Sixth Grade

Everyday Mathematics®

Teacher's Lesson Gui

Volume 2

The University of Chicago
School Mathematics Project

Chicago, Illinois

UCSMP Elementary Materials Component

Max Bell, Director

Authors

Max Bell
John Bretzlauf
Amy Dillard
Robert Hartfield
Andy Isaacs
James McBride, Director
Kathleen Pitvorec
Peter Saecker
Robert Balfanz*
William Carroll*

Technical Art

Diana Barrie

*First Edition only

Everyday Learning Development Staff

Editorial: Anna Belluomini, Fran Brown, Molly Coe, Mary Cooney, Amy Feun Lee, Elizabeth Glosniak, Joan Green, Bernadette Lopez
Production: Hector Cuadra, Julie Dalton, Annette Davis, Tina Dunlap, Elizabeth Gabbard, Luis Leal, Silvana Valenzuela

Additional Credit: Black Dot Group, Kathleen Burke, Lindaanne Donohoe, Mary Ghislin, Susan Halko, Herman Adler Design Group, Scott LaPierre, Lucy Lesiak, Yoshi Miyake, Precision Graphics, Randi Robin Design, Rasa Sutkus, Regina Thoeming, Ann Tomasic

Photo Credits

Phil Martin/Photography
Cover: Bill Burlingham/Photography
Photo Collage: Herman Adler Design Group

Contributors

Ann Brown, Sarah Busse, Terry DeJong, Craig Dezell, John Dini, James Flanders, Donna Goffron, Steve Heckley, Karen Hedberg, Deborah Arron Leslie, Sharon McHugh, Janet M. Meyers, Donna Owen, William D. Pattison, Marilyn Pavlak, Jane Picken, Denise Porter, Kelly Porto, John Sabol, Rose Ann Simpson, Debbi Suhajda, Laura Sunseri, Andrea Tyrance, Kim Van Haitsma, Mary Wilson, Nancy Wilson, Jackie Winston, Carl Zmola, Theresa Zmola

This material is based upon work supported by the National Science Foundation under Grant No. ESI-9252984. Any opinions, findings, and conclusions or recommendations expressed in this material are those of the authors and do not necessarily reflect the views of the National Science Foundation.

ISBN 1-57039-921-2

Everyday Learning Corporation
P.O. Box 812960
Chicago, IL 60681
www.everydaylearning.com

1 2 3 4 5 6 7 8 9 QW 05 04 03 02 01 00

Contents

Volume 1

Welcome **xxiv**

Unit 1 Collection, Display, and Interpretation of Data **2**

1.1 Introduction to the *Student Reference Book* **16**
1.2 Line Plots **20**
1.3 Median and Mean **24**
1.4 The *Landmark Shark Game* **29**
1.5 Broken-Line Graphs **33**
1.6 Bar Graphs **38**
1.7 Step Graphs **42**
1.8 The Percent Circle and Circle Graphs **47**
1.9 Using a Graph to Investigate Perimeter and Area **52**
1.10 Persuasive Data and Graphs **57**
1.11 Kitchen Units of Capacity **62**
1.12 Unit 1 Review and Assessment **67**

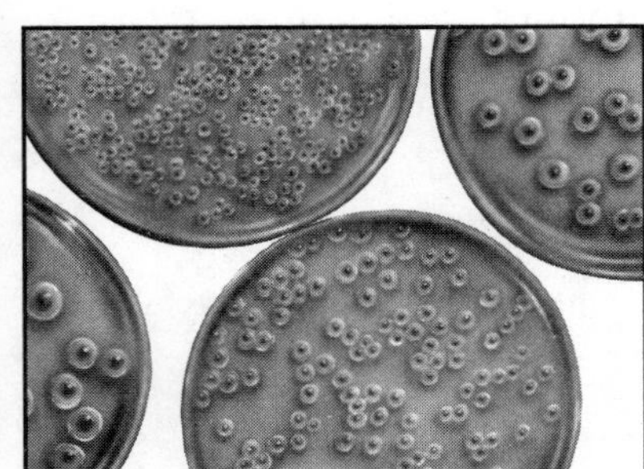

Unit 2 Operations with Whole Numbers and Decimals **72**

2.1 Addition and Subtraction of Decimals **86**
2.2 Multiplication of Decimals: Part 1 **91**
2.3 Multiplication of Decimals: Part 2 **95**
2.4 Multiplying by Powers of 10 **99**
2.5 Analyzing Large Numbers **103**
2.6 Reading and Writing Small Numbers **108**
2.7 Exponential Notation and the Powers Key on a Calculator **112**
2.8 Scientific Notation for Large and Small Numbers **116**
2.9 Scientific Notation on a Calculator **121**
2.10 Division of Whole Numbers **125**
2.11 Division of Decimals **132**
2.12 Unit 2 Review and Assessment **137**

Unit 3 Variables, Formulas, and Graphs **142**

3.1 Using Variables to Describe Number Patterns **154**
3.2 General Patterns (Two Variables) **158**
3.3 Algebraic Expressions **162**
3.4 Formulas **166**
3.5 Formulas, Tables, and Graphs: Part 1 **171**
3.6 A Science Experiment **176**
3.7 Variables and Formulas in Spreadsheets: Part 1 **182**
3.8 Variables and Formulas in Spreadsheets: Part 2 **187**
3.9 Reading and Drawing Graphs **191**
3.10 Formulas, Tables, and Graphs: Part 2 **196**
3.11 Unit 3 Review and Assessment **201**

Unit 4 Rational Number Uses and Operations **206**

4.1 Equivalent Fractions **218**
4.2 Comparing Fractions **224**
4.3 Adding and Subtracting Fractions **229**
4.4 Adding and Subtracting Mixed Numbers with Like Denominators **235**
4.5 Adding and Subtracting Mixed Numbers with Unlike Denominators **240**
4.6 Fraction Multiplication **245**
4.7 Multiplication of Mixed Numbers **249**
4.8 Fractions, Decimals, and Percents **253**
4.9 More Difficult Conversions **258**
4.10 Graphing Garbage **263**
4.11 Percent of a Number **268**
4.12 Unit 4 Review and Assessment **272**

Unit 5 Geometry: Congruence, Constructions, and Parallel Lines **278**

5.1 Measuring and Drawing Angles **290**
5.2 Reasoning with Angle Measures **295**
5.3 Using a Protractor to Make Circle Graphs **299**
5.4 Coordinate Geometry **304**
5.5 Isometry Transformations **309**
5.6 Congruent Figures **314**
5.7 Compass-and-Straightedge Constructions 1 **320**
5.8 Compass-and-Straightedge Constructions 2 **325**
5.9 Parallel Lines and Angle Relationships **330**
5.10 Parallelograms **336**
5.11 Unit 5 Review and Assessment **341**

Appendices **347**

Projects **348**
Sixth Grade Key Vocabulary **391**
Scope and Sequence **407**
Index **428**

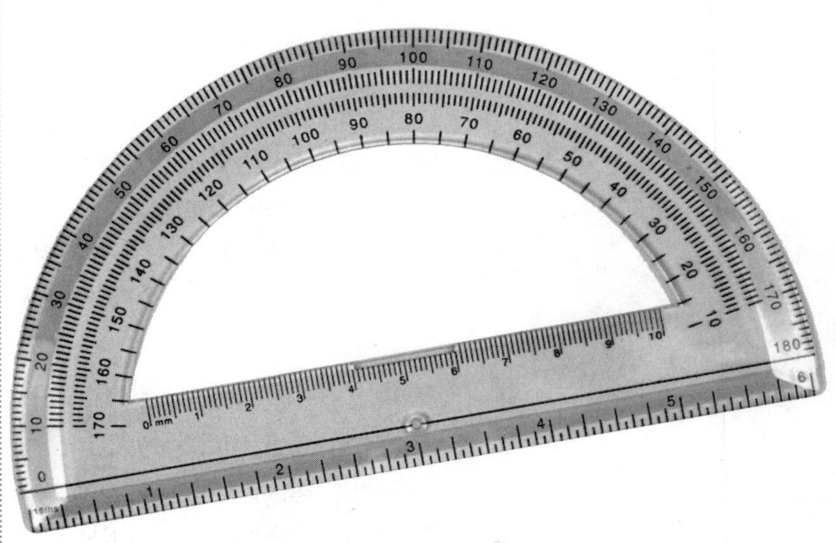

Volume 2

Unit 6 Number Systems and Algebra Concepts 438

6.1	Multiplication of Fractions and Mixed Numbers	452
6.2	Division of Fractions and Mixed Numbers	457
6.3	Review: Addition and Subtraction of Positive and Negative Numbers	462
6.4	Multiplication and Division of Positive and Negative Numbers	470
6.5	The Properties of Number Systems	475
6.6	Order of Operations	481
6.7	Review: Number Sentences	487
6.8	Solving Simple Equations	493
6.9	Review: Pan-Balance Problems	499
6.10	Pan-Balance Equations	507
6.11	The Equivalent-Equations Method of Solving Equations	512
6.12	Inequalities	517
6.13	Unit 6 Review and Assessment	523

Unit 7 Probability and Discrete Mathematics 528

7.1	The Probability of Equally Likely Outcomes	540
7.2	Generating Random Numbers	546
7.3	A Random-Number Simulation	551
7.4	Tree Diagrams	556
7.5	Using Tree Diagrams to Calculate Probabilities	561
7.6	Venn Diagrams	567
7.7	Fair and Unfair Games	573
7.8	Strategies for Multiple-Choice Tests	579
7.9	Unit 7 Review and Assessment	585

Unit 8 Rates and Ratios 590

8.1	Rates, Rate Tables, and Unit Rates	602
8.2	Solving Rate Problems with Proportions	609
8.3	Solving Proportions by Cross Multiplication	615
8.4	Calorie Use	621
8.5	Using Nutrition Information	627
8.6	Ratios	634
8.7	Using Proportions to Solve Percent Problems	641
8.8	Calculating the Fat Content of Foods	646

8.9 Using Ratios to Describe Size Changes **652**
8.10 Similar Polygons **659**
8.11 Comparing Ratios **667**
8.12 The Golden Ratio **674**
8.13 Unit 8 Review and Assessment **680**

Unit 9 More about Variables, Formulas, and Graphs **686**

9.1 Area Models for the Distributive Property **700**
9.2 The Distributive Property **704**
9.3 Simplifying Expressions: Combining Like Terms **710**
9.4 Simplifying Expressions: Removing Parentheses **715**
9.5 Simplifying and Solving Equations **720**
9.6 Using Equations to Solve Mobile Problems **725**
9.7 Computer Spreadsheets **732**
9.8 Area Formulas with Applications **738**
9.9 Volume Formulas with Applications **743**
9.10 Solving Equations by Trial and Error **749**
9.11 Formula Equations **755**
9.12 The Pythagorean Theorem **761**
9.13 Indirect Measurement Problems **768**
9.14 Unit 9 Review and Assessment **773**

Unit 10 Geometry Topics **778**

10.1 Semiregular Tessellations **788**
10.2 Escher-Type Translation Tessellations **795**
10.3 Rotation Symmetry **800**
10.4 Cross Sections of Clay Solids **806**
10.5 Introduction to Topology **812**
10.6 Möbius Strips **818**
10.7 Unit 10 Review and Assessment **823**

Appendices **827**

Projects **828**
Sixth Grade Key Vocabulary **871**
Scope and Sequence **887**
Index **908**

Unit 6
Number Systems and Algebra Concepts

overview

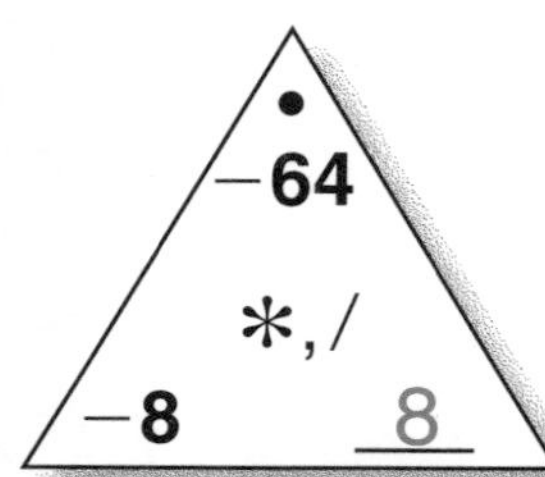

Unit 6 has two main objectives. The first objective is to complete the arithmetic system by showing that the standard operations are possible with rational numbers. This includes a review of the algorithms for addition and subtraction of positive and negative numbers, an introduction to a division of fractions algorithm, and an introduction to multiplication and division of positive and negative numbers. The second objective is to review and extend previous work with equations and inequalities.

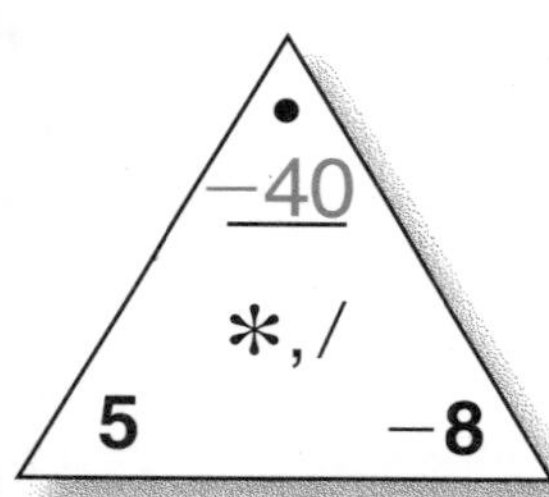

Between the work on these two objectives are lessons providing a bridge between arithmetic and algebra. Lesson 6.5 summarizes the relationship between the set of rational numbers and some of its subsets (whole numbers, integers, and positive rational numbers); Lesson 6.6 reviews the rules for the order in which operations in expressions are performed. Most students who complete this unit successfully will have the necessary background to take a substantial pre-algebra course in seventh grade. Many will even be prepared for a secondary school algebra course.

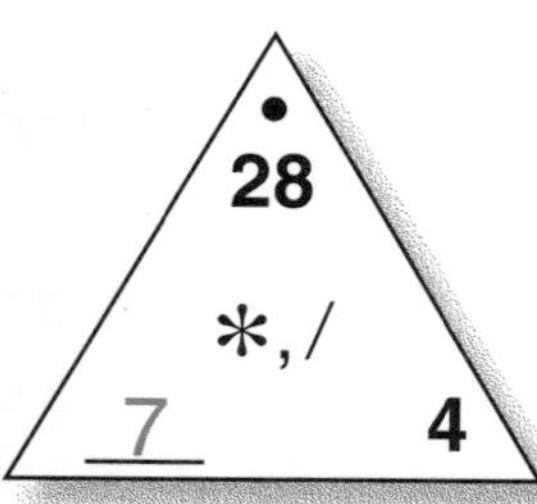

contents

UNIT 6

Lesson	Objective	Page
6.1	**Multiplication of Fractions and Mixed Numbers** *To review multiplying fractions and mixed numbers.*	452
6.2	**Division of Fractions and Mixed Numbers** *To introduce an algorithm for the division of fractions.*	457
6.3	**Review: Addition and Subtraction of Positive and Negative Numbers** *To practice adding and subtracting positive and negative numbers.*	462
6.4	**Multiplication and Division of Positive and Negative Numbers** *To develop rules for multiplying and dividing positive and negative numbers; and to practice these operations.*	470
6.5	**The Properties of Number Systems** *To summarize the properties of number systems and operations.*	475
6.6	**Order of Operations** *To review the rules for the order of operations; and to evaluate expressions containing parentheses.*	481
6.7	**Review: Number Sentences** *To review relation symbols, number sentences, and equations; to identify number sentences as true or false; and to translate between English and number sentences.*	487
6.8	**Solving Simple Equations** *To solve equations by trial and error and by a cover-up method.*	493
6.9	**Review: Pan-Balance Problems** *To solve pan-balance problems as models for equation-solving techniques.*	499
6.10	**Pan-Balance Equations** *To explore a method for solving equations by transforming them into equivalent equations of the form* $x = a$.	507
6.11	**The Equivalent-Equations Method of Solving Equations** *To solve equations by transforming them into equivalent equations of the form* $x = a$.	512
6.12	**Inequalities** *To graph inequalities in one variable on a number line.*	517
6.13	**Unit 6 Review and Assessment** *To review and assess students' progress on the material covered in Unit 6.*	523

learning goals in perspective

	learning goals	links to the past	links to the future
6a	**Beginning Goal** Solve and graph solutions for inequalities. **(Lesson 6.12)**	Grades 3–5: Use the relation symbols (=, >, <). Compare and order numbers. Draw and interpret graphs.	After Grade 6: Convert inequalities to equivalent forms to solve problems.
6b	**Developing Goal** Solve equations. **(Lessons 6.8–6.11)**	Grades 4 and 5: Review number sentences, open sentences, and variables; solve addition/subtraction number stories by modeling with open sentences.	Grade 6: Simplify and solve equations (Unit 9). After Grade 6: Convert equations to equivalent forms to solve problems.
6c	**Developing Goal** Use an algorithm to add, subtract, multiply, and divide fractions and mixed numbers. **(Lessons 6.1 and 6.2)**	Grades 5: Use algorithms to add, subtract, and multiply fractions and mixed numbers. Grade 6: Use an algorithm to add, subtract, and multiply fractions and mixed numbers (Unit 4).	Grade 6: Applications and maintenance. After Grade 6: Operations with fractions and mixed numbers will be important in mathematics and daily life.
6d	**Developing/Secure Goal** Find opposites and reciprocals of numbers. **(Lessons 6.1 and 6.2)**	Grades 3–5: Review meanings and uses of negative numbers. Understand the use of positive and negative numbers to relate numbers to a zero point.	Grade 6: Applications and maintenance.
6e	**Developing/Secure Goal** Add, subtract, multiply, and divide positive and negative numbers. **(Lessons 6.3 and 6.4)**	Grade 5: Develop rules for adding and subtracting positive and negative numbers. Add and subtract positive and negative numbers. Grade 6: Practice spreadsheet computation (Unit 3).	Grade 6: Applications and maintenance. After Grade 6: Displaying and performing operations with positive and negative numbers will be important in mathematics, science, and business.
6f	**Developing/Secure Goal** Perform operations in the correct order. **(Lessons 6.6 and 6.8)**	Grade 5: Understand and apply the order of operations to evaluate expressions and solve number sentences.	Grade 6: Applications and maintenance.
6g	**Developing/Secure Goal** Identify number sentences as true or false. **(Lesson 6.7)**	Grade 4: Insert parentheses to make number sentences true. Grade 5: Tell whether number sentences are true or false.	Grade 6: Simplify and solve equations (Unit 9). After Grade 6: Convert equations and inequalities to equivalent forms to solve.
6h	**Secure Goal** Compare and order positive and negative numbers. **(Lesson 6.3)**	Grades 4 and 5: Graph, compare, and order positive and negative numbers on a number line.	Grade 6: Applications and maintenance.
6i	**Secure Goal** Understand and apply the identity property for multiplication. **(Lessons 6.4 and 6.5)**	Grades 2–5: Use multiplication shortcuts: multiplication by 1.	Grade 6: Apply properties of operations to simplify expressions and simplify and solve equations (Unit 9). After Grade 6: Properties of operations will be important in algebra and other mathematics courses.
6j	**Secure Goal** Understand and apply the commutative property for addition and multiplication. **(Lessons 6.1 and 6.3)**	Grades 2–5: Review and use addition and multiplication shortcuts: "turn-around" rule.	See Goal 6i.
6k	**Secure Goal** Understand and apply the associative property for addition and multiplication. **(Lessons 6.3–6.5)**	Grades 3–5: Solve problems with parentheses. Applications and maintenance.	

assessment

ongoing • product • periodic

Informal Assessment

Math Boxes These *Math Journal* pages provide opportunities for cumulative review or assessment of concepts and skills.

Ongoing Assessment: Kid Watching Use the Ongoing Assessment suggestions in the following lessons to make quick, on-the-spot observations about students' understanding of:

- Operations and Computation **(Lesson 6.2, Part 1; Lesson 6.3, Part 1; Lesson 6.4, Part 1)**
- Patterns, Functions, and Algebra **(Lesson 6.5, Part 1; Lesson 6.6, Part 1; Lesson 6.7, Part 1; Lesson 6.8, Part 1; Lesson 6.9, Part 1; Lesson 6.10, Part 1; Lesson 6.11, Part 1)**

Portfolio Ideas Samples of students' work may be obtained from the following assignments:

- Completing Fact Triangles **(Lesson 6.4)**
- Exploring Scientific Calculators **(Lesson 6.6)**
- Solving Challenging Equations **(Lesson 6.8)**
- Solving Pan-Balance Problems **(Lesson 6.9)**
- Solving More Challenging Pan-Balance Problems **(Lesson 6.9)**
- Balancing Pans **(Lesson 6.10)**
- Graphing Inequalities **(Lesson 6.12)**

Unit 6 Review and Assessment

Math Message Use Question 4 from Time to Reflect in Lesson 6.13 to assess students' progress toward the following learning goals: **Goals 6i–6k**

Oral and Slate Assessments Use oral or slate assessments during Lesson 6.13 to assess students' progress toward the following learning goals: **Goals 6b–6e**

Written Assessment Use a written review during Lesson 6.13 to assess students' progress toward the following learning goals: **Goals 6a–6k**

Alternative Assessment Options Use independent alternative assessments in Lesson 6.13 to assess students' progress toward the following learning goals: **Goals 6b and 6f**

assessmenthandbook

For more information on how to use different types of assessment in Unit 6, see the Assessment Overview on pages 54–57 in the *Assessment Handbook.* The following Assessment Masters can be found in the *Math Masters* book:

- Unit 6 Checking Progress, pp. 403–405
- Unit 6 Individual Profile of Progress, p. 445
- Unit 6 Class Checklist, p. 444
- Class Progress Indicator, p. 470
- Math Logs, pp. 473–474
- Self-Assessment Forms, pp. 476–477
- Interest Inventories, pp. 471–472

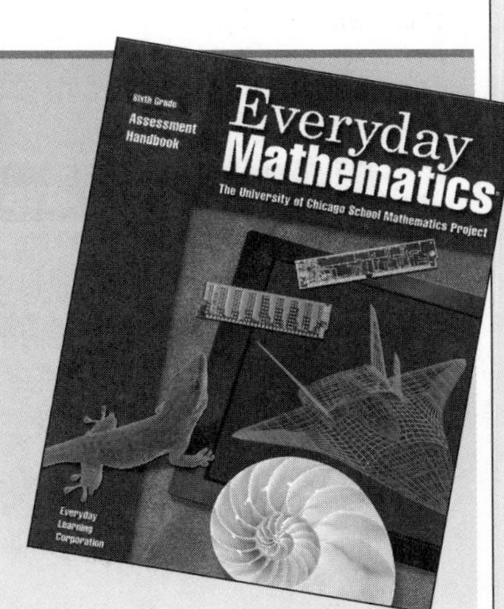

problem solving

A process of modeling everyday situations using tools from mathematics

Encourage students to use a variety of strategies when attacking a given problem–and to explain those strategies. *Strategies students might use in this unit:*

- Use computation
- Write a number model
- Act out the problem
- Find a pattern
- Use a formula
- Try and check
- Use logical reasoning
- Use a picture
- Use a number line

Four Problem-Solving REPRESENTATIONS

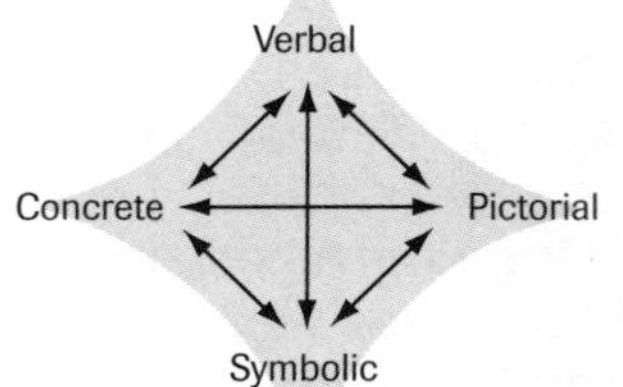

Lessons that teach *through* problem solving, not just *about* problem solving

Lesson	Activity	Lesson	Activity
6.1, 6.6	Solve number stories involving fractions.	**6.7**	Solve problems involving the areas of rectangles.
6.2	Find the number of segments of a particular size in a given length.	**6.8**	Use the cover-up method to solve equations.
6.3	Develop a rule for subtracting positive and negative numbers.	**6.9**	Use the pan-balance method to solve equations.
6.4	Develop rules for multiplying and dividing positive and negative numbers.	**6.12**	Graph solutions of inequalities.
6.5	Solve multistep number stories.		

For more information about problem solving in *Everyday Mathematics,* see the *Teacher's Reference Manual.*

cross-curricular links

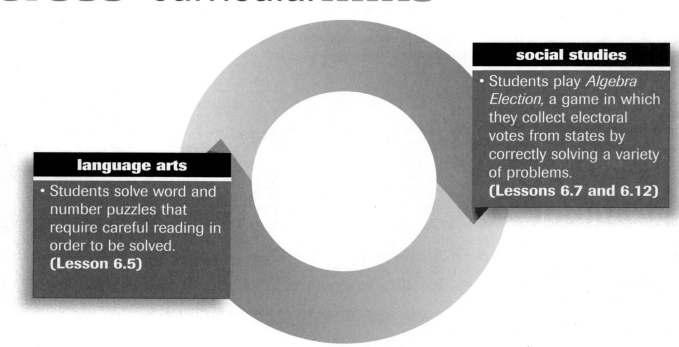

social studies

- Students play *Algebra Election,* a game in which they collect electoral votes from states by correctly solving a variety of problems. **(Lessons 6.7 and 6.12)**

language arts

- Students solve word and number puzzles that require careful reading in order to be solved. **(Lesson 6.5)**

meeting INDIVIDUAL needs

UNIVERSAL ACCESS

✦ RETEACHING

The following features provide additional instructional support:

Adjusting the Activity

- **Lesson 6.1, Part 1**
- **Lesson 6.2, Part 1**
- **Lesson 6.3, Part 1**
- **Lesson 6.4, Part 1**
- **Lesson 6.5, Part 1**
- **Lesson 6.6, Part 1**
- **Lesson 6.8, Part 1**
- **Lesson 6.9, Part 1**

Options for Individualizing

- **Lesson 6.3** Modeling Positive and Negative Numbers with Colored Chips or Counters

✦ ENRICHMENT

The following features suggest enrichment and extension activities:

Adjusting the Activity

- **Lesson 6.1, Part 1**
- **Lesson 6.7, Part 1**
- **Lesson 6.8, Part 1**
- **Lesson 6.9, Part 1**
- **Lesson 6.10, Part 1**

Options for Individualizing

- **Lesson 6.2** Studying a Proof
- **Lesson 6.3** Adding and Subtracting Positive and Negative Numbers Using Absolute Value
- **Lesson 6.4** Reading about Division by Zero
- **Lesson 6.5** Investigating Properties of Rational Numbers
- **Lesson 6.5** Solving Puzzles
- **Lesson 6.6** Exploring Scientific Calculators
- **Lesson 6.8** Solving Challenging Equations
- **Lesson 6.9** Solving More Challenging Pan-Balance Problems
- **Lesson 6.12** Graphing Inequalities
- **Lesson 6.12** Playing *Solution Search* with Student-Created Cards

✦ LANGUAGE DIVERSITY

The following features suggest ways to support students who are acquiring proficiency in English:

Adjusting the Activity

- **Lesson 6.11, Part 1**

Options for Individualizing

- **Lesson 6.7** Making Reminder Cards

✦ MULTIAGE CLASSROOM

The following chart lists related lessons from Grade 5 that can help you meet your instructional needs:

Grade 5	8.7 8.8	8.12	7.7 7.8	2.8		7.5	7.4		10.1 10.2	10.1 10.2			
Grade 6	6.1	6.2	6.3	6.4	6.5	6.6	6.7	6.8	6.9	6.10	6.11	6.12	6.13

materials

lesson	math masters pages	manipulative kit items	other items
6.1	Study Link Master, p. 312 Teaching Master, p. 92		calculator Geometry Template
6.2	Study Link Master, p. 313 Teaching Master, p. 93		inch and centimeter ruler calculator
6.3	Study Link Master, p. 314 Teaching Masters, pp. 94 and 95	Per partnership: complete deck of number cards (from the Everything Math Deck, if available)	calculator Real Number Line Poster chalk or masking tape (optional) Geometry Template 10 chips or counters of one color per student 10 chips or counters of another color per student Per partnership: penny ***See* Advance Preparation, p. 462**
6.4	Study Link Master, p. 315 Teaching Master, p. 96	number cards (from the Everything Math Deck, if available)	calculator slate
6.5	Study Link Master, p. 316 Teaching Masters, pp. 97 and 98		calculator; Real Number Line Poster ***See* Advance Preparation, p. 475**
6.6	Study Link Master, p. 317 Teaching Masters, pp. 99 and 100		calculators (both scientific and non-scientific) Geometry Template ***See* Advance Preparation, p. 481**
6.7	Study Link Master, p. 318 Teaching Masters, pp. 101–103 ***See* Advance Preparation, p. 487**	six-sided die	calculator 4 counters scissors
6.8	Study Link Master, p. 319 Teaching Masters, p. 104 Assessment Master, p. 478 (optional)	number cards (from the Everything Math Deck, if available)	calculator Geometry Template
6.9	Study Link Master, p. 320 transparency of Teaching Master, p. 105 (optional) Teaching Masters, pp. 106 and 107 ***See* Advance Preparation, p. 499**		For every 4 students: pan balance variety of small objects, such as paper clips, pattern blocks, and pencils (optional) calculator ***See* Advance Preparation, p. 499**
6.10	Study Link Master, p. 321 Teaching Master, p. 108		
6.11	Study Link Master, p. 322 Teaching Master, p. 109 Assessment Master, p. 478 (optional) ***See* Advance Preparation, p. 512**		calculator
6.12	Study Link Master, p. 323 Teaching Masters, pp. 102, 103, 110 (per group), and 111 ***See* Advance Preparation, p. 517**	Per group: 4 each of number cards 1–10 and 1 each of number cards 11–20 (from the Everything Math Deck, if available) six-sided die	counters; calculator *Algebra Election* materials (see Lesson 6.7) ***See* Advance Preparation, p. 517**
6.13	Study Link Masters, pp. 324–327 Teaching Masters, pp. 100 and 107 Assessment Masters, pp. 403–405		

planningtips

Pacing

Pacing depends on a number of factors, such as students' individual needs and how long your school has been using *Everyday Mathematics*. At the beginning of Unit 6, review your Content by Strand Poster to help you set a monthly pace.

JANUARY	FEBRUARY	MARCH
← MOST CLASSROOMS →		

Using the Projects

Use Project 6, Anthropometry Project: Formulas for Body Height and Neck Circumference, during or after Unit 6, to provide an interesting application of formulas. The projects can be found at the back of the *Teacher's Lesson Guide*.

Home Communication

Share Study Links 6.1–6.12 with families to help them understand the content and procedures in this unit. At the end of the unit, use Study Link 6.13 to introduce Unit 7. Supplemental information can be found in the *Home Connection Handbook*.

NCTM Standards

Standard	1	2	3	4	5	6	7	8	9	10
Unit 6 Lessons	6.1–6.6, 6.8	6.5–6.12	6.1, 6.2, 6.5–6.7, 6.10, 6.12	6.1–6.3, 6.5–6.7, 6.9	6.1, 6.3, 6.13	6.1–6.13	6.1–6.13	6.1–6.13	6.1–6.13	6.1–6.13

Content Standards
1 Number and Operations
2 Algebra
3 Geometry
4 Measurement
5 Data Analysis and Probability

Process Standards
6 Problem Solving
7 Reasoning and Proof
8 Communication
9 Connections
10 Representation

PRACTICE through Games

Everyday Mathematics uses games to help students develop good fact power and other math skills.

- *Credits/Debits Game (Advanced Version)* to practice adding and subtracting positive and negative numbers **(Lesson 6.3)**
- *Top-It* to practice adding, subtracting, and comparing positive and negative numbers **(Lesson 6.4)**
- *Algebra Election* to practice solving problems involving variables in the context of electoral votes in an election **(Lessons 6.7 and 6.12)**
- *Broken Calculator* to practice finding solutions for equations by trial and error **(Lessons 6.8, 6.9, and 6.11)**
- *Name That Number* to practice writing number sentences using order of operations **(Lesson 6.8)**
- *Solution Search* to practice identifying a solution to an inequality **(Lesson 6.12)**

unit 6 content highlights

The discussion below highlights the major content ideas presented in Unit 6 and may help you establish instructional priorities.

Reciprocals; Multiplication and Division of Fractions and Mixed Numbers (Lessons 6.1 and 6.2)

Situations that involve quotients of rational numbers in *decimal* form are fairly common in everyday life. On the other hand, the same kinds of situations involving quotients of numbers in *fraction* form are rare. Indeed, few adults have a need to divide fractions once they leave school. Therefore, division of fractions is taught in *Everyday Mathematics* not in order to develop a practical, needed skill, but to accomplish the following goals:

- ▷ To complete the arithmetic system. Since we can add, subtract, multiply, and divide counting numbers and decimals, we should verify that all of these operations, including division, are also possible with fractions.
- ▷ To anticipate some of the work with rational number expressions found in standard algebra courses.

Most adults were taught the "Don't ask why— just invert and multiply" rule to divide fractions. The advantage of this algorithm is that it is easy to use. However, few people understand why the algorithm works. The essay on pages 89 and 90 of the *Student Reference Book* presents a "proof" of the algorithm through an example; you are encouraged to discuss this proof with your class.

Another, less mysterious way to divide fractions exploits the use of common denominators, very much as they are used with addition and subtraction of fractions. While this method might make more sense to students than the "invert and multiply" method, it may prove less efficient. Students should use whichever method they are most comfortable with.

Division of Fractions

$\frac{2}{3} \div \frac{4}{5} = ?$

"Invert and multiply" method

$$\frac{2}{3} \div \frac{4}{5} = \frac{2}{3} \times \frac{5}{4} = \frac{10}{12} \text{ or } \frac{5}{6}$$

Common denominator method

$$\frac{2}{3} \div \frac{4}{5} = \frac{10}{15} \div \frac{12}{15} = 10 \div 12 = \frac{10}{12} \text{ or } \frac{5}{6}$$

Operations with Positive and Negative Numbers (Lessons 6.3 and 6.4)

In *Fourth* and *Fifth Grade Everyday Mathematics,* students explored addition and subtraction of positive and negative numbers through business situations involving credits and debits. They used red counters (debits) and black counters (credits) to model account balances before and after gain and loss transactions. In *Fifth Grade Everyday Mathematics,* students constructed a "slide rule" and used it to solve addition and subtraction problems with both positive and negative numbers. Students also explored how to use the (−) key on their calculators to enter negative numbers and to find the opposite of any number. This key makes it possible to add, subtract, multiply, and divide positive and negative numbers with a calculator.

Lesson 6.3 is a review of addition and subtraction of positive and negative numbers. By now, students may have generated a variety of rules for subtraction. Lesson 6.3 focuses on the following rule: To subtract a number b from a number a, add the opposite of the number b to the number a. This is the preferred method, since it is the most useful for later work in algebra.

Lesson 6.4 gives students their first exposure to multiplication and division of positive and negative numbers. As with division of fractions, there are few situations outside of mathematics courses that call for multiplication and division with positive and negative numbers, but it is useful to show students that all of the standard operations are possible in the rational number system. Although the rules for multiplication and division are easy to learn and easy to remember, they are difficult to justify. To illustrate the fact that the product or quotient of two negative numbers is a positive number, you might use an analogy to the double negative in everyday language. (If I never never give homework, it means that I always give homework.)

Development of Number Systems (Lesson 6.5)

Whole numbers were originally developed for counting. Eventually, fractions and decimals were invented to deal with measures that cannot be represented by whole numbers, that is, measures that fall within intervals between two consecutive whole numbers. The invention of negative numbers came later, prompted by both mathematical and practical considerations.

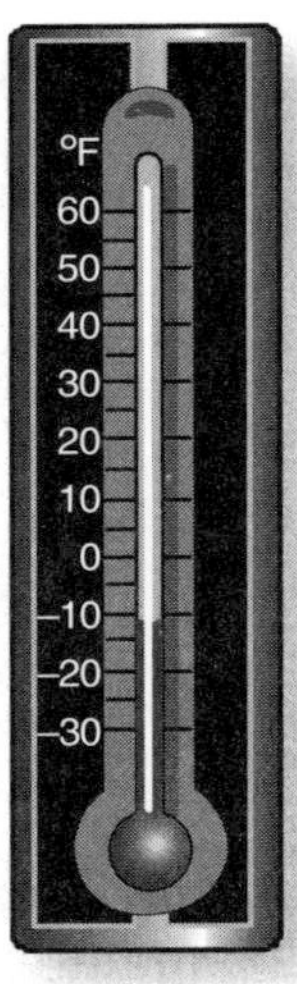

From a mathematical point of view, negative numbers are needed

- ▷ to make subtraction "closed"—that is, there is an answer to every subtraction problem (including such problems as $10 - 13$).
- ▷ so that there are number names for the points on both sides of zero on the number line.
- ▷ so that every number has an "additive inverse," which, when added to the number, results in a sum of zero.

In the real world, negative numbers answer the need for specifying locations in reference frames in relation to a starting point (the zero point) and for naming measures that extend in both directions from the zero point. Examples include temperatures above and below a zero point, elevations above and below sea level, years B.C. and A.D. on historical time lines, and profits and losses in business.

The purpose of Lesson 6.5 is to present the "big picture"—to show that the expansion of the whole-number system to include positive and negative rational numbers was necessary to meet the needs described above. You may find it helpful to read pages 62–65 in the *Student Reference Book* before the start of the lesson.

Order of Operations (Lesson 6.6)

Mathematical expressions and sentences obey many of the same underlying rules of structure and punctuation as phrases, clauses, and sentences in spoken and written language. In both verbal language and mathematics, the purpose of these rules is to avoid ambiguities. In mathematics, this is accomplished by the proper use of parentheses and other grouping symbols and, in their absence, by rules that determine the order in which operations are to be performed. For example, the expression $3 * 8 + 4 * 6$, which contains no parentheses, might have the following values:

P	( )
E	2^x
M	∗ or ×
D	/ or ÷
A	+
S	–

Order of operations

- ▷ $3 * 8 + 4 * 6 = 48$
  (Multiply $3 * 8$ and $4 * 6$ first; add the results.)
- ▷ $3 * 8 + 4 * 6 = 216$
  (Add $8 + 4$; multiply the result by 3 and then by 6.)
- ▷ $3 * 8 + 4 * 6 = 168$
  (Multiply $3 * 8$; add 4 to the result; multiply the result by 6.)

According to the accepted rules of order, the first expression gives the correct value of the expression. Lesson 6.6 focuses on these rules, which many people remember by the mnemonic **P**lease **E**xcuse **M**y **D**ear **A**unt **S**ally—first do whatever is inside **P**arentheses; then find the value of numbers with **E**xponents; then do **M**ultiplications and **D**ivisions in order from left to right; and finally, **A**dd and **S**ubtract in order from left to right.

Scientific calculators are programmed to follow the rules of order, so it is usually safe to enter the numbers in an expression without parentheses in the order in which they occur. This is not the case with the four-function calculators often used in earlier grades. For example, if the expression $9^2 + 12^2$ is entered in a scientific calculator, it will first calculate $9 * 9$ $(= 81)$, then $12 * 12$ $(= 144)$, and then find the sum of the results $(81 + 144 = 225)$. A four-function calculator will calculate $9 * 9$ $(= 81)$ first but then might add 12 $(= 93)$ and finish by multiplying by 12 $(= 1{,}116)$.

In general, it is good practice to use parentheses to make the meanings of expressions and number sentences perfectly clear. But because parentheses can become cumbersome, they are often omitted in mathematics books and other printed works.

Solving Equations (Lessons 6.7–6.11)

In mathematics, as in spoken and written language, a sentence may be true or false, or it may not contain enough information to make it possible to determine whether it is true or false. For example, the sentence "John Kennedy was the president of the United States in 1961" is true. The sentence "Ronald Reagan was the president of the United States in 1961" is false. The sentence "He was the president of the United States" is true for fewer than 50 people and false for billions of others. We cannot tell whether it is true or false unless the pronoun "he" is replaced by someone's name. Similarly, the equation "$5 + 3 = 8$" is true, and the inequality "$27 < 25$" is false. The open sentence "$2x > 10$" is true for many numbers and false for many others. We cannot tell whether it is true or false until the variable x is replaced by a number. If the replacement for x results in a true sentence, then the replacement is a solution of the open sentence. When solving equations and inequalities, it is important that students never lose sight of this fundamental definition of "solution."

Notice that the open sentence was written "$2x > 10$" instead of "$2 * x > 10$." It is customary, especially in texts used in secondary school and beyond, to omit the multiplication sign in equations, inequalities, and formulas that contain variables. Although this may seem to be an easy convention to learn, it takes some students time to get used to it, so the authors suggest that, for awhile, you use both notations.

Notations for Multiplication	
$a \times b$	ab
$a * b$	$(a)(b)$
$a \cdot b$	

Expressions and mathematical sentences are often used to model a situation. For example, the equation "$13 = 2A + 5$" can be used to represent the sentence "John is 13 years old, and he is 5 years older than twice Ann's age." In this way, a relationship among numbers can be represented in a compact way without, for the moment, committing to specific numbers.

The ideas discussed on the previous page are reviewed in Lessons 6.7 and 6.8. Lesson 6.8 focuses on two methods for solving equations. The trial-and-error method has been featured in *Everyday Mathematics* for several years, as students were invited to consider algebra equations as "puzzles" to be solved. This method encourages mental arithmetic, and, for students with good "number sense," it is quite efficient for many of the equation problems given in high school algebra books. What the authors call the "cover-up method" is equivalent to finding missing addends or missing factors, as has been done in *Everyday Mathematics* since first grade. This is a more systematic method and can be used to solve equations that might be too difficult to solve by trial and error.

A third, more systematic method for solving equations in one variable is introduced in Lesson 6.11. Using this method, a rather complex equation is transformed into a succession of simpler, equivalent equations, until an equation results that can be solved by inspection. Students apply this method in an algorithmic, step-by-step fashion, justifying each step in shorthand notation.

Before the equivalent-equations method is introduced in Lessons 6.10 and 6.11, students solve pan-balance problems (Lesson 6.9) by acting out situations in which the weight of a single object is found by removing objects from both pans, until the object in question is balanced with one or more remaining objects. The pan balance is used more as a metaphor than as an actual tool—if the pans are balanced, they can be kept in balance by adding or removing objects of the same weight from both pans. First introduced in fifth grade, pan-balance problems offer a concrete model of the equivalent-equations method. Lesson 6.10 provides a transition from working with the pan-balance model to solving equations without that model.

Pan-balance problem

The same procedure that is used to make complex equations simpler can be used to make simple equations more complex. Oddly enough, making expressions somewhat more complex is sometimes useful in high school and university courses, usually in order to put them in a recognizable standard form. It is also true that the rule "do the same thing to both sides" is easily adapted to solving inequalities and to solving systems of several equations with several variables. In other words, what begins as a simple pan-balance metaphor turns out to be very adaptable and useful in many of the future courses your students may take.

In Unit 9, students will solve more complicated equations, in which they must simplify an equation before they can apply the solution method taught in Lesson 6.11.

Inequalities (Lesson 6.12)

Inequalities look very much like equations, except that the symbol $=$ (*equal*) is replaced by such symbols as $\neq$ (*not equal to*), $>$ (*greater than*), or $\geq$ (*greater than or equal to*). Most equations, such as $2 + x = 5$, have just one solution, whereas inequalities usually have many solutions. For example, there are infinitely many rational numbers that, when used as a replacement for x in $x < 100$, result in a true sentence. (For example, 50, 39, 1, 13, 98.5, -37.8, and $-1{,}057$ are all less than 100.)

Lesson 6.12 introduces inequalities and ways of finding and describing sets of solutions for inequalities. The ideas and methods are informal and easy to follow; they are an important part of the "pre-algebra" experience.

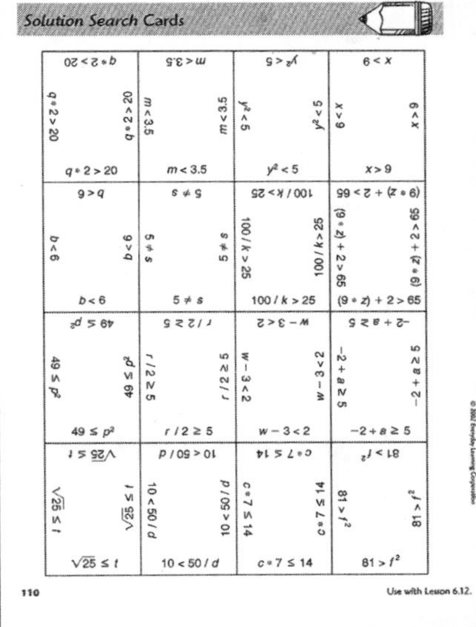
Name Date Time

Solution Search Cards

$q * 2 > 20$	$m < 3.5$	$y^2 < 5$	$x > 9$
$b < 6$	$5 \neq s$	$100 / k > 25$	$(9 * z) + 2 > 65$
$49 \leq p^2$	$r / 2 \geq 5$	$w - 3 < 2$	$-2 + a \geq 5$
$\sqrt{25} \leq t$	$10 < 50 / d$	$c * 7 \leq 14$	$81 > f^2$

Use with Lesson 6.12.

Review and Assessment (Lesson 6.13)

Like every unit in *Sixth Grade Everyday Mathematics*, Unit 6 ends with a review and assessment lesson. This lesson provides a list of unit goals, as well as suggested questions for oral and slate evaluation. Assessment Masters provide review items for students to complete in writing; each item is keyed to a unit goal.

For additional information on the following topics, see the *Teacher's Reference Manual*:

- calculators
- operations with positive and negative numbers
- positive and negative numbers
- reading and writing number sentences
- solving open sentences
- uses of variables

6.1 Multiplication of Fractions and Mixed Numbers

OBJECTIVE **To review multiplying fractions and mixed numbers.**

summaries	materials
1 Teaching the Lesson	
Students review several properties that are the basis for an introduction to division of fractions in Lesson 6.2. They practice multiplying fractions and mixed numbers. Finally, they practice finding the reciprocal of a number. [Operations and Computation; Numeration]	☐ *Math Journal 2,* pp. 207–209 ☐ *Student Reference Book,* pp. 84–86 (optional) ☐ calculator
2 Ongoing Learning & Practice	
Students practice renaming equivalent fractions. [Numeration] Students practice and maintain skills through Math Boxes and Study Link activities.	☐ *Math Journal 2,* pp. 210 and 211 ☐ Study Link Master *(Math Masters,* p. 312) ☐ Geometry Template
3 Options for Individualizing	
Extra Practice Students practice finding reciprocals. [Numeration]	☐ Teaching Master *(Math Masters,* p. 92)

Additional Information

Vocabulary • **reciprocal**

Getting Started

Mental Math and Reflexes

If fractions are equivalent, students indicate "thumbs up." If fractions are not equivalent, students indicate "thumbs down." *Suggestions:*

- $1\frac{5}{6}$ and $\frac{22}{12}$ up
- $\frac{3}{12}$ and $\frac{1.5}{5}$ down
- $1\frac{7}{8}$ and $\frac{15}{16}$ down
- $\frac{15}{45}$ and $\frac{4}{6}$ down
- $\frac{4}{5}$ and $\frac{28}{35}$ up
- $\frac{7}{6}$ and $1\frac{1}{7}$ down

Math Message

Complete the problems on journal page 207.

Teaching the Lesson

✦ Math Message Follow-Up
(*Math Journal 2,* p. 207)

WHOLE-CLASS DISCUSSION

Briefly go over the answers to Problems 1–3. Then ask a few volunteers to share their answers to Problem 4.

✦ Reviewing Multiplication of Fractions
(*Math Journal 2,* p. 208)

PARTNER ACTIVITY

Multiplication of fractions and mixed numbers was covered in Lessons 4.6 and 4.7. Pose several multiplication of fractions and mixed numbers problems to check students' understanding. Then assign Problems 1–17 on journal page 208. Circulate and assist as needed.

✦ Defining the Reciprocal of a Number
(*Math Journal 2,* p. 208)

WHOLE-CLASS DISCUSSION

Bring the class together to discuss Problem 17. Students may have discovered a visual pattern: If a fraction is multiplied by the same fraction turned "upside down," the product is 1. Pairs of numbers whose product is 1 are called **reciprocals** of each other. For example, 2 is the reciprocal of $\frac{1}{2}$, and $\frac{1}{2}$ is the reciprocal of 2 because the product of $\frac{1}{2}$ and 2 is 1. The numbers 1 and -1 are their own reciprocals ($1 * 1 = 1$ and $-1 * -1 = 1$). Zero has no reciprocal, since the product of 0 and any number is 0. Every other number has a reciprocal that is not equal to itself. Point out that reciprocals need not be in fraction form. For example, 0.8 and 1.25 are reciprocals of each other because $0.8 * 1.25 = 1$.

Adjusting the Activity Students can use a calculator to check that 0.8 and 1.25 are reciprocals of each other. Or, they could write the numbers in fraction form: $\frac{8}{10} * 1\frac{1}{4} = \frac{4}{5} * \frac{5}{4}$.

Have students do the remaining problems on journal page 208 (Problems 18–20).

Multiplication and Division Properties

1. a. If you multiply a number by 1, what number do you get? That number
   b. Give an example for each kind of number. Sample answers:
   Whole number $5 * 1 = 5$ Fraction $\frac{1}{3} * 1 = \frac{1}{3}$
   Decimal $0.084 * 1 = 0.084$
   c. Complete: If y is a whole number, fraction, or decimal, then $y * 1 =$ y and $1 * y =$ y.
2. a. If you divide a number by 1, what number do you get? That number
   b. Give an example for each kind of number. Sample answers:
   Whole number $58 / 1 = 58$ Fraction $\frac{3}{8} / 1 = \frac{3}{8}$
   Decimal $7.02 / 1 = 7.02$
   c. Complete: If y is a whole number, fraction, or decimal, then $y / 1 =$ y and $\frac{y}{1} =$ y.
3. a. If you divide any number, except 0, by itself, what number do you get? 1
   b. Give an example for each kind of number. Sample answers:
   Whole number $3 / 3 = 1$ Fraction $\frac{7}{12} / \frac{7}{12} = 1$
   Decimal $0.89 / 0.89 = 1$
   c. Complete: If y is any whole number, fraction, or decimal, except 0, then $y / y =$ 1 and $\frac{y}{y} =$ 1.
4. Suppose you want to explain to a third grader how to solve the problem $\frac{2}{3} * \frac{3}{5}$. What will you say? Be sure to use words the third grader already knows or define any words he or she may not know.
   Sample answer: Multiply the top numbers to get the numerator of the answer; then multiply the bottom numbers to get the denominator.

STUDENT PAGE

✧ *Math Journal 2,* p. 207

Adjusting the Activity You may want to go over pages 84–86 in the *Student Reference Book* with students who need additional review of multiplication of fractions and mixed numbers.

Fraction Multiplication

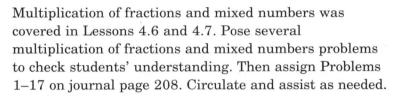

Multiply. Write your answers in simplest form. When you and your partner have finished solving the problems, compare your answers. If you disagree on an answer, check it with a calculator.

1. $\frac{5}{6} * \frac{3}{10} =$ $\frac{1}{4}$
2. $6 * \frac{2}{3} =$ 4
3. $7 * \frac{3}{7} =$ 3
4. $2\frac{3}{4} * \frac{4}{1} =$ 11
5. $2\frac{3}{5} * 1\frac{2}{3} =$ $4\frac{1}{3}$
6. $\frac{7}{3} * \frac{1}{3} =$ $\frac{7}{9}$
7. $\frac{1}{4} * \frac{2}{5} =$ $\frac{1}{10}$
8. $3\frac{3}{8} * \frac{3}{4} =$ $2\frac{17}{32}$
9. $1\frac{5}{6} * 4\frac{2}{3} =$ $8\frac{5}{9}$
10. $\frac{7}{10} * 2\frac{3}{5} =$ $1\frac{41}{50}$
11. $\frac{5}{6} * \frac{6}{5} =$ 1
12. $\frac{3}{4} * \frac{4}{3} =$ 1
13. $\frac{4}{1} * \frac{1}{4} =$ 1
14. $\frac{1}{100} * \frac{100}{1} =$ 1
15. $\frac{7}{8} * \frac{8}{7} =$ 1
16. $\frac{11}{12} * \frac{12}{11} =$ 1
17. What pattern do you notice in Problems 11–16?
    Sample answer: When a fraction is turned "upside down" and multiplied, the answer is always 1.
18. $\frac{2}{3} *$ $\frac{3}{2}$ $= 1$
19. $\frac{3}{5} *$ $\frac{5}{3}$ $= 1$
20. Make up three multiplication problems that have 1 as the answer. Sample answers:
    a. $\frac{7}{8} * \frac{8}{7} = 1$ b. $\frac{4}{5} * \frac{5}{4} = 1$
    c. $\frac{6}{3} * \frac{3}{6} = 1$

STUDENT PAGE

✧ *Math Journal 2,* p. 208

Reciprocals

Reciprocal Property

If a and b are any numbers, except 0, then $\frac{a}{b} * \frac{b}{a} = 1$.

$\frac{a}{b}$ and $\frac{b}{a}$ are called reciprocals of each other.

$a * \frac{1}{a} = 1$, so a and $\frac{1}{a}$ are reciprocals of each other.

Find the reciprocal of each number. Then check your answers with a calculator.

1. 6 $\frac{1}{6}$
2. 17 $\frac{1}{17}$
3. $\frac{3}{4}$ $\frac{4}{3}$, or $1\frac{1}{3}$
4. $\frac{1}{3}$ 3
5. $\frac{3}{8}$ $\frac{8}{3}$, or $2\frac{2}{3}$
6. $\frac{13}{16}$ $\frac{16}{13}$, or $1\frac{3}{13}$
7. $8\frac{1}{2}$ $\frac{2}{17}$
8. $3\frac{5}{6}$ $\frac{6}{23}$
9. $4\frac{2}{3}$ $\frac{3}{14}$
10. $6\frac{1}{4}$ $\frac{4}{25}$
11. 0.1 10
12. 0.4 $\frac{5}{2}$, or $2\frac{1}{2}$
13. 0.75 $\frac{4}{3}$, or $1\frac{1}{3}$
14. 2.5 $\frac{2}{5}$
15. 0.375 $\frac{8}{3}$, or $2\frac{2}{3}$
16. 5.6 $\frac{5}{28}$
17. π (*Hint:* Use either 3.14 or $3\frac{1}{7}$ as an approximate value for π.) $\frac{50}{157}$, or $\frac{7}{22}$

The year didn't always begin in January. Thousands of years ago, the Roman new year began in March. This is why our months September, October, November, and December have the prefixes they do—they used to be the seventh, eighth, ninth, and tenth months, respectively. Later, the Romans added January and February to the beginning of the year. The old names for the months September through December didn't make sense then, but the Romans kept them anyway.

STUDENT PAGE

◇ *Math Journal 2,* p. 209

◆ Finding Reciprocals (*Math Journal 2,* p. 209)

WHOLE-CLASS ACTIVITY

One way to test whether two numbers are reciprocals of each other is to find their product. If the product is 1, then the numbers are reciprocals of each other. Write the following number pairs on the board and ask the class to multiply to determine which pairs are reciprocals.

- ▷ 4 and $\frac{1}{4}$ yes
- ▷ $\frac{7}{4}$ and $\frac{4}{7}$ yes
- ▷ $3\frac{1}{3}$ and $\frac{3}{10}$ yes
- ▷ $\frac{2}{3}$ and $\frac{1}{3}$ no
- ▷ $\frac{2}{5}$ and 5 no
- ▷ 2.5 and 0.4 yes

Write the following numbers on the board and ask students to find their reciprocals:

- ▷ $\frac{5}{6}$ $\frac{6}{5}$, or $1\frac{1}{5}$
- ▷ $\frac{7}{5}$ $\frac{5}{7}$
- ▷ $\frac{1}{9}$ 9
- ▷ 8 $\frac{1}{8}$
- ▷ $2\frac{5}{8}$ $\frac{8}{21}$
- ▷ $3\frac{1}{4}$ $\frac{4}{13}$

◆ Practicing Finding Reciprocals (*Math Journal 2,* p. 209)

PARTNER ACTIVITY

Students complete the problems on journal page 209.

Adjusting the Activity If students have difficulty with Problems 11–16, remind them of the F↔D key on the calculator. They can use it to rename the decimals as fractions, find the reciprocal, and then use the key again to get the decimal form.

NOTE: It is important that students understand that the reciprocal of a number may be represented in many ways, not just as a fraction turned "upside down."

✦ Optional: Finding Reciprocals Using a Calculator

WHOLE-CLASS DISCUSSION

Some calculators have keys such as [1/x] or [x^{-1}], which can be used to find reciprocals.

For example, to find the reciprocal of $\frac{5}{6}$ using a calculator that displays fractions and has the [1/x] key, enter 5/6 [1/x]. The display shows 6/5.

Calculators with the [x^{-1}] key may be a little more troublesome, since students must understand that x^{-1} equals $\frac{1}{x}$.

The Texas Instruments TI-15, the calculator recommended for *Sixth Grade Everyday Mathematics,* does not have a key that allows the reciprocal to be found directly. Instead, students can use the reciprocal property stating that the product of a number and its reciprocal is equal to 1 and that the reciprocal of a number a can be expressed as $\frac{1}{a}$. For example, to find the reciprocal of $\frac{5}{8}$, key in 1 (÷) 5 (n) 8 (d) (Enter). The display shows $1\frac{3}{5}$.

As always, check the instructions supplied with the calculator.

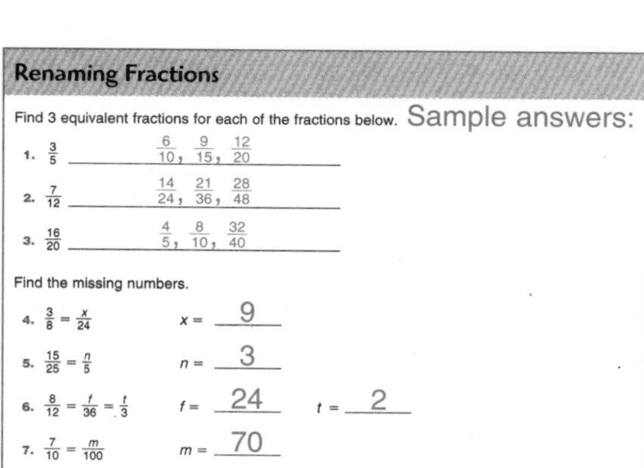

Renaming Fractions

Find 3 equivalent fractions for each of the fractions below. Sample answers:

1. $\frac{3}{5}$ $\frac{6}{10}$, $\frac{9}{15}$, $\frac{12}{20}$
2. $\frac{7}{12}$ $\frac{14}{24}$, $\frac{21}{36}$, $\frac{28}{48}$
3. $\frac{16}{20}$ $\frac{4}{5}$, $\frac{8}{10}$, $\frac{32}{40}$

Find the missing numbers.

4. $\frac{3}{8} = \frac{x}{24}$ $x =$ 9
5. $\frac{15}{25} = \frac{n}{5}$ $n =$ 3
6. $\frac{8}{12} = \frac{f}{36} = \frac{t}{3}$ $f =$ 24 $t =$ 2
7. $\frac{7}{10} = \frac{m}{100}$ $m =$ 70
8. $\frac{6}{9} = \frac{y}{3} = \frac{z}{6}$ $y =$ 2 $z =$ 4
9. $\frac{10}{15} = \frac{w}{6}$ $w =$ 4
10. Explain how you found w in Problem 9.
Sample answer: I reduced $\frac{10}{15}$ to $\frac{2}{3}$; then I found the fraction with a denominator of 6 equivalent to $\frac{2}{3}$, which is $\frac{4}{6}$.
11. Make up one of your own problems. Answers vary.
_____ = _____ = _____
12. Solve Problem 11 in your partner's journal.

STUDENT PAGE

✧ *Math Journal 2,* p. 210

Ongoing Learning & Practice

✦ Finding Equivalent Fractions (*Math Journal 2,* p. 210)

INDEPENDENT ACTIVITY 

Students practice finding equivalent fractions. They also explain the computation process they used.

✦ Math Boxes 6.1 (*Math Journal 2,* p. 211)

INDEPENDENT ACTIVITY 

Mixed Review Math Boxes in this lesson are paired with Math Boxes in Lesson 6.3. The skill in Problem 1 is a prerequisite for Unit 7.

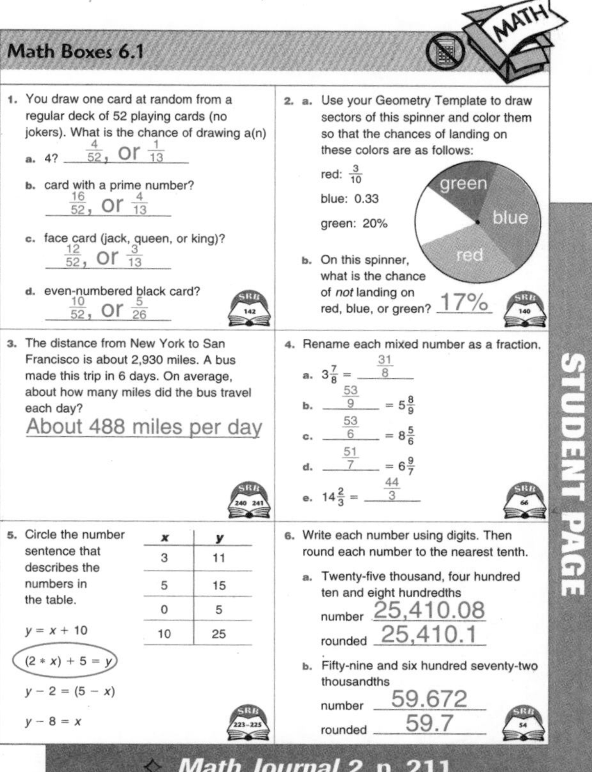

Math Boxes 6.1

1. You draw one card at random from a regular deck of 52 playing cards (no jokers). What is the chance of drawing a(n)
a. 4? $\frac{4}{52}$, or $\frac{1}{13}$
b. card with a prime number? $\frac{16}{52}$, or $\frac{4}{13}$
c. face card (jack, queen, or king)? $\frac{12}{52}$, or $\frac{3}{13}$
d. even-numbered black card? $\frac{10}{52}$, or $\frac{5}{26}$
SRB 142

2. a. Use your Geometry Template to draw sectors of this spinner and color them so that the chances of landing on these colors are as follows:
red: $\frac{3}{10}$
blue: 0.33
green: 20%
(spinner: green, blue, red)
b. On this spinner, what is the chance of *not* landing on red, blue, or green? 17%
SRB 140

3. The distance from New York to San Francisco is about 2,930 miles. A bus made this trip in 6 days. On average, about how many miles did the bus travel each day?
About 488 miles per day
SRB 240 241

4. Rename each mixed number as a fraction.
a. $3\frac{7}{8} = \frac{31}{8}$
b. $\frac{53}{9} = 5\frac{8}{9}$
c. $\frac{53}{6} = 8\frac{5}{6}$
d. $\frac{51}{7} = 6\frac{9}{7}$
e. $14\frac{2}{3} = \frac{44}{3}$
SRB 66

5. Circle the number sentence that describes the numbers in the table.

x	y
3	11
5	15
0	5
10	25

$y = x + 10$
($(2 * x) + 5 = y$) (circled)
$y - 2 = (5 - x)$
$y - 8 = x$
SRB 223–225

6. Write each number using digits. Then round each number to the nearest tenth.
a. Twenty-five thousand, four hundred ten and eight hundredths
number 25,410.08
rounded 25,410.1
b. Fifty-nine and six hundred seventy-two thousandths
number 59.672
rounded 59.7
SRB 54

STUDENT PAGE

✧ *Math Journal 2,* p. 211

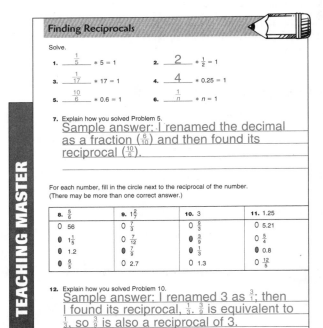

STUDY LINK MASTER

Practice with Fractions — Study Link 6.1

Put a check mark next to each pair of equivalent fractions.

1. ____ $\frac{2}{3}$ and $\frac{5}{6}$
2. ✓ $1\frac{3}{4}$ and $\frac{28}{16}$
3. ✓ $\frac{24}{30}$ and $\frac{4}{5}$
4. ____ $\frac{7}{3}$ and $\frac{3}{7}$
5. ✓ $\frac{56}{8}$ and $\frac{49}{7}$
6. ____ $2\frac{3}{8}$ and $\frac{19}{4}$

Find the reciprocal of each number. Check your answers with a calculator.

7. 19 $\frac{1}{19}$
8. $\frac{2}{5}$ $\frac{5}{2}$, or $2\frac{1}{2}$
9. $3\frac{5}{7}$ $\frac{7}{26}$
10. $\frac{1}{6}$ 6

Multiply. Write your answers in simplest form. Show your work.

11. $\frac{2}{5} * 7 =$ $2\frac{4}{5}$
12. $\frac{2}{3} * 1\frac{1}{8} =$ $\frac{3}{4}$
13. $2\frac{1}{6} * 1\frac{5}{6} =$ $3\frac{35}{36}$
14. $3\frac{1}{7} * \frac{7}{22} =$ 1

Solve the number stories.

15. How much does a box containing 5 horseshoes weigh, if each horseshoe weighs about $2\frac{1}{2}$ pounds? $12\frac{1}{2}$ lb
16. One and a half dozen golf tees are laid in a straight line, end to end. If each tee is $2\frac{1}{8}$ inches long, how long is the line of tees? $38\frac{1}{4}$ in.
17. A standard-size brick is 8 inches long and $2\frac{1}{4}$ inches high and has a depth of $3\frac{3}{4}$ inches. What is the volume of a standard-size brick? $67\frac{1}{2}$ $in.^3$

✦ *Math Masters,* **p. 312**

✦ Study Link 6.1 (*Math Masters,* p. 312)

Home Connection Students find pairs of equivalent fractions, find the reciprocals of numbers, and multiply fractions and mixed numbers.

3 Options for Individualizing

✦ EXTRA PRACTICE Finding Reciprocals (*Math Masters,* p. 92)

INDEPENDENT ACTIVITY  **15–30 min** 

Students find reciprocals of whole numbers, fractions, and decimals.

TEACHING MASTER

Finding Reciprocals

Solve.

1. $\frac{1}{5}$ $* 5 = 1$
2. 2 $* \frac{1}{2} = 1$
3. $\frac{1}{17}$ $* 17 = 1$
4. 4 $* 0.25 = 1$
5. $\frac{10}{6}$ $* 0.6 = 1$
6. $\frac{1}{n}$ $* n = 1$

7. Explain how you solved Problem 5.
Sample answer: I renamed the decimal as a fraction ($\frac{6}{10}$) and then found its reciprocal ($\frac{10}{6}$).

For each number, fill in the circle next to the reciprocal of the number. (There may be more than one correct answer.)

8. $\frac{5}{6}$	9. $1\frac{2}{7}$	10. 3	11. 1.25
○ 56	○ $\frac{7}{3}$	○ $\frac{9}{3}$	○ 5.21
● $1\frac{1}{5}$	○ $\frac{7}{12}$	● $\frac{3}{9}$	○ $\frac{5}{4}$
● 1.2	● $\frac{7}{9}$	● $\frac{1}{3}$	● 0.8
● $\frac{6}{5}$	○ 2.7	○ 1.3	○ $\frac{12}{5}$

12. Explain how you solved Problem 10.
Sample answer: I renamed 3 as $\frac{3}{1}$; then I found its reciprocal, $\frac{1}{3}$. $\frac{3}{9}$ is equivalent to $\frac{1}{3}$, so $\frac{3}{9}$ is also a reciprocal of 3.

✦ *Math Masters,* **p. 92**

6.2 Division of Fractions and Mixed Numbers

OBJECTIVE **To introduce an algorithm for the division of fractions.**

summaries	materials
1 Teaching the Lesson	
Students learn a division algorithm for fractions and use it to divide fractions and mixed numbers. [Operations and Computation]	☐ *Math Journal 2,* pp. 212 and 213 ☐ *Student Reference Book,* p. 89 ☐ Study Link 6.1 ☐ inch and centimeter ruler ☐ calculator
2 Ongoing Learning & Practice	
Students practice and maintain skills through Math Boxes and Study Link activities.	☐ *Math Journal 2,* p. 214 ☐ Study Link Master (*Math Masters,* p. 313)
3 Options for Individualizing	
Extra Practice Students practice dividing fractions and mixed numbers. [Operations and Computation] **Enrichment** Students study a "proof" of the Division of Fractions Property. [Operations and Computation; Patterns, Functions, and Algebra]	☐ *Student Reference Book,* pp. 89 and 90 ☐ Teaching Master (*Math Masters,* p. 93)

Additional Information

Vocabulary • **Division of Fractions Property**

Getting Started

Mental Math and Reflexes

Students give the reciprocal of each number. *Suggestions:* $\frac{1}{6}$ 6, $\frac{3}{5}$ $\frac{5}{3}$, $\frac{2}{3}$ $\frac{3}{2}$, 3 $\frac{1}{3}$, $\frac{7}{4}$ $\frac{4}{7}$, $1\frac{1}{3}$ $\frac{3}{4}$

Students give an equivalent fraction with a denominator of 24. *Suggestions:* $\frac{1}{6}$ $\frac{4}{24}$, $\frac{2}{3}$ $\frac{16}{24}$, $\frac{3}{4}$ $\frac{18}{24}$, $\frac{1}{2}$ $\frac{12}{24}$, $\frac{5}{8}$ $\frac{15}{24}$, $\frac{7}{12}$ $\frac{14}{24}$, $\frac{32}{48}$ $\frac{16}{24}$

Students give an equivalent fraction with a denominator of 60. *Suggestions:* $\frac{1}{6}$ $\frac{10}{60}$, $\frac{2}{3}$ $\frac{40}{60}$, $\frac{3}{4}$ $\frac{45}{60}$, $\frac{1}{2}$ $\frac{30}{60}$, $\frac{3}{5}$ $\frac{36}{60}$, $\frac{9}{10}$ $\frac{54}{60}$, $\frac{9}{20}$ $\frac{27}{60}$, $\frac{7}{12}$ $\frac{35}{60}$, $\frac{100}{120}$ $\frac{50}{60}$

Math Message

Solve Problems 1–4 on journal page 212.

Study Link 6.1 Follow-Up

Briefly go over the answers.

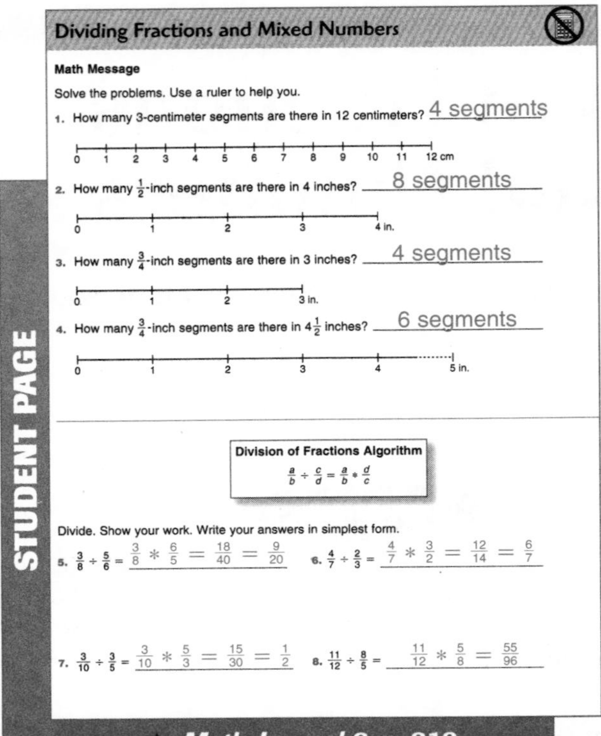

Dividing Fractions and Mixed Numbers

Math Message

Solve the problems. Use a ruler to help you.

1. How many 3-centimeter segments are there in 12 centimeters? 4 segments
2. How many $\frac{1}{2}$-inch segments are there in 4 inches? 8 segments
3. How many $\frac{3}{4}$-inch segments are there in 3 inches? 4 segments
4. How many $\frac{3}{4}$-inch segments are there in $4\frac{1}{2}$ inches? 6 segments

Division of Fractions Algorithm

$\frac{a}{b} \div \frac{c}{d} = \frac{a}{b} * \frac{d}{c}$

Divide. Show your work. Write your answers in simplest form.

5. $\frac{3}{8} \div \frac{5}{6} = \frac{3}{8} * \frac{6}{5} = \frac{18}{40} = \frac{9}{20}$
6. $\frac{4}{7} \div \frac{2}{3} = \frac{4}{7} * \frac{3}{2} = \frac{12}{14} = \frac{6}{7}$
7. $\frac{3}{10} \div \frac{3}{5} = \frac{3}{10} * \frac{5}{3} = \frac{15}{30} = \frac{1}{2}$
8. $\frac{11}{12} \div \frac{8}{5} = \frac{11}{12} * \frac{5}{8} = \frac{55}{96}$

STUDENT PAGE

◇ *Math Journal 2,* p. 212

Teaching the Lesson

◆ Math Message Follow-Up (*Math Journal 2,* p. 212)

WHOLE-CLASS DISCUSSION

Ask volunteers to describe how they solved the problems. Students should see that Problem 1 can be solved by division.

Problem 1: $12 \div 3 = 4$

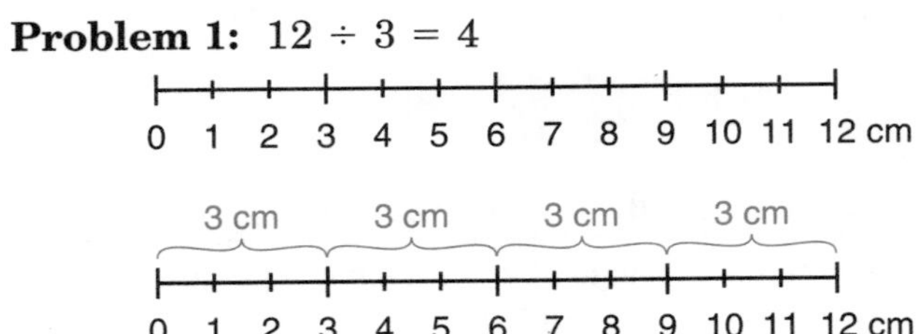

Point out that the rest of the problems are similar, except they use fractions or mixed numbers. Therefore, they too can be solved by division. Go over each problem. Draw a picture on the board showing the partition of the whole line segment into equal segments. Then write a division sentence.

Problem 2: $4 \div \frac{1}{2} = 8$

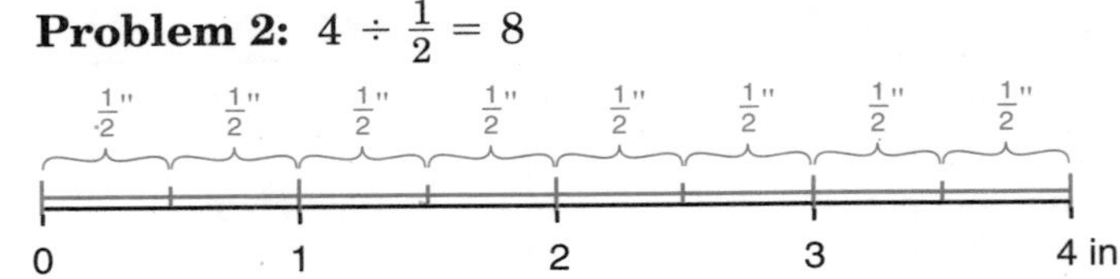

Problem 3: $3 \div \frac{3}{4} = 4$

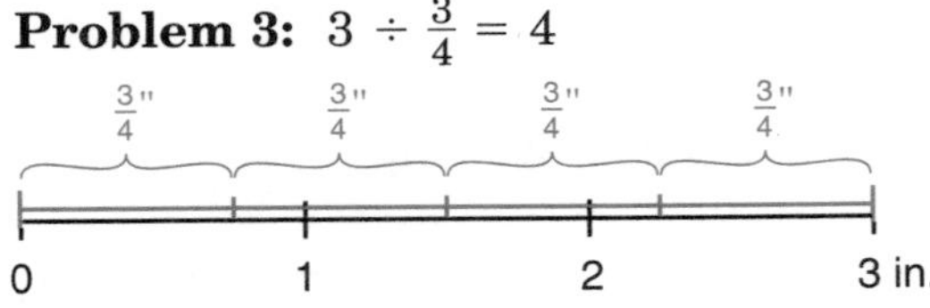

Problem 4: $4\frac{1}{2} \div \frac{3}{4} = 6$

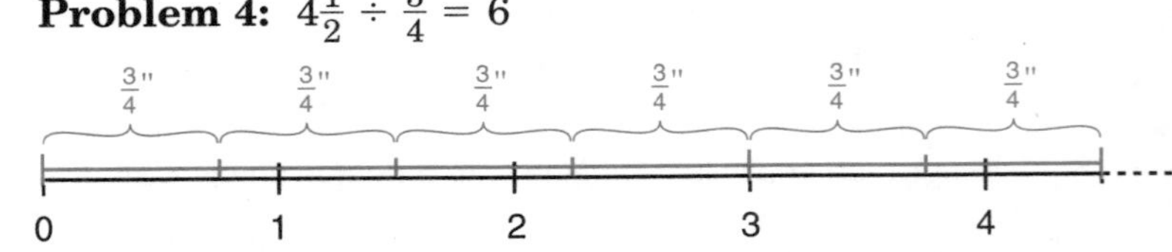

Now draw a line segment on the board and ask: *How many $\frac{3}{8}$-inch segments are in $1\frac{1}{2}$ inches?*

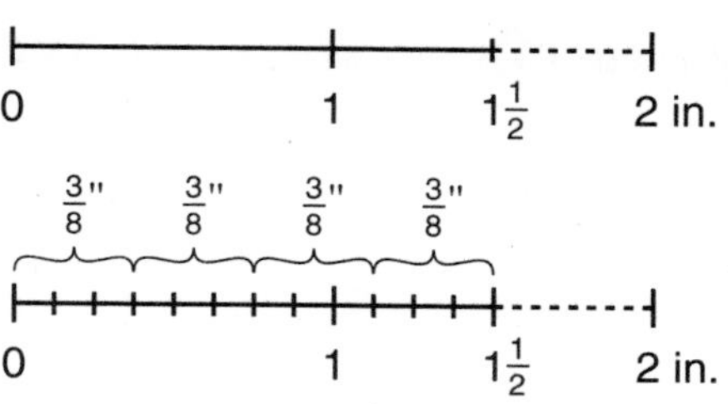

Point out that one way to solve the problem is to divide the $1\frac{1}{2}$-inch segment into eighths. Then it is easy to see that there are four $\frac{3}{8}$-inch segments in $1\frac{1}{2}$ inches.

Remind students that in *Fifth Grade Everyday Mathematics,* they learned to divide fractions using the common denominator method: renaming fractions so that they all have a common denominator. By dividing the $1\frac{1}{2}$-inch segment into eighths, we renamed the $1\frac{1}{2}$ inches so that both fractions have the same denominator: 8.

Demonstrate how to solve the problem by using the common denominator method.

Example: $1\frac{1}{2} \div \frac{3}{8} = ?$

▷ Rename $1\frac{1}{2}$ as a fraction: $1\frac{1}{2} \div \frac{3}{8} = \frac{3}{2} \div \frac{3}{8}$

▷ Rename $\frac{3}{2}$ as eighths: $\frac{3}{2} \div \frac{3}{8} = \frac{12}{8} \div \frac{3}{8}$

▷ Divide the numerators: $12 \div 3 = 4$

NOTE: Some students may wonder why, when using this method, we can ignore the denominators. Remind them of the original problem: *How many $\frac{3}{8}$-inch segments are in $1\frac{1}{2}$ inches?* Think of the question as: *How many segments of a "certain size" are in $1\frac{1}{2}$ inches?* The answer is 4 segments of a "certain size," which is the result of dividing the numerators.

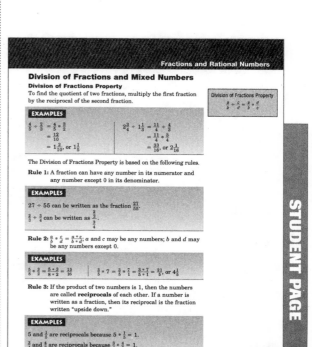

With the class, solve problems in which the answer is a mixed number or fraction.

Example: $\frac{2}{3} \div \frac{4}{9} = ?$

▷ Rename $\frac{2}{3}$ as ninths: $\frac{2}{3} \div \frac{4}{9} = \frac{6}{9} \div \frac{4}{9}$

▷ Divide the numerators: $6 \div 4 = \frac{6}{4} = 1\frac{2}{4}$, or $1\frac{1}{2}$

Example: $\frac{1}{4} \div \frac{2}{3} = ?$

▷ Rename both fractions: $\frac{1}{4} \div \frac{2}{3} = \frac{3}{12} \div \frac{8}{12}$

▷ Divide the numerators: $3 \div 8 = \frac{3}{8}$

Pose several problems for students to solve. *Suggestions:*

- $1\frac{1}{2} \div \frac{3}{8}$ 4
- $\frac{2}{3} \div \frac{3}{5}$ $1\frac{1}{9}$
- $\frac{5}{6} \div \frac{2}{3}$ $1\frac{1}{4}$
- $\frac{3}{4} \div \frac{1}{3}$ $2\frac{1}{4}$

✦ Introducing the Division of Fractions Property (*Student Reference Book,* p. 89)

WHOLE-CLASS ACTIVITY 

Ask a volunteer to solve this problem on the board:

$\frac{4}{5} \div \frac{2}{3} = ?$

$\frac{4}{5} \div \frac{2}{3} = \frac{12}{15} \div \frac{10}{15} = 12 \div 10 = \frac{12}{10}$, or $1\frac{1}{5}$

Ask whether anyone knows how to solve the problem using the "invert and multiply" rule. If so, have a volunteer demonstrate it. If no one is able to, have the class turn to the **Division of Fractions Property** at the top of page 89 in the *Student Reference Book.*

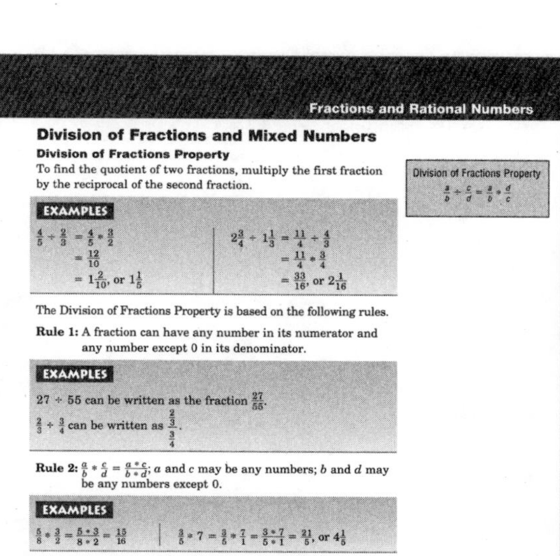

Fractions and Rational Numbers

Division of Fractions and Mixed Numbers

Division of Fractions Property

To find the quotient of two fractions, multiply the first fraction by the reciprocal of the second fraction.

Division of Fractions Property: $\frac{a}{b} \div \frac{c}{d} = \frac{a}{b} * \frac{d}{c}$

EXAMPLES

$\frac{4}{5} \div \frac{2}{3} = \frac{4}{5} * \frac{3}{2} = \frac{12}{10} = 1\frac{2}{10}$, or $1\frac{1}{5}$

$2\frac{3}{4} \div 1\frac{1}{3} = \frac{11}{4} \div \frac{4}{3} = \frac{11}{4} * \frac{3}{4} = \frac{33}{16}$, or $2\frac{1}{16}$

The Division of Fractions Property is based on the following rules.

Rule 1: A fraction can have any number in its numerator and any number except 0 in its denominator.

EXAMPLES

$27 \div 55$ can be written as the fraction $\frac{27}{55}$.

$\frac{2}{3} \div \frac{3}{4}$ can be written as $\frac{\frac{2}{3}}{\frac{3}{4}}$.

Rule 2: $\frac{a}{b} * \frac{c}{d} = \frac{a * c}{b * d}$; a and c may be any numbers; b and d may be any numbers except 0.

EXAMPLES

$\frac{5}{8} * \frac{3}{2} = \frac{5 * 3}{8 * 2} = \frac{15}{16}$

$\frac{3}{5} * 7 = \frac{3}{5} * \frac{7}{1} = \frac{3 * 7}{5 * 1} = \frac{21}{5}$, or $4\frac{1}{5}$

Rule 3: If the product of two numbers is 1, then the numbers are called **reciprocals** of each other. If a number is written as a fraction, then its reciprocal is the fraction written "upside down."

EXAMPLES

5 and $\frac{1}{5}$ are reciprocals because $5 * \frac{1}{5} = 1$.

$\frac{3}{4}$ and $\frac{4}{3}$ are reciprocals because $\frac{3}{4} * \frac{4}{3} = 1$.

$2\frac{3}{5}$ and $\frac{5}{13}$ are reciprocals because $2\frac{3}{5} = \frac{13}{5}$ and $\frac{13}{5} * \frac{5}{13} = 1$.

eighty-nine SRB 89

STUDENT PAGE

✧ *Student Reference Book,* p. 89

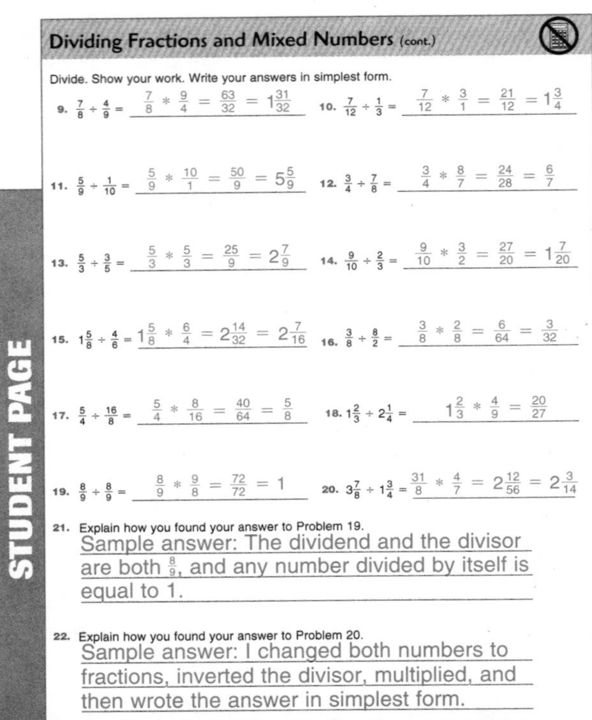

Dividing Fractions and Mixed Numbers (cont.)

Divide. Show your work. Write your answers in simplest form.

9. $\frac{7}{8} \div \frac{4}{9} = \frac{7}{8} * \frac{9}{4} = \frac{63}{32} = 1\frac{31}{32}$

10. $\frac{7}{12} \div \frac{1}{3} = \frac{7}{12} * \frac{3}{1} = \frac{21}{12} = 1\frac{3}{4}$

11. $\frac{5}{9} \div \frac{1}{10} = \frac{5}{9} * \frac{10}{1} = \frac{50}{9} = 5\frac{5}{9}$

12. $\frac{3}{4} \div \frac{7}{8} = \frac{3}{4} * \frac{8}{7} = \frac{24}{28} = \frac{6}{7}$

13. $\frac{5}{3} \div \frac{3}{5} = \frac{5}{3} * \frac{5}{3} = \frac{25}{9} = 2\frac{7}{9}$

14. $\frac{9}{10} \div \frac{2}{3} = \frac{9}{10} * \frac{3}{2} = \frac{27}{20} = 1\frac{7}{20}$

15. $1\frac{5}{8} \div \frac{4}{6} = 1\frac{5}{8} * \frac{6}{4} = 2\frac{14}{32} = 2\frac{7}{16}$

16. $\frac{3}{8} \div \frac{8}{2} = \frac{3}{8} * \frac{2}{8} = \frac{6}{64} = \frac{3}{32}$

17. $\frac{5}{4} \div \frac{16}{8} = \frac{5}{4} * \frac{8}{16} = \frac{40}{64} = \frac{5}{8}$

18. $1\frac{2}{3} \div 2\frac{1}{4} = 1\frac{2}{3} * \frac{4}{9} = \frac{20}{27}$

19. $\frac{8}{9} \div \frac{8}{9} = \frac{8}{9} * \frac{9}{8} = \frac{72}{72} = 1$

20. $3\frac{7}{8} \div 1\frac{3}{4} = \frac{31}{8} * \frac{4}{7} = 2\frac{12}{56} = 2\frac{3}{14}$

21. Explain how you found your answer to Problem 19.
Sample answer: The dividend and the divisor are both $\frac{8}{9}$, and any number divided by itself is equal to 1.

22. Explain how you found your answer to Problem 20.
Sample answer: I changed both numbers to fractions, inverted the divisor, multiplied, and then wrote the answer in simplest form.

STUDENT PAGE

◇ *Math Journal 2,* p. 213

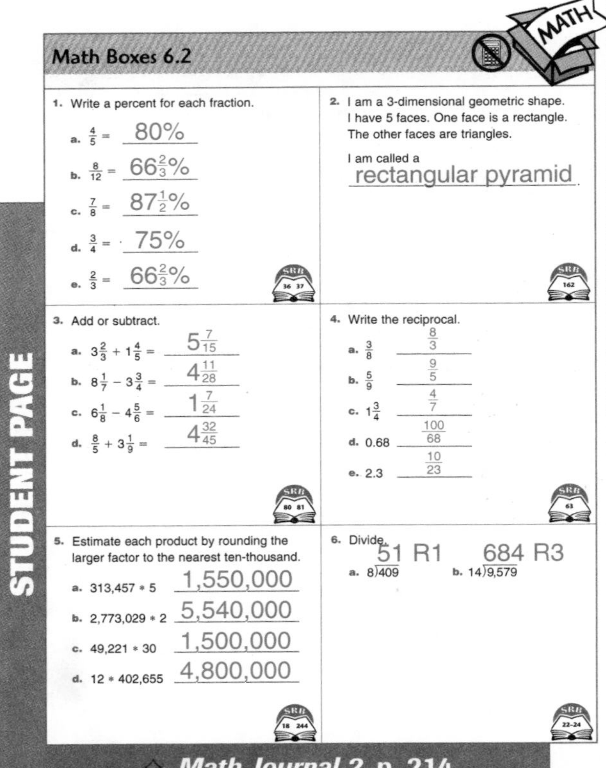

Math Boxes 6.2

1. Write a percent for each fraction.
   a. $\frac{4}{5} =$ 80%
   b. $\frac{8}{12} =$ $66\frac{2}{3}$%
   c. $\frac{7}{8} =$ $87\frac{1}{2}$%
   d. $\frac{3}{4} =$ 75%
   e. $\frac{2}{3} =$ $66\frac{2}{3}$%

SRB 36 37

2. I am a 3-dimensional geometric shape. I have 5 faces. One face is a rectangle. The other faces are triangles.
   I am called a rectangular pyramid

SRB 162

3. Add or subtract.
   a. $3\frac{2}{3} + 1\frac{4}{5} =$ $5\frac{7}{15}$
   b. $8\frac{1}{7} - 3\frac{3}{4} =$ $4\frac{11}{28}$
   c. $6\frac{1}{8} - 4\frac{5}{6} =$ $1\frac{7}{24}$
   d. $\frac{8}{5} + 3\frac{1}{9} =$ $4\frac{32}{45}$

SRB 80 81

4. Write the reciprocal.
   a. $\frac{3}{8}$ $\frac{8}{3}$
   b. $\frac{5}{9}$ $\frac{9}{5}$
   c. $1\frac{3}{4}$ $\frac{4}{7}$
   d. 0.68 $\frac{100}{68}$
   e. 2.3 $\frac{10}{23}$

SRB 63

5. Estimate each product by rounding the larger factor to the nearest ten-thousand.
   a. 313,457 * 5 1,550,000
   b. 2,773,029 * 2 5,540,000
   c. 49,221 * 30 1,500,000
   d. 12 * 402,655 4,800,000

SRB 18 244

6. Divide.
   a. 8)409 51 R1
   b. 14)9,579 684 R3

SRB 22-24

STUDENT PAGE

◇ *Math Journal 2,* p. 214

Example 1 shows how to solve the problem by multiplying the dividend by the reciprocal of the divisor.

Students will probably be puzzled by this procedure, since it doesn't make sense intuitively. To help them accept its validity, ask them to use the procedure to solve the same problems they solved earlier by the common denominator method. You might also suggest that they solve the problems on their calculators. (See page 459.)

NOTE: A common error in using this algorithm is to take the reciprocal of the *dividend* instead of the divisor. Be sure to caution students to use the correct reciprocal.

✦ Dividing Fractions and Mixed Numbers

(*Math Journal 2,* pp. 212 and 213)

PARTNER ACTIVITY 

Have students complete these pages on their own. Then they should compare their answers to those of their partners and use a calculator to resolve disagreements. Remind students to write their answers in simplest form.

Adjusting the Activity If students are struggling with the algorithm, you might want to skip Problems 15, 18, and 20 (involving mixed numbers) on journal page 213 today and come back to them in a few days.

ONGOING ASSESSMENT

Use students' answers to Problems 21 and 22 to assess their understanding. Expect that some students will perform the algorithm without realizing that $\frac{8}{9} \div \frac{8}{9}$ (any non-zero number divided by itself) equals 1.

2 Ongoing Learning & Practice

✦ Math Boxes 6.2 (*Math Journal 2,* p. 214)

INDEPENDENT ACTIVITY 

Mixed Review Math Boxes in this lesson are paired with Math Boxes in Lesson 6.4. The skill in Problem 1 is a prerequisite for Unit 7.

✦ Study Link 6.2 (*Math Masters,* p. 313)

Home Connection Students practice dividing fractions and mixed numbers.

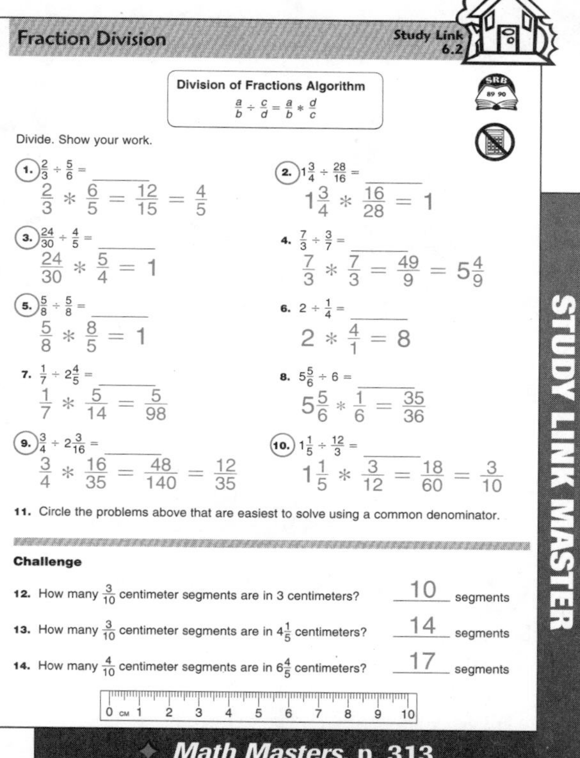

Fraction Division — Study Link 6.2

Division of Fractions Algorithm

$\frac{a}{b} \div \frac{c}{d} = \frac{a}{b} * \frac{d}{c}$

Divide. Show your work.

1. $\frac{2}{3} \div \frac{5}{6} =$ ____ $\quad \frac{2}{3} * \frac{6}{5} = \frac{12}{15} = \frac{4}{5}$
2. $1\frac{3}{4} \div \frac{28}{16} =$ ____ $\quad 1\frac{3}{4} * \frac{16}{28} = 1$
3. $\frac{24}{30} \div \frac{4}{5} =$ ____ $\quad \frac{24}{30} * \frac{5}{4} = 1$
4. $\frac{7}{3} \div \frac{3}{7} =$ ____ $\quad \frac{7}{3} * \frac{7}{3} = \frac{49}{9} = 5\frac{4}{9}$
5. $\frac{5}{8} \div \frac{5}{8} =$ ____ $\quad \frac{5}{8} * \frac{8}{5} = 1$
6. $2 \div \frac{1}{4} =$ ____ $\quad 2 * \frac{4}{1} = 8$
7. $\frac{1}{7} \div 2\frac{4}{5} =$ ____ $\quad \frac{1}{7} * \frac{5}{14} = \frac{5}{98}$
8. $5\frac{5}{6} \div 6 =$ ____ $\quad 5\frac{5}{6} * \frac{1}{6} = \frac{35}{36}$
9. $\frac{3}{4} \div 2\frac{3}{16} =$ ____ $\quad \frac{3}{4} * \frac{16}{35} = \frac{48}{140} = \frac{12}{35}$
10. $1\frac{1}{5} \div \frac{12}{3} =$ ____ $\quad 1\frac{1}{5} * \frac{3}{12} = \frac{18}{60} = \frac{3}{10}$
11. Circle the problems above that are easiest to solve using a common denominator.

Challenge

12. How many $\frac{3}{10}$ centimeter segments are in 3 centimeters? 10 segments
13. How many $\frac{3}{10}$ centimeter segments are in $4\frac{1}{5}$ centimeters? 14 segments
14. How many $\frac{4}{10}$ centimeter segments are in $6\frac{4}{5}$ centimeters? 17 segments

STUDY LINK MASTER

✦ *Math Masters,* p. 313

3 Options for Individualizing

✦ EXTRA PRACTICE Practicing Division of Fractions and Mixed Numbers (*Math Masters,* p. 93)

INDEPENDENT ACTIVITY  **15–30 min** 

If students need more practice, have them complete this master.

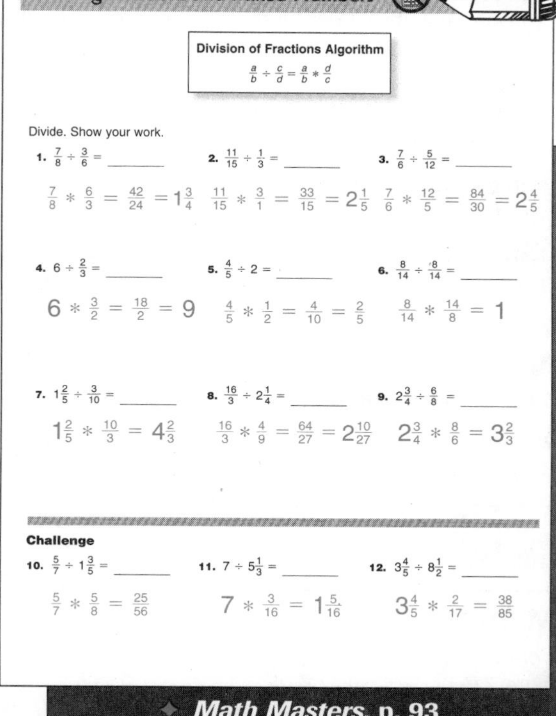

Dividing Fractions and Mixed Numbers

Division of Fractions Algorithm

$\frac{a}{b} \div \frac{c}{d} = \frac{a}{b} * \frac{d}{c}$

Divide. Show your work.

1. $\frac{7}{8} \div \frac{3}{6} =$ ____ $\quad \frac{7}{8} * \frac{6}{3} = \frac{42}{24} = 1\frac{3}{4}$
2. $\frac{11}{15} \div \frac{1}{3} =$ ____ $\quad \frac{11}{15} * \frac{3}{1} = \frac{33}{15} = 2\frac{1}{5}$
3. $\frac{7}{6} \div \frac{5}{12} =$ ____ $\quad \frac{7}{6} * \frac{12}{5} = \frac{84}{30} = 2\frac{4}{5}$
4. $6 \div \frac{2}{3} =$ ____ $\quad 6 * \frac{3}{2} = \frac{18}{2} = 9$
5. $\frac{4}{5} \div 2 =$ ____ $\quad \frac{4}{5} * \frac{1}{2} = \frac{4}{10} = \frac{2}{5}$
6. $\frac{8}{14} \div \frac{8}{14} =$ ____ $\quad \frac{8}{14} * \frac{14}{8} = 1$
7. $1\frac{2}{5} \div \frac{3}{10} =$ ____ $\quad 1\frac{2}{5} * \frac{10}{3} = 4\frac{2}{3}$
8. $\frac{16}{3} \div 2\frac{1}{4} =$ ____ $\quad \frac{16}{3} * \frac{4}{9} = \frac{64}{27} = 2\frac{10}{27}$
9. $2\frac{3}{4} \div \frac{6}{8} =$ ____ $\quad 2\frac{3}{4} * \frac{8}{6} = 3\frac{2}{3}$

Challenge

10. $\frac{5}{7} \div 1\frac{3}{5} =$ ____ $\quad \frac{5}{7} * \frac{5}{8} = \frac{25}{56}$
11. $7 \div 5\frac{1}{3} =$ ____ $\quad 7 * \frac{3}{16} = 1\frac{5}{16}$
12. $3\frac{4}{5} \div 8\frac{1}{2} =$ ____ $\quad 3\frac{4}{5} * \frac{2}{17} = \frac{38}{85}$

TEACHING MASTER

✦ *Math Masters,* p. 93

✦ ENRICHMENT Studying a Proof (*Student Reference Book,* pp. 89 and 90)

INDEPENDENT ACTIVITY  **15–30 min** 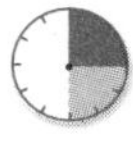

Further justification for the Division of Fractions Property can be found on pages 89 and 90 of the *Student Reference Book* in the "proof by example," which utilizes the five rules demonstrated in the essay. While some students may not fully understand the example, reviewing it is a worthwhile exercise in logic and the reading of mathematical text.

6.3 Review: Addition and Subtraction of Positive and Negative Numbers

OBJECTIVE **To practice adding and subtracting positive and negative numbers.**

summaries	materials
1 Teaching the Lesson	
Students review how to add and subtract positive and negative numbers on a number line. They also use the rule for subtraction of positive and negative numbers. [Patterns, Functions, and Algebra]	□ *Math Journal 2,* pp. 215 and 216 □ *Student Reference Book,* pp. 91, 252, and 262 □ Study Link 6.2 □ calculator □ Real Number Line Poster □ chalk or masking tape (optional) ***See* Advance Preparation**
2 Ongoing Learning & Practice	
Students practice and maintain skills through Math Boxes and Study Link activities.	□ *Math Journal 2,* p. 217 □ Study Link Master (*Math Masters,* p. 314) □ Geometry Template
3 Options for Individualizing	
Enrichment Students learn to add and subtract positive and negative numbers by the absolute value method. [Patterns, Functions, and Algebra] **Reteaching** Students use colored counters to model positive and negative numbers. [Patterns, Functions, and Algebra] **Extra Practice** Students play the advanced version of the *Credits/Debits Game.* [Operations and Computation] **Extra Practice** Students add and subtract positive and negative numbers. [Patterns, Functions, and Algebra]	□ *Student Reference Book,* pp. 94 and 283 □ Teaching Masters (*Math Masters,* pp. 94 and 95) □ 10 chips or counters of one color per student □ 10 chips or counters of another color per student Per partnership: □ complete deck of number cards (from the Everything Math Deck, if available) □ penny

Additional Information

Advance Preparation For Part 1, review the functions of the following calculator keys: (,) , ^ , (-) .

Vocabulary • **opposite of a number**

Getting Started

Math Message

Complete Problems 1 and 2 on journal page 215.

Study Link 6.2 Follow-Up

Go over the answers with the class. Ask students to indicate which problems they circled and to give their reasons for doing so.

Mental Math and Reflexes

Pose problems like the following to give students practice comparing positive and negative numbers, an important prerequisite for this lesson. Allow extra time if students need more practice. Refer to the Real Number Line Poster when discussing the answers to problems.

Which is warmer,

- 5° above zero or 2° below zero? 5° above zero
- 12° below zero or 7° below zero? 7° below zero
- +15° or −20°? +15°
- −10° or 0°? 0°

Which is less,

- −7 or +2? −7
- −45 or −54? −54
- +3.6 or −1.5? −1.5
- 0 or −6? −6

1 Teaching the Lesson

✦Math Message Follow-Up
(*Math Journal 2,* p. 215; *Student Reference Book,* pp. 91, 252, and 262)

WHOLE-CLASS DISCUSSION 

Briefly go over the section on keying positive and negative numbers into a calculator at the top of page 252 of the *Student Reference Book*. Go over the functions of the following keys: (,) , ∧ , and (−) . Partners then correct each other's answers to Problems 1 and 2 on the journal page and use their calculators to resolve any disagreements.

Some students are likely to be confused by the symbol "−," which may be used in three different ways: as a minus sign to indicate subtraction, as a negative sign to represent a negative number, and as a symbol to represent the **opposite of a number.** The symbol (OPP), meaning the opposite of, is introduced to ease potential confusion.

STUDENT PAGE

Negative Numbers on a Calculator

Math Message

Read the section "Negative Numbers" on page 91 in your *Student Reference Book.* Then use your calculator to solve the problems below. You will use the following keys: (,) , ∧ , and (−) .

1. Enter each number into your calculator. Press Enter. Record the calculator display.

Enter	−236	−4.85	$-(\frac{2}{3})$	−0.006	$(-4)^2$	$(-8)^5$
Display	−236	−4.85	$-\frac{2}{3}$	−0.006	16	−32768

The negative sign can be used to represent the phrase "the opposite of." For example, to enter the opposite of 12, key in (−) 12 Enter. The display shows −12. To enter the opposite of −12, key in (−) (−) 12 Enter. The display shows 12. We can write "the opposite of −12" as "−(−12)" or as "(OPP) (−12)." The symbol (OPP) is read "the opposite of."

2. Enter each number into your calculator. Record the calculator display. Clear.

Enter	(OPP) 75	(OPP) (−89)	(OPP) (−312)	(OPP) (27 − 16)	(OPP) (−18 + 56)
Display	−75	89	312	−11	−38

Add or subtract with a calculator. *Remember:* The term (OPP) means "use the opposite of the number."

3. −26 − 17 = −43
   −26 + (OPP) 17 = −43
4. −34 − 68 = −102
   −34 + (−68) = −102
5. 56 − 24 = 32
   56 + (OPP) 24 = 32
6. 18 − 84 = −66
   18 + (−84) = −66
7. 43 − (−97) = 140
   43 + (OPP) (−97) = 140
   43 + 97 = 140
8. 31 − (−13) = 44
   31 + (−(−13)) = 44
   31 + 13 = 44
9. −130 − (−62) = −68
   −130 + (OPP) (−62) = −68
   −130 + 62 = −68
10. −2 − (−22) = 20
    −2 + (−(−22)) = 20
    −2 + 22 = 20

✧ *Math Journal 2,* p. 215

NOTE: Students were introduced to addition and subtraction of positive and negative numbers in *Fourth* and *Fifth Grade Everyday Mathematics.* The number-line models for these operations appear on pages 92 and 93 of the *Student Reference Book.*

✦Adding Positive and Negative Numbers on a Number Line

WHOLE-CLASS ACTIVITY 

Use the following procedure to demonstrate addition of positive and negative numbers on a number line.

Example 1: $-6 + 2 = ?$

▷ Locate the first addend, −6, on the number line. This is your starting point.

▷ To add, face right on the number line.

▷ If the second addend is positive, walk forward that number of spaces, 2. If the second addend is negative, walk backward.

▷ The answer is the number you land on, −4.
$-6 + 2 = -4$

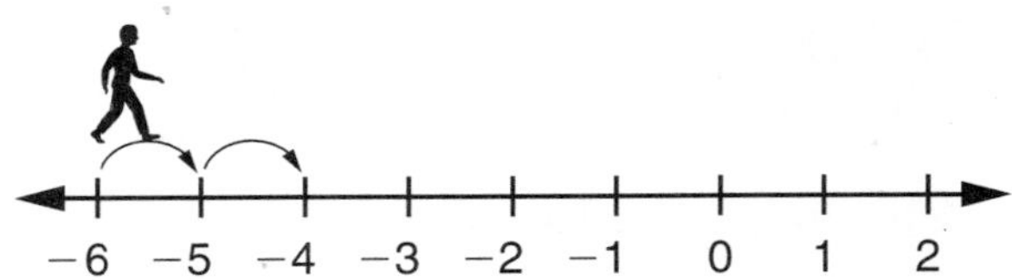

Example 2: $4 + (-3) = ?$

▷ Locate the first addend, 4, on the number line.

▷ Face right.

▷ Since the second addend, −3, is a negative number, walk 3 steps *backward.*

▷ You end up at 1.
$4 + (-3) = 1$

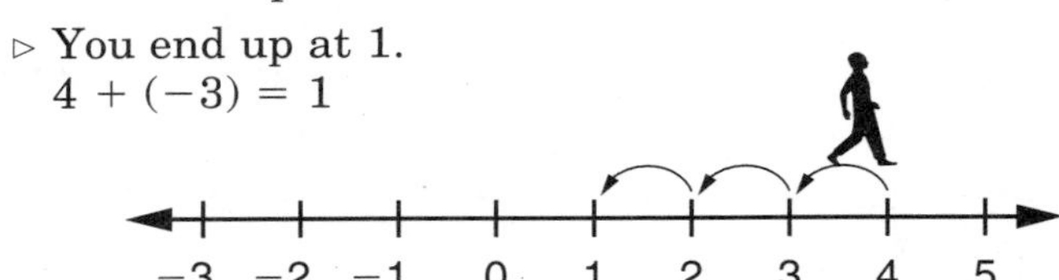

Emphasize that the operation sign indicates which direction to face and that it is the *second* addend, not the first, that determines whether to walk forward or backward.

✦Subtracting Positive and Negative Numbers on a Number Line

WHOLE-CLASS ACTIVITY

The procedure for subtracting positive and negative numbers is exactly the same as the one for addition, except that you face left on the number line.

Adjusting the Activity The rule for subtracting positive and negative numbers requires students to know how to add such numbers. If students need more practice with addition, pose a few addition problems.

Suggestions

- $9 + (-7)$ 2
- $0 + (-12)$ −12
- $-7 + 3$ −4
- $-8 + (-5)$ −13

Example 1: $-5 - 3 = ?$

▷ Locate the first number, −5, on the number line. This is your starting point.

▷ To subtract, face left on the number line.

▷ If the second number is positive, walk forward. If the second number is negative, walk backward. Since 3 is a positive number, walk 3 steps forward.

▷ The answer is the number you land on, −8.
$-5 - 3 = -8$

Example 2: $-2 - (-6) = ?$

▷ Start at −2.

▷ Face left, since this is a subtraction problem.

▷ Walk 6 steps *backward,* because the second number is negative.

▷ You end at 4.
$-2 - (-6) = 4$

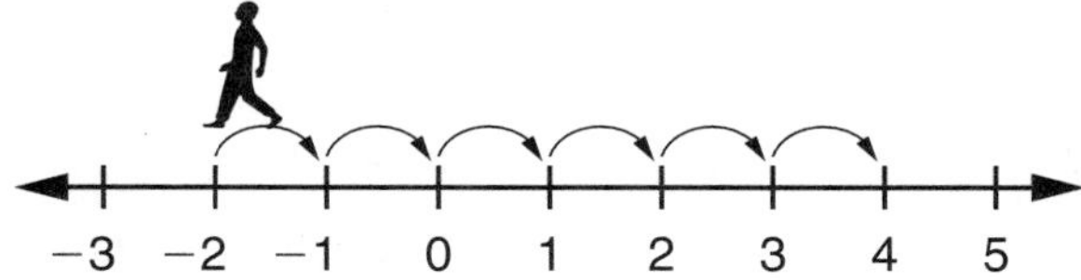

Emphasize that the operation sign (addition or subtraction) determines whether you face right or left. The positive or negative sign with the *second* number tells whether to walk forward or backward.

Adjusting the Activity Students having difficulty might want to act out subtraction problems with a floor number line. Draw a number line from −15 to +15 on the floor with chalk (or use masking tape). Alternatively, students can model the problems on the Real Number Line Poster which also appears on page 100 in the *Student Reference Book.*

Finally, pose a combination of addition and subtraction problems to make sure that students are able to make the two basic decisions correctly—whether to *face* right or left and whether to *move* forward or backward.

Suggestions

- $10 + (-8)$ 2
- $-5 + 4$ −1
- $4 - 6$ −2
- $-7 - (-3)$ −4

STUDENT PAGE

Negative Numbers on a Calculator

Math Message

Read the section "Negative Numbers" on page 91 in your *Student Reference Book*. Then use your calculator to solve the problems below. You will use the following keys: (,), ^ , and (−).

1. Enter each number into your calculator. Press Enter. Record the calculator display.

Enter	-236	-4.85	$-(\frac{2}{3})$	-0.006	$(-4)^2$	$(-8)^5$
Display	-236	-4.85	$-\frac{2}{3}$	-0.006	16	-32768

The negative sign can be used to represent the phrase "the opposite of." For example, to enter the opposite of 12, key in (−) 12 Enter. The display shows −12. To enter the opposite of −12, key in (−) (−) 12 Enter. The display shows 12. We can write "the opposite of −12" as "−(−12)" or as "(OPP) (−12)." The symbol (OPP) is read "the opposite of."

2. Enter each number into your calculator. Record the calculator display. Clear.

Enter	(OPP) 75	(OPP) (−89)	(OPP) (−312)	(OPP) (27 − 16)	(OPP) (−18 + 56)
Display	−75	89	312	−11	−38

Add or subtract with a calculator. *Remember:* The term (OPP) means "use the opposite of the number."

3. −26 − 17 = −43
   −26 + (OPP) 17 = −43
4. −34 − 68 = −102
   −34 + (−68) = −102
5. 56 − 24 = 32
   56 + (OPP) 24 = 32
6. 18 − 84 = −66
   18 + (−84) = −66
7. 43 − (−97) = 140
   43 + (OPP) (−97) = 140
   43 + 97 = 140
8. 31 − (−13) = 44
   31 + (−(−13)) = 44
   31 + 13 = 44
9. −130 − (−62) = −68
   −130 + (OPP) (−62) = −68
   −130 + 62 = −68
10. −2 − (−22) = 20
    −2 + (−(−22)) = 20
    −2 + 22 = 20

✧ **Math Journal 2, p. 215**

STUDENT PAGE

Subtracting Positive and Negative Numbers

One way to subtract one number from another number is to change the subtraction problem into an addition problem.

> **Subtraction Rule**
> To subtract a number *b* from a number *a*, add the opposite of *b* to *a*.
> Thus, for any numbers *a* and *b*, $a - b = a + \text{(OPP)}\ b$, or $a - b = a + (-b)$.

Examples

6 − 9 = 6 + (OPP) 9 = 6 + (−9) = −3
−15 − (−23) = −15 + (OPP) (−23) = −15 + 23 = 8

Rewrite each subtraction problem as an addition problem. Then solve the problem.

1. 22 − (15) = 22 + (OPP) 15 = 7
2. −35 − 20 = −35 + (OPP) 20 = −55
3. −3 − (−4.5) = −3 + (OPP) (−4.5) = 1.5
4. −27 − (−27) = −27 + (OPP) (−27) = 0

Subtract.

5. −23 − (−5) = −18
6. 9 − (−54) = 63
7. $-(\frac{4}{5}) - 1\frac{1}{5}$ = −2
8. \$1.25 − (−\$6.75) = \$8.00
9. −76 − (−56) = −20
10. −27 − 100 = −127
11. Explain how you solved Problem 9. Sample answer: I used the subtraction rule. I changed the problem to an addition problem and took the opposite of −56. I found −76 + (+56) = −20.

Fill in the missing numbers.

12. −15 + 5 = −10
    −10 − 5 = −15
13. −5 + (−5) = −10
    −10 − (−5) = −5
14. −9 + 9 = 0
    0 − (−9) = 9
15. 16 + −23 = −7
    −7 − 16 = −23
16. −25 + 40 = 15
    15 − (−25) = 40
17. −21 + 13 = −8
    −8 − 13 = −21

✧ **Math Journal 2, p. 216**

✦ Developing a Rule for Subtraction of Positive and Negative Numbers

(*Math Journal 2,* pp. 215 and 216)

WHOLE-CLASS DISCUSSION 

Use the Real Number Line Poster to review the meaning of the opposite of a number. Opposites are the same distance from zero on the number line but on opposite sides of zero. For example, +7 is 7 units from 0 on the positive side of the number line. The opposite is −7; it is 7 units from 0 on the negative side.

Pose problems, such as the following: the opposite of 9 −9; the opposite of −4 4; the opposite of the opposite of (−12) −12.

Have students do Problems 3–10 on journal page 215. Then discuss patterns in each set of problems. Students should notice several facts:

- ▷ All of the problems in a set have the same answer.
- ▷ The first problem is subtraction.
- ▷ The second problem is addition.
- ▷ The second numbers in each problem set are opposites.
- ▷ In Problem sets 7–10, a positive number has been substituted for the opposite of a negative number.

Guide students to see that subtracting a number is the same as adding the opposite of that number.

Demonstrate this fact on the number line, using the following description:

- ▷ Subtracting a *positive* number is the same as adding a negative number. (Facing left and walking forward is the same as facing right and walking backward.)
- ▷ Subtracting a *negative* number is the same as adding a positive number. (Facing left and walking backward is the same as facing right and walking forward.)

Stated as a general case:

> **Subtraction Rule**
>
> To subtract a number *b* from a number *a,* add the opposite of *b* to *a:*
>
> $a - b = a + \text{(OPP)}\ b$ or $a - b = a + (-b)$.

The Subtraction Rule is displayed at the top of journal page 216. Go over the two examples below the rule.

✦ Practicing Subtraction of Positive and Negative Numbers (*Math Journal 2,* p. 216)

PARTNER ACTIVITY 

Assign journal page 216. Students may *not* use their calculators. You might want to ask students to work individually and then have partners *check* each other's work, using a calculator.

Adjusting the Activity Encourage students to use a number line if they need to.

ONGOING ASSESSMENT

Use students' answers to Problem 11 to assess their understanding of the Subtraction Rule.

When students have completed the page, ask volunteers to describe how they solved a few of the problems. Discuss the relationship between addition and subtraction, as illustrated in Problems 12–17: Any subtraction problem can be solved in terms of addition. For example, to solve $12 - (-8)$, think: *What is the distance from −8 to 12 on the number line?* or *What number, when added to −8, is equal to 12?* 20

Ongoing Learning & Practice

✦ Math Boxes 6.3 (*Math Journal 2,* p. 217)

INDEPENDENT ACTIVITY 

Mixed Review Math Boxes in this lesson are paired with Math Boxes in Lesson 6.1. The skill in Problem 1 is a prerequisite for Unit 7.

✦ Study Link 6.3 (*Math Masters,* p. 314)

Home Connection Students practice subtracting positive and negative numbers.

Math Boxes 6.3

STUDENT PAGE

1. You roll 2 six-sided dice. Give the probability of rolling the following totals.
   a. 2 $\frac{1}{36}$ b. 12 $\frac{1}{36}$
   c. 11 $\frac{1}{18}$ d. 7 $\frac{1}{6}$
   e. 0 0 f. 3 or 4 $\frac{5}{36}$
   g. An even number $\frac{1}{2}$

2. a. Use your Geometry Template to draw sectors of this spinner and color them so that the chances of landing on these colors are as follows:
   red: 1 out of 4
   blue: $\frac{3}{8}$ 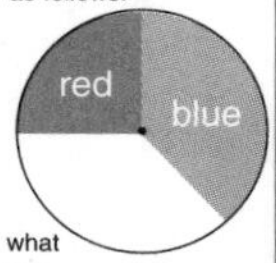
   (spinner: red, blue)
   b. On this spinner, what is the chance of *not* landing on red or blue? $\frac{3}{8}$

3. The distance from Chicago to Los Angeles is about 2,060 miles. A family drove this distance in 4 days. On average, about how many miles did the family travel each day?
   About 515 miles per day

4. Write a mixed number for each fraction.
   a. $\frac{320}{25} = 12\frac{20}{25}$, or $12\frac{4}{5}$
   b. $6\frac{1}{7} = \frac{43}{7}$
   c. $20\frac{1}{5} = \frac{101}{5}$
   d. $9\frac{3}{8} = \frac{75}{8}$
   e. $\frac{147}{4} = 36\frac{3}{4}$

5. Circle the number sentence that describes the numbers in the table.

m	*p*
8	16
0	−8
4	4
10	22

   $p = m * 2$
   $(3 - m) = p + 8$
   $p = (3 * m) - 8$ (circled)
   $m - 8 = p$

6. Write each number using digits. Then round each number to the nearest ten-thousand.
   a. Four million, three hundred seventy-two thousand, nine hundred five
   number 4,372,905
   rounded 4,370,000
   b. Thirteen million, sixty-eight thousand, four hundred twenty-three
   number 13,068,423
   rounded 13,070,000

✦ *Math Journal 2,* p. 217

Subtraction of Positive and Negative Numbers — Study Link 6.3

STUDY LINK MASTER

SRB 92 93

To subtract *b* from *a*, add the opposite of *b* to *a*. For any numbers *a* and *b*, $a - b = a + (OPP)\ b$, or $a - b = a + (-b)$.

1. Rewrite each subtraction problem as an addition problem. Then solve the problem.
   a. $46 - 19 = 46 + (-19) = 27$
   b. $-43 - 17 = -43 + (-17) = -60$
   c. $-5 - (-6.8) = -5 + 6.8 = 1.8$
   d. $21 - (-21) = 21 + 21 = 42$

2. Subtract.
   a. $-72 - (-43) = -29$
   b. $43 = 4 - (-39)$
   c. $-\left(\frac{7}{10}\right) - 1\frac{1}{2} = -2\frac{1}{5}$
   d. $4.8 - (-3.6) = 8.4$
   e. $-3\frac{1}{4} = -2\frac{1}{2} - \frac{3}{4}$
   f. $-\left(\frac{5}{6}\right) - \left(-\frac{1}{3}\right) = -\frac{1}{2}$
   g. $-12.3 - 5.9 = -18.2$
   h. $-8.5 - (-2.7) = -5.8$

3. Fill in the missing numbers.
   a. $19 = 17 - (-2)$
   b. $-43 = -26 - 17$
   c. $\frac{1}{2} - 2\frac{1}{4} = -1\frac{3}{4}$
   d. $\frac{9}{10} - \left(-2\frac{4}{5}\right) = 3\frac{7}{10}$
   e. $-17.6 = -3.7 - 13.9$
   f. $83.5 = -62.7 - (-146.2)$
   g. $-\frac{7}{16} = 5\frac{3}{4} - 6\frac{3}{16}$
   h. $9.6 - (-0.4) = 10$

✦ *Math Masters,* p. 314

STUDENT PAGE

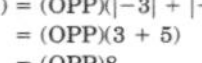

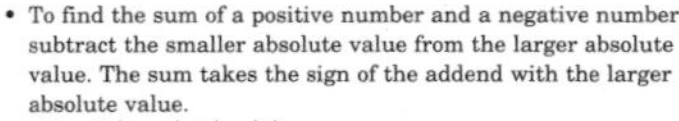

Using Absolute Value to Add Positive and Negative Numbers

Here is another way to think about addition of positive and negative rational numbers.

- The **absolute value** of a positive number is the number itself. The absolute value of a negative number is the opposite of the number. Absolute value is shown by vertical lines before and after a number.
  absolute value of $-6 = |-6| = (\text{OPP})(-6) = 6$
  absolute value of $3 = |3| = 3$
- The sum of two positive numbers is the sum of their absolute values. For example, $3 + 5 = |3| + |5| = 8$.
- To find the sum of two negative numbers, add the absolute values of the addends. The sum is the opposite of the result.
  $-3 + (-5) = (\text{OPP})(|-3| + |-5|)$
  $= (\text{OPP})(3 + 5)$
  $= (\text{OPP})8$
  $= -8$
- To find the sum of a positive number and a negative number, subtract the smaller absolute value from the larger absolute value. The sum takes the sign of the addend with the larger absolute value.
  $-7 + 3 = -(|-7| - |3|)$
  $= -(7 - 3)$
  $= -4$ The sum takes the sign of -7.
  $-2 + 8 = (|8| - |-2|)$
  $= 8 - 2$
  $= 6$ The sum takes the sign of 8.
- The sum of two opposites is zero. For example, $-5 + 5 = 0$.

NOTE
The symbol (OPP) before a number means "the opposite of." See page 103.
(OPP)5 = −5
(OPP)(−7) = 7

CHECK YOUR UNDERSTANDING

Add or subtract.

1. $-9 + (-6)$	**2.** $-14 + 38$	**3.** $5.2 + (-5.6)$	**4.** $9 + (-27)$
5. $3 - 7$	**6.** $-5 - (-2)$	**7.** $-6 - 4$	**8.** $8 - (-9)$

Check your answers on page 374.

Student Reference Book, p. 94

3 Options for Individualizing

ENRICHMENT Adding and Subtracting Positive and Negative Numbers Using Absolute Value (*Student Reference Book*, p. 94)

SMALL-GROUP ACTIVITY  **15–30 min** 

Have students use the absolute-value strategy described on *Student Reference Book,* page 94 to solve addition and subtraction problems.

RETEACHING Modeling Positive and Negative Numbers with Colored Chips or Counters

SMALL-GROUP ACTIVITY  **15–30 min** 

Give each student 10 chips or counters of one color and 10 of another color. Designate one color as positive numbers and one color as negative numbers. Do several problems like the one below.

Show the number +5 using five counters.

Show the number +5 using nine counters.

NOTE: You may need to remind students that adding one positive chip and one negative chip to the number represented does not change the number. The positive and negative cancel each other out: Adding one of each is like adding a zero.

Repeat the above procedure for several numbers.

When students are ready, pose problems like the ones below. Have students use their chips or counters to model each problem. For example: $+5 - (-3) = ?$

Show +5

Rename

Take away −3

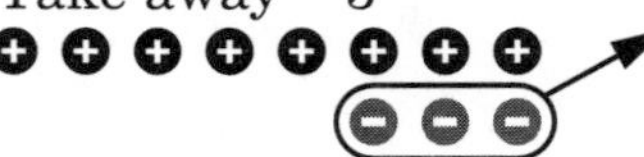

Continue as time allows. *Suggestions:*

- $+6 - (-2) = ?$ $+8$
- $+4 + (-2) = ?$ $+2$
- $-5 + 3 = ?$ -2
- $-5 - (-3) = ?$ -2

✦ EXTRA PRACTICE Playing the Advanced Version of *Credits/Debits Game* (*Student Reference Book,* p. 283; *Math Masters,* p. 94)

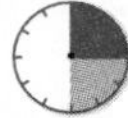

PARTNER ACTIVITY **15–30 min**

Students who need more practice adding and subtracting with positive and negative numbers can play the advanced version of the *Credits/Debits Game,* first introduced in *Fourth Grade Everyday Mathematics.*

✦ EXTRA PRACTICE Practicing Addition and Subtraction of Positive and Negative Numbers (*Math Masters,* p. 95)

INDEPENDENT ACTIVITY **15–30 min**

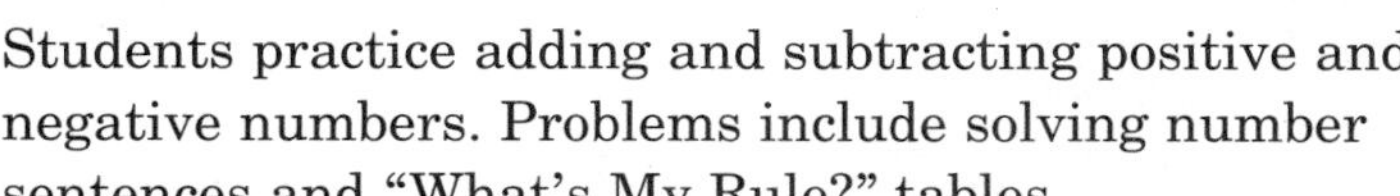

Students practice adding and subtracting positive and negative numbers. Problems include solving number sentences and "What's My Rule?" tables.

Credits/Debits Game Recording Sheets

TEACHING MASTER

Game 1

	Start	Change: Addition or Subtraction	Change: Credit or Debit	End, and Next Start
1	+$10			
2				
3				
4				
5				
6				
7				
8				
9				
10				

Game 2

	Start	Change: Addition or Subtraction	Change: Credit or Debit	End, and Next Start
1	+$10			
2				
3				
4				
5				
6				
7				
8				
9				
10				

✦ *Math Masters,* p. 94

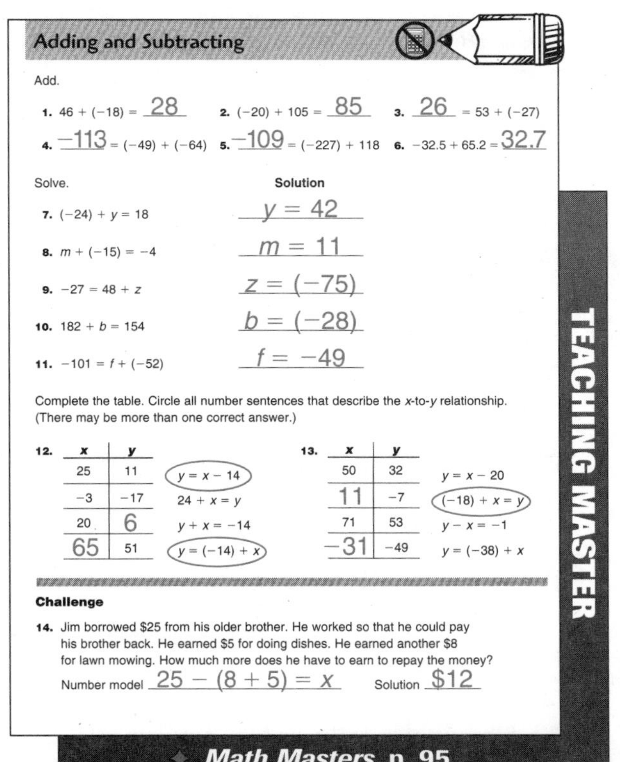

Adding and Subtracting

TEACHING MASTER

Add.

1. $46 + (-18) =$ 28
2. $(-20) + 105 =$ 85
3. 26 $= 53 + (-27)$
4. −113 $= (-49) + (-64)$
5. −109 $= (-227) + 118$
6. $-32.5 + 65.2 =$ 32.7

Solve. **Solution**

7. $(-24) + y = 18$ — $y = 42$
8. $m + (-15) = -4$ — $m = 11$
9. $-27 = 48 + z$ — $z = (-75)$
10. $182 + b = 154$ — $b = (-28)$
11. $-101 = f + (-52)$ — $f = -49$

Complete the table. Circle all number sentences that describe the *x*-to-*y* relationship. (There may be more than one correct answer.)

12.

x	y
25	11
−3	−17
20	6
65	51

(circled) $y = x - 14$
$24 + x = y$
$y + x = -14$
(circled) $y = (-14) + x$

13.

x	y
50	32
11	−7
71	53
−31	−49

$y = x - 20$
(circled) $(-18) + x = y$
$y - x = -1$
$y = (-38) + x$

Challenge

14. Jim borrowed $25 from his older brother. He worked so that he could pay his brother back. He earned $5 for doing dishes. He earned another $8 for lawn mowing. How much more does he have to earn to repay the money?

Number model $25 - (8 + 5) = x$ Solution $12

✦ *Math Masters,* p. 95

Games

Credits/Debits Game (Advanced Version)

STUDENT PAGE

Materials ☐ 1 complete deck of number cards
☐ 1 penny
☐ recording sheet for each player (*Math Masters,* p. 94)

Players 2

Directions

Pretend that you are an accountant for a business. Your job is to keep track of the company's current balance. The current balance is also called the "bottom line."

1. Shuffle the deck and lay it facedown between the players.
2. The black-numbered cards are the "credits," and the blue- or red-numbered cards are the "debits."
3. The heads side of the coin tells you to **add** a credit to the bottom line. The tails side of the coin tells you to **subtract** a credit or debit from the bottom line.
4. Each player begins with a bottom line of +$10.
5. Players take turns. On your turn, do the following:
   - Flip the coin. This tells you whether to add or subtract.
   - Draw a card. The card tells you what amount in dollars (positive or negative) to add or subtract from the bottom line. Red or blue numbers are negative numbers.
   - Record the result in the table.

Recording Sheet

	Start	Change: Addition or Subtraction	Change: Credit or Debit	End, and next start
1	+$10			
2				
3				
4				
5				
6				
7				
8				
9				
10				

EXAMPLES Max has a new "Start" balance of $5. He draws a red 8 and records −$8 in the "Credit or Debit" column. His coin lands heads-side up and he records + in the "Addition or Subtraction" column. Max adds: $5 + (−$8) = −$3. He records −$3 in the "End" balance column. He also records −$3 in the "Start" column on the next line.

Beth has a new "Start" balance of −$20. Her coin lands tails-side up, which means subtract. She draws a black 11 (+$11). She subtracts: −$20 − (+$11) = −$31. Her "End" balance is −$31.

Scoring: After 10 turns each, the player with more money is the winner of the round. If both players have negative dollar amounts, the player whose amount is closer to 0 wins.

two hundred eighty-three  283

✦ *Student Reference Book,* p. 283

6.4 Multiplication and Division of Positive and Negative Numbers

OBJECTIVES **To develop rules for multiplying and dividing positive and negative numbers; and to practice these operations.**

summaries	materials
1 Teaching the Lesson	
Students learn to multiply positive and negative numbers by observing patterns in sets of number sentences. They also learn to divide these numbers by applying previous knowledge about fact families. [Patterns, Functions, and Algebra]	☐ *Math Journal 2,* pp. 218–220 ☐ Study Link 6.3 ☐ calculator ☐ slate
2 Ongoing Learning & Practice	
Students play *Top-It* games with positive and negative numbers. [Patterns, Functions, and Algebra; Numeration] Students practice and maintain skills through Math Boxes and Study Link activities.	☐ *Math Journal 2,* p. 221 ☐ *Student Reference Book,* p. 310 ☐ Study Link Master (*Math Masters,* p. 315) ☐ number cards (from the Everything Math Deck, if available)
3 Options for Individualizing	
Enrichment Students learn why it is not possible to divide by 0. [Operations and Computation] **Extra Practice** Students solve multiplication/division Fact Triangles with positive and negative numbers. [Patterns, Functions, and Algebra]	☐ *Student Reference Book,* p. 96 ☐ Teaching Master (*Math Masters,* p. 96)

Additional Information

Vocabulary • **multiplication property of −1**

Getting Started

Mental Math and Reflexes

Pose subtraction problems with positive and negative numbers.
Suggestions

- −30 − (−10) −20
- −12 − 5 −17
- 5 − (−23) 28
- 18 − 20 −2
- −15 − (−20) 5
- 25 − 12 13

Math Message

Complete the problems on journal page 218.

Study Link 6.3 Follow-Up

Go over the answers with the class.

Teaching the Lesson

✦ Math Message Follow-Up (*Math Journal 2,* p. 218)

WHOLE-CLASS DISCUSSION

Students should be able to complete the patterns. In each set of number sentences in Problems 1–4, one factor remains the same, while the other factor in the set decreases by 1 each time. The *products* in each set also decrease in a pattern. For example, in Problem 1a, 6 is one of the factors in each number sentence. The second factor decreases by 1 from one sentence to the next (4, 3, 2, 1, 0). The product decreases by 6 (24, 18, 12, 6, 0).

Be sure that students have circled the correct words in the multiplication rules in Problems 1–4. Briefly discuss the **multiplication property of −1** in Problem 5. (The product of a number and −1 is the opposite of the number.) Point out that the turn-around rule also holds for multiplication with negative numbers. For example, $5 * (-2) = -2 * 5 = -10$.

Spend a few minutes practicing multiplication. Pose problems that students can easily solve mentally. They should write the products on their slates or on scratch paper and then check their answers with a calculator.

Suggestions

- $8 * (-6)$ −48
- $-3 * 5$ −15
- $1.2 * (-5)$ −6
- $(-8)^2$ 64
- $-\frac{2}{3} * \frac{6}{5}$ $-\frac{4}{5}$
- $0.5 * (-2)$ −1

✦ Deriving the Rules for Division of Positive and Negative Numbers (*Math Journal 2,* p. 219)

PARTNER ACTIVITY

Students of *Everyday Mathematics* have been using addition/subtraction and multiplication/division fact families since first grade. In this lesson, they use fact families to derive the rules for dividing positive and negative numbers.

Review the example at the top of journal page 219.

Do Problem 1a as a class. Students can apply the multiplication rules to solve the first two problems: $5 * (-3) = -15$ and $-3 * 5 = -15$. The three numbers used to build this fact family are 5, −3, and −15. This information can be used to complete the division facts in the family.

Multiplication Patterns

In each of Problems 1–4, complete the patterns in Part a. Check your answers with a calculator. Then circle the word in parentheses that correctly completes the statement in Part b.

1. a. 6 * 4 = 24; 6 * 3 = 18; 6 * 2 = 12; 6 * 1 = 6; 6 * 0 = 0

b. Positive * Positive Rule: When a positive number is multiplied by a positive number, the product is a (positive or negative) number. [positive circled]

2. a. 5 * 2 = 10; 5 * 1 = 5; 5 * 0 = 0; 5 * (−1) = −5; 5 * (−2) = −10

b. Positive * Negative Rule: When a positive number is multiplied by a negative number, the product is a (positive or negative) number. [negative circled]

3. a. 2 * 3 = 6; 1 * 3 = 3; 0 * 3 = 0; −1 * 3 = −3; −2 * 3 = −6

b. Negative * Positive Rule: When a negative number is multiplied by a positive number, the product is a (positive or negative) number. [negative circled]

4. a. −4 * 1 = −4; −4 * 0 = 0; −4 * (−1) = 4; −4 * (−2) = 8; −4 * (−3) = 12

b. Negative * Negative Rule: When a negative number is multiplied by a negative number, the product is a (positive or negative) number. [positive circled]

5. a. Solve. −1 * 6 = −6; −1 * (−7.7) = 7.7; $-1 * -(\frac{1}{2})$ = $-\frac{1}{2}$; −1 * *m* = −*m*

b. Multiplication Property of −1: For any number *a*, −1 * *a* = *a* * −1 = (OPP) *a*, or −*a*. Since the number *a* can be a negative number, (OPP) *a* or −*a* can be a positive number. For example, if *a* = −5, then −*a* = (OPP) −5 = 5.

STUDENT PAGE

✦ Math Journal 2, p. 218

Fact Families for Multiplication and Division

A fact family is a group of four basic, related multiplication and division facts.

Example The multiplication and division fact family for 6, 3, and 18 is made up of the following facts: 6 * 3 = 18, 3 * 6 = 18, 18 / 6 = 3, 18 / 3 = 6

As you already know, when a positive number is divided by a positive number, the quotient is a positive number. Problems 1 and 2 will help you discover the rules for division with negative numbers. Complete the fact families. Check your answers with a calculator. Then complete each rule.

1. a. 5 * (−3) = −15; −3 * 5 = −15; −15 / (−3) = 5; −15 / 5 = −3

b. 6 * (−8) = −48; −8 * 6 = −48; −48 / (−8) = 6; −48 / 6 = −8

c. 5 * (−5) = −25; −5 * 5 = −25; −25 / −5 = 5; −25 / 5 = −5

d. Negative / Negative Rule: When a negative number is divided by a negative number, the quotient is a (positive or negative) number. [positive circled]

e. Negative / Positive Rule: When a negative number is divided by a positive number, the quotient is a (positive or negative) number. [negative circled]

2. a. −4 * (−3) = 12; −3 * (−4) = 12; 12 / (−3) = −4; 12 / (−4) = −3

b. −7 * (−5) = 35; −5 * (−7) = 35; 35 / (−5) = −7; 35 / (−7) = −5

c. −2 * (−10) = 20; −10 * (−2) = 20; 20 / (−10) = −2; 20 /−2 = (−10)

d. Positive / Negative Rule: When a positive number is divided by a negative number, the quotient is a (positive or negative) number. [negative circled]

3. Solve. Check your answers with a calculator.

a. −6 * (−4) = 24 (*Think:* What number multiplied by −4 is equal to 24?)

b. −9 * 9 = −81 **c.** −6 * −8 = 48 **d.** 9 * (−3) = −27

e. −81 / 9 = −9 **f.** 48 / (−6) = −8 **g.** −27 / (−3) = 9

STUDENT PAGE

✦ Math Journal 2, p. 219

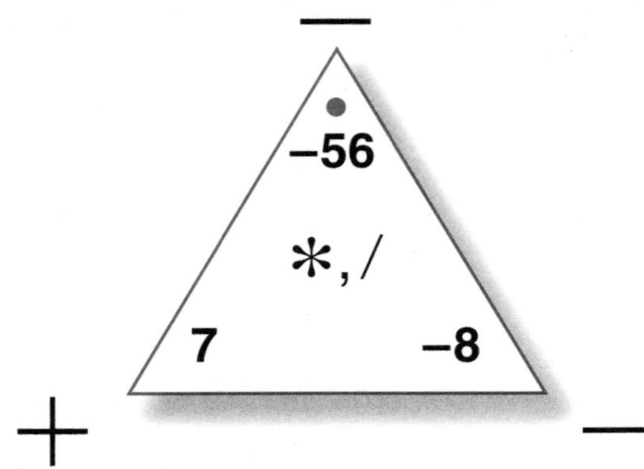

Multiplication fact family for 7, −8, and −56:

$7 * (-8) = -56$
$-8 * 7 = -56$
$-56 / 7 = -8$
$-56 / -8 = 7$

Adjusting the Activity If students have difficulty with Problem 1 on journal page 219, use Fact Triangles with both positive and negative numbers to illustrate the patterns. For example, draw a Fact Triangle for 7, −8, and −56 on the board (*see margin*). Draw large + (positive) and − (negative) signs at the corners for emphasis. Discuss the pattern of signs for the facts from the triangle (negative times positive equals negative, negative divided by negative equals positive, and so on). Repeat for other examples, such as −6, 8, and −48 and −3, −4, and 12.

Spend a few minutes practicing division. *Suggestions:*

- 54 / (−9) −6
- −49 / 7 −7
- −60 / (−12) 5
- $(-8)^2 / (-8)$ −8

Students complete journal page 219 independently. Partners then check each other's answers with a calculator.

Review the rules for division. Discuss the relationship between multiplication and division, as illustrated in Problem 3; that is, any division problem can be solved in terms of multiplication. For example, to solve 35 / (−5), think: *What number, multiplied by −5, is equal to 35?* −7

✦ Practicing Multiplication and Division of Positive and Negative Numbers

(*Math Journal 2,* p. 220)

PARTNER ACTIVITY

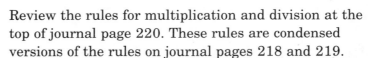

Review the rules for multiplication and division at the top of journal page 220. These rules are condensed versions of the rules on journal pages 218 and 219.

Students complete journal page 220 independently. Partners then check answers with a calculator.

Adjusting the Activity If some students are still struggling, have them complete as much of journal page 220 as they can now. Return to the page later in the year when students have had more experience.

STUDENT PAGE

*, / of Positive and Negative Numbers

Multiplication Property	Division Property
For all numbers *a* and *b*, if the values of *a* and *b* are both positive or both negative, then the product *a* * *b* is a positive number. If one of the values is positive and the other is negative, then the product *a* * *b* is a negative number.	For all numbers *a* and *b*, if the values of *a* and *b* are both positive or both negative, then the quotient *a* / *b* is a positive number. If one of the values is positive and the other is negative, then the quotient *a* / *b* is a negative number.

Solve. Use a calculator to check your answers.

1. $-7 * 8 =$ −56
2. $73 * (-45) =$ −3,285
3. −700 $\div (-10) = 70$
4. $\frac{1}{2} * (-\frac{3}{4}) =$ $-\frac{3}{8}$
5. $0.5 * (-15) =$ −7.5
6. −1 $* 3.3 = -3.3$
7. $-3 * 4 * (-7) =$ 84
8. −2 $* (-8) * (-3) = -48$
9. $-54 / 9 =$ −6
10. $36 / (-12) =$ −3
11. $-\frac{3}{5} \div (-\frac{4}{5}) =$ $\frac{3}{4}$
12. $45 / (-5) / (-3) =$ 3
13. −90 $\div 15 = -6$
14. $72 / (-8) =$ −9
15. $-99 /$ 9 $= -11$
16. $\frac{1}{2} \div (-\frac{3}{4}) =$ $-\frac{2}{3}$
17. $-3 * (-4 + 6) =$ −6
18. $32 \div (-5 - 3) =$ −4
19. $(-9 * 4) + 6 =$ −30
20. $(-75 / 5) + (-20) =$ −35
21. $(-6 * 3) + (-6 * 5) =$ −48
22. $(4 * (-7)) - (4 * (-3)) =$ −16

Evaluate each expression for $y = -4$.

23. $3 - (-y) =$ −1
24. $-y / (-6) =$ $-\frac{2}{3}$
25. $y - (-7 + 3) =$ 0
26. $y - (y + 2) =$ −2
27. $(-8 * y) - 6 =$ 26
28. $(-8 * 6) - (-8 * y) =$ −80

✧ *Math Journal 2,* p. 220

ONGOING ASSESSMENT

Use journal page 220 to assess students' ability to correctly apply the rules for multiplication and division of positive and negative numbers in increasingly complex situations. Expect that some students may still feel unsure of the rules. There will be future opportunities for practice.

2 Ongoing Learning & Practice

✦ Playing *Top-It* Games with Positive and Negative Numbers

(*Student Reference Book,* p. 310)

PARTNER ACTIVITY 

The versions of the *Top-It* games described on page 310 of the *Student Reference Book* provide practice with comparison, addition, and subtraction of positive and negative numbers. For extra practice, encourage students to play the games often, both in school and at home.

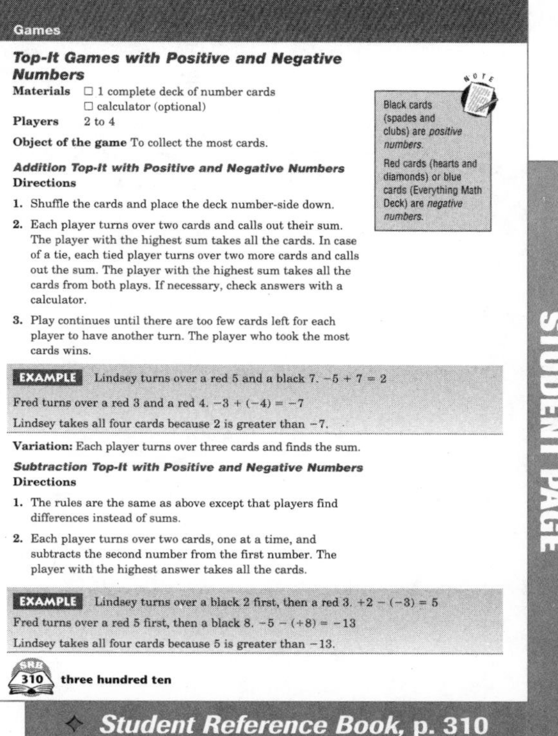

Games

Top-It Games with Positive and Negative Numbers

Materials □ 1 complete deck of number cards
□ calculator (optional)

Players 2 to 4

Object of the game To collect the most cards.

NOTE: Black cards (spades and clubs) are *positive numbers.* Red cards (hearts and diamonds) or blue cards (Everything Math Deck) are *negative numbers.*

Addition Top-It with Positive and Negative Numbers

Directions

1. Shuffle the cards and place the deck number-side down.
2. Each player turns over two cards and calls out their sum. The player with the highest sum takes all the cards. In case of a tie, each tied player turns over two more cards and calls out the sum. The player with the highest sum takes all the cards from both plays. If necessary, check answers with a calculator.
3. Play continues until there are too few cards left for each player to have another turn. The player who took the most cards wins.

EXAMPLE Lindsey turns over a red 5 and a black 7. $-5 + 7 = 2$
Fred turns over a red 3 and a red 4. $-3 + (-4) = -7$
Lindsey takes all four cards because 2 is greater than -7.

Variation: Each player turns over three cards and finds the sum.

Subtraction Top-It with Positive and Negative Numbers

Directions

1. The rules are the same as above except that players find differences instead of sums.
2. Each player turns over two cards, one at a time, and subtracts the second number from the first number. The player with the highest answer takes all the cards.

EXAMPLE Lindsey turns over a black 2 first, then a red 3. $+2 - (-3) = 5$
Fred turns over a red 5 first, then a black 8. $-5 - (+8) = -13$
Lindsey takes all four cards because 5 is greater than -13.

SRB 310 three hundred ten

STUDENT PAGE

✦ *Student Reference Book,* p. 310

✦ Math Boxes 6.4 (*Math Journal 2,* p. 221)

INDEPENDENT ACTIVITY 

Mixed Review Math Boxes in this lesson are paired with Math Boxes in Lesson 6.2. The skill in Problem 1 is a prerequisite for Unit 7.

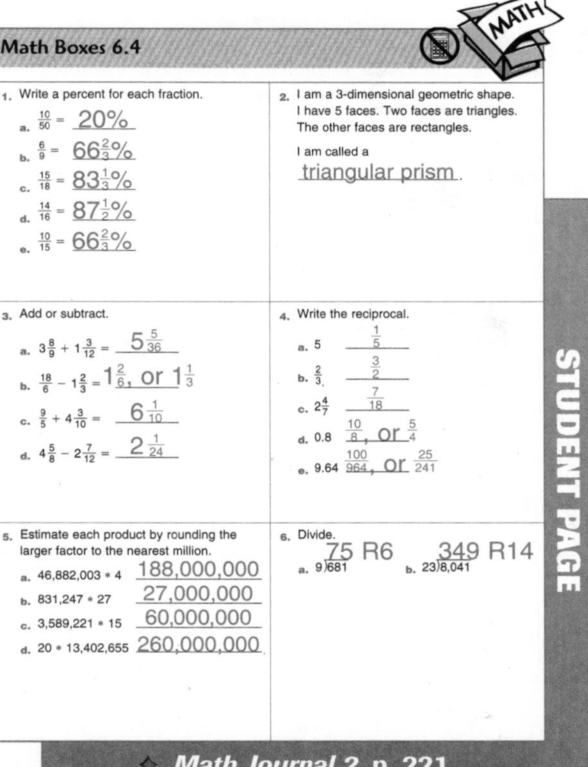

Math Boxes 6.4

1. Write a percent for each fraction.
   a. $\frac{10}{50}$ = 20%
   b. $\frac{6}{9}$ = $66\frac{2}{3}\%$
   c. $\frac{15}{18}$ = $83\frac{1}{3}\%$
   d. $\frac{14}{16}$ = $87\frac{1}{2}\%$
   e. $\frac{10}{15}$ = $66\frac{2}{3}\%$

2. I am a 3-dimensional geometric shape. I have 5 faces. Two faces are triangles. The other faces are rectangles.
   I am called a triangular prism.

3. Add or subtract.
   a. $3\frac{8}{9} + 1\frac{3}{12} =$ $5\frac{5}{36}$
   b. $\frac{18}{6} - 1\frac{2}{3} =$ $1\frac{2}{6}$, or $1\frac{1}{3}$
   c. $\frac{9}{5} + 4\frac{3}{10} =$ $6\frac{1}{10}$
   d. $4\frac{5}{8} - 2\frac{7}{12} =$ $2\frac{1}{24}$

4. Write the reciprocal.
   a. 5 $\frac{1}{5}$
   b. $\frac{2}{3}$ $\frac{3}{2}$
   c. $2\frac{4}{7}$ $\frac{7}{18}$
   d. 0.8 $\frac{10}{8}$, or $\frac{5}{4}$
   e. 9.64 $\frac{100}{964}$, or $\frac{25}{241}$

5. Estimate each product by rounding the larger factor to the nearest million.
   a. 46,882,003 * 4 188,000,000
   b. 831,247 * 27 27,000,000
   c. 3,589,221 * 15 60,000,000
   d. 20 * 13,402,655 260,000,000

6. Divide.
   a. 9)681 75 R6
   b. 23)8,041 349 R14

STUDENT PAGE

✦ *Math Journal 2,* p. 221

✦ Study Link 6.4 (*Math Masters,* p. 315)

Home Connection Students practice multiplication and division of positive and negative numbers.

STUDY LINK MASTER

*, / of Positive and Negative Numbers

Study Link 6.4

SRB 95

Multiplication Property	Division Property
For all numbers *a* and *b*, if the values of *a* and *b* are both positive or both negative, then the product *a* * *b* is a positive number. If one of the values is positive and the other is negative, then the product *a* * *b* is a negative number.	For all numbers *a* and *b*, if the values of *a* and *b* are both positive or both negative, then the quotient *a* / *b* is a positive number. If one of the values is positive and the other is negative, then the quotient *a* / *b* is a negative number.

Solve. Use a calculator to check your answers.

1. −12 * 5 = −60
2. −63 / 7 = −9
3. 24 ÷ (−4) = −6
4. −9 * −6 = 54
5. −50 / −5 = 10
6. −6 * 5 * 8 = −240
7. 48 / (−6 − 2) = −6
8. (−8 * 5) + 12 = −28
9. 50 * (−23) = −1,150
10. 6 * (12 + 15) = 162
11. (−90 ÷ 10) + (−45) = −54
12. 56 / (−7) / (−4) = 2
13. −2 * (−7) * (−4) = −56
14. −360 ÷ 40 = −9

Challenge

15. $\frac{2}{3} * (-\frac{5}{6}) = -\frac{5}{9}$
16. (8 * (−3)) − (8 * (−9)) = 48
17. 0.25 * (−8) = −2
18. $(-\frac{3}{4}) \div (-\frac{1}{2}) = 1\frac{1}{2}$
19. Evaluate each expression for *b* = −7.
    - a. (−9 * *b*) − 27 = 36
    - b. 11 * (−*b*) = 77
    - c. −*b* / (−14) = −0.5
    - d. *b* − (*b* + 16) = −16

✦ *Math Masters,* p. 315

3 Options for Individualizing

✦ ENRICHMENT Reading about Division by Zero (*Student Reference Book,* p. 96)

WHOLE-CLASS DISCUSSION 5–15 min

Students read and discuss page 96 in the *Student Reference Book.*

✦ EXTRA PRACTICE Completing Fact Triangles (*Math Masters,* p. 96)

INDEPENDENT ACTIVITY 5–15 min

Students practice solving basic multiplication and division facts with positive and negative numbers.

STUDENT PAGE

Fractions and Rational Numbers

Multiplication and Division with Zero

Multiplication with Zero: a * 0 = 0

If one (or more) of the factors in a multiplication problem is 0, the product is 0.

EXAMPLES −38 * 0 = 0 5 * 12 * 0 * 4 = 0 0 * 0 = 0

Division of Zero: 0 / a = 0

When 0 is divided by any number (except 0), the answer is 0.

To understand this, think about multiplication. Any division problem can be rewritten as a multiplication problem with a missing factor. The missing factor in every such multiplication problem is 0.

Division Problem	Multiplication Problem	Missing Factor
0 / 8 = □	8 * □ = 0	0
0 / 75 = □	75 * □ = 0	0
0 / *a* = □ (if *a* ≠ 0)	*a* * □ = 0	0

Division by Zero: a / 0 = ?

Division by 0 is not allowed.

Again, thinking about multiplication can help you understand this fact. Any division problem can be rewritten as a multiplication problem with a missing factor.

Division Problem	Multiplication Problem	Missing Factor
8 / 0 = □	0 * □ = 8	no solution
75 / 0 = □	0 * □ = 75	no solution
a / 0 = □ (if *a* ≠ 0)	0 * □ = *a*	no solution

Any number multiplied by 0 is 0, so there are no solutions to the multiplication problems above. This means *none* of the division problems have answers either. This is why we say division by 0 is not allowed: There is no answer.

NOTE: The problem 0 / 0 = □ is interesting. It is equivalent to the multiplication problem 0 * □ = 0. Since any number at all (5, 73, −245, $\frac{1}{2}$, and so on) will make 0 * □ = 0 true, there are too many answers. So, people usually say 0 / 0 is not allowed. (If you study calculus in high school or college, you may learn about special cases when 0 / 0 is allowed, but for elementary mathematics, division of 0 by 0 is not allowed.)

CHECK YOUR UNDERSTANDING

Multiply or divide.

1. 0 * (−1,234)
2. 5 * 15 * 3 * 0
3. 0 / 75
4. 27 / 0

Check your answers on page 374.

SRB 96 ninety-six

✧ *Student Reference Book,* p. 96

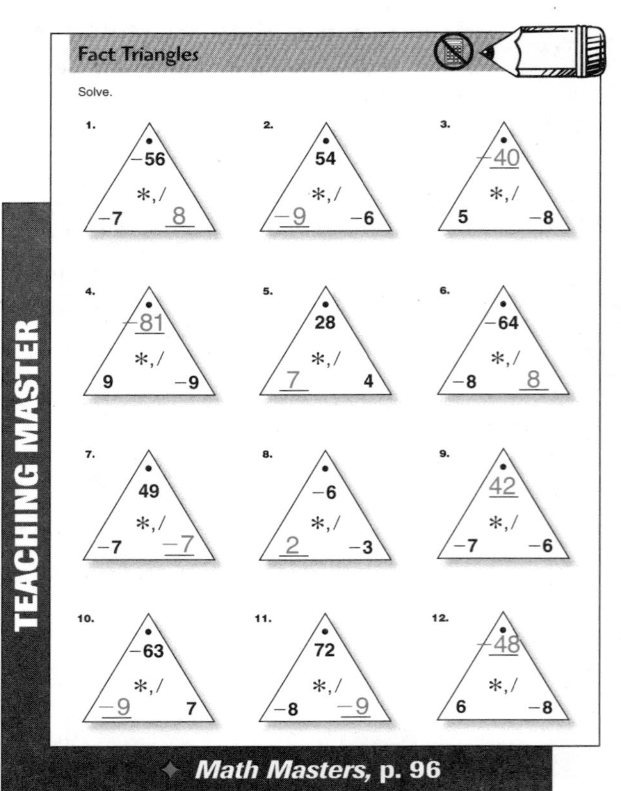
TEACHING MASTER

Fact Triangles

Solve.

1. −56; −7, 8; *, /
2. 54; −9, −6; *, /
3. −40; 5, −8; *, /
4. −81; 9, −9; *, /
5. 28; 7, 4; *, /
6. −64; −8, 8; *, /
7. 49; −7, −7; *, /
8. −6; 2, −3; *, /
9. 42; −7, −6; *, /
10. −63; −9, 7; *, /
11. 72; −8, −9; *, /
12. −48; 6, −8; *, /

✦ *Math Masters,* p. 96

6.5 The Properties of Number Systems

OBJECTIVE **To summarize the properties of number systems and operations.**

summaries	materials
1 Teaching the Lesson	
Students are presented with an overview of the real number system. They take part in a mathematical "scavenger hunt" that focuses on the composition of various sets of numbers and the properties of the rational numbers. [Numeration]	□ *Math Journal 2,* pp. 222–224 □ *Student Reference Book,* pp. 97–100 and 102–104 □ Study Link 6.4 □ calculator □ Real Number Line Poster ***See* Advance Preparation**
2 Ongoing Learning & Practice	
Students review a problem-solving diagram and solve multi-step number stories. [Operations and Computation] Students practice and maintain skills through Math Boxes and Study Link activities.	□ *Math Journal 2,* pp. 224 and 225 □ *Student Reference Book,* pp. 240 and 241 □ Study Link Master (*Math Masters,* p. 316)
3 Options for Individualizing	
Enrichment Students investigate whether general statements about rational numbers are true or false. [Numeration] **Enrichment** Students solve number and word puzzles.	□ Teaching Masters (*Math Masters,* pp. 97 and 98)

Additional Information

Advance Preparation For Part 1, read pages 97–100 in the *Student Reference Book.* For more information, read about the rational number system and its properties in the *Teacher's Reference Manual.*

Vocabulary • **counting numbers** • **whole numbers** • **integers** • **rational numbers** • **terminating decimals** • **repeating decimals** • **irrational numbers** • **real numbers**

Getting Started

Mental Math and Reflexes

Pose problems such as the following:

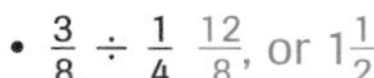

- $\frac{3}{8} \div \frac{1}{4}$ $\frac{12}{8}$, or $1\frac{1}{2}$
- $\frac{3}{4} \div \frac{5}{8}$ $1\frac{4}{20}$, or $1\frac{1}{5}$
- $\frac{5}{4} \div \frac{1}{3}$ $\frac{15}{4}$, or $3\frac{3}{4}$
- $\frac{2}{3} \div \frac{2}{5}$ $\frac{10}{6}$, or $1\frac{2}{3}$
- $\frac{1}{9} \div \frac{1}{2}$ $\frac{2}{9}$
- $\frac{4}{9} \div \frac{1}{6}$ $\frac{24}{9}$, or $2\frac{2}{3}$

Math Message

- *How many positive numbers are there?*
- *How many negative numbers are there?*
- *How many numbers are there that are neither positive nor negative?*
- *Name one positive and one negative number, each of which is very close to 0.*

Study Link 6.4 Follow-Up

Briefly go over the answers.

1 Teaching the Lesson

✦ Math Message Follow-Up

WHOLE-CLASS DISCUSSION 

Most students probably know that there are infinitely many positive and negative numbers. Ask students to express this fact in a variety of ways: *Positive numbers go on without end. No matter how large (small) a positive (negative) number I think of, I can always think of one that is larger (smaller).* Zero is the only number that is neither positive nor negative. Ask students to share the positive and negative numbers they chose that are close to zero. Record them on the board and have students put them in ascending order.

✦ Presenting an Overview of Our Number System (*Student Reference Book,* pp. 97–100)

WHOLE-CLASS DISCUSSION 

Unlike most activities in *Everyday Mathematics,* for this one you might want to present the information on our number system in a short lecture. Or you may want to read pages 97 through 100 in the *Student Reference Book* as a class, but students will probably get more out of this discussion if you present the ideas yourself. Keep in mind that this is an introduction to very sophisticated ideas, to which students will return over and over again in the next few years, so you need not dwell on these topics. Here is one way to present the information.

1. Identify the counting numbers.

Draw a number line on the board with 11 evenly-spaced marks on it.

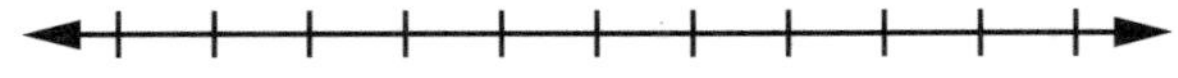

Write the numbers 1 through 5, as shown below.

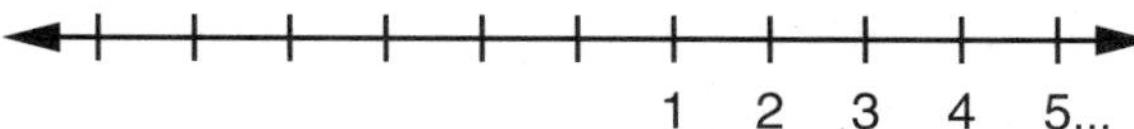

These are called counting numbers. As the name implies, they are used to count things. There are infinitely many **counting numbers.** Ask students to name some counting numbers *not* shown on the number line.

2. Identify the whole numbers.

Add the number 0 to the number line. All of the counting numbers and 0 make up the set of **whole numbers.**

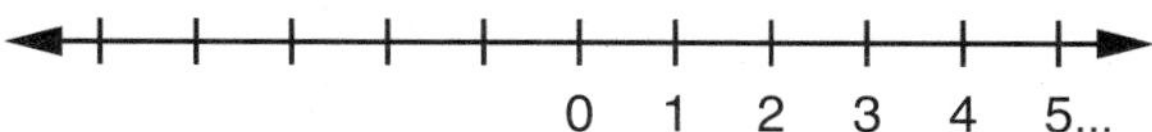

3. Identify the integers.

Now write the numbers -1 through -5 to the left of 0.

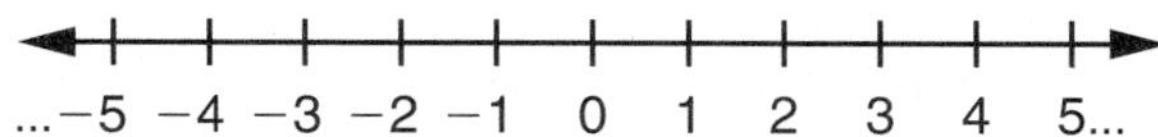

All of the whole numbers and all of the negative whole numbers make up the set of **integers.** Ask students to name some integers *not* shown on the number line.

4. Identify the rational numbers.

Ask students to name situations in which integers do not accurately apply. For example, the length of an object or a temperature reading may be represented by a number between two consecutive integers.

Ask students to name some numbers that are *between* consecutive numbers on the number line. Look for students to name fractions and decimals, such as $\frac{1}{2}$, 2.5, $-4\frac{1}{4}$, and $\frac{1}{3}$. Write a few of them in the appropriate places on the number line. These are called **rational numbers.**

A rational number is any number that can be written as a simple fraction $\frac{a}{b}$, where a and b are integers and $b \neq 0$. Rational numbers can be positive, negative, or 0. They can be whole numbers, since any whole number can be expressed as a fraction (for example, $3 = \frac{3}{1}$). They can also be mixed numbers or percents, since any mixed number or percent can be renamed as a fraction.

Students have learned that any fraction can be renamed as a decimal. For example, $\frac{1}{2} = 0.5$ and $\frac{1}{3} = 0.33333....$ Renaming $\frac{1}{2}$ as a decimal by dividing 1 by 2 results in a remainder of zero. The division comes to an end. Decimals that end are called **terminating decimals.**

Scavenger Hunt

Use *Student Reference Book* pages 1–24 and 91–104 to find answers to as many of these questions as you can. Try to get as high a score as possible.

1. How many rational numbers are there? (10 points) An infinite number
2. Give an example of each of the following. (5 points each) Sample answers:
   a. A counting number 5
   b. A negative rational number $-\frac{1}{2}$
   c. A positive rational number $\frac{3}{4}$
   d. A real number $\sqrt{5}$
   e. An integer 0
   f. An irrational number π
3. Name two examples of uses of negative rational numbers. (5 points each) Sample answers: To express measures below sea level and; to express temperatures below the freezing point
4. Explain why numbers like 4, $\frac{3}{5}$, and 3.5 are rational numbers. (10 points) Sample answer: They can be expressed as simple fractions: 4 can be expressed as $\frac{4}{1}$; $\frac{3}{5}$ is already a fraction; and 3.5 can be expressed as $3\frac{1}{2}$.
5. Explain why numbers like π and $\sqrt{2}$ are irrational numbers. (10 points) They are non-terminating and non-repeating decimals.
6. $n + n = n$ What is n? 0 (15 points)
7. $k = (\text{OPP})\ k$ What is k? 0 (15 points)
8. $j * j = j$ Which two numbers could j be? 1 or 0 (15 points each)
9. $a + (-a) =$ 0 (15 points)
10. $b * \frac{1}{b} =$ 1 (15 points)

STUDENT PAGE

Math Journal 2, p. 222

STUDENT PAGE

Scavenger Hunt (cont.)

11. Match each sentence in Column 1 with the property in Column 2 that it illustrates. (5 points each)

Column 1	Column 2
A. $a + (b + c) = (a + b) + c$	D Distributive property of multiplication over subtraction
B. $a + b = b + a$	B Commutative property of addition
C. $a * (b + c) = (a * b) + (a * c)$	C Distributive property of multiplication over addition
D. $a * (b - c) = (a * b) - (a * c)$	F Associative property of multiplication
E. $a * b = b * a$	E Commutative property of multiplication
F. $a * (b * c) = (a * b) * c$	A Associative property of addition

12. $-a > 0$. How can that be? (15 points)
If a is a negative number, then its opposite will always be greater than 0. For example, $-(-8) > 0$, since $-(-8) = 8$.

13. Complete. (2 points each, except the last problem, which is worth 25 points)

(OPP) 1 = −1
(OPP) (OPP) 1 = 1
(OPP) (OPP) (OPP) 1 = −1
(OPP) (OPP) (OPP) (OPP) 1 = 1
(OPP) (OPP) (OPP) (OPP) (OPP) 1 = −1
(OPP) (OPP) (OPP) (OPP) (OPP) (OPP) 1 = 1
(OPP) (OPP) (OPP) (OPP) (OPP) (OPP) ... (OPP) (OPP) 1 = 1
100 (OPP)s

Explain how you found the answer to the last problem. Sample answer: Taking the opposite an even number of times gives a positive number because every pair of (OPP)s, gives a positive number.

◆ *Math Journal 2*, p. 223

STUDENT PAGE

Scavenger Hunt (cont.)

14. Is 5^{-2} a positive or negative number? Explain. (15 points)
Sample answer: It is positive. By the powers of a number property, 5^{-2} is 1 divided by 5 used as a factor 2 times which is $\frac{1}{5*5}$ or $\frac{1}{25}$.

15. Two numbers are their own reciprocals. What are they? 1 and −1 (15 points each)

16. What number has no reciprocal? 0 (15 points)

Number Stories

1. Diana wants to make a 15'-by-20' section of her yard into a garden. She will plant flowers in $\frac{2}{3}$ of the garden and vegetables in the rest of the garden. How many square feet of vegetable garden will she have?
100 ft^2
Explain how you got your answer. Sample answer: I multiplied 15 by 20 to get the total square footage of 300 ft^2; then I multiplied 300 by $\frac{2}{3}$ to find out the amount for the flower garden: 200 ft^2. Finally, I subtracted 200 from 300 to find the amount used for vegetables.

2. Leo is in charge of buying hot dogs for family math night. Out of 300 people, he expects about $\frac{3}{5}$ of them to attend. Hot dogs come 8 to a package, and Leo figures he will need to buy 22 packages so that each person can get 1 hot dog.
   a. How do you think he calculated to get 22 packages?
   Sample answer: He first multiplied $\frac{3}{5}$ by 300 to find out that about 180 people will come. Then he divided 180 by 8. He should have gotten 22.5.
   b. What was Leo's mistake? He did not interpret the remainder properly. He needs to buy 23 packages.

◆ *Math Journal 2*, p. 224

Renaming $\frac{1}{3}$ as a decimal by dividing 1 by 3 does not result in a zero remainder no matter how many places there are after the decimal point. Not only do the digits go on and on, but they do so in a repeating pattern—in this case, 3 is repeated over and over. Such decimals are called **repeating decimals.**

5. Identify the irrational numbers.

There are some numbers that can be written as decimals that go on without end, such that the digits do *not* follow a repeating pattern. They are called **irrational numbers.** The number π is an example of an irrational number that students have used in the past. Ask students to key in π on a calculator. With a 10-place calculator, the display is 3.141592654. With a 20-place calculator, the display is 3.1415926535897932384. Even on a million-place calculator, the display will still show a decimal that neither comes to an end nor exhibits a repeating pattern.

6. Identify the real numbers.

The set of numbers consisting of all rational numbers and all irrational numbers is called the set of **real numbers.** Examples of these numbers are displayed on the Real Number Line Poster. At one time or another, students have worked with all of the notations shown on the number line with the exception of the tangent of 30° (tan 30°), the number *e,* and the irrational square roots, all of which are represented by non-terminating, non-repeating decimals.

◆ Taking Part in a Mathematical Scavenger Hunt (*Math Journal 2*, pp. 222–224; *Student Reference Book*, pp. 97–100 and 102–104)

PARTNER ACTIVITY

Ask students to browse through *Student Reference Book* pages 102–104. These pages formally summarize many of the properties of rational numbers that students have been working with for years. For example, the commutative properties are just the familiar turn-around rules that students used to simplify learning the addition and multiplication facts.

Explain that students will work in partnerships to complete the Scavenger Hunt on journal pages 222 through 224. Encourage students to read all of the questions first and then to search the *Student Reference Book* pages to find answers. Most answers require thinking beyond the information provided in the book.

Let students know that some questions are very challenging, so they shouldn't be discouraged if they cannot solve them all.

When most partnerships have finished, or after a predetermined length of time, review the answers.

You might also want to discuss some of these ideas:

- Numbers like $\sqrt{12}$ and $\sqrt{5}$ can be written as non-terminating, non-repeating decimals; thus, they name irrational numbers. Point out that not all square roots are irrational; for example, $\sqrt{16} = 4$, which is a counting number. *What other square roots on the number line are counting numbers?* Sample answers: $\sqrt{9}$ 3, $\sqrt{4}$ 2, $\sqrt{1}$ 1
- Note that $-\sqrt{1}$ is shown at the -1 point on the number line, since $-1 * -1 = 1$. $\sqrt{1}$ is also equal to 1. All square roots have both a positive and a negative value.
- 10^{-1} is a positive number, since it is equivalent to the fraction $\frac{1}{10}$.

ONGOING ASSESSMENT

Use students' answers to Problems 1–5 on journal page 222 to assess their understanding of number systems. Are they able to describe the various kinds of numbers? Use students' answers to Problems 9 and 10 to assess their understanding of the sum of opposites property and the multiplication of reciprocals property.

Ongoing Learning & Practice

Reviewing a Problem-Solving Diagram and Solving Number Stories (*Math Journal 2,* p. 224; *Student Reference Book,* pp. 240 and 241)

PARTNER ACTIVITY

With the whole class, review the general approach to problem solving described on the *Student Reference Book* pages. Use the strategies and diagram to discuss how the Check Your Understanding problem at the bottom of page 241 might be solved.

Over the next few days, students can estimate an answer and write an explanation of how they arrived at their estimate.

Students solve the multi-step number stories on the journal page and explain their thinking.

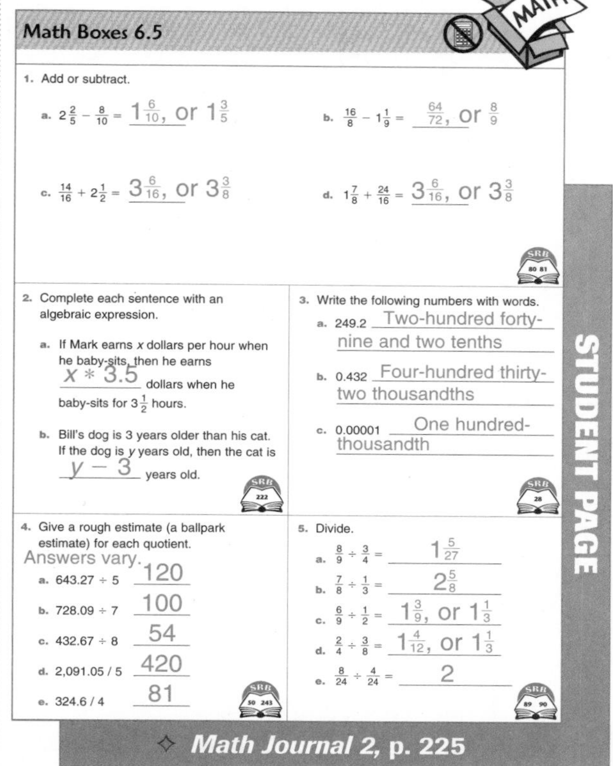

Math Boxes 6.5

1. Add or subtract.

a. $2\frac{2}{5} - \frac{8}{10} =$ $1\frac{6}{10}$, or $1\frac{3}{5}$

b. $\frac{16}{8} - 1\frac{1}{9} =$ $\frac{64}{72}$, or $\frac{8}{9}$

c. $\frac{14}{16} + 2\frac{1}{2} =$ $3\frac{6}{16}$, or $3\frac{3}{8}$

d. $1\frac{7}{8} + \frac{24}{16} =$ $3\frac{6}{16}$, or $3\frac{3}{8}$

2. Complete each sentence with an algebraic expression.

a. If Mark earns x dollars per hour when he baby-sits, then he earns $x * 3.5$ dollars when he baby-sits for $3\frac{1}{2}$ hours.

b. Bill's dog is 3 years older than his cat. If the dog is y years old, then the cat is $y - 3$ years old.

3. Write the following numbers with words.

a. 249.2 Two-hundred forty-nine and two tenths

b. 0.432 Four-hundred thirty-two thousandths

c. 0.00001 One hundred-thousandth

4. Give a rough estimate (a ballpark estimate) for each quotient.
Answers vary.

a. 643.27 ÷ 5 120

b. 728.09 ÷ 7 100

c. 432.67 ÷ 8 54

d. 2,091.05 / 5 420

e. 324.6 / 4 81

5. Divide.

a. $\frac{8}{9} \div \frac{3}{4} =$ $1\frac{5}{27}$

b. $\frac{7}{8} \div \frac{1}{3} =$ $2\frac{5}{8}$

c. $\frac{6}{9} \div \frac{1}{2} =$ $1\frac{3}{9}$, or $1\frac{1}{3}$

d. $\frac{2}{4} \div \frac{3}{8} =$ $1\frac{4}{12}$, or $1\frac{1}{3}$

e. $\frac{8}{24} \div \frac{4}{24} =$ 2

STUDENT PAGE

Math Journal 2, p. 225

Adjusting the Activity For Problems 6–10 on journal page 222, suggest to struggling students that they replace the variables with numbers (special cases) and then look for patterns.

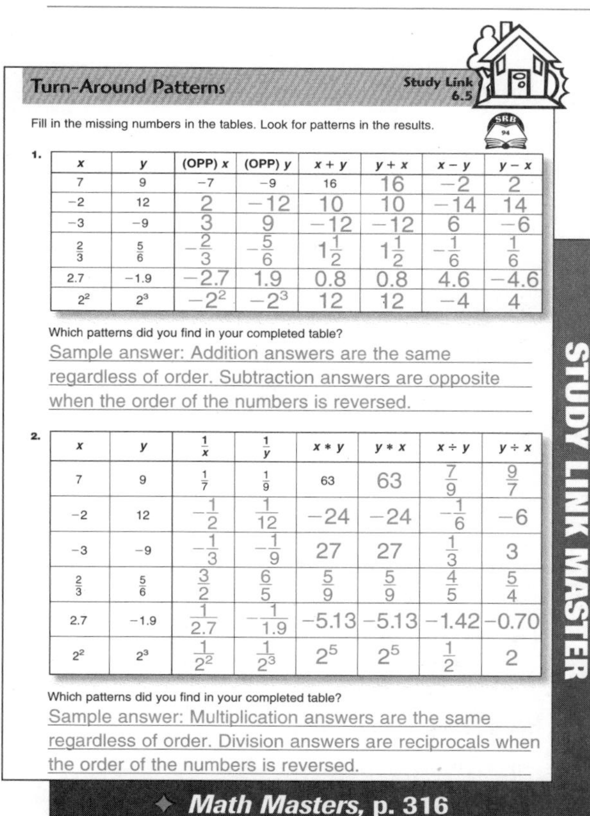

Turn-Around Patterns Study Link 6.5

Fill in the missing numbers in the tables. Look for patterns in the results.

1.

x	y	(OPP) x	(OPP) y	$x + y$	$y + x$	$x - y$	$y - x$
7	9	−7	−9	16	16	−2	2
−2	12	2	−12	10	10	−14	14
−3	−9	3	9	−12	−12	6	−6
$\frac{2}{3}$	$\frac{5}{6}$	$-\frac{2}{3}$	$-\frac{5}{6}$	$1\frac{1}{2}$	$1\frac{1}{2}$	$-\frac{1}{6}$	$\frac{1}{6}$
2.7	−1.9	−2.7	1.9	0.8	0.8	4.6	−4.6
2^2	2^3	-2^2	-2^3	12	12	−4	4

Which patterns did you find in your completed table?
Sample answer: Addition answers are the same regardless of order. Subtraction answers are opposite when the order of the numbers is reversed.

2.

x	y	$\frac{1}{x}$	$\frac{1}{y}$	$x * y$	$y * x$	$x \div y$	$y \div x$
7	9	$\frac{1}{7}$	$\frac{1}{9}$	63	63	$\frac{7}{9}$	$\frac{9}{7}$
−2	12	$-\frac{1}{2}$	$\frac{1}{12}$	−24	−24	$-\frac{1}{6}$	−6
−3	−9	$-\frac{1}{3}$	$-\frac{1}{9}$	27	27	$\frac{1}{3}$	3
$\frac{2}{3}$	$\frac{5}{6}$	$\frac{3}{2}$	$\frac{6}{5}$	$\frac{5}{9}$	$\frac{5}{9}$	$\frac{4}{5}$	$\frac{5}{4}$
2.7	−1.9	$\frac{1}{2.7}$	$-\frac{1}{1.9}$	−5.13	−5.13	−1.42	−0.70
2^2	2^3	$\frac{1}{2^2}$	$\frac{1}{2^3}$	2^5	2^5	$\frac{1}{2}$	2

Which patterns did you find in your completed table?
Sample answer: Multiplication answers are the same regardless of order. Division answers are reciprocals when the order of the numbers is reversed.

STUDY LINK MASTER

Math Masters, p. 316

TEACHING MASTER

Properties of Numbers

For each of the statements below, indicate whether it is always true. If the statement is not always true, give an example that is false.

	Statement	True or false?	Example
1.	$\frac{a}{b} + \frac{c}{d} = \frac{a+c}{b+d}$	false	$\frac{3}{4} + \frac{2}{5} \neq \frac{5}{9}$
2.	$\frac{a}{b} * \frac{c}{d} = \frac{a*c}{b*d}$	true	
3.	$\frac{a}{b} - \frac{c}{d} = \frac{a-c}{b-d}$	false	$\frac{9}{10} - \frac{4}{8} \neq \frac{5}{2}$
4.	$\frac{a}{b} \div \frac{c}{d} = \frac{a \div c}{b \div d}$	true (See below.)	

5. Explain why one example for a true statement is not enough to prove that it is true.
Sample answer: *True* means *true in every case,* not just true in one case.

Challenge

6. Correct each false statement in Problems 1–4 so that it is true for all special cases. Give one example for each statement.

1. $\frac{a}{b} + \frac{c}{d} = \frac{(a*d)+(c*b)}{b*d}; \frac{3}{4} + \frac{2}{5} = \frac{(3*5)+(2*4)}{20} = 1\frac{3}{20}$

3. $\frac{a}{b} - \frac{c}{d} = \frac{(a*d)-(c*b)}{b*d}; \frac{7}{9} - \frac{3}{4} = \frac{(7*4)-(3*9)}{36} = \frac{1}{36}$

Proof of Problem 4:

$\frac{a}{b} \div \frac{c}{d} = \frac{a}{b} * \frac{d}{c} = \frac{ad}{bc}$

$\frac{a \div c}{b \div d} = \frac{a}{c} \div \frac{b}{d} = \frac{a}{c} * \frac{d}{b} = \frac{ad}{cb}$

✦ *Math Masters,* p. 97

TEACHING MASTER

Brain Teasers

1. Trevor had 12 cookies. He ate all but 5. How many were left? 5 cookies
2. What is the exact opposite of "not in"? in
3. How many prime numbers are there between 0 and 10? 4: 2, 3, 5, and 7
4. As I was going to St. Ives, I met a man with seven wives. Every wife had seven sacks, every sack had seven cats. Every cat had seven kits. Kits, cats, sacks, and wives, How many were going to St. Ives? 1 person
5. $3 * \frac{1}{3} * 3 * \frac{1}{3} * 3 =$ 3
6. $\frac{(415 + 415 + 415 + 415 + 415)}{5} =$ 415
7. What is the only even prime number? 2
8. $(1 + 2 + 3 + 4) + (9 + 8 + 7 + 6) =$ 40
9. What word does every teacher in your school always pronounce wrong? "wrong"
10. Divide 10 by $\frac{1}{2}$ and add 5. What is the answer? 25
11. How many months have 28 days? 12 months
12. Describe an easy way to solve Problem 6.
Sample answer: The problem is asking for an average. You are adding the same number 5 times and then dividing by 5; multiplying by 5 and then dividing by 5 undo each other.

✦ *Math Masters,* p. 98

✦ Math Boxes 6.5 (*Math Journal 2,* p. 225)

INDEPENDENT ACTIVITY 

Mixed Review Math Boxes in this lesson are paired with Math Boxes in Lesson 6.7. The skill in Problem 1 is a prerequisite for Unit 7.

✦ Study Link 6.5 (*Math Masters,* p. 316)

Home Connection Students explore the relationships between addition and subtraction and between multiplication and division of rational numbers.

3 Options for Individualizing

✦ ENRICHMENT Investigating Properties of Rational Numbers (*Math Masters,* p. 97)

INDEPENDENT ACTIVITY  **15–30 min** 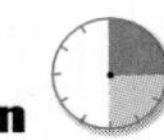

Students investigate whether general statements about rational numbers are true or false.

✦ ENRICHMENT Solving Puzzles (*Math Masters,* p. 98)

INDEPENDENT ACTIVITY  **15–30 min** 

Language Arts Link Students solve number and word puzzles, some of which use the properties discussed in this lesson.

6.6 Order of Operations

OBJECTIVES **To review the rules for the order of operations; and to evaluate expressions containing parentheses.**

summaries	materials
1 Teaching the Lesson	
Students review the rules for the order of operations by solving problems on a scientific calculator. They also evaluate expressions according to these rules. [Patterns, Functions, and Algebra; Operations and Computation]	□ *Math Journal 2,* pp. 226 and 227 □ *Student Reference Book,* p. 229 □ Teaching Master (*Math Masters,* p. 99; optional) □ Study Link 6.5 □ calculator ***See* Advance Preparation**
2 Ongoing Learning & Practice	
Students solve number stories using division of fractions. [Operations and Computation] Students practice and maintain skills through Math Boxes and Study Link activities.	□ *Math Journal 2,* pp. 228 and 229 □ Study Link Master (*Math Masters,* p. 317) □ Geometry Template
3 Options for Individualizing	
Extra Practice Students practice using the order of operations rules. [Patterns, Functions, and Algebra; Operations and Computation] **Enrichment** Students explore the differences between scientific and non-scientific calculators. [Operations and Computation]	□ Teaching Masters (*Math Masters,* pp. 99 and 100) □ calculators (both scientific and non-scientific)

Additional Information

Advance Preparation For Part 1, read the essay on page 251 of the *Student Reference Book.* Check that your students' calculators are programmed for order of operations by entering the first Math Message problem into a calculator. If the display shows 10, then the calculator is programmed to follow these rules. Note that all scientific calculators on the market today follow these rules, but most standard four-function calculators do not.

Vocabulary • **order of operations**

Getting Started

Mental Math and Reflexes

Have students evaluate the following expressions:

- $(55 - 44) * 8$ 88
- $(-\frac{2}{3} + -\frac{2}{3}) * -3$ 4
- $18 / (-6 + 4)$ −9
- $-6 * (\frac{3}{4} / \frac{1}{4})$ −18
- $27 + (11 * 3)$ 60
- $(7 + 23) / [(14 / 2) + 0.5]$ 4

Math Message

Evaluate the following expressions.

1. $12 - 8 / 4$ **2.** $24 / 3 + 6$

3. $6 * 5 + 7$ **4.** $17 - 9 * 3$

5. $15 + 6^2 / 3$ **6.** $2^3 / 8 + 3$

Study Link 6.5 Follow-Up

Ask students to share the patterns they found in the tables. Make sure that the following patterns are mentioned:

- $x + y = y + x$
- $x * y = y * x$
- $y - x$ is the opposite of $x - y$.
- $y \div x$ is the reciprocal of $x \div y$.

1 Teaching the Lesson

✦Math Message Follow-Up

WHOLE-CLASS ACTIVITY

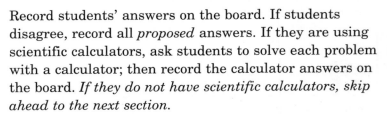

Record students' answers on the board. If students disagree, record all *proposed* answers. If they are using scientific calculators, ask students to solve each problem with a calculator; then record the calculator answers on the board. *If they do not have scientific calculators, skip ahead to the next section.*

In an expression with at least two operations, the order in which the operations are carried out can be indicated with parentheses. Without parentheses, the value of the expression depends on rules for the order in which the operations are to be done.

Unless students know the rules for the order of operations, they probably solved the problems by calculating from left to right. If they did, their answers to Problems 1, 4, and 5 will differ from the answers they obtained with their calculators.

Ask students to insert parentheses in each expression to show which operation the calculator did first. Record these expressions on the board. (See the table below.)

Problem Number	Expression	Left to Right	Calculator	Parentheses
1.	$12 - 8 / 4$	1	10	$12 - (8 / 4)$
2.	$24 / 3 + 6$	14	14	$(24 / 3) + 6$
3.	$6 * 5 + 7$	37	37	$(6 * 5) + 7$
4.	$17 - 9 * 3$	24	-10	$17 - (9 * 3)$
5.	$15 + 6^2 / 3$	17	27	$15 + (6^2 / 3)$
6.	$2^3 / 8 + 3$	4	4	$(2^3 / 8) + 3$

For Problems 1, 4, and 5, the scientific calculator clearly did not evaluate the expressions in the order in which the numbers and operations were entered. In each of these expressions, the calculator carried out the addition or subtraction last. A scientific calculator will follow the rules for order of operations, regardless of the order in which an expression is keyed in.

✦ Reviewing the Rules for the Order of Operations (*Student Reference Book,* p. 229)

WHOLE-CLASS DISCUSSION

The use of parentheses in an expression and the rules for the **order of operations** make up a mathematical "punctuation" system. As a class, read and work through the examples on *Student Reference Book,* page 229.

Discuss why, in the absence of parentheses, the rules of operations are necessary. They are necessary so that everyone can agree on the same value for any expression.

Summarize the rules. Point out that in expressions with addition and subtraction only, or multiplication and division only, neither operation has priority over the other. The operations are done in order from left to right. So, for example, the answer to $4 - 3 + 1$ should be 2, not 0, and the answer to $24 / 3 * 4$ should be 32, not 2.

Check that students understand how to use the mnemonic "Please Excuse My Dear Aunt Sally." Ask students if they can make up their own mnemonic.

Students solve the Check Your Understanding problems and explain how they got their answers. Suggest that they follow the format of the examples in the *Student Reference Book,* in which each step is written on a separate line. This format makes it easy to keep track of the order in which the operations are done. Have students check their answers with a calculator. Pose additional problems if students need more practice.

NOTE: The rules for the order of operations were formally introduced in *Fifth Grade Everyday Mathematics* but have not been emphasized until now. Prior to this lesson, *Everyday Mathematics* has stressed the use of parentheses to give an expression an unambiguous value because the authors feel that students benefit from a more explicit approach.

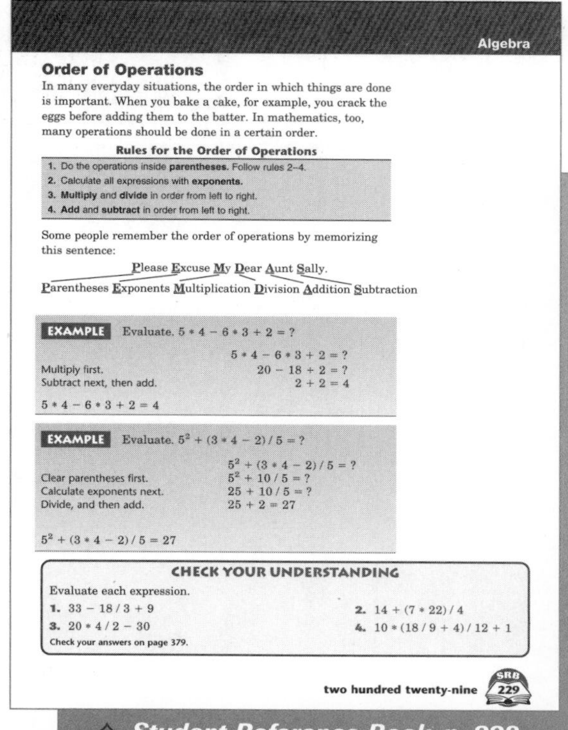

Algebra

STUDENT PAGE

Order of Operations

In many everyday situations, the order in which things are done is important. When you bake a cake, for example, you crack the eggs before adding them to the batter. In mathematics, too, many operations should be done in a certain order.

Rules for the Order of Operations

1. Do the operations inside **parentheses.** Follow rules 2–4.
2. Calculate all expressions with **exponents.**
3. **Multiply** and **divide** in order from left to right.
4. **Add** and **subtract** in order from left to right.

Some people remember the order of operations by memorizing this sentence:

Please Excuse My Dear Aunt Sally.

Parentheses Exponents Multiplication Division Addition Subtraction

EXAMPLE Evaluate. $5 * 4 - 6 * 3 + 2 = ?$

	$5 * 4 - 6 * 3 + 2 = ?$
Multiply first.	$20 - 18 + 2 = ?$
Subtract next, then add.	$2 + 2 = 4$

$5 * 4 - 6 * 3 + 2 = 4$

EXAMPLE Evaluate. $5^2 + (3 * 4 - 2) / 5 = ?$

	$5^2 + (3 * 4 - 2) / 5 = ?$
Clear parentheses first.	$5^2 + 10 / 5 = ?$
Calculate exponents next.	$25 + 10 / 5 = ?$
Divide, and then add.	$25 + 2 = 27$

$5^2 + (3 * 4 - 2) / 5 = 27$

CHECK YOUR UNDERSTANDING

Evaluate each expression.

1. $33 - 18 / 3 + 9$
2. $14 + (7 * 22) / 4$
3. $20 * 4 / 2 - 30$
4. $10 * (18 / 9 + 4) / 12 + 1$

Check your answers on page 379.

two hundred twenty-nine SRB 229

✧ *Student Reference Book,* p. 229

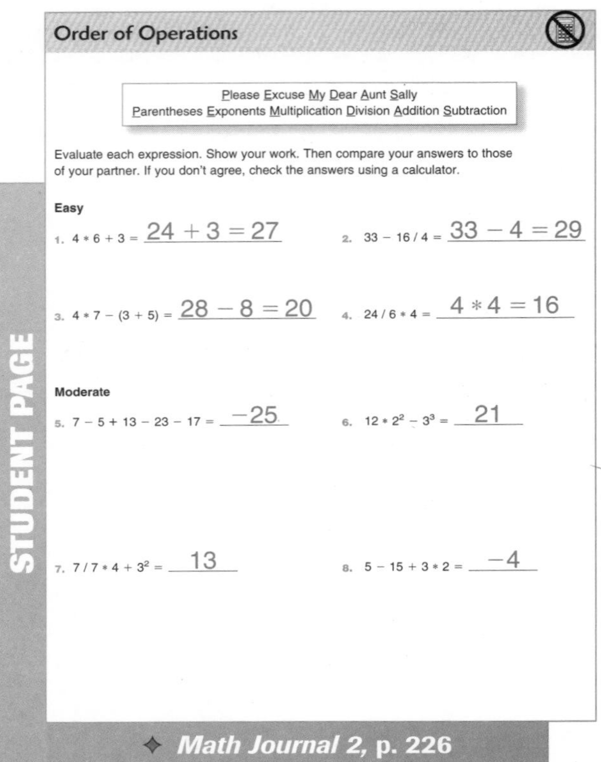
STUDENT PAGE

Order of Operations

Please Excuse My Dear Aunt Sally
Parentheses Exponents Multiplication Division Addition Subtraction

Evaluate each expression. Show your work. Then compare your answers to those of your partner. If you don't agree, check the answers using a calculator.

Easy

1. $4 * 6 + 3 =$ $24 + 3 = 27$
2. $33 - 16 / 4 =$ $33 - 4 = 29$
3. $4 * 7 - (3 + 5) =$ $28 - 8 = 20$
4. $24 / 6 * 4 =$ $4 * 4 = 16$

Moderate

5. $7 - 5 + 13 - 23 - 17 =$ -25
6. $12 * 2^2 - 3^3 =$ 21
7. $7 / 7 * 4 + 3^2 =$ 13
8. $5 - 15 + 3 * 2 =$ -4

✦ *Math Journal 2*, p. 226

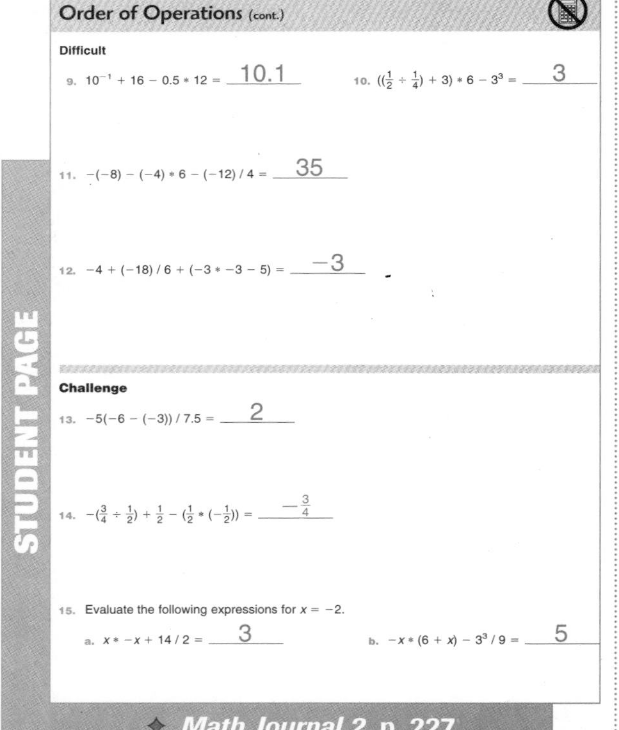
STUDENT PAGE

Order of Operations (cont.)

Difficult

9. $10^{-1} + 16 - 0.5 * 12 =$ 10.1
10. $((\frac{1}{2} \div \frac{1}{4}) + 3) * 6 - 3^3 =$ 3
11. $-(-8) - (-4) * 6 - (-12) / 4 =$ 35
12. $-4 + (-18) / 6 + (-3 * -3 - 5) =$ -3

Challenge

13. $-5(-6 - (-3)) / 7.5 =$ 2
14. $-(\frac{3}{4} \div \frac{1}{2}) + \frac{1}{2} - (\frac{1}{2} * (-\frac{1}{2})) =$ $-\frac{3}{4}$
15. Evaluate the following expressions for $x = -2$.
   a. $x * -x + 14 / 2 =$ 3
   b. $-x * (6 + x) - 3^3 / 9 =$ 5

✦ *Math Journal 2*, p. 227

✦ Evaluating Expressions (*Math Journal 2*, pp. 226 and 227; *Math Masters*, p. 99)

PARTNER ACTIVITY

Assign journal pages 226 and 227. Students can solve the problems independently and then compare their answers to those of their partners. Disagreements can be resolved by doing the problems with a calculator.

Some of the problems use two sets of parentheses in the same expression. When this occurs, the operation inside the "inner" parentheses is done before the operation in the "outer" parentheses. Double parentheses are often referred to as *nested* parentheses.

NOTE: Omission of the multiplication symbol in algebraic expressions can confuse students. Remind them that expressions like $2 * N$ and $2N$ have the same meaning. Also, expressions like $5(4 + 3)$ mean $5 * (4 + 3)$.

Adjusting the Activity For students who need more foundation with the basic rules for the order of operations, assign *Math Masters*, page 99 (see Part 3) and revisit journal page 227 at a later date, when students are ready for more challenging situations.

Circulate and assist as needed. When most students have finished, bring the class together and go over any problems that students found to be particularly difficult.

ONGOING ASSESSMENT

Most students should be able to do the "easy" and "moderate" problems on journal page 226. Use all of these problems to assess students' understanding of the rules for the order of operations.

Ongoing Learning & Practice

Solving Number Stories Involving Division with Fractions (*Math Journal 2,* p. 228)

PARTNER ACTIVITY 

Students solve number stories that require dividing fractions. They also write number stories for given number models.

Math Boxes 6.6 (*Math Journal 2,* p. 229)

INDEPENDENT ACTIVITY 

Mixed Review Math Boxes in this lesson are paired with Math Boxes in Lesson 6.8. The skill in Problem 1 is a prerequisite for Unit 7.

Study Link 6.6 (*Math Masters,* p. 317)

Home Connection Students use the rules for the order of operations to evaluate expressions.

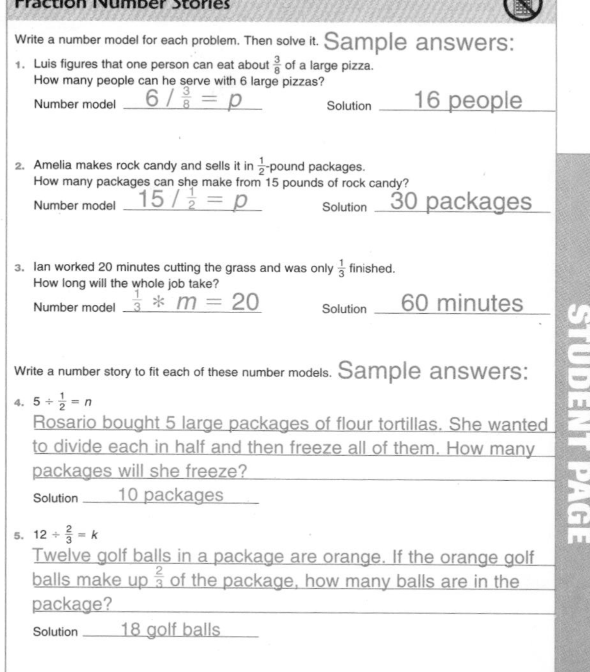

Fraction Number Stories

Write a number model for each problem. Then solve it. Sample answers:

1. Luis figures that one person can eat about $\frac{3}{8}$ of a large pizza. How many people can he serve with 6 large pizzas?
   Number model $6 / \frac{3}{8} = p$ Solution 16 people
2. Amelia makes rock candy and sells it in $\frac{1}{2}$-pound packages. How many packages can she make from 15 pounds of rock candy?
   Number model $15 / \frac{1}{2} = p$ Solution 30 packages
3. Ian worked 20 minutes cutting the grass and was only $\frac{1}{3}$ finished. How long will the whole job take?
   Number model $\frac{1}{3} * m = 20$ Solution 60 minutes

Write a number story to fit each of these number models. Sample answers:

4. $5 \div \frac{1}{2} = n$
   Rosario bought 5 large packages of flour tortillas. She wanted to divide each in half and then freeze all of them. How many packages will she freeze?
   Solution 10 packages
5. $12 \div \frac{2}{3} = k$
   Twelve golf balls in a package are orange. If the orange golf balls make up $\frac{2}{3}$ of the package, how many balls are in the package?
   Solution 18 golf balls

STUDENT PAGE

Math Journal 2, p. 228

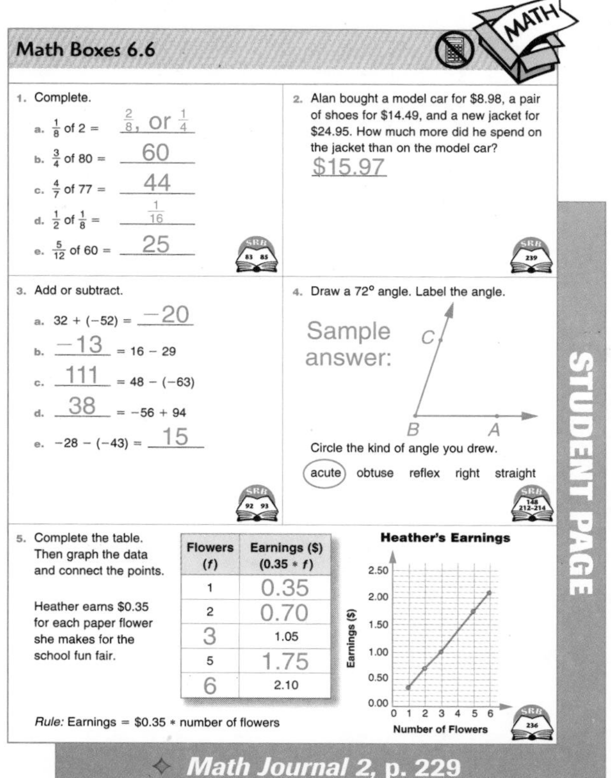

Math Boxes 6.6

1. Complete.
   a. $\frac{1}{8}$ of 2 = $\frac{2}{8}$, or $\frac{1}{4}$
   b. $\frac{3}{4}$ of 80 = 60
   c. $\frac{4}{7}$ of 77 = 44
   d. $\frac{1}{2}$ of $\frac{1}{8}$ = $\frac{1}{16}$
   e. $\frac{5}{12}$ of 60 = 25
2. Alan bought a model car for $8.98, a pair of shoes for $14.49, and a new jacket for $24.95. How much more did he spend on the jacket than on the model car? $15.97
3. Add or subtract.
   a. 32 + (−52) = −20
   b. −13 = 16 − 29
   c. 111 = 48 − (−63)
   d. 38 = −56 + 94
   e. −28 − (−43) = 15
4. Draw a 72° angle. Label the angle. Sample answer: (C, B, A)
   Circle the kind of angle you drew. (acute) obtuse reflex right straight
5. Complete the table. Then graph the data and connect the points.
   Heather earns $0.35 for each paper flower she makes for the school fun fair.

Flowers (f)	Earnings ($) (0.35 * f)
1	0.35
2	0.70
3	1.05
5	1.75
6	2.10

Rule: Earnings = $0.35 * number of flowers

Heather's Earnings (Earnings ($) vs. Number of Flowers)

STUDENT PAGE

Math Journal 2, p. 229

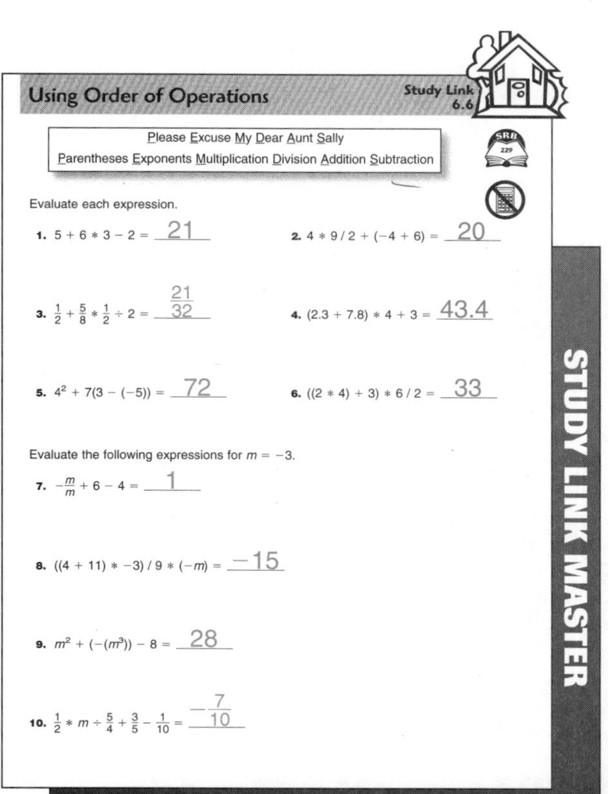

Using Order of Operations Study Link 6.6

Please Excuse My Dear Aunt Sally
Parentheses Exponents Multiplication Division Addition Subtraction

Evaluate each expression.

1. $5 + 6 * 3 - 2 =$ 21
2. $4 * 9 / 2 + (-4 + 6) =$ 20
3. $\frac{1}{2} + \frac{5}{8} * \frac{1}{2} \div 2 =$ $\frac{21}{32}$
4. $(2.3 + 7.8) * 4 + 3 =$ 43.4
5. $4^2 + 7(3 - (-5)) =$ 72
6. $((2 * 4) + 3) * 6 / 2 =$ 33

Evaluate the following expressions for $m = -3$.

7. $-\frac{m}{m} + 6 - 4 =$ 1
8. $((4 + 11) * -3) / 9 * (-m) =$ −15
9. $m^2 + (-(m^3)) - 8 =$ 28
10. $\frac{1}{2} * m \div \frac{5}{4} + \frac{3}{5} - \frac{1}{10} =$ $-\frac{7}{10}$

STUDY LINK MASTER

Math Masters, p. 317

Order of Operations

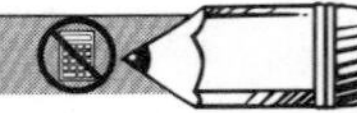

Please Excuse My Dear Aunt Sally
Parentheses Exponents Multiplication Division Addition Subtraction

Evaluate each expression. Compare your answer to a partner's. If you don't agree, discuss how you each solved the problem to decide which answer is correct.

1. 26 + 15 * 2 − 6 = 50
2. 18 − 5 + 10^2 = 113
3. 50 + 70 / 2 = 85
4. 39 + 1 − 24 / 6 = 36
5. 18 / 3 + (37 + 13) = 56
6. 18 / 3 + 37 + 13 = 56
7. 42 + 6 / 6 − 8 = 35
8. 5 + 3^2 * 4 / 2 = 23

TEACHING MASTER

✦ *Math Masters,* p. 99

3 Options for Individualizing

✦ EXTRA PRACTICE Evaluating Expressions (*Math Masters,* p. 99)

PARTNER ACTIVITY  **15–30 min** 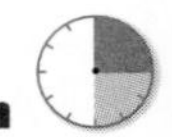

Students practice applying the rules for the order of operations by evaluating expressions. This page provides practice with the order of operations without the distraction of difficult computations.

✦ ENRICHMENT Exploring Scientific Calculators (*Math Masters,* p. 100)

INDEPENDENT ACTIVITY  **15–30 min**

Students explore the differences between scientific and non-scientific calculators. They enter problems into both kinds of calculators and record the answers. For each problem, they rewrite the number sentence using parentheses to show how the calculator performed the operations.

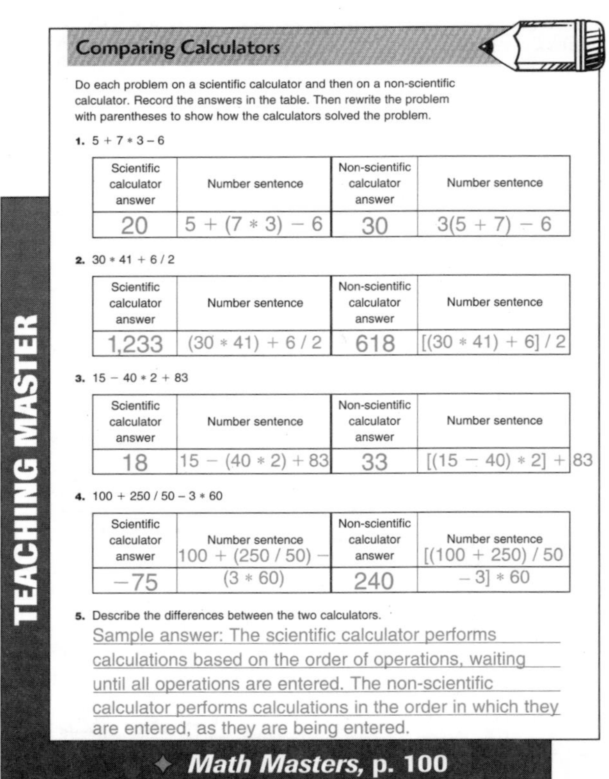

Comparing Calculators

Do each problem on a scientific calculator and then on a non-scientific calculator. Record the answers in the table. Then rewrite the problem with parentheses to show how the calculators solved the problem.

1. 5 + 7 * 3 − 6

Scientific calculator answer	Number sentence	Non-scientific calculator answer	Number sentence
20	5 + (7 * 3) − 6	30	3(5 + 7) − 6

2. 30 * 41 + 6 / 2

Scientific calculator answer	Number sentence	Non-scientific calculator answer	Number sentence
1,233	(30 * 41) + 6 / 2	618	[(30 * 41) + 6] / 2

3. 15 − 40 * 2 + 83

Scientific calculator answer	Number sentence	Non-scientific calculator answer	Number sentence
18	15 − (40 * 2) + 83	33	[(15 − 40) * 2] + 83

4. 100 + 250 / 50 − 3 * 60

Scientific calculator answer	Number sentence	Non-scientific calculator answer	Number sentence
−75	100 + (250 / 50) − (3 * 60)	240	[(100 + 250) / 50 − 3] * 60

5. Describe the differences between the two calculators.
Sample answer: The scientific calculator performs calculations based on the order of operations, waiting until all operations are entered. The non-scientific calculator performs calculations in the order in which they are entered, as they are being entered.

TEACHING MASTER

✦ *Math Masters,* p. 100

6.7 Review: Number Sentences

OBJECTIVES **To review relation symbols, number sentences, and equations; to identify number sentences as true or false; and to translate between English and number sentences.**

summaries	materials
1 Teaching the Lesson	
Students review the parts of a number sentence. They also determine, when possible, whether a number sentence is true or false. [Patterns, Functions, and Algebra]	□ *Math Journal 2,* pp. 230 and 231 □ *Student Reference Book,* p. 223 □ Study Link 6.6
2 Ongoing Learning & Practice	
Students solve challenging problems involving areas of rectangles. [Measurement and Reference Frames] Students practice and maintain skills through Math Boxes and Study Link activities.	□ *Math Journal 2,* pp. 231 and 232 □ Study Link Master (*Math Masters,* p. 318) □ calculator
3 Options for Individualizing	
Extra Practice Students translate expressions given in words into mathematical symbols. [Patterns, Functions, and Algebra] **Extra Practice** Students play *Algebra Election.* [Patterns, Functions, and Algebra] **Language Diversity** Students make cards to remember the meanings of relation symbols. [Patterns, Functions, and Algebra]	□ *Math Journal 2,* Activity Sheets 5 and 6 □ *Student Reference Book,* pp. 276 and 277 □ Teaching Masters (*Math Masters,* pp. 101–103) □ 4 counters □ 1 six-sided die □ calculator □ scissors ***See* Advance Preparation**

Additional Information

Advance Preparation For the first optional Extra Practice activity in Part 3, make one copy of *Math Masters,* page 101 for each group of students.

Vocabulary • **relation symbol** • **equation** • **inequality** • **operation symbol** • **false number sentence** • **true number sentence**

Getting Started

Mental Math and Reflexes

Have students solve simple number sentences. *Suggestions:*

- $6 + x = 15$ $x = 9$
- $8 + y = 15$ $y = 7$
- $12 = 2 * z$ $z = 6$
- $28 = n + (-5)$ $n = 33$
- $10 = 8 + y$ $y = 2$
- $40 = b * 0.4$ $b = 100$

Math Message

Read page 223 in your Student Reference Book. *With a partner, solve the Check Your Understanding problems at the bottom of page 223.*

Study Link 6.6 Follow-Up

Briefly go over the answers with the class.

1 Teaching the Lesson

✦ Math Message Follow-Up
(*Student Reference Book,* p. 223)

WHOLE-CLASS DISCUSSION

Some of the terms and ideas in the *Student Reference Book* will be discussed in the next lesson. In *this* lesson, make sure that students understand the following terms and ideas:

- ▷ A number sentence must contain a **relation symbol** ($=$, $\neq$, $<$, $>$, $\leq$, or $\geq$). A number sentence that contains an $=$ symbol is called an **equation.** A number sentence that contains any of the other relation symbols is called an **inequality.** Ask students to give examples of both. Point out that an expression like $15 + 7$ is not a number sentence, because it does not contain a relation symbol.
- ▷ A number sentence usually contains one or more **operation symbols** ($+$, $-$, $\times$, $*$, $\div$, or $/$). Some number sentences do not. For example, $14 \neq 20$ and $17 < 22$ are number sentences without operation symbols.
- ▷ If a number sentence contains only numbers (and no variables), it is *always* possible to tell whether the sentence is true or false.
- ▷ A common misconception is that a number sentence must be true—that if it is false, the statement is not a number sentence. Explain that a **false sentence** is no less a number sentence than a **true sentence.**

Students of *Everyday Mathematics* have worked with number sentences containing the relation symbols $=$, $<$, and $>$ since first grade. They are probably less familiar with the symbols $\neq$, $\leq$, and $\geq$. Present several examples to clarify the meanings of these symbols. *Suggestions:*

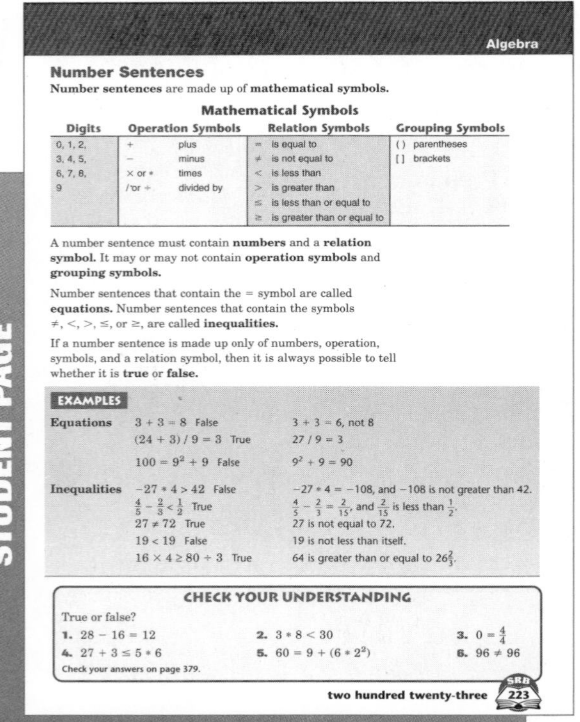

STUDENT PAGE

Algebra

Number Sentences

Number sentences are made up of **mathematical symbols.**

Mathematical Symbols

Digits	Operation Symbols		Relation Symbols		Grouping Symbols	
0, 1, 2,	+	plus	=	is equal to	( )	parentheses
3, 4, 5,	–	minus	≠	is not equal to	[ ]	brackets
6, 7, 8,	× or *	times	<	is less than		
9	/ or ÷	divided by	>	is greater than		
			≤	is less than or equal to		
			≥	is greater than or equal to		

A number sentence must contain **numbers** and a **relation symbol.** It may or may not contain **operation symbols** and **grouping symbols.**

Number sentences that contain the = symbol are called **equations.** Number sentences that contain the symbols $\neq$, $<$, $>$, $\leq$, or $\geq$, are called **inequalities.**

If a number sentence is made up only of numbers, operation, symbols, and a relation symbol, then it is always possible to tell whether it is **true** or **false.**

EXAMPLES

Equations	$3 + 3 = 8$ False	$3 + 3 = 6$, not 8
	$(24 + 3) / 9 = 3$ True	$27 / 9 = 3$
	$100 = 9^2 + 9$ False	$9^2 + 9 = 90$
Inequalities	$-27 * 4 > 42$ False	$-27 * 4 = -108$, and -108 is not greater than 42.
	$\frac{4}{5} - \frac{2}{3} < \frac{1}{2}$ True	$\frac{4}{5} - \frac{2}{3} = \frac{2}{15}$, and $\frac{2}{15}$ is less than $\frac{1}{2}$.
	$27 \neq 72$ True	27 is not equal to 72.
	$19 < 19$ False	19 is not less than itself.
	$16 \times 4 \geq 80 \div 3$ True	64 is greater than or equal to $26\frac{2}{3}$.

CHECK YOUR UNDERSTANDING

True or false?

1. $28 - 16 = 12$
2. $3 * 8 < 30$
3. $0 = \frac{4}{4}$
4. $27 + 3 \leq 5 * 6$
5. $60 = 9 + (6 * 2^2)$
6. $96 \neq 96$

Check your answers on page 379.

two hundred twenty-three SRB 223

✧ Student Reference Book, p. 223

- $6 + 4 \neq 7$ is an inequality. It is true because the sum of 6 and 4 is 10, not 7.
- $2 * 5 \neq 10$ is a false inequality because the product of 2 and 5 is, in fact, 10.
- $7 \leq 14$ is a true inequality because 7 is less than 14.
- $7 + 7 \leq 14$ is a true inequality because $7 + 7$ is equal to 14.
- $8 \geq 2 + 10$ is a false inequality because $2 + 10$ is not less than 8, nor is it equal to 8.

Go over the answers to the Check Your Understanding problems on page 223 in the *Student Reference Book.* Remind the class that parentheses in a number sentence tell which operation to do first (see Problem 5).

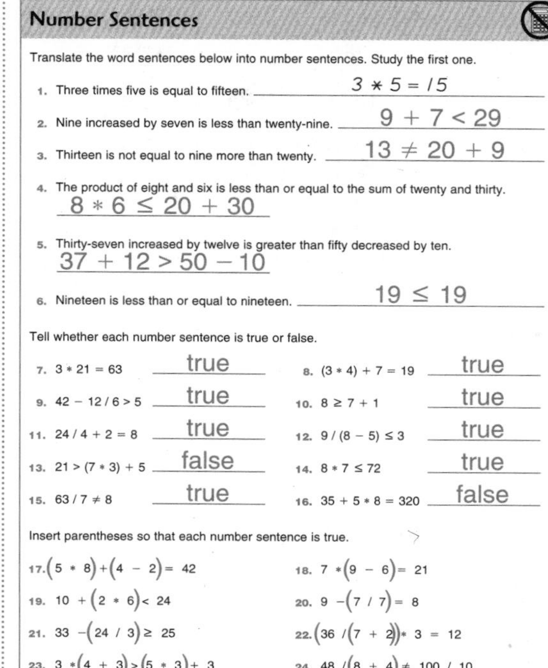
Number Sentences

Translate the word sentences below into number sentences. Study the first one.

1. Three times five is equal to fifteen. $3 * 5 = 15$
2. Nine increased by seven is less than twenty-nine. $9 + 7 < 29$
3. Thirteen is not equal to nine more than twenty. $13 \neq 20 + 9$
4. The product of eight and six is less than or equal to the sum of twenty and thirty. $8 * 6 \leq 20 + 30$
5. Thirty-seven increased by twelve is greater than fifty decreased by ten. $37 + 12 > 50 - 10$
6. Nineteen is less than or equal to nineteen. $19 \leq 19$

Tell whether each number sentence is true or false.

7. $3 * 21 = 63$ true
8. $(3 * 4) + 7 = 19$ true
9. $42 - 12 / 6 > 5$ true
10. $8 \geq 7 + 1$ true
11. $24 / 4 + 2 = 8$ true
12. $9 / (8 - 5) \leq 3$ true
13. $21 > (7 * 3) + 5$ false
14. $8 * 7 \leq 72$ true
15. $63 / 7 \neq 8$ true
16. $35 + 5 * 8 = 320$ false

Insert parentheses so that each number sentence is true.

17. $(5 * 8) + (4 - 2) = 42$
18. $7 * (9 - 6) = 21$
19. $10 + (2 * 6) < 24$
20. $9 - (7 / 7) = 8$
21. $33 - (24 / 3) \geq 25$
22. $(36 / (7 + 2)) * 3 = 12$
23. $3 * (4 + 3) > (5 * 3) + 3$
24. $48 / (8 + 4) \neq 100 / 10$

STUDENT PAGE

Math Journal 2, p. 230

✦ Solving Problems Involving Number Sentences (*Math Journal 2,* pp. 230 and 231)

PARTNER ACTIVITY 

Assign Problems 1–25 on journal pages 230 and 231. Circulate and assist as needed. Remind students to pay attention to the inequalities in Problems 3, 4, 6, 10, 12, 14, 15, 21, and 24, each of which contains a ≠, ≤, or ≥ symbol. Remind students to observe the rules for the order of operations.

When most students have completed the problems, bring the class together to go over the answers. Volunteers might want to share their translated number sentences.

Adjusting the Activity For Problems 7–16, you might want to extend the activity by having students write the number sentences in words.

ONGOING ASSESSMENT

Use student number sentences in Problem 25 to assess students' ability to determine whether a number sentence is true or false. You may want to give students parameters for their number sentences to better assess their understanding. For example, require that at least one number sentence have three operations on at least one side of the relation symbol.

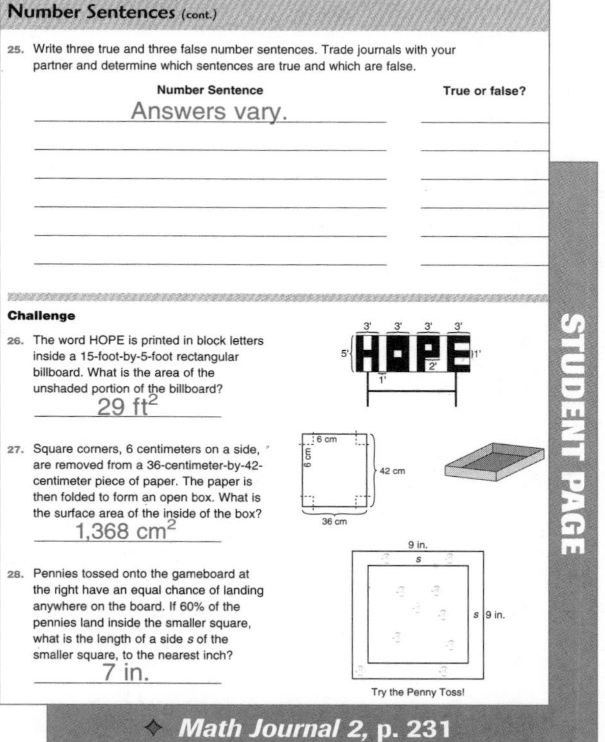
Number Sentences (cont.)

25. Write three true and three false number sentences. Trade journals with your partner and determine which sentences are true and which are false.

Number Sentence	True or false?
Answers vary.	

Challenge

26. The word HOPE is printed in block letters inside a 15-foot-by-5-foot rectangular billboard. What is the area of the unshaded portion of the billboard? 29 ft²

27. Square corners, 6 centimeters on a side, are removed from a 36-centimeter-by-42-centimeter piece of paper. The paper is then folded to form an open box. What is the surface area of the inside of the box? 1,368 cm²

28. Pennies tossed onto the gameboard at the right have an equal chance of landing anywhere on the board. If 60% of the pennies land inside the smaller square, what is the length of a side *s* of the smaller square, to the nearest inch? 7 in.

STUDENT PAGE

Math Journal 2, p. 231

Math Boxes 6.7

1. Add or subtract.

a. $\frac{8}{10} + 8\frac{1}{3} =$ $9\frac{4}{30}$, or $9\frac{2}{15}$

b. $5\frac{4}{5} - 2\frac{7}{8} =$ $2\frac{37}{40}$

c. $\frac{15}{4} + \frac{9}{7} =$ $5\frac{1}{28}$

d. $\frac{23}{10} - 1\frac{1}{5} =$ $1\frac{1}{10}$

2. Complete each sentence with an algebraic expression.

a. If each bag of potatoes weighs at least *p* pounds, then 6 bags weigh at least $p * 6$ pounds.

b. Jack is 6 inches taller than Michael. If Jack is *h* inches tall, then Michael is $h - 6$ inches tall.

3. Write the following numbers with words.

a. 0.001 One-thousandth

b. 0.017 Seventeen thousandths

c. 0.0001 One ten-thousandth

d. 2.603 Two and six hundred three thousandths

4. Give a rough estimate (a ballpark estimate) for each quotient. Sample answers:

a. 137.8 ÷ 6 20

b. 248.19 ÷ 12 20

c. 4,507.08 ÷ 9 500

d. 26,991.05 / 3 9,000

e. 2,804.79 / 4 700

5. Divide.

a. $\frac{5}{6} \div \frac{1}{2} =$ $1\frac{4}{6}$, or $1\frac{2}{3}$

b. $\frac{3}{8} \div \frac{3}{4} =$ $\frac{12}{24}$, or $\frac{1}{2}$

c. $\frac{2}{3} \div \frac{5}{6} =$ $\frac{12}{15}$, or $\frac{4}{5}$

d. $\frac{20}{25} \div \frac{5}{25} =$ 4

e. $\frac{7}{12} \div \frac{2}{5} =$ $1\frac{11}{24}$

STUDENT PAGE

Math Journal 2, p. 232

Number Sentences

Study Link 6.7

1. a. Draw a circle around each number sentence.

17 < 27 (circled)   3 ∗ 15 < 100 (circled)   56 / 8

(5 − 4) ∗ 20 = 20 (circled)   (4 + 23) / 9   12 ≠ 12 (circled)

b. Choose one item that you did not circle. Explain why it is not a number sentence.

Sample answer: A number sentence must contain a relation symbol. 56 / 8 does not include one.

2. Tell whether each number sentence is true or false.

a. 9 − (6 + 2) > 0.5 true

b. 94 = 49 − 2 ∗ 2 false

c. $\frac{24}{6}$ < 33 / 11 false

d. 70 − 25 = 45 true

3. Insert parentheses so that each number sentence is true.

a. (28 − 6) + 9 = 31

b. 20 < (40 − 9) + 11

c. (36 / 6) / 2 < 12

d. 4 ∗ (8 − 4) = 16

4. Write a number sentence for each word sentence. Tell whether the number sentence is true or false.

Word sentence	Number sentence	True or false?
a. If 14 is subtracted from 60, the result is 50.	60 − 14 = 50	false
b. 90 is three times as much as 30.	90 = 3 ∗ 30	true
c. 21 increased by 7 is less than 40.	21 + 7 < 40	true
d. The square root of 36 is greater than half of 10.	$\sqrt{36} > \frac{1}{2} * 10$	true

STUDY LINK MASTER

Math Masters, p. 318

2 Ongoing Learning & Practice

Solving Challenging Area Problems (*Math Journal 2,* p. 231)

PARTNER ACTIVITY 

Assign Problems 26–28 on journal page 231. While some students may not be able to solve all of the problems, encourage everyone to try. Have students share their solution strategies.

- Problem 26: Some students may calculate the area of the word HOPE and then subtract it from the area of the rectangle. 75 − 46 or 29 ft^2 Others may add the areas of the unshaded rectangles. (1 ∗ 2) + (1 ∗ 2) + (1 ∗ 5) + (1 ∗ 1) + (1 ∗ 5) + (1 ∗ 1) + (3 ∗ 2) + (1 ∗ 3) + (2 ∗ 1) + (2 ∗ 1) or 29 ft^2
- Problem 27: The surface area of the open box is the same as the area of the original rectangular piece of paper (36 ∗ 42 or 1,512 cm^2) minus the area of the four square corners that are removed (4 ∗ (6 ∗ 6) or 144 cm^2). 1,512 cm^2 − 144 cm^2 = 1,368 cm^2
- Problem 28: The area of the entire gameboard is 81 square inches. The area of the smaller square is 60% of the area of the entire board, or 48.6 square inches. This is almost 49 square inches. Therefore, the length of a side of the smaller square is almost 7 inches, since 7 ∗ 7 = 49. Some students may notice that, by using the square root key on their calculators, they will be able to find the solution quickly.

Math Boxes 6.7 (*Math Journal 2,* p. 232)

INDEPENDENT ACTIVITY 

Mixed Review Math Boxes in this lesson are paired with Math Boxes in Lesson 6.5. The skill in Problem 1 is a prerequisite for Unit 7.

Study Link 6.7 (*Math Masters,* p. 318)

Home Connection Students practice inserting parentheses to make true number sentences, identifying true and false number sentences, and translating word sentences into number sentences.

Options for Individualizing

✦ EXTRA PRACTICE Interpreting and Evaluating Expressions (*Math Masters,* p. 101)

SMALL-GROUP ACTIVITY  **15–30 min**

In groups of three, students translate expressions written in words into expressions written with mathematical symbols. They also evaluate expressions.

✦ EXTRA PRACTICE Playing *Algebra Election* (*Math Journal 2,* Activity Sheets 5 and 6; *Math Masters,* pp. 102 and 103; *Student Reference Book,* pp. 276 and 277)

SMALL-GROUP ACTIVITY  **15–30 min**

Social Studies Link *Algebra Election* is a popular game that was introduced in *Fifth Grade Everyday Mathematics*. Students collect electoral votes from states by correctly solving a variety of problems. The game is identical in both fifth and sixth grades with two exceptions. In fifth grade, a different set of 32 cards is used, and students can use a calculator three times during one game.

Mathematical Expressions

Write the following expressions with symbols. Write *x* for the unknown number.

Sample answers:

Example
7 less than a number $x - 7$

1. 5 more than a number $x + 5$
2. Twice a number $x * 2$
3. A number decreased by 10 $x - 10$
4. A number increased by 10 $x + 10$
5. A number added to $\frac{1}{2}$ $x + \frac{1}{2}$
6. A number divided by 6 $x / 6$
7. 18 more than double a number $18 + 2x$
8. 3 times a number squared $3 * x^2$

Evaluate each of the expressions if the unknown number is 5.

9. 5 more than a number $5 + 5 = 10$
10. Twice a number $5 * 2 = 10$
11. A number decreased by 10 $5 - 10 = -5$
12. A number increased by 10 $5 + 10 = 15$
13. A number added to $\frac{1}{2}$ $5 + \frac{1}{2} = 5\frac{1}{2}$
14. A number divided by 6 $5 / 6 = 0.833$
15. 18 more than double a number $18 + (2 * 5) = 28$
16. 3 times a number squared $3 * 5^2 = 75$
17. Do you think it is easier to evaluate an expression written in words or as a number sentence? Explain.
Sample answer: Numbers and operations can be recognized more quickly than words and, therefore, it is easier to evaluate an expression written algebraically.

TEACHING MASTER

✦ *Math Masters,* p. 101

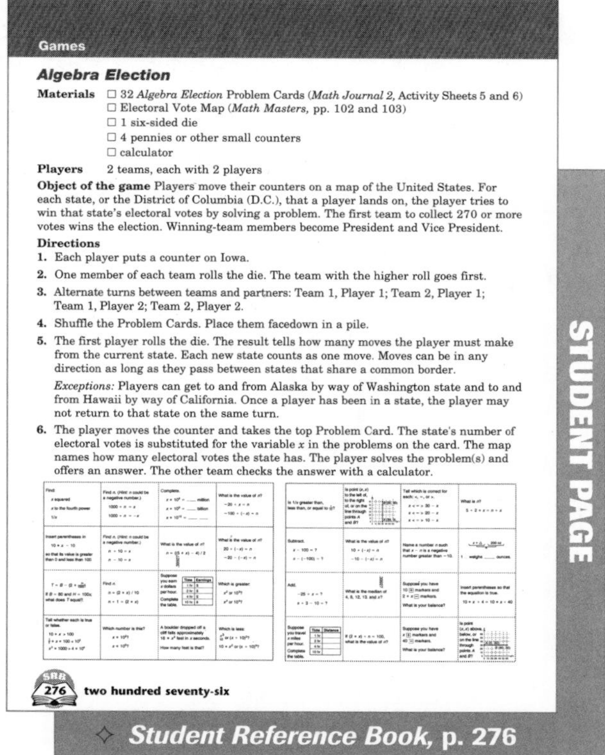
Games

Algebra Election

Materials ☐ 32 *Algebra Election* Problem Cards (*Math Journal 2,* Activity Sheets 5 and 6)
☐ Electoral Vote Map (*Math Masters,* pp. 102 and 103)
☐ 1 six-sided die
☐ 4 pennies or other small counters
☐ calculator

Players 2 teams, each with 2 players

Object of the game Players move their counters on a map of the United States. For each state, or the District of Columbia (D.C.), that a player lands on, the player tries to win that state's electoral votes by solving a problem. The first team to collect 270 or more votes wins the election. Winning-team members become President and Vice President.

Directions

1. Each player puts a counter on Iowa.
2. One member of each team rolls the die. The team with the higher roll goes first.
3. Alternate turns between teams and partners: Team 1, Player 1; Team 2, Player 1; Team 1, Player 2; Team 2, Player 2.
4. Shuffle the Problem Cards. Place them facedown in a pile.
5. The first player rolls the die. The result tells how many moves the player must make from the current state. Each new state counts as one move. Moves can be in any direction as long as they pass between states that share a common border.
Exceptions: Players can get to and from Alaska by way of Washington state and to and from Hawaii by way of California. Once a player has been in a state, the player may not return to that state on the same turn.
6. The player moves the counter and takes the top Problem Card. The state's number of electoral votes is substituted for the variable *x* in the problems on the card. The map names how many electoral votes the state has. The player solves the problem(s) and offers an answer. The other team checks the answer with a calculator.

SRB 276 two hundred seventy-six

STUDENT PAGE

✧ *Student Reference Book,* p. 276

Games

7. If the answer is correct, the player's team wins the state's electoral votes. They do the following:
• Write the state's name and its electoral votes on a piece of scratch paper.
• Write their first initials in pencil on the state to show that they have won it.
Once a state is won, it is out of play. The opposing team may land on the state, but they cannot get its votes.

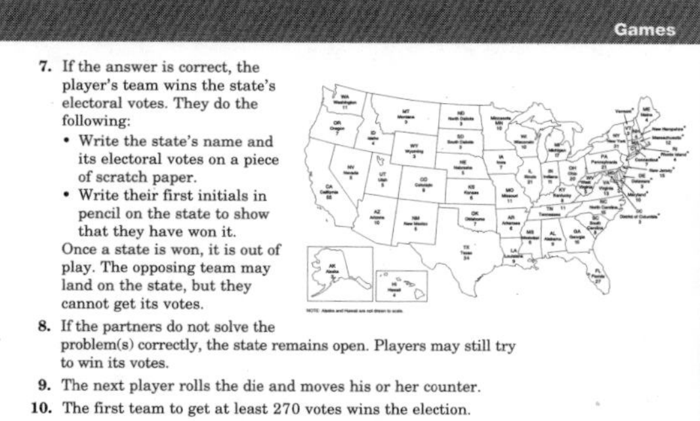

8. If the partners do not solve the problem(s) correctly, the state remains open. Players may still try to win its votes.
9. The next player rolls the die and moves his or her counter.
10. The first team to get at least 270 votes wins the election.
11. When all the Problem Cards have been used, shuffle the deck and use it again.
12. Each player begins a turn from the last state he or she landed on.

Notes

• "A state" means "a state or the District of Columbia (D.C.)."
• Partners may discuss the problem with one another. Each player, however, has to answer the problem on his or her own.
• If a player does not want to answer a Problem Card, the player may say "Pass," and draw another card. A player may "Pass" 3 times during a game.
• If a Problem Card contains several problems, a player must answer all the questions on a card correctly to win a state's votes.
• Suggested strategy: Look at the map to see which states have the most votes, then work with your partner to win those states.

Variations:

1. Agree on a time limit for answering problems.
2. Give one extra point if the player can name the capital of the state landed on.
3. A shorter version of the game can be played by going through all 32 cards just once. The team with the most votes at that time is the winner.

two hundred seventy-seven 

STUDENT PAGE

✧ *Student Reference Book,* p. 277

NOTE: The map on *Math Masters,* pages 102 and 103 shows electoral votes as determined by the U.S. Census of 2000. A state's electoral votes equal the number of its representatives and senators in the U.S. Congress. The number of representatives a state has depends on its population, but the total number of representatives for all 50 states is fixed at 435. There are 100 senators, and the District of Columbia has 3 electoral votes. Thus, the total number of electoral votes is 538, and 270 electoral votes are necessary to win the presidency.

A set of problem cards is supplied on Activity Sheets 5 and 6. You can tailor the game to address any skills you wish to review, including those covered on standardized tests, simply by writing a new set of problem cards.

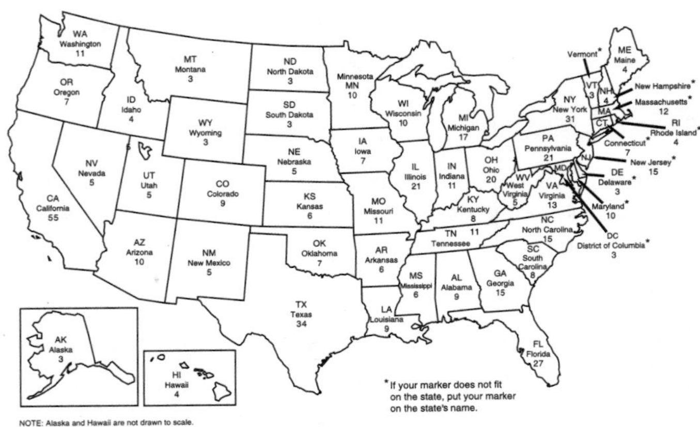

Math Masters, pages 102 and 103 show the electoral votes for each state.

✦ LANGUAGE DIVERSITY
Making Reminder Cards

SMALL-GROUP ACTIVITY **5–15 min** 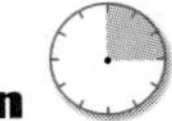

Students who are learning English may need "reminder cards" to help them remember the relation symbols' meanings. Guide them to draw each symbol and to write next to it a word or phrase that explains its meaning. They might want to use index cards and to keep their cards on their desks for easy reference.

STUDENT PAGE

Algebra Election Cards, Set 1

Find: x squared x to the fourth power 1/x	Insert parentheses in $10 * x - 10$ so that its value is greater than 0 and less than 100.	$T = B - (2 * \frac{H}{1000})$ If $B = 80$ and $H = 100x$, what does T equal?	Tell whether each is true or false. $10 * x > 100$ $\frac{1}{2} * x * 100 < 10^3$ $x^3 * 1000 > 4 * 10^4$
Find n. (*Hint: n* could be a negative number.) $1000 + n = x$ $1000 + n = -x$	Find n. (*Hint: n* could be a negative number.) $n + 10 = x$ $n - 10 = x$	Find n. $n = (2 * x) / 10$ $n + 1 = (2 * x)$	Which number is this? $x * 10^2$? $x * 10^5$?
Complete. $x * 10^6 =$ ____ million $x * 10^9 =$ ____ billion $x * 10^{12} =$ ____ ____	What is the value of n? $n = ((5 * x) - 4) / 2$	Suppose you earn x dollars per hour. Complete the table. Time / Earnings: 1 hr $; 2 hr $; 4 hr $; 10 hr $	A boulder dropped off a cliff falls approximately $16 * x^2$ feet in x seconds. How many feet is that?
What is the value of n? $-20 + x = n$ $-100 + (-x) = n$	What is the value of n? $20 + (-x) = n$ $-20 - (-x) = n$	Which is greater: x^2 or 10^3? x^3 or 10^4?	Which is less: $\frac{x^3}{10}$ or $(x + 10)^2$? $10 * x^2$ or $(x + 10)^3$?

✦ *Math Journal 2,* Activity Sheet 5

STUDENT PAGE

Algebra Election Cards, Set 2

What is n? $5 + 2 * x = n + x$	$x + \triangle$ | 200 oz 1 △ weighs ____ ounces.	Insert parentheses so that the equation is true. $10 * x + 4 = 10 * x + 40$	Is point (x,x) above, below, or on the line through points A and B? [graph: A (0, 30), B (60, 30)]
Tell which is correct for each: <, =, or >. $x <=> 30 - x$ $x <=> 20 - x$ $x <=> 10 - x$	Name a number n such that $x - n$ is a negative number greater than -10.	Suppose you have 10 ⊞ markers and $2 * x$ ⊟ markers. What is your balance?	Suppose you have x ⊞ markers and 40 ⊟ markers. What is your balance?
Is point (x,x) to the left of, to the right of, or on the line through points A and B? [graph: B (30, 60), A (30, 0)]	What is the value of n? $10 + (-x) = n$ $-10 - (-x) = n$	What is the median of 4, 8, 12, 13, and x?	If $(2 * x) + n = 100$, what is the value of n?
Is $1/x$ greater than, less than, or equal to $\frac{1}{10}$?	Subtract. $x - 100 = ?$ $x - (-100) = ?$	Add. $-25 + x = ?$ $x + 3 - 10 = ?$	Suppose you travel x miles per hour. Complete the table. Time / Distance: 1 hr; 2 hr; 4 hr; 10 hr

✦ *Math Journal 2,* Activity Sheet 6

6.8 Solving Simple Equations

OBJECTIVE **To solve equations by trial and error and by a cover-up method.**

summaries	materials
1 Teaching the Lesson	
To practice solving equations by the trial-and-error method, students play *Broken Calculator*. They also learn how to solve equations using the cover-up method. [Patterns, Functions, and Algebra]	☐ *Math Journal 2,* p. 233 ☐ *Student Reference Book,* pp. 224 and 225 ☐ Study Link 6.7 ☐ Assessment Master (*Math Masters,* p. 478; optional) ☐ calculator
2 Ongoing Learning & Practice	
Students play *Name That Number.* [Patterns, Functions, and Algebra; Operations and Computation] Students practice and maintain skills through Math Boxes and Study Link activities.	☐ *Math Journal 2,* p. 234 ☐ *Student Reference Book,* p. 301 ☐ Study Link Master (*Math Masters,* p. 319) ☐ number cards (from the Everything Math Deck, if available) ☐ Geometry Template
3 Options for Individualizing	
Enrichment Students solve challenging equations. [Patterns, Functions, and Algebra]	☐ Teaching Master (*Math Masters,* p. 104)

Additional Information

Vocabulary • **variable** • **open sentence** • **solution** • **trial-and-error method** • **cover-up method** • **consecutive**

Getting Started

Mental Math and Reflexes

Write problems like the following on the board or an overhead transparency.

What are the next two numbers in each pattern?

- $1, \frac{1}{2}, \frac{1}{4}, \frac{1}{8}, \ldots$ $\frac{1}{16}, \frac{1}{32}$
- 16, 8, 0, −8, ... −16, −24
- 2, 3, 5, 7, 11, ... 13, 17 (prime numbers)
- 4, 6, 8, 9, 10, 12, ... 14, 15 (composite numbers)
- 2.9, 3.3, 3.7, ... 4.1, 4.5

Math Message

Be ready to explain what it means "to solve an open sentence." If you are not sure, look it up on pages 224 and 225 in your Student Reference Book.

Study Link 6.7 Follow-Up

Go over the answers with the class.

STUDENT PAGE

Algebra

Parentheses

When there is more than one operation in a number sentence, parentheses can be used to tell which operation to do first. The parentheses in the following examples tell you which operation to do first.

EXAMPLE Evaluate. $(24 - 6) * 2 = ?$

The parentheses tell you to subtract $24 - 6$ first, and then multiply by 2.

$(24 - 6) * 2 = ?$

$18 * 2 = 36$

So, $(24 - 6) * 2 = 36$.

EXAMPLE Evaluate. $24 - (6 * 2) = ?$

The parentheses tell you to multiply $6 * 2$ first, and then subtract.

$24 - (6 * 2) = ?$

$24 - 12 = 12$

So, $24 - (6 * 2) = 12$.

Open Sentences

There are number sentences in which one or more of the numbers are missing. Symbols such as □, ?, a blank line, or a letter are written in place of a missing number. Such sentences are called **open sentences.** The number sentence $3 + x = 5$, for example, is open. Open sentences are neither true nor false.

A symbol used in place of a missing number is called a **variable.** For example, $5 + x = 12$ is an open sentence in which the variable x stands for some number. If the letter x is replaced by a number, then the number sentence is either true or false.

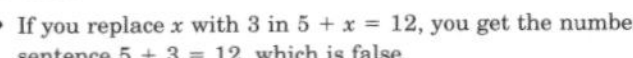

- If you replace x with 3 in $5 + x = 12$, you get the number sentence $5 + 3 = 12$, which is false.
- If you replace x with 7 in $5 + x = 12$, you get the number sentence $5 + 7 = 12$, which is true.

two hundred twenty-four

✦ Student Reference Book, p. 224

STUDENT PAGE

Algebra

If the number used in place of the variable makes the number sentence true, this number is called a **solution** of the open sentence. For example, the number 7 is a solution of the open sentence $5 + x = 12$ because the number sentence $5 + 7 = 12$ is true. Finding a solution for an open number sentence is called **solving** the number sentence.

Many simple equations have just one solution, but inequalities may have many solutions. For example, 9, 3.5, $2\frac{1}{2}$, and -8 are all solutions of the inequality $x < 10$. In fact, $x < 10$ has infinitely many solutions—any number that is less than 10.

Number Models

In *Everyday Mathematics,* a number sentence that fits or describes some situation is called a **number model.** Suppose, for example, that you had $20, spent $8.50, and ended up with $11.50. The number model $20 − $8.50 = $11.50 fits this situation. The number model $20 = $8.50 + $11.50 also fits.

Number models can be useful in solving problems. For example, the problem "Juan is saving for a bicycle that costs $119. He has $55. How much more does he need?" can be modeled by "$119 = $55 + *x*" or by "$119 − $55 = *x*." The first of these number models suggests counting up to find how much more Juan needs; the second suggests subtracting to find the answer.

Other kinds of mathematical models are discussed in the section on problem solving.

CHECK YOUR UNDERSTANDING

Find the solution of each equation.

1. $8 + c = 20$
2. $35 = 5 * z$
3. $(2 * f) + 7 = 28$

Write a number model that fits each problem.

4. Hunter used a $20 bill to pay for a CD that cost $11.49. How much change did he get?
5. Eve earns $10 a week baby-sitting. How many weeks will it take her to earn $70?

Check your answers on page 379.

two hundred twenty-five

✦ Student Reference Book, p. 225

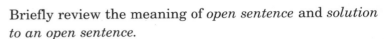

1 Teaching the Lesson

✦ Math Message Follow-Up

(*Student Reference Book,* pp. 224 and 225)

WHOLE-CLASS DISCUSSION

Briefly review the meaning of *open sentence* and *solution to an open sentence.*

- ▷ Number sentences may contain one or more **variables**—letters or other symbols that each stand for a missing number. Such number sentences are called **open sentences.** (Note that an open sentence is a special kind of number sentence.)
- ▷ An *open sentence* is neither true nor false. However, when the variables in an open sentence are replaced by numbers, the *resulting* number sentence *is* either true or false. If the sentence is true, then the number used to replace a variable is called a **solution** of the sentence.
- ▷ To solve an open sentence, find one or more numbers that, when substituted for the variables, result in a true number sentence.

Do the Check Your Understanding problems on page 225 in the *Student Reference Book* with the class. Make a chart on the board and record the results as follows:

Equation	Solution	Replace variable with solution	
$8 + c = 20$	12	$8 + 12 = 20$	True
$35 = 5 * z$	7	$35 = 5 * 7$	True

The last step is important—it serves to check the solution. Throughout this unit, remind students to check solutions by substituting them for the variables in the open sentences.

Briefly review what a *number model* is—a number sentence that fits some real or hypothetical situation—and how number models can be useful in solving problems and in recording solutions. Remind students of other uses of variables: in "What's My Rule?" tables; in formulas; and to state properties of number systems. Ask students to name formulas they have used in the past.

✦ Playing *Broken Calculator*

WHOLE-CLASS ACTIVITY

The *Broken Calculator* game offers practice in finding solutions by **trial and error.** Students generate values for a variable and test them as solutions. They observe how close these test values are to the solution and use this information to select *new* test numbers, attempting to get closer results.

Too often, when students develop more sophisticated solution methods, they lose sight of the fact that a solution of an open sentence is a number that makes the sentence true. Play *Broken Calculator* periodically to provide practice with estimation and solving open sentences.

Ask students to pretend that the minus key on their calculators is broken. Write the following equation on the board and ask students to solve it on their calculators, without using the minus key.

$792 + n = 3{,}518$

After a few minutes, bring the class together to share solution strategies. Students who are very skilled in mental computation may have subtracted 792 from 3,518 mentally. Others probably replaced the variable n with various numbers until they obtained a true number sentence. *For example:*

▷ $792 + \mathbf{2{,}000} = 2{,}792$ Too little

▷ $792 + \mathbf{2{,}500} = 3{,}292$ Too little, but closer

▷ $792 + \mathbf{2{,}800} = 3{,}592$ Just a little over

▷ $792 + \mathbf{2{,}726} = 3{,}518$ Got it!

The solution to $792 + n = 3{,}518$ is 2,726 because $792 + 2{,}726 = 3{,}518$ is a true number sentence.

Try a few more problems. *Suggestions:*

Equation	Broken key	Solution
$59 + x = 515$	⊖	456
$z + 647 = 1{,}310$	⊖	663
$d - 468 = 1{,}387$	⊕	1,855
$p / 54 = 29$	⊗	1,566
$y / 33 = 76$	⊗	2,508
$17 * t = 867$	⊕÷	51
$s * 39 = 1{,}833$	⊕÷	47

Broken-Calculator Games

Broken Number Keys

Materials 1 calculator

Players 2 or more

Directions

1. Partners pretend that one of the number keys is broken.
2. One partner says a number.
3. The other partner tries to display that number on the calculator without using the "broken" key.

EXAMPLE Suppose the 8 key is "broken." The number 18 can be displayed by pressing 9 (+) 7 (+) 2 (=), or 9 (×) 2 (=), or 72 (÷) 4 (=).

Scoring: A player's score is the number of keys pressed to display the number. Scores for five rounds are totaled. The player with the lowest total wins.

Broken Operation Keys

Directions

1. In this version of the game, partners pretend that one of the operation keys on their calculator is broken.
2. One partner says an open sentence.
3. The other tries to solve the sentence on the calculator without using the "broken" key.

EXAMPLE Pretend the (−) key is broken. What is the solution to the open sentence $452 + x = 735$?

Replace the variable x with a number and see if you get a true number sentence. If it is not true, try other numbers until you get a true sentence. Here is one solution:

Try **400:** $452 + \mathbf{400} = 852$ 400 is too big.

Try **300:** $452 + \mathbf{300} = 752$ 300 is 17 away.

Try **317:** $452 + \mathbf{317} = 769$ Wrong way!

Try **283:** $452 + \mathbf{283} = 735$ True sentence.

283 is the answer.

Scoring: A player's score is the number of guesses it takes to get a true number sentence. Scores for five rounds are totaled. The player with the lowest total wins.

NOTE: The activities in this lesson focus on two methods for solving equations: the trial-and-error method and the cover-up method. A third method, a systematic approach, for solving equations is explored beginning in Lesson 6.10. Trial and error is not guessing; it is a legitimate approach that students should have in their mathematical tool kit. People often use it when they have problems that are too difficult to solve by more direct methods.

STUDENT PAGE

Solving Equations

Find the solution to each equation. Write a number sentence with the solution in place of the variable. Check that the number sentence is true.

	Equation	Solution	Number Sentence
1.	$12 + x = 32$	$x = 20$	$12 + 20 = 32$
2.	$y + 89 = 93$	$y = 4$	$4 + 89 = 93$
3.	$b - 32 = 15$	$b = 47$	$47 - 32 = 15$
4.	$m * 8 = 35 - 19$	$m = 2$	$2 * 8 = 35 - 19$
5.	$p + (4 * 9) = 55$	$p = 19$	$19 + (4 * 9) = 55$
6.	$42 = 7 * (a - 4)$	$a = 10$	$42 = 7 * (10 - 4)$
7.	$(9 + w) / 2 = 6 + (6 / 6)$	$w = 5$	$(9 + 5) / 2 = 6 + (6 / 6)$
8.	$4 + (3n - 6) = 1 + (3 * 6)$	$n = 7$	$4 + (21 - 6) = 1 + (3 * 6)$

Find the solution to each equation.

9. $4 * 6 = 35 - t$ $t = 11$
10. $9 * (11 - c) = 81$ $c = 2$
11. $17 - 11 = k / 8$ $k = 48$
12. $(m + 14) / 4 = 6$ $m = 10$
13. $36 / 9 = 2 + p$ $p = 2$
14. $23 - a = 15$ $a = 8$
15. $(3 * p) + 5 = 26$ $p = 7$
16. $2 - d = 3 * 4$ $d = -10$
17. Make up four equations whose solutions are whole numbers. Ask your partner to solve each one. Answers vary.

	Equation	Solution
a.		
b.		
c.		
d.		

✦ Math Journal 2, p. 233

✦ Writing and Solving Equations

(*Math Journal 2,* p. 233)

PARTNER ACTIVITY

Assign Problems 1–8 and give students 5 to 10 minutes to solve as many equations as they can. Have them share their solutions with the class. Then introduce the **cover-up method.**

Write the equation $y + 89 = 93$ on the board and cover the variable with your hand or a sheet of paper. Ask: *Which number plus 89 equals 93?* 4

Repeat this procedure with Problems 3, 4, and 5. For Problems 4 and 5, you need to simplify the equation first: For Problem 4, rewrite $m * 8 = 35 - 19$ as $m * 8 = 16$; for Problem 5, rewrite $p + (4 * 9) = 55$ as $p + 36 = 55$.

Although Problems 6, 7, and 8 are a little more complicated, they too can be solved using the cover-up method. For Problem 6, cover $(a - 4)$ and ask: *42 is equal to 7 times which number?* 6 Write $a - 4 = 6$ on the board and ask: *Which number, decreased by 4, gives 6?* 10 Then replace the variable with 10 in the original equation to check that 10 is the correct solution. $42 = 7 * (10 - 4)$ is a true sentence, so 10 is the solution to the equation.

For Problem 7, simplify the right side of the equation. Then cover up $(9 + w)$ and proceed as before.

Assign the rest of the problems on journal page 233. Remind students to check their solutions by replacing the variables in the equations with them. Circulate and assist.

Adjusting the Activity Some students may make up equations for Problem 17 that do not have whole-number solutions. One way to be sure of a whole-number solution is first to write a correct number sentence with *no variables* and then to substitute a variable for one of the numbers. For example, a student might first write "$5 * 3 - 8 = 7$" and then replace the 3 with a *t*: "$5 * t - 8 = 7$."

Challenge students by giving them additional parameters for the equations they create. For example, require that one of the equations includes division of fractions or that one of the equations contains exponents.

When most students have completed the problems, bring the class together to go over solution strategies. Ask volunteers to share the equations they wrote for Problem 17.

ONGOING ASSESSMENT

Have students use an Exit Slip (*Math Masters,* page 478) to explain how they found the solution to Problem 10.

2 Ongoing Learning & Practice

✦ Playing *Name That Number* (*Student Reference Book,* p. 301)

PARTNER ACTIVITY 

Students play *Name That Number* to practice working with equations and order of operations. Have students record their number sentences for each target number so that they can practice using order of operations.

✦ Math Boxes 6.8 (*Math Journal 2,* p. 234)

INDEPENDENT ACTIVITY

Mixed Review Math Boxes in this lesson are paired with Math Boxes in Lesson 6.6. The skill in Problem 1 is a prerequisite for Unit 7.

✦ Study Link 6.8 (*Math Masters,* p. 319)

Home Connection Students solve equations and translate English sentences into equations. They also write expressions equivalent to target numbers.

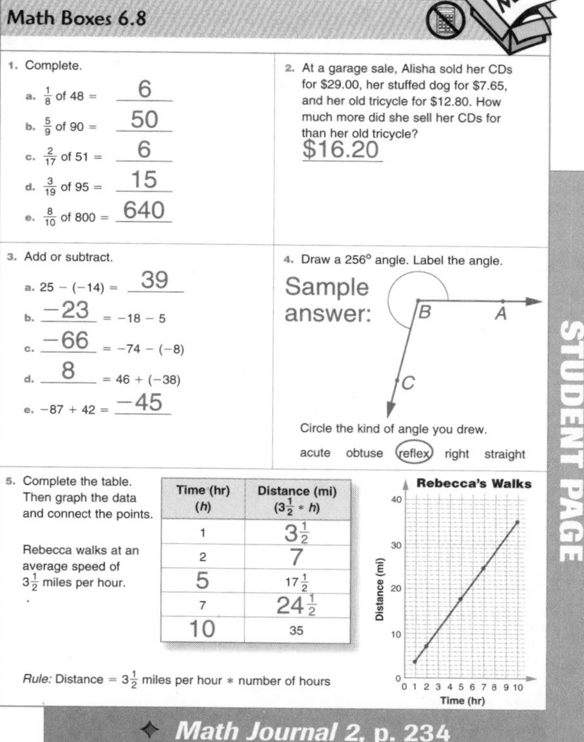

Math Boxes 6.8

1. Complete.
   a. $\frac{1}{8}$ of 48 = 6
   b. $\frac{5}{9}$ of 90 = 50
   c. $\frac{2}{17}$ of 51 = 6
   d. $\frac{3}{19}$ of 95 = 15
   e. $\frac{8}{10}$ of 800 = 640

2. At a garage sale, Alisha sold her CDs for $29.00, her stuffed dog for $7.65, and her old tricycle for $12.80. How much more did she sell her CDs for than her old tricycle? $16.20

3. Add or subtract.
   a. 25 − (−14) = 39
   b. −23 = −18 − 5
   c. −66 = −74 − (−8)
   d. 8 = 46 + (−38)
   e. −87 + 42 = −45

4. Draw a 256° angle. Label the angle.
   Sample answer:
   Circle the kind of angle you drew.
   acute obtuse (reflex) right straight

5. Complete the table. Then graph the data and connect the points.
   Rebecca walks at an average speed of $3\frac{1}{2}$ miles per hour.

Time (hr) (h)	Distance (mi) ($3\frac{1}{2} * h$)
1	$3\frac{1}{2}$
2	7
5	$17\frac{1}{2}$
7	$24\frac{1}{2}$
10	35

Rule: Distance = $3\frac{1}{2}$ miles per hour * number of hours

STUDENT PAGE

✦ *Math Journal 2,* p. 234

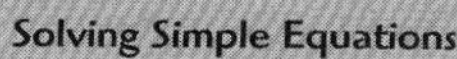

Solving Simple Equations — Study Link 6.8

1. Find the solution to each equation.
   a. $b - 7 = 12$ — $b = 19$
   b. $53 = n + 29$ — $n = 24$
   c. $x = 63 / 9$ — $x = 7$
   d. $\frac{1}{2} * k = \frac{4}{12}$ — $k = \frac{4}{6}$, or $\frac{2}{3}$
   e. $45 / y^2 = 5$ — $y = 3$
   f. $m * \frac{2}{3} = 1 - \frac{13}{15}$ — $m = \frac{1}{5}$

2. Translate the English sentences below into equations. Then find the solution to each equation.

	English sentence	Equation	Solution
a.	If you divide a number by 6, the result is 10.	$\frac{x}{6} = 10$	$x = 60$
b.	Which number is 7 less than 200?	$200 - 7 = n$	$n = 193$
c.	A number multiplied by 48 is equal to 2,928.	$b * 48 = 2{,}928$	$b = 61$
d.	27 is equal to 13 increased by which number?	$27 = 13 + n$	$n = 14$

3. For each problem, use parentheses and as many numbers and operations as you can to write an expression equal to the target number. You may use each number just once in an expression. For example, for Problem 3a, you can write the expression 3 * 12. Try to write expressions with more than two numbers.

   Sample answers:
   a. Numbers: 3, 9, 11, 12, 19 Target number: 36 — (3 * 11) + (12 − 9)
   b. Numbers: 1, 2, 6, 14, 18 Target number: 50 — 2 * 18 + 14
   c. Numbers: 3, 9, 10, 15, 16 Target number: 45 — (10 * 3) + 15
   d. Numbers: 4, 5, 8, 14, 17 Target number: 22 — (17 − 5) + 14 − 4
   e. Numbers: 6, 7, 12, 14, 20 Target number: 41 — (20 + 14) + 7

STUDY LINK MASTER

✦ *Math Masters,* p. 319

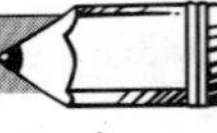

Solving Challenging Equations

TEACHING MASTER

1. $x - x = 0$ $n + 5 = 1$ $a + 8 < 3$ $y \neq y$ $\frac{0}{g} \geq 1$

Which of the above sentences have

a. no solution? $y \neq y$; $\frac{0}{g} \geq 1$

b. more than one solution? $x - x = 0$; $a + 8 < 3$

c. a solution that is a negative number? $n + 5 = 1$; $a + 8 < 3$; $x - x = 0$

2. Find the solution to each equation.

a. $x + (x + 1) + (x + 2) = 90$ $x = 29$

(*Hint:* Think of this equation as a sum of three numbers.)

b. $a + (a + 1) + (a + 2) + (a + 3) + (a + 4) = 90$ $a = 16$

3. Whole numbers are said to be **consecutive** if they follow one another in an uninterrupted pattern. For example, 5, 6, 7, 8, 9, and 10 are six consecutive whole numbers.

a. What are three consecutive whole numbers whose sum is 90?

(*Hint:* Replace each variable x in Problem 2a with the solution of the equation.)

29 + 30 + 31 = 90

b. What are five consecutive whole numbers whose sum is 90?

16 + 17 + 18 + 19 + 20 = 90

c. What are four consecutive whole numbers whose sum is 90?

21 + 22 + 23 + 24 = 90

4. Each letter in the subtraction problem below represents a different digit from 0 through 9. The digits 3 and 5 do not appear in the problem. Replace each letter so that the answer to the subtraction problem is correct.

GRAPE −PLUM	G = 9	R = 4	A = 8	P = 7
APPLE	E = 2	L = 1	U = 6	M = 0

✦ *Math Masters,* p. 104

3 Options for Individualizing

✦ ENRICHMENT Solving Challenging Equations

(*Math Masters,* p. 104)

PARTNER ACTIVITY  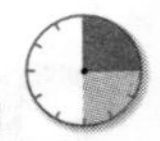

15–30 min

These problems may prove difficult for some students, but everyone should be encouraged to try them. Plan to spend some time sharing solution strategies.

Possible strategies:

▷ Problem 1a: $y \neq y$ has no solution, since any number is equal to itself; that is, there is no replacement for y that will make the sentence true. Also, $\frac{0}{g} \geq 1$ has no solution, since 0 divided by any number equals 0, and 0 is not greater than or equal to 1.

▷ Problem 1b: $x - x = 0$ has an infinite number of solutions, since any number subtracted from itself equals 0. Similarly, $a + 8 < 3$ has many solutions, such as −8, −9, and −10.

▷ Problem 1c: $n + 5 = 1$, $a + 8 < 3$, and $x - x = 0$ each have a solution that is a negative number. (The solution to $n + 5 = 1$ is −4.)

▷ Problem 2: The first equation is an algebraic representation of 90 as the sum of three **consecutive** whole numbers; the second equation consists of five consecutive whole numbers.

▷ Problem 3: The answers to Problems 3a and 3b require replacing the variables in Problems 2a and 2b with the solutions to the equations. For example, to solve Problem 3a, replace x in $x + (x + 1) + (x + 2) = 90$ with 29 and combine the numbers in parentheses.

$(29 + (29 + 1) + (29 + 2) = 29 + 30 + 31 = 90)$

To solve Problem 3c, solve the equation

$n + (n + 1) + (n + 2) + (n + 3) = 90.$

$(21 + 22 + 23 + 24 = 90)$

▷ Problem 4: Students may be able to reason through some relationships to get started. For example, M must be 0, L + U must equal P, A must be 1 less than G, and P must be half of R + 10. Encourage students to use trial and error to solve the problem. (This is a challenging problem.)

6.9 Review: Pan-Balance Problems

OBJECTIVE **To solve pan-balance problems as models for equation-solving techniques.**

summaries	materials
1 Teaching the Lesson	
Students solve pan-balance problems. They find the weight of an object in a balanced pan-balance by removing objects from both pans without unbalancing the pans. This procedure models equation-solving techniques that will be introduced in Lesson 6.11. [Patterns, Functions, and Algebra]	☐ *Math Journal 2,* pp. 235–237 ☐ Study Link 6.8 ☐ Transparency (*Math Masters,* p. 105; optional) For every 4 students: ☐ pan balance ☐ variety of small objects, such as paper clips, pattern blocks, and pencils (optional) ***See* Advance Preparation**
2 Ongoing Learning & Practice	
Students play *Broken Calculator.* [Patterns, Functions, and Algebra] Students practice and maintain skills through Math Boxes and Study Link activities.	☐ *Math Journal 2,* p. 238 ☐ Study Link Master (*Math Masters,* p. 320) ☐ calculator
3 Options for Individualizing	
Enrichment Students solve challenging pan-balance problems. [Patterns, Functions, and Algebra] **Extra Practice** Students solve pan-balance problems. [Patterns, Functions, and Algebra]	☐ Teaching Masters (*Math Masters,* pp. 106 and 107) ***See* Advance Preparation**

Additional Information

Advance Preparation For Part 1, if pan balances are available, ensure that they balance before beginning this lesson by moving or sliding the fine-tuning adjustment. If necessary, tape paper clips to the underside of one pan to make the two pans balance.

You may want to use semi-permanent chalk to draw a pan balance on the board for use in the activities. Or, you can make a transparency of *Math Masters,* page 105. You might also choose to use the rocker balance in the manipulatives kit.

For the second optional activity in Part 3, write pan-balance problems on a copy of *Math Masters,* page 107. Then copy the master for each student.

Vocabulary • **pan balance**

Getting Started

Mental Math and Reflexes

Ask students to draw geometric figures. *Suggestions:*

- Two lines that are parallel to each other
- Two parallel lines and a transversal
- Two lines that are perpendicular to each other
- An acute angle
- A reflex angle
- Concentric circles

Math Message

Solve the following equations:

1. $(3 * x) + 7 = 13$ 2

2. $34 - 15 = 1 + 6t$ 3

3. $10 = 60 - (m * 4)$ 12.5

4. $3y + 1 = 25$ 8

Study Link 6.8 Follow-Up

Briefly go over answers with the class. Ask volunteers to share expressions they found for Problem 3.

1 Teaching the Lesson

✦ Math Message Follow-Up

WHOLE-CLASS DISCUSSION 

Go over the answers to the Math Message. Algebraic notation for products is often confusing for students: The product $3 * x$ is usually written as $3x$, without the multiplication sign. Ask students to rewrite the first and third equations without using a multiplication sign. $3x + 7 = 13$ and $10 = 60 - 4m$ If necessary, pose a few additional problems using such notation before continuing with the lesson.

ONGOING ASSESSMENT

Have students record the equations in the Math Message, along with their answers, on a half-sheet of paper. Before reviewing the answers, ask students to explain in words their steps for solving Problem 2. Collect the papers to assess students' understanding of how to solve equations.

Reviewing How to Solve Pan-Balance Problems (*Math Journal 2,* p. 235; *Math Masters,* p. 105)

WHOLE-CLASS ACTIVITY

Draw a **pan balance** on the board or use a transparency of *Math Masters,* page 105, as you work through the example on journal page 235 as a class. Help students come to the following conclusions:

- The pans balance if the objects in one pan weigh the same amount as the objects in the other pan.
- If objects of equal weight are added to or taken from both pans of a balanced pan balance, the pan balance remains balanced.
- If the pans are balanced, the number of objects in both pans may be doubled, tripled, quadrupled, ... Or the same fraction of objects may be removed from each pan.

Adjusting the Activity If a pan balance is available, you might want to let students explore how it works, using a variety of small objects, such as pattern blocks, paper clips, and pencils. The pans should always begin in balance.

Have students work in partnerships to solve Problems 1 and 2. Be sure to emphasize that whatever students do, the pans must always remain balanced. Ask students to share their solution strategies.

Solving Pan-Balance Problems (*Math Journal 2,* pp. 236 and 237)

PARTNER ACTIVITY 

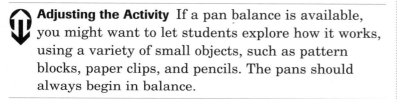

Students work in pairs to complete journal pages 236 and 237. Problems 1–7 show pictures of objects on the pan balance. Problems 8–10 show variables. Problem 1 requires no change to the content of the pans. Problems 2, 3, and 6 can be solved in one step; Problems 4 and 8 in two steps; and Problems 5, 7, 9, and 10 in three steps.

STUDENT PAGE

Pan-Balance Problems

A pan balance can be used to compare the weights of objects or to weigh objects. If the objects in one pan weigh as much as those in the other pan, the pans will balance.

The diagram at the right shows a balanced pan balance.

Example In each of the diagrams below, the pans are balanced. Your job is to figure out how many marbles weigh as much as an orange. The best way to do this is to move oranges and marbles so that a single orange is in one pan and only marbles are in the other pan. When moving the oranges and marbles, you must follow these simple rules: *Whatever you do, the pans must always remain balanced. You must do the same thing to both pans.*

The pan balance shows that 3 oranges weigh as much as 1 orange and 12 marbles.

If you remove 1 orange from each pan, the pans remain balanced.

If you then remove half of the objects from each pan, the pans will still be balanced.

Success! One orange weighs as much as 6 marbles.

Solve the pan-balance problems with a partner. Be ready to share your strategies with the class.

1. One pencil weighs as much as 10 paper clips.
2. One *P* (pencil) weighs as much as 2 *C*s (paper clips).

◆ *Math Journal 2,* p. 235

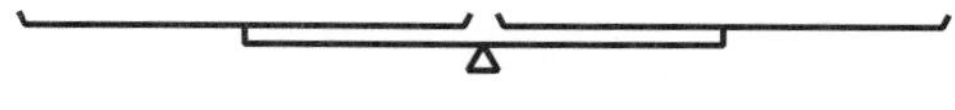

Pan balance shown on *Math Masters,* page 105

Adjusting the Activity For problems that require more than one step, suggest that struggling students draw pictures to show what they do at each step. The pictures should be simple, with a short line representing each pan and a small triangle between the pans to represent the fulcrum.

To extend the activity, have students write equations that describe the pan-balance problems.

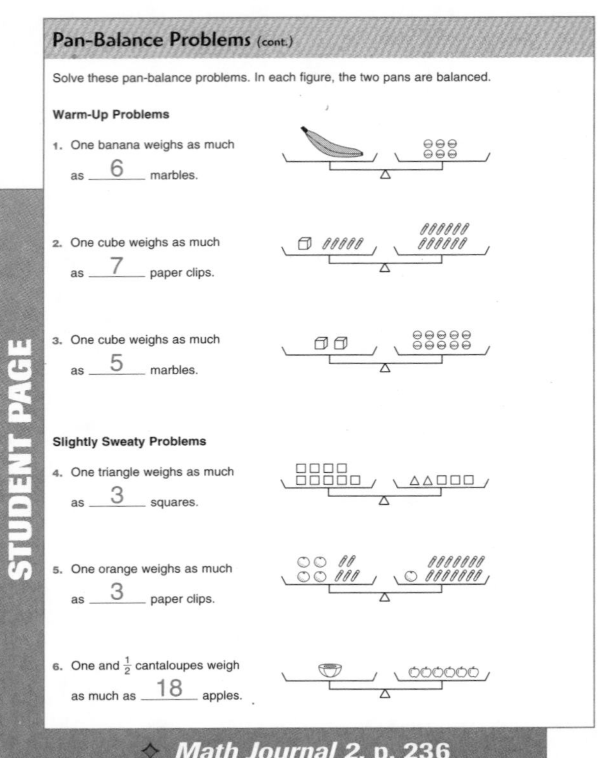
Pan-Balance Problems (cont.)

Solve these pan-balance problems. In each figure, the two pans are balanced.

Warm-Up Problems

1. One banana weighs as much as 6 marbles.
2. One cube weighs as much as 7 paper clips.
3. One cube weighs as much as 5 marbles.

Slightly Sweaty Problems

4. One triangle weighs as much as 3 squares.
5. One orange weighs as much as 3 paper clips.
6. One and $\frac{1}{2}$ cantaloupes weigh as much as 18 apples.

STUDENT PAGE

✧ *Math Journal 2*, p. 236

Circulate and assist as needed. When most students have finished, gather the class together to discuss solution strategies. The following procedure is suggested:

Draw a large pan balance on the board. For each problem, draw the objects in the pan balance at the outset. Then, as students propose a series of steps to solve the problem, draw or erase the appropriate objects. Use an arithmetic operation to record each step. (This is important preparation for the equation-solving technique introduced in the next lesson.)

Problem 2

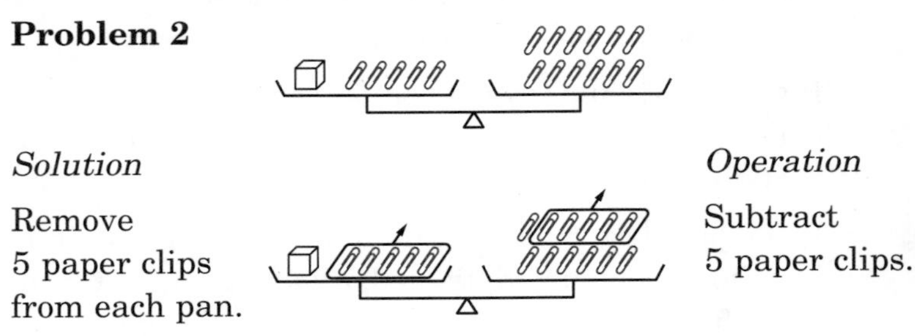

Solution

Remove 5 paper clips from each pan.

Operation

Subtract 5 paper clips.

Problem 3

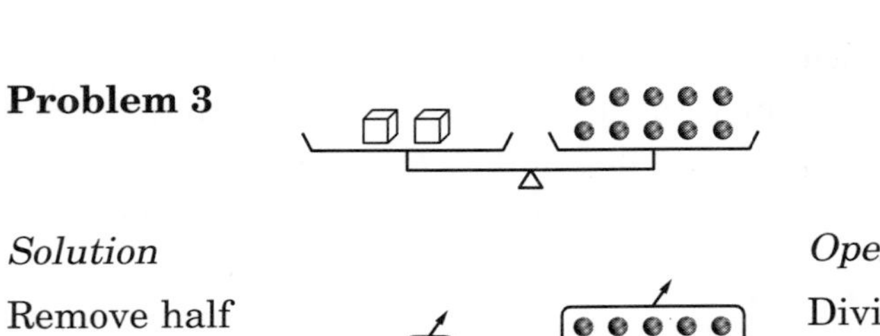

Solution

Remove half of the objects from each pan.

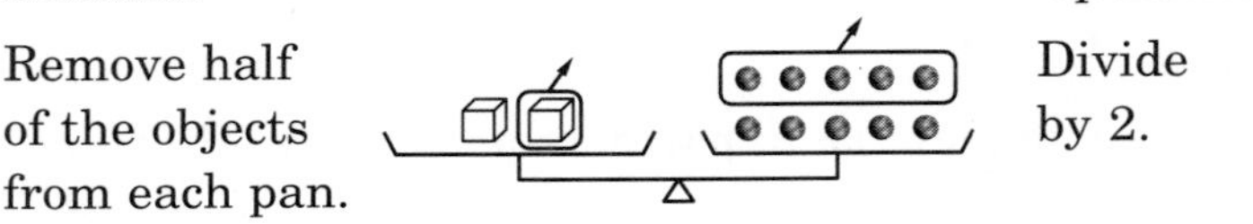

Operation

Divide by 2.

Problem 4

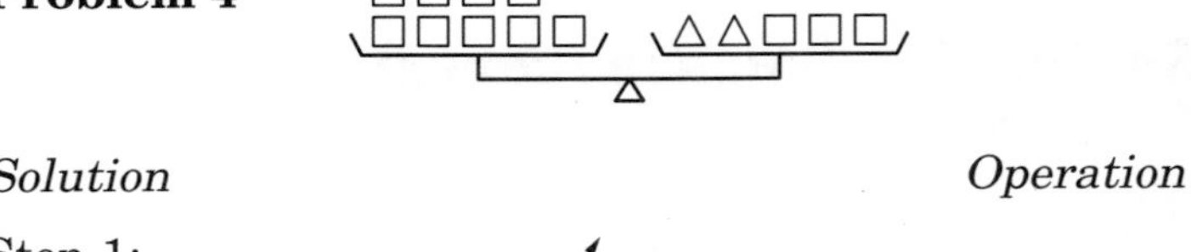

Solution

Step 1: Remove 3 squares from each pan.

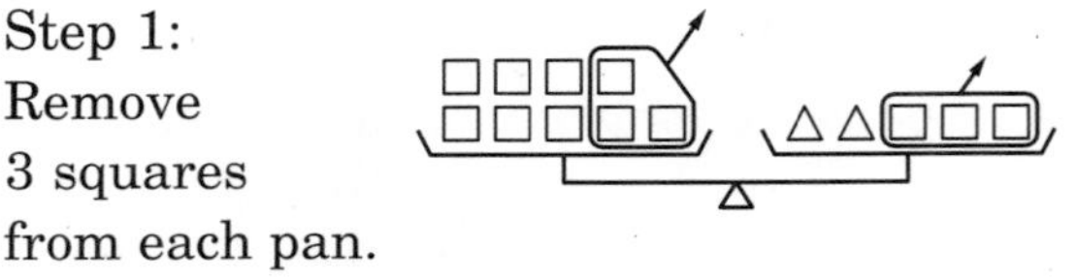

Operation

Subtract 3 squares.

Step 2: Remove half of the objects from each pan.

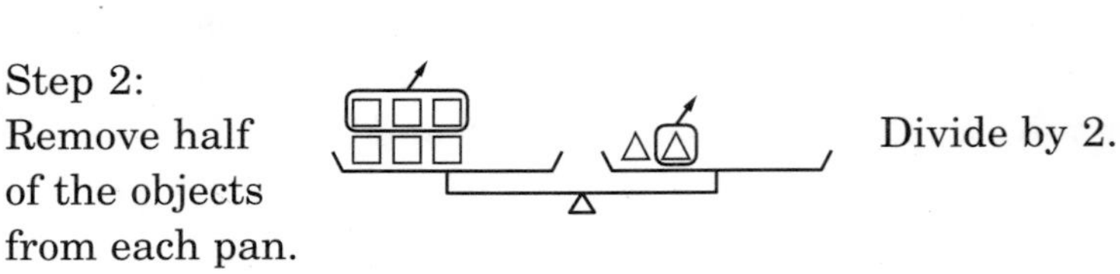

Divide by 2.

Problem 5

Solution | *Operation*

Step 1:
Remove 1 orange from each pan.

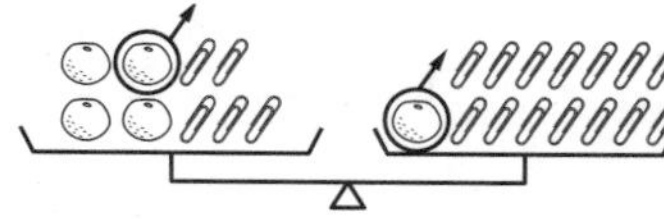

Subtract 1 orange.

Step 2:
Remove 5 paper clips from each pan.

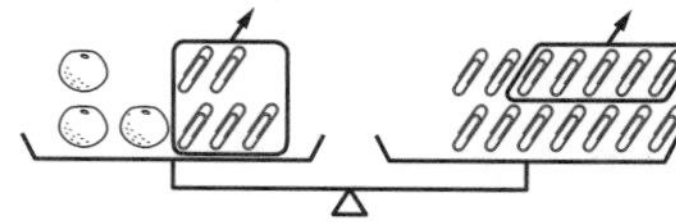

Subtract 5 paper clips.

Step 3:
Remove $\frac{2}{3}$ of the objects from each pan so that $\frac{1}{3}$ of the objects are left in each pan.

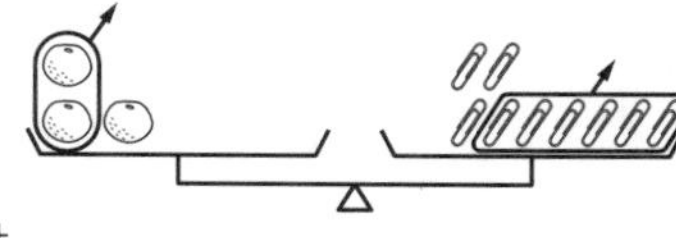

Divide by 3.

Problem 6

Solution | *Operation*

Triple the number of objects in each pan.

Multiply by 3.

Problem 7

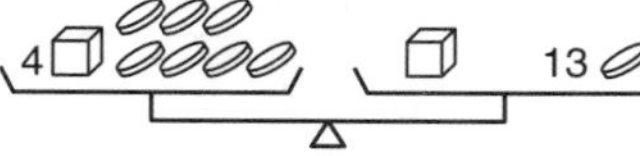

Solution | *Operation*

Step 1:
Remove 1 cube from each pan.

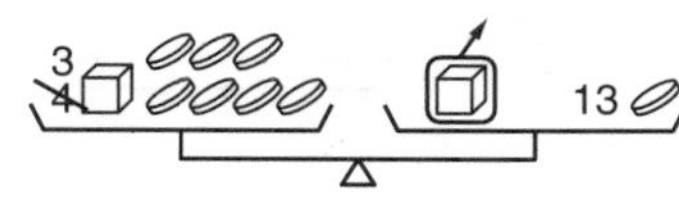

Subtract 1 cube.

Step 2:
Remove 7 coins from each pan.

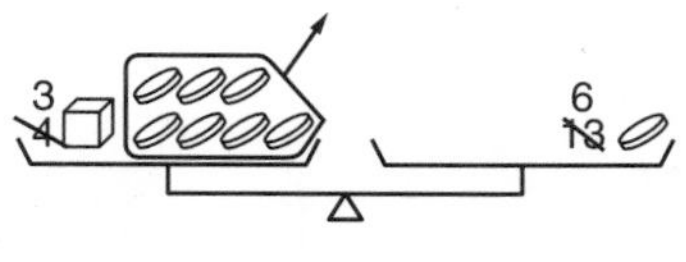

Subtract 7 coins.

Step 3:
Remove $\frac{2}{3}$ of the objects from each pan so that $\frac{1}{3}$ of the objects are left in the pan.

Divide by 3.

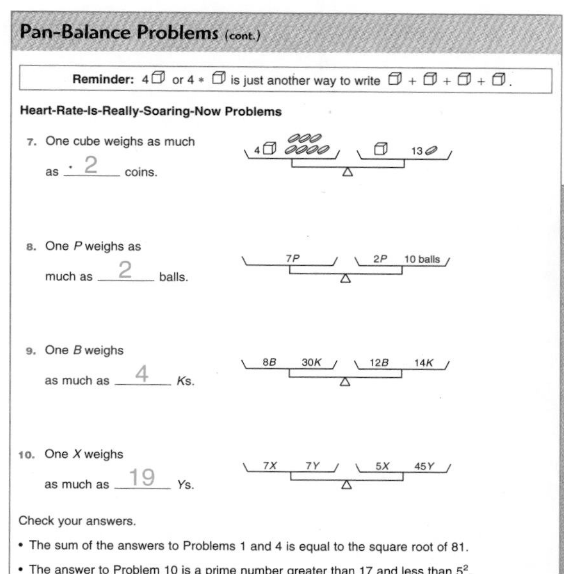

Pan-Balance Problems (cont.)

Reminder: 4□ or 4 ∗ □ is just another way to write □ + □ + □ + □.

Heart-Rate-Is-Really-Soaring-Now Problems

7. One cube weighs as much as 2 coins.

8. One *P* weighs as much as 2 balls.

9. One *B* weighs as much as 4 *K*s.

10. One *X* weighs as much as 19 *Y*s.

Check your answers.

- The sum of the answers to Problems 1 and 4 is equal to the square root of 81.
- The answer to Problem 10 is a prime number greater than 17 and less than 5^2.
- The product of the answers to Problems 6 and 7 is 36.
- The sum of the answers to Problems 1 and 10 is the solution to the equation $4n = 10^2$.
- The product of the answers to Problems 5, 7, and 9 is 24.

STUDENT PAGE

Math Journal 2, p. 237

Problem 8 7*P* | 2*P* 10 balls

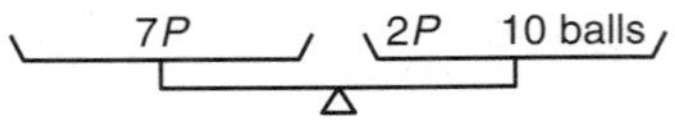

Solution

Step 1:
Subtract 2*P*.

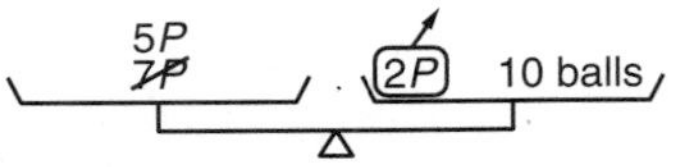

Step 2:
Divide by 5.

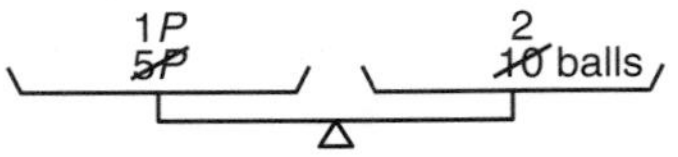

Problem 9 8*B* 30*K* | 12*B* 14*K*

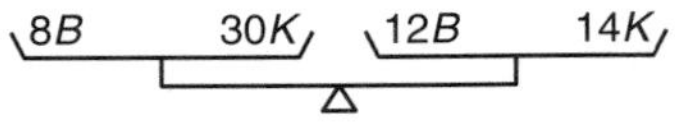

Solution

Step 1:
Subtract 8*B*.

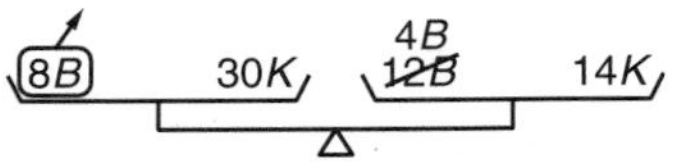

Step 2:
Subtract 14*K*.

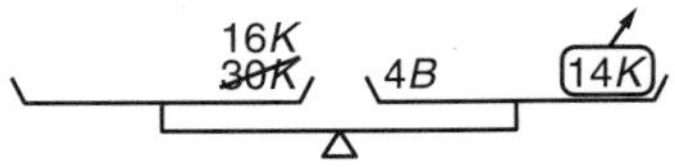

Step 3:
Divide by 4.

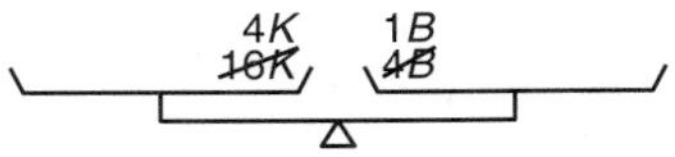

Problem 10 7*X* 7*Y* | 5*X* 45*Y*

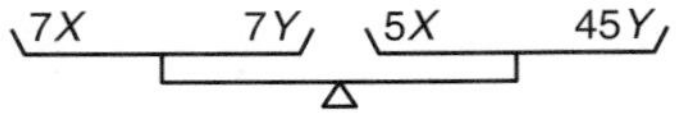

Solution

Step 1:
Subtract 5*X*.

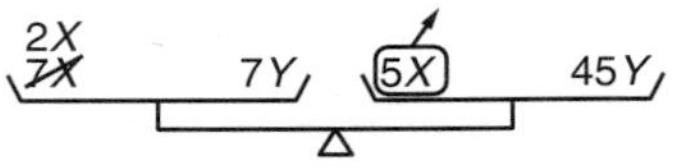

Step 2:
Subtract 7*Y*.

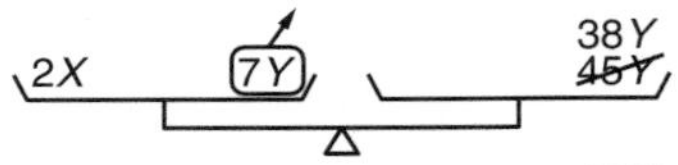

Step 3:
Divide by 2.

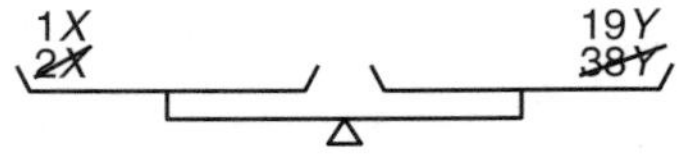

Equation	Broken key	Solution
214 + n = 305	(−)	91
L / 38 = 27	(×)	1,026
43 ∗ t = 2,537	(÷)	59
M ∗ 26 = 1,924	(÷)	74
E − 593 = 457	(+)	1,050

2 Ongoing Learning & Practice

Playing *Broken Calculator*

WHOLE-CLASS ACTIVITY

Students practice solving equations by playing *Broken Calculator*. See the table in the margin for suggestions. Game directions appear on page 495.

◆ Math Boxes 6.9 (*Math Journal 2,* p. 238)

INDEPENDENT ACTIVITY 

Mixed Review Math Boxes in this lesson are paired with Math Boxes in Lesson 6.11. The skill in Problem 1 is a prerequisite for Unit 7.

◆ Study Link 6.9 (*Math Masters,* p. 320)

Home Connection Students practice solving pan-balance problems.

3 Options for Individualizing

◆ ENRICHMENT Solving More Challenging Pan-Balance Problems (*Math Masters,* p. 106)

PARTNER ACTIVITY  **15–30 min**

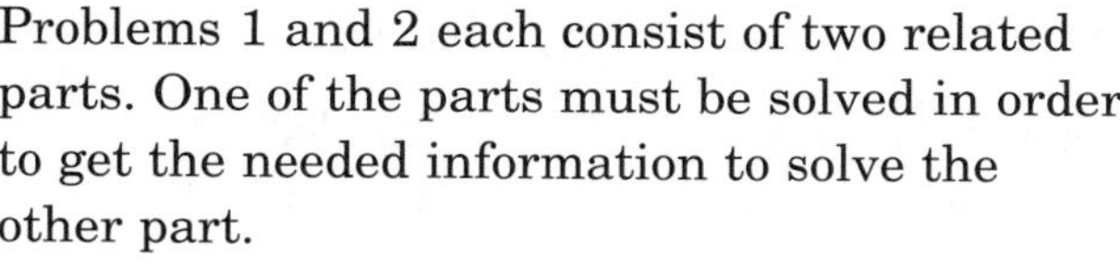

Problems 1 and 2 each consist of two related parts. One of the parts must be solved in order to get the needed information to solve the other part.

Problem 1: Complete the second statement first: One coin weighs as much as 8 marbles.

The first statement can be reasoned in this way: Since 1 coin weighs as much as 8 marbles, replace the coin on the first balance with 8 marbles. Then subtract 8 marbles from both pans; the 2 cubes must weigh as much as 14 marbles. Therefore, 1 cube weighs as much as 7 marbles.

Problem 2: The first statement can be reasoned in this way: The first balance shows that 1 can weighs as much as 3 marbles. If each can on the second balance is replaced by 3 marbles, then 10 marbles are balanced by 15 paper clips. Therefore, 1 marble weighs as much as $1\frac{1}{2}$ paper clips.

The second statement can be reasoned in this way: If 1 can weighs as much as 3 marbles and each marble weighs as much as $1\frac{1}{2}$ paper clips, then one can must weigh as much as $4\frac{1}{2}$ paper clips.

Math Boxes 6.9

1. Complete the table.

Fraction	Decimal	Percent
$\frac{5}{8}$	0.625	$62\frac{1}{2}\%$
$\frac{65}{100}$	0.65	65%
$\frac{47}{100}$	0.47	47%
$\frac{8}{12}$	$0.\overline{6}$	$66\frac{2}{3}\%$

SRB 32 33 36 37

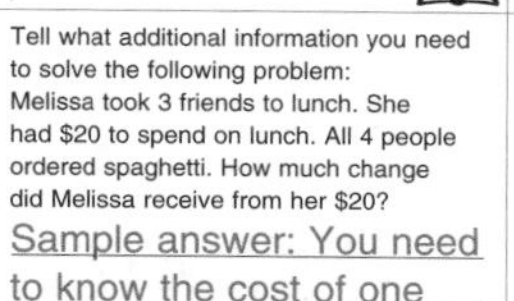

2. Multiply or divide.
   a. $-3 * 5 = -15$
   b. $-10 * -8 = 80$
   c. $120 = -4 * -30$
   d. $-4 = 28 \div -7$
   e. $7 = -56 \div -8$

SRB 95

3. Use the following formula to calculate about how long it will take an object to reach the bottom of a well:
$t = \frac{1}{4} * \sqrt{d}$
where *d* is the distance in feet the object falls and *t* is the time in seconds it takes to reach the bottom. This formula does not account for air resistance. About how long would it take a bowling ball to hit the bottom of a well 100 feet deep?
2.5 seconds

SRB 227 228

4. Tell what additional information you need to solve the following problem:
Melissa took 3 friends to lunch. She had \$20 to spend on lunch. All 4 people ordered spaghetti. How much change did Melissa receive from her \$20?
Sample answer: You need to know the cost of one order of spaghetti.

SRB 240 241

5. Make each sentence true by inserting parentheses.
   a. $(4 * 7) - (6 / 3) = 26$
   b. $3^3 - [(49 / 7) + 12] = 8$
   c. $(2\frac{5}{8} - 3 / 4) + 1 / 2 = 2\frac{3}{8}$
   d. $[6 + (15 / 3)] - 2 * 5 = 1$
   e. $2\frac{5}{8} - (3 / 4 + 1 / 2) = 1\frac{3}{8}$

SRB 229

STUDENT PAGE

◆ *Math Journal 2,* p. 238

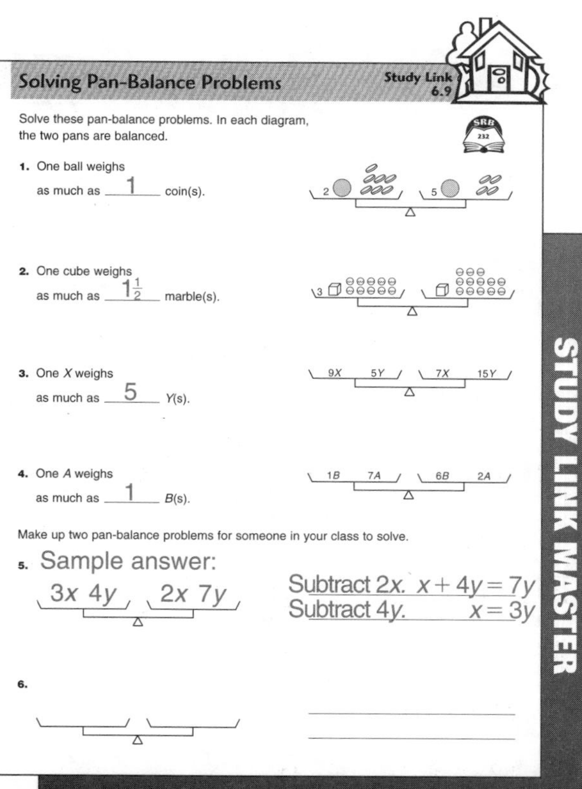

Solving Pan-Balance Problems

Study Link 6.9

Solve these pan-balance problems. In each diagram, the two pans are balanced.

SRB 232

1. One ball weighs as much as 1 coin(s).
2. One cube weighs as much as $1\frac{1}{2}$ marble(s).
3. One *X* weighs as much as 5 *Y*(s).

4. One *A* weighs as much as 1 *B*(s).

Make up two pan-balance problems for someone in your class to solve.

5. Sample answer:

Subtract 2x. $x + 4y = 7y$
Subtract 4y. $x = 3y$

6.

STUDY LINK MASTER

◆ *Math Masters,* p. 320

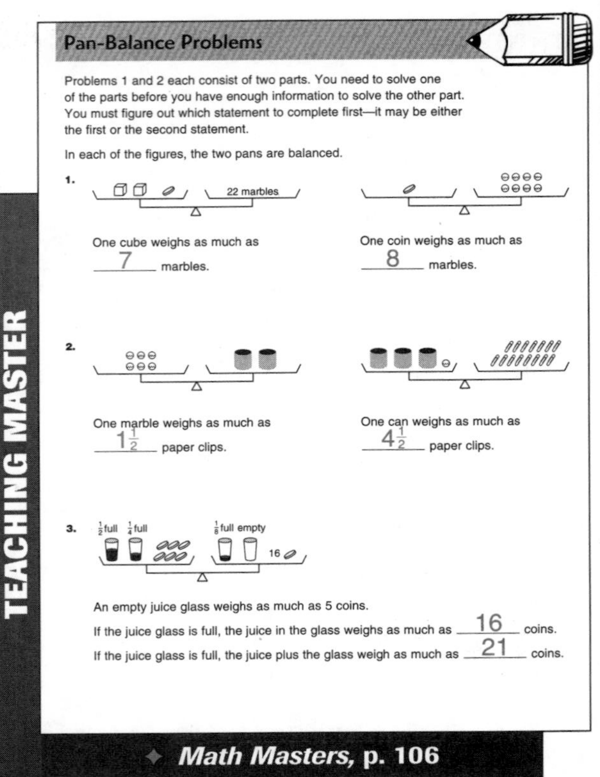

TEACHING MASTER

Pan-Balance Problems

Problems 1 and 2 each consist of two parts. You need to solve one of the parts before you have enough information to solve the other part. You must figure out which statement to complete first—it may be either the first or the second statement.

In each of the figures, the two pans are balanced.

1. One cube weighs as much as 7 marbles. One coin weighs as much as 8 marbles.

2. One marble weighs as much as $1\frac{1}{2}$ paper clips. One can weighs as much as $4\frac{1}{2}$ paper clips.

3. An empty juice glass weighs as much as 5 coins.
If the juice glass is full, the juice in the glass weighs as much as 16 coins.
If the juice glass is full, the juice plus the glass weigh as much as 21 coins.

✦ *Math Masters,* p. 106

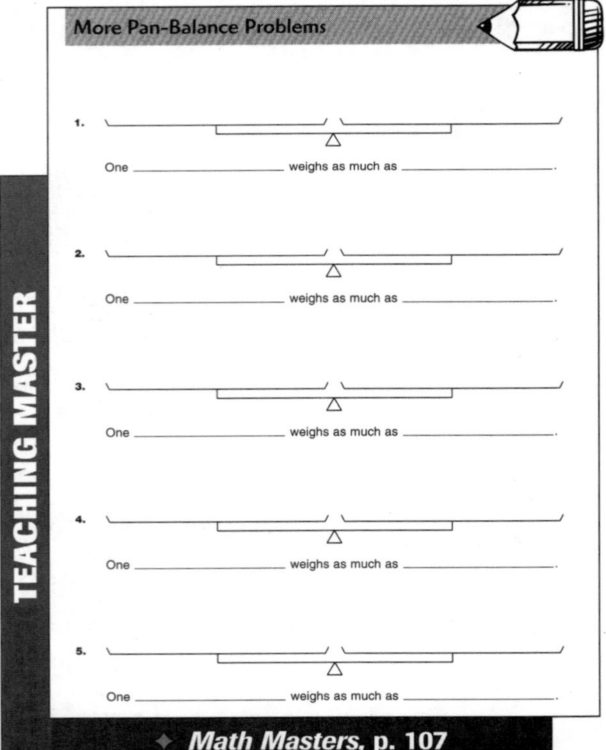

TEACHING MASTER

More Pan-Balance Problems

1. One ________ weighs as much as ________.

2. One ________ weighs as much as ________.

3. One ________ weighs as much as ________.

4. One ________ weighs as much as ________.

5. One ________ weighs as much as ________.

✦ *Math Masters,* p. 107

Problem 3 is very challenging, so don't expect many students to find the correct answers.

One strategy: Pour the juice from the $\frac{1}{4}$-full glass into the $\frac{1}{2}$-full glass. This leaves an empty glass in each pan, which can be removed. Remove 6 coins from each pan. Remove $\frac{1}{8}$ of a glass of juice from each side. This leaves an empty glass in the second pan. Replace it with 5 coins. This leaves the following: $\frac{5}{8}$-full glass in the first pan and 15 coins in the second pan. Five of the coins weigh as much as the glass in the first pan, so the juice in the glass weighs as much as 10 coins. Therefore, the juice in a full glass weighs as much as 16 coins ($\frac{5}{8}$ of 16 equals 10), and the juice and the glass together weigh 21 coins.

✦ EXTRA PRACTICE Solving Pan-Balance Problems (*Math Masters,* p. 107)

INDEPENDENT ACTIVITY  **15–30 min**

Portfolio Ideas

Prepare a page of pan-balance problems on *Math Masters,* page 107 for students to solve. *Suggestions*

Pan 1: 2 apples Pan 2: 6 blocks
One apple weighs as much as 3 blocks.

Pan 1: 4 balls Pan 2: 1 ball; 6 blocks
One ball weighs as much as 2 blocks.

Pan 1: 3 pencils; 1 block Pan 2: 10 blocks
One pencil weighs as much as 3 blocks.

Pan 1: 3 apples; 4 blocks Pan 2: 2 apples; 6 blocks
One apple weighs as much as 2 blocks.

Pan 1: 2 balls; 1 pencil Pan 2: 1 pencil; 4 blocks
One ball weighs as much as 2 blocks.

6.10 Pan-Balance Equations

OBJECTIVE **To explore a method for solving equations by transforming them into equivalent equations of the form $x = a$.**

summaries	materials
1 Teaching the Lesson	
Students perform operations on the elements on both sides of simple equations, transforming them into more complex equations; then they reverse the procedure to derive simple equations from complex ones. Students also use the procedure to write their own equations for group members to solve. [Patterns, Functions, and Algebra]	☐ *Math Journal 2,* pp. 240–243 ☐ *Student Reference Book,* p. 232 ☐ Study Link 6.9
2 Ongoing Learning & Practice	
Students practice and maintain skills through Math Boxes and Study Link activities.	☐ *Math Journal 2,* p. 239 ☐ Study Link Master (*Math Masters,* p. 321)
3 Options for Individualizing	
Extra Practice Students solve pan-balance equations. [Patterns, Functions, and Algebra]	☐ Teaching Master (*Math Masters,* p. 108)

Additional Information

Vocabulary • **equivalent equations**

Getting Started

Mental Math and Reflexes

For each of the following statements, students show "thumbs up" if the statement is true and "thumbs down" if the statement is false:

- $\frac{1}{3}$ of a day is 9 hours. down
- $\frac{3}{4}$ of a day is 16 hours. down
- $\frac{5}{6}$ of a day is 20 hours. up
- $\frac{1}{4}$ of a day is 6 hours. up
- $\frac{3}{6}$ of a day is 14 hours. down
- $\frac{9}{12}$ of a day is 18 hours. up
- $\frac{10}{12}$ of a day is 35 hours. down
- $\frac{7}{4}$ of a day is 42 hours. up

Math Message

Read page 232 in your Student Reference Book. *Solve the Check Your Understanding problems.*

Study Link 6.9 Follow-Up

Review the answers with the class. Students share the pan-balance problems that they created.

Algebra

Pan Balance Problems and Equations

If two different kinds of objects are placed in the pans of a balance so that they balance, then you can find the weight of one kind of object in terms of the other kind of object.

EXAMPLE The pan balance at the right has 2 balls and 6 marbles in one pan and 1 ball and 8 marbles in the other pan. How many marbles weigh as much as 1 ball?

Step 1: If 1 ball is removed from each pan, the pan balance will remain balanced. One ball and 6 marbles will be left in the pan on the left and 8 marbles will be left in the pan on the right.

Step 2: If 6 marbles are removed from each pan, the pan balance will remain balanced. One ball will be left in the pan on the left and 2 marbles will be left in the pan on the right.

1 ball weighs as much as 2 marbles.

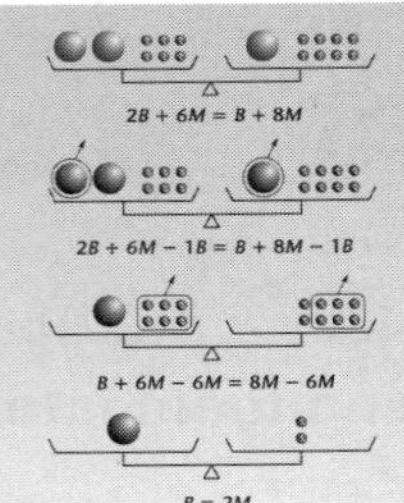

When solving a pan balance problem, the pans must balance after each step. If you do the same thing to the objects in both pans, then the pans will remain balanced. For example, you might remove the same number of the same kinds of objects from both pans, or you might remove half of each kind of object.

You can think of pan balance problems as models for equations. Suppose that B stands for the weight of 1 ball and M stands for the weight of 1 marble. The pan balance problem in the example above can then be expressed by the equation $2B + 6M = B + 8M$.

CHECK YOUR UNDERSTANDING

Write an equation for each pan balance problem.

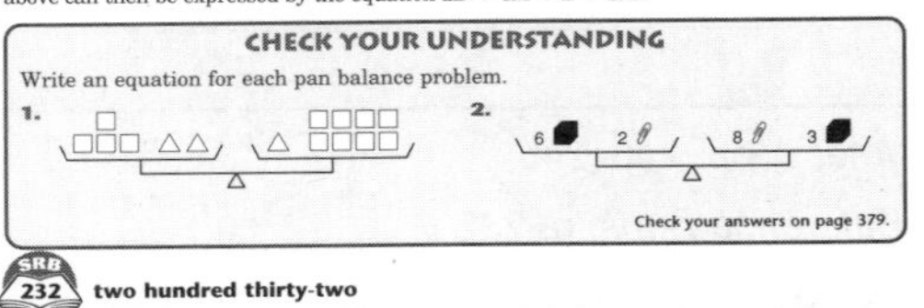

Check your answers on page 379.

SRB 232 two hundred thirty-two

STUDENT PAGE

✦ *Student Reference Book,* p. 232

Pan-Balance Equations

1. Start with the original pan-balance equation. Do the first operation on both sides of the pan balance, and write the result on the second pan balance. Do the second operation on both sides of the second pan balance, and write the result on the third pan balance. Fill in the fourth pan balance in the same way.

Operation (in words)	Operation (abbreviation)	Pan balance		
Original pan-balance equation		X	=	10
Multiply by 3.	M 3	$(3 * X)$	=	30
Add 18.	A 18	$(3 * X) + 18$	=	48
Add 2 ∗ X.	A 2 ∗ X	$(5 * X) + 18$	=	$(2 * X) + 48$

Equations that have the same solution are called **equivalent equations.**

2. Check that the pan-balance equations above are equivalent equations (that is, that 10 is the solution to each equation).

3. Now do the opposite of what you did in Problem 1. Record on each pan balance the operation used to obtain the results.

Operation (in words)	Operation (abbreviation)	Pan balance		
Original pan-balance equation		$(5 * X) + 18$	=	$(2 * X) + 48$
Subtract 2 ∗ X.	S 2 ∗ X	$(3 * X) + 18$	=	48
Subtract 18.	S 18	$3 * X$	=	30
Divide by 3.	D 3	X	=	10

STUDENT PAGE

✦ *Math Journal 2,* p. 240

1 Teaching the Lesson

✦ Math Message Follow-Up
(*Student Reference Book,* p. 232)

WHOLE-CLASS DISCUSSION

The purpose of this essay is to introduce the idea that pan-balance problems can be viewed as models for equations. Remind students of the basic principle of pan-balance problems: In order for the pans to remain in balance, what you do to the objects in one pan you must also do to the objects in the other pan. Go over the answers to the Check Your Understanding problems.

✦ Generating Equivalent Equations
(*Math Journal 2,* pp. 240 and 241)

WHOLE-CLASS ACTIVITY

NOTE: The pan-balance problems in Lesson 6.9 offered a concrete model of a systematic method for solving equations in which an equation is transformed into a succession of simpler, equivalent equations. Lesson 6.10 provides a transition from working with the model itself to solving equations without the model.

Complete Problem 1 on journal page 240 as a class. Follow these steps:

1. A simple pan-balance equation, $X = 10$, is given. Transform this equation into the equation $3 * X = 30$ by multiplying both sides of the original pan-balance equation, $X = 10$, by 3.
2. Transform the pan-balance equation $3 * X = 30$ into the equation $(3 * X) + 18 = 48$ by adding 18 to both sides of the equation $3 * X = 30$.
3. Finally, transform the pan-balance equation $(3 * X) + 18 = 48$ into the equation $(5 * X) + 18 = (2 * X) + 48$ by adding $2 * X$ to both sides of the equation.

The solution to the original equation, $X = 10$, is 10. Have students check that 10 is also the solution to each of the other equations by replacing X with 10. Equations having the same solution are called **equivalent equations.**

As you work the problem with the class, make sure that students understand both the arrangement of the stacked pan balances and operations instructions. Each operation acts on the balance *above* it, and the result is recorded on the balance *next* to it.

Check that students understand these underlying ideas:

- ▷ Each operation must be carried out on both sides of the equation (both pans of the balance).
- ▷ Any operation that is carried out in the same way for both pans keeps the pan balance in a balanced position.
- ▷ Any operation (except $* \ 0$ and $\div \ 0$) performed on both sides of an equation ensures that the resulting equation has the same solution as the original equation.

Adjusting the Activity Ask students to write an equation and then to use it to illustrate why multiplying both sides by 0 will not give the solution to the original equation.

The pan-balance equations in Problem 1 are displayed in reverse order in Problem 3. As a class, find the operation that was used to obtain each equation. Note that the instructions for the operations in Problem 1 were stated in two ways—in words and in abbreviated form. Students may find the abbreviated notation easier to use and should be encouraged to do so. But if some students want to write operation instructions as well, that is fine, too.

Note also that each operation in Problem 3 is the inverse of the corresponding operation in Problem 1. For example, the first operation in Problem 3 (subtract $2 * X$) is the inverse of the last operation in Problem 1 (add $2 * X$): It "undoes" the result of the last operation in Problem 1.

Adjusting the Activity Point out that addition and multiplication are the only operations required for manipulating these equations. Any subtraction instruction can be restated as a related addition instruction. (Subtract $2 * X$ and add OPP $(2 * X)$ produce the same result.) Similarly, any division instruction can be restated as a related multiplication instruction. (Divide by 3 and multiply by $\frac{1}{3}$) produce the same result.

To reinforce the routines on journal page 240, have students complete journal page 241 with a partner. Remind them that the multiplication symbol may be omitted (for example, $2n$ for $2 * n$). Circulate and assist.

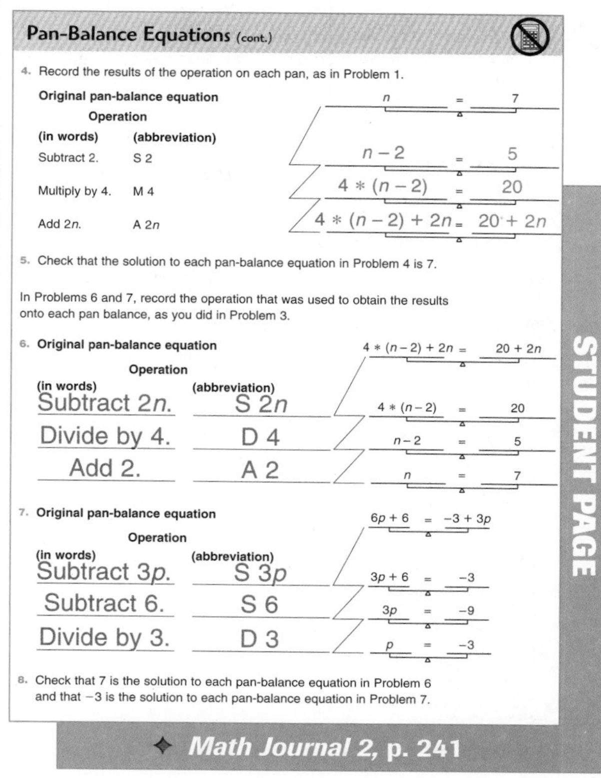

Pan-Balance Equations (cont.)

4. Record the results of the operation on each pan, as in Problem 1.

Operation (in words)	Operation (abbreviation)	Left pan		Right pan
Original pan-balance equation		n	=	7
Subtract 2.	S 2	$n - 2$	=	5
Multiply by 4.	M 4	$4 * (n - 2)$	=	20
Add $2n$.	A $2n$	$4 * (n - 2) + 2n$	=	$20 + 2n$

5. Check that the solution to each pan-balance equation in Problem 4 is 7.

In Problems 6 and 7, record the operation that was used to obtain the results onto each pan balance, as you did in Problem 3.

6.

Operation (in words)	Operation (abbreviation)	Left pan		Right pan
Original pan-balance equation		$4 * (n - 2) + 2n$	=	$20 + 2n$
Subtract $2n$.	S $2n$	$4 * (n - 2)$	=	20
Divide by 4.	D 4	$n - 2$	=	5
Add 2.	A 2	n	=	7

7.

Operation (in words)	Operation (abbreviation)	Left pan		Right pan
Original pan-balance equation		$6p + 6$	=	$-3 + 3p$
Subtract $3p$.	S $3p$	$3p + 6$	=	-3
Subtract 6.	S 6	$3p$	=	-9
Divide by 3.	D 3	p	=	-3

8. Check that 7 is the solution to each pan-balance equation in Problem 6 and that -3 is the solution to each pan-balance equation in Problem 7.

STUDENT PAGE

✦ *Math Journal 2*, p. 241

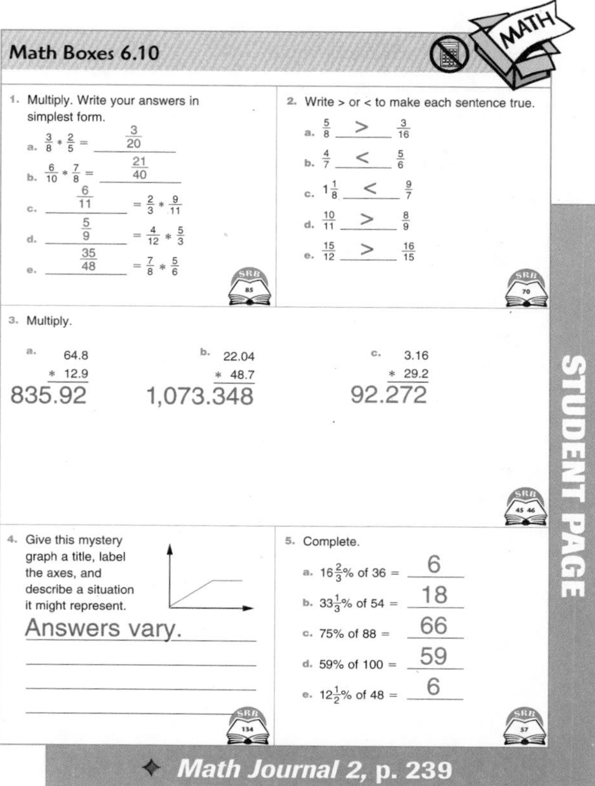

Math Boxes 6.10

1. Multiply. Write your answers in simplest form.
   a. $\frac{3}{8} * \frac{2}{5} = \frac{3}{20}$
   b. $\frac{6}{10} * \frac{7}{8} = \frac{21}{40}$
   c. $\frac{6}{11} = \frac{2}{3} * \frac{9}{11}$
   d. $\frac{5}{9} = \frac{4}{12} * \frac{5}{3}$
   e. $\frac{35}{48} = \frac{7}{8} * \frac{5}{6}$

2. Write > or < to make each sentence true.
   a. $\frac{5}{8} > \frac{3}{16}$
   b. $\frac{4}{7} < \frac{5}{6}$
   c. $1\frac{1}{8} < \frac{9}{7}$
   d. $\frac{10}{11} > \frac{8}{9}$
   e. $\frac{15}{12} > \frac{16}{15}$

3. Multiply.
   a. $64.8 * 12.9$ = 835.92
   b. $22.04 * 48.7$ = 1,073.348
   c. $3.16 * 29.2$ = 92.272

4. Give this mystery graph a title, label the axes, and describe a situation it might represent.
   Answers vary.

5. Complete.
   a. $16\frac{2}{3}\%$ of 36 = 6
   b. $33\frac{1}{3}\%$ of 54 = 18
   c. 75% of 88 = 66
   d. 59% of 100 = 59
   e. $12\frac{1}{2}\%$ of 48 = 6

STUDENT PAGE

✦ *Math Journal 2*, p. 239

Inventing and Solving Equations

Work in groups of three. Each of you will invent two equations and then ask the other two group members to solve them. You will show your solutions on page 243. Here is what you should do for each equation.

Step 1 Choose any positive or negative integer and record it on the first line to complete the original equation.

Step 2 Apply any operation you wish to both sides of the equation. Record the operation and write the new (equivalent) equation on the lines below the original equation.

Step 3 Repeat Step 2. Apply a new operation and show the new equation that results.

Step 4 Check your work by substituting the original value of x in each equation you have written. You should get a true number sentence every time.

Step 5 Give the other members of your group the final equation to solve.

1. Make up an equation from two equivalent equations. Selected integer

Original equation x = ______

Operation

Answers vary.

2. Make up an equation from three equivalent equations. Selected integer

Original equation x = ______

Operation

Answers vary.

STUDENT PAGE

◆ *Math Journal 2*, p. 242

Inventing and Solving Equations (cont.)

Use this page to solve your partners' equations. Answers vary.

First, record the equation. Then solve it. For each step, record the operation you use and the equation that results. Check your solution by substituting it for the variable in your partners' equation. Finally, compare the steps you used to solve your partners' equation to the steps your partners used in inventing the equation.

1. Partners' equation ______ = ______

Operation

2. Partners' equation ______ = ______

Operation

3. Partners' equation ______ = ______

Operation

4. Partners' equation ______ = ______

Operation

STUDENT PAGE

◆ *Math Journal 2*, p. 243

◆ Inventing and Solving Equations

(*Math Journal 2*, pp. 242–243)

SMALL-GROUP ACTIVITY 

Divide the class into groups of three students. Go over the directions for this activity which appear at the top of journal page 242 and work through an example or two.

Each group member "builds" two equations, following the procedure for Problem 1 on journal page 240, and records his or her work on journal page 242. Note that the equation for Problem 1 (on page 242) is obtained after performing two operations and that the equation for Problem 2 requires three operations.

Each student then solves the equations created by the other members of the group—by reversing the steps as in Problem 3 on journal page 240—and records his or her work on journal page 243.

Students check their solutions. They compare the steps they used to solve the equations to the steps the writers of the equations used to create them.

Remind students that there are no restrictions on the operations or the order of the operations they apply to the initial equation they choose. Any operation is permissible, except for multiplication and division by zero.

Caution students to check that the integer value selected in the initial equation is in fact a solution for each of the equations they generate along the way. Such checking has two advantages:

▷ It develops student confidence that any operation carried out on both sides of an equation will produce an equivalent equation.

▷ It ensures that a correct solution of the invented equation will match the intended solution.

ONGOING ASSESSMENT

Keep in mind that this is an exploratory activity. Because students construct their own equations, you have no control over how "nice" the equations will be. Some may be very difficult. Also, in solving their partners' equations, students will perform operations that don't advance the solution process: They will do things they will want to undo; they will multiply at the wrong time, producing coefficients that are unwieldy; and so on. These trials are all part of the learning process. It is important that students become involved in the development of this equation-solving procedure. The work in this lesson will help them in Lesson 6.11 when this procedure is formalized.

Ongoing Learning & Practice

✦Math Boxes 6.10 (*Math Journal 2,* p. 239)

INDEPENDENT ACTIVITY 

Mixed Review Math Boxes in this lesson are paired with Math Boxes in Lesson 6.12. The skill in Problem 1 is a prerequisite for Unit 7.

NOTE: The reproduction of journal page 239 with answers appears on page 509.

✦Study Link 6.10 (*Math Masters,* p. 321)

Home Connection Students practice recording the operations used to obtain their results in a variety of pan-balance equations.

3 Options for Individualizing

✦EXTRA PRACTICE Balancing Pans (*Math Masters,* p. 108)

INDEPENDENT ACTIVITY  **15–30 min** 

Students solve for variables in a variety of pan-balance equations.

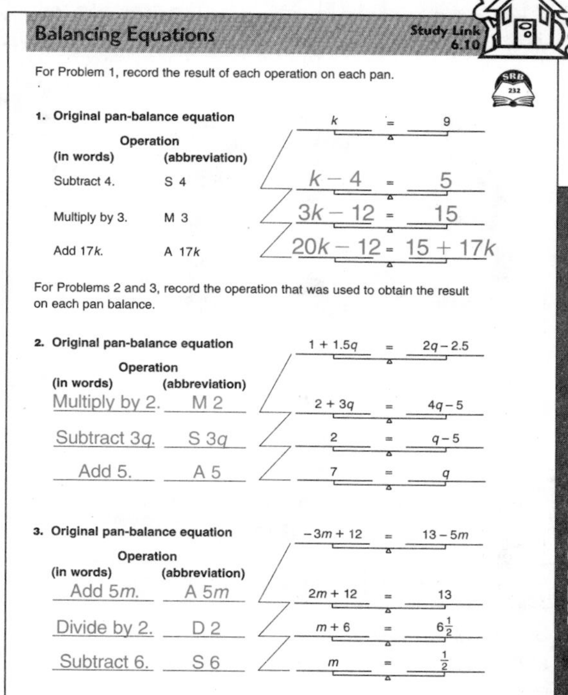

Balancing Equations — Study Link 6.10

For Problem 1, record the result of each operation on each pan.

1. Original pan-balance equation: $k = 9$

Operation (in words)	(abbreviation)		
Subtract 4.	S 4	$k - 4$	5
Multiply by 3.	M 3	$3k - 12$	15
Add 17*k*.	A 17*k*	$20k - 12$	$15 + 17k$

For Problems 2 and 3, record the operation that was used to obtain the result on each pan balance.

2. Original pan-balance equation: $1 + 1.5q = 2q - 2.5$

Operation (in words)	(abbreviation)		
Multiply by 2.	M 2	$2 + 3q$	$4q - 5$
Subtract 3*q*.	S 3*q*	2	$q - 5$
Add 5.	A 5	7	q

3. Original pan-balance equation: $-3m + 12 = 13 - 5m$

Operation (in words)	(abbreviation)		
Add 5*m*.	A 5*m*	$2m + 12$	13
Divide by 2.	D 2	$m + 6$	$6\frac{1}{2}$
Subtract 6.	S 6	m	$\frac{1}{2}$

STUDY LINK MASTER

✦ Math Masters, p. 321

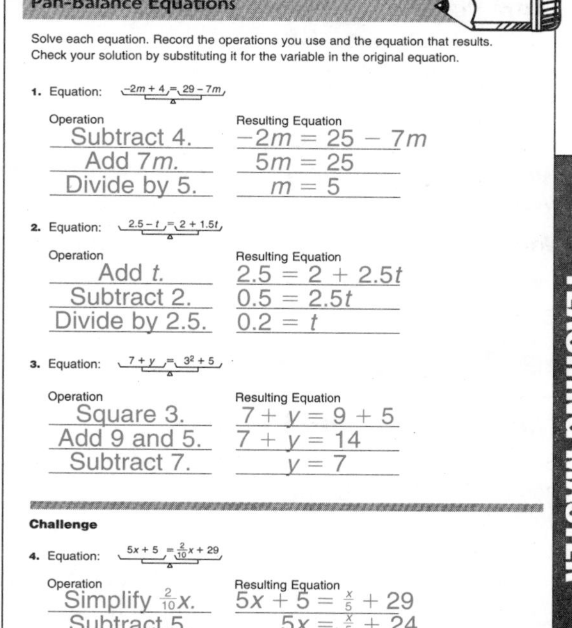

Pan-Balance Equations

Solve each equation. Record the operations you use and the equation that results. Check your solution by substituting it for the variable in the original equation.

1. Equation: $-2m + 4 = 29 - 7m$

Operation	Resulting Equation
Subtract 4.	$-2m = 25 - 7m$
Add 7*m*.	$5m = 25$
Divide by 5.	$m = 5$

2. Equation: $2.5 - t = 2 + 1.5t$

Operation	Resulting Equation
Add *t*.	$2.5 = 2 + 2.5t$
Subtract 2.	$0.5 = 2.5t$
Divide by 2.5.	$0.2 = t$

3. Equation: $7 + y = 3^2 + 5$

Operation	Resulting Equation
Square 3.	$7 + y = 9 + 5$
Add 9 and 5.	$7 + y = 14$
Subtract 7.	$y = 7$

Challenge

4. Equation: $5x + 5 = \frac{2}{10}x + 29$

Operation	Resulting Equation
Simplify $\frac{2}{10}x$.	$5x + 5 = \frac{x}{5} + 29$
Subtract 5.	$5x = \frac{x}{5} + 24$
Subtract $\frac{x}{5}$.	$4\frac{4}{5}x = 24$
Divide by $4\frac{4}{5}$.	$x = 5$

TEACHING MASTER

✦ Math Masters, p. 108

6.11 The Equivalent-Equations Method of Solving Equations

OBJECTIVE **To solve equations by transforming them into equivalent equations of the form $x = a$.**

summaries	materials
1 Teaching the Lesson	
Students solve equations by transforming them into a succession of equations, each equivalent to the original equation, culminating in an equation of the form "$x =$ some number," which can then be solved by inspection. [Patterns, Functions, and Algebra]	□ *Math Journal 2,* pp. 244 and 245 □ Study Link 6.10 □ Assessment Master (*Math Masters,* p. 478; optional) □ calculator
2 Ongoing Learning & Practice	
Students play *Broken Calculator.* [Patterns, Functions, and Algebra] Students practice and maintain skills through Math Boxes and Study Link activities.	□ *Math Journal 2,* p. 246 □ Study Link Master (*Math Masters,* p. 322) □ calculator
3 Options for Individualizing	
Extra Practice Students solve equations. [Patterns, Functions, and Algebra]	□ Teaching Master (*Math Masters,* p. 109) ***See* Advance Preparation**

Additional Information

Advance Preparation For Part 3, write equations appropriate for the level of your class on a copy of *Math Masters,* page 109. Make one copy of the master for each student.

Vocabulary • **terms of an equation** • **variable term** • **constant term** • **coefficient**

Getting Started

Mental Math and Reflexes

Students write *A, P,* or *V* to indicate whether they need to find the area, the perimeter, or the volume in each of the following situations:

- Filling a sandbox in a playground with sand *V*
- Finding the square footage of a house *A*
- Buying carpet *A*
- Finding the distance around the school *P*
- Buying a wallpaper border for a bedroom *P*
- Buying a refrigerator *V, A*

Math Message

Solve the equation $4x - 6 = x + 3$. *Check your solution.*

Study Link 6.10 Follow-Up

Review the answers with the class.

Teaching the Lesson

✦ Math Message Follow-Up

WHOLE-CLASS DISCUSSION 

Students share their solution strategies. While some students may have solved the equation by trial and error, most should have used the method they learned in Lesson 6.10. Emphasize that the same operation must be performed on both sides of the equal sign. Record the operation for each step in abbreviated form, using the following format:

Original equation	$4x - 6 = x + 3$
Operation	
S x, or A $-x$	$3x - 6 = 3$
A 6, or S -6	$3x = 9$
D 3, or M $\frac{1}{3}$	$x = 3$

The solution is 3. Check the solution by substituting it for the variable in the original equation. Since subtraction is the inverse of addition, and division is the inverse of multiplication, each operation may be recorded in two ways. For example, adding 6 is the same as subtracting -6.

Define the following terms:

▷ In the equation $4x - 6 = x + 3$, "$4x$," "6," "x," and "3" are the **terms of the equation.**

▷ The terms $4x$ and x are **variable terms,** since they each contain a variable.

▷ The terms 6 and 3, which do not contain a variable, are called **constant terms** (or constants).

▷ The number part of a variable term is called the **coefficient.** The coefficient of the variable term $4x$ is 4.

Do not expect students to memorize these terms at the present time. With repeated use, they will gradually become part of students' vocabulary.

Solve a few more equations with the class. *Suggestions:*

▷ $4n + 6 = n + 3$ -1 ▷ $3w + 6.4 = 6.4 - 2w$ 0

▷ $8 - h = h + 5$ 1.5 ▷ $\frac{1}{5}k + 3 = \frac{3}{5}k - 5$ 20

NOTE: In Lesson 6.10, students informally explored a strategy for solving an equation that contains a variable term and/or a constant on both sides of the equal sign, as in $8 - 3x = 5x + 1$. In the current lesson, that strategy is formalized.

Adjusting the Activity To help students become more familiar with the newly defined terms, display the words on a word list or on posters in the classroom. Include an example of an equation with the new vocabulary words appropriately labeled.

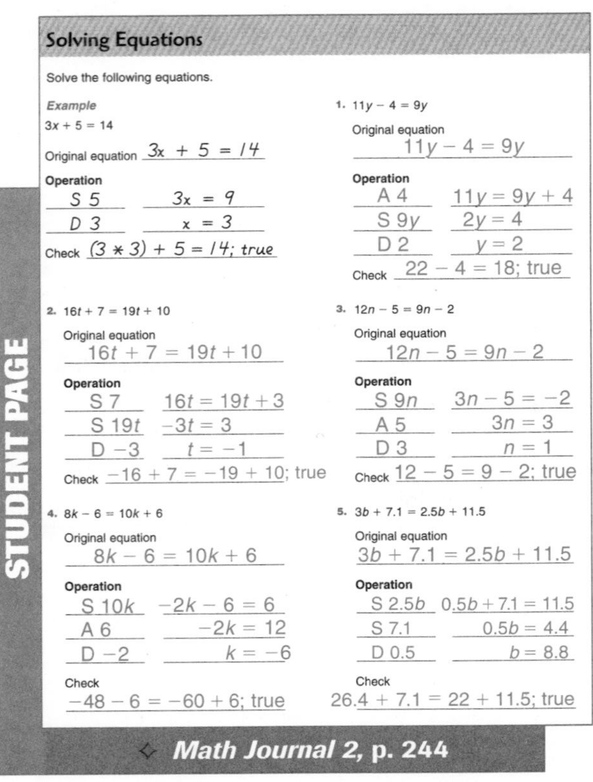

STUDENT PAGE

Solving Equations

Solve the following equations.

Example
$3x + 5 = 14$
Original equation $3x + 5 = 14$
Operation
S 5 — $3x = 9$
D 3 — $x = 3$
Check $(3 * 3) + 5 = 14$; true

1. $11y - 4 = 9y$
Original equation $11y - 4 = 9y$
Operation
A 4 — $11y = 9y + 4$
S 9y — $2y = 4$
D 2 — $y = 2$
Check $22 - 4 = 18$; true

2. $16t + 7 = 19t + 10$
Original equation $16t + 7 = 19t + 10$
Operation
S 7 — $16t = 19t + 3$
S 19t — $-3t = 3$
D −3 — $t = -1$
Check $-16 + 7 = -19 + 10$; true

3. $12n - 5 = 9n - 2$
Original equation $12n - 5 = 9n - 2$
Operation
S 9n — $3n - 5 = -2$
A 5 — $3n = 3$
D 3 — $n = 1$
Check $12 - 5 = 9 - 2$; true

4. $8k - 6 = 10k + 6$
Original equation $8k - 6 = 10k + 6$
Operation
S 10k — $-2k - 6 = 6$
A 6 — $-2k = 12$
D −2 — $k = -6$
Check $-48 - 6 = -60 + 6$; true

5. $3b + 7.1 = 2.5b + 11.5$
Original equation $3b + 7.1 = 2.5b + 11.5$
Operation
S 2.5b — $0.5b + 7.1 = 11.5$
S 7.1 — $0.5b = 4.4$
D 0.5 — $b = 8.8$
Check $26.4 + 7.1 = 22 + 11.5$; true

✧ *Math Journal 2*, p. 244

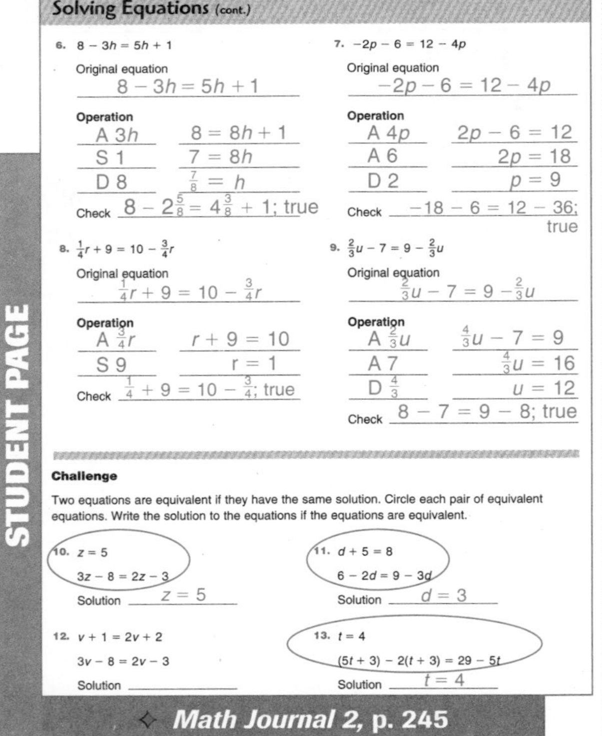

STUDENT PAGE

Solving Equations (cont.)

6. $8 - 3h = 5h + 1$
Original equation $8 - 3h = 5h + 1$
Operation
A 3h — $8 = 8h + 1$
S 1 — $7 = 8h$
D 8 — $\frac{7}{8} = h$
Check $8 - 2\frac{5}{8} = 4\frac{3}{8} + 1$; true

7. $-2p - 6 = 12 - 4p$
Original equation $-2p - 6 = 12 - 4p$
Operation
A 4p — $2p - 6 = 12$
A 6 — $2p = 18$
D 2 — $p = 9$
Check $-18 - 6 = 12 - 36$; true

8. $\frac{1}{4}r + 9 = 10 - \frac{3}{4}r$
Original equation $\frac{1}{4}r + 9 = 10 - \frac{3}{4}r$
Operation
A $\frac{3}{4}r$ — $r + 9 = 10$
S 9 — $r = 1$
Check $\frac{1}{4} + 9 = 10 - \frac{3}{4}$; true

9. $\frac{2}{3}u - 7 = 9 - \frac{2}{3}u$
Original equation $\frac{2}{3}u - 7 = 9 - \frac{2}{3}u$
Operation
A $\frac{2}{3}u$ — $\frac{4}{3}u - 7 = 9$
A 7 — $\frac{4}{3}u = 16$
D $\frac{4}{3}$ — $u = 12$
Check $8 - 7 = 9 - 8$; true

Challenge

Two equations are equivalent if they have the same solution. Circle each pair of equivalent equations. Write the solution to the equations if the equations are equivalent.

10. $z = 5$
$3z - 8 = 2z - 3$
Solution $z = 5$

11. $d + 5 = 8$
$6 - 2d = 9 - 3d$
Solution $d = 3$

12. $v + 1 = 2v + 2$
$3v - 8 = 2v - 3$
Solution ______

13. $t = 4$
$(5t + 3) - 2(t + 3) = 29 - 5t$
Solution $t = 4$

✧ *Math Journal 2*, p. 245

Summary

To solve equations in which a variable term and/or a constant appear on both sides of the equal sign:

▷ Eliminate the variable term from one side of the equal sign by adding or subtracting the variable term or its opposite from both sides of the equation.

▷ Eliminate the constant term from the other side of the equal sign by adding or subtracting the constant or its opposite from both sides of the equation.

▷ Divide both sides of the equation by the coefficient of the variable term. (Or, multiply both sides of the equation by the reciprocal of the coefficient of the variable term.)

Remind students that the equations at each step are equivalent to the original equation—that is, the solution to the original equation is also the solution to each subsequent equation. Thus, the method of solving equations involves transforming each equation into a simpler equation that is equivalent to the original equation, culminating in an equation of the form "x = some number," which can then be solved by inspection.

✦Practicing Solving Equations (*Math Journal 2*, pp. 244 and 245)

PARTNER ACTIVITY 

Problems 1–9 provide practice in solving equations. If students have difficulty, you might want to work through several problems, one at a time, checking each one before going on to the next.

ONGOING ASSESSMENT

Before sharing strategies for Problems 10–13, have students complete an Exit Slip (*Math Masters*, page 478) responding to the following:

- **For one of the pairs of equations that you did not circle in Problems 10–13, explain how you decided that the equations are not equivalent.**

Problems 10–13 reinforce the concept that two equations are equivalent if they have the same solution. Some students may discover that they need *not* solve both equations in order to determine whether they are equivalent. They can solve just one equation (preferably the simpler one) and substitute the solution into the other equation. For example, in Problem 10, the solution to $z = 5$ is, obviously, 5. If you replace z with 5 in the second equation, you obtain a true sentence. Therefore, 5 is also the solution to the second equation, and the two equations are equivalent.

Plan to have students share their solution strategies with the class *for each problem* before you begin the next lesson. Note that the second equation in Problem 13 looks very complicated, but if students substitute the solution to the first equation, 4, for the variable, they will see that the two equations are equivalent. Some students, however, may want to try to solve the second equation.

Math Boxes 6.11

1. Complete the table.

Fraction	Decimal	Percent
$\frac{15}{20}$	0.75	75%
$\frac{9}{10}$	0.9	90%
$\frac{24}{100}$, or $\frac{6}{25}$	0.24	24%
$\frac{35}{100}$, or $\frac{7}{20}$	0.35	35%

2. Multiply or divide.
   a. $-3 * -12 =$ 36
   b. $-50 * 70 =$ −3,500
   c. 100,000 $= -200 * -500$
   d. −9 $* 70 = -630$
   e. −40 $* -40 = 1,600$

3. Suppose N is a 2-digit whole number that ends in 5, such as 15. It is easy to calculate the square of N by using the formula
   $N^2 = (t * (t + 1) * 100) + 25$
   where t is the tens digit of the number you are squaring. Use this formula to find the following. (*Hint:* In Problem a, $t = 3$.)
   a. $35^2 =$ 1,225
   b. $75^2 =$ 5,625
   c. $95^2 =$ 9,025

4. Tell what additional information you need to solve the following problem:
   Sam has 2 baseball cards that are worth \$4.20 each and 3 baseball cards that are worth \$7 each. The rest of his cards are worth \$1 each. How much is his collection worth in all?
   Sample answer: You need to know how many cards Sam has in his whole collection.

5. Make each sentence true by inserting parentheses.
   a. $[4 * (7 - 6)] / 3 = \frac{4}{3}$
   b. $3^2 - 38 / (7 + 12) = 7$
   c. $2\frac{5}{8} - 3 / (4 - 1) + 1 / 2 = 2\frac{1}{8}$
   d. $6 + (15 / 3) - (2 * 5) = 1$
   e. $[18 / (3^2 - 6)] + 8 = 14$

STUDENT PAGE

✧ *Math Journal 2,* p. 246

2 Ongoing Learning & Practice

✦ Playing *Broken Calculator*

WHOLE-CLASS ACTIVITY

Students play *Broken Calculator,* which was introduced in Lesson 6.8. *Suggestions:*

Equation	Broken key	Solution
$382 + n = 771$	⊖	389
$L / 84 = 49$	⊗	4,116
$57 * t = 3,705$	⊕̶ (÷)	65
$M * 104 = 6,864$	÷	66
$E - 779 = 438$	⊕	1,217

✦ Math Boxes 6.11 (*Math Journal 2,* p. 246)

INDEPENDENT ACTIVITY 

Mixed Review Math Boxes in this lesson are paired with Math Boxes in Lesson 6.9. The skill in Problem 1 is a prerequisite for Unit 7.

✦ Study Link 6.11 (*Math Masters,* p. 322)

Home Connection Students practice solving equations.

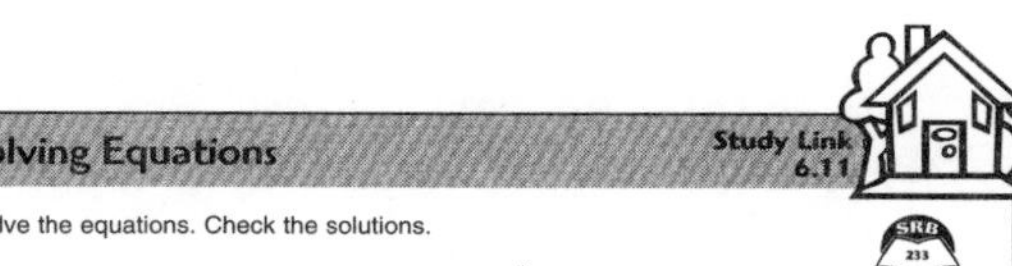

Solve the equations. Check the solutions.

1. $9 + 5k = 45 + 2k$
   Original equation: $9 + 5k = 45 + 2k$
   Operation: S 9 — $5k = 36 + 2k$; S 2k — $3k = 36$; D 3 — $k = 12$
   Check: $9 + 60 = 45 + 24$

2. $\frac{9}{2}m - 8 = -5.5 + 4m$
   Original equation: $\frac{9}{2}m - 8 = -5.5 + 4m$
   Operation: A 8 — $\frac{9}{2}m = 2.5 + 4m$; S 4m — $\frac{1}{2}m = 2.5$; M 2 — $m = 5$
   Check: $22.5 - 8 = -5.5 + 20$

3. $24x - 10 = 18x - 4$
   Original equation: $24x - 10 = 18x - 4$
   Operation: S 18x — $6x - 10 = -4$; A 10 — $6x = 6$; D 6 — $x = 1$
   Check: $24 - 10 = 18 - 4$

4. $12d - 9 = 15d + 9$
   Original equation: $12d - 9 = 15d + 9$
   Operation: S 15d — $-3d - 9 = 9$; A 9 — $-3d = 18$; D −3 — $d = -6$
   Check: $-72 - 9 = -90 + 9$

5. $-6r - 5 = 7 - 12r$
   Original equation: $-6r - 5 = 7 - 12r$
   Operation: A 12r — $6r - 5 = 7$; A 5 — $6r = 12$; D 6 — $r = 2$
   Check: $-12 - 5 = 7 - 24$

6. $\frac{1}{3}p + 7 = 12 - \frac{2}{3}p$
   Original equation: $\frac{1}{3}p + 7 = 12 - \frac{2}{3}p$
   Operation: A $\frac{2}{3}p$ — $p + 7 = 12$; S 7 — $p = 5$
   Check: $1\frac{2}{3} + 7 = 12 - 3\frac{1}{3}$

STUDY LINK MASTER

✦ *Math Masters,* p. 322

TEACHING MASTER

Solving Equations

Solve the following equations.

1. Original equation

Operation

Check

2. Original equation

Operation

Check

3. Original equation

Operation

Check

4. Original equation

Operation

Check

5. Original equation

Operation

Check

6. Original equation

Operation

Check

✦ *Math Masters,* **p. 109**

3 Options for Individualizing

✦ EXTRA PRACTICE Solving Equations
(*Math Masters,* p. 109)

INDEPENDENT ACTIVITY  **15–30 min** 

On *Math Masters,* page 109, write equations appropriate to the level of your class for students to solve.
Suggestions

▷ $3y - 7 = 4y - 16$ $y = 9$

▷ $18 + 5k = 2k + 24$ $k = 2$

▷ $7n + 40 = 2n + 8 * 8 - 4$ $n = 4$

▷ $\frac{1}{3}b + 15 = 2b - 25$ $b = 24$

▷ $2t + 3 = 4.5 + 1.75t$ $(t = 6)$

▷ $\frac{(e - 12)}{2} = \sqrt{100} + \frac{1}{2}e - 16$ e = any number

6.12 Inequalities

OBJECTIVE **To graph inequalities in one variable on a number line.**

summaries	materials
1 Teaching the Lesson	
Students extend their work with equations to finding the solution sets of inequalities. [Patterns, Functions, and Algebra]	□ *Math Journal 2,* pp. 247 and 248 □ Study Link 6.11 □ *Student Reference Book,* pp. 226 and 304 Per group: □ Teaching Master (*Math Masters,* p. 110) □ 4 each of number cards 1–10 and 1 each of number cards 11–20 (from the Everything Math Deck, if available) ***See* Advance Preparation**
2 Ongoing Learning & Practice	
Students practice adding, subtracting, multiplying, and dividing positive and negative numbers. [Patterns, Functions, and Algebra] Students practice and maintain skills through Math Boxes and Study Link activities.	□ *Math Journal 2,* pp. 249 and 250 □ Study Link Master (*Math Masters,* p. 323)
3 Options for Individualizing	
Enrichment Students graph inequalities. [Patterns, Functions, and Algebra] **Enrichment** Students make their own *Solution Search* cards. [Patterns, Functions, and Algebra] **Extra Practice** Students play *Algebra Election.* [Patterns, Functions, and Algebra]	□ *Student Reference Book,* pp. 276 and 277 □ Teaching Master (*Math Masters,* p. 111) □ Electoral Vote map (*Math Masters,* pp. 102 and 103) □ counters □ six-sided die □ calculator □ *Algebra Election* cards (*Math Journal 2,* Activity Sheets 5 and 6) ***See* Advance Preparation**

Additional Information

Advance Preparation For Part 1, make a copy of *Math Masters,* page 110 for every three or four students. For the optional Extra Practice activity in Part 3, make sure that each group of students has an Electoral Vote map (*Math Masters,* pp. 102 and 103).

Vocabulary • **inequality** • **solution set**

Getting Started

Mental Math and Reflexes

Have students estimate the answers to the following problems by showing "thumbs up" for an answer greater than 1 and "thumbs down" for an answer less than 1. *Suggestions:*

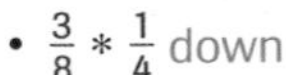

- $\frac{3}{8} * \frac{1}{4}$ down
- $\frac{7}{8} \div \frac{3}{4}$ up
- $5 * \frac{8}{6}$ up
- $6 \div \frac{2}{5}$ up
- $\frac{1}{2} \div \frac{3}{8}$ up
- $\frac{3}{10} \div 4$ down
- $6 \div \frac{3}{5}$ up
- $\frac{1}{2} \div \frac{1}{4}$ up

Math Message

Complete the problems on journal page 247.

Study Link 6.11 Follow-Up

Go over the answers with the class. Ask volunteers to share solution strategies.

1 Teaching the Lesson

✦ Math Message Follow-Up
(*Math Journal 2,* p. 247)

WHOLE-CLASS DISCUSSION 

These problems serve as a reminder of some of the ideas covered in Lesson 6.7, which are extended in this lesson. Ask a few students to share their answers to Problem 4. Their responses indicate whether students can extend the concept of open sentences to include **inequalities.**

STUDENT PAGE

Introduction to Inequalities

1. Translate each inequality into an English sentence.
   a. $15 \neq 3 * 7$ *15 is not equal to 3 times 7.*
   b. $(9 / 9) + 13 \le 14$ 13 more than 9 divided by 9 is less than or equal to 14.
   c. $7 > 1 * \frac{2}{3}$ 7 is greater than 1 times $\frac{2}{3}$.
   d. $23 < 6 * 3$ 23 is less than 6 times 3.
   e. $20 \ge 5^2$ 20 is greater than or equal to 5 squared.
2. Are all of the inequalities in Problem 1 true? no
   If not, which are false? Inequalities d. and e. are false.
3. Some of the inequalities below are true, and some are false. Write "true" or "false" after each one.
   a. $5 * 4 < 20$ false
   b. $(7 + 3) * 6 \neq 60$ false
   c. $54 / 9 > 7$ false
   d. $9 - (3 * 2) < 10$ true
   e. $45 \ge 9 * 5$ true
   f. $3 \le -1 + 6$ true
   g. $15 \le 12 + 2$ false
   h. $17 - 6 \ge 9$ true
4. a. Write an inequality that is neither true nor false.
   Sample answer: $x + 3 < 6$
   b. Explain how you can change it into an inequality that is true.
   Sample answer: Let $x = 2$. Then the inequality $2 + 3 < 6$ is true.

✧ *Math Journal 2,* p. 247

✦ Introducing Solution Sets to Inequalities

(*Student Reference Book,* p. 226)

WHOLE-CLASS DISCUSSION 

Read page 226 in the *Student Reference Book* as a class and discuss the examples. The following points should be part of the discussion:

▷ While most equations that students have solved so far have only one solution, most inequalities have an infinite number of solutions.

▷ The solutions to an inequality comprise its **solution set.**

▷ The solution set of an inequality can be described in words.

▷ The solution set can also be graphed by shading the appropriate parts of a number line.

If an inequality contains the relation symbol $<$, $>$, or $\neq$, the endpoint of the graph is shown with an open circle, indicating that the circled point is *not* part of the solution set. If an inequality contains the relation symbol $\geq$ or $\leq$, the endpoint of the graph is shown with a solid dot, indicating that the circled point *is* part of the solution set.

Ask students to describe and graph the inequality $n \neq 5$. The solution set includes any number less than 5 and any number greater than 5. Five is the only number *not* in the solution set. Therefore, the graph at 5 is an open circle. The rest of the number line, on each side of 5, should be shaded.

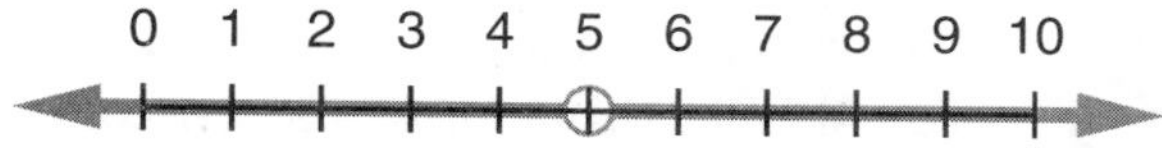

Before assigning independent journal practice, ask students to solve the Check Your Understanding problems at the bottom of the *Student Reference Book* page.

✦ Solving Inequalities (*Math Journal 2,* p. 248)

PARTNER ACTIVITY

Circulate and assist as students complete the problems on the journal page. The problems should present little difficulty for most students.

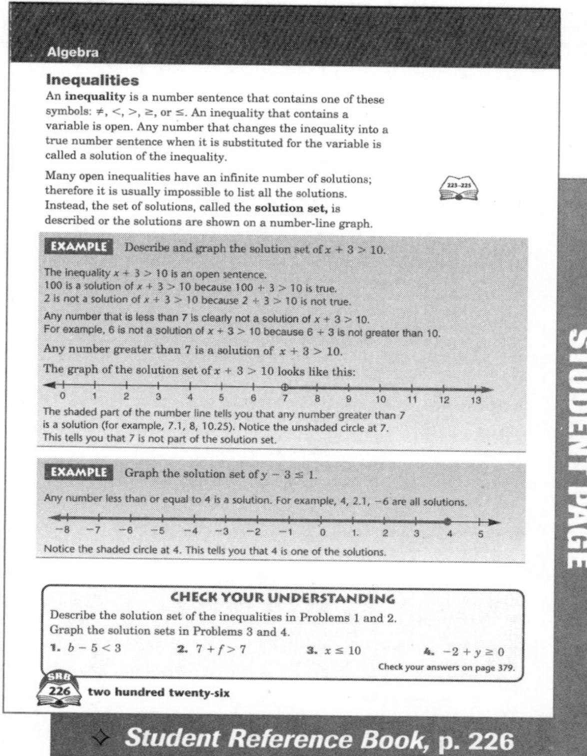

Algebra

Inequalities

An **inequality** is a number sentence that contains one of these symbols: $\neq$, $<$, $>$, $\geq$, or $\leq$. An inequality that contains a variable is open. Any number that changes the inequality into a true number sentence when it is substituted for the variable is called a solution of the inequality.

Many open inequalities have an infinite number of solutions; therefore it is usually impossible to list all the solutions. Instead, the set of solutions, called the **solution set,** is described or the solutions are shown on a number-line graph.

223–225

EXAMPLE Describe and graph the solution set of $x + 3 > 10$.

The inequality $x + 3 > 10$ is an open sentence.
100 is a solution of $x + 3 > 10$ because $100 + 3 > 10$ is true.
2 is not a solution of $x + 3 > 10$ because $2 + 3 > 10$ is not true.

Any number that is less than 7 is clearly not a solution of $x + 3 > 10$.
For example, 6 is not a solution of $x + 3 > 10$ because $6 + 3$ is not greater than 10.

Any number greater than 7 is a solution of $x + 3 > 10$.

The graph of the solution set of $x + 3 > 10$ looks like this:

0 1 2 3 4 5 6 7 8 9 10 11 12 13

The shaded part of the number line tells you that any number greater than 7 is a solution (for example, 7.1, 8, 10.25). Notice the unshaded circle at 7. This tells you that 7 is not part of the solution set.

EXAMPLE Graph the solution set of $y - 3 \leq 1$.

Any number less than or equal to 4 is a solution. For example, 4, 2.1, −6 are all solutions.

−8 −7 −6 −5 −4 −3 −2 −1 0 1. 2 3 4 5

Notice the shaded circle at 4. This tells you that 4 is one of the solutions.

CHECK YOUR UNDERSTANDING

Describe the solution set of the inequalities in Problems 1 and 2. Graph the solution sets in Problems 3 and 4.

1. $b - 5 < 3$ **2.** $7 + f > 7$ **3.** $x \leq 10$ **4.** $-2 + y \geq 0$

Check your answers on page 379.

SRB 226 two hundred twenty-six

STUDENT PAGE

✧ Student Reference Book, p. 226

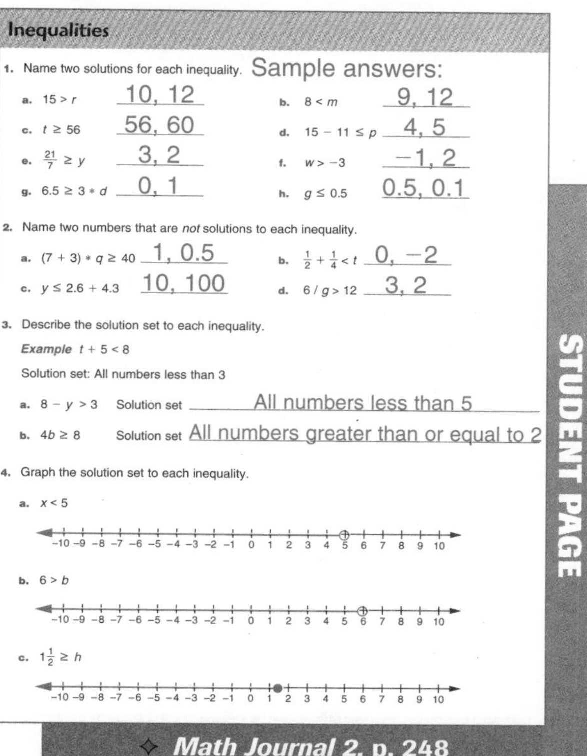

Inequalities

1. Name two solutions for each inequality. Sample answers:

a. $15 > r$ 10, 12 b. $8 < m$ 9, 12
c. $t \geq 56$ 56, 60 d. $15 - 11 \leq p$ 4, 5
e. $\frac{21}{7} \geq y$ 3, 2 f. $w > -3$ −1, 2
g. $6.5 \geq 3 * d$ 0, 1 h. $g \leq 0.5$ 0.5, 0.1

2. Name two numbers that are *not* solutions to each inequality.

a. $(7 + 3) * q \geq 40$ 1, 0.5 b. $\frac{1}{2} + \frac{1}{4} < t$ 0, −2
c. $y \leq 2.6 + 4.3$ 10, 100 d. $6 / g > 12$ 3, 2

3. Describe the solution set to each inequality.

Example $t + 5 < 8$

Solution set: All numbers less than 3

a. $8 - y > 3$ Solution set All numbers less than 5
b. $4b \geq 8$ Solution set All numbers greater than or equal to 2

4. Graph the solution set to each inequality.

a. $x < 5$

−10 −9 −8 −7 −6 −5 −4 −3 −2 −1 0 1 2 3 4 5 6 7 8 9 10

b. $6 > b$

−10 −9 −8 −7 −6 −5 −4 −3 −2 −1 0 1 2 3 4 5 6 7 8 9 10

c. $1\frac{1}{2} \geq h$

−10 −9 −8 −7 −6 −5 −4 −3 −2 −1 0 1 2 3 4 5 6 7 8 9 10

STUDENT PAGE

✧ Math Journal 2, p. 248

STUDENT PAGE

Games

Solution Search

Materials □ 1 set of *Solution Search* cards (*Math Masters,* p. 110)
□ 1 complete deck of number cards

Players 3 or 4

Object of the game To discard all cards first.

Directions

1. Shuffle the *Solution Search* cards and place them facedown in the center of the playing surface.
2. Shuffle the deck of playing cards and deal eight cards to each player. Place the remainder of the deck facedown in the center of the playing surface.
3. Player 1 begins the first round by turning over the top *Solution Search* card. For example, Player 1 may turn over $x > 9$. Player 1 then does one of the following:
   - Discards a card that is a solution to the inequality.
   - If Player 1 does not have a card that is a solution, he or she must continue to draw from the deck of number cards until a possible solution is drawn. Player 1 then discards this card.
4. Play continues in a clockwise direction. Each player must discard a solution card. The round is over when each player has had a turn.
5. Player 2 starts the next round by turning over the top *Solution Search* card. The round proceeds as above.
6. When a player completes a round, the player on his or her left starts the next round by turning over the top *Solution Search* card. The round proceeds as above.
7. When no more *Solution Search* cards remain, turn the pile facedown and, without shuffling, take the top *Solution Search* card.
8. The winner is the first player to discard all of his or her cards.

Variation: 2s and 7s are special cards: 2s are WILD. A player may choose to play a 2 card with its given value of 2, or a player may assign any value he or she wishes to the 2 card. The value of the 7 card is always 7. However, if a player plays the 7 card, the next player loses his or her turn.

three hundred four

Student Reference Book, p. 304

TEACHING MASTER

Solution Search Cards

$q * 2 > 20$	$m < 3.5$	$y^2 < 5$	$x > 9$
$b < 6$	$5 \neq s$	$100 / k > 25$	$(9 * z) + 2 > 65$
$49 \leq p^2$	$r / 2 \geq 5$	$w - 3 < 2$	$-2 + a \geq 5$
$\sqrt{25} \leq t$	$10 < 50 / d$	$c * 7 \leq 14$	$81 > f^2$

Math Masters, p. 110

✦Playing *Solution Search* (*Student Reference Book,* p. 304; *Math Masters,* p. 110)

SMALL-GROUP ACTIVITY

Go over the directions for *Solution Search.* You might want to play a few rounds of the game with three students while the rest of the class observes. Use this opportunity to answer any questions regarding rules of play. Then students should play *Solution Search* in groups of three or four. Circulate and assist as needed.

2 Ongoing Learning & Practice

✦Computing with Positive and Negative Numbers (*Math Journal 2,* p. 249)

INDEPENDENT ACTIVITY 

Students calculate with positive and negative numbers. This journal page can serve as a before-the-end-of-unit review assessment.

✦Math Boxes 6.12 (*Math Journal 2,* p. 250)

INDEPENDENT ACTIVITY 

Mixed Review Math Boxes in this lesson are paired with Math Boxes in Lesson 6.10. The skill in Problem 1 is a prerequisite for Unit 7.

✦Study Link 6.12 (*Math Masters,* p. 323)

Home Connection Students review some of the major concepts from this unit in preparation for the end-of-unit assessment.

3 Options for Individualizing

✦ ENRICHMENT Graphing Inequalities
(*Math Masters,* p. 111)

INDEPENDENT ACTIVITY  **15–30 min** 

These problems are challenging. For Problem 4, expect that many students will graph all numbers equal to or greater than 3, neglecting all numbers less than or equal to -3. Remind them that $(-3) * (-3) = 9$. For Problems 5–7, there are many possible inequalities. Watch for students who do not use the proper relation symbol.

Portfolio Ideas

NOTE: The reproduction of *Math Masters,* page 111 with answers appears on page 522.

✦ ENRICHMENT Playing *Solution Search* with Student-Created Cards

SMALL-GROUP ACTIVITY **15–30 min** 

Encourage students to create their own sets of *Solution Search* cards to be used in place of the ones provided.

Operations with Positive and Negative Numbers

1. $17 - (-17) =$ 34
2. $-24 + 50 =$ 26
3. $-43 - (-21) =$ -22
4. $34 + (-75) =$ -41
5. a. Is the answer to Problem 2 positive or negative? positive
   b. Why? Sample answer: Imagine you are standing at -24 on a number line. Since you're adding, face right. You're adding positive 50, so move forward 50 paces. You'll move 24 spaces to get to zero, and then you'll go another 26 spaces. You will end up at positive 26.
6. $20 * (-8) =$ -160
7. $-6 * (-15) =$ 90
8. $48 \div (-6) =$ -8
9. $-81 \div (-9) =$ 9
10. $-35 \div (-7) =$ 5
11. $-7 * 50 =$ -350
12. a. Is the answer to Problem 7 positive or negative? positive
    b. Why? Sample answer: Multiplying two negative numbers results in a positive product.

Use order of operations to solve the problems below.

13. $-5 * 3 + 24 - 4 * 8 =$ -23
14. $23 + 15 * 2 - (-6)^2 =$ 17

STUDENT PAGE

✦ *Math Journal 2,* p. 249

Math Boxes 6.12

MATH

1. Multiply. Write your answer in simplest form.
   a. $\frac{7}{9} * \frac{2}{3} = \frac{14}{27}$
   b. $\frac{5}{6} * \frac{4}{10} = \frac{1}{3}$
   c. $\frac{4}{7} = \frac{4}{5} * \frac{5}{7}$
   d. $\frac{8}{9} = \frac{4}{3} * \frac{10}{15}$
   e. $\frac{14}{27} = \frac{8}{12} * \frac{7}{9}$
2. Write > or < to make each sentence true.
   a. $\frac{5}{9} < \frac{6}{10}$
   b. $\frac{7}{12} > \frac{8}{15}$
   c. $\frac{15}{8} > 1\frac{6}{7}$
   d. $\frac{11}{12} > \frac{8}{9}$
   e. $\frac{4}{7} > \frac{5}{9}$
3. Multiply.
   a. $42.6 * 38.15$ = 1,625.19
   b. $12.7 * 60.3$ = 765.81
   c. $80.2 * 4.3$ = 344.86
4. Give this mystery graph a title, label the axes, and describe a situation it might represent.
   Answers vary.
5. Complete.
   a. 80% of 50 = 40
   b. 10% of 83 = 8.3
   c. 25% of 48 = 12
   d. 35% of 100 = 35
   e. 50% of 72 = 36

STUDENT PAGE

✦ *Math Journal 2,* p. 250

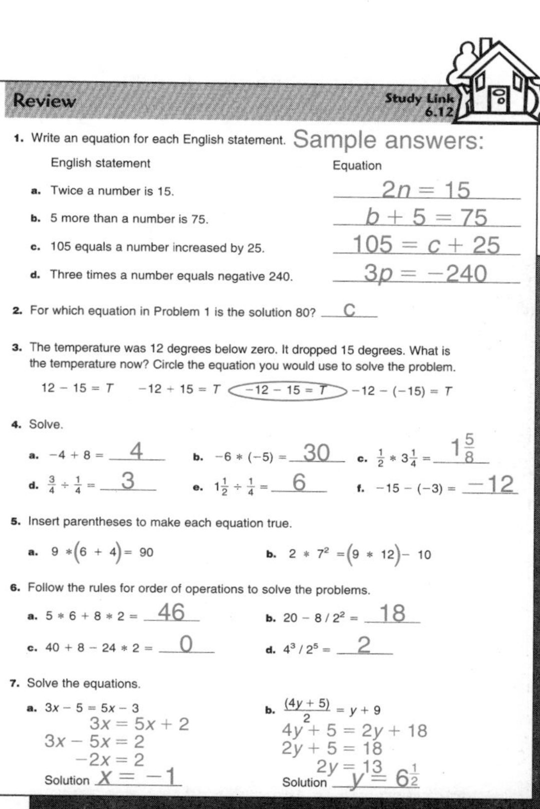

Review Study Link 6.12

1. Write an equation for each English statement. Sample answers:

English statement	Equation
a. Twice a number is 15.	$2n = 15$
b. 5 more than a number is 75.	$b + 5 = 75$
c. 105 equals a number increased by 25.	$105 = c + 25$
d. Three times a number equals negative 240.	$3p = -240$

2. For which equation in Problem 1 is the solution 80? c
3. The temperature was 12 degrees below zero. It dropped 15 degrees. What is the temperature now? Circle the equation you would use to solve the problem.
   $12 - 15 = T$ $\quad -12 + 15 = T \quad$ ($-12 - 15 = T$ circled) $\quad -12 - (-15) = T$
4. Solve.
   a. $-4 + 8 =$ 4
   b. $-6 * (-5) =$ 30
   c. $\frac{1}{2} * 3\frac{1}{4} =$ $1\frac{5}{8}$
   d. $\frac{3}{4} \div \frac{1}{4} =$ 3
   e. $1\frac{1}{2} \div \frac{1}{4} =$ 6
   f. $-15 - (-3) =$ -12
5. Insert parentheses to make each equation true.
   a. $9 * (6 + 4) = 90$
   b. $2 * 7^2 = (9 * 12) - 10$
6. Follow the rules for order of operations to solve the problems.
   a. $5 * 6 + 8 * 2 =$ 46
   b. $20 - 8 / 2^2 =$ 18
   c. $40 + 8 - 24 * 2 =$ 0
   d. $4^3 / 2^5 =$ 2
7. Solve the equations.
   a. $3x - 5 = 5x - 3$
      $3x = 5x + 2$
      $3x - 5x = 2$
      $-2x = 2$
      Solution $x = -1$
   b. $\frac{(4y + 5)}{2} = y + 9$
      $4y + 5 = 2y + 18$
      $2y + 5 = 18$
      $2y = 13$
      Solution $y = 6\frac{1}{2}$

STUDY LINK MASTER

✦ *Math Masters,* p. 323

Graphing Inequalities

Graph all solutions of each inequality.

1. $8 > x \geq -1$
   (*Hint:* "$8 > x \geq -1$" means "$8 > x$" and "$x \geq -1$." In order for a number to be a solution, it must make both number sentences true.)
2. $3 < y + 2 \leq 7$
3. $m \neq -2$
4. $x^2 \geq 9$

Write an inequality for each graph.

5. $5 \geq x \geq -8$
6. $-1 > x \geq -7$
7. $x \neq 1$

TEACHING MASTER

◆ *Math Masters,* p. 111

◆ EXTRA PRACTICE Playing *Algebra Election*

(*Algebra Election* cards; *Math Masters,* pp. 102 and 103; *Student Reference Book,* pp. 276 and 277)

SMALL-GROUP ACTIVITY **15–30 min**

Social Studies Link Students practice solving equations and inequalities by playing *Algebra Election,* which was introduced in Lesson 6.7.

Algebra Election Cards, Set 1

- Find: x squared; x to the fourth power; 1/x
- Find n. (*Hint:* n could be a negative number.) $1000 + n = x$; $1000 + n = -x$
- Complete. $x * 10^6 =$ ___ million; $x * 10^9 =$ ___ billion; $x * 10^{12} =$ ___ ___
- What is the value of n? $-20 + x = n$; $-100 + (-x) = n$
- Insert parentheses in $10 * x - 10$ so that its value is greater than 0 and less than 100.
- Find n. (*Hint:* n could be a negative number.) $n + 10 = x$; $n - 10 = x$
- What is the value of n? $n = ((5 * x) - 4) / 2$
- What is the value of n? $20 + (-x) = n$; $-20 - (-x) = n$
- $T = B - (2 * \frac{H}{1000})$. If $B = 80$ and $H = 100x$, what does T equal?
- Find n. $n = (2 * x) / 10$; $n + 1 = (2 * x)$
- Suppose you earn x dollars per hour. Complete the table.

Time	Earnings
1 hr	$
2 hr	$
4 hr	$
10 hr	$

- Which is greater: x^2 or 10^3? x^3 or 10^4?
- Tell whether each is true or false. $10 * x > 100$; $\frac{1}{2} * x * 100 < 10^3$; $x^3 * 1000 > 4 * 10^4$
- Which number is this? $x * 10^2$? $x * 10^5$?
- A boulder dropped off a cliff falls approximately $16 * x^2$ feet in x seconds. How many feet is that?
- Which is less: $\frac{x^3}{10}$ or $(x + 10)^2$? $10 * x^2$ or $(x + 10)^3$?

STUDENT PAGE

◆ *Math Journal 2,* Activity Sheet 5

Algebra Election Cards, Set 2

- What is n? $5 + 2 * x = n + x$
- Tell which is correct for each: <, =, or >. $x <=> 30 - x$; $x <=> 20 - x$; $x <=> 10 - x$
- Is point (x,x) to the left of, to the right of, or on the line through points A and B? [B (30, 60), A (30, 0)]
- Is 1/x greater than, less than, or equal to $\frac{1}{10}$?
- [$x + \triangle$ balances 200 oz] 1 △ weighs ___ ounces.
- Name a number n such that $x - n$ is a negative number greater than −10.
- What is the value of n? $10 + (-x) = n$; $-10 - (-x) = n$
- Subtract. $x - 100 = ?$; $x - (-100) = ?$
- Insert parentheses so that the equation is true. $10 * x + 4 = 10 * x + 40$
- Suppose you have 10 [+] markers and $2 * x$ [−] markers. What is your balance?
- What is the median of 4, 8, 12, 13, and x?
- Add. $-25 + x = ?$; $x + 3 - 10 = ?$
- Is point (x,x) above, below, or on the line through points A and B? [A (0, 30), B (60, 30)]
- Suppose you have x [+] markers and 40 [−] markers. What is your balance?
- If $(2 * x) + n = 100$, what is the value of n?
- Suppose you travel x miles per hour. Complete the table.

Time	Distance
1 hr	
2 hr	
4 hr	
10 hr	

STUDENT PAGE

◆ *Math Journal 2,* Activity Sheet 6

6.13 Unit 6 Review and Assessment

OBJECTIVE **To review and assess students' progress on the material covered in Unit 6.**

1 Assess Progress

learning goals	activities
6a **Beginning Goal** Solve and graph solutions for inequalities. **(Lesson 6.12)**	❑ Written Assessment, Problems 53–55
6b **Developing Goal** Solve equations. **(Lessons 6.8–6.11)**	❑ Slate Assessment, Problem 4 ❑ Written Assessment, Problems 39–52
6c **Developing Goal** Use an algorithm to add, subtract, multiply, and divide fractions and mixed numbers. **(Lessons 6.1 and 6.2)**	❑ Slate Assessment, Problem 2 ❑ Written Assessment, Problems 1, 8, 9, and 20–29
6d **Developing/Secure Goal** Find opposites and reciprocals of numbers. **(Lessons 6.1 and 6.2)**	❑ Slate Assessment, Problem 1 ❑ Written Assessment, Problems 18, 19, and 23
6e **Developing/Secure Goal** Add, subtract, multiply, and divide positive and negative numbers. **(Lessons 6.3 and 6.4)**	❑ Oral Assessment, Problem 1 ❑ Written Assessment, Problems 2–7, 10–19, 25, and 33
6f **Developing/Secure Goal** Perform operations in the correct order. **(Lessons 6.6 and 6.8)**	❑ Written Assessment, Problems 1 and 31–38
6g **Developing/Secure Goal** Identify number sentences as true or false. **(Lesson 6.7)**	❑ Written Assessment, Problem 1
6h **Secure Goal** Compare and order positive and negative numbers. **(Lesson 6.3)**	❑ Written Assessment, Problems 2–7
6i **Secure Goal** Understand and apply the identity property for multiplication. **(Lessons 6.4 and 6.5)**	❑ Written Assessment, Problem 1
6j **Secure Goal** Understand and apply the commutative property for addition and multiplication. **(Lessons 6.1 and 6.3)**	❑ Written Assessment, Problem 1
6k **Secure Goal** Understand and apply the associative property for addition and multiplication. **(Lessons 6.3–6.5)**	❑ Written Assessment, Problems 1 and 30

materials

- ☐ *Math Journal 2,* p. 251
- ☐ Study Link 6.12
- ☐ *Student Reference Book*
- ☐ Teaching Masters (*Math Masters,* pp. 100 and 107)
- ☐ Assessment Masters (*Math Masters,* pp. 403–405)

2 Build Background for Unit 7

summaries	materials
Students practice and maintain skills through Math Boxes and Study Link activities.	☐ *Math Journal 2,* p. 252 ☐ Study Link Masters (*Math Masters,* pp. 324–327)

Each **learning goal** listed above indicates a level of performance that might be expected at this point in the *Everyday Mathematics* K–6 curriculum. For a variety of reasons, the levels indicated may not accurately portray your class's performance.

Additional Information

For additional information on assessment for Unit 6, see the *Assessment Handbook,* pages 54–57. For assessment checklists, see *Math Masters,* pages 444, 445, and 468–470.

Getting Started

Math Message

Complete the Time to Reflect *questions on journal page 251.*

Study Link 6.12 Follow-Up

Briefly review answers.

Time to Reflect

1. In this unit, you have been studying algebra concepts and practicing algebra skills. How would you explain to someone what algebra is?
Look for students to include the idea that algebra is a way to express and work with relationships expressed in general terms. (See pages 220 and 221 in the *Student Reference Book.*)

2. Explain why 3 + *x* is not a number sentence but 15 > 9 is a number sentence.
Students' answers should indicate that they understand that a number sentence must include a relation symbol: >, <, =, ≠, ≥, or ≤.

3. Why do you think patterns were used to introduce the rules for multiplying and dividing signed numbers?
Using patterns allows students to focus on the single element that is changing; in this case, students see how the introduction of a negative term affects the product. Using patterns also establishes a basis for the continuation of a pattern so that students can find a rule for getting an answer.

4. Which properties of numbers and number systems did you learn about in this unit?
Multiplication Property of −1; Reciprocal Property; Division of Fractions Property; Commutative Properties (turn-around rules) of Addition and Multiplication; Associative Properties of Addition and Multiplication; Distributive Property of Multiplication over Addition

STUDENT PAGE

✧ *Math Journal 2,* p. 251

NOTE: Some of these assessment suggestions relate to learning goals that have been addressed in previous units. Now is a good time to evaluate students' progress toward those goals.

1 Assess Progress

✦ Math Message Follow-Up (*Math Journal 2,* p. 251)

WHOLE-CLASS DISCUSSION 

Students share their answers. Questions 1–4 provide students with an opportunity to assess their own progress on algebraic concepts and number properties covered in Unit 6.

✦ Oral and Slate Assessments

WHOLE-CLASS ACTIVITY

If the suggested problems below are not appropriate for your class's level of performance, adjust the numbers or the problems themselves to better assess your students' abilities.

Oral Assessment Suggestions

1. Students show thumbs up if the sum or difference is greater than 1 and thumbs down if it is less than 1. **Goal 6c** *Suggestions:*
   - $\frac{3}{4} + \frac{1}{8}$ down
   - $\frac{2}{3} + \frac{4}{5}$ up
   - $1\frac{2}{5} - \frac{8}{10}$ down
   - $1\frac{1}{4} - \frac{3}{16}$ up
   - $\frac{3}{8} + \frac{2}{5}$ down
   - $1\frac{3}{6} - \frac{1}{8}$ up
2. Students use their arms to model various types of angles. *Suggestions:* acute, obtuse, right, reflex, straight, adjacent, supplementary, vertical.
3. Students show thumbs up if the fractions are equivalent and thumbs down if the fractions are not equivalent. *Suggestions:*
   - $\frac{2}{3}$ and $\frac{10}{15}$ up
   - $\frac{3}{4}$ and $\frac{5}{12}$ down
   - $\frac{7}{8}$ and $\frac{7}{12}$ down
   - $\frac{9}{12}$ and $\frac{6}{8}$ up
   - $\frac{4}{9}$ and $\frac{2}{3}$ down
   - $\frac{12}{16}$ and $\frac{6}{8}$ up

Slate Assessment Suggestions

1. Find reciprocals. (Remind students to think, "The number times which number equals 1?") **Goal 6d**
   Suggestions
   - $\frac{1}{4}$ 4
   - $-\frac{1}{2}$ -2
   - $\frac{2}{3}$ $\frac{3}{2}$
   - 3 $\frac{1}{3}$
   - $1\frac{1}{4}$ $\frac{4}{5}$
   - 0.1 10
2. Multiply fractions. **Goal 6c**
   Suggestions
   - $\frac{1}{3} * \frac{2}{5}$ $\frac{2}{15}$
   - $\frac{3}{8} * \frac{2}{3}$ $\frac{6}{24}$, or $\frac{1}{4}$
   - $\frac{4}{5} * \frac{1}{10}$ $\frac{4}{50}$, or $\frac{2}{25}$
   - $\frac{6}{7} * \frac{1}{2}$ $\frac{6}{14}$, or $\frac{3}{7}$
   - $\frac{3}{4} * \frac{2}{5}$ $\frac{6}{20}$, or $\frac{3}{10}$
   - $\frac{1}{4} * \frac{5}{8}$ $\frac{5}{32}$
3. Solve "percent of" problems. Encourage students to solve the problems mentally. They can use calculators to solve the last three in the second column.
   - 20% of 80 16
   - 75% of 200 150
   - 5% of 40 2
   - 50% of 640 320
   - 10% of 15 1.5
   - $33\frac{1}{3}$% of 120 40
   - 15% of 40 6
   - 29% of 73 21.17
   - 8% of 324 25.92
   - 67.5% of 56 37.8
4. Solve equations. **Goal 6b**
   Suggestions
   - $5 + x = 3$ $x = -2$
   - $27 - y = 53$ $y = -26$
   - $d * 40 = 200$ $d = 5$
   - $p / 15 = 4$ $p = 60$

✦ Written Assessment
(*Math Masters,* pp. 403–405)

INDEPENDENT ACTIVITY 

Depending on the needs of students, you may want to work through an example together, reading a problem aloud, discussing it, and providing additional examples as necessary before students work the problem independently.

Each of the problems is listed below and paired with one or more of this unit's learning goals.

- Tell whether number sentences are true or false. (Problem 1) **Goal 6g**
- Solve equations. (Problems 39–52) **Goal 6b**
- Perform operations in the correct order. (Problems 1 and 31–38) **Goal 6f**

Unit 6 Checking Progress 

1. Circle the number sentences below that are true.

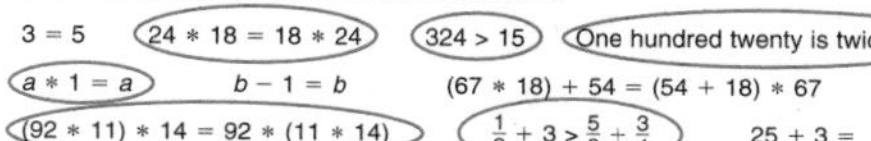

$3 = 5$ $24 * 18 = 18 * 24$ $324 > 15$ One hundred twenty is twice sixty.
$a * 1 = a$ $b - 1 = b$ $(67 * 18) + 54 = (54 + 18) * 67$
$(92 * 11) * 14 = 92 * (11 * 14)$ $\frac{1}{2} + 3 > \frac{5}{2} + \frac{3}{4}$ $25 + 3 =$

Write >, <, or = to complete each number sentence.

2. 54 __>__ -58
3. -25 __>__ -47
4. -16 __<__ $5 + (-20)$
5. $-18 - (-26)$ __=__ $50 + (-42)$
6. $-34 + (-15)$ __<__ $17 - 60$
7. $15 * (-20)$ __<__ $-600 \div (-2)$
8. $\frac{2}{5} + \frac{3}{10}$ __<__ 1
9. $\frac{6}{8} - \frac{4}{12}$ __>__ $\frac{2}{3} - \frac{6}{9}$

Solve.

10. $24 * (-11) =$ __-264__
11. __360__ $= -30 * (-12)$
12. $(13 + 12) * (-6) =$ __-150__
13. __-59__ $= 13 + 12 * (-6)$
14. $-3 * (8 * 5) =$ __-120__
15. __120__ $= (-3 * 8) * (-5)$
16. $28 / (-7) =$ __-4__
17. __29__ $= 25 + (-36) \div (-9)$
18. (OPP)(5) + (OPP)(−24) = __19__
19. __-16__ = (OPP)(OPP)(−8) + (−8)
20. $-\left(\frac{3}{4}\right) - \left(\frac{1}{4}\right) =$ __-1__
21. $\frac{2}{3} \div \frac{1}{3} =$ __2__
22. $3\frac{1}{4} \div 4 =$ __$\frac{13}{16}$__
23. $\frac{3}{4} *$ __$\frac{4}{3}$__ $= 1$
24. $1\frac{1}{4} \div \frac{1}{2} =$ __$2\frac{1}{2}$__
25. $\frac{1}{5} *$ __-5__ $= -1$
26. $6\frac{5}{8} - 3\frac{3}{4} =$ __$2\frac{7}{8}$__
27. __$2\frac{1}{2}$__ $= 1\frac{5}{6} + \frac{2}{3}$
28. $5 \div \frac{2}{3} =$ __$7\frac{1}{2}$__
29. $2\frac{3}{4} * \frac{2}{3} =$ __$1\frac{5}{6}$__
30. Explain how solving Problem 14 can help you solve Problem 15.
    Sample answer: Once you have the answer to Problem 14, all you have to do is look at the number of negative signs in Problem 15 to see that the answer is merely the opposite.

ASSESSMENT MASTER

✦ *Math Masters,* p. 403

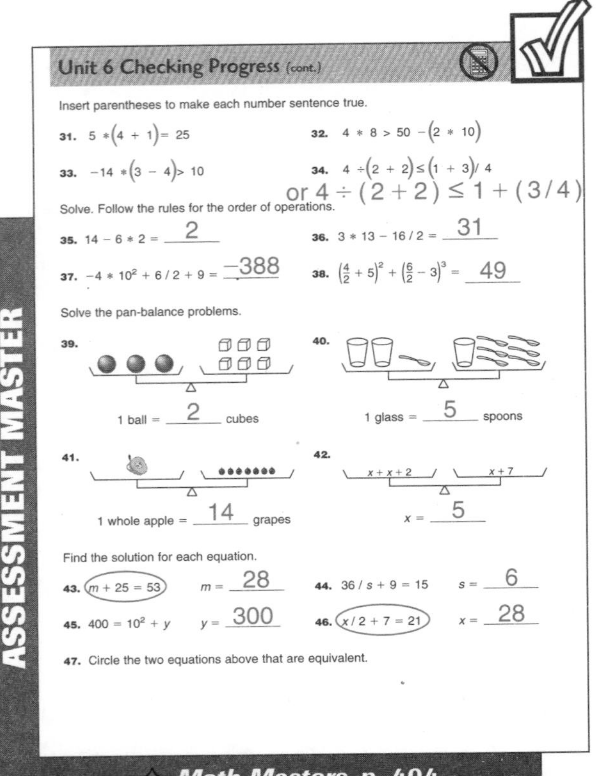
ASSESSMENT MASTER

Unit 6 Checking Progress (cont.)

Insert parentheses to make each number sentence true.

31. $5 * (4 + 1) = 25$

32. $4 * 8 > 50 - (2 * 10)$

33. $-14 * (3 - 4) > 10$

34. $4 \div (2 + 2) \leq (1 + 3) / 4$ or $4 \div (2 + 2) \leq 1 + (3/4)$

Solve. Follow the rules for the order of operations.

35. $14 - 6 * 2 =$ 2

36. $3 * 13 - 16 / 2 =$ 31

37. $-4 * 10^2 + 6 / 2 + 9 =$ −388

38. $(\frac{4}{2} + 5)^2 + (\frac{6}{2} - 3)^3 =$ 49

Solve the pan-balance problems.

39. 1 ball = 2 cubes

40. 1 glass = 5 spoons

41. 1 whole apple = 14 grapes

42. $x + x + 2$ | $x + 7$; $x =$ 5

Find the solution for each equation.

43. $m + 25 = 53$ $m =$ 28

44. $36 / s + 9 = 15$ $s =$ 6

45. $400 = 10^2 + y$ $y =$ 300

46. $x / 2 + 7 = 21$ $x =$ 28

47. Circle the two equations above that are equivalent.

Math Masters, p. 404

- Graph solutions to inequalities. (Problems 53–55) **Goal 6a**
- Add, subtract, multiply, and divide fractions and mixed numbers. (Problems 1, 8, 9, and 20–29) **Goal 6c**
- Find opposites and reciprocals of numbers. (Problems 18, 19, and 23) **Goal 6d**
- Add, subtract, multiply, and divide positive and negative numbers. (Problems 2–7, 10–19, 25, and 33) **Goal 6e**
- Compare and order positive and negative numbers. (Problems 2–7) **Goal 6h**

✦ ALTERNATIVE ASSESSMENT OPTION

Explore Scientific Calculators

(*Math Masters,* p. 100)

INDEPENDENT ACTIVITY 

Use this activity from Part 3 of Lesson 6.6 to assess students' understanding of the order of operations.

✦ ALTERNATIVE ASSESSMENT OPTION

Play *Name That Number*

(*Student Reference Book,* p. 301)

PARTNER ACTIVITY

Use this game from Part 2 of Lesson 6.8 to assess students' ability to write expressions to name target numbers and to assess their understanding of the rules for the order of operations. As students play the game, have them record their final number sentences for each target number on a half-sheet of paper.

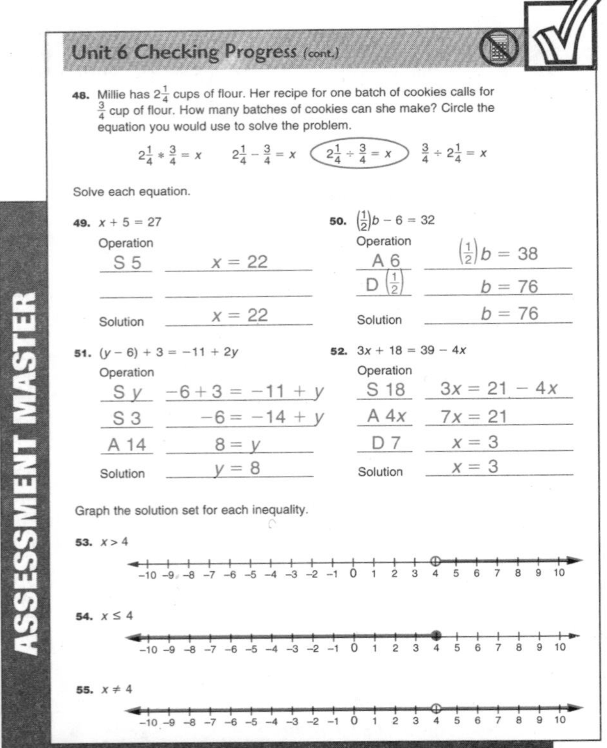
ASSESSMENT MASTER

Unit 6 Checking Progress (cont.)

48. Millie has $2\frac{1}{4}$ cups of flour. Her recipe for one batch of cookies calls for $\frac{3}{4}$ cup of flour. How many batches of cookies can she make? Circle the equation you would use to solve the problem.

$2\frac{1}{4} * \frac{3}{4} = x$ $2\frac{1}{4} - \frac{3}{4} = x$ $2\frac{1}{4} \div \frac{3}{4} = x$ $\frac{3}{4} \div 2\frac{1}{4} = x$

Solve each equation.

49. $x + 5 = 27$

Operation	
S 5	$x = 22$
Solution	$x = 22$

50. $(\frac{1}{2})b - 6 = 32$

Operation	
A 6	$(\frac{1}{2})b = 38$
D $(\frac{1}{2})$	$b = 76$
Solution	$b = 76$

51. $(y - 6) + 3 = -11 + 2y$

Operation	
S y	$-6 + 3 = -11 + y$
S 3	$-6 = -14 + y$
A 14	$8 = y$
Solution	$y = 8$

52. $3x + 18 = 39 - 4x$

Operation	
S 18	$3x = 21 - 4x$
A $4x$	$7x = 21$
D 7	$x = 3$
Solution	$x = 3$

Graph the solution set for each inequality.

53. $x > 4$

54. $x \leq 4$

55. $x \neq 4$

−10 −9 −8 −7 −6 −5 −4 −3 −2 −1 0 1 2 3 4 5 6 7 8 9 10

Math Masters, p. 405

✦ ALTERNATIVE ASSESSMENT OPTION

Solve Pan-Balance Problems

(*Math Masters,* p. 107)

INDEPENDENT ACTIVITY 

Use this master from Part 3 of Lesson 6.9 to assess students' ability to solve equations using the pan-balance model. Make up problems of an appropriate level before making copies. You may want to mix operations and include some two-step problems to assess a wider range of abilities.

2 Build Background for Unit 7

✦ Math Boxes 6.13 (*Math Journal 2,* p. 252)

INDEPENDENT ACTIVITY 

Mixed Review The skills covered in Problems 1–5 are prerequisites for Unit 7.

✦ Study Link 6.13: Unit 7 Family Letter (*Math Masters,* pp. 324–327)

Home Connection This Study Link is a four-page newsletter that introduces parents and guardians to Unit 7's topics and terms. The letter also offers ideas for mathematics activities that are supportive of classroom work and can be done at home.

Math Boxes 6.13

MATH

1. The following table shows the results of rolling a six-sided die 50 times.

Number Showing	1	2	3	4	5	6
Number of Times	10	5	11	12	4	8

Tell whether each sentence below is true or false.

a. On the next roll of the die, a 5 is more likely to come up than a 1. false

b. There is a 50-50 chance of rolling a prime number. true

c. There is a 50-50 chance of rolling a composite number. false

2. Multiply. Write your answer in simplest form.

a. $\frac{6}{8} * \frac{2}{5} = \frac{3}{10}$

b. $\frac{3}{9} * \frac{9}{12} = \frac{1}{4}$

c. $\frac{24}{35} = \frac{4}{7} * \frac{6}{5}$

d. $\frac{24}{47} = \frac{8}{10} * \frac{30}{47}$

e. $\frac{21}{100} = \frac{7}{25} * \frac{75}{100}$

3. Rewrite each fraction as a percent.

a. $\frac{20}{40} = 50\%$

b. $\frac{35}{50} = 70\%$

c. $\frac{18}{24} = 75\%$

d. $\frac{7}{8} = 87\frac{1}{2}\%$

e. $\frac{15}{75} = 20\%$

4. Add.

a. $\frac{3}{8} + 1\frac{3}{4} = 2\frac{1}{8}$

b. $\frac{2}{3} + 5\frac{1}{5} = 5\frac{13}{15}$

c. $\frac{7}{8} + \frac{2}{4} + \frac{1}{3} = 1\frac{17}{24}$

d. $\frac{3}{5} + \frac{3}{8} = \frac{39}{40}$

e. $\frac{2}{9} + 2\frac{1}{3} = 2\frac{5}{9}$

5. Solve.

a. $\frac{4}{7}$ of 56 = 32

b. $\frac{2}{3}$ of 15 = 10

c. $\frac{8}{9}$ of 72 = 64

d. $\frac{3}{8}$ of 32 = 12

e. $\frac{9}{10}$ of 31 = $27\frac{9}{10}$

STUDENT PAGE

✦ Math Journal 2, p. 252

Family Letter

Study Link 6.13

Unit 7: Probability and Discrete Mathematics

All of us are aware that the world is filled with uncertainties. As Ben Franklin wrote, "Nothing is certain except death and taxes!" Of course, there are some things we can be sure of: The sun will rise tomorrow, for example. We also know that there are degrees of uncertainty—some things are more likely to happen than others. There are occurrences that, although uncertain, can be predicted with reasonable accuracy.

While predictions are usually most reliable when they deal with general trends, it is possible and often helpful to predict the outcomes of specific situations. In Unit 7, your child will learn how to simulate a situation with random outcomes and how to determine the likelihood of various outcomes. Additionally, the class will analyze games of chance to determine whether or not they are fair—that is, whether or not all players have the same chance of winning.

We will be looking at two tools for analyzing probability situations—tree diagrams (familiar from single-elimination sports tournaments) and Venn diagrams (circle diagrams that show relationships between overlapping groups).

One lesson concerns strategies for taking multiple-choice tests based on probability. Should test takers guess at answers they don't know? Your child will learn some of the advantages and disadvantages of guessing on this type of test.

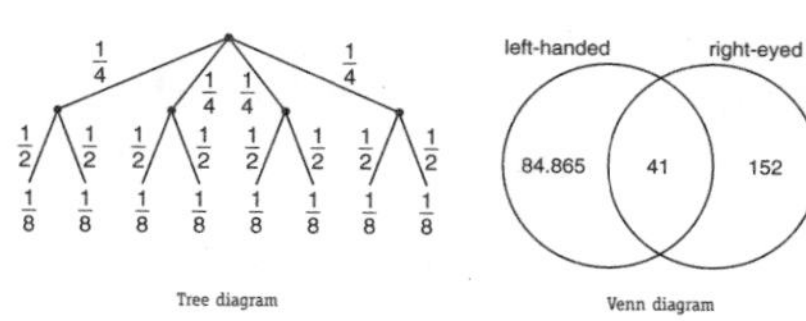

Tree diagram

Venn diagram

Please keep this Family Letter for reference as your child works through Unit 7.

STUDY LINK MASTERS

✦ Math Masters, pp. 324–327

Unit 7 Probability and Discrete Mathematics

overview

This unit begins with a review of the basic concepts and vocabulary associated with chance events. The remainder of the unit deals in a playful manner with a variety of topics, all linked to finding or using probabilities and judging the "fairness" of situations.

Everyday Mathematics not only connects mathematics to the everyday lives of people, but also tries to anticipate mathematics that students may be asked to learn beyond sixth grade. Many activities in this unit come from "discrete mathematics" and involve tools that are used in various occupations. These include "random walk" simulations, which exploit random numbers; tree diagrams, which help to analyze complex events; and Venn diagrams, which can be used to sort out interactions.

Please don't be concerned if these topics are unfamiliar. The topics can be enjoyed by sixth graders and are likely to play a significant role in mathematics education in the future.

contents

UNIT 7

Lesson	Objective	Page
7.1	**The Probability of Equally Likely Outcomes** *To review the basic vocabulary and concepts of probability; and to find probabilities for outcomes when they are equally likely.*	540
7.2	**Generating Random Numbers** *To investigate random numbers; and to use number cards to generate random numbers within a given range.*	546
7.3	**A Random-Number Simulation** *To simulate a situation using random numbers; and to use simulation results to estimate the chance of each possible outcome.*	551
7.4	**Tree Diagrams** *To use tree diagrams to find expected outcomes for chance events; and to compare actual results of a simulation to expected outcomes.*	556
7.5	**Using Tree Diagrams to Calculate Probabilities** *To use tree diagrams to help calculate the probabilities of the outcomes of chance events.*	561
7.6	**Venn Diagrams** *To use Venn diagrams to analyze situations.*	567
7.7	**Fair and Unfair Games** *To analyze games of chance to determine whether or not they are fair games.*	573
7.8	**Strategies for Multiple-Choice Tests** *To investigate the effects of guessing on multiple-choice tests.*	579
7.9	**Unit 7 Review and Assessment** *To review and assess students' progress on the material covered in Unit 7.*	585

learning goals in perspective

	learning goals	links to the past	links to the future
7a	**Beginning Goal** Understand and use probability tree diagrams to solve problems. **(Lessons 7.4, 7.5, and 7.7)**	Grade 3: Find all possible combinations of pants and socks in four colors. Grade 4: Analyze data from a random-outcome game. Grade 5: Use tree diagrams to find all possible ways a sequence of choices can be made.	After Grade 6: Tree diagrams are useful in analyzing and quantifying situations involving choice.
7b	**Developing Goal** Construct and interpret Venn diagrams. **(Lesson 7.6)**	Grade 4: Use a grid to solve logic problems. Grade 5: Solve logic problems.	After Grade 6: Venn diagrams are useful in studying combinations, probability, and logic.
7c	**Developing/Secure Goal** Calculate probability in simple situations. **(Lessons 7.1, 7.3, and 7.4)**	Grade 3: Introduce the vocabulary of chance events. Do probability activities with blocks, dice, coins, spinners: predict results; test predictions; display results. Grade 4: Review basic ideas of probability. Compare predicted and actual results from a random-outcome experiment. Solve probability problems. Grade 5: Perform experiments to estimate the probability of a chance event. Record results on the Probability Meter.	Grade 6: Applications and maintenance. After Grade 6: Probability is a major topic in mathematics.
7d	**Developing/Secure Goal** Understand what constitutes a fair game. **(Lesson 7.7)**	Grades 1-4: Combine individual and partner results from surveys and experiments to generate more reliable estimates; play games that involve the idea of fairness "in the long run." Grade 4: Predict outcomes for games and experiments that are repeated many times. Grade 5: Collect data samples and analyze them to determine whether a game is fair.	After Grade 6: Fairness is an important concept in probability, statistics, and game design.
7e	**Developing/Secure Goal** Understand and apply the concept of random numbers to probability situations. **(Lessons 7.2 and 7.3)**	Grade 4: Review basic ideas of probability. Compare predicted and actual results from a random-outcome experiment. Solve probability problems. Grade 5: Introduce the Probability Meter; perform experiments to estimate the probability of chance events, and record results on the Probability Meter (Unit 2).	After Grade 6: Randomness is an important concept in statistics, product testing, and survey design.
7f	**Secure Goal** Solve "fraction-of-a-fraction" problems. **(Lesson 7.3)**	Grade 4: Solve "fraction-of" and "percent-of" number stories. Grade 5: Use an algorithm to multiply fractions. Grade 6: Use an algorithm to multiply fractions (Unit 6).	Grade 6: Applications and maintenance.
7g	**Secure Goal** Understand how increasing the number of trials affects experimental results. **(Lesson 7.2)**	Grades 1-4: Combine results from surveys and experiments to generate more reliable estimates; play games that involve the idea of fairness "in the long run." Grade 4: Predict outcomes for games and experiments that are repeated many times. Grade 5: Understand how sample size affects results.	After Grade 6: Sample size is important in statistics, product testing, and survey design.

assessment

ongoing • product • periodic

Informal Assessment

Math Boxes These *Math Journal* pages provide opportunities for cumulative review or assessment of concepts and skills.

Ongoing Assessment: Kid Watching Use the Ongoing Assessment suggestions in the following lessons to make quick, on-the-spot observations about students' understanding of:

- Numeration **(Lesson 7.5, Part 1)**
- Patterns, Functions, and Algebra **(Lesson 7.8, Part 2)**
- Data and Chance **(Lesson 7.1, Part 1; Lesson 7.2, Part 1; Lesson 7.3, Part 1; Lesson 7.4, Part 1; Lesson 7.5, Part 1; Lesson 7.6, Part 1)**

Portfolio Ideas Samples of students' work may be obtained from the following assignments:

- Playing Carnival Games **(Lesson 7.1)**
- Running an Amazing Contest **(Lesson 7.4)**
- Improving Scores on Multiple-Choice Tests **(Lesson 7.8)**
- Make a Fair Game **(Lesson 7.9)**
- Make Venn Diagrams from Internet Searches **(Lesson 7.9)**

Unit 7 Review and Assessment

Math Message Use Time to Reflect questions 2 and 3 in Lesson 7.9 to assess students' progress toward the following learning goals: **Goals 7a and 7d**

Oral and Slate Assessments Use oral or slate assessments during Lesson 7.9 to assess students' progress toward the following learning goal: **Goal 7f**

Written Assessment Use a written review during Lesson 7.9 to assess students' progress toward the following learning goals: **Goals 7a–7g**

Alternative Assessment Options Use small-group and partner alternative assessments in Lesson 7.9 to assess students' progress toward the following learning goals: **Goals 7b, 7d, and 7g**

assessmenthandbook

For more information on how to use different types of assessment in Unit 7.9, see the Assessment Overview on pages 58–60 in the *Assessment Handbook.* The following Assessment Masters can be found in the *Math Masters* book:

- Unit 7 Checking Progress, pp. 406–409
- Unit 7 Individual Profile of Progress, p. 447
- Unit 7 Class Checklist, p. 446
- Class Progress Indicator, p. 470
- Math Logs, pp. 473 and 474
- Self-Assessment Forms, pp. 476 and 477
- Interest Inventories, pp. 471 and 472

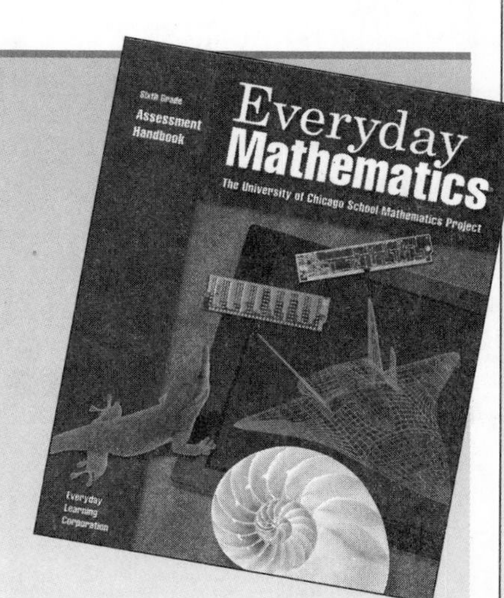

problem solving

A process of modeling everyday situations using tools from mathematics

Encourage students to use a variety of strategies when attacking a given problem—and to explain those strategies. *Strategies students might use in this unit:*

- Use a picture
- Act out the problem
- Make a table
- Use computation
- Make a (tree, Venn) diagram
- Write a number sentence

Four Problem-Solving **REPRESENTATIONS**

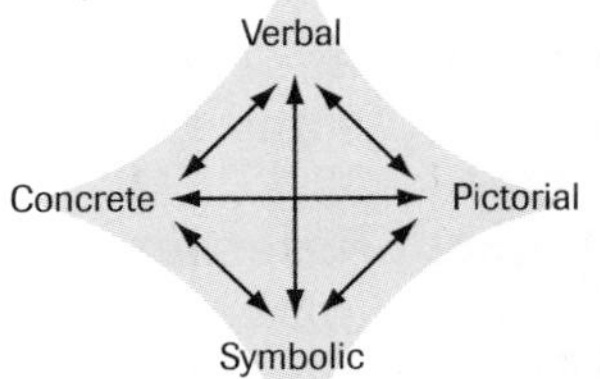

Lessons that teach *through* problem solving, not just *about* problem solving

Lesson	Activity	Lesson	Activity
7.1, 7.3	Find the probability of specific outcomes involving dominoes and dice.	7.5	Solve probability problems about random draws of clothing and letters.
7.2	Use number cards to generate random numbers; decide if situations involve randomness.	7.6	Solve problems involving relationships between different groups.
7.2, 7.7	Solve pan-balance problems and number stories with variables.	7.7	Determine the fairness of a game and revise a game to make it fair.
7.3	Simulate a "best-of-five" tournament by using random numbers.	7.8	Determine when guessing is an advantage or disadvantage on multiple-choice tests.
7.4	Find expected outcomes for random-walk (maze) problems and compare them with simulated results.		

For more information about problem solving in *Everyday Mathematics,* see the *Teacher's Reference Manual.*

cross-curricular links

consumer education

- Students experiment with a maze contest to explore the balance between the entry fee, prize, and profits. **(Lesson 7.4)**
- Students make Venn diagrams from Internet searches. **(Lesson 7.6)**

science

- Students study biological data presented in tables and Venn diagrams. **(Lesson 7.6)**
- Students examine the results of guessing on multiple-choice science questions. **(Lesson 7.8)**

social studies

- Students examine the results of guessing on multiple-choice social studies questions. **(Lesson 7.8)**

literature

- Students read short stories and try activities from *Do You Wanna Bet?* that illustrate probability in everyday situations. **(Lesson 7.1)**

language arts

- Students study the language of questions in sample standardized tests and discuss the effects of changing different key words. **(Lesson 7.8)**

meeting INDIVIDUAL needs

UNIVERSAL ACCESS

✦ RETEACHING

The following features provide additional instructional support:

Adjusting the Activity

- **Lesson 7.1, Part 1**
- **Lesson 7.3, Part 1**
- **Lesson 7.4, Part 1**
- **Lesson 7.5, Part 1**

Options for Individualizing

- **Lesson 7.2** Predicting Which Blocks Are in a Bag

✦ ENRICHMENT

The following features suggest enrichment and extension activities:

Adjusting the Activity

- **Lesson 7.1, Part 3**
- **Lesson 7.5, Part 3**
- **Lesson 7.7, Part 1 and Part 3**
- **Lesson 7.8, Part 1**

Options for Individualizing

- **Lesson 7.1** Playing Carnival Games; Reading a Book about Probability
- **Lesson 7.2** Examining a Table of Random Digits
- **Lesson 7.4** Running an Amazing Contest
- **Lesson 7.6** Relating Tables and Venn Diagrams; Making Venn Diagrams from Internet Searches
- **Lesson 7.7** Investigating a Coin-Flipping Problem

✦ LANGUAGE DIVERSITY

The following feature suggests ways to support students who are acquiring proficiency in English:

Options for Individualizing

- **Lesson 7.8** Studying the Language of Questions

✦ MULTIAGE CLASSROOM

The following chart lists related lessons from Grade 5 that can help you meet your instructional needs:

Grade 5	12.1			12.2				
Grade 6	7.1	7.2	7.3	7.4	7.5	7.6	7.7	7.8

materials

lesson	math masters pages	manipulative kit items	other items
7.1	Study Link Master, p. 328 Teaching Masters, pp. 112, 113, and 486 *See* **Advance Preparation, p. 540**	Per partnership: 2 six-sided dice	Geometry Template *Do You Wanna Bet?* Per partnership: 1 coin *See* **Advance Preparation, p. 540**
7.2	Study Link Master, p. 329 transparency of Teaching Master, p. 114 (optional) Teaching Masters, pp. 115 and 116 Assessment Master, p. 478 (optional)	Per partnership: number cards 1–5 (from the Everything Math Deck, if available) *See* **Advance Preparation, p. 546**	calculator Per group: brown paper bag (size of a lunch bag) 5 blocks in each of 3 colors (15 total)
7.3	Study Link Master, p. 330 Teaching Master, p. 117 *See* **Advance Preparation, p. 551**	2 six-sided dice (optional)	Per partnership: 1 coin
7.4	Study Link Master, p. 331 transparencies of Teaching Masters, pp. 118 (optional) and 119 Teaching Masters, pp. 67–78, 120, and 121 Assessment Master, p. 478 (optional)	Per partnership: number cards 1–4 (from the Everything Math Deck, if available) 4 each of number cards 0–10 (from the Everything Math Deck, if available)	penny or other counter calculator
7.5	Study Link Master, p. 332 transparency of Teaching Master, p. 118 (optional) Teaching Master, p. 122 Assessment Master, p. 473 (optional)		Geometry Template straightedge and protractor, if Geometry Template is not available Per partnership: 1 coin (optional)
7.6	Study Link Master, p. 333 transparency of Teaching Master, p. 123 (optional) Teaching Master, p. 124 Assessment Master, p. 478 (optional)		*See* **Advance Preparation, p. 567**
7.7	Study Link Master, p. 334 Teaching Masters, pp. 125 and 126	Per group: number cards 1 (or ace), 3, 6, and 10 (from the Everything Math Deck, if available)	3 black and 2 white counters small paper bag 2 or 3 small objects, such as a paperweight, tissue box, small book, and so on ruler; scale (bathroom and postal) *See* **Advance Preparation, p. 573**
7.8	Study Link Master, p. 335 Teaching Masters, pp. 127 and 128	number cards (from the Everything Math Deck, if available)	
7.9	Study Link Masters, pp. 336–339 Teaching Masters, pp. 115 and 125 Assessment Masters, pp. 406–409 and 478		

planningtips

Pacing

Pacing depends on a number of factors, such as students' individual needs and how long your school has been using *Everyday Mathematics*. At the beginning of Unit 7, review your Content by Strand Poster to help you set a monthly pace.

← MOST CLASSROOMS →		
FEBRUARY	MARCH	APRIL

Using the Projects

Use Project 6, Anthropometry Project: Formulas for Body Height and Neck Circumference, during or after Unit 7, to measure body parts and plot measurements as data pairs. Investigate formulas that relate body measurements. The Projects can be found at the back of this book.

Home Communication

Share Study Links 7.1–7.8 with families to help them understand the content and procedures in this unit. At the end of the unit, use Study Link 7.9 to introduce Unit 8. Supplemental information can be found in the *Home Connection Handbook*.

NCTM Standards

Standard	1	2	3	4	5	6	7	8	9	10
Unit 7 Lessons	7.1, 7.3, 7.4	7.2, 7.7, 7.8		7.5	7.1–7.9	7.1–7.9	7.1–7.9	7.1–7.9	7.1–7.9	7.1–7.9

Content Standards
1 Number and Operations
2 Algebra
3 Geometry
4 Measurement
5 Data Analysis and Probability

Process Standards
6 Problem Solving
7 Reasoning and Proof
8 Communication
9 Connections
10 Representations

PRACTICE *through* Games

Everyday Mathematics uses games to help students develop good fact power and other math skills.

- *Fraction Action, Fraction Friction* to practice estimating sums of fractions **(Lesson 7.1)**
- *Greedy* to learn about probability by using random-number simulations **(Lesson 7.3)**
- *Frac-Tac-Toe* to practice renaming fractions as decimals **(Lesson 7.4)**
- *Angle Tangle* to practice estimating and measuring the size of angles **(Lesson 7.5)**
- *Name That Number* to practice writing number sentences and using order of operations **(Lessons 7.6 and 7.8)**

unit 7 content highlights

The discussion below highlights the major content ideas presented in Unit 7 and may help you establish instructional priorities.

NOTE: Courses in discrete mathematics are recent additions to the offerings at colleges and universities and are as likely to be in the engineering or business school as in the mathematics department. More recently, such courses are being offered in high schools. The UCSMP secondary school course *Probability and Discrete Mathematics* was a pioneer. The increasing importance of discrete mathematics is indicated by the publication in 1991 of the Yearbook of the National Council of Teachers of Mathematics, *Discrete Mathematics across the Curriculum.*

Many activities in Unit 7 use the following approach:

Students first calculate the probability of each possible outcome of a random process. For example, when a coin is flipped, it can be expected to land HEADS up about one-half of the time.

Students then conduct an experiment many times and compare the results to the expected outcomes. For example, they flip three coins repeatedly to test whether the coins land all HEADS up or all TAILS up the expected number of times.

It is important that students understand the difference between expected outcomes and actual results. In a real-world trial, the two results may be very different, even in a fair game or truly random process. But if the outcomes depend only on chance, the more often the random process occurs, the closer the actual results should resemble the expected results. (If they don't, it is a signal that something other than chance may be operating, as in some of the games played in Lesson 7.7.)

Be sure to reiterate this idea throughout the unit, whenever students compare expected outcomes to actual results. A fair coin can land HEADS up 8 out of 10 times; since coins have no memory, past results have nothing to do with what will happen on the next flip. But if a coin were to land HEADS up 81 out of 100 times, it is probably not a fair coin or the person flipping it has learned how to control the flips.

The Probability of Chance Outcomes (Lesson 7.1)

All students have had experience comparing the chances of outcomes in various situations; for example, "It is more likely to rain tomorrow than to be dry." It is important that students become comfortable talking about chance outcomes. They may use such terms as *sure, certain, probable, 50-50 chance, not likely, impossible,* and so on.

In Lesson 7.1, students review the basic vocabulary and concepts associated with probability. They then calculate the probabilities of spinner outcomes, and of selecting, at random, dominoes meeting various criteria: a double, exactly 1 blank side, sum of the dots is 7, and so on.

Random Numbers (Lessons 7.2 and 7.3)

The concept of "randomness" is implicit in *Everyday Mathematics* in work with card decks, dice, coins, and so on. Besides its importance in mathematics and statistics, randomness plays important roles in scientific research and daily life. For example, in testing a new medicine, researchers usually give some subjects the medicine and others a placebo, or neutral substance. Random numbers are used to ensure that there is no bias in the selection of the subjects who will receive the medicine. States that hold lotteries must guarantee that the winning numbers are generated "at random" and do not follow a pattern. Several decades ago, a scandal resulted when it was discovered that a draft lottery (to determine which young men had to serve in the military) was not random.

A truly random set of numbers (with equal representation of all numbers and without any patterns) is surprisingly difficult to achieve without mechanical or electronic help. It is nearly impossible for a person to list 50 whole numbers less than 100 in a truly random way. (Try it.) In Lesson 7.2, random numbers are used to simulate the outcome of a tournament with evenly matched teams. In the world outside school, random numbers are usually generated by computers or taken from books.

Tree Diagrams (Lessons 7.4 and 7.5)

Tree diagrams are familiar to anyone who has followed certain sports events, such as single-elimination tournaments. Tree diagrams are introduced as a way to model complex situations, especially those in which later outcomes depend on earlier outcomes.

In Lessons 7.4 and 7.5, students calculate how many people entering a maze can be expected to follow each path, assuming that there is an equal chance of taking any path at an intersection. Students use a random-number generator to move "people" (coins) through the maze, and they compare their actual results to the expected results. Then they use tree diagrams to help determine probabilities at each intersection and at the ends of the maze. Students should note that the sum of the final probabilities must be 1.

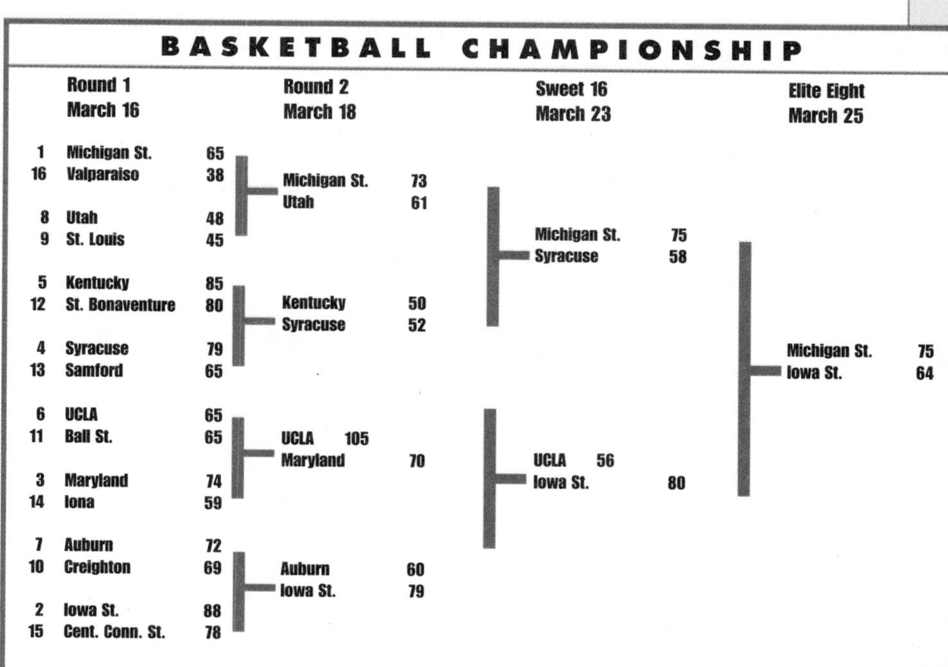

Venn Diagrams (Lesson 7.6)

Venn diagrams are named for John Venn (1834–1923), a British mathematician. In mathematics, they are used to analyze composite events, whose descriptions include words such as *in either, in both, not in both*, and *in at least one*.

Students may have encountered Venn diagrams in other subject areas, as well. For example, in language arts, students may have used a Venn diagram to compare two characters in a story.

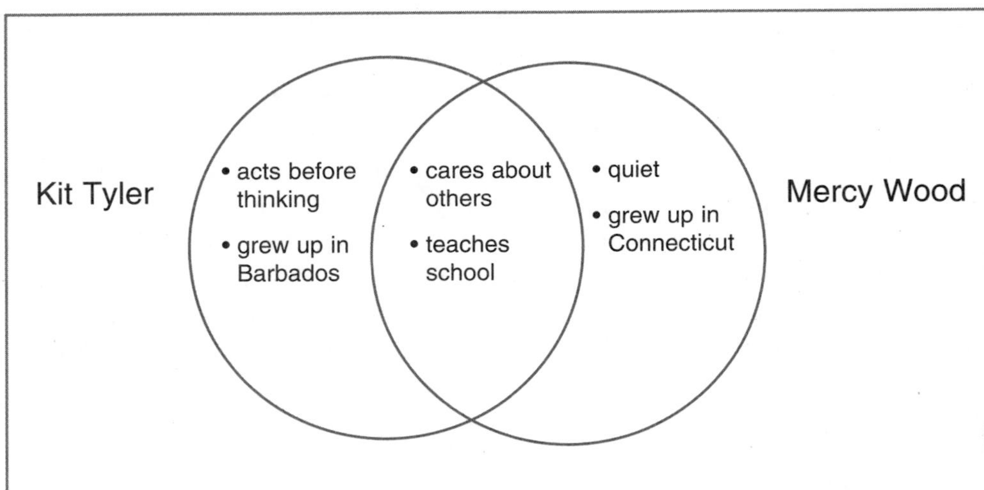

A comparison of characters from *The Witch of Blackbird Pond* by Elizabeth George Speare

Fair and Unfair Games (Lesson 7.7)

A game for two or more players is **fair** if each player has the same chance of winning. A game for one player is **fair** if the player has an equal chance of winning or losing.

In Lesson 7.7, students calculate the probabilities of winning and losing four different games and decide whether or not each game is fair. An enrichment activity is provided in which students figure out how to make a game fair.

Strategies for Taking Multiple-Choice Tests (Lesson 7.8)

If you knew nothing about a subject and had to take a true-false or multiple-choice test on it, one strategy would be to mark responses at random, by flipping a coin or generating random numbers to determine which answer to choose. The expected score for random guessing on true-false questions would be 50%. If each question on a multiple-choice test had four possible answers, the expected score might be 25%.

Test makers prefer that truly ignorant test takers get scores near zero. To discourage random guessing, a penalty is sometimes assessed for choosing a wrong answer, but there is no penalty for not answering. If a test had four choices for each question, the penalty might be $\frac{1}{3}$ times the number of wrong answers. (For 100 questions, each with four choices, pure guessing for every question would give an expected score of 25 right and 75 wrong; with a penalty of $\frac{1}{3}$ times the number of wrong answers, the final score would be $25 - (\frac{1}{3} * 75)$, or 0, the score a truly uninformed person ought to receive.)

But if test takers have enough knowledge to eliminate some wrong choices, even when they can't pick the one correct answer, then guessing among the remaining options has a higher probability of success than pure guessing and would justify a reward for knowing something rather than nothing. This lesson explores the strategy of educated rather than random guessing, not only to get students thinking about test-taking strategies, but also to offer another interesting application of probability.

End-of-Unit Assessment (Lesson 7.9)

The Unit 7 assessment in Lesson 7.9 includes oral, slate, and written assessments of the following concepts and skills:

- ▷ calculating probabilities in simple situations
- ▷ constructing and using tree diagrams and Venn diagrams
- ▷ identifying a fair game
- ▷ applying the concept of random numbers to probability situations
- ▷ understanding how increasing the number of trials affects experimental results

For **additional information** on the following topics, see the *Teacher's Reference Manual:*

- collecting and recording data
- making predictions
- organizing and displaying data
- the language of chance
- tools for exploring data and chance

7.1 The Probability of Equally Likely Outcomes

OBJECTIVES **To review the basic vocabulary and concepts of probability; and to find probabilities for outcomes when they are equally likely.**

summaries	materials
1 Teaching the Lesson	
Students use such terms as *certain, likely, 50-50 chance, unlikely,* and *impossible* to describe the likelihood of an outcome. They calculate the probabilities for various experiments with equally likely outcomes. [Data and Chance]	□ *Math Journal 2,* pp. 253 and 254 □ Transparency of Probability Meter (*Math Journal 2,* Reference Page 2; optional)
2 Ongoing Learning & Practice	
Students play *Fraction Action, Fraction Friction* to practice adding fractions. [Operations and Computation] Students practice and maintain skills through Math Boxes and Study Link activities.	□ *Math Journal 2,* p. 255 □ *Student Reference Book,* p. 293 □ Study Link Master (*Math Masters,* p. 328) □ Geometry Template □ Fraction Cards (*Math Masters,* p. 486 or index cards)
3 Options for Individualizing	
Enrichment Students play carnival games and determine a winning strategy based on probability. [Data and Chance] **Enrichment** Students read a short story about probability in an everyday situation. [Data and Chance]	□ Teaching Masters (*Math Masters,* p. 112, 1 per partnership; and p. 113) □ *Do You Wanna Bet?* □ Per partnership: 2 six-sided dice; 1 coin ***See* Advance Preparation**

Additional Information

Advance Preparation For the second optional Enrichment activity in Part 3, obtain a copy of *Do You Wanna Bet?* by Jean Cushman (Clarion Books, 1991). It contains a collection of short stories and activities that can be used throughout this unit.

Vocabulary • **outcome** • **equally likely** • **probability**

Getting Started

Mental Math and Reflexes

Dictate fractions for students to rename in simplest form. *Suggestions:*

- $\frac{9}{12}$ $\frac{3}{4}$
- $\frac{12}{28}$ $\frac{3}{7}$
- $\frac{6}{18}$ $\frac{1}{3}$
- $\frac{8}{16}$ $\frac{1}{2}$
- $\frac{16}{24}$ $\frac{2}{3}$
- $\frac{25}{30}$ $\frac{5}{6}$

Dictate fractions for students to rename as decimals and percents. *Suggestions:*

- $\frac{3}{4}$ 0.75, 75%
- $\frac{4}{6}$ $0.\overline{6}$, $66\frac{2}{3}$%
- $\frac{7}{20}$ 0.35, 35%
- $\frac{7}{8}$ 0.875, 87.5%
- $\frac{9}{25}$ 0.36, 36%
- $\frac{3}{100}$ 0.03, 3%

Math Message

Complete the problems on journal page 253.

Teaching the Lesson

Math Message Follow-Up
(*Math Journal 2,* p. 253)

WHOLE-CLASS DISCUSSION

Journal page 253 reviews the basic vocabulary and concepts of probability. Remind students of their work with the Probability Meter in *Fifth Grade Everyday Mathematics* and of the use of such terms as *certain, likely, 50-50 chance, unlikely,* and *impossible* to describe the likelihood of an event.

Ask students to use a variety of "probability phrases" to rephrase some of the statements on the journal page. For example, the statement "There is about a $\frac{1}{4}$ chance that this spinner will land on gray" might also be stated as follows:

- If I spin the spinner many times, I expect it to land on gray about 1 out of 4 times.
- The spinner will land on gray about 25% of the time.
- The spinner is unlikely to land on gray.
- The probability that the spinner will land on gray is $\frac{1}{4}$.
- The probability that the spinner will land on gray is 0.25.
- The ratio of the number of times the spinner will land on gray to the total number of spins is about 1 to 4.
- The spinner will land on gray about $\frac{1}{3}$ as often as it will land on white.

Adjusting the Activity If your students need practice with the language of probability, consider making a transparency of the Probability Meter. (Students have a copy on page 342 of the *Student Reference Book* and on Reference Page 2 of *Math Journal 2.*) Consider regularly projecting the transparency, writing students' predictions on the transparency, and checking them the next day. *Suggestions: What is the probability that everyone will bring his or her homework tomorrow? What do you predict the average spelling test score will be? What is the chance that there will be rain tomorrow?*

Probability

In a probability experiment, each possible result is called an **outcome.** If each possible result has the *same chance of happening,* the outcomes are **equally likely.**

When you roll a fair 6-sided die, each of the numbers from 1 to 6 has an equal chance of coming up: The possible outcomes are 1, 2, 3, 4, 5, and 6. This fact does *not* mean that in six rolls each number will come up exactly once. A 2 might come up three times; a 6 might not come up at all. But in 100 rolls, each number is likely to come up about $\frac{1}{6}$ of the time. In 1,000 rolls, it's even *more* likely that each number will come up about $\frac{1}{6}$ of the time. So, we say that the **probability** of rolling a 1 (or a 2, 3, 4, 5, or 6) is $\frac{1}{6}$.

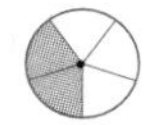

The spinner at the right has 5 equal parts; two parts are blue. If you spin it often enough, the spinner is likely to land on blue about $\frac{2}{5}$ of the time. The probability of landing on blue is $\frac{2}{5}$, or 40%.

Here are pictures of 6 spinners. Next to each statement below, write the letter of the spinner it describes. A spinner may be matched with more than one statement.

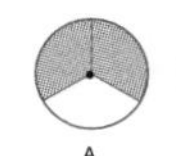
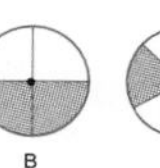
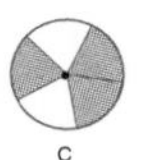
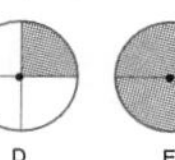
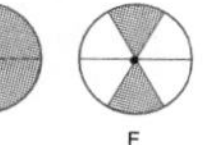

A B C D E F

Example This spinner will land on blue about 2 out of 3 times. A

1. There is about a $\frac{1}{4}$ chance that this spinner will land on blue. D
2. This spinner will land on blue 100% of the time. E
3. There is about a 50-50 chance that this spinner will land on white. B
4. This spinner will never land on white. E
5. The probability that this spinner will land on blue is $\frac{3}{5}$. C
6. This spinner will land on white about twice as often as on blue. F
7. This spinner will land on white a little less than half of the time. A, or C
8. The probability that this spinner will land on white is 75%. D

STUDENT PAGE

Math Journal 2, p. 253

ONGOING ASSESSMENT

Use students' answers from journal page 253 to assess their understanding of probability. Have volunteers explain their answers. Expect that most of your students will correctly answer the problems.

✦ Finding Probabilities of Equally Likely Outcomes (*Math Journal 2,* p. 254)

PARTNER ACTIVITY

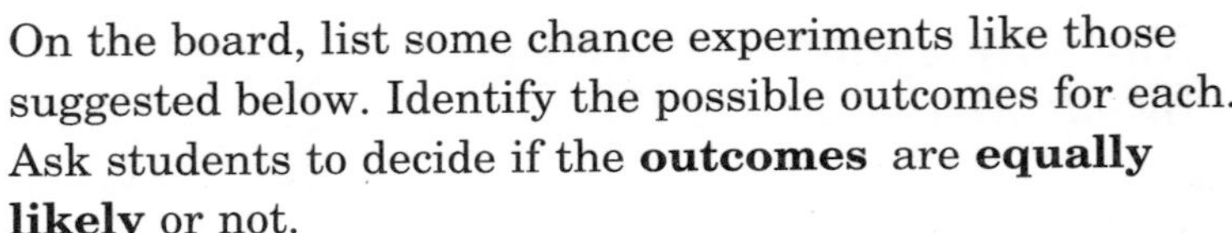

On the board, list some chance experiments like those suggested below. Identify the possible outcomes for each. Ask students to decide if the **outcomes** are **equally likely** or not.

Experiment	Possible Outcomes	Outcomes Equally Likely?
Flip a coin.	HEADS, TAILS	Yes
Roll a fair die.	1, 2, 3, 4, 5, 6	Yes
Roll a loaded die (a die with one face weighted heavier than the other faces).	1, 2, 3, 4, 5, 6	No. The face opposite the weighted face will come up more than $\frac{1}{6}$ of the time.
	Black, white	Yes. The black and white areas are equal.
	Black, white	Yes. The black and white areas are equal.
	Black, white	No. The black area is larger than the white area.
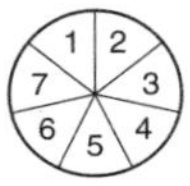	1, 2, 3, 4, 5, 6, 7	Yes. The numbered areas are equal.
Drop a thumbtack.	Lands point up, lands point down	Can't tell. Must collect data by experimenting.
Send a letter.	Delivered, returned, lost	No. The chance of the letter being returned and the chance of it getting lost are both very small.
People write their names on cards and put them in a bag. A volunteer picks one card without looking.	Name of each person who filled out a card	Yes, if all cards are the same size. Probably no, if cards are different sizes.

Assign journal page 254 for students to complete in partnerships or independently. Make sure students understand that selecting a domino is a chance experiment with equally likely outcomes. There are 28 dominoes. Each domino has the same $\frac{1}{28}$ chance of being selected. After most students have finished, gather the class together and discuss students' answers.

For each situation listed in Problems 4–10, students must identify and count the number of dominoes satisfying that situation. Once students have counted the dominoes that satisfy the situation, they may think in different ways to name the **probability.** *For example:*

Problem 4: Select a double.

▷ The *favorable outcomes* are the dominoes that are doubles. There are 7 favorable outcomes: 6-6, 5-5, 4-4, 3-3, 2-2, 1-1, and blank-blank.

▷ The number of *possible outcomes* is 28. There are 28 dominoes in the double-6 set.

▷ The fraction $\frac{\text{number of favorable outcomes}}{\text{number of possible outcomes}} = \frac{7}{28}$ is the probability.

Problem 7: The sum of the dots is 7. *Possible strategies:*

▷ Three dominoes have a sum equal to 7: the 6-1, 5-2, and 4-3 dominoes. That's 3 out of 28 dominoes. So the chance, or probability, of picking a domino with a sum equal to 7 is $\frac{3}{28}$.

▷ Three dominoes have a sum equal to 7. Each one of these has a $\frac{1}{28}$ chance of being picked. So the total chance of picking a domino with a sum equal to 7 is $\frac{1}{28} + \frac{1}{28} + \frac{1}{28}$, or $\frac{3}{28}$.

For Problems 4–10, students' answers should agree with probabilities found using the formula.

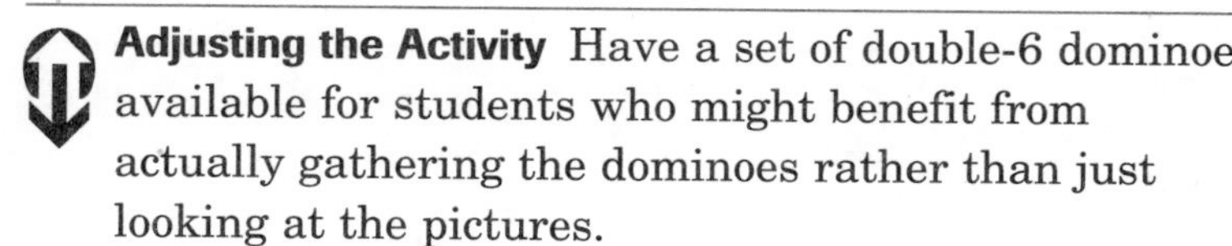

Adjusting the Activity Have a set of double-6 dominoes available for students who might benefit from actually gathering the dominoes rather than just looking at the pictures.

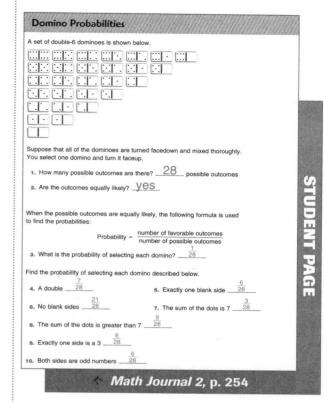

Domino Probabilities

A set of double-6 dominoes is shown below.

Suppose that all of the dominoes are turned facedown and mixed thoroughly. You select one domino and turn it faceup.

1. How many possible outcomes are there? 28 possible outcomes
2. Are the outcomes equally likely? yes

When the possible outcomes are equally likely, the following formula is used to find the probabilities:

$$\text{Probability} = \frac{\text{number of favorable outcomes}}{\text{number of possible outcomes}}$$

3. What is the probability of selecting each domino? $\frac{1}{28}$

Find the probability of selecting each domino described below.

4. A double $\frac{7}{28}$
5. Exactly one blank side $\frac{6}{28}$
6. No blank sides $\frac{21}{28}$
7. The sum of the dots is 7 $\frac{3}{28}$
8. The sum of the dots is greater than 7 $\frac{9}{28}$
9. Exactly one side is a 3 $\frac{6}{28}$
10. Both sides are odd numbers $\frac{6}{28}$

STUDENT PAGE

Math Journal 2, p. 254

2 Ongoing Learning & Practice

✦ Playing *Fraction Action, Fraction Friction* (*Student Reference Book,* p. 293, *Math Masters,* p. 486)

PARTNER ACTIVITY 

Have students play this game from Lesson 4.3 to practice fraction addition. Students can make a set of cards by cutting apart *Math Masters,* page 486, or by copying the fractions onto index cards. You may want to have students keep a written record of each round to assess their mastery of simple fraction addition.

✦ Math Boxes 7.1 (*Math Journal 2,* p. 255)

INDEPENDENT ACTIVITY

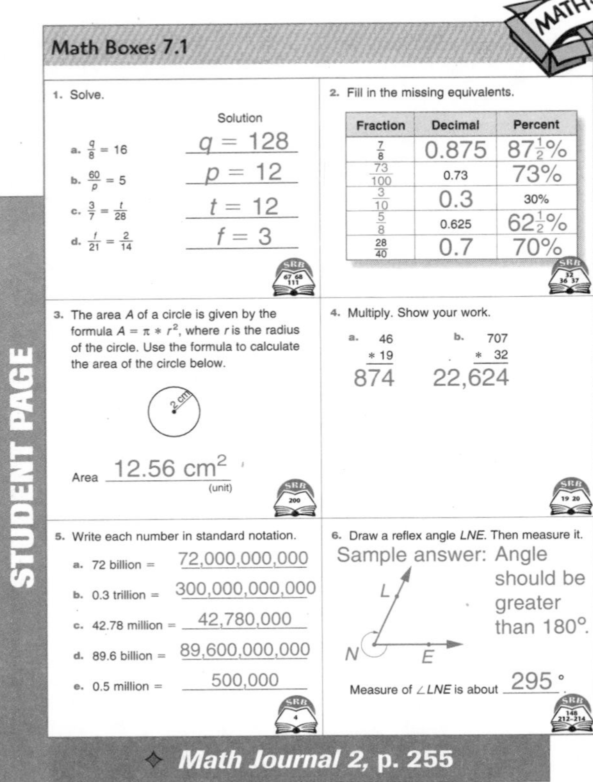

STUDENT PAGE

Math Boxes 7.1

1. Solve.

	Solution
a. $\frac{q}{8} = 16$	$q = 128$
b. $\frac{60}{p} = 5$	$p = 12$
c. $\frac{3}{7} = \frac{t}{28}$	$t = 12$
d. $\frac{f}{21} = \frac{2}{14}$	$f = 3$

2. Fill in the missing equivalents.

Fraction	Decimal	Percent
$\frac{7}{8}$	0.875	$87\frac{1}{2}\%$
$\frac{73}{100}$	0.73	73%
$\frac{3}{10}$	0.3	30%
$\frac{5}{8}$	0.625	$62\frac{1}{2}\%$
$\frac{28}{40}$	0.7	70%

3. The area A of a circle is given by the formula $A = \pi * r^2$, where r is the radius of the circle. Use the formula to calculate the area of the circle below.

2 cm

Area 12.56 cm² (unit)

4. Multiply. Show your work.

a. 46 * 19 = 874

b. 707 * 32 = 22,624

5. Write each number in standard notation.

a. 72 billion = 72,000,000,000

b. 0.3 trillion = 300,000,000,000

c. 42.78 million = 42,780,000

d. 89.6 billion = 89,600,000,000

e. 0.5 million = 500,000

6. Draw a reflex angle LNE. Then measure it.

Sample answer: Angle should be greater than 180°.

Measure of $\angle LNE$ is about 295°

✦ *Math Journal 2,* p. 255

Mixed Review Math Boxes in this lesson are paired with Math Boxes in Lesson 7.3. The skill in Problem 1 is a prerequisite for Unit 8.

✦ Study Link 7.1 (*Math Masters,* p. 328)

Home Connection Students complete a "Blast from the Past" review page that focuses on some of the skills that will be covered in this unit.

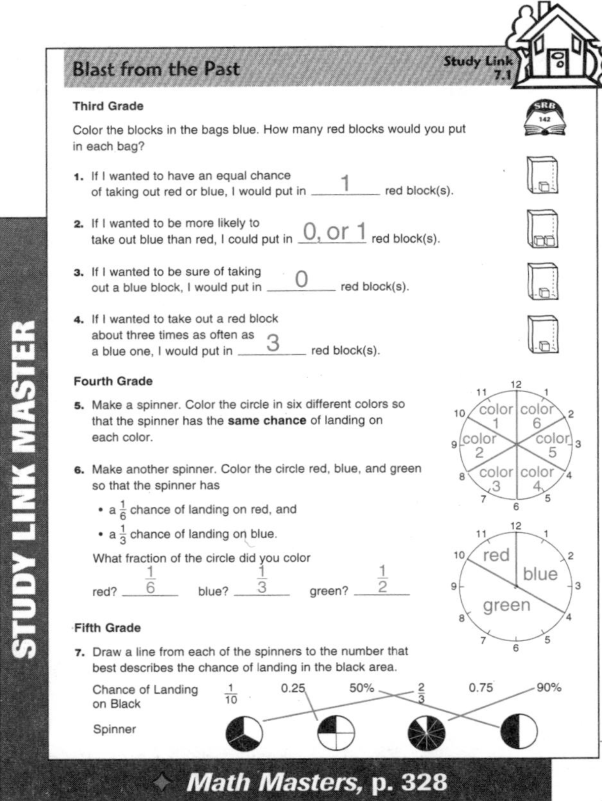

STUDY LINK MASTER

Blast from the Past Study Link 7.1

Third Grade

Color the blocks in the bags blue. How many red blocks would you put in each bag?

1. If I wanted to have an equal chance of taking out red or blue, I would put in 1 red block(s).
2. If I wanted to be more likely to take out blue than red, I could put in 0, or 1 red block(s).
3. If I wanted to be sure of taking out a blue block, I would put in 0 red block(s).
4. If I wanted to take out a red block about three times as often as a blue one, I would put in 3 red block(s).

Fourth Grade

5. Make a spinner. Color the circle in six different colors so that the spinner has the **same chance** of landing on each color.
6. Make another spinner. Color the circle red, blue, and green so that the spinner has
   - a $\frac{1}{6}$ chance of landing on red, and
   - a $\frac{1}{3}$ chance of landing on blue.

   What fraction of the circle did you color red? $\frac{1}{6}$ blue? $\frac{1}{3}$ green? $\frac{1}{2}$

Fifth Grade

7. Draw a line from each of the spinners to the number that best describes the chance of landing in the black area.

Chance of Landing on Black: $\frac{1}{10}$, 0.25, 50%, $\frac{2}{3}$, 0.75, 90%

Spinner

✦ *Math Masters,* p. 328

3 Options for Individualizing

✦ ENRICHMENT Playing Carnival Games (*Math Masters,* pp. 112 and 113)

PARTNER ACTIVITY **15–30 min**

Students explore the probabilities of rolling dice and flipping coins for a set of carnival games. They find the best possible combination of booths to visit, based on playing 10 games.

The following is a summary of the outcomes of the six game booths. Share it with students or write the headings on the board and work with them to fill it in.

Booth	Number of Winning Outcomes	Number of Possible Outcomes	$\frac{\text{Winning Outcomes}}{\text{Possible Outcomes}}$	Probability of Winning
1	2	4	$\frac{2}{4}$, or $\frac{1}{2}$	50.0%
2	3	12	$\frac{3}{12}$, or $\frac{1}{4}$	25.0%
3	15	36	$\frac{15}{36}$, or $\frac{5}{12}$	41.7%
4	4	36	$\frac{4}{36}$, or $\frac{1}{9}$	11.1%
5	1	6	$\frac{1}{6}$	16.7%
6	21	36	$\frac{21}{36}$, or $\frac{7}{12}$	58.3%

Ask if anyone can suggest a winning strategy based on the probabilities. The best theoretical combination would be visiting Booth 6 eight times, and Booths 1 and 3 each one time.

Have partners compare their individual tallies with the probabilities. They will likely notice that their individual results often differ. Ask why this might be so. Their samples are too small to reliably reflect the probabilities.

Adjusting the Activity To extend the activity, have students design their own set of fair games that are easy or difficult to win.

✦ ENRICHMENT Reading a Book about Probability

WHOLE-CLASS ACTIVITY  **5–15 min**

Literature Link Read a short story to the class from the following book:

Do You Wanna Bet?

Summary: Two boys find that the most ordinary events and activities such as card games, coin flips, same birth dates, raffle chances, sports statistics, and even weather predictions involve concepts of chance and probability.

After each story is a brief description of the probability concepts illustrated as well as suggestions for similar activities students could try.

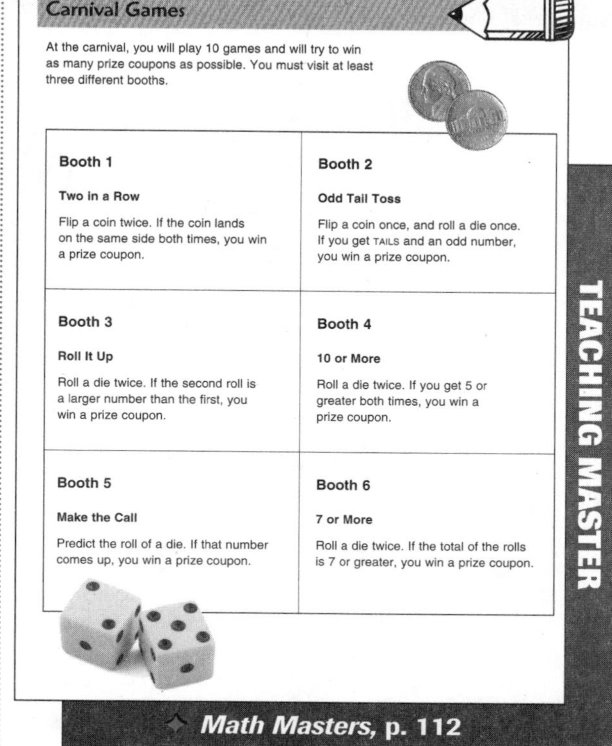

Carnival Games

At the carnival, you will play 10 games and will try to win as many prize coupons as possible. You must visit at least three different booths.

Booth 1	Booth 2
Two in a Row Flip a coin twice. If the coin lands on the same side both times, you win a prize coupon.	**Odd Tail Toss** Flip a coin once, and roll a die once. If you get TAILS and an odd number, you win a prize coupon.
Booth 3	**Booth 4**
Roll It Up Roll a die twice. If the second roll is a larger number than the first, you win a prize coupon.	**10 or More** Roll a die twice. If you get 5 or greater both times, you win a prize coupon.
Booth 5	**Booth 6**
Make the Call Predict the roll of a die. If that number comes up, you win a prize coupon.	**7 or More** Roll a die twice. If the total of the rolls is 7 or greater, you win a prize coupon.

TEACHING MASTER

✦ *Math Masters,* p. 112

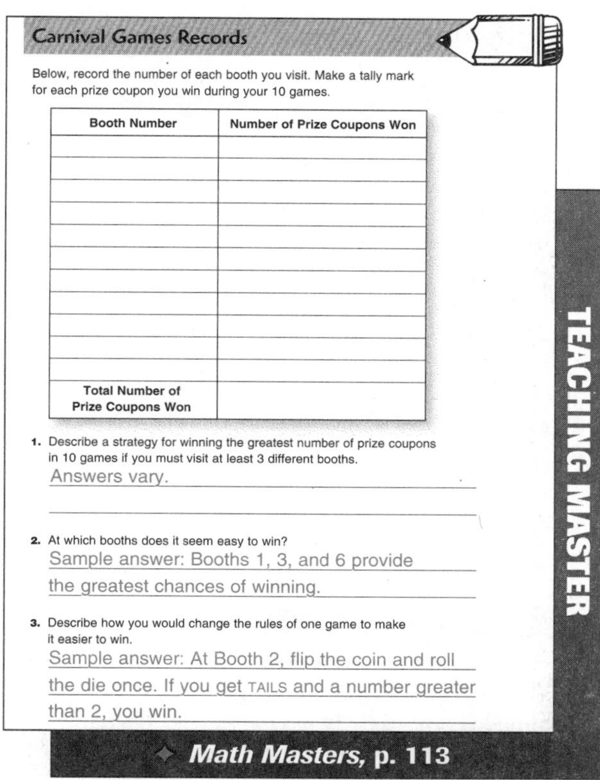

Carnival Games Records

Below, record the number of each booth you visit. Make a tally mark for each prize coupon you win during your 10 games.

Booth Number	Number of Prize Coupons Won
Total Number of Prize Coupons Won	

1. Describe a strategy for winning the greatest number of prize coupons in 10 games if you must visit at least 3 different booths.
Answers vary.

2. At which booths does it seem easy to win?
Sample answer: Booths 1, 3, and 6 provide the greatest chances of winning.

3. Describe how you would change the rules of one game to make it easier to win.
Sample answer: At Booth 2, flip the coin and roll the die once. If you get TAILS and a number greater than 2, you win.

TEACHING MASTER

✦ *Math Masters,* p. 113

7.2 Generating Random Numbers

OBJECTIVES To investigate random numbers; and to use number cards to generate random numbers within a given range.

summaries	materials
1 Teaching the Lesson	
Students learn to generate random numbers using number cards. They discover that the more times they generate a number within a given range, the more likely they are to obtain an equal distribution of possible outcomes. [Data and Chance]	☐ *Math Journal 2,* pp. 256 and 257 ☐ Study Link 7.1 ☐ Assessment Master (*Math Masters,* p. 478; optional) ☐ Transparency (*Math Masters,* p. 114; optional) ☐ Per partnership: number cards 1–5 (from the Everything Math Deck, if available) ☐ calculator ***See* Advance Preparation**
2 Ongoing Learning & Practice	
Students practice solving pan-balance problems and equations. [Patterns, Functions, and Algebra] Students practice and maintain skills through Math Boxes and Study Link activities.	☐ *Math Journal 2,* pp. 258 and 259 ☐ Study Link Master (*Math Masters,* p. 329)
3 Options for Individualizing	
Reteaching Students predict the colors of blocks in a bag, based on repeated random draws with replacement. They find that the more draws they make, the more reliable their predictions are. [Data and Chance] **Enrichment** Students make a tally chart to help them decide whether the digits in a random digits table are actually random. [Data and Chance]	☐ Teaching Master (*Math Masters,* p. 116) Per group: ☐ Teaching Master (*Math Masters,* p. 115) ☐ brown paper bag (size of a lunch bag) ☐ 5 blocks in each of 3 colors (15 total)

Additional Information

Advance Preparation You may use any number cards 1–5, or have groups make a set using index cards.

Vocabulary • **outcome** • **generate random numbers** • **random number**

Getting Started

Math Message

Complete Problem 1 at the top of journal page 256.

Study Link 7.1 Follow-Up

Briefly go over the answers to the "Blast from the Past."

Mental Math and Reflexes

Write numbers in exponential and scientific notation on the board or overhead projector. Students rewrite them in standard notation. Remind students that it is sometimes easier to write out all of the necessary digits and then go back and insert commas. *Suggestions:*

- 10^5 100,000
- 10^{12} 1,000,000,000,000
- 10^7 10,000,000
- $2 * 10^2$ 200
- $5.6 * 10^9$ 5,600,000,000
- $8.92 * 10^4$ 89,200

Teaching the Lesson

✦ Math Message Follow-Up
(*Math Journal 2,* p. 256)

WHOLE-CLASS DISCUSSION

Students share their answers. Each number generated is an **outcome.** There are five possible outcomes for this card-picking activity—the numbers 1, 2, 3, 4, and 5.

Each pick **generates random numbers** from 1–5. A **random number** is a number that has the same chance of appearing as any other number. There is no pattern, and the next number to appear is unpredictable.

Since each of the five numbers is as likely to appear as any other, each should appear about 20% of the time in a large sample.

✦ Generating Random Numbers
(*Math Journal 2,* pp. 256 and 257)

SMALL-GROUP ACTIVITY

Divide the class into groups of four students each and name them Group 1, Group 2, and so on. Each group should then divide into two partnerships. The goal is for each group of four to quickly generate 50 random numbers.

Each partnership generates 25 random numbers from the set of numbers 1, 2, 3, 4, and 5 as described on journal page 256. One partner handles the deck of cards, while the other partner picks a card without looking and tallies the outcome on a piece of paper. Then each student records the results generated by the other partnership in the group (for a total of 50 random numbers), adds the results for each outcome, and calculates the percent of the total that each number was picked.

Generating Random Numbers

Math Message

Suppose you have a deck of number cards, one card for each of the numbers 1 through 5. When you shuffle the cards and pick a card without looking, you get a number 1 through 5. Each number has the same chance of being picked. Numbers found in this way are **random numbers.**

Suppose you continue finding random numbers using these steps.

- Shuffle
- Pick a card
- Replace the card
- Repeat

1. If you did this many times, about what percent of the time would you expect to pick the number 5? About 20 percent

An Experiment

2. Work with a partner in a group of 4 students. Use a deck of 5 number cards, one card for each of the numbers 1 through 5.
3. One of you shuffles the deck of 5 number cards and fans them out, facedown. Your partner then picks one without looking. The pick **generates a random number** from 1 to 5. The number is an **outcome.**
4. The person picking the card tallies the outcome in the table below while the person with the deck replaces the card and shuffles the deck. Generate exactly 25 random numbers.

Outcome	Tally	Number of Times Picked
1		
2		
3		
4		
5		
	Total Random Numbers	25

Math Journal 2, p. 256

Generating Random Numbers (cont.)

5. Record the results in the table below. In the My Partnership column, write the number of times each of the numbers 1 through 5 appeared.

6. In the Other Partnership column, record the results of the other partnership in your group.

7. For each outcome, add the two results and write the sum in the Both Partnerships column.

8. Convert each result under Both Partnerships to a percent. Write it in the % of Total column. (For example, 10 out of 50 would be 20%.) Answers vary.

Outcome	My Partnership	Other Partnership	Both Partnerships	% of Total
1			____ out of 50	
2			____ out of 50	
3			____ out of 50	
4			____ out of 50	
5			____ out of 50	
Total	25	25	50 out of 50	100%

STUDENT PAGE

Math Journal 2, p. 257

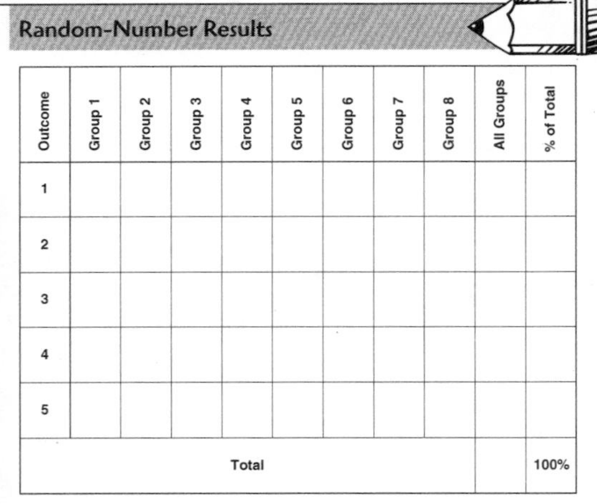

Random-Number Results

Outcome	Group 1	Group 2	Group 3	Group 4	Group 5	Group 6	Group 7	Group 8	All Groups	% of Total
1										
2										
3										
4										
5										
Total										100%

TEACHING MASTER

Math Masters, p. 114

Observing the Effect of Increasing the Number of Trials (*Math Journal 2,* p. 257; *Math Masters,* p. 114)

WHOLE-CLASS DISCUSSION 

Copy the Random-Number Results table (*Math Masters,* page 114) onto the board, or display an overhead transparency. Ask each group to report its results while you record them in the table.

Results are likely to vary considerably. For example, some students may think that the cards were not shuffled well enough or that the other person looked when picking, because the number 3 came up only 8 times in 50 tries. For several partnerships, however, the number 3 may have occurred most often.

By combining the results for all groups, students should realize that uneven results are not the fault of the students picking or shuffling the cards but lie in the nature of randomness.

For each outcome, add the results for all groups and record them in the All Groups column in the Random-Number Results table. For example, suppose 6 groups generated 300 random numbers. Record 300 as the Total beneath the All Groups column. If the number 1 was generated 90 times, enter 90 in the All Groups column for Outcome 1. In the % of Total column, enter 30% for Outcome 1, since 90 out of 300 is equivalent to $\frac{90}{300}$, which equals 0.3, or 30%.

Repeat this process for Outcomes 2, 3, 4, and 5. Students may need to use their calculators to find some of the entries in the % of Total column.

When the table is complete, ask students to compare the single-group results to the combined-group results. Help them summarize:

▷ The results for a single group may be very uneven. Some numbers may come up frequently, while other numbers come up rarely.

▷ The combined-group results will be much more even. Each of the numbers 1, 2, 3, 4, and 5 should appear close to 20% of the time.

▷ If the class were to continue to generate random numbers, the percents would eventually "settle down" to 20% for each number.

ONGOING ASSESSMENT

To assess students' understanding of how sample size affects outcomes, have students complete an Exit Slip (*Math Masters,* page 478) explaining how they think sample size affects *actual* results compared to *predicted* results.

2 Ongoing Learning & Practice

✦ Solving Pan-Balance Problems and Equations (*Math Journal 2,* p. 258)

INDEPENDENT ACTIVITY 

Students complete a journal page of pan-balance problems and equations.

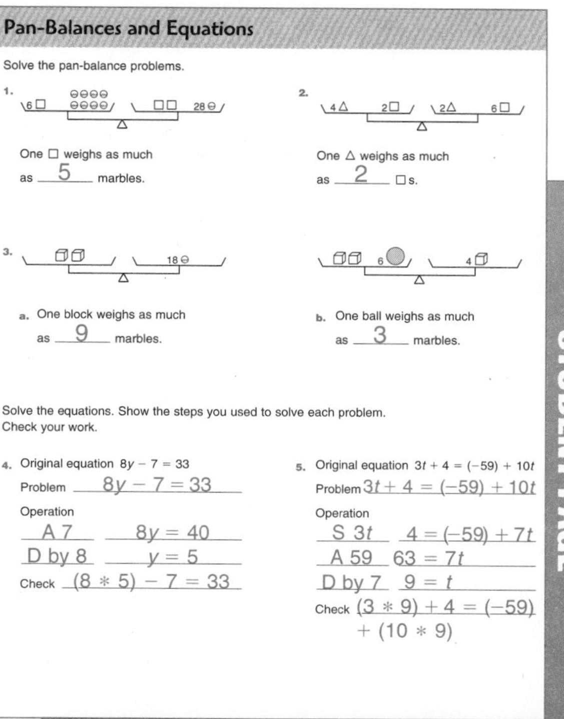

Pan-Balances and Equations

Solve the pan-balance problems.

1. One □ weighs as much as 5 marbles.

2. One △ weighs as much as 2 □s.

3. a. One block weighs as much as 9 marbles.
   b. One ball weighs as much as 3 marbles.

Solve the equations. Show the steps you used to solve each problem. Check your work.

4. Original equation $8y - 7 = 33$
   Problem $8y - 7 = 33$
   Operation
   A 7 — $8y = 40$
   D by 8 — $y = 5$
   Check $(8 * 5) - 7 = 33$

5. Original equation $3t + 4 = (-59) + 10t$
   Problem $3t + 4 = (-59) + 10t$
   Operation
   S $3t$ — $4 = (-59) + 7t$
   A 59 — $63 = 7t$
   D by 7 — $9 = t$
   Check $(3 * 9) + 4 = (-59) + (10 * 9)$

STUDENT PAGE

✦ *Math Journal 2,* p. 258

✦ Math Boxes 7.2 (*Math Journal 2,* p. 259)

INDEPENDENT ACTIVITY 

Mixed Review Math Boxes in this lesson are paired with Math Boxes in Lesson 7.4. The skill in Problem 1 is a prerequisite for Unit 8.

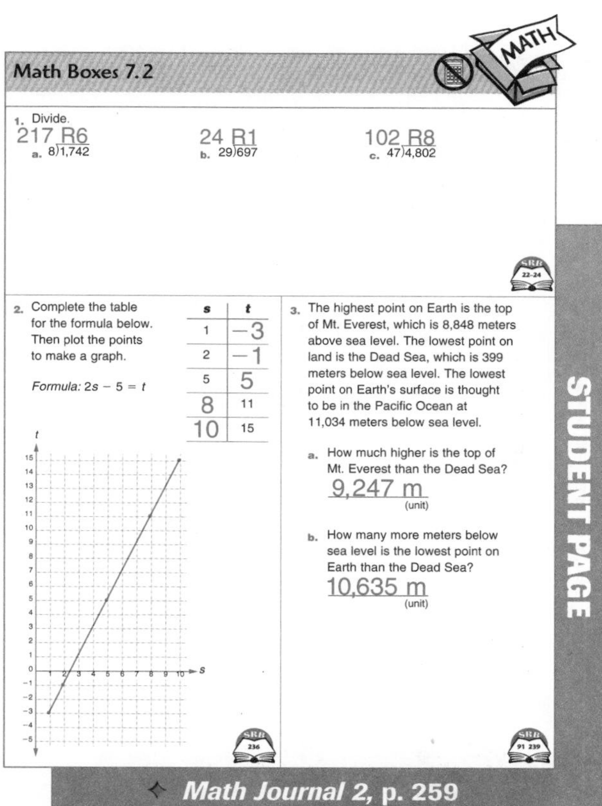

Math Boxes 7.2

1. Divide.
   a. 8)1,742 — 217 R6
   b. 29)697 — 24 R1
   c. 47)4,802 — 102 R8

2. Complete the table for the formula below. Then plot the points to make a graph.
   Formula: $2s - 5 = t$

s	t
1	−3
2	−1
5	5
8	11
10	15

3. The highest point on Earth is the top of Mt. Everest, which is 8,848 meters above sea level. The lowest point on land is the Dead Sea, which is 399 meters below sea level. The lowest point on Earth's surface is thought to be in the Pacific Ocean at 11,034 meters below sea level.
   a. How much higher is the top of Mt. Everest than the Dead Sea? 9,247 m (unit)
   b. How many more meters below sea level is the lowest point on Earth than the Dead Sea? 10,635 m (unit)

STUDENT PAGE

✦ *Math Journal 2,* p. 259

✦ Study Link 7.2 (*Math Masters,* p. 329)

Home Connection Students answer questions about randomness.

Using Random Numbers

Study Link 7.2

STUDY LINK MASTER

1. A gym teacher is dividing her class into two teams to play soccer. Do you think she should choose the teams "at random"? no

   Explain. Sample answer: Teams should be evenly matched. A team selected at random might not have a balance of skilled and unskilled players.

2. The entire school is going to a baseball game. Some seats are better than others. Should the principal select the section where each class will sit "at random"? Yes and no

   Explain. Sample answer: In an elementary school, preference for the better seats should go to the youngest children so that they can see the game. But starting in Grades 3 through 6, the principal should choose seat assignments randomly.

3. The spinner at the right has landed on the shaded part 5 times in a row. Renee says, "On the next spin, the spinner is more likely to land on white than on the shaded part."

   Do you agree or disagree with Renee? disagree

   Explain. Sample answer: There is always an even chance of landing on black or white. The previous spins do not affect the outcome.

4. The spinner at the right has landed on the shaded part 5 times in row. Matthew says, "On the next spin, the spinner has a better chance of landing on white than on the shaded part."

   Do you agree or disagree with Matthew? agree

   Explain. Sample answer: There is always a better chance that the spinner will land on white because the white area is larger. The outcome does not depend on the previous spins.

◆ **Math Masters, p. 329**

3 Options for Individualizing

◆ RETEACHING Predicting Which Blocks Are in a Bag (*Math Masters,* p. 115)

SMALL-GROUP ACTIVITY  **15–30 min** 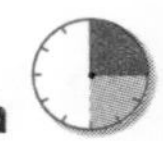

Students predict the numbers and colors of blocks in a bag, based on drawing blocks out of the bag. The blocks are replaced after each draw. Students discover that the more draws they make, the easier it is to make a prediction.

◆ ENRICHMENT Examining a Table of Random Digits (*Math Masters,* p. 116)

 **30+ min** 

Students check the randomness of digits in a table of random digits by making a tally chart. The group should divide the chart into rows so that each student tallies a few of the rows.

Predict Which Blocks Are in a Bag

TEACHING MASTER

1. Pick one person in your group to be the "Director."
2. The Director selects 5 blocks and hides them in a bag. The blocks should NOT all be the same color. The group members should NOT see the blocks.
3. Group members take turns drawing one block out of the bag without looking. Each time a block is drawn, group members tally the color.

   Example (for first 5 draws)

red	////
blue	/

4. The person who drew the block puts it back into the bag, shakes the bag, and gives it to the next person to draw.
5. After 5 draws, each person writes a prediction for how many blocks of each color are in the bag.
6. Discuss your prediction with the group. If everyone has the same prediction, the Director shows the contents of the bag and checks the prediction.
7. If your group does not agree on a prediction, take turns making 5 more draws (for a total of 10). Everyone predicts again and compares predictions.
8. Continue until the group agrees on a prediction. Then the Director shows the contents of the bag.

Repeat this experiment with a different number of blocks in the bag. Try it with 3 blocks. Try it with 7 blocks.

9. Does the number of blocks in the bag make a difference? yes

   Explain. Sample answer: With fewer blocks, finding the ratio of one color to another is easier.

10. Do you think that there must be a minimum number of draws to be certain of the contents of the bag? yes

    Explain. Sample answer: With 10 draws you can make an informed decision. As more and more draws are made, the decision becomes more reliable.

◆ **Math Masters, p. 115**

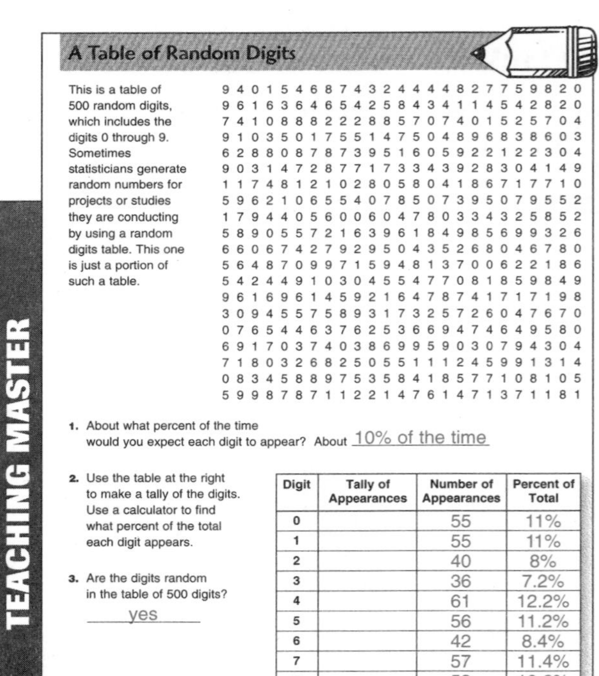

A Table of Random Digits

TEACHING MASTER

This is a table of 500 random digits, which includes the digits 0 through 9. Sometimes statisticians generate random numbers for projects or studies they are conducting by using a random digits table. This one is just a portion of such a table.

9 4 0 1 5 4 6 8 7 4 3 2 4 4 4 4 8 2 7 7 5 9 8 2 0
9 6 1 6 3 6 4 6 5 4 2 5 8 4 3 4 1 1 4 5 4 2 8 2 0
7 4 1 0 8 8 8 2 2 2 8 8 5 7 0 7 4 0 1 5 2 5 7 0 4
9 1 0 3 5 0 1 7 5 5 1 4 7 5 0 4 8 9 6 8 3 8 6 0 3
6 2 8 8 0 8 7 8 7 3 9 5 1 6 0 5 9 2 2 1 2 2 3 0 4
9 0 3 1 4 7 2 8 7 7 1 7 3 3 4 3 9 2 8 3 0 4 1 4 9
1 1 7 4 8 1 2 1 0 2 8 0 5 8 0 4 1 8 6 7 1 7 7 1 0
5 9 6 2 1 0 6 5 5 4 0 7 8 5 0 7 3 9 5 0 7 9 5 5 2
1 7 9 4 4 0 5 6 0 0 6 0 4 7 8 0 3 3 4 3 2 5 8 5 2
5 8 9 0 5 5 7 2 1 6 3 9 6 1 8 4 9 8 5 6 9 9 3 2 6
6 6 0 6 7 4 2 7 9 2 9 5 0 4 3 5 2 6 8 0 4 6 7 8 0
5 6 4 8 7 0 9 9 7 1 5 9 4 8 1 3 7 0 0 6 2 2 1 8 6
5 4 2 4 4 9 1 0 3 0 4 5 5 4 7 7 0 8 1 8 5 9 8 4 9
9 6 1 6 9 6 1 4 5 9 2 1 6 4 7 8 7 4 1 7 1 7 1 9 8
3 0 9 4 5 5 7 5 8 9 3 1 7 3 2 5 7 2 6 0 4 7 6 7 0
0 7 6 5 4 4 6 3 7 6 2 5 3 6 6 9 4 7 4 6 4 9 5 8 0
6 9 1 7 0 3 7 4 0 3 8 6 9 9 5 9 0 3 0 7 9 4 3 0 4
7 1 8 0 3 2 6 8 2 5 0 5 5 1 1 1 2 4 5 9 9 1 3 1 4
0 8 3 4 5 8 8 9 7 5 3 5 8 4 1 8 5 7 7 1 0 8 1 0 5
5 9 9 8 7 8 7 1 1 2 2 1 4 7 6 1 4 7 1 3 7 1 1 8 1

1. About what percent of the time would you expect each digit to appear? About 10% of the time
2. Use the table at the right to make a tally of the digits. Use a calculator to find what percent of the total each digit appears.
3. Are the digits random in the table of 500 digits? yes

Digit	Tally of Appearances	Number of Appearances	Percent of Total
0		55	11%
1		55	11%
2		40	8%
3		36	7.2%
4		61	12.2%
5		56	11.2%
6		42	8.4%
7		57	11.4%
8		53	10.6%
9		45	9%
Total	500	500	100%

◆ **Math Masters, p. 116**

7.3 A Random-Number Simulation

OBJECTIVES **To simulate a situation using random numbers; and to use simulation results to estimate the chance of each possible outcome.**

summaries	materials
1 Teaching the Lesson	
Students toss a coin to simulate a tournament with equally matched teams. They estimate the chances of various outcomes of the tournament. [Data and Chance]	□ *Math Journal 2,* pp. 260 and 261 □ Study Link 7.2 □ Per partnership: 1 coin □ 2 six-sided dice (optional)
2 Ongoing Learning & Practice	
Students review computation with a page of mixed practice. [Operations and Computation] Students practice and maintain skills through Math Boxes and Study Link activities.	□ *Math Journal 2,* pp. 262 and 263 □ Study Link Master (*Math Masters,* p. 330)
3 Options for Individualizing	
Extra Practice Students play the game *Greedy* to practice probability skills. [Data and Chance]	□ Teaching Master (*Math Masters,* p. 117) □ 1 six-sided die ***See* Advance Preparation**

Additional Information

Advance Preparation For the optional Extra Practice game in Part 3, make one copy of *Math Masters,* page 117 for every four students.

Vocabulary • **simulation** • **simulate**

Getting Started

Mental Math and Reflexes

Pose "fraction-of-a-fraction" problems. If students do not immediately recognize this type of problem, remind them that it is the same as multiplying. You could demonstrate by folding a sheet of paper in half and then in half again to illustrate the first problem below. Continue as time allows. *Suggestions:*

- $\frac{1}{2}$ of $\frac{1}{2}$ $\frac{1}{4}$
- $\frac{1}{4}$ of $\frac{1}{2}$ $\frac{1}{8}$
- $\frac{1}{3}$ of $\frac{1}{2}$ $\frac{1}{6}$
- $\frac{2}{5}$ of $\frac{1}{9}$ $\frac{2}{45}$
- $\frac{2}{3}$ of $\frac{1}{5}$ $\frac{2}{15}$
- $\frac{3}{10}$ of $\frac{2}{3}$ $\frac{6}{30}$

Math Message

List all of the 2-digit whole numbers you can using only the digits 1 and 2. Digits may be repeated. What percent of the numbers are made up of the same digit?

Study Link 7.2 Follow-Up

Answers to Problems 1 and 2 may vary. However, it is important that students understand that something done "at random" is without pattern or favoritism. Problems 3 and 4 emphasize that the outcomes of random events frequently repeat in clusters or runs. Devices used to generate random numbers, such as spinners and dice, have no memory. The previous spin or roll cannot affect the next spin or roll. In Problem 3, the probability of landing on the shaded part or the white part is the same—$\frac{1}{2}$. In Problem 4, the probability of landing on the white part is greater than the probability of landing on the shaded part. However, this is not because the spinner has landed on the shaded part 5 times in a row, but because of the sizes of the regions. On any spin, the probability of landing on the white part is $\frac{3}{4}$, and the probability of landing on the shaded part is $\frac{1}{4}$.

This might be a good time to point out that some people can, with practice, learn to control devices like spinners and dice so that certain outcomes will be more likely. In the hands of such people, the device is no longer a random-number generator.

STUDENT PAGE

Using Random Numbers

Suppose two evenly matched teams play a game that cannot end in a tie—one team must win. Because the teams have an equal chance of winning, you could get about the same results by randomly generating the numbers 1 and 2: You can do this by tossing a coin. If the coin lands on HEADS, Team 1 wins; if it lands on TAILS, Team 2 wins. In this way, tossing a coin **simulates** the outcome of a game. In a **simulation,** an object or event is represented by something else.

Suppose Team 1 and Team 2 play a "best-of-5" tournament. The first team to win three games wins. The team might win the first three games played; or three of the first four games; or three of five games. Use a coin to simulate the tournament, as follows:

Game 1 — If the coin lands on HEADS, Team 1 wins. If the coin lands on TAILS, Team 2 wins.

Games 2 and 3 — Repeat the instructions for Game 1.

Games 4 and 5 — Play only if necessary. Repeat the instructions for Game 1.

Sample results:

If the coin tosses are HEADS, HEADS, HEADS, Team 1 wins the tournament.
If the coin tosses are HEADS, HEADS, TAILS, HEADS, Team 1 wins.
If the coin tosses are TAILS, HEADS, HEADS, TAILS, TAILS, Team 2 wins.

1. Fill in the table as described on the next page. Answers vary.

Number of Games Needed to Win the Tournament	Winner	Tally of Tournaments Won	Total Tournaments Won
3	Team 1		
	Team 2		
4	Team 1		
	Team 2		
5	Team 1		
	Team 2		
		Total	25

✦ *Math Journal 2,* p. 260

1 Teaching the Lesson

✦ Math Message Follow-Up

WHOLE-CLASS DISCUSSION

The numbers are 11, 12, 21, and 22. One-half, or 50%, of the numbers are made up of the same digit.

✦ Using Random Numbers to Simulate a Tournament (*Math Journal 2,* pp. 260 and 261)

PARTNER ACTIVITY

Read and discuss journal page 260 with the class. Then review the **simulation** procedure with students.

▷ The teams are evenly matched—that is, in the long run, each team will win about 50% of the time. Tossing a coin **simulates** the outcome of a game by randomly generating HEADS or TAILS to represent Team 1 or Team 2.

▷ Partners toss a coin to play individual games. If HEADS appears, Team 1 wins the game. If TAILS appears, Team 2 wins the game.

▷ Partners play a series of games until one team wins three games. That team wins the tournament. This type of tournament is sometimes called a "best-of-five" tournament even though fewer than five games might be played. The ways a team can win are listed in the table on the next page.

Best-of-Five Tournament

Games Played	Team Results
3	win-win-win
4	lose-win-win-win win-lose-win-win win-win-lose-win
5	lose-lose-win-win-win lose-win-lose-win-win lose-win-win-lose-win win-lose-lose-win-win win-lose-win-lose-win win-win-lose-lose-win

Model several tournaments with the class before students begin working on their own.

One partner tosses the coin, while the other partner acts as record keeper. The record keeper keeps track of the games and announces when one team has won three games (has won the tournament). The record keeper also makes a tally mark in the table on journal page 260 to show the winner and the number of games played in that tournament. Directions for filling in the table appear at the top of journal page 261.

Partners play a total of 25 tournaments. They switch roles as coin tosser and record keeper midway through the activity. After completing the table, partners should do Problem 2 on journal page 261. Circulate and assist.

✦ Estimating the Chances of Tournament Outcomes (*Math Journal 2,* p. 261)

WHOLE-CLASS DISCUSSION

Discuss students' answers to Problem 4 on journal page 261. There is no need to combine students' results or make one large combined tally. Tally totals will vary from partnership to partnership, so students' estimates will vary. Focus instead on following the correct procedure and interpreting the results. *For example:*

"In our 25 tournaments, there were 11 times when it took 4 games. The chance of a tournament taking 4 games is about $\frac{11}{25}$ or $\frac{44}{100}$. That's a chance of about 44%."

Using Random Numbers (cont.)

2. Use coin tosses to play a "best-of-5" tournament. Make a tally mark in the Tally of Tournaments Won column of the table on page 260. The tally mark shows which team won the tournament and in how many games.

3. Play exactly 24 more tournaments. Make a tally mark to record the result for each tournament. Then convert the tally marks into numbers in the Total Tournaments Won column.

4. Use the table on page 260 to estimate the chance that a tournament takes
Answers vary.
   a. exactly 3 games. ______% b. exactly 4 games. ______%
   c. exactly 5 games. ______% d. fewer than 5 games. ______%

Discuss the following situations with a partner. Record your ideas.

5. Suppose that there is a list of jobs that need to be done for your class (such as distributing supplies, collecting books, and taking messages to the office). How might you use random numbers to assign the jobs "at random," without using any pattern or showing favoritism?
Sample answer: Assign a number to each student (such as 1 to 25 in a 25-student class). Select a job, generate a random number from 1 to 25, and give the job to the student whose number comes up.

6. You want to play a game. The rules are, "Roll 2 dice and add the numbers. Move your marker ahead that many spaces." You do not have any dice. How can you use number cards to play the game?
Sample answer: Use a deck of cards consisting of two cards for each number 1 through 6. For each move, draw two cards and add the numbers. Return the cards to the deck and shuffle the deck.

STUDENT PAGE

✧ *Math Journal 2*, p. 261

NOTE: The theoretical probabilities are as follows: 25% that the tournament will take 3 games; 37.5% that it will take 4 games; and 37.5% that it will take 5 games. Students' tally totals will vary but will generally resemble this pattern.

Mixed Practice

1. $(-49) + 52 =$ 3
2. $100 - (-35) =$ 135
3. $7 * (-90) =$ −630
4. $(-2{,}000) - 300 =$ −2,300
5. $(-40) * (-500) =$ 20,000
6. $2{,}100 \div (-3) =$ −700
7. $\frac{1}{2} * \frac{1}{2} =$ $\frac{1}{4}$
8. $\frac{3}{4} + \frac{1}{2} =$ $1\frac{1}{4}$
9. $4 - \frac{3}{4} =$ $3\frac{1}{4}$
10. $\frac{1}{2}$ of 24 = 12
11. $1.25 + $3.45 = $4.70
12. $1\frac{1}{2} + (-\frac{3}{4}) =$ $\frac{3}{4}$
13. There are 11 classes at Washington School. Each class has about 28 students. What is a good estimate of the number of students at Washington School?
    About 300 students (unit)
14. Stacy has saved $100.37. The picture frame she wants to buy for her parents' anniversary present is $47.56. Does she have enough money to buy two frames?
    yes
    Explain how you know. Sample answer: The cost of the frame is less than $50.00, which is half of $100.00. So Stacy has enough money to buy 2 of them.

STUDENT PAGE

Math Journal 2, p. 262

✦ Using Random Numbers (*Math Journal 2,* p. 261)

PARTNER ACTIVITY

Partners discuss ways in which random numbers might be used in the situations described in Problems 5 and 6 on journal page 261, and they record their ideas. Then volunteers share their ideas with the class.

Adjusting the Activity To show that sums 2 through 12 do not have equal chances of appearing, have 6 partnerships roll pairs of dice 10 times each. One partner counts the number of 7s, 2s, and 12s that result. In 60 rolls, you can expect about ten 7s, two 2s, and two 12s.

ONGOING ASSESSMENT

Use students' answers to Problem 5 to assess their understanding of random numbers.

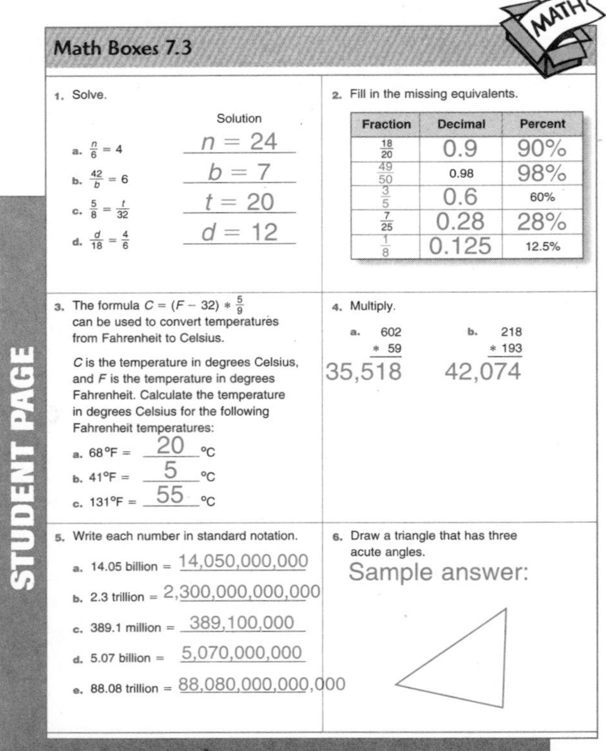

Math Boxes 7.3

1. Solve.

	Solution
a. $\frac{n}{6} = 4$	$n = 24$
b. $\frac{42}{b} = 6$	$b = 7$
c. $\frac{5}{8} = \frac{t}{32}$	$t = 20$
d. $\frac{d}{18} = \frac{4}{6}$	$d = 12$

2. Fill in the missing equivalents.

Fraction	Decimal	Percent
$\frac{18}{20}$	0.9	90%
$\frac{49}{50}$	0.98	98%
$\frac{3}{5}$	0.6	60%
$\frac{7}{25}$	0.28	28%
$\frac{1}{8}$	0.125	12.5%

3. The formula $C = (F - 32) * \frac{5}{9}$ can be used to convert temperatures from Fahrenheit to Celsius.
   C is the temperature in degrees Celsius, and F is the temperature in degrees Fahrenheit. Calculate the temperature in degrees Celsius for the following Fahrenheit temperatures:
   a. 68°F = 20 °C
   b. 41°F = 5 °C
   c. 131°F = 55 °C

4. Multiply.
   a. 602 * 59 = 35,518
   b. 218 * 193 = 42,074

5. Write each number in standard notation.
   a. 14.05 billion = 14,050,000,000
   b. 2.3 trillion = 2,300,000,000,000
   c. 389.1 million = 389,100,000
   d. 5.07 billion = 5,070,000,000
   e. 88.08 trillion = 88,080,000,000,000

6. Draw a triangle that has three acute angles.
   Sample answer:

STUDENT PAGE

Math Journal 2, p. 263

2 Ongoing Learning & Practice

✦ Practicing Computation (*Math Journal 2,* p. 262)

INDEPENDENT ACTIVITY 

Students complete a page of mixed computation practice.

✦ Math Boxes 7.3 (*Math Journal 2,* p. 263)

INDEPENDENT ACTIVITY 

Mixed Review Math Boxes in this lesson are paired with Math Boxes in Lesson 7.1. The skill in Problem 1 is a prerequisite for Unit 8.

✦ Study Link 7.3 (*Math Masters,* p. 330)

Home Connection Students complete a set of probability problems.

Options for Individualizing

✦ EXTRA PRACTICE Playing *Greedy*
(*Math Masters,* p. 117)

WHOLE-CLASS ACTIVITY  **5–15 min** 

The object of *Greedy* is to accumulate the most points by rolling a die.

All students stand up. You roll a die twice. These rolls are free—everyone gets the total of the rolls with no risk.

Before each subsequent roll, ask whether anyone would like to sit down. Students who sit down keep the points they have accumulated. Students who remain standing receive the points from the next roll—unless that roll is a 2. If it is a 2, the students standing lose all of their points for the round, and the round is over. If the roll is not a 2, they add the points to their total. The round continues until everyone is sitting or a 2 is rolled.

Play a total of six rounds. Start each round with everyone standing and two free rolls. Keep a running total during each round, so students can record their scores when they choose to sit. Score sheets are provided on *Math Masters,* page 117. Some students may want to record each roll so that they can sit when they expect a roll of 2. You might keep a record of the rolls on the board for later discussion.

At the end of six rounds, have students find their cumulative totals. The highest "grand total" wins. After each game of six rounds, discuss strategies for winning. Ask questions like the following:

- What is the probability that a 2 will come up on the first roll? $\frac{1}{6}$ On the second roll? $\frac{1}{6}$ The twentieth roll? $\frac{1}{6}$
- Why do more students sit down as the number of rolls in a round increases? They think that the higher the number of rolls, the more likely it is that the next roll will be a 2.
- Why are there streaks of 10 or more rolls without a 2 coming up? The die has no memory. On each roll, the probability is still the same—1 out of 6.
- Does winning seem to rely more on strategy or luck? Expect a variety of answers. Luck is a key factor.

Probability Problems — Study Link 7.3

1. Ron hates to decide what to wear. He made spinners to help him pick his clothes each day. The statements below describe his spinners. Draw spinners to match the statements. Label or color each section with the correct color.

Pants

He is twice as likely to wear his blue pants as his tan pants.

He will wear his black pants about $\frac{1}{4}$ of the time.

About 50% of the time, he will wear his blue pants.

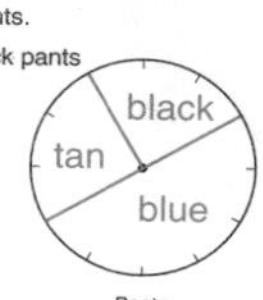

Shirts

He will wear his yellow shirt the least often.

He will wear his red shirt about half as often as his white shirt.

About $37\frac{1}{2}$% of the time, he will wear his blue shirt.

He will wear his white shirt about 1 out of every 3 times.

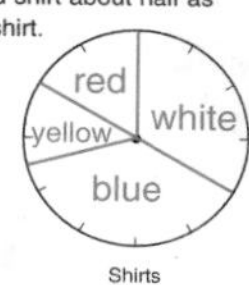

Marlene played a game with a friend. The rules were, "Take turns rolling a die. The first player to roll a 6 wins." Marlene figured she would win if she let her friend roll first.

2. Why did Marlene think she would win if her friend rolled first?
Sample answer: The chance that a 6 will come up is $\frac{1}{6}$; therefore, the more the die is rolled, the more likely it is that a 6 will come up.

3. Do you think she won when her friend rolled first?
Sample answer: It is impossible to tell.
Explain. Although the probability that a 6 will come up is 1 out of 6 times, in a small sample of actual trial results, the outcomes are nearly impossible to predict.

4. Explain how the game changes if the die does not have 6 sides. (There are dice with 4 sides, 8 sides, 12 sides, and 20 sides.)
Sample answer: The chances of rolling a die so that a particular face comes up increases or decreases with the number of faces on the die.

STUDY LINK MASTER

✦ *Math Masters,* p. 330

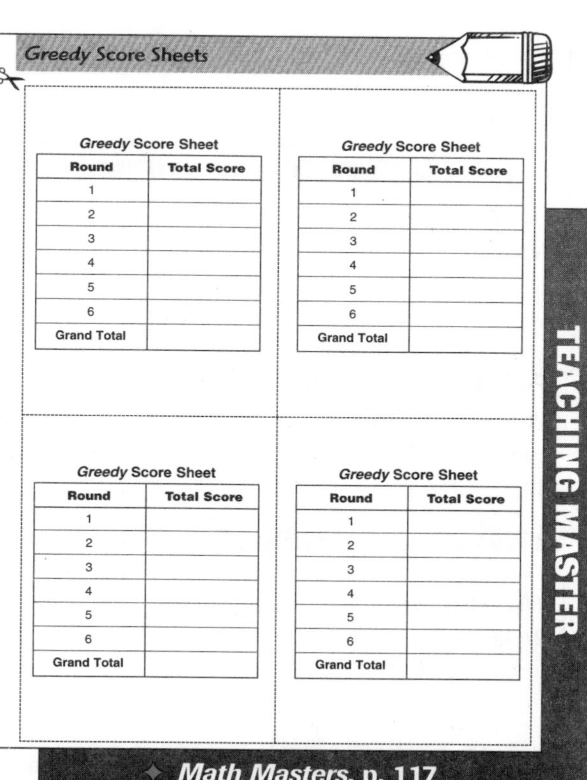

***Greedy* Score Sheets**

Greedy Score Sheet

Round	Total Score
1	
2	
3	
4	
5	
6	
Grand Total	

Greedy Score Sheet

Round	Total Score
1	
2	
3	
4	
5	
6	
Grand Total	

Greedy Score Sheet

Round	Total Score
1	
2	
3	
4	
5	
6	
Grand Total	

Greedy Score Sheet

Round	Total Score
1	
2	
3	
4	
5	
6	
Grand Total	

TEACHING MASTER

✦ *Math Masters,* p. 117

7.4 Tree Diagrams

OBJECTIVES **To use tree diagrams to find expected outcomes for chance events; and to compare actual results of a simulation to expected outcomes.**

summaries	materials
1 Teaching the Lesson	
Students are introduced to tree diagrams and use them to find expected outcomes for random-walk (maze) problems. They carry out a series of simulations and compare the actual results to the expected outcomes. [Data and Chance]	☐ *Math Journal 2,* pp. 264 and 265 ☐ Study Link 7.3 ☐ Assessment Master (*Math Masters,* p. 478; optional) ☐ Transparencies (*Math Masters,* p. 118, optional; and p. 119) ☐ Per partnership: number cards 1–4 (from the Everything Math Deck, if available); penny or counter
2 Ongoing Learning & Practice	
Students play *Frac-Tac-Toe* to practice fraction, decimal, and percent conversions. [Numeration] Students practice and maintain skills through Math Boxes and Study Link activities.	☐ *Math Journal 2,* p. 266 ☐ *Student Reference Book,* pp. 290–292 ☐ Teaching Masters (*Math Masters,* pp. 67–78) ☐ Study Link Master (*Math Masters,* p. 331) ☐ calculator ☐ 4 each of number cards 0–10 (from the Everything Math Deck, if available)
3 Options for Individualizing	
Enrichment Students use tree diagrams to make predictions about winning in a maze contest. [Data and Chance]	☐ Teaching Masters (*Math Masters,* pp. 120 and 121) ☐ Per partnership: number cards 1–4 (from the Everything Math Deck, if available); counter

Additional Information

Vocabulary • **tree diagram** • **expected outcomes** • **actual results**

Getting Started

Mental Math and Reflexes

Write fractions, mixed numbers, and decimals on the board. Students find their reciprocals. *Suggestions:*

- $\frac{3}{8}$ $\frac{8}{3}$
- $\frac{6}{7}$ $\frac{7}{6}$
- $\frac{10}{5}$ $\frac{5}{10}$
- $4\frac{1}{4}$
- $1\frac{1}{2}$ $\frac{2}{3}$
- 0.3 $\frac{10}{3}$, or $3.\overline{3}$
- 1.15 $\frac{100}{115}$, or 0.87 rounded

Math Message

Complete the problems on journal page 264.

Study Link 7.3 Follow-Up

Have volunteers explain their strategies for figuring out the spinner sections and Marlene's incorrect strategy. If you have polyhedral dice available, show them to the class. Ask students whether they think that dice with more or fewer than six sides are fair. If all of the faces are congruent, the interior angles are equal, and the material is uniform, the dice should be fair.

1 Teaching the Lesson

✦ Math Message Follow-Up (*Math Journal 2,* p. 264)

WHOLE-CLASS DISCUSSION 

Briefly discuss students' answers as well as their solution strategies.

✦ Finding Expected Outcomes with a Tree Diagram (*Math Journal 2,* p. 264; *Math Masters,* p. 118)

WHOLE-CLASS DISCUSSION 

Call students' attention to the **tree diagram** at the bottom of journal page 264. You may want to display the top diagram on *Math Masters,* page 118 on an overhead transparency. (*See margin on next page.*) Use the diagram to demonstrate how a tree diagram can help solve maze problems. The following procedure is suggested:

1. In the first box of the tree diagram, record the number 80—the number of people who enter the maze and reach the first intersection.
2. The path then divides into four paths. Since there is an equal chance of selecting any one of the paths, one-fourth of the people will select each path. Write 20 in each of the four boxes.
3. At the next intersection, each path divides into two more paths. One-half of the 20 people at an intersection will follow one path, and one-half will follow the other. Record 10 in each of the eight boxes.

Five of the boxes represent exits into Room A, and three boxes represent exits into Room B. Therefore, 50 people are expected to end up in Room A, and 30 people are expected to end up in Room B. These are the **expected outcomes,** if 80 people take turns walking through the maze.

Mazes and Tree Diagrams

The diagram at the right shows a maze. A person walking through the maze does not know in advance how many paths there are or how they divide.

Pretend that you are walking through the maze. Each time the path divides, you select your next path at random. The paths that you can take next all have the same chance of being selected. You may not retrace your steps.

Enter

Room A

Room B

Depending on which paths you follow, you will end up in either Room A or Room B.

1. In which room are you more likely to end up—Room A or Room B? Room A
2. Suppose 80 people took turns walking through the maze.
   a. About how many people would you expect to end up in Room A? 50 people
   b. About how many people would you expect to end up in Room B? 30 people

Your teacher will show you how to complete the following tree diagram. Or you can find out for yourself by reading pages 143 and 144 in the *Student Reference Book.*

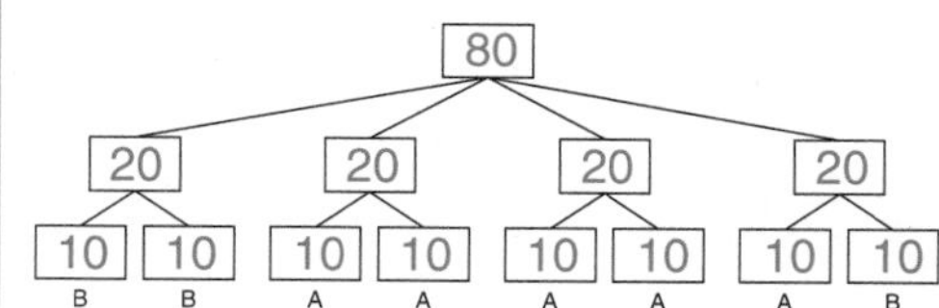

STUDENT PAGE

✦ *Math Journal 2,* p. 264

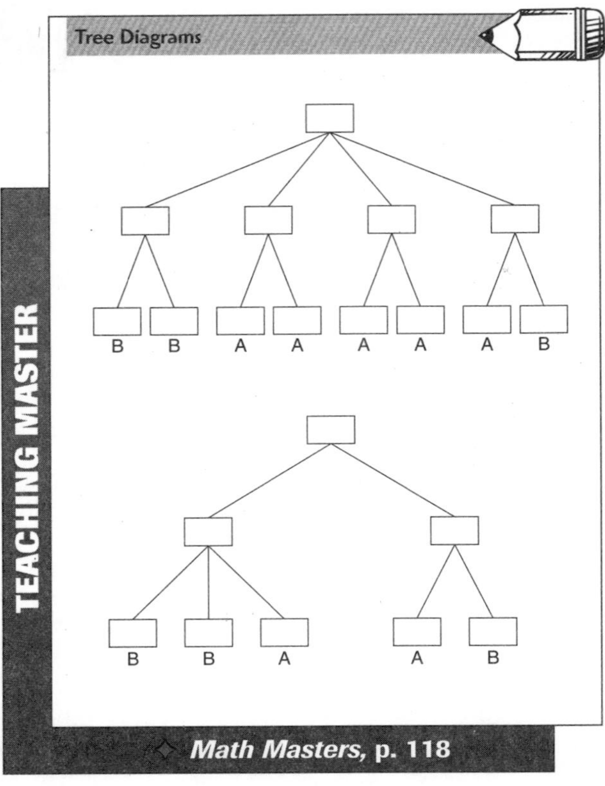

Math Masters, p. 118

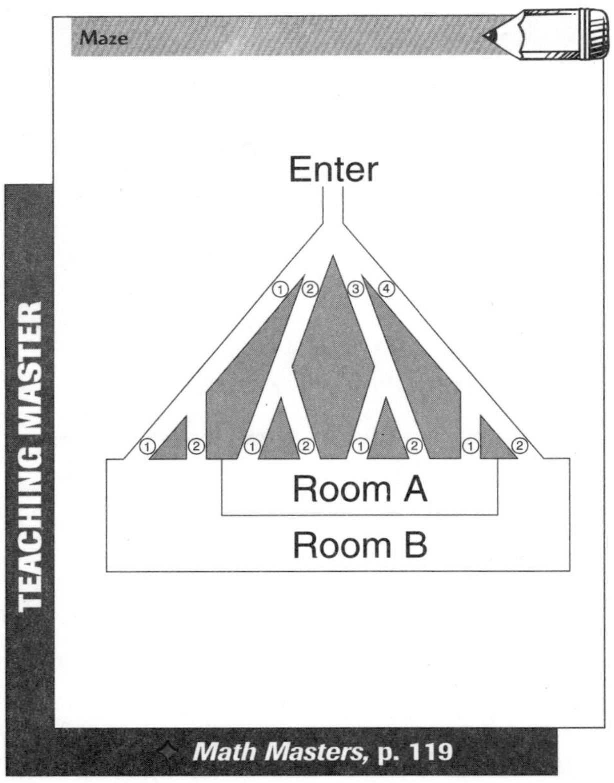

Math Masters, p. 119

✦ Simulating Results with a Tree Diagram
(*Math Journal 2,* p. 264; *Math Masters,* pp. 119)

PARTNER ACTIVITY

With the class, simulate a random walk through the maze on journal page 264. Use an overhead transparency of *Math Masters,* page 119, number cards to generate random numbers, and a counter.

Suggested procedure

1. Place the counter at the entry to the maze and move it along the path to the first intersection. Here the path divides into four paths, numbered 1, 2, 3, and 4.
2. Use number cards 1, 2, 3, and 4 to generate a random number. Shuffle the cards and draw one without looking. The number on the card determines which path to follow.
3. Move the counter along that path to the next intersection. No matter which of the four paths was previously selected, the path now divides into two paths, numbered 1 and 2.
4. Using number cards 1 and 2, draw a card to determine which path to follow next. Move the counter along that path, to either Room A or Room B.

NOTE: Once the choices are narrowed to 2, students may use a coin to determine the path chosen: HEADS, path 1; TAILS, path 2.

Repeat the random walk through the maze several more times, or as needed in order for students to understand.

Then divide the class into partnerships. Each partnership takes 10 random walks through the maze and tallies the number of times they end up in Room A and the number of times in Room B.

Select eight partnerships and record their results on the board. Combine the results to get a total of 80 random walks. These are the **actual results** from simulating the walks of 80 people through the maze.

Compare the expected outcomes to the actual results for 80 random walks through the maze. Emphasize that expected outcomes need not match actual results.

It is important that students understand the difference between *expected outcomes* and the *actual results* from simulating or observing a chance event. These may be similar or very different. However, the more times a chance event occurs, the closer the actual results are likely to come to the expected outcomes. Be sure to reiterate this idea throughout the unit, when students compare actual results to expected outcomes.

ONGOING ASSESSMENT

To assess students' understanding of the concepts of expected outcomes and actual results, have students complete an Exit Slip (*Math Masters,* page 478) describing the differences between them.

✦ Solving Maze Problems (*Math Journal 2,* p. 265)

PARTNER ACTIVITY

Partners work through the problems on journal page 265. A tree diagram is provided in Problem 1. Students draw their own tree diagram for Problem 2. Circulate and assist.

Adjusting the Activity If students are having difficulty, you may want to go over the solution to Problem 1, using the bottom diagram on the transparency of *Math Masters,* page 118, before they attempt Problem 2.

When discussing Problem 1, point out that although there are five exits, it does not necessarily follow that one-fifth of the 60 people (12 people) reach each exit.

Maze Problems

1. Use the tree diagram below to help you solve the following problem. Suppose that 60 people walk through the maze below.
   a. About how many people would you expect to end up in Room A? 25 people
   b. About how many people would you expect to end up in Room B? 35 people

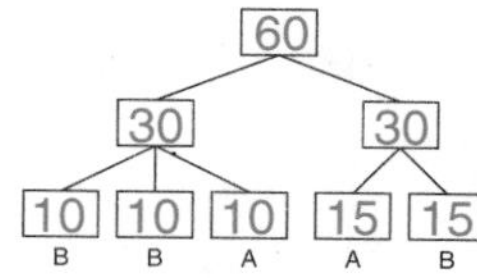

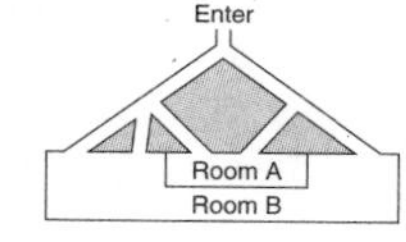

2. Make your own tree diagram to help you solve the following problem. Suppose that 120 people walk through the maze below.
   a. About how many people would you expect to end up in Room A? 50 people
   b. About how many people would you expect to end up in Room B? 70 people

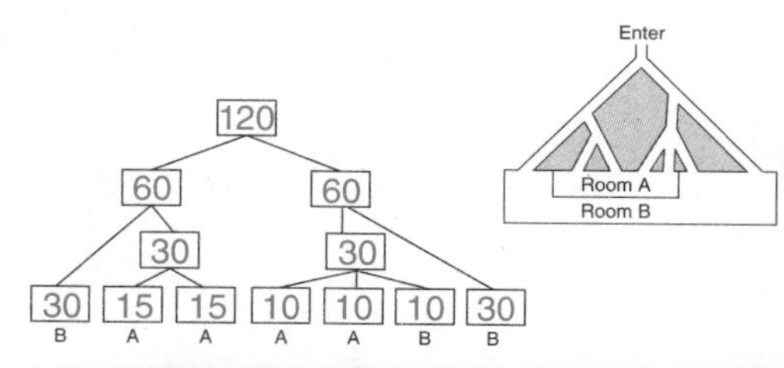

STUDENT PAGE

✧ *Math Journal 2,* p. 265

2 Ongoing Learning & Practice

✦ Playing *Frac-Tac-Toe* (*Student Reference Book,* pp. 290–292; *Math Masters,* pp. 67–78)

PARTNER ACTIVITY

Students play *Frac-Tac-Toe* (the version of your choice) to practice finding equivalent fractions, decimals, and percents.

✦ Math Boxes 7.4 (*Math Journal 2,* p. 266)

INDEPENDENT ACTIVITY

Mixed Review Math Boxes in this lesson are paired with Math Boxes in Lesson 7.2. The skill in Problem 1 is a prerequisite for Unit 8.

Math Boxes 7.4

1. Divide.
   a. 7)2,045 — 292 R1
   b. 46)552 — 12
   c. 32)2,714 — 84 R26

2. Complete the table for the formula below. Then plot the points to make a graph.

   Formula: $4h = g$

h	g
1	4
2	8
3	12
5	20
6.5	26

3. The highest point in North America is the top of Mt. McKinley, Alaska, with an elevation of 20,320 feet. The highest point in the lower 48 states of the United States is the top of Mt. Whitney, California, with an elevation of 14,494 feet. The lowest point in the United States is in Death Valley, California, at 282 feet below sea level.
   a. How much higher is the top of Mt. McKinley than Mt. Whitney? 5,826 ft
   b. How many feet below Mt. McKinley is Death Valley? 20,602 ft

STUDENT PAGE

✧ *Math Journal 2,* p. 266

Tree Diagrams

Study Link 7.4

Suppose you are walking through a maze. When the path divides, you randomly select the next path to follow. Each path has an equal chance of being selected. You may not retrace your steps. Depending on which paths you follow, you will end up in one room or another.

You may wish to make tree diagrams to help you solve the following problems.

1. Suppose 300 people take turns walking through the maze below.

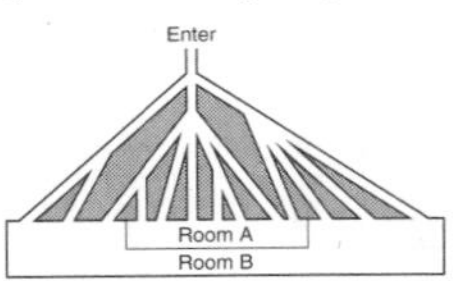

a. About how many people would you expect to end up in Room A? 115 people

b. About how many people would you expect to end up in Room B? 185 people

2. Suppose 112 people take turns walking through the maze below.

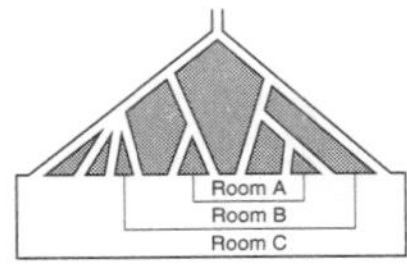

a. About how many people would you expect to end up in Room A? 35 people

b. About how many people would you expect to end up in Room B? 28 people

c. About how many people would you expect to end up in Room C? 49 people

STUDY LINK MASTER

Math Masters, p. 331

◆ Study Link 7.4 (*Math Masters*, p. 331)

Home Connection Students solve maze problems similar to those in the lesson.

3 Options for Individualizing

◆ ENRICHMENT Running an Amazing Contest (*Math Masters*, pp. 120 and 121)

PARTNER ACTIVITY

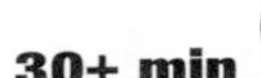

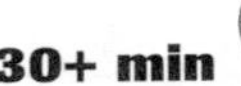

30+ min

Consumer Education Link Students experiment with a maze contest. They try to determine a balance between the entry fee and the winnings, so that contestants will believe they can win and the class will make some money at the same time.

An Amazing Contest

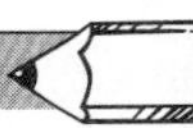

The sixth graders at Bailey School want to raise money to buy a microscope. Students have created the maze shown below, which they will use for a contest. Each contestant pays a fee and tries to go from Start to Exit without retracing any steps. Anyone not ending up at a dead end wins a prize.

The paths at each intersection are numbered. When a contestant reaches an intersection, the contestant chooses the next path at random, using number cards.

Suppose that you are going to try the maze. There are 3 different paths at Start. To decide which path to follow, pick a card without looking from a set of cards having 1, 2, and 3. If the card you choose is 1, follow Path 1. This leads to a dead end, so you lose.

If the card you choose at Start is 2, follow Path 2. This leads to an intersection that divides into 4 different paths. Pick from a set of cards having 1, 2, 3, and 4 to see which path to follow next. You win if you follow Path 3.

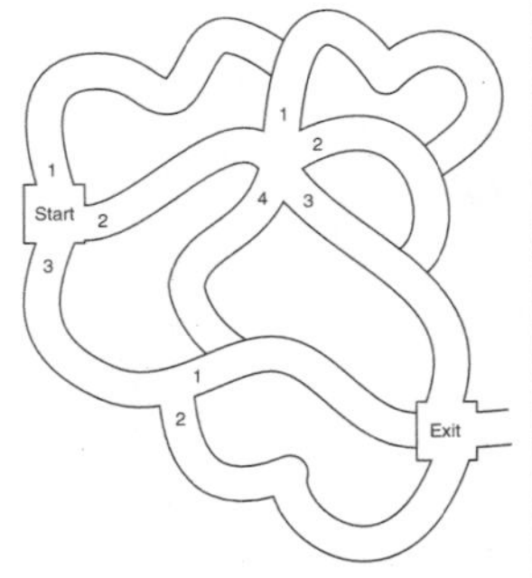

If you choose the number 3 at Start, follow Path 3. This leads to an intersection that divides into 2 different paths. Pick from a set of cards having 1 and 2 to see which path to follow next. You win if you follow Path 2.

Work with a partner. Take turns trying to get through the maze. Each of you should try a total of 6 times. What fraction of the time did you and your partner reach the Exit? Answers vary.

I reached the Exit ________ of the time.

My partner reached the Exit ________ of the time.

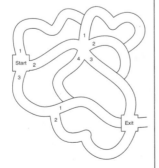

TEACHING MASTER

Math Masters, p. 120

Analyzing the Amazing Contest

Make a tree diagram of the contest maze to help you solve the following problems.

Start: 60 → (1) 20; (2) 20; (3) 20
(2) 20 → (1) 5; (2) 5; (3) 5 Exit; (4) 5
(3) 20 → (1) 10; (2) 10 Exit

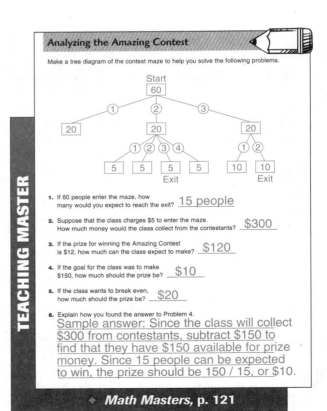

1. If 60 people enter the maze, how many would you expect to reach the exit? 15 people

2. Suppose that the class charges $5 to enter the maze. How much money would the class collect from the contestants? $300

3. If the prize for winning the Amazing Contest is $12, how much can the class expect to make? $120

4. If the goal for the class was to make $150, how much should the prize be? $10

5. If the class wants to break even, how much should the prize be? $20

6. Explain how you found the answer to Problem 4.
Sample answer: Since the class will collect $300 from contestants, subtract $150 to find that they have $150 available for prize money. Since 15 people can be expected to win, the prize should be 150 / 15, or $10.

TEACHING MASTER

Math Masters, p. 121

7.5 Using Tree Diagrams to Calculate Probabilities

OBJECTIVE **To use tree diagrams to help calculate the probabilities of the outcomes of chance events.**

summaries	materials
1 Teaching the Lesson	
Students use tree diagrams to help them calculate the probabilities of the outcomes of random walks and other chance events. [Data and Chance]	□ *Math Journal 2,* pp. 268 and 269 □ Study Link 7.4 □ Assessment Master (*Math Masters,* p. 473; optional) □ Transparency (*Math Masters,* p. 118; optional)
2 Ongoing Learning & Practice	
Students play *Angle Tangle* to review how to estimate and measure the sizes of angles. [Measurement and Reference Frames; Geometry] Students practice and maintain skills through Math Boxes and Study Link activities.	□ *Math Journal 2,* p. 267 □ *Student Reference Book,* p. 278 □ Study Link Master (*Math Masters,* p. 332) □ Geometry Template, or straightedge and protractor
3 Options for Individualizing	
Extra Practice Students use tree diagrams to predict outcomes in a coin-flipping experiment. [Data and Chance]	□ Teaching Master (*Math Masters,* p. 122) □ Per partnership: 1 coin (optional)

Additional Information

Vocabulary • **probability tree diagram**

Getting Started

Mental Math and Reflexes

Play "What number am I?" Consider writing the clues on the board or overhead projector.

Suggestions

- Square me and add 10 to get 74. 8
- Cube me. Add 36. Divide by 4 to get 25. 4
- Divide 10 to the fifth power by me and add 100 to get 50,100. 2
- Take $\frac{1}{2}$ of me. Add 43. Divide by 3 to get 21. 40
- Multiply me by 25. Take my square root. Double that to get 20. 4

Math Message

Tim is late to school about 1 day out of 10. About how many times will Tim be late in 30 school days? In 200 school days?

Study Link 7.4 Follow-Up

Review the answers as necessary.

1 Teaching the Lesson

✦Math Message Follow-Up

WHOLE-CLASS DISCUSSION

The *probability* that Tim will be late on any particular school day is $\frac{1}{10} = 0.1 = 10\%$. This probability does not change. It is $\frac{1}{10}$ every school day. But the *expected number* of late arrivals depends on the number of days being considered.

▷ For 30 school days, Tim is expected to be late $\frac{1}{10}$ of 30 days, or 3 days.

▷ For 200 school days, Tim is expected to be late $\frac{1}{10}$ of 200 days, or 20 days.

✦Revisiting Probability Tree Diagrams

(*Math Journal 2,* p. 268; *Math Masters,* p. 118)

WHOLE-CLASS ACTIVITY

Problems 1 and 2 on journal page 268 show the same mazes used in Lesson 7.4. (See journal pages 264 and 265.) The mazes remain the same, but the questions change. In Lesson 7.4, students were told the number of people who entered a maze and were asked how many could be expected to enter Rooms A and B.

In this lesson, students calculate the probability that a person walking through the maze enters Room A and the probability that the person enters Room B.

Do Problem 1 with the class. If you have an overhead transparency of *Math Masters,* page 118, use the top diagram. Go through each step carefully, making sure that students understand the procedure.

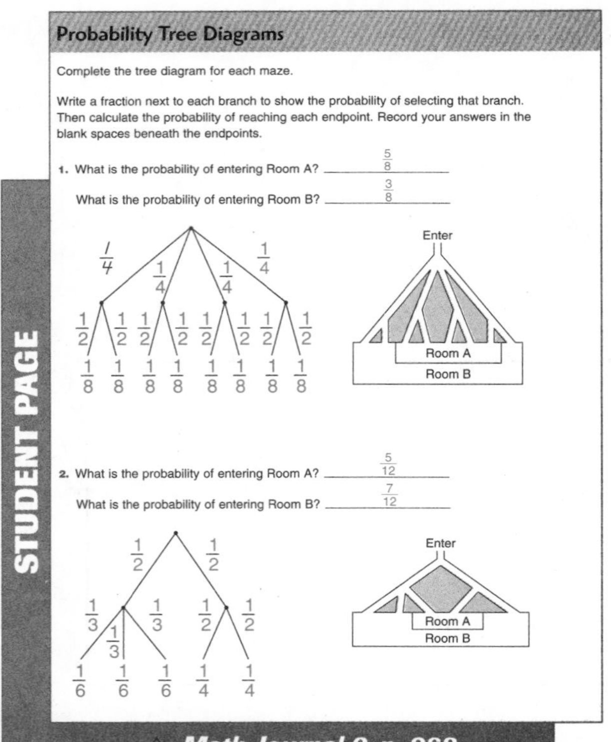

STUDENT PAGE

Probability Tree Diagrams

Complete the tree diagram for each maze.

Write a fraction next to each branch to show the probability of selecting that branch. Then calculate the probability of reaching each endpoint. Record your answers in the blank spaces beneath the endpoints.

1. What is the probability of entering Room A? $\frac{5}{8}$

   What is the probability of entering Room B? $\frac{3}{8}$

2. What is the probability of entering Room A? $\frac{5}{12}$

   What is the probability of entering Room B? $\frac{7}{12}$

Math Journal 2, p. 268

Step 1: Calculate the probability of reaching each of the endpoints.

▷ Since the tree diagram divides into 4 branches at the first intersection, the probability of following any one of these branches is $\frac{1}{4}$. Write $\frac{1}{4}$ next to each branch.

▷ For each of the second set of intersections, the probability of following any one of the branches is $\frac{1}{2}$. Write $\frac{1}{2}$ next to each branch.

▷ Next, calculate the probabilities of reaching each of the endpoints of the tree diagram. To reach these endpoints, the first branch is taken $\frac{1}{4}$ of the time, and each of the second branches $\frac{1}{2}$ of $\frac{1}{4}$ of the time, or $\frac{1}{2} * \frac{1}{4}$ of the time.

▷ $\frac{1}{2} * \frac{1}{4} = \frac{1}{8}$, so the probability of reaching any one of the endpoints is $\frac{1}{8}$. Record this probability at each endpoint.

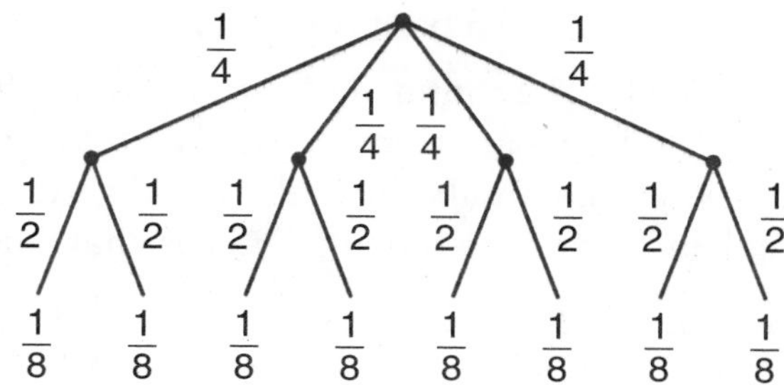

Students should notice that to calculate the probability of any of the endpoints in the diagram, they can multiply the probabilities of the branches that lead to that endpoint (that is, $\frac{1}{2} * \frac{1}{4}$, or $\frac{1}{8}$).

Step 2: Calculate the probabilities of entering each room.

▷ Use the **probability tree diagram** to calculate the probability of entering Room A and the probability of entering Room B.

▷ There are 5 different endpoints in Room A. Add the probabilities of reaching these endpoints. The probability of entering Room A is

$$\frac{1}{8} + \frac{1}{8} + \frac{1}{8} + \frac{1}{8} + \frac{1}{8}\text{, or } \frac{5}{8}.$$

▷ There are 3 different endpoints in Room B. Add the probabilities of reaching these endpoints. The probability of entering Room B is

$$\frac{1}{8} + \frac{1}{8} + \frac{1}{8}\text{, or } \frac{3}{8}.$$

From Step 2, we know the chances that a person will enter Rooms A and B. If a large number of people enter the maze, the expected number entering each room can be found. Use the example on the following page to illustrate this.

Example

Suppose 80 people walk through the maze.

The probability of entering Room A is $\frac{5}{8}$.

The number of people who can be expected to enter Room A is $\frac{5}{8}$ of 80, or 50 people. Similarly, 30 people ($\frac{3}{8}$ of 80) can be expected to enter Room B.

Adjusting the Activity You may want to refer students back to journal page 264, where they worked with numbers on the tree diagram. Relate the numbers at each step to the fraction of people walking a given path. Remind students that the *whole* changes as each new intersection is reached. In the beginning, the whole is 80 people, and $\frac{1}{4}$ of 80 people, or 20 people, walk down each path. At the next intersection, the whole is 20 people. One-half of 20 people, or 10 people, continue down each path from there.

This idea can be confusing to students. In the first problem, it appears that the original total can be divided by the number of exits. Looking at the second problem, however, students will see that this is a faulty strategy.

Ask students to work on Problem 2 on their own. After a few minutes, bring the class together to discuss the answers. You might want to use the diagram at the bottom of the transparency of *Math Masters,* page 118 to discuss the problem. The probability of entering Room B is $\frac{1}{6} + \frac{1}{6} + \frac{1}{4}$, or $\frac{7}{12}$.

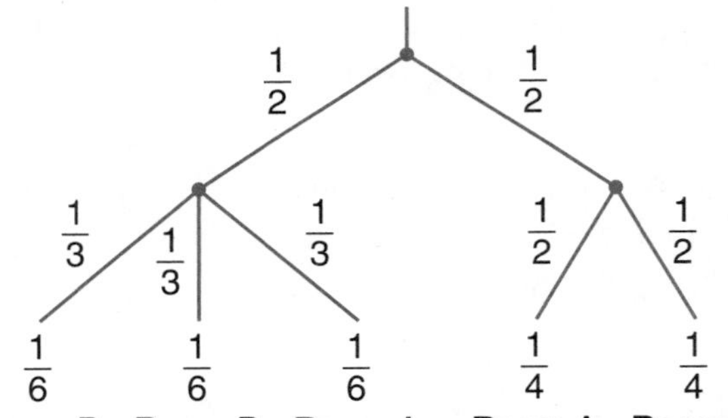

The probability of entering Room A is $\frac{1}{6} + \frac{1}{4}$, or $\frac{5}{12}$.

Pose a problem related to this diagram. Ask: *If 60 people walk through the maze, about how many would enter Room A?* $\frac{5}{12}$ of 60, or 25 people *About how many would enter Room B?* $\frac{7}{12}$ of 60, or 35 people

✦Calculating Probabilities with Tree Diagrams
(*Math Journal 2,* p. 269)

INDEPENDENT ACTIVITY 

Read the introduction to the problem as a class so that students know what to do. The tree diagram has already been drawn and labeled. Students should quickly notice that the probability of taking any path in Problem 3 is $\frac{1}{3} * \frac{1}{2}$, or $\frac{1}{6}$. Circulate and assist.

ONGOING ASSESSMENT

Use a Math Log page (*Math Masters,* page 473) to have students answer the following question:

- **Consider what the following numbers represent: $\frac{1}{4}$ of a probability of an outcome; $\frac{1}{4}$ of a pizza. What are the similarities?** The notation is the same; they both stand for 1 out of 4 of something; the "something" or whole is different.

Probability Tree Diagrams (cont.)

3. Josh has 3 clean shirts (red, blue, and green) and 2 clean pairs of pants (tan and black). He randomly selects one shirt. Then he randomly selects a pair of pants.

   a. Complete the tree diagram. Write a fraction next to each branch to show the probability of selecting that branch.

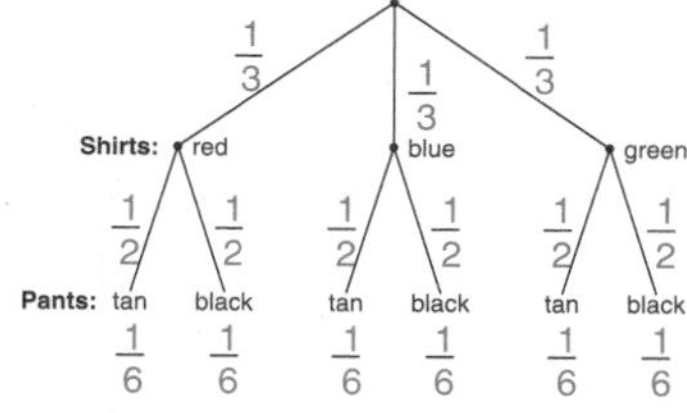

   b. List all possible shirt-pants combinations. One has been done for you.
   red–tan red-black, blue-tan, blue-black, green-tan, green-black

   c. How many different shirt-pants combinations are there? 6 combinations

   d. Do all of the shirt-pants combinations have the same chance of being selected? yes

   e. What is the probability that Josh will select
   the blue shirt? $\frac{1}{3}$ the blue shirt and the tan pants? $\frac{1}{6}$
   the tan pants? $\frac{1}{2}$ a shirt that is not red? $\frac{2}{3}$
   the black pants and a shirt that is not red? $\frac{1}{3}$

STUDENT PAGE

✧ *Math Journal 2,* p. 269

Ongoing Learning & Practice

✦Playing *Angle Tangle*
(*Student Reference Book,* p. 278)

PARTNER ACTIVITY 

Students play this game, introduced in Lesson 5.1, to practice estimating and measuring the sizes of angles.

✦Math Boxes 7.5 (*Math Journal 2,* p. 267)

INDEPENDENT ACTIVITY 

Mixed Review Math Boxes in this lesson are paired with Math Boxes in Lesson 7.7. The skill in Problem 1 is a prerequisite for Unit 8.

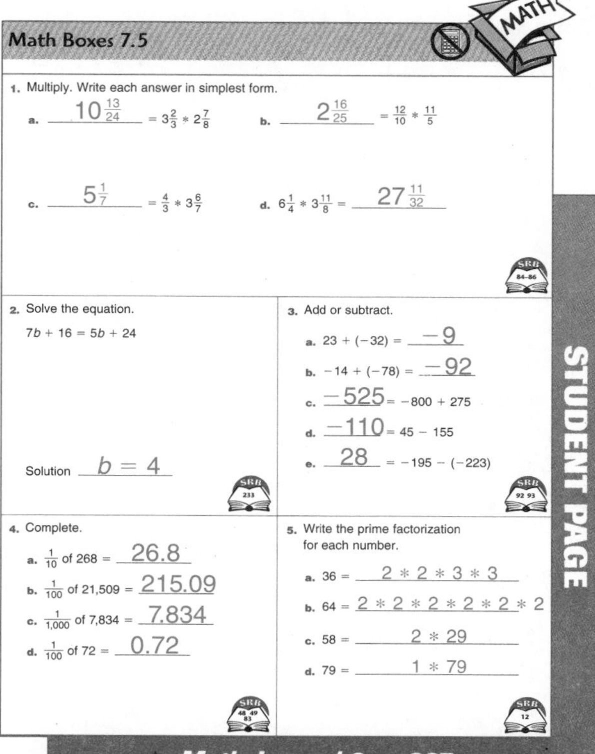

Math Boxes 7.5

1. Multiply. Write each answer in simplest form.
   a. $10\frac{13}{24} = 3\frac{2}{3} * 2\frac{7}{8}$
   b. $2\frac{16}{25} = \frac{12}{10} * \frac{11}{5}$
   c. $5\frac{1}{7} = \frac{4}{3} * 3\frac{6}{7}$
   d. $6\frac{1}{4} * 3\frac{11}{8} = 27\frac{11}{32}$

2. Solve the equation.
   $7b + 16 = 5b + 24$
   Solution $b = 4$

3. Add or subtract.
   a. $23 + (-32) = -9$
   b. $-14 + (-78) = -92$
   c. $-525 = -800 + 275$
   d. $-110 = 45 - 155$
   e. $28 = -195 - (-223)$

4. Complete.
   a. $\frac{1}{10}$ of 268 = 26.8
   b. $\frac{1}{100}$ of 21,509 = 215.09
   c. $\frac{1}{1,000}$ of 7,834 = 7.834
   d. $\frac{1}{100}$ of 72 = 0.72

5. Write the prime factorization for each number.
   a. 36 = 2 * 2 * 3 * 3
   b. 64 = 2 * 2 * 2 * 2 * 2 * 2
   c. 58 = 2 * 29
   d. 79 = 1 * 79

STUDENT PAGE

✧ *Math Journal 2,* p. 267

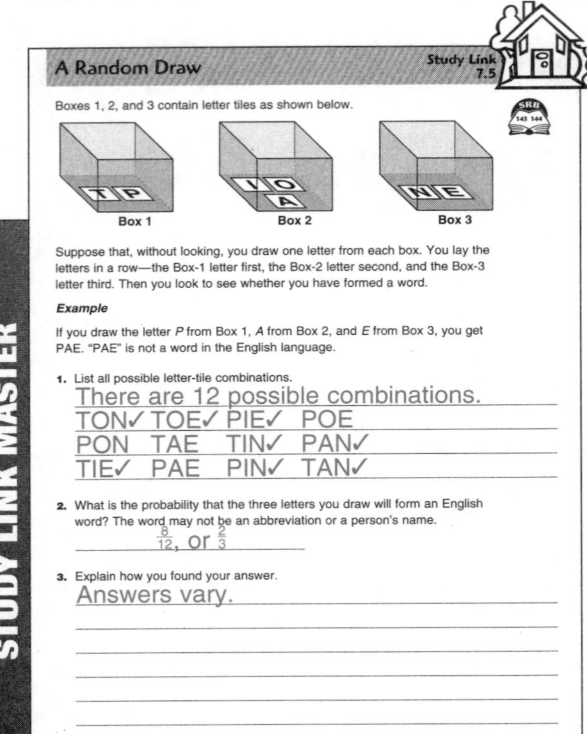

A Random Draw

Study Link 7.5

SRB 143 144

Boxes 1, 2, and 3 contain letter tiles as shown below.

Box 1: T P — Box 2: I O A — Box 3: N E

Suppose that, without looking, you draw one letter from each box. You lay the letters in a row—the Box-1 letter first, the Box-2 letter second, and the Box-3 letter third. Then you look to see whether you have formed a word.

Example

If you draw the letter *P* from Box 1, *A* from Box 2, and *E* from Box 3, you get PAE. "PAE" is not a word in the English language.

1. List all possible letter-tile combinations.
   There are 12 possible combinations.
   TON✓ TOE✓ PIE✓ POE
   PON TAE TIN✓ PAN✓
   TIE✓ PAE PIN✓ TAN✓
2. What is the probability that the three letters you draw will form an English word? The word may not be an abbreviation or a person's name.
   $\frac{8}{12}$, or $\frac{2}{3}$
3. Explain how you found your answer.
   Answers vary.

STUDY LINK MASTER

Math Masters, p. 332

✦ Study Link 7.5 (*Math Masters,* p. 332)

Home Connection Students solve a problem involving random draws.

3 Options for Individualizing

✦ EXTRA PRACTICE Experimenting with Coin Flips (*Math Masters,* p. 122)

PARTNER ACTIVITY **15–30 min**

Students predict the results of a coin-flipping experiment with the help of tree diagrams. They analyze the results and answer questions about the experiment.

Adjusting the Activity Students can extend the activity by actually carrying out the experiment, doing 3 flips of the coin a large number of times and keeping a record of the results. They should compare the actual results with the predicted results.

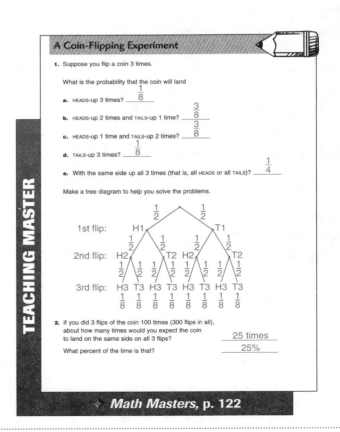

A Coin-Flipping Experiment

1. Suppose you flip a coin 3 times.

   What is the probability that the coin will land

   a. HEADS-up 3 times? $\frac{1}{8}$

   b. HEADS-up 2 times and TAILS-up 1 time? $\frac{3}{8}$

   c. HEADS-up 1 time and TAILS-up 2 times? $\frac{3}{8}$

   d. TAILS-up 3 times? $\frac{1}{8}$

   e. With the same side up all 3 times (that is, all HEADS or all TAILS)? $\frac{1}{4}$

   Make a tree diagram to help you solve the problems.

   1st flip: H1 ($\frac{1}{2}$), T1 ($\frac{1}{2}$)

   2nd flip: H2 ($\frac{1}{2}$), T2 ($\frac{1}{2}$), H2 ($\frac{1}{2}$), T2 ($\frac{1}{2}$)

   3rd flip: H3 T3 H3 T3 H3 T3 H3 T3 (each branch $\frac{1}{2}$)

   $\frac{1}{8}$ $\frac{1}{8}$ $\frac{1}{8}$ $\frac{1}{8}$ $\frac{1}{8}$ $\frac{1}{8}$ $\frac{1}{8}$ $\frac{1}{8}$

2. If you did 3 flips of the coin 100 times (300 flips in all), about how many times would you expect the coin to land on the same side on all 3 flips? 25 times

   What percent of the time is that? 25%

TEACHING MASTER

Math Masters, p. 122

7.6 Venn Diagrams

OBJECTIVE **To use Venn diagrams to analyze situations.**

summaries	materials
1 Teaching the Lesson	
Students use Venn diagrams to analyze situations whose descriptions include words such as *in either, in both, not in both,* and *in at least one.* [Data and Chance]	☐ *Math Journal 2,* pp. 270 and 271 ☐ Study Link 7.5 ☐ Assessment Master (*Math Masters,* p. 478; optional) ☐ Transparency (*Math Masters,* p. 123; optional)
2 Ongoing Learning & Practice	
Students use a tree diagram to help them answer questions about a train schedule. [Data and Chance] Students practice and maintain skills through Math Boxes and Study Link activities.	☐ *Math Journal 2,* pp. 272 and 273 ☐ Study Link Master (*Math Masters,* p. 333)
3 Options for Individualizing	
Enrichment Students consider the relationship between data in tables and data in Venn diagrams. [Data and Chance] **Enrichment** Students investigate the relationship between Venn diagrams and Internet searches. [Data and Chance]	☐ Teaching Master (*Math Masters,* p. 124) ***See* Advance Preparation**

Additional Information

Advance Preparation To do the second optional Enrichment activity in Part 3, you will need a computer with Internet access and a search engine.

Vocabulary • **Venn diagram**

Getting Started

Mental Math and Reflexes

Students show "thumbs up" if a number sentence is true and "thumbs down" if a number sentence is false.

Suggestions

- $12 + (-10) = -2$ down
- $-14 + 5 = -9$ up
- $30 - 4 = -4$ down
- $50 - (-28) = 78$ up
- $25 - 28 = -3$ up
- $-14 - (-5) = 9$ down
- $100 + -75 = -25$ down
- $-23 - (-8) = -15$ up

Math Message

Complete the problems on journal page 270.

Study Link 7.5 Follow-Up

With the help of the class, make a tree diagram to find the possible 3-letter combinations. (*See below.*) Remind students that the first letter must come from Box 1, the second letter from Box 2, and the third letter from Box 3. There are 12 possible combinations.

The probability of any one of these combinations is $\frac{1}{2} * \frac{1}{3} * \frac{1}{2} = \frac{1}{12}$.

Eight of the 12 combinations are words in the English language (shown in boldface type). Therefore, the probability of forming an English word is $\frac{8}{12}$, or $\frac{2}{3}$.

Box 1:	T			P		
Box 2:	O	I	A	O	I	A
Box 3:	N E	N E	N E	N E	N E	N E
	TON	**TIN**	**TAN**	PON	**PIN**	**PAN**
	TOE	**TIE**	TAE	POE	**PIE**	PAE

1 Teaching the Lesson

✦Math Message Follow-Up
(*Math Journal 2,* p. 270; *Math Masters,* p. 123)

NOTE: Venn diagrams are named for John Venn (1834–1923), a British mathematician, who introduced them in 1880.

WHOLE-CLASS DISCUSSION

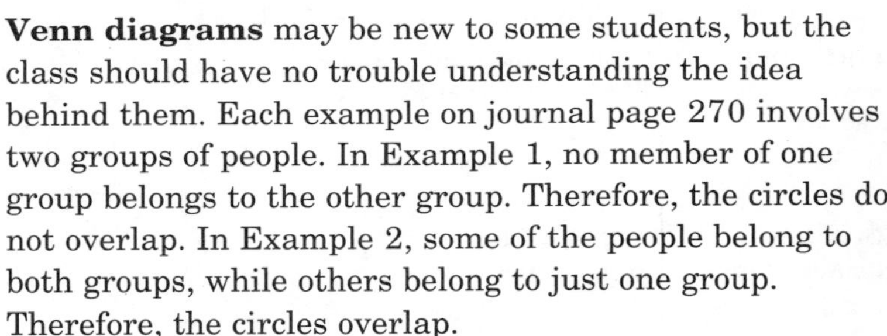

Venn diagrams may be new to some students, but the class should have no trouble understanding the idea behind them. Each example on journal page 270 involves two groups of people. In Example 1, no member of one group belongs to the other group. Therefore, the circles do not overlap. In Example 2, some of the people belong to both groups, while others belong to just one group. Therefore, the circles overlap.

Make sure that students understand Example 2. You might want to use a transparency of *Math Masters,* page 123.

- What do the numbers 21, 5, and 19 mean? 21 students are in the math class but not in the science class. 19 are in the science class but not in the math class. 5 are in both classes.
- How were the numbers 21 and 19 obtained? There are 26 students in the math class, but 5 are in both classes. Subtract the number of students in both classes from 26: 26 − 5 = 21. Similarly, 24 − 5 = 19.

STUDENT PAGE

Venn Diagrams

A Venn diagram is a picture in which circles show relationships between sets.

Example 1

At Lincoln Middle School, every student is required to take a music class. 75 students play an instrument. They take a band or orchestra class. The remaining 300 students take a general music class. Students who take a band or orchestra class do not take the general music class.

A Venn diagram illustrates this situation. The circles are drawn so that they do not overlap. This is because students who take a band or orchestra class do not take a general music class, and students who take a general music class do not take a band or orchestra class.

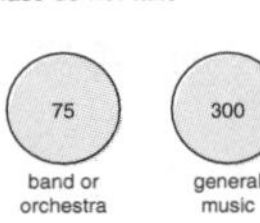

1. How many students are there at Lincoln Middle School? 375 students

Example 2

Ms. Barrie teaches both math and science. There are 26 students in her math class. There are 24 students in her science class. 5 of the students in her science class are also in her math class.

A Venn diagram of this situation shows overlapping circles. The overlapping part of the diagram represents the students who are in both Ms. Barrie's math class and her science class.

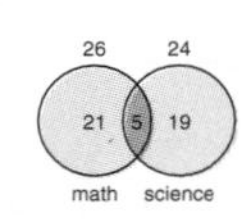

2. Ms. Barrie made a list of all of the students in her math and science classes. How many different names are on her list? 45 names

3. Write a number story for the Venn diagram at the right.
Sample answer: One hundred people surveyed were asked whether they preferred wheat bread or rye bread. Seventy said wheat, 20 preferred rye, and 10 said they liked both.

70 | 10 | 20

Math Journal 2, p. 270

There are two ways to calculate the total number of students in both classes.

- ▷ Add the numbers of students in the three distinct subgroups: $21 + 5 + 19 = 45$.
- ▷ Add the numbers of students in the math class (26) and in the science class (24). Then subtract the number of students in both classes (5), because these students have been *counted twice*—once in the math class and again in the science class: $26 + 24 - 5 = 45$.

Ask a few students to share the number stories they wrote. If no one was able to make up a story, you might pose a few stories of your own.

✦Solving Venn Diagram Problems
(*Math Journal 2,* p. 271)

PARTNER ACTIVITY

Assign journal page 271. Circulate and assist.

ONGOING ASSESSMENT

To assess students' understanding of Venn diagrams, have them complete an Exit Slip (*Math Masters,* page 478) describing how they would explain a Venn diagram to someone who had never seen one before. You may need to give some students an example from which to work. Refer them to the test-scores Venn diagram on journal page 271.

More about Venn Diagrams

1. The sixth graders at Lincoln Middle School were asked whether they write with their left hands or right hands. A small number of students reported that they write equally well with either hand.

The survey results are shown in the Venn diagram at the right.

left 15 3 82 right

a. How many students were surveyed? 100 students

b. How many are *ambidextrous* (can write with either hand)? 3 students

c. How many always write with their left hands? 15 students

d. How many always write with their right hands? 82 students

e. How many never write with their left hands? 82 students

2. Mr. Carlson has 30 students in his sixth grade homeroom. After receiving their final test scores, he identified all students who scored 90% or above on each test. Mr. Carlson then drew this Venn diagram.

math, history, science; Elise, Latisha, Sancho, Jill, Cory, Hasni, Ron, Purnima

a. Whose performance was best overall? Jill's

b. Who scored 90% or above on *at least 2* tests? Jill, Ron, Cory, Hasni

c. Who scored 90% or above on *exactly 1* test? Purnima, Sancho, Elise, Latisha

d. Who scored 90% or above in both math and science? Cory, Hasni, Jill

e. Which two tests had the least overlap? History and math

f. What percent of the students in Mr. Carlson's homeroom had a score of 90% or above on *exactly 2* tests? 10%

STUDENT PAGE

✧ Math Journal 2, p. 271

2 Ongoing Learning & Practice

✦Calculating Travel Options from a Train Schedule (*Math Journal 2,* p. 272)

INDEPENDENT ACTIVITY 

Students use a tree diagram to answer probability questions about a train schedule.

Probability Tree Diagrams

Mr. Gulliver travels to and from work by train. Trains to work leave at 6, 7, 8, 9, and 10 A.M. Trains from work leave at 3, 4, and 5 P.M. Suppose Mr. Gulliver selects a morning train at random and then selects an afternoon train at random.

To work: 6 7 8 9 10 A.M.

From work: 3 4 5 3 4 5 3 4 5 3 4 5 3 4 5 P.M.

1. How many different combinations of trains to and from work can Mr. Gulliver take? 15 combinations

Calculate the probability of each of the following.

2. Mr. Gulliver takes the 7 A.M. train to work. $\frac{1}{5}$

3. He returns home on the 4 P.M. train. $\frac{1}{3}$

4. He takes the 7 A.M. train to work and returns on the 4 P.M. train. $\frac{1}{15}$

5. He leaves for work on the 9 A.M. train and returns home on the 5 P.M. train. $\frac{1}{15}$

6. He leaves for work *before* 9 A.M. $\frac{3}{5}$

7. He leaves for work at 6 A.M. or 7 A.M. and returns home at 3 P.M. $\frac{2}{15}$

8. He returns home, but not on the 5 P.M. train. $\frac{2}{3}$

9. He boards the return train 9 hours after leaving for work. $\frac{1}{5}$

STUDENT PAGE

✧ Math Journal 2, p. 272

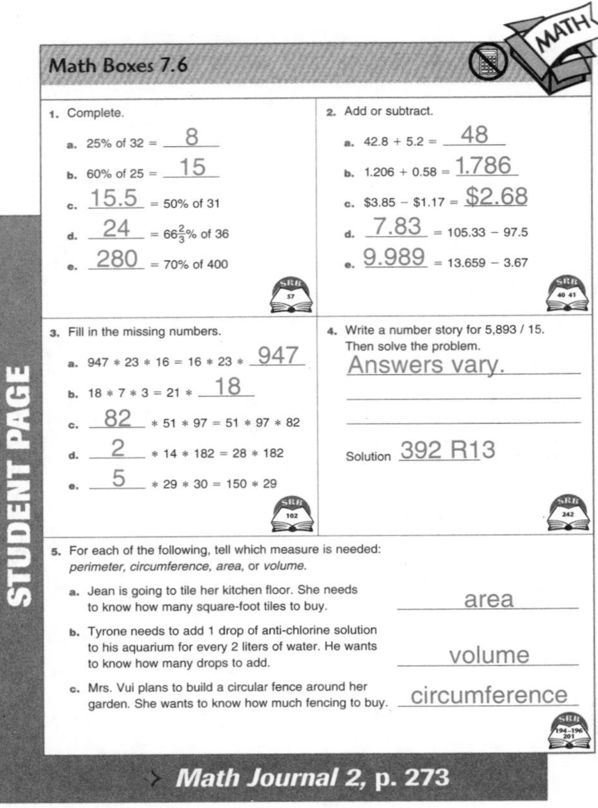

STUDENT PAGE

Math Boxes 7.6

1. Complete.
   a. 25% of 32 = 8
   b. 60% of 25 = 15
   c. 15.5 = 50% of 31
   d. 24 = $66\frac{2}{3}$% of 36
   e. 280 = 70% of 400

2. Add or subtract.
   a. 42.8 + 5.2 = 48
   b. 1.206 + 0.58 = 1.786
   c. \$3.85 − \$1.17 = \$2.68
   d. 7.83 = 105.33 − 97.5
   e. 9.989 = 13.659 − 3.67

3. Fill in the missing numbers.
   a. 947 * 23 * 16 = 16 * 23 * 947
   b. 18 * 7 * 3 = 21 * 18
   c. 82 * 51 * 97 = 51 * 97 * 82
   d. 2 * 14 * 182 = 28 * 182
   e. 5 * 29 * 30 = 150 * 29

4. Write a number story for 5,893 / 15. Then solve the problem.
   Answers vary.
   Solution 392 R13

5. For each of the following, tell which measure is needed: *perimeter, circumference, area,* or *volume.*
   a. Jean is going to tile her kitchen floor. She needs to know how many square-foot tiles to buy. area
   b. Tyrone needs to add 1 drop of anti-chlorine solution to his aquarium for every 2 liters of water. He wants to know how many drops to add. volume
   c. Mrs. Vui plans to build a circular fence around her garden. She wants to know how much fencing to buy. circumference

Math Journal 2, p. 273

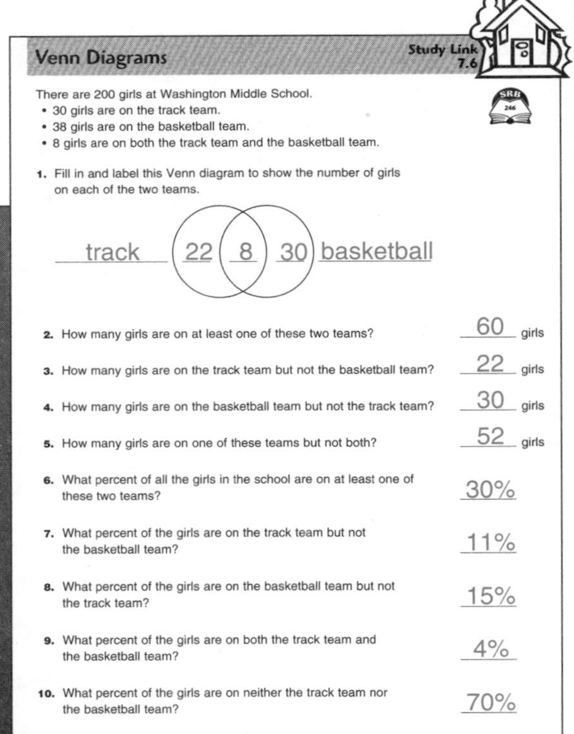

STUDY LINK MASTER

Venn Diagrams Study Link 7.6

There are 200 girls at Washington Middle School.
- 30 girls are on the track team.
- 38 girls are on the basketball team.
- 8 girls are on both the track team and the basketball team.

1. Fill in and label this Venn diagram to show the number of girls on each of the two teams.
   track 22 | 8 | 30 basketball
2. How many girls are on at least one of these two teams? 60 girls
3. How many girls are on the track team but not the basketball team? 22 girls
4. How many girls are on the basketball team but not the track team? 30 girls
5. How many girls are on one of these teams but not both? 52 girls
6. What percent of all the girls in the school are on at least one of these two teams? 30%
7. What percent of the girls are on the track team but not the basketball team? 11%
8. What percent of the girls are on the basketball team but not the track team? 15%
9. What percent of the girls are on both the track team and the basketball team? 4%
10. What percent of the girls are on neither the track team nor the basketball team? 70%

Math Masters, p. 333

◆ Math Boxes 7.6 (*Math Journal 2,* p. 273)

INDEPENDENT ACTIVITY 

Mixed Review Math Boxes in this lesson are paired with Math Boxes in Lesson 7.8. The skill in Problem 1 is a prerequisite for Unit 8.

◆ Study Link 7.6 (*Math Masters,* p. 333)

Home Connection Students draw a Venn diagram to help them solve problems that involve members of overlapping groups.

3 Options for Individualizing

◆ ENRICHMENT Relating Tables and Venn Diagrams (*Math Masters,* p. 124)

PARTNER ACTIVITY **15–30 min** 

Science Link The research described on *Math Masters,* page 124 involves four groups, some of which overlap. Because a Venn diagram of the relationships between the four groups would be complicated to create and decipher, it is preferable to show the relationships in a table. However, the underlying idea is the same.

To illustrate the relationship between the table and the Venn diagram, Problem 4 asks students to represent a subset of the data in the table with a Venn diagram.

If students have trouble understanding the situation, you might guide them by asking questions such as those on the next page.

- What is the largest number in the table? 700 What does that number mean? 700 people are right-handed and right-eyed.
- What is the sum of the four numbers in the table? 1,000 Why should it be 1,000? Since 1,000 people were sampled, the total number of people in the four groups should equal 1,000.
- How many left-eyed and right-handed people were in the sample? 200
- There are two numbers in the bottom row of the table. What does each represent? 30 right-eyed, left-handed people; and 700 right-eyed, right-handed people What is their sum? 30 + 700 = 730 What do these 730 people have in common? They're all right-eyed.
- How many left-handed people were in the sample of 1,000 persons? 100 How did you find that answer? Add the number of left-handed, left-eyed people and the number of left-handed, right-eyed people: 70 + 30 = 100.

NOTE: According to the *Encyclopaedia Britannica,* about $\frac{9}{10}$ of people are right-handed; about $\frac{3}{4}$ of right-handed people are right-eyed; and about $\frac{1}{3}$ of left-handed people are right-eyed.

✦ ENRICHMENT Making Venn Diagrams from Internet Searches

PARTNER ACTIVITY **15–30 min** 

Consumer Education Link Briefly discuss the role of search engines for finding information on the Internet. Your discussion should include the following points:

▷ A search engine scans for Web sites that fit prescribed criteria.

▷ Sometimes searching by a single word results in too many hits.

▷ If you refine the search by adding words or phrases that narrow the description, you can reduce the number of hits and find sites that include all of the specified keywords.

▷ The number of hits is reduced because the search engine is finding sites where all of your search words and phrases appear. Looking at the search results is like looking at an overlapping region of a Venn diagram.

See sample demonstrations on the next page.

Tables and Venn Diagrams

Suppose researchers chose 1,000 adults at random and tested them to find out how many were right-handed and how many were left-handed. People who showed no preference were classified according to the hand they used most often when writing.

Each person was also tested to determine which eye was dominant—the right eye or the left eye.

The possible results are shown in the table at the right. For example, the table shows that 30 people were both left-handed and right-eyed.

		Dominant Hand	
		Left	Right
Dominant Eye	Left	70	200
	Right	30	700

Refer to the table to answer the following questions.

1. The sum of the numbers in the table is 1,000.
2. a. How many people in the sample were both right-handed and right-eyed? 700 people
   b. How many people were both right-handed and left-eyed? 200 people
   c. How many people were right-handed? 900 people
3. a. How many people in the sample were both left-handed and left-eyed? 70 people
   b. How many people were left-handed? 100 people
   c. How many people were left-eyed? 270 people
4. Use your answers from Problem 3 to complete the Venn diagram. Fill in the missing numbers.

left-handed 30 | 70 | 200 left-eyed

5. What percent of the people in the sample have their dominant hand and dominant eye on the same side? 77%

TEACHING MASTER

✦ Math Masters, p. 124

Demonstrate a few searches. For example, search for *left-handed*. Expect tens of thousands of hits. Search for *right-eyed*. Expect over 100 hits. Now enter both terms into a search. Doing so should narrow the hits to fewer than 50.

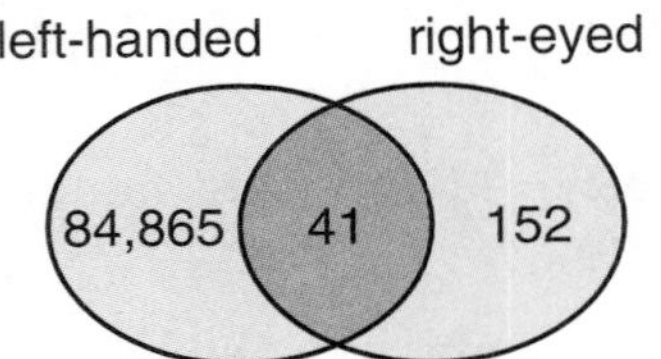

Research report on dominant hand/eye

Try another search. Suppose you want to plan a vacation. First search for *hike and camp*. Expect about 800 hits. Now search for *Arizona*. Expect over 2 million hits. When you put both of these terms into a search, expect approximately 50 hits.

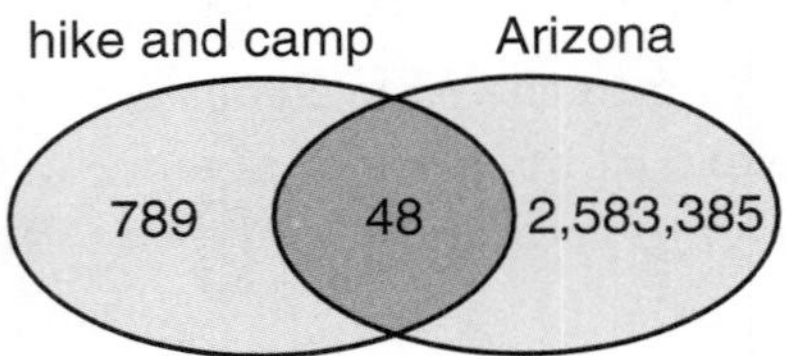

Have students choose subjects they would like to research on the Internet. Discuss the keyword searches they might perform. Students should try the individual keywords and then combinations of keywords. They make Venn diagrams to represent the number of hits they get.

7.7 Fair and Unfair Games

OBJECTIVE **To analyze games of chance to determine whether or not they are fair games.**

summaries	materials
1 Teaching the Lesson	
Students play four simple games of chance, estimate the probability of winning each game, and decide which of the games are fair. [Data and Chance]	☐ *Math Journal 2,* pp. 274 and 275 ☐ Study Link 7.6 ☐ 3 black and 2 white counters ☐ small paper bag ☐ 2 or 3 small objects, such as a paperweight, tissue box, small book, and so on ☐ ruler; scale (bathroom and postal) ***See* Advance Preparation**
2 Ongoing Learning & Practice	
Students review algebraic expressions. [Patterns, Functions, and Algebra] Students practice and maintain skills through Math Boxes and Study Link activities.	☐ *Math Journal 2,* pp. 276 and 277 ☐ Study Link Master (*Math Masters,* p. 334)
3 Options for Individualizing	
Enrichment Students investigate a coin-flipping experiment with the help of tree diagrams. [Data and Chance] **Extra Practice** Students figure out how to make a game fair. [Data and Chance]	☐ Teaching Masters (*Math Masters,* pp. 125 and 126) ☐ Per group: number cards 1 (or ace), 3, 6, and 10 (from the Everything Math Deck, if available)

Additional Information

Advance Preparation For Part 1, each student will need a small paper bag (such as a brown lunch bag) and 5 counters—3 black and 2 white. You may use other colors instead if you prefer. If you do, tell students to revise the directions in their journals accordingly. Place bags and counters near the Math Message.

Vocabulary • **fair game** • **unfair game**

Getting Started

Mental Math and Reflexes

Show an object to the class. Have students record estimates of the object's length, height, volume, weight, and so on. Have a student actually measure and weigh the object to check the estimates. Repeat with other objects.

Math Message

Take 3 black counters, 2 white counters, and a paper bag. Play each of Games 1, 2, and 3 on journal page 274 six times. Record the results. Answer the question about Game 4.

Study Link 7.6 Follow-Up

Review answers.

1 Teaching the Lesson

✦ Math Message Follow-Up
(*Math Journal 2,* p. 274)

WHOLE-CLASS DISCUSSION

Briefly review the definition of a **fair game.**

▷ A game for two or more players is fair if each player has the same chance of winning.

▷ A game for one player is fair if the player has an equal chance of winning or losing.

All four games on journal page 274 are for one player, and each is played in the same way. A player draws a counter from a bag and then draws a second counter *without replacing the first one*. The player wins if both counters are the same color.

For each of the first three games, ask students to raise their hands if they think it is a fair game. (Game 4 is not fair, since the player always wins.) Then combine all students' results for each game. You might ask students to suggest an efficient way to do this.

▷ One possibility: Each student reports his or her results. These are recorded on the board and added to find the total number of wins and losses.

▷ Another possibility, perhaps less time-consuming: Count the number of students who won 6 games, then the number who won 5 games, 4 games, and so on. Calculate the totals.

Example: A class of 26 students reported the following results for Game 1:

Wins	0	1	2	3	4	5	6
Students	2	6	8	6	3	1	0

STUDENT PAGE

Fair and Unfair Games

A game of chance for two or more players is a **fair game** if each player has the same chance of winning. A game for one player is fair if the player has an equal chance of winning or losing. Any other game is an **unfair game.**

Each of the four games described below is for one player. Play Games 1, 2, and 3 a total of 6 times each. Tally the results. Later, the class will combine results for each game.

Answers vary.

Game 1 Put 2 black counters and 1 white counter into a paper bag and shake the bag. Without looking, draw one counter. Then draw a second counter without putting the first counter back into the bag. If the 2 counters are the same color, you win. Otherwise, you lose. Play 6 games, and tally your results.

Tally for 6 games: Win ________ Lose ________

Do you think the game is fair? ________

Combined class data: Win ________ Lose ________

Game 2 Use 2 black counters and 2 white counters. The rules are the same.

Tally for 6 games: Win ________ Lose ________

Do you think the game is fair? ________

Combined class data: Win ________ Lose ________

Game 3 Use 3 black counters and 1 white counter. The rules are the same.

Tally for 6 games: Win ________ Lose ________

Do you think the game is fair? ________

Combined class data: Win ________ Lose ________

Game 4 Suppose you use 4 black counters. The rules are the same.

Do you think the game is fair? no

Explain your answer. Sample answer: You will always draw two counters of the same color, so you will always win.

✧ *Math Journal 2,* p. 274

To find the total number of wins, calculate as follows:

$$(2 * 0) + (6 * 1) + (8 * 2) + (6 * 3) + (3 * 4) + (1 * 5) + (0 * 6) = 57$$

Since there are 26 students, each of whom played 6 games, a total of $6 * 26$, or 156 games was played. Thus, students won 57 out of 156 games, or about $\frac{1}{3}$ of the games. The chances of winning and losing are not equal. The game is not fair.

NOTE: On journal page 274, students play the games and determine the probabilities of winning and losing by actual experience. On journal page 275, students use tree diagrams to calculate the expected probabilities of winning and losing, and they determine whether a game is fair or unfair. The games referred to on page 275 are those described on page 274.

✦ Determining the Probabilities of Winning the Games (*Math Journal 2,* pp. 274 and 275)

PARTNER ACTIVITY

In preceding lessons, students calculated the probabilities for random processes in which one outcome *did not affect* the other outcomes. For example, if a coin lands HEADS-up 10 times in a row, the probability that it will land HEADS-up on the eleventh try remains $\frac{1}{2}$.

The games in this lesson are examples of random processes whose outcomes *do* affect the outcomes that follow. For example, in Game 1, if the first draw is a black counter, the probability of getting a black counter on the second draw is $\frac{1}{2}$, since there are two counters left in the bag—1 black and 1 white. On the other hand, if the first draw is a white counter, the second draw is certain to be a black counter.

Read the analysis of Game 1 and discuss the tree diagram on journal page 275 with the class.

Fair Games and Probability

You can use a tree diagram to decide whether a game is fair or unfair. This tree diagram represents Game 1 on page 274.

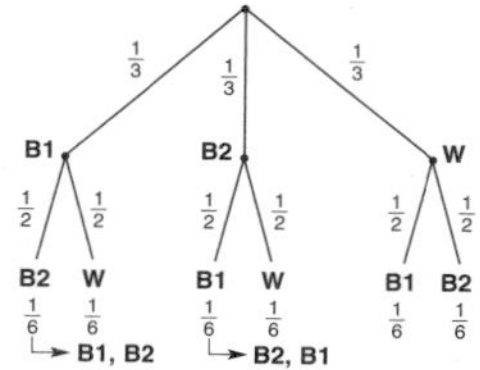

Before you draw the first counter, there are 3 counters in the bag. Although the 2 black counters look alike, they are not the same. To tell them apart, they are labeled B1 and B2. The probability of drawing either B1, B2, or W is $\frac{1}{3}$.

After the first draw, there are 2 counters left in the bag. The probability of drawing either of the 2 remaining counters is $\frac{1}{2}$.

There are 6 possible ways to draw the 2 remaining counters. The probability of each outcome is $\frac{1}{3} * \frac{1}{2}$, or $\frac{1}{6}$. There are 2 ways to draw the same color counters:

Draw B1 on the first draw and B2 on the second draw.
Draw B2 on the first draw and B1 on the second draw.

The chance of drawing 2 black counters is $\frac{1}{6} + \frac{1}{6}$, which is $\frac{2}{6}$, or $\frac{1}{3}$. Therefore, Game 1 is not a fair game.

Make tree diagrams to help you answer these questions.

1. What is the probability of winning Game 2? $\frac{1}{3}$
2. Is Game 2 a fair game? no
3. What is the probability of winning Game 3? $\frac{1}{2}$
4. Is Game 3 a fair game? yes

STUDENT PAGE

✦ *Math Journal 2,* p. 275

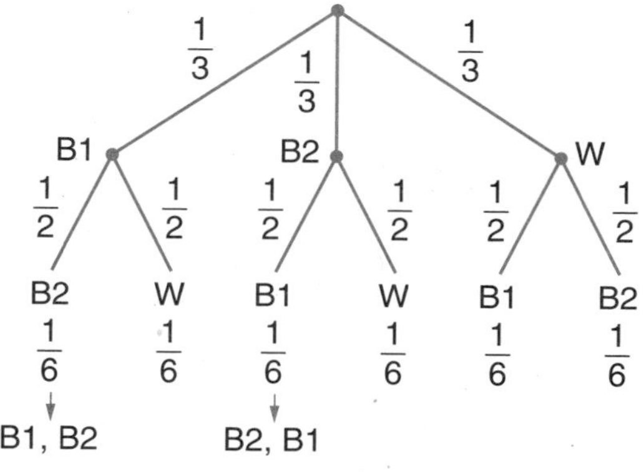

Counter not put back

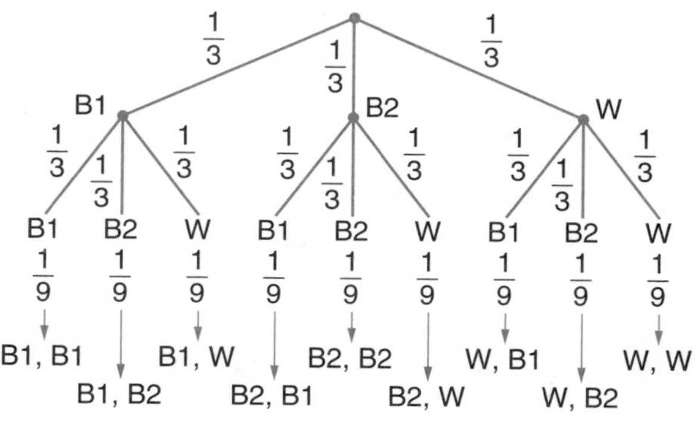

Counter put back

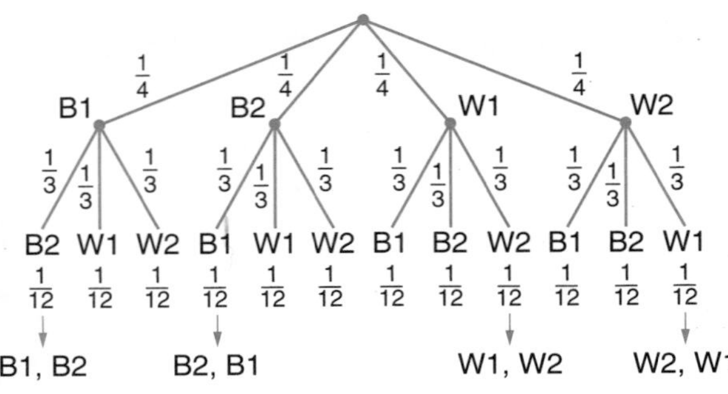

Tree diagram for Game 2
(See journal pages 274 and 275.)

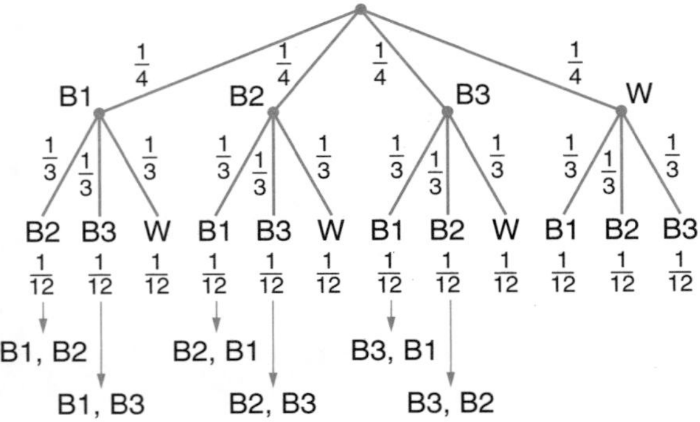

Tree diagram for Game 3
(See journal pages 274 and 275.)

If students seem to understand how the probabilities were obtained for Game 1, they can work with partners to analyze Games 2 and 3. Otherwise, analyze Game 2 as a whole-class activity, and let students analyze Game 3 on their own.

From their analyses, students should conclude that Games 1 and 2 are **unfair games** and that Game 3 is fair.

Adjusting the Activity Extend the activity by asking students how the results would change if they replace the counters after each draw. The probability of winning each game would change because the outcomes would change.

Have students make tree diagrams for the games showing the counters replaced after each draw. Ask them to judge again which (if any) of the games are fair. Game 2 becomes the fair game. You have an equal chance of drawing either color. There are 16 possible outcomes. Eight of them result in the same color on both draws.

2 Ongoing Learning & Practice

✦ Reviewing Algebraic Expressions
(Math Journal 2, p. 276)

INDEPENDENT ACTIVITY 

Students complete a review of algebraic expressions in several contexts.

STUDENT PAGE

Algebraic Expressions

1. Write an algebraic expression for each situation. Use the suggested variable.
   a. Jessica is 14 inches taller than Gerry. If Gerry is H inches tall, how many inches tall is Jessica? $H + 14$ inches
   b. Sam ran for $\frac{4}{5}$ the length of time that Justin ran. If Justin ran R minutes, how long did Sam run? $R * \frac{4}{5}$ minutes
   c. Mary has X CDs in her collection. If Ann has 9 fewer CDs than Mary, how many CDs does Ann have? $X - 9$ CDs
   d. Charlie has d dollars. Leanna has 6 times as much money as Charlie. How much money does Leanna have? $6 * d$ dollars
   e. Erica has been a lifeguard for y years. That is 3 times as many years as Tom. How long has Tom been a lifeguard? $\frac{y}{3}$ years

2. Write the rule for the numbers in the table.

x	y
1.5	6.75
2	9
−3	−13.5
0.25	1.125

Rule $y = x * 4.5$

3. Write the rule for the numbers in the table.

a	b
$\frac{2}{3}$	$\frac{4}{15}$
$\frac{1}{6}$	$\frac{1}{15}$
$\frac{3}{4}$	$\frac{3}{10}$
$\frac{4}{5}$	$\frac{8}{25}$

Rule $b = a * \frac{2}{5}$

First translate each situation from words into an algebraic expression. Then solve the problem that follows.

4. Claire has 7 more crayons than 3 times the number of crayons Royce has. If Royce has C crayons, how many does Claire have? $7 + 3C$
   If Royce has 12 crayons, how many does Claire have? 43 crayons (unit)

5. Alinda has seen 4 fewer than $\frac{1}{2}$ the number of movies that her sister has seen. If her sister has seen M movies, how many has Alinda seen? $\frac{1}{2}M - 4$
   If her sister has seen 20 movies, how many has Alinda seen? 6 movies (unit)

✦ *Math Journal 2,* p. 276

✦ Math Boxes 7.7 (*Math Journal 2,* p. 277)

INDEPENDENT ACTIVITY 

Mixed Review Math Boxes in this lesson are paired with Math Boxes in Lesson 7.5. The skill in Problem 1 is a prerequisite for Unit 8.

✦ Study Link 7.7 (*Math Masters,* p. 334)

Home Connection Students design spinners to match probability statements. They decide whether any of the spinners could be used to play a fair game.

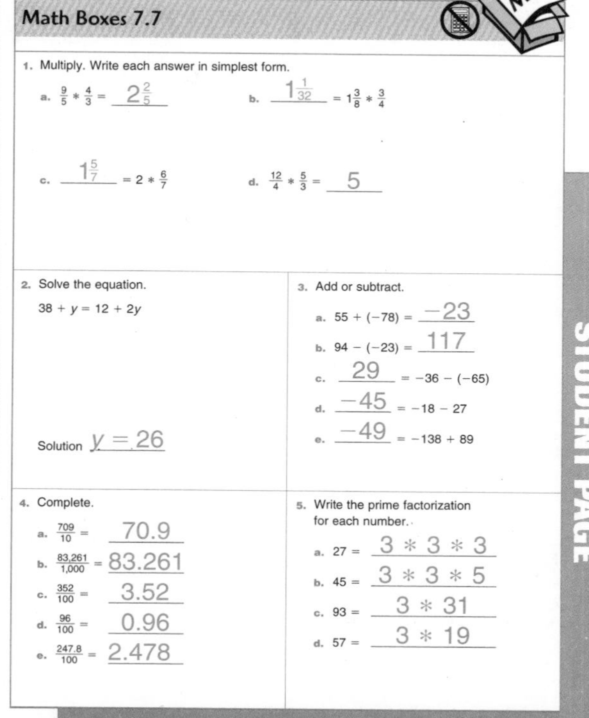

Math Boxes 7.7

1. Multiply. Write each answer in simplest form.

a. $\frac{9}{5} * \frac{4}{3} =$ $2\frac{2}{5}$

b. $1\frac{1}{32}$ $= 1\frac{3}{8} * \frac{3}{4}$

c. $1\frac{5}{7}$ $= 2 * \frac{6}{7}$

d. $\frac{12}{4} * \frac{5}{3} =$ 5

2. Solve the equation.

$38 + y = 12 + 2y$

Solution $y = 26$

3. Add or subtract.

a. $55 + (-78) =$ -23

b. $94 - (-23) =$ 117

c. 29 $= -36 - (-65)$

d. -45 $= -18 - 27$

e. -49 $= -138 + 89$

4. Complete.

a. $\frac{709}{10} =$ 70.9

b. $\frac{83,261}{1,000} =$ 83.261

c. $\frac{352}{100} =$ 3.52

d. $\frac{96}{100} =$ 0.96

e. $\frac{247.8}{100} =$ 2.478

5. Write the prime factorization for each number.

a. 27 = $3 * 3 * 3$

b. 45 = $3 * 3 * 5$

c. 93 = $3 * 31$

d. 57 = $3 * 19$

STUDENT PAGE

✦ *Math Journal 2,* p. 277

3 Options for Individualizing

✦ ENRICHMENT Investigating a Coin-Flipping Problem (*Math Masters,* p. 126)

PARTNER ACTIVITY  **5–15 min** 

Students make a tree diagram to help them solve a challenging coin-flipping problem.

A Coin-Flipping Experiment

1. Draw a tree diagram to show all of the possible outcomes when you flip a coin four times.

1st flip: H1 T1
2nd flip: H2 T2 H2 T2
3rd flip: H3 T3 H3 T3 H3 T3 H3 T3
4th flip: H4 T4 H4 T4 H4 T4 H4 T4 H4 T4 H4 T4 H4 T4 H4 T4

2. How many possible outcomes are there? 16 possible outcomes

3. What is the probability that the coin will land TAILS-up once and HEADS-up three times? $\frac{4}{16}$, or $\frac{1}{4}$

4. What is the probability that the coin will land TAILS-up the same number of times it lands HEADS-up? $\frac{6}{16}$, or $\frac{3}{8}$

5. What is the probability that the coin will land with the same side up all four times? $\frac{2}{16}$, or $\frac{1}{8}$

6. What is the probability that the coin will land TAILS-up more often than HEADS-up? $\frac{4}{16}$, or $\frac{1}{4}$

7. What is the probability that the coin will land TAILS-up 75% of the time? $\frac{4}{16}$, or $\frac{1}{4}$

8. What is the probability that the coin will land HEADS-up *at least* once? $\frac{15}{16}$

Optional Experiment

9. Do the coin-flipping experiment several times and record the actual results. Combine your results with those of your classmates. Do the actual results come close to the predicted results?

Actual Results Answers vary.

Conclusions

TEACHING MASTER

✦ *Math Masters,* p. 126

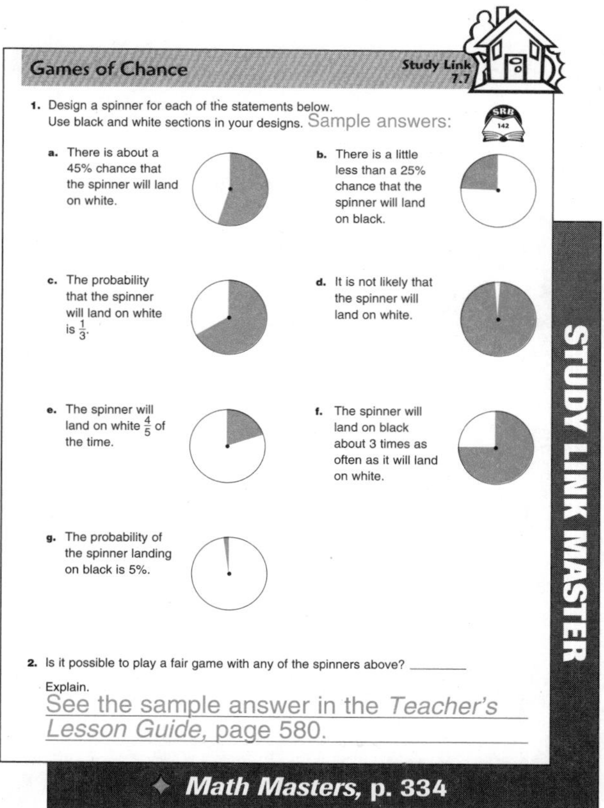

Games of Chance — Study Link 7.7

1. Design a spinner for each of the statements below. Use black and white sections in your designs. Sample answers:

a. There is about a 45% chance that the spinner will land on white.

b. There is a little less than a 25% chance that the spinner will land on black.

c. The probability that the spinner will land on white is $\frac{1}{3}$.

d. It is not likely that the spinner will land on white.

e. The spinner will land on white $\frac{4}{5}$ of the time.

f. The spinner will land on black about 3 times as often as it will land on white.

g. The probability of the spinner landing on black is 5%.

2. Is it possible to play a fair game with any of the spinners above?

Explain. See the sample answer in the *Teacher's Lesson Guide,* page 580.

STUDY LINK MASTER

✦ *Math Masters,* p. 334

TEACHING MASTER

Making a Fair Game

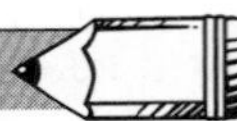

Work with your group to figure out how to make the following game fair.

Sum Game

Materials Four each of number cards 1, 3, 6, and 10 (from the Everything Math Deck, if available)

Players 1

Directions

1. Mix the cards and place them facedown on the playing surface.
2. Turn over two of the cards.
3. Add the numbers on the two cards. The 1-card (or ace) is worth 1, the 3-card is worth 3, and so on. The sum is your score for the game.
4. You win if you score at least a *certain number* of points. Otherwise, you lose.

Your group's job is to figure out the *certain number*, so that the game is fair. In other words, you must find the answer to the following question:

What is the smallest number of points you must score in order to win half of the time?

Answer: You win if you score at least 11 points.

Explain how you found the answer.

Sample answer: I used a tree diagram to determine the probability of each score—4, 7, 9, 11, 13, and 16. Since each score has an equal chance of coming up, the game will be fair if 11, 13, and 16 are winning scores and 4, 7, and 9 are losing scores.

Math Masters, p. 125

EXTRA PRACTICE Creating a Fair Game (*Math Masters,* p. 125)

SMALL-GROUP ACTIVITY  **15–30 min** 

Each group should have one each of number cards 1 (or ace), 3, 6, and 10. Introduce the activity on *Math Masters,* page 125, and go over the instructions. When a group has figured out how to make the *Sum Game* a fair game, group members should write a report describing what they did.

Students may use either of these two approaches:

▷ Play the game repeatedly. Keep track of the actual scores, and estimate the probabilities of the different scores.

▷ Use a tree diagram. Determine the possible scores and the probabilities of these scores.

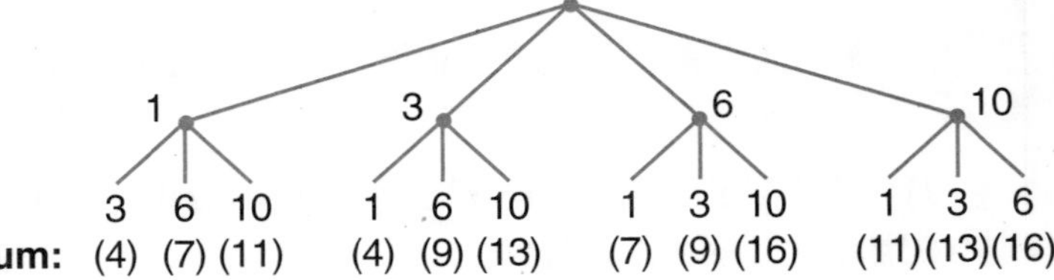

Bring the groups together to share solution strategies. There are six possible scores: 4, 7, 9, 11, 13, and 16 points. Each score has an equal chance of coming up—$\frac{1}{6}$ of the time. Therefore, the game is fair if 11, 13, and 16 are winning scores and 4, 7, and 9 are losing scores. Thus, the *certain number* is 11.

Adjusting the Activity To extend the activity, encourage students to invent a fair game of their own.

7.8 Strategies for Multiple-Choice Tests

OBJECTIVE **To investigate the effects of guessing on multiple-choice tests.**

summaries	materials
1 Teaching the Lesson	
Students investigate the effects of guessing on multiple-choice tests when they can eliminate one or two possible answer choices. They calculate expected scores, as well as the probabilities of improved scores and lowered scores. [Data and Chance]	□ *Math Journal 2,* pp. 279–283 □ Study Link 7.7 ***See* Advance Preparation**
2 Ongoing Learning & Practice	
Students play *Name That Number* to practice writing number sentences and using the correct order of operations. [Patterns, Functions, and Algebra] Students practice and maintain skills through Math Boxes and Study Link activities.	□ *Math Journal 2,* p. 278 □ *Student Reference Book,* p. 301 □ Study Link Master (*Math Masters,* p. 335) □ number cards (from the Everything Math Deck, if available)
3 Options for Individualizing	
Extra Practice Students calculate expected scores on multiple-choice tests and continue to investigate test-taking strategies. [Data and Chance] **Language Diversity** Students study the key words in test questions. [Data and Chance]	□ Teaching Masters (*Math Masters,* pp. 127 and 128)

Additional Information

Advance Preparation For Part 1, you may want to copy the tables from Problem 6 on journal page 281 and Problem 12 on journal page 283 onto an overhead transparency or the board. You can then use the tables to record the class tallies during the discussion.

Getting Started

Mental Math and Reflexes

If you roll a 6-sided die, what is the probability that the following numbers will come up?

- An odd number $\frac{3}{6}$, or $\frac{1}{2}$
- A composite number $\frac{2}{6}$, or $\frac{1}{3}$
- A factor of 4 $\frac{3}{6}$, or $\frac{1}{2}$
- An even number $\frac{3}{6}$, or $\frac{1}{2}$
- A multiple of 2 $\frac{3}{6}$, or $\frac{1}{2}$
- A multiple of 4 $\frac{1}{6}$

Math Message

Complete Problems 1–3 on journal page 279.

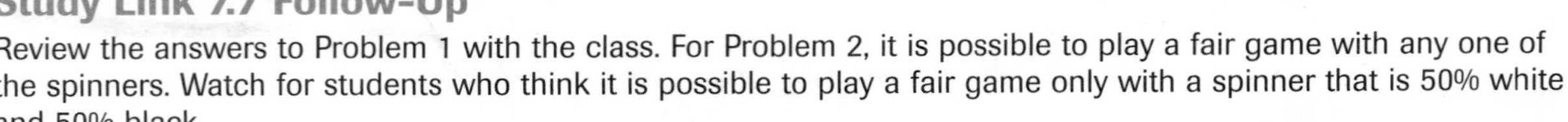

Study Link 7.7 Follow-Up

Review the answers to Problem 1 with the class. For Problem 2, it is possible to play a fair game with any one of the spinners. Watch for students who think it is possible to play a fair game only with a spinner that is 50% white and 50% black.

For example, a fair game using the spinner in Part e might be played as follows: The winner is the player with more points. Each time the spinner lands on white, Player 1 gets 1 point. Each time the spinner lands on black, Player 2 gets 4 points. Suppose 100 rounds are played. We would expect the spinner to land on white 80 times ($\frac{4}{5}$ of 100) and on black 20 times ($\frac{1}{5}$ of 100). Then the scores would be as follows: white, 80 * 1 point = 80 points; black, 20 * 4 points = 80 points. This is a fair game, because the players have an equal chance of winning.

Suppose the rule for Part f is that every time the spinner lands on black, Player 1 gets 1 point. Every time the spinner lands on white, Player 2 gets 3 points. The probability of landing on black is $\frac{3}{4}$; so for every 4 spins, Player 1 would expect to score 3 points. The probability of landing on white is $\frac{1}{4}$, so for every 4 spins, Player 2 would expect to score 3 points. Again, players have an equal chance of winning.

1 Teaching the Lesson

Math Message Follow-Up
(*Math Journal 2,* p. 279)

WHOLE-CLASS DISCUSSION 

Briefly go over the answers. Analyze Problem 3 using the strategy discussed above for Problem 2 of Study Link 7.7.

- ▷ The chance of guessing correctly is $\frac{1}{4}$. Expect that guessing on 20 questions leads to 5 correct answers ($\frac{1}{4}$ of 20) and 15 incorrect answers ($\frac{3}{4}$ of 20).
- ▷ 5 correct answers raises the test score by 5 * 1 point, or 5 points. 15 incorrect answers lowers the test score by 15 * $\frac{1}{3}$ point, or 5 points.
- ▷ The penalty points for incorrect answers should be the same as the extra points for correct guesses. The net gain is then 0 points, which is what a person who is guessing deserves to receive.

Guessing on Multiple-Choice Tests
(*Math Journal 2,* pp. 279–283)

WHOLE-CLASS ACTIVITY

Use your usual class reading procedure to read the two paragraphs at the bottom of journal page 279.

Social Studies Link Give students time to complete journal page 280. Emphasize that the test is not meant to assess their knowledge. In fact, it would be unusual if students knew the correct answers to most questions. They are written so that two answers are obviously incorrect and the other answers are so similar

STUDENT PAGE

Narrowing Your Choices on Multiple-Choice Tests

Imagine that you are taking a multiple-choice test. Four possible answers are given for each question. You are to circle the correct answer. Suppose there are 20 questions for which you don't know the correct answer. You decide to guess for each of these questions.

1. What is the probability (chance) of answering a question correctly? $\frac{1}{4}$
2. How many of the 20 questions would you expect to answer correctly by guessing? 5 questions
   Explain. Sample answer: $\frac{1}{4}$ of 20 is 5.
3. In scoring the test, each correct answer is worth 1 point. To discourage guessing, there is a penalty of $\frac{1}{3}$ point for each incorrect answer. Do you think this is a fair penalty for an incorrect answer? yes
   Explain. Sample answer: The chance of guessing the correct answer is 1 out of 4. If I get 1 point for the 1 answer out of 4 guessed correctly, I lose only 1 point for the 3 of the 4 guessed incorrectly.

When you play board games or card games or answer fun quizzes in which there is no penalty for guessing incorrectly, guessing can be a valuable tool for improving your score. You can improve your chances of guessing correctly, if you are able to eliminate some of the choices before you guess. On the following pages, you will investigate the advantages (or disadvantages) that can result from guessing on multiple-choice tests.

Guessing is usually not encouraged for school tests or achievement tests, even if a penalty is not imposed for incorrect answers. A score that is inflated by guessing gives a misleading view of the test taker's skills and knowledge.

Math Journal 2, p. 279

that it is hard to tell which is likely to be correct. The purpose is to examine the probable effects of eliminating unlikely answers and guessing which of the remaining answers is correct.

Circulate and assist. When most students have finished the test, briefly go over the answers to Problem 1. Answers are on the reproduced student page. Have students check their answers and record the number they got correct.

Go over the answers to Problem 2. For each test question, 2 of the 4 answers are clearly wrong. The other 2 answers are so similar that most students must guess. The chance of guessing correctly is $\frac{1}{2}$. The expected outcome is that a student should get $\frac{1}{2}$, or 3 of the 6, answers correct by guessing.

Ask several volunteers to predict what the results of a class tally will be. The tallies should cluster around 3, because 3 is the expected number of correct answers. Some students will get more than 3 answers correct; some, fewer than 3 correct. But many will get exactly 3 correct, and the class average should be close to 3 correct.

Ask for a show of hands and record a class tally on the board or a transparency. Students should also record the class tally in their journals. (*See margin note.*)

Narrow Choices to 2

Correct/ Incorrect	Probability	Expected Number of Students (out of 25)
6-0	0.016	0.4
5-1	0.094	2.35
4-2	0.234	5.85
3-3	0.312	7.8
2-4	0.234	5.85
1-5	0.094	2.35
0-6	0.016	0.4

Adjusting the Activity To extend the activity, verify that the class average is about 3 correct answers. For example, a class tally for 25 students might look like the following:

Number Correct	6	5	4	3	2	1	0
Class Tally	0	1	6	8	7	1	2

To find the total number of correct answers, calculate as follows: $(0 * 6) + (1 * 5) + (6 * 4) + (8 * 3) + (7 * 2) + (1 * 1) + (2 * 0) = 68$

Then divide by 25 to find the average number of correct answers: $68 / 25 = 2.72$.

Guessing on Multiple-Choice Tests

1. For each question on the following test, first draw a line through each answer that you know is not correct. Then circle one answer for each question. If you do not know the correct answer, guess.

Number correct Answers vary.

1. A nautical mile is equal to
   a. ~~1 foot.~~
   b. ~~1 yard.~~
   c. 1,832 meters.
   d. 1,852 meters. (circled)

2. In 1994, the population of Nevada was
   a. ~~1 billion.~~
   b. 1,475,028.
   c. 1,457,028. (circled)
   d. ~~14,628.~~

3. Which region receives the greatest average annual rainfall?
   a. Atlanta, Georgia (circled)
   b. New Orleans, Louisiana
   c. ~~Mojave Desert, California~~
   d. ~~Sahara Desert, Africa~~

4. The addition sign (+) was introduced into mathematics by
   a. Johann Widman. (circled)
   b. Johann Rahn.
   c. ~~Abraham Lincoln.~~
   d. ~~Martin Luther King, Jr.~~

5. How many diagonals does a 13-sided polygon (13-gon) have?
   a. ~~1~~
   b. 54
   c. 65 (circled)
   d. ~~13,000~~

6. The leading cause of death in the United States is
   a. ~~bungee jumping.~~
   b. cancer.
   c. ~~drowning.~~
   d. heart disease. (circled)

STUDENT PAGE

Math Journal 2, p. 280

NOTE: The table in the main column shows the probabilities and expected numbers of students in a class of 25 for the classroom tally in Problem 6.

Guessing on Multiple-Choice Tests (cont.)

2. When you can narrow the choices for a question to two possible answers, what is the chance of guessing the correct answer? $\frac{1}{2}$

3. How many of the 6 questions on page 280 do you think you answered correctly? Answers vary. questions

4. Is it likely that you got all 6 correct? no

5. Is it likely that you got all 6 wrong? no

6. Suppose each correct answer is worth 1 point and each incorrect answer carries a penalty of $\frac{1}{3}$ point. Complete the Total Points column of the table. You will complete the Class Tally column later.

Number Correct	Number Incorrect	Total Points	Class Tally
6	0	6	
5	1	$4\frac{2}{3}$	
4	2	$3\frac{1}{3}$	
3	3	2	
2	4	$2 - \frac{4}{3} = \frac{2}{3}$	
1	5	$-\frac{2}{3}$	
0	6	-2	

STUDENT PAGE

Math Journal 2, p. 281

STUDENT PAGE

Guessing on Multiple-Choice Tests (cont.)

7. For each question on the following test, first draw a line through each answer that you know is not correct. Then circle one answer for each question. If you do not know the correct answer, guess.

Number correct Answers vary.

1. The neck of a 152-pound person weighs about
   a. ~~100 pounds.~~
   b. $12\frac{1}{2}$ pounds.
   c. $11\frac{1}{2}$ pounds.
   d. $10\frac{1}{2}$ pounds. (circled)

2. The average height of a full grown weeping willlow tree is
   a. 50 feet. (circled)
   b. 45 feet.
   c. 35 feet.
   d. ~~2 feet.~~

3. The normal daily high temperature for July in Cleveland, Ohio, is
   a. 84°F.
   b. 82°F. (circled)
   c. 80°F.
   d. ~~0°F.~~

4. The circumference of Earth at the equator is about
   a. 24,901.6 miles. (circled)
   b. 24,801.6 miles.
   c. 24,701.6 miles.
   d. ~~2,000 miles.~~

5. In 1994, the average American consumed about 141 pounds of which food?
   a. sugar
   b. ~~spinach~~
   c. potatoes (circled)
   d. rice

6. A slice of white bread has about how many calories?
   a. ~~3~~
   b. 65 (circled)
   c. 70
   d. 75

✦ *Math Journal 2,* p. 282

STUDENT PAGE

Guessing on Multiple-Choice Tests (cont.)

8. When you can narrow the choices for a question to three possible answers, what is the chance of guessing the correct answer? $\frac{1}{3}$

9. How many of the six questions do you think you answered correctly? Answers vary. questions

10. Is it likely that you got all six correct? no

11. Is it likely that you got all six wrong? no

12. Suppose each correct answer is worth 1 point and each incorrect answer carries a penalty of $\frac{1}{3}$ point. Complete the Total Points column of the table below.

Number Correct	Number Incorrect	Total Points	Class Tally
6	0	6	
5	1	$4\frac{2}{3}$	
4	2	$3\frac{1}{3}$	
3	3	2	
2	4	$2 - \frac{4}{3} = \frac{2}{3}$	
1	5	$-\frac{2}{3}$	
0	6	-2	

✦ *Math Journal 2,* p. 283

Science Link Repeat the above procedure with the test on journal page 282. When most students have completed the page, briefly go over the answers to the test in Problem 7. Have students check their answers and record the number they got correct.

Discuss students' answers to Problem 8. This time, only 1 of the 4 answers for each test question is clearly wrong. The other 3 answers are so similar that most students must guess. The chance of guessing correctly is $\frac{1}{3}$. The expected outcome is that a student should get $\frac{1}{3}$, or 2 of the 6, answers correct by guessing.

Record a class tally for the number of correct answers on the board or a transparency. Students should also record the class tally on journal page 283. The tallies should cluster around 2, because 2 is the expected number of correct answers. Some students will get more than 2 answers correct; some, fewer than 2 answers correct. But many will get exactly 2 correct, and the class average should be close to 2 correct.

NOTE: The table below shows the probabilities and expected numbers of students in a class of 25 for the classroom tally in Problem 12.

Narrow Choices to 3

Correct/ Incorrect	Probability	Expected Number of Students (out of 25)
6-0	0.001	0.04
5-1	0.016	0.4
4-2	0.082	2.06
3-3	0.220	5.49
2-4	0.329	8.23
1-5	0.263	6.58
0-6	0.088	2.2

✦ Discussing Advantages and Disadvantages of Guessing on Multiple-Choice Tests
(*Math Journal 2,* pp. 281 and 283)

WHOLE-CLASS DISCUSSION

Remind students that the point system is the same for both tests they have taken—1 point for each correct answer and $\frac{1}{3}$ point off for each incorrect answer. Therefore, the score for a particular number of answers correct is the same for both tests.

The advantage of guessing is that guessing correctly on 2 or more of 6 problems raises the test score. The disadvantage of guessing is that guessing correctly on none or only 1 of 6 problems lowers the test score.

Have students use the class tallies in Problems 6 and 12 to estimate the probabilities of raising and lowering their test scores by guessing.

Example: A class of 25 students reported results for the test on journal page 280. (*See margin.*)

$\frac{22}{25} = \frac{88}{100}$, or 88% of the students, raised their scores by guessing correctly on 2 or more of 6 problems.

$\frac{3}{25} = \frac{12}{100}$, or 12% of the students, lowered their scores by guessing correctly on none or only 1 of 6 problems.

It is very likely (but not certain!) that a greater percent of your students lowered their test scores on the second test than on the first. The probabilities for lowered test scores (negative scores) are 11% on the first test and 35% on the second test. Many teachers report that students seem willing to guess when they can narrow the choices to 2, but do not like the "odds" for improving their scores by guessing when they can narrow their choices to only 3.

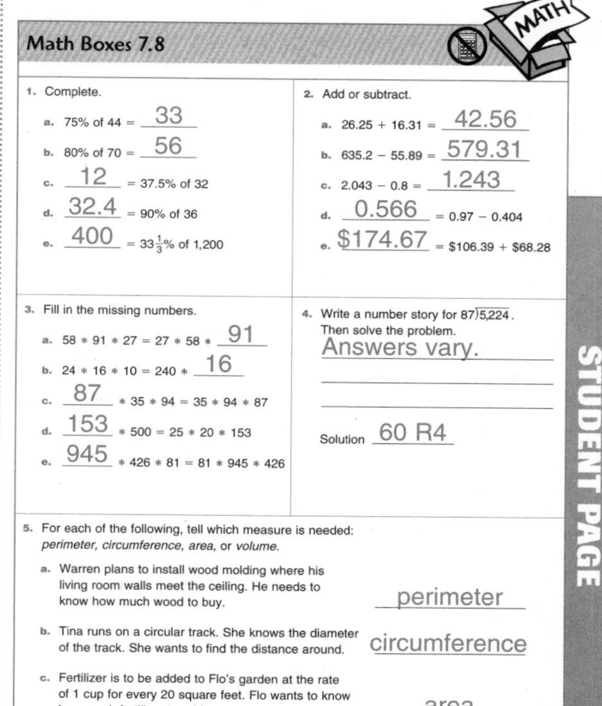
Math Boxes 7.8

1. Complete.
   a. 75% of 44 = 33
   b. 80% of 70 = 56
   c. 12 = 37.5% of 32
   d. 32.4 = 90% of 36
   e. 400 = $33\frac{1}{3}$% of 1,200

2. Add or subtract.
   a. 26.25 + 16.31 = 42.56
   b. 635.2 − 55.89 = 579.31
   c. 2.043 − 0.8 = 1.243
   d. 0.566 = 0.97 − 0.404
   e. $174.67 = $106.39 + $68.28

3. Fill in the missing numbers.
   a. 58 * 91 * 27 = 27 * 58 * 91
   b. 24 * 16 * 10 = 240 * 16
   c. 87 * 35 * 94 = 35 * 94 * 87
   d. 153 * 500 = 25 * 20 * 153
   e. 945 * 426 * 81 = 81 * 945 * 426

4. Write a number story for 87)5,224. Then solve the problem.
   Answers vary.
   Solution 60 R4

5. For each of the following, tell which measure is needed: *perimeter, circumference, area,* or *volume.*
   a. Warren plans to install wood molding where his living room walls meet the ceiling. He needs to know how much wood to buy. perimeter
   b. Tina runs on a circular track. She knows the diameter of the track. She wants to find the distance around. circumference
   c. Fertilizer is to be added to Flo's garden at the rate of 1 cup for every 20 square feet. Flo wants to know how much fertilizer to add. area

Math Journal 2, p. 278

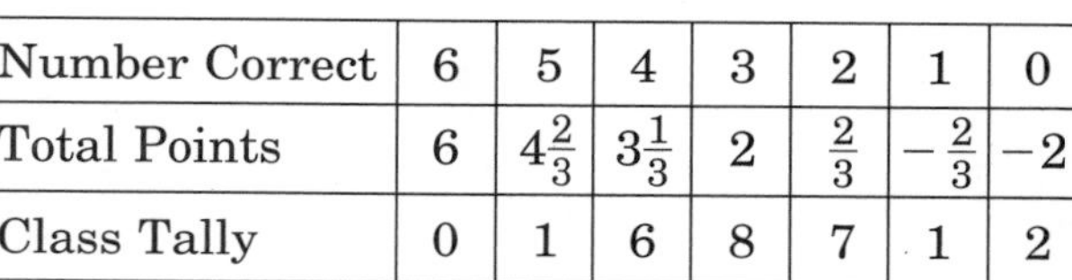
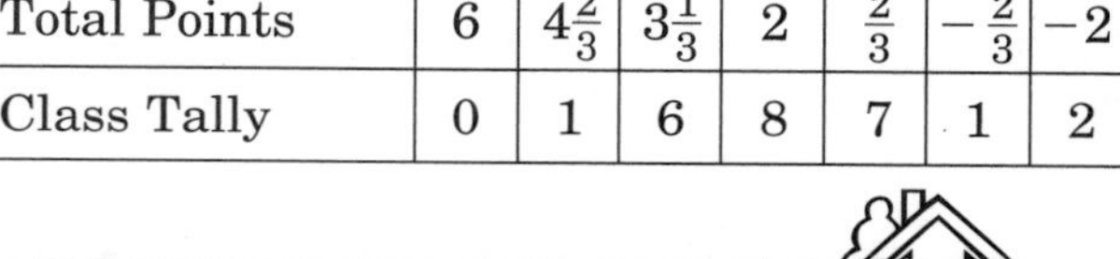

Number Correct	6	5	4	3	2	1	0
Total Points	6	$4\frac{2}{3}$	$3\frac{1}{3}$	2	$\frac{2}{3}$	$-\frac{2}{3}$	−2
Class Tally	0	1	6	8	7	1	2

2 Ongoing Learning & Practice

✦ Playing *Name That Number* (*Student Reference Book,* p. 301)

PARTNER ACTIVITY

Students play this game, introduced in Lesson 1.3, to practice writing number sentences using the correct order of operations. For each round, students write their answers as a single number sentence. They should try whenever possible to organize their number sentences so that parentheses are not needed.

ONGOING ASSESSMENT

To assess students' understanding of the order of operations, for one round have students write their strategies for reaching the target number in words, and then translate the words into a number sentence. For example, suppose the cards are 1, 2, 3, 4, and 8. The target number is 9. A student might write, "I added 1 to 3 times 4 to get 13. Then I divided 8 by 2 to get 4 and subtracted the 4 from 13 to get 9." The number sentence would be $1 + 3 * 4 - \frac{8}{2} = 9$; or $[1 + (3 * 4)] - (8 \div 2) = 9$.

Reviewing Probability Study Link 7.8

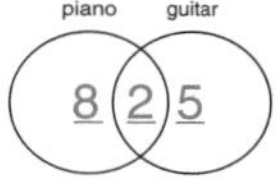

1. Each fraction in the left column below shows the probability of a chance event. Match each fraction with the correct description.
   - $\frac{1}{3}$ — The probability of getting HEADS if you flip a coin.
   - $\frac{1}{4}$ — The probability that 3 will come up if you roll a 6-sided die.
   - $\frac{1}{2}$ — The probability of choosing a red ball from a bag containing 2 red balls, 3 white balls, and 1 green ball.
   - $\frac{1}{6}$ — The probability of drawing a heart from a deck of playing cards.

2. Sandy is planning her outfit for the school dance. She has narrowed her choices to a red, white, or blue dress and to a pair of red or white shoes. Make a tree diagram to show all possible combinations of dresses and shoes.

   Dress: red, white, blue
   Shoes: red white, red white, red white

3. How many different combinations are there? 6 combinations

4. If Sandy chooses her outfit at random, what is the probability that she will choose a dress and shoes of the same color? $\frac{2}{6}$, or $\frac{1}{3}$

5. Ten of the students in Mrs. Moore's class play the piano. Two of the 10 also play the guitar. In all, 15 students play the piano, the guitar, or both the piano and guitar. Use this information to complete the Venn diagram at the right.

   piano: 8 | both: 2 | guitar: 5

6. How many students play the guitar but not the piano? 5 students

7. There are 25 students in Mrs. Moore's class. If you choose a student's name at random, what is the probability that the student plays the piano, the guitar, or both the piano and the guitar? $\frac{15}{25}$, or $\frac{3}{5}$

STUDY LINK MASTER

Math Masters, p. 335

TEACHING MASTER

Guessing on Multiple-Choice Tests

1. Draw a line through each answer that you know cannot be correct. Then circle one answer for each question. If you do not know the answer, guess. Make sure to answer all questions. Scoring is the same as on previous tests: 1 point for each correct answer and $\frac{1}{3}$ point off for each incorrect answer. Number correct Answers vary.

1. The area of a standard playing card is about
   - ~~a. 25 in.^{2}~~
   - b. 7.9 in.^{2}
   - c. 7.6 in.^{2}
   - ~~d. 1 in.^{2}~~
2. The fastest speed a base runner has circled the bases in baseball is almost
   - ~~a. 2 km/hr.~~
   - b. 30 km/hr.
   - c. 28 km/hr.
   - d. 32 km/hr.
3. It took about 33,000 worker-years (number of workers * number of years) to complete which of the following?
   - ~~a. Yankee Stadium~~
   - ~~b. first McDonald's restaurant in the U.S.~~
   - c. Great Pyramid at Giza, Egypt
   - d. Great Wall of China
4. The average number of quills on a porcupine is about
   - a. 30,000
   - b. 25,000.
   - ~~c. 100.~~
   - ~~d. 10.~~
5. The size of the smallest dust particle is about
   - a. 0.01 cm
   - ~~b. 5 cm.~~
   - ~~c. 50 cm.~~
   - ~~d. 100 cm.~~
6. What is the fastest crawling insect, with a speed of almost 3 mph?
   - a. cockroach
   - b. ladybug
   - ~~c. inchworm~~
   - d. carpenter ant
7. At age 120, the oldest person alive in 1995 was
   - ~~a. Ronald Reagan.~~
   - b. Shigeychico Izumi
   - ~~c. Michael Jordan.~~
   - ~~d. Hillary Clinton.~~
8. A modern lightbulb lasts about 2,500 hours. About how long did Edison's first successful lightbulb last?
   - ~~a. 5,000 hours~~
   - b. 60 hours
   - c. 50 hours
   - d. 40 hours
9. About how much water can a camel drink in 10 minutes?
   - ~~a. 1 cup~~
   - ~~b. 1 pint~~
   - c. 30 gal
   - d. 35 gal

◆ *Math Masters,* p. 127

TEACHING MASTER

Guessing on Multiple-Choice Tests (cont.)

Sample answers:

2. How many questions could you answer without guessing? 2 questions
3. a. For how many questions did you have 2 realistic choices? 4 questions
   b. What would your maximum score for these questions be? 4
   c. What would your minimum score for these questions be? $-\frac{4}{3}$
   d. What would your expected score for these questions be? $1\frac{1}{3}$
4. a. For how many questions did you have 3 realistic choices? 3 questions
   b. What would your maximum score for these questions be? 3
   c. What would your minimum score for these questions be? -1
   d. What would your expected score for these questions be? $\frac{1}{3}$
5. a. Overall, what is the highest possible score you could achieve? 9
   b. Overall, what is the lowest possible score you could achieve? -3
   c. What would your expected score be? $3\frac{2}{3}$
   d. How did you calculate your expected score? Sample answer: I added my expected scores from Problems 2, 3d, and 4d. Since $2 + 1\frac{1}{3} + \frac{1}{3}$ is $3\frac{2}{3}$, that is my expected score.
6. If you were not instructed to guess on the problems you weren't sure about, would you have skipped some? yes

   Explain. Sample answer: If I did as well as expected on the problems I guessed on, I would have added $1\frac{2}{3}$ points to my score.
7. If the scoring were changed to 1 point for each correct answer and $\frac{1}{2}$ off for each incorrect answer, would you have answered all of the questions on the test, guessing when necessary? yes

   Explain. Sample answer: I would still guess, hoping to do as well as expected, and add 1 point to my score.

◆ *Math Masters,* p. 128

◆ Math Boxes 7.8 (*Math Journal 2,* p. 278)

INDEPENDENT ACTIVITY 

Mixed Review Math Boxes in this lesson are paired with Math Boxes in Lesson 7.6. The skill in Problem 1 is a prerequisite for Unit 8.

◆ Study Link 7.8 (*Math Masters,* p. 335)

Home Connection Students review several of the concepts and skills covered in this unit in preparation for the end-of-unit written assessment.

3 Options for Individualizing

◆ EXTRA PRACTICE Improving Scores on Multiple-Choice Tests (*Math Masters,* pp. 127 and 128)

INDEPENDENT ACTIVITY  **15–30 min**

Students continue to practice multiple-choice test-taking strategies by analyzing another testing situation.

NOTE: Problem 7 on *Math Masters,* page 128 is challenging. Provide time for students to discuss their answers.

◆ LANGUAGE DIVERSITY Studying the Language of Questions

SMALL-GROUP ACTIVITY  **15–30 min** 

Language Arts Link Group students learning English with a couple of proficient English speakers. Have them study the questions on *Math Masters,* pages 127 and 128. Students are to look for the key words in each question. For example, in the question about "the average number of quills on a porcupine ...," the key word is *average.* The group discusses how the question would change if the key word were different.

7.9 Unit 7 Review and Assessment

OBJECTIVE **To review and assess students' progress on the material covered in Unit 7.**

1 Assess Progress

learning goals	activities
7a **Beginning Goal** Understand and use probability tree diagrams to solve problems. **(Lessons 7.4, 7.5, and 7.7)**	❑ Written Assessment, Problems 12 and 14–17
7b **Developing Goal** Construct and interpret Venn diagrams. **(Lesson 7.6)**	❑ Written Assessment, Problem 22
7c **Developing/Secure Goal** Calculate probability in simple situations. **(Lessons 7.1, 7.3, and 7.4)**	❑ Written Assessment, Problems 8–11, 13, 14, and 18–20
7d **Developing/Secure Goal** Understand what constitutes a fair game. **(Lesson 7.7)**	❑ Written Assessment, Problems 16 and 17
7e **Developing/Secure Goal** Understand and apply the concept of random numbers to probability situations. **(Lessons 7.2 and 7.3)**	❑ Written Assessment, Problems 8–11
7f **Secure Goal** Solve "fraction-of-a-fraction" problems. **(Lesson 7.3)**	❑ Slate Assessment, Problem 2 ❑ Written Assessment, Problems 1–7
7g **Secure Goal** Understand how increasing the number of trials affects experimental results. **(Lesson 7.2)**	❑ Written Assessment, Problem 21

materials

- ☐ *Math Journal 2,* p. 284
- ☐ Study Link 7.8
- ☐ Teaching Masters (*Math Masters,* pp. 115 and 125)
- ☐ Assessment Masters (*Math Masters,* pp. 406–409 and 478)

2 Build Background for Unit 8

summaries	materials
Students practice and maintain skills through Math Boxes and Study Link activities.	☐ *Math Journal 2,* p. 285 ☐ Study Link Masters (*Math Masters,* pp. 336–339)

Each **learning goal** listed above indicates a level of performance that might be expected at this point in the *Everyday Mathematics* K–6 curriculum. For a variety of reasons, the levels indicated may not accurately portray your class's performance.

Additional Information

Advance Preparation For additional information on assessment for Unit 7, see the *Assessment Handbook,* pages 58–60. For assessment checklists, see *Math Masters,* pages 446, 447, and 468–470.

Getting Started

Math Message

Complete the Time to Reflect *questions on journal page 284.*

Study Link 7.8 Follow-Up

Review students' answers.

Time to Reflect

1. In this unit, you have been studying probability. Describe at least one way in which probability is part of your daily life.
   Answers vary.

2. How would you describe a fair game to someone who didn't know what it was?
   Sample answer: A fair game provides every player with an equal chance of winning or losing.

3. Explain how drawing a probability tree diagram might help you solve a problem.
   Sample answer: A probability tree diagram is a picture of all of the possible outcomes. It allows you to see results, and this helps you to solve a problem.

4. Explain how you can get a better score on a multiple-choice test even if you don't know all of the answers.
   Sample answer: Guessing is most helpful when you can narrow down the possible answers to 2. Then you have a better chance of guessing correctly.

STUDENT PAGE

Math Journal 2, p. 284

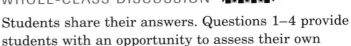

1 Assess Progress

✦ Math Message Follow-Up
(*Math Journal 2*, p. 284)

WHOLE-CLASS DISCUSSION

Students share their answers. Questions 1–4 provide students with an opportunity to assess their own progress on probability concepts.

✦ Oral and Slate Assessments

WHOLE-CLASS ACTIVITY

If the suggested problems below are not appropriate for your class's level of performance, adjust the numbers or the problems themselves to better assess your students' abilities.

NOTE: Some of these assessment suggestions relate to learning goals that have been addressed in previous units. Now is a good time to evaluate students' progress toward those goals.

Oral Assessment Suggestions

1. Students show "thumbs up" if the sum or difference is greater than 1 and "thumbs down" if it is less than 1.
   - $\frac{1}{4} + \frac{3}{8}$ down
   - $\frac{1}{3} + \frac{4}{5}$ up
   - $\frac{8}{5} - \frac{9}{10}$ down
   - $1\frac{3}{4} - \frac{2}{8}$ up
   - $\frac{6}{7} + \frac{1}{10}$ down
   - $\frac{5}{6} + \frac{5}{12}$ up

2. Students show "thumbs up" if the fractions and mixed numbers are equivalent and "thumbs down" if they are not equivalent.
   - $\frac{4}{3}$ and $1\frac{1}{3}$ up
   - $1\frac{3}{4}$ and $\frac{13}{4}$ down
   - $\frac{14}{8}$ and $1\frac{1}{2}$ down
   - $\frac{8}{3}$ and $2\frac{6}{9}$ up
   - $1\frac{7}{10}$ and $\frac{17}{100}$ down
   - $\frac{9}{6}$ and $1\frac{1}{2}$ up

Slate Assessment Suggestions

1. Find reciprocals. (Remind students to think, "The number times what other number equals 1?")
   - $\frac{3}{4}$ $\frac{4}{3}$
   - $\frac{7}{8}$ $\frac{8}{7}$
   - $6\frac{4}{5}$ $\frac{5}{34}$
   - 0.3 $\frac{10}{3}$, or $3.\overline{3}$
   - $2\frac{1}{3}$ $\frac{3}{7}$
   - 0.09 $\frac{100}{9}$, or $11.\overline{1}$

2. Solve "fraction of" problems. Remind students that "of" indicates multiplication. **Goal 7f**
   - $\frac{1}{4}$ of $\frac{2}{3}$ $\frac{2}{12}$, or $\frac{1}{6}$
   - $\frac{3}{8}$ of $\frac{1}{2}$ $\frac{3}{16}$
   - $\frac{1}{8}$ of $\frac{3}{4}$ $\frac{3}{32}$
   - $\frac{3}{4}$ of $\frac{4}{7}$ $\frac{12}{28}$, or $\frac{3}{7}$
   - $\frac{4}{5}$ of $\frac{6}{10}$ $\frac{24}{50}$, or $\frac{12}{25}$

3. Solve equations.
   - $8 + x = 13$ $x = 5$
   - $d * 60 = 240$ $d = 4$
   - $35 - y = 27$ $y = 8$
   - $p / 90 = 400$ $p = 36{,}000$

4. Write each fraction as a decimal and a percent.
   - $\frac{3}{4}$ 0.75, 75%
   - $\frac{5}{8}$ 0.625, $62\frac{1}{2}$%
   - $\frac{2}{6}$ $0.\overline{3}$, $33\frac{1}{3}$%
   - $\frac{7}{20}$ 0.35, 35%
   - $\frac{4}{5}$ 0.8, 80%

5. Write numbers in standard notation.
   - 52 thousand 52,000
   - 6 million 6,000,000
   - 10^5 100,000
   - 4.8 million 4,800,000
   - $3 * 10^3$ 3,000

✦ Written Assessment
(*Math Masters*, pp. 406–409)

INDEPENDENT ACTIVITY 

Depending on the needs of students, you may want to work through an example together, reading a problem aloud, discussing it, and providing additional examples as necessary before students work the problem independently.

Unit 7 Checking Progress

Solve.

1. $\frac{1}{2}$ of $\frac{1}{3}$ = $\frac{1}{6}$
2. $\frac{2}{3}$ of $\frac{4}{5}$ = $\frac{8}{15}$
3. $\frac{1}{5}$ of $\frac{2}{3}$ = $\frac{2}{15}$
4. $\frac{2}{9}$ of $\frac{3}{8}$ = $\frac{1}{12}$
5. $\frac{1}{3} * \frac{1}{2}$ = $\frac{1}{6}$
6. $\frac{3}{2} * \frac{6}{7}$ = $1\frac{2}{7}$
7. Explain why Problems 1 and 5 have the same answer.
   Sample answer: They are the same problem. They demonstrate the commutative property of multiplication, or the turn-around rule. Also, "of" means "times."

Answer the following questions about making random draws from a deck of five cards numbered 1, 2, 3, 4, and 5.

8. If you draw a card 50 times, putting the card back and mixing the deck after each draw, about how many times would you expect to draw the number 4? 10 times
9. What percent of the time would you expect to draw a 1? 20%
10. Suppose you draw the number 2. What is the probability that 2 will come up on the next draw? (Circle one.)
    $\frac{1}{4}$ ($\frac{1}{5}$ circled) $\frac{2}{5}$
11. Explain your answer to Problem 10.
    Sample answer: The cards have no memory, so the probability remains the same with each draw.

ASSESSMENT MASTER

✦ *Math Masters*, p. 406

Unit 7 Checking Progress (cont.)

12. Balls are dropped, one at a time, into the chute shown below. Each time the chute divides, the ball has an equal chance of going down any of the chutes. Sixty balls are dropped into the chute. Fill in the boxes in the tree diagram to show how many balls you would expect to go down each chute.

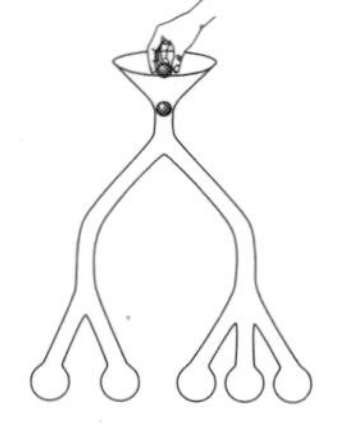

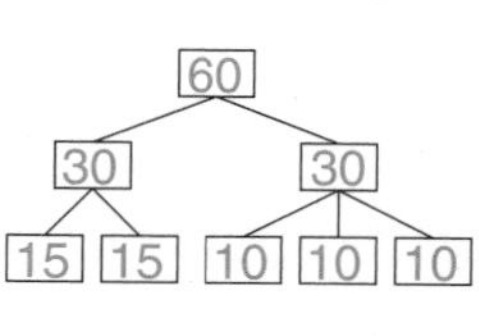

13. For each probability described below, write its letter next to the correct fraction.

a. The probability of getting HEADS when you flip a coin	$\frac{1}{6}$	e
b. The probability of drawing a diamond from a deck of playing cards	$\frac{1}{2}$	a
c. The probability of drawing the white marble from a jar with 1 white, 2 red, and 2 green marbles	$\frac{1}{13}$	d
d. The probability of drawing a jack from a deck of playing cards	$\frac{1}{4}$	b
e. The probability of getting a 4 when you roll a six-sided die	$\frac{1}{5}$	c

ASSESSMENT MASTER

✦ *Math Masters*, p. 407

ASSESSMENT MASTER

Unit 7 Checking Progress *(cont.)*

Jamie and Vern designed the game *Lucky Coin* for their school carnival. To play, flip a coin. If it lands TAILS-up, you lose. If it lands HEADS-up, you get to flip again. If it lands HEADS-up on the second flip, you win a prize. If it lands TAILS-up, you lose. Make a tree diagram to help you answer the questions below.

14. What is the probability of winning *Lucky Coin*? $\frac{1}{4}$

15. If 100 people play *Lucky Coin*, how many would you expect to win? 25 people

16. Explain why this is not a fair game.
Sample answer: The chances of winning and losing are not equal.

17. How would you change the rules to make *Lucky Coin* a fair game?
Sample answer: Flip a coin twice. If it lands on the same side both times, you win.

✦ ***Math Masters*, p. 408**

ASSESSMENT MASTER

Unit 7 Checking Progress *(cont.)*

Refer to the spinner at the right. Name the color that fits each of the following statements.

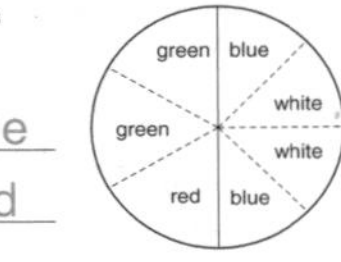

18. The spinner will land on this color about as often as it lands on white. blue

19. The chance of getting this color is $\frac{1}{6}$. red

20. The probability of landing on this color is greater than 30%. green

21. In 6 spins, the spinner lands on red 4 times. Explain how this is possible if the spinner should only land on red 1 out of every 6 times.
Sample answer: The actual results, in a small sample of trials, is often very different from the expected probability. The more trials that are done, the closer the results will be to the expected probability.

22. In the space below, draw and label a Venn diagram showing the following information about Mr. Penn's class:
- 21 students have either a dog, a cat, or both a dog and a cat.
- 14 students have a dog.
- 4 of the students who have a dog also have a cat.

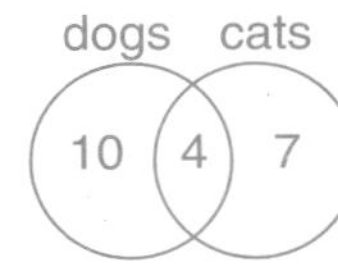

How many students have a cat but no dog? 7 students

✦ ***Math Masters*, p. 409**

Each of the problems is listed below and paired with one or more of this unit's learning goals.

- Multiply fractions. (Problems 1–7) **Goal 7f**
- Determine probabilities of outcomes. (Problems 8–11, 13, 14, and 18–20) **Goal 7c**
- Use randomly generated numbers in probability situations. (Problems 8–11) **Goal 7e**
- Draw Venn diagrams. (Problem 22) **Goal 7b**
- Determine fairness in games. (Problems 16 and 17) **Goal 7d**
- Distinguish between expected outcomes and actual results. (Problems 8, 9, 12, 15, and 21) **Goal 7g**
- Use probability tree diagrams. (Problems 12 and 14–17) **Goal 7a**

✦ ALTERNATIVE ASSESSMENT OPTION
Predict the Number and Colors of Blocks in a Bag (*Math Masters,* p. 115; *Math Masters,* p. 478)

SMALL-GROUP ACTIVITY

Use this activity from Part 3 of Lesson 7.2 to assess students' understanding of how the number of trials affects experimental results.

After students have played several rounds, have them complete an Exit Slip (*Math Masters,* page 478). They should explain how many random draws they think are necessary to make an accurate prediction about how many blocks of each color are in the bag if there are 5 blocks in total. You may want to extend the question by asking students how their answer would change if instead of 5, there were 3 or 10 blocks in the bag.

✦ ALTERNATIVE ASSESSMENT OPTION
Make a Fair Game (*Math Masters,* p. 125)

PARTNER ACTIVITY

Use this activity from Part 3 of Lesson 7.7 to assess students' understanding of a fair game. Look for successful strategies for creating a fair game in student reports.

✦ ALTERNATIVE ASSESSMENT OPTION

Make Venn Diagrams from Internet Searches

PARTNER ACTIVITY

Use this activity from Part 3 of Lesson 7.6 to assess students' understanding of Venn diagrams. Select a "research" topic that is related to a current topic in your class. For example, if you are studying the solar system, you might have students plan how they would research the travel time from Earth to Venus. They should first decide what information they require. Then they must decide which key words might give them good "hits." They should then consider how they can narrow and refine the range of "hits." Suggest that students draw a Venn diagram to represent the intersecting set of information.

Build Background for Unit 8

✦ Math Boxes 7.9 (*Math Journal 2,* p. 285)

INDEPENDENT ACTIVITY 

Mixed Review The skills in Problems 1–4 are prerequisites for Unit 8.

✦ Study Link 7.9: Unit 8 Family Letter (*Math Masters,* pp. 336–339)

Home Connection This Study Link is a four-page newsletter that introduces parents and guardians to Unit 8's topics and terms. The letter also offers ideas for mathematics activities that are supportive of classroom work and can be done at home.

PLANNING AHEAD

For Lesson 8.1, you will need a sample nutrition label from a food can or package.

STUDENT PAGE

Math Boxes 7.9

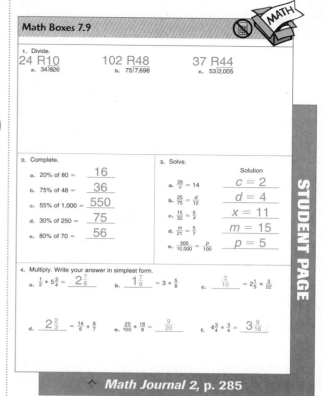

1. Divide.
   a. $34\overline{)826}$ 24 R10
   b. $75\overline{)7,698}$ 102 R48
   c. $53\overline{)2,005}$ 37 R44

2. Complete.
   a. 20% of 80 = 16
   b. 75% of 48 = 36
   c. 55% of 1,000 = 550
   d. 30% of 250 = 75
   e. 80% of 70 = 56

3. Solve. (Solution)
   a. $\frac{28}{c} = 14$ — $c = 2$
   b. $\frac{25}{75} = \frac{d}{12}$ — $d = 4$
   c. $\frac{15}{33} = \frac{5}{x}$ — $x = 11$
   d. $\frac{m}{21} = \frac{5}{7}$ — $m = 15$
   e. $\frac{500}{10,000} = \frac{p}{100}$ — $p = 5$

4. Multiply. Write your answer in simplest form.
   a. $\frac{1}{2} * 5\frac{3}{4} = 2\frac{7}{8}$
   b. $1\frac{7}{8} = 3 * \frac{5}{8}$
   c. $\frac{3}{10} = 2\frac{1}{5} * \frac{3}{22}$
   d. $2\frac{2}{3} = \frac{14}{6} * \frac{8}{7}$
   e. $\frac{20}{100} * \frac{18}{8} = \frac{9}{20}$
   f. $4\frac{3}{4} * \frac{3}{4} = 3\frac{9}{16}$

✦ *Math Journal 2,* p. 285

STUDY LINK MASTERS

Family Letter Study Link 7.9

Unit 8: Rates and Ratios

The next unit is devoted to the study of rates and ratios. Both fraction and decimal notation will be used to express rates and ratios and to solve problems.

Ratios compare quantities that have the same unit. These units "cancel" each other in the comparison, so the resulting ratio has no units. For example, the fraction $\frac{2}{20}$ could mean that 2 out of 20 people in a class got an A on a test or that 20,000 out of 200,000 people voted for a certain candidate in an election.

Another frequent use of ratios is to indicate relative size. For example, a picture in a dictionary drawn to $\frac{1}{10}$ scale means that every length in the picture is $\frac{1}{10}$ the corresponding length in the actual object. Students will use ratios to characterize relative size as they examine map scales and compare geometric figures.

Rates, on the other hand, compare quantities that have different units. For example, rate of travel, or speed, may be expressed in miles per hour (55 mph); food costs may be expressed in cents per ounce (17 cents per ounce) or dollars per pound ($2.49 per pound).

Easy ratio and rate problems can be solved intuitively by making tables, similar to "What's My Rule?" tables. Problems requiring more complicated calculations are best solved by writing and solving proportions. Students will learn to solve proportions by cross multiplication. This method is based on the idea that two fractions are equivalent, if the product of the denominator of the first fraction and the numerator of the second fraction is equal to the product of the numerator of the first fraction and the denominator of the second fraction. For example, the fractions $\frac{4}{6}$ and $\frac{6}{9}$ are equivalent because $6 * 6 = 4 * 9$. This method is especially powerful because proportions can be used to solve any ratio and rate problem. It will be used extensively in algebra and trigonometry.

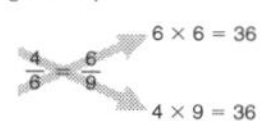

Students will apply these rate and ratio skills as they explore nutrition guidelines. The class will collect nutrition labels and design balanced meals based on recommended daily allowances of fat, protein, and carbohydrate. You may wish to participate by planning a balanced dinner together and by examining food labels while shopping with your child. Your child will also collect and tabulate various kinds of information about your family and your home and then compare the data by converting them to ratios. In a final application lesson, your child will learn about the Golden Ratio—a ratio that is found in many works of art and architecture.

✦ *Math Masters,* pp. 336–339

Unit 8 Rates and Ratios

overview

Rates, ratios, and what is sometimes called "proportional thinking" are very common in the everyday world. There is probably no better indication of good "number sense" and "measure sense" than the ability to handle such problems with ease. Unfortunately, for many people, everyday uses of rates seem to be among the most difficult aspects of mathematics. Many of the reports of poor achievement in mathematics, found in professional literature and in the popular press, are based on failures with rate or ratio problems on inventory tests, or with proportional thinking in the everyday workplace.

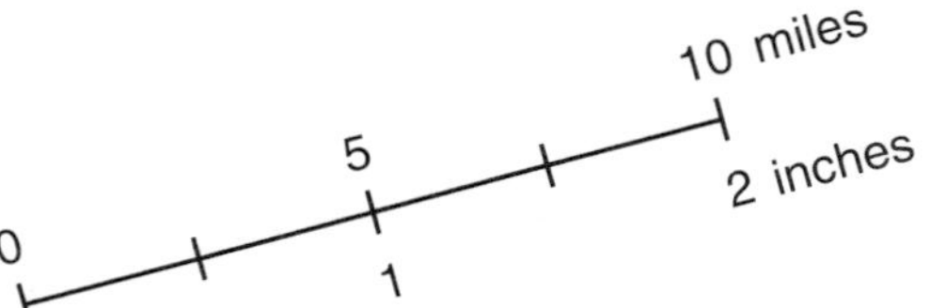

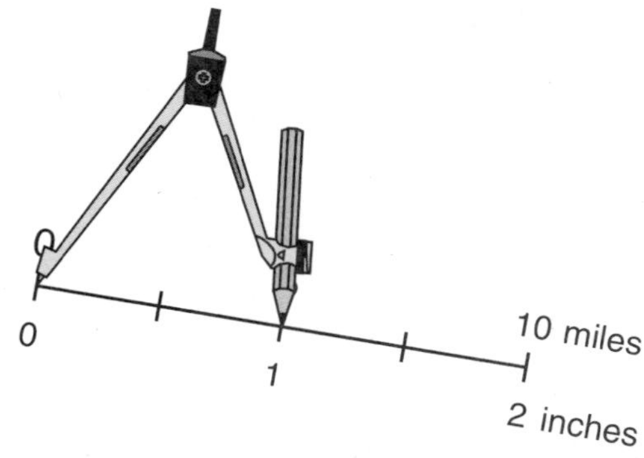

contents

Lesson	Objective	Page
8.1	**Rates, Rate Tables, and Unit Rates** *To review rates; to use the per-unit-rate and rate-table methods of solving rate problems; and to introduce proportions as models for rate situations.*	602
8.2	**Solving Rate Problems with Proportions** *To use proportions to model and solve rate problems.*	609
8.3	**Solving Proportions by Cross Multiplication** *To introduce cross multiplication as a way to test whether two fractions are equivalent; and to use cross multiplication to solve proportions.*	615
8.4	**Calorie Use** *To estimate students' calorie use per day; and to practice solving rate problems.*	621
8.5	**Using Nutrition Information** *To use nutrition information to plan a healthful meal.*	627
8.6	**Ratios** *To review notations for and meanings of ratios; and to solve problems involving part-to-part and part-to-whole ratios.*	634
8.7	**Using Proportions to Solve Percent Problems** *To solve percent problems by writing and solving proportions.*	641
8.8	**Calculating the Fat Content of Foods** *To estimate percent equivalents for fractions; and to calculate what percent of total calories comes from fat, protein, and carbohydrate.*	646
8.9	**Using Ratios to Describe Size Changes** *To explore the use of ratios to describe size changes; and to use a variety of notations to show the size-change factor.*	652
8.10	**Similar Polygons** *To explore the properties of similar polygons; and to use ratios to find the lengths of corresponding sides of similar polygons.*	659
8.11	**Comparing Ratios** *To compare ratios by renaming them as* n-to-1 *ratios; and to introduce the Golden Ratio.*	667
8.12	**The Golden Ratio** *To explore Golden Rectangles and the Golden Ratio.*	674
8.13	**Unit 8 Review and Assessment** *To review and assess students' progress on the material covered in Unit 8.*	680

learning goals in perspective

	learning goals	links to the past	links to the future
8a	**Developing Goal** Write open proportions to model problems. **(Lessons 8.1, 8.2, and 8.6)**	Grades 4 and 5: Review number sentences, open sentences, and variables; solve number stories by modeling with open sentences.	After Grade 6: Proportions are a useful problem-solving tool in mathematics, science, art, and business.
8b	**Developing Goal** Solve percent problems. **(Lessons 8.5, 8.7, and 8.8)**	Grade 4: Solve "percent-of" number stories. Grade 5: Find the whole, given a fraction or percent of the whole. Find a percent of a number. Grade 6: Find a percent of a number (Unit 4).	Grade 6: Applications and maintenance. After Grade 6: Percent skills are essential in school courses and daily life.
8c	**Developing Goal** Solve problems that involve a size-change factor. **(Lessons 8.9 and 8.10)**	Grade 5: Explore transformations of polygons using a coordinate grid.	After Grade 6: Transformations are studied in geometry and other branches of mathematics.
8d	**Developing/Secure Goal** Use cross multiplication to solve open proportions. **(Lessons 8.3, 8.6, and 8.7)**	Grades 4 and 5: Solve number stories by modeling with open sentences. Develop and apply the multiplication rule for finding equivalent fractions.	After Grade 6: Cross-multiplication is a useful technique in solving equations.
8e	**Developing/Secure Goal** Solve rate number stories. **(Lessons 8.1–8.4)**	Grade 4: Introduce and explore rates; create a Rates Museum. Use a rate table to record rate information and solve rate problems. Solve number stories involving rates. Convert rates to equivalent rates with different units. Grade 5: Represent rate problems as formulas, graphs, and tables. Grade 6: Review the concept of rates. Represent and interpret rates in words, rules, formulas, tables, and graphs (Unit 3).	Grade 6: Applications and maintenance. After Grade 6: Rates are an important tool in school courses and daily life.
8f	**Developing/Secure Goal** Solve ratio number stories. **(Lessons 8.6 and 8.9–8.12)**	Grade 3: Use ratios to compare numbers. Grade 4: Compare numbers. Use division to calculate the ratio of two areas. Grade 5: Solve ratio number stories.	Grade 6: Applications and maintenance. After Grade 6: Ratios are an important tool in school courses and daily life.
8g	**Developing/Secure Goal** Estimate equivalent percents for fractions. **(Lesson 8.8)**	Grade 4: Shade 10-by-10 grids to represent percents, then rename each percent as a fraction. Rename "easy" fractions (fourths, fifths, and tenths) as percents. Use a calculator to rename fractions as percents. Grade 5: Develop reflexes for fraction-decimal-percent equivalencies.	Grade 6: Applications and maintenance.
8h	**Developing/Secure Goal** Solve division problems that involve decimals. **(Lessons 8.9 and 8.11)**	Grade 6: Use the partial-quotients algorithm to divide whole numbers by decimals, using estimation to place the decimal point. Extend the partial-quotients algorithm to include quotients to a given number of decimal places (Unit 2).	Grade 6: Applications and maintenance. After Grade 6: Division skills with all types of divisors and dividends are important.
8i	**Secure Goal** Use rate tables to solve problems. **(Lessons 8.1 and 8.2)**	See Goal 8e.	See Goal 8e.

assessment

ongoing • product • periodic

Informal Assessment

Math Boxes These *Math Journal* pages provide opportunities for cumulative review or assessment of concepts and skills.

Ongoing Assessment: Kid Watching Use the Ongoing Assessment suggestions in the following lessons to make quick, on-the-spot observations about students' understanding of:

- Data and Chance **(Lesson 8.7, Part 2)**
- Operations and Computation **(Lesson 8.2, Part 2; Lesson 8.3, Part 2; Lesson 8.9, Part 2; Lesson 8.10, Part 2; Lesson 8.11, Part 2)**
- Patterns, Functions, and Algebra **(Lesson 8.1, Part 1; Lesson 8.3, Part 1; Lesson 8.4, Part 1; Lesson 8.5, Part 1; Lesson 8.6, Part 1; Lesson 8.7, Part 1; Lesson 8.8, Part 1, Lesson 8.9, Part 1)**

Portfolio Ideas Samples of students' work may be obtained from the following assignments:

- Calculating Amounts of Ingredients for Making Peanut Butter Fudge **(Lesson 8.3)**
- Making a Circle Graph to Represent a Meal **(Lesson 8.5)**
- Using a Grid to Draw an Enlargement of a Picture; Reducing Designs **(Lesson 8.10)**
- Reading Ratios **(Lesson 8.11)**
- Calculate Amounts of Ingredients; Write Ratio Number Stories; Enlarge a Picture **(Lesson 8.13)**

Unit 8 Review and Assessment

Math Message Use Time to Reflect questions 1–3 in Lesson 8.13 to assess students' progress toward the following learning goals: **Goals 8e and 8f**

Oral and Slate Assessments Use oral or slate assessments during Lesson 8.13 to assess students' progress toward the following learning goals: **Goals 8b and 8g**

Written Assessment Use a written review during Lesson 8.13 to assess students' progress toward the following learning goals: **Goals 8a-8f, 8h, and 8i**

Alternative Assessment Options Use independent alternative assessments in Lesson 8.13 to assess students' progress toward the following learning goals: **Goals 8c, 8e, and 8f**

assessmenthandbook

For more information on how to use different types of assessment in Unit 8, see the Assessment Overview on pages 61–63 in the *Assessment Handbook*. The following Assessment Masters can be found in the *Math Masters* book:

- Unit 8 Checking Progress, pp. 410–413
- Unit 8 Individual Profile of Progress, p. 449
- Unit 8 Class Checklist, p. 448
- Class Progress Indicator, p. 470
- Math Logs, pp. 473 and 474
- Self-Assessment Forms, pp. 476 and 477
- Interest Inventories, pp. 471 and 472

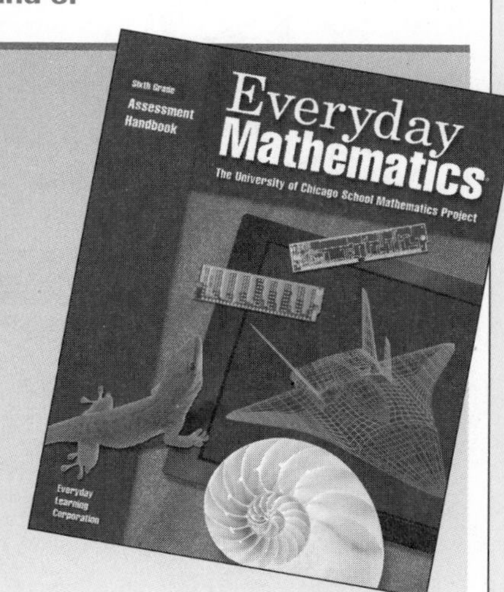

problemsolving

A process of modeling everyday situations using tools from mathematics

Encourage students to use a variety of strategies when attacking a given problem—and to explain those strategies. *Strategies students might use in this unit:*

- Make a table
- Write an equation (proportion)
- Use computation
- Use estimation
- Use data from a table
- Use a picture

Four Problem-Solving **REPRESENTATIONS**

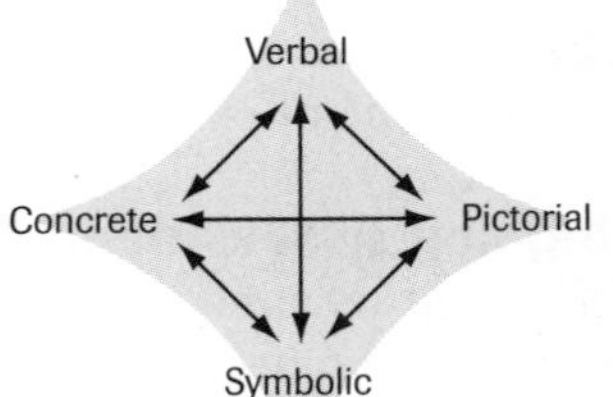

Lessons that teach *through* problem solving, not just *about* problem solving

Lesson	Activity	Lesson	Activity
8.1, 8.2, 8.3	Solve rate problems.	**8.7**	Solve percent problems (including discount problems) in which the percent, or the part, or the whole is unknown.
8.3	Find amounts of ingredients when increasing a recipe.	**8.7**	Make a stem-and-leaf plot and describe a situation based on given data landmarks.
8.4	Find how many calories you use per day.	**8.8**	Use food label information to find percents of total calories that come from fat, protein, and carbohydrates.
8.5	Plan a lunch that meets the recommended percent of calories from protein, fat, and carbohydrates.	**8.9**	Solve size-change problems involving geometric figures, map scales, and scale drawings.
8.6	Solve ratio number stories.	**8.11**	Compare ratios based on collected data about a variety of objects found at home.

For more information about problem solving in *Everyday Mathematics,* see the *Teacher's Reference Manual.*

cross-curricularlinks

physical education

- Students calculate how many calories a sixth grader uses in a triathlon. **(Lesson 8.4)**

social studies

- Students compare the ratio of females and males in their households to the same ratio in the total U.S. population. **(Lesson 8.11)**

health

- Students make a circle graph to represent a meal. **(Lesson 8.5)**
- Students examine examples of nutrition labels. **(Lesson 8.8)**

literature

- Students find rate stories in *Math Curse.* **(Lesson 8.3)**
- Students read "The Golden Mean." **(Lesson 8.12)**

art

- Students read about the use of the Golden Ratio in art. **(Lesson 8.12)**

consumer education

- Students explore how to express the ratio of a sale price to a regular price. **(Lesson 8.7)**

language arts

- Students define *calorie* and look at the word *calorie* in other languages. **(Lesson 8.4)**

meeting INDIVIDUAL needs

UNIVERSAL ACCESS

✦ RETEACHING

The following features provide additional instructional support:

Adjusting the Activity

- **Lesson 8.2, Part 1**
- **Lesson 8.3, Part 1**
- **Lesson 8.4, Part 1**
- **Lesson 8.6, Part 1**
- **Lesson 8.7, Part 1**
- **Lesson 8.8, Part 1**
- **Lesson 8.10, Part 1**
- **Lesson 8.11, Part 1**

Options for Individualizing

- **Lesson 8.1** Reading about Rates
- **Lesson 8.2** Reading an Essay about Using Proportions to Solve Rate Problems
- **Lesson 8.6** Reading an Essay about Ratios

✦ ENRICHMENT

The following features suggest enrichment and extension activities:

Adjusting the Activity

- **Lesson 8.2, Parts 1 and 3**
- **Lesson 8.3, Part 1**
- **Lesson 8.4, Part 1**
- **Lesson 8.5, Parts 1 and 3**
- **Lesson 8.9, Part 1**
- **Lesson 8.10, Part 1**
- **Lesson 8.11, Part 1**

Options for Individualizing

- **Lesson 8.3** Finding Rates in the Story *Math Curse*
- **Lesson 8.5** Making a Circle Graph to Represent a Meal
- **Lesson 8.6** Solving Challenging Ratio Problems
- **Lesson 8.9** Investigating Map Scales
- **Lesson 8.10** Using a Grid to Draw an Enlargement of a Picture; Reducing Designs; Enlarging a Triangle with Rubber Bands
- **Lesson 8.12** Reading about the Golden Ratio; Exploring the Relationship between the Fibonacci Sequence and the Golden Ratio; Reading the Poem "The Golden Mean"

✦ LANGUAGE DIVERSITY

The following feature suggests ways to support students who are acquiring proficiency in English:

Options for Individualizing

- **Lesson 8.5** Recognizing Technical Language
- **Lesson 8.6** Writing Ratio Number Stories
- **Lesson 8.9** Illustrating Terms
- **Lesson 8.11** Reading Ratios

✦ MULTIAGE CLASSROOM

The following chart lists related lessons from Grade 5 that can help you meet your instructional needs:

Grade 5						12.4 12.5							
Grade 6	8.1	8.2	8.3	8.4	8.5	8.6	8.7	8.8	8.9	8.10	8.11	8.12	8.13

materials

lesson	math masters pages	manipulative kit items	other items
8.1	Study Link Master, p. 340 Teaching Master, p. 129 Assessment Master, p. 478 (optional)		nutrition label (for demonstration purposes) ***See* Advance Preparation, p. 602**
8.2	Study Link Masters, pp. 341 and 342 Teaching Master, p. 130		slate Geometry Template
8.3	Study Link Masters, pp. 343 and 344 Teaching Master, p. 131 Assessment Master, p. 478 (optional) ***See* Advance Preparation, p. 615**		*Math Curse* ***See* Advance Preparation, p. 615**
8.4	Study Link Master, p. 344 Teaching Master, p. 132		calculator Geometry Template
8.5	Study Link Master, p. 345 Teaching Masters, pp. 133 and 134 Assessment Master, p. 478 (optional)		calculator; Geometry Template *World Almanac for Kids,* health books (optional) computer with Internet access (optional) nutrition labels ***See* Advance Preparation, p. 627**
8.6	Study Link Master, p. 346	Per partnership: deck of playing cards (from the Everything Math Deck, if available)	
8.7	Study Link Master, p. 347 Teaching Master, p. 135		blank overhead transparency (optional)
8.8	Study Link Masters, pp. 348 and 349 Teaching Master, p. 136 Assessment Master, p. 478 (optional) ***See* Advance Preparation, p. 646**		calculator slate protractor
8.9	Study Link Master, p. 350 Teaching Masters, pp. 137–139 ***See* Advance Preparation, p. 652**		calculator; inch and cm ruler Geometry Template (optional) computer with Internet access (optional)
8.10	Study Link Master, p. 351 Teaching Masters, pp. 8, 9, 140, and 141 ***See* Advance Preparation, p. 659**	Per partnership: 16 green triangle and 10 red trapezoid pattern blocks ***See* Advance Preparation, p. 659**	overhead pattern blocks (optional) protractor; compass; ruler Geometry Template (optional) Per group of 4 students: 3 spoons *Spoon Scramble* cards (See Lesson 4.12) 3" × by 5" index cards (optional) 2 identical, small rubber bands ***See* Advance Preparation, p. 659**
8.11	Study Link Master, p. 352 Teaching Master, p. 142 ***See* Advance Preparation, p. 667**		calculator posterboard (or chart paper) and markers
8.12	Study Link Masters, pp. 353 and 354 transparency of Teaching Master, p. 143 (optional) Teaching Master, p. 144	compass	compass and yardstick for demonstration purposes calculator; compass; ruler *Math Talk: Mathematical Ideas in Poems for Two Voices* ***See* Advance Preparation, p. 674**
8.13	Study Link Masters, pp. 355–358 Teaching Master, p. 8 Assessment Masters, pp. 410–413		recipes

planningtips

Pacing

Pacing depends on a number of factors, such as students' individual needs and how long your school has been using *Everyday Mathematics.* At the beginning of Unit 8, review your Content by Strand Poster to help you set a monthly pace.

	←MOST CLASSROOMS→	
FEBRUARY	MARCH	APRIL

Using the Projects

Use Project 6, Anthropometry Project: Formulas for Body Height and Neck Circumference, during or after Unit 6, to provide an interesting application of formulas and proportions. The projects can be found at the back of the *Teacher's Lesson Guide.*

Home Communication

Share Study Links 8.1–8.12 with families to help them understand the content and procedures in this unit. At the end of the unit, use Study Link 8.13 to introduce Unit 9. Supplemental information can be found in the *Home Connection Handbook.*

NCTM Standards

Standard	1	2	3	4	5	6	7	8	9	10
Unit 8 Lessons	8.1, 8.3–8.6, 8.8–8.11	8.1–8.12	8.10, 8.12	8.5, 8.9	8.5, 8.7, 8.8	8.1–8.10	8.1–8.10	8.1–8.10	8.1–8.10	8.1–8.10

Content Standards
1 Number and Operations
2 Algebra
3 Geometry
4 Measurement
5 Data Analysis and Probability

Process Standards
6 Problem Solving
7 Reasoning and Proof
8 Communication
9 Connections
10 Representation

PRACTICE *through* Games

Everyday Mathematics uses games to help students develop good fact power and other math skills.

- *Spoon Scramble* to practice identifying equivalent fraction expressions **(Lesson 8.10)**

unit 8 content highlights

The discussion below highlights the major content ideas presented in Unit 8, and may help you establish instructional priorities.

Rates and Ratios

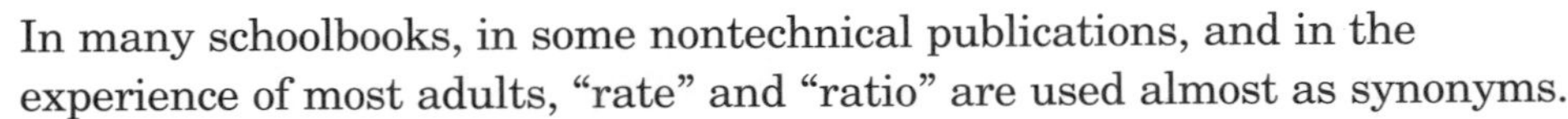

In many schoolbooks, in some nontechnical publications, and in the experience of most adults, “rate” and “ratio” are used almost as synonyms.

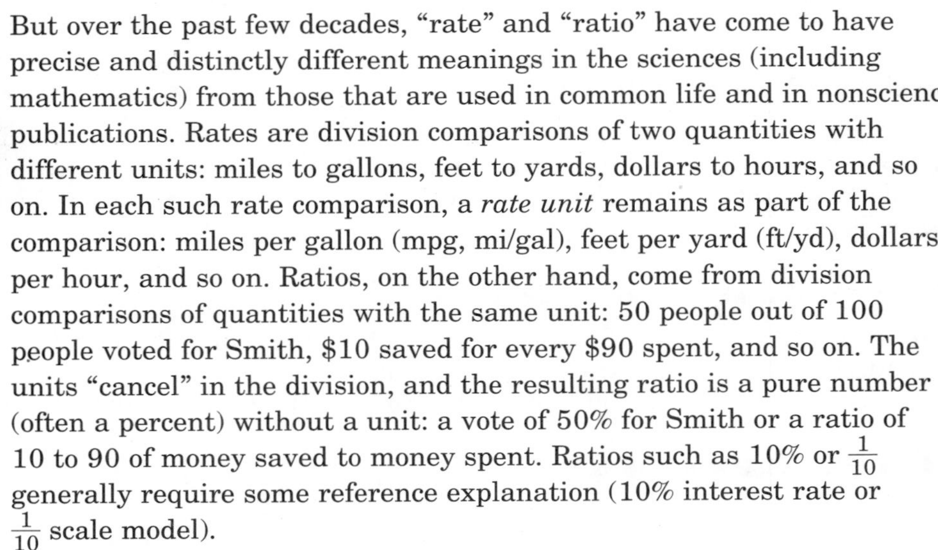

But over the past few decades, “rate” and “ratio” have come to have precise and distinctly different meanings in the sciences (including mathematics) from those that are used in common life and in nonscience publications. Rates are division comparisons of two quantities with different units: miles to gallons, feet to yards, dollars to hours, and so on. In each such rate comparison, a *rate unit* remains as part of the comparison: miles per gallon (mpg, mi/gal), feet per yard (ft/yd), dollars per hour, and so on. Ratios, on the other hand, come from division comparisons of quantities with the same unit: 50 people out of 100 people voted for Smith, \$10 saved for every \$90 spent, and so on. The units “cancel” in the division, and the resulting ratio is a pure number (often a percent) without a unit: a vote of 50% for Smith or a ratio of 10 to 90 of money saved to money spent. Ratios such as 10% or $\frac{1}{10}$ generally require some reference explanation (10% interest rate or $\frac{1}{10}$ scale model).

Throughout *Everyday Mathematics,* a serious effort has been made to be consistent with modern scientific use of the words and ideas of *rate* versus *ratio* and, in this and other matters, to insist on proper use of count and measure units. You are urged to make this effort also—your students’ future science teachers will thank you. But little harm will be caused by occasional errors or inconsistencies.

Solving Rate Problems (Lessons 8.1–8.3)

Three methods for solving rate problems are discussed in Lessons 8.1–8.3, as illustrated with the following example:

> A gray whale’s heart beats 72 times in 9 minutes. At this rate, how many times does the whale’s heart beat in 5 minutes?

The per-unit-rate method was first introduced in *Fourth Grade Everyday Mathematics*. Using this method, you first find the number of times the whale’s heart beats in 1 minute by dividing 72 by 9—a rate of 8 beats per minute. Then, to find the number of heartbeats in 5 minutes, multiply 8 by 5: the whale’s heart would beat 40 times in 5 minutes.

In the rate-table method, equivalent rates are shown in a table similar to a “What’s My Rule?” table. By completing such tables, students develop a sense that rate problems usually involve a search for equivalent rates, leading to the solution of a problem. A rate table for the previous example might look like this:

heartbeats	72	24	48	8	40
minutes	9	3	6	1	5

Using a rate table, there are many ways of arriving at the answer. For example, a student might have focused on the rates in the third and fourth columns of the table and reasoned that if the heart beats 48 times in 6 minutes, or 8 times in 1 minute, then it beats (48 − 8) times in (6 − 1) minutes, or 40 times in 5 minutes.

A third approach is to model the problem with an open proportion and to solve the proportion using the multiplication or division rule for equivalent fractions or by finding cross products. A proportion for the above problem would look like this:

$$\frac{\text{heartbeats}}{\text{minutes}} \quad \frac{72}{9} = \frac{n}{5} \quad \begin{matrix} 9 * n \\ 72 * 5 \end{matrix}$$

In a true proportion, the cross products are equal. Thus,

$$9 * n = 72 * 5$$
$$9 * n = 360$$
$$n = 360 \div 9 = 40$$

The proportion method, while more formal than the first two methods, can be used to solve any rate problem. Students should adapt the method they use to the particular problem. For the above example, students may find either of the first two methods easier to use than the proportion method. But it is usually easier to use proportions to solve more complex problems.

Heart Rate Chart

Heart Rate Target (10 Second Count)

Age	55%	60%	70%	80%	85%
15	19	21	24	27	29
20	18	20	23	27	28
25	18	19	23	26	28
30	17	19	22	25	27
35	17	19	22	25	26
40	17	18	21	24	26
45	16	18	20	23	25
50	16	17	20	23	24

Nutrition Applications (Lessons 8.4, 8.5, and 8.8)

Nutrition is used as a context to provide students with practice in many of the skills encountered in this unit and in previous units. In Lesson 8.4, students practice solving rate problems as they estimate how many calories they use in a typical 24-hour day. In Lesson 8.5, students discuss elements of a balanced diet, as well as plan meals that meet the recommended guidelines for fat, carbohydrate, and protein calories. In Lesson 8.8, they examine information from food labels to estimate and then calculate the percent (ratio) of total calories that comes from fat.

Nutrition Facts
Serving Size 2 Tbsp (32g)
Servings Per Container about 24

Amount Per Serving	
Calories 190	Calories from Fat 130
	% Daily Value*
Total Fat 16g	25%
Saturated Fat 3g	15%
Cholesterol 0mg	0%
Sodium 140mg	6%
Total Carbohydrate 7g	2%
Dietary Fiber 2g	8%
Sugars 3g	
Protein 7g	

Ratios (Lessons 8.6–8.12)

As noted in the Introduction, ratios result from comparison by division of two quantities having the same unit. The comparisons are often expressed as fractions (half as big), multiples (three times as many), or percents. Also as noted earlier, ratios have no units, but they do nearly always need explanation—25% of the calories from fat is quite a different piece of information from 25% of the vote or 25% wrong on a test.

Part-to-whole and part-to-part comparisons are very common and closely related. For example, if a school class consists of 15 boys and 10 girls, the ratio of boys to girls (15 to 10) expresses a part-to-part comparison; the ratio of boys to the whole class (15 to 25) expresses a part-to-whole comparison. Note that part-to-part comparisons often resemble rates: The ratio of boys to girls can be expressed as 1.5 boys per girl.

Using Ratios to Describe Size Changes (Lessons 8.9 and 8.10)

In countless everyday situations, pictures, diagrams, maps, and models represent real-life objects; the representations have the same shapes as the real-life objects, but they may be uniformly enlarged or reduced in size. If the representation is "similar" to the object, then every length in the representation is exactly the same multiple or fraction of the corresponding length in the object. The ratio expressing this constant fraction or multiple is often called a "scale factor," which is expressed in various ways. For example, for a geometric figure enlarged by 2X on a copying machine, the relationship of every length in the copy is double that in the original. This relationship can be expressed with any of these scale factor notations when changing from smaller to larger:

2:1, 2X, $\frac{2}{1}$, 2 / 1, double;

or the corresponding scales when changing from larger to smaller:

1:2, $\frac{1}{2}$X, $\frac{1}{2}$, 1 / 2, half

It is important to note that these size-change factors are applicable only to exactly corresponding lengths. These initial experiences with size changes should make work with "similar figures" in high school geometry much easier for your students.

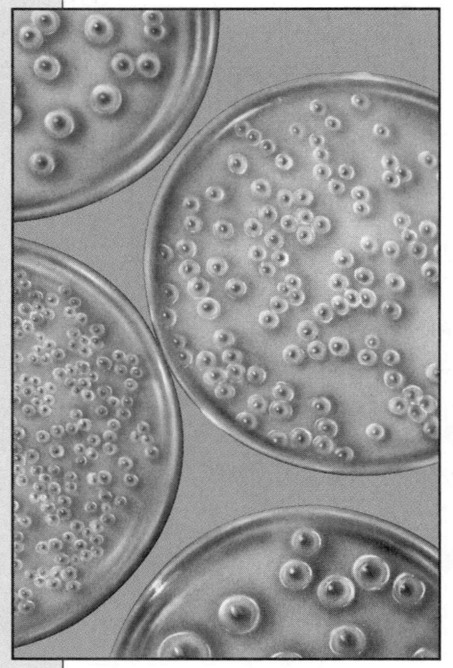

Reduced by about $\frac{1}{2}$X

Comparing Ratios (Lesson 8.11)

Many applications of ratios involve comparing one ratio to another. Such comparisons are made easier if the ratios have a common term. For example, it is easy to compare percents because they are ratios whose second term is 100. But percents are applicable only to part-to-whole comparisons. An alternative is to rename ratios as n-to-1 ratios—ratios of a number to 1.

One key to understanding rates and ratios is repeated exposure to their many uses in everyday life. To this end, Study Link 8.8 asks students to collect a variety of counts and measures, such as the number of left-handed and right-handed people in their homes and the length and width of a television screen. Then, in Lesson 8.11, students write n-to-1 ratios for the data they collected so that they can easily compare their data to the data collected by the other students in their groups.

The Golden Ratio (Lesson 8.12)

A special ratio, called the Golden Ratio, has been an intriguing idea in art, architecture, and mathematics for centuries. In Lesson 8.12, students calculate the ratio of length to width for various rectangles and find that in certain rectangles, known as Golden Rectangles, the ratio of length to width is the Golden Ratio. They have the opportunity to learn a compass construction of the Golden Rectangles and to explore the connection between the Golden Ratio and the Fibonacci sequence.

Review and Assessment (Lesson 8.13)

The Unit 8 assessment in Lesson 8.13 includes oral, slate, and written assessments of the concepts and skills covered in the unit.

For additional information on the following topics, see the *Teacher's Reference Manual:*

- percents
- rates, ratios, and proportions
- rational numbers and decimals
- size-change transformations
- use of variables

8.1 Rates, Rate Tables, and Unit Rates

OBJECTIVES **To review rates; to use the per-unit-rate and rate-table methods of solving rate problems; and to introduce proportions as models for rate situations.**

summaries	materials
1 Teaching the Lesson	
Students review the meaning of rates, along with rate terminology and notation. Students solve rate problems by first finding unit rates. They also solve rate problems by completing rate tables and by using proportions to model rate situations. [Patterns, Functions, and Algebra]	☐ *Math Journal* 2, pp. 286 and 287 ☐ Assessment Master (*Math Masters,* p. 478; optional)
2 Ongoing Learning & Practice	
Students divide whole numbers by whole numbers. They express some quotients as mixed numbers and round other quotients to the nearest whole number. [Operations and Computation] Students practice and maintain skills through Math Boxes and Study Link activities.	☐ *Math Journal* 2, pp. 288 and 289 ☐ Study Link Master (*Math Masters,* p. 340) ☐ nutrition label (for demonstration purposes) ***See* Advance Preparation**
3 Options for Individualizing	
Reteaching Students read an essay on rates in the *Student Reference Book.* [Patterns, Functions, and Algebra] **Extra Practice** Students collect examples of rates in ads, labels, and newspaper and magazine articles. [Patterns, Functions, and Algebra] **Extra Practice** Students solve rate problems. [Patterns, Functions, and Algebra]	☐ *Student Reference Book,* p. 107 ☐ Teaching Master (*Math Masters,* p. 129)

Additional Information

Advance Preparation To introduce Study Link 8.1 in Part 2, bring in a nutrition label from a food package to show students.

Vocabulary • **rate** • **per-unit rate** • **rate table** • **equivalent rate** • **proportion**

Getting Started

Mental Math and Reflexes

Rename each percent as a decimal and as a fraction. Write the fraction in simplest form. *Suggestions:*

- 50% 0.5, $\frac{1}{2}$
- 75% 0.75, $\frac{3}{4}$
- 40% 0.40, $\frac{2}{5}$
- 70% 0.70, $\frac{7}{10}$
- 25% 0.25, $\frac{1}{4}$
- 17% 0.17, $\frac{17}{100}$
- 35% 0.35, $\frac{7}{20}$
- $66\frac{2}{3}$% $0.6\bar{6}$, $\frac{2}{3}$

Math Message

Complete Problems 1 and 2 at the top of page 286 in your journal.

Teaching the Lesson

✦ Math Message Follow-Up
(*Math Journal 2,* p. 286)

WHOLE-CLASS DISCUSSION 

Mention that Problems 1 and 2 are examples of rate situations. Ask students for other examples of rates. If students are unable to suggest examples, give a few and ask for more: 89 cents per liter, 60 miles per hour, 17 points per game, 18 chairs per row, 8 legs per spider, 12 buns per package.

Briefly discuss rates, eventually leading students to the understanding that a **rate** tells how many of something there are for a given number of another thing.

Next, discuss Problems 1 and 2. Many students may have solved them "intuitively" and might be unable to explain their solutions. Point out that although intuitive approaches may work for easy problems, such methods will not help when solving harder problems. In the next several lessons, students will learn methods that will work for all rate problems. So even though many problems in this lesson and the next will be simple enough to solve intuitively, students should also solve them using more formal techniques.

✦ Introducing Two Methods for Solving Rate Problems

WHOLE-CLASS DISCUSSION 

This lesson focuses on two approaches to solving rate problems: using **per-unit rates** and using **rate tables.**

Solving Rate Problems

Math Message

1. A computer printer prints 6 pages in 2 minutes. How many pages will it print in 5 minutes? 15 pages
2. Jessica trains at an indoor track during the winter. She can run 24 laps in 8 minutes. At this rate, how many laps can Jessica run in 12 minutes? 36 laps
3. Ms. Marquez is reading stories her students wrote. She has read 5 stories in 40 minutes.
   a. At this rate, how long would it take her to read 1 story? 8 minutes
   b. How long will it take her to read all 30 of her students' stories? 240 min, or 4 hr
   c. Complete the proportion to show your solution. $\frac{5 \text{ stories}}{40 \text{ minutes}} = \frac{30 \text{ stories}}{240 \text{ minutes}}$
4. Sam scored 75 points in the first 5 basketball games.
   a. On average, how many points did he score per game? 15 points
   b. At this rate, how many points might he score in a 15-game season? 225 points
   c. Complete the proportion to show your solution. $\frac{75 \text{ points}}{5 \text{ games}} = \frac{225 \text{ points}}{15 \text{ games}}$
5. Last year, 55 students sold \$1,210 worth of candy for their band's fund-raiser.
   a. On average, how many dollars' worth of candy did each student sell? \$22
   b. This year, 67 students will be selling candy. If they sell at the same rate as last year, how much money can they expect to raise? \$1,474
   c. Complete the proportion to show your solution. $\frac{55 \text{ students}}{\$1{,}210} = \frac{67 \text{ students}}{\$1{,}474}$
6. Art worked at the checkout counter from 5:30 P.M. to 11 P.M. He earned \$33.
   a. How much did he earn per hour? \$6
   b. Art works $27\frac{1}{2}$ hours per week. How much will he earn in 1 week? \$165
   c. Complete the proportion to show your solution. $\frac{\$33}{5\frac{1}{2} \text{ hours}} = \frac{\$165}{27\frac{1}{2} \text{ hours}}$

STUDENT PAGE

✧ *Math Journal 2,* p. 286

The Per-Unit-Rate Method

Many of your students may have used the per-unit-rate method to solve the Math Message problems even if they cannot explain what they did. Here is how to solve Problem 1 by using the per-unit-rate method:

Step 1: Find the number of pages printed in 1 minute. Since 6 pages can be printed in 2 minutes, the number of pages printed in 1 minute is 6 / 2, or 3 pages.

Step 2: Use the number of pages printed in 1 minute to find the number of pages printed in 5 minutes. The number of pages printed in 5 minutes is 5 * 3, or 15 pages.

Point out that the number of pages printed in 1 minute is an example of a per-unit rate. Rates like this are often written "3 pages per minute" or "3 pages/minute," but in this unit we will use fraction notation: $\frac{3 \text{ pages}}{1 \text{ minute}}$. Fraction notation is clearer and usually used in more complex rate situations, especially those involving scientific data.

Discuss Problem 2 using the per-unit-rate method.

Step 1: Find the number of laps Jessica can run in 1 minute. She can run 24 laps in 8 minutes. At this rate, the number of laps she can run in 1 minute is 24 / 8, or 3 laps per minute.

Step 2: Use the number of laps she can run in 1 minute to find the number of laps she can run in 12 minutes. At this rate, the number of laps she can run in 12 minutes is 12 * 3, or 36 laps.

The Rate-Table Method

A rate table looks like a "What's My Rule?" table, except it's horizontal instead of vertical. There are many ways to set up a rate table. One approach is to enter the known quantities and then use a question mark for the unknown. A rate table for Problem 1 might look like this:

pages	6			?		
minutes	2			5		

One advantage to using rate tables is that it's usually possible to fill in *something*. This means that students can make progress step by step. Eventually, as enough of the table is filled in, the answer will be found.

pages	6	12	9	?		
minutes	2	4	3	5		

For example, the numbers in the third column are double the numbers in the second column. The numbers in the fourth column are halfway between the numbers in the second and third columns. To fill in the fifth column, students can reason in the following way: Since 2 minutes + 3 minutes = 5 minutes, the number of pages printed in 5 minutes is the sum of the number of pages printed in 2 minutes and 3 minutes:

$$6 \text{ pages} + 9 \text{ pages} = 15 \text{ pages}$$

With the class, make a rate table for Problem 2 that shows both the given numbers and the unknown numbers. Ask students to help you fill in the table until it looks like the following:

laps	24	3	6	12	?		
minutes	8	1	2	4	12		

Lead students to the conclusion that each number in the second row is $\frac{1}{3}$ of the corresponding number in the first row. Ask: *At this rate, how long would it take Jessica to run 1 lap?* $\frac{1}{3}$ minute, or 20 seconds

ONGOING ASSESSMENT

Have students explain in writing how they can use a rate table to find the number of laps that Jessica can run in 1 minute. Some students may say that they can divide 24 by 8 to get 3. Others may use patterns in the table to solve the problem. Either approach is fine.

Extend the assessment by having students explain how they can find the number of laps that Jessica can run in 12 minutes. They can multiply 12 by 3, or they might extend the pattern in the table by adding 24 laps in 8 minutes to 12 laps in 4 minutes.

✦ Using Proportions to Model Solutions to Rate Problems

WHOLE-CLASS ACTIVITY

In order to have a good understanding of rates, it is important that students summarize rate situations in words. For example, Math Message Problem 1 can be summarized as follows: If a printer can print 6 pages in 2 minutes, it can print 15 pages in 5 minutes.

This verbal statement can be translated into the following number model:

$$\frac{6 \text{ pages}}{2 \text{ minutes}} = \frac{15 \text{ pages}}{5 \text{ minutes}}$$

Help students see how this number model corresponds to the problem. The left-hand side is the original rate that was given in the problem. The right-hand side is an **equivalent rate** that names the number of pages printed in 5 minutes—15 pages. Such number models are called **proportions.** A proportion is a number sentence that states that two fractions are equivalent.

Repeat this procedure for Problem 2:

Verbal statement: Jessica can run 24 laps in 8 minutes. At this rate, she can run 36 laps in 12 minutes.

Proportion: $\frac{24 \text{ laps}}{8 \text{ minutes}} = \frac{36 \text{ laps}}{12 \text{ minutes}}$

Again, help students see how this proportion corresponds to the problem.

Solving Rate Problems

Math Message

1. A computer printer prints 6 pages in 2 minutes. How many pages will it print in 5 minutes? 15 pages

2. Jessica trains at an indoor track during the winter. She can run 24 laps in 8 minutes. At this rate, how many laps can Jessica run in 12 minutes? 36 laps

3. Ms. Marquez is reading stories her students wrote. She has read 5 stories in 40 minutes.
   a. At this rate, how long would it take her to read 1 story? 8 minutes
   b. How long will it take her to read all 30 of her students' stories? 240 min, or 4 hr
   c. Complete the proportion to show your solution. $\frac{5 \text{ stories}}{40 \text{ minutes}} = \frac{30 \text{ stories}}{240 \text{ minutes}}$

4. Sam scored 75 points in the first 5 basketball games.
   a. On average, how many points did he score per game? 15 points
   b. At this rate, how many points might he score in a 15-game season? 225 points
   c. Complete the proportion to show your solution. $\frac{75 \text{ points}}{5 \text{ games}} = \frac{225 \text{ points}}{15 \text{ games}}$

5. Last year, 55 students sold $1,210 worth of candy for their band's fund-raiser.
   a. On average, how many dollars' worth of candy did each student sell? $22
   b. This year, 67 students will be selling candy. If they sell at the same rate as last year, how much money can they expect to raise? $1,474
   c. Complete the proportion to show your solution. $\frac{55 \text{ students}}{\$1{,}210} = \frac{67 \text{ students}}{\$1{,}474}$

6. Art worked at the checkout counter from 5:30 P.M. to 11 P.M. He earned $33.
   a. How much did he earn per hour? $6
   b. Art works $27\frac{1}{2}$ hours per week. How much will he earn in 1 week? $165
   c. Complete the proportion to show your solution. $\frac{\$33}{5\frac{1}{2} \text{ hours}} = \frac{\$165}{27\frac{1}{2} \text{ hours}}$

STUDENT PAGE

✦ *Math Journal 2,* p. 286

Solving Rate Problems (cont.)

7. The furlong is a unit of distance. This unit is now most commonly used in horse racing. There are 40 furlongs in 5 miles.
   a. Fill in the rate table.

miles	1	2	3	5	8	10
furlongs	8	16	24	40	64	80

   b. How many furlongs are there in 8 miles? 64 furlongs

   Complete the proportion to show your solution. $\frac{5 \text{ miles}}{40 \text{ furlongs}} = \frac{8 \text{ miles}}{64 \text{ furlongs}}$

   c. How many miles are there in 8 furlongs? 1 mile

   Complete the proportion to show your solution. $\frac{5 \text{ miles}}{40 \text{ furlongs}} = \frac{1 \text{ miles}}{8 \text{ furlongs}}$

8. Nico read a 240-page book in 6 hours.
   a. Fill in the rate table.

pages	40	120	160	240	80	320
hours	1	3	4	6	2	8

   b. At this rate, how long would it take him to read a 160-page book? 4 hours

   Complete the proportion to show your solution. $\frac{240 \text{ pages}}{6 \text{ hours}} = \frac{160 \text{ pages}}{4 \text{ hours}}$

   c. How many hours did it take him to read 80 pages? 2 hours

   Complete the proportion to show your solution. $\frac{40 \text{ pages}}{1 \text{ hours}} = \frac{80 \text{ pages}}{2 \text{ hours}}$

Use any method you wish to solve the following problems. Write a proportion to show your solution.

9. A recipe for a 2-pound loaf of bread calls for 4 cups of flour. How many 2-pound loaves can you make with 12 cups of flour? 3 loaves $\frac{1 \text{ loaves}}{4 \text{ cups}} = \frac{3 \text{ loaves}}{12 \text{ cups}}$

10. Two inches of rain fell between 7 A.M. and 3 P.M. It continued to rain at the same rate until 7 P.M. How many inches of rain fell between 7 A.M. and 7 P.M.? 3 inches $\frac{2 \text{ inches}}{8 \text{ hours}} = \frac{3 \text{ inches}}{12 \text{ hours}}$

STUDENT PAGE

✦ *Math Journal 2,* p. 287

✦ Solving Rate Problems
(*Math Journal 2,* pp. 286 and 287)

PARTNER ACTIVITY

Assign journal pages 286 and 287. Note that Problems 3–6 use the per-unit-rate method and Problems 7 and 8 use the rate-table method. Students may use any method they choose to solve Problems 9 and 10. It is important that they practice both methods, since one method will be more appropriate for some applications and the other method for other applications in the lessons that follow. If necessary, work through one or more problems with the class. Circulate and assist as needed.

ONGOING ASSESSMENT

Have students complete an Exit Slip (*Math Masters,* page 478) explaining which method they used to solve Problem 10 and why they chose that method.

Division Practice

Divide. Show your work in the space below.
In Problems 1–3, write your answer as a mixed number.

1. 5,875 ÷ 34 = $172\frac{27}{34}$
2. 958 / 18 = $53\frac{4}{18}$, or $53\frac{2}{9}$
3. 2,509 / 64 = $39\frac{13}{64}$

In Problems 4–6, round your answer to the nearest whole number.

4. 38,419 ÷ 57 = 674
5. 7,648 ÷ 84 = 91
6. 10,063 / 23 = 438

7. Write a number story for Problem 6.
Sample answer: A stadium for a minor league baseball team is divided into 23 equal sections. The entire stadium can hold 10,063 people. How many people can sit in each section?

STUDENT PAGE

✦ *Math Journal 2,* p. 288

Ongoing Learning & Practice

✦ Dividing a Whole Number by a Whole Number (*Math Journal 2,* p. 288)

INDEPENDENT ACTIVITY 

Students may use the partial-quotients algorithm or another algorithm to solve division of whole numbers problems on journal page 288. In Problems 1–3, they express quotients as mixed numbers. In Problems 4–6, they round quotients to the nearest whole number.

Before assigning the problems, you might want to review these two ways of expressing the quotient:

- ▷ In a mixed-number quotient, the remainder is the numerator of the fraction part and the divisor is the denominator.
- ▷ When rounding the quotient, round down if the remainder is less than half of the divisor. Round up if the remainder is at least half of the divisor.

✦ Math Boxes 8.1 (*Math Journal 2,* p. 289)

INDEPENDENT ACTIVITY 

Mixed Review Math Boxes in this lesson are paired with Math Boxes in Lesson 8.3. The skill in Problem 1 is a prerequisite for Unit 9.

✦ Study Link 8.1 (*Math Masters,* p. 340)

Home Connection In preparation for Lesson 8.5, students collect nutrition labels from a variety of foods. Show them a sample nutrition label. See sample on page 610 of the *Teacher's Lesson Guide.* Designate display space on a bulletin board so that the labels can be displayed as students bring them to class. Students also solve problems involving the rate of change in the U.S. population.

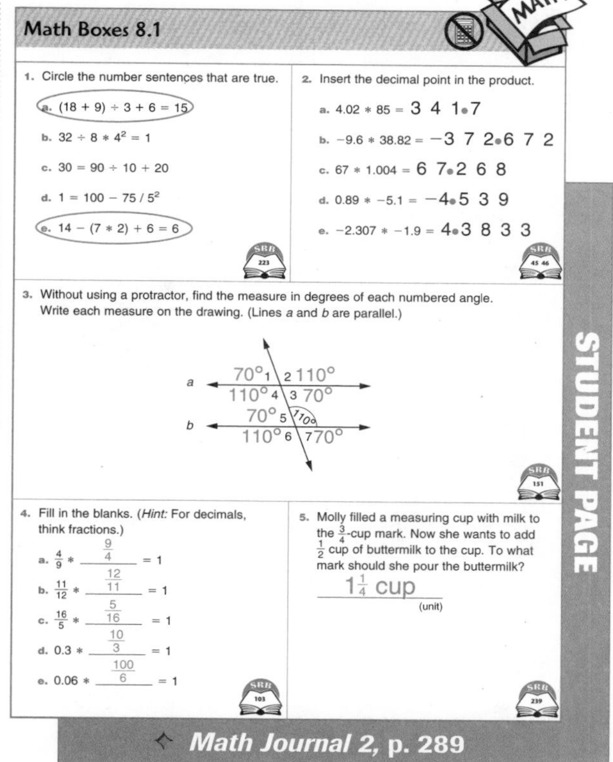

Math Boxes 8.1

1. Circle the number sentences that are true.
   a. (18 + 9) ÷ 3 + 6 = 15
   b. 32 ÷ 8 ∗ 4² = 1
   c. 30 = 90 ÷ 10 + 20
   d. 1 = 100 − 75 / 5²
   e. 14 − (7 ∗ 2) + 6 = 6

2. Insert the decimal point in the product.
   a. 4.02 ∗ 85 = 3 4 1.7
   b. −9.6 ∗ 38.82 = −3 7 2.6 7 2
   c. 67 ∗ 1.004 = 6 7.2 6 8
   d. 0.89 ∗ −5.1 = −4.5 3 9
   e. −2.307 ∗ −1.9 = 4.3 8 3 3

3. Without using a protractor, find the measure in degrees of each numbered angle. Write each measure on the drawing. (Lines *a* and *b* are parallel.)

4. Fill in the blanks. (*Hint:* For decimals, think fractions.)
   a. $\frac{4}{9} * \frac{9}{4} = 1$
   b. $\frac{11}{12} * \frac{12}{11} = 1$
   c. $\frac{16}{5} * \frac{5}{16} = 1$
   d. $0.3 * \frac{10}{3} = 1$
   e. $0.06 * \frac{100}{6} = 1$

5. Molly filled a measuring cup with milk to the $\frac{3}{4}$-cup mark. Now she wants to add $\frac{1}{2}$ cup of buttermilk to the cup. To what mark should she pour the buttermilk?
   $1\frac{1}{4}$ cup (unit)

STUDENT PAGE

✦ Math Journal 2, p. 289

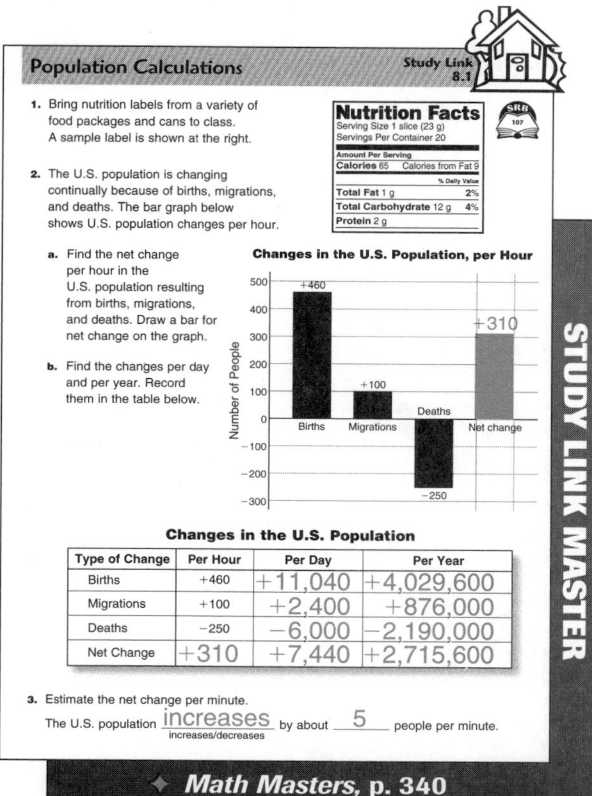

Population Calculations — Study Link 8.1

1. Bring nutrition labels from a variety of food packages and cans to class. A sample label is shown at the right.

2. The U.S. population is changing continually because of births, migrations, and deaths. The bar graph below shows U.S. population changes per hour.
   a. Find the net change per hour in the U.S. population resulting from births, migrations, and deaths. Draw a bar for net change on the graph.
   b. Find the changes per day and per year. Record them in the table below.

Changes in the U.S. Population

Type of Change	Per Hour	Per Day	Per Year
Births	+460	+11,040	+4,029,600
Migrations	+100	+2,400	+876,000
Deaths	−250	−6,000	−2,190,000
Net Change	+310	+7,440	+2,715,600

3. Estimate the net change per minute.
   The U.S. population increases (increases/decreases) by about 5 people per minute.

STUDY LINK MASTER

✦ Math Masters, p. 340

STUDENT PAGE

Rates, Ratios, and Proportions

Rates and Rate Tables

A **rate** tells how many of one thing there are for a certain number of another thing. Rates often contain the word **per** meaning *for each, for every,* or a similar phrase.

Some rates use special abbreviations. For example, *miles per hour* can be written as "mph" and *miles per gallon* can be written as "mpg."

EXAMPLE Alan rode his bicycle 12 miles in 1 hour. He traveled at a rate of 12 *miles per hour,* or 12 *mph.* This rate describes the distance Alan traveled and the time it took him.

Here are other examples of rates.

typing speed	50 words per minute	$\frac{\text{50 words}}{\text{1 minute}}$
price	$14\frac{1}{2}$ cents per ounce	$\frac{14\frac{1}{2}¢}{\text{1 ounce}}$
scoring average	17 points per game	$\frac{\text{17 points}}{\text{1 game}}$
exchange rate	5.4 French francs for each U.S. dollar	$\frac{\text{5.4 French francs}}{\text{1 U.S. dollar}}$

Rate information can be organized in **rate tables.**

EXAMPLE Make a rate table for the statement, "A computer printer prints 4 pages per minute."

The table shows that if a printer prints 4 pages per minute, it will print 8 pages in 2 minutes, 12 pages in 3 minutes, and so on.

pages	4	8	12	16	20	24	28
minutes	1	2	3	4	5	6	7

Rates are often written with a slash (/) or as a fraction. The slash and fraction bar can be read as "per" or "for each."

Rate	Slash	Fraction
per-hour rate: 65 miles per hour	65 miles/hour	$\frac{\text{65 miles}}{\text{1 hour}}$
per-candy rate: $\frac{1}{2}$ cent per candy	$\frac{1}{2}$ cent/candy	$\frac{\frac{1}{2}\text{ cent}}{\text{1 candy}}$

CHECK YOUR UNDERSTANDING

Write each rate with a slash and as a fraction. Make a rate table for each rate.

1. Rebecca earns $4 per hour helping her neighbor in the garden.
2. Todd can type 35 words per minute.

Check your answers on page 375.

one hundred seven SRB 107

◆ *Student Reference Book,* p. 107

TEACHING MASTER

Solving Rate Problems

Solve the problems below using rate tables or unit rates. Write proportions to show your solutions.

1. Melissa planted 10 flowers in 30 minutes. At this rate, how long would it take her to plant 50 flowers? 150 minutes

   $\frac{\text{10 flowers}}{\text{30 minutes}} = \frac{\text{50 flowers}}{\text{150 minutes}}$

2. Rudy was filling his fish tank. He was adding 1 quart every 4 minutes. How many quarts did he add in 28 minutes? 7 quarts

   $\frac{\text{1 quarts}}{\text{4 minutes}} = \frac{\text{7 quarts}}{\text{28 minutes}}$

3. Fred rode 240 kilometers on a bike trip. He converted this distance to miles. (16 kilometers = 10 miles) How many miles did he ride? 150 miles

   $\frac{\text{10 miles}}{\text{16 km}} = \frac{\text{150 miles}}{\text{240 km}}$

4. For which problems did you use rate tables and for which problems did you use unit rates? Explain why you chose the methods you used for each problem. Use the back of this page. Answers vary.

Challenge

5. Louis drinks 1 gallon of water a day. How many days will it take him to drink 28 pints of water? 3.5 days

   $\frac{\text{1 day}}{\text{8 pints}} = \frac{\text{3.5 days}}{\text{28 pints}}$

◆ *Math Masters,* p. 129

3 Options for Individualizing

◆ RETEACHING Reading about Rates (*Student Reference Book,* p. 107)

SMALL-GROUP ACTIVITY  **15–30 min** 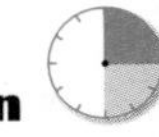

Students read an essay about rates in the *Student Reference Book*. Then they complete the Check Your Understanding problem set.

◆ EXTRA PRACTICE Collecting Examples of Rates

INDEPENDENT ACTIVITY  **30+ min** 

Have students bring to class advertisements, labels, or newspaper and magazine articles that contain references to rates. They should underline or highlight the rates. You may also want to ask students to list and illustrate examples of rates. This collection can be displayed on a "Rates in Our World" bulletin board.

◆ EXTRA PRACTICE Solving Number Stories Involving Rates (*Math Masters,* p. 129)

INDEPENDENT ACTIVITY  **15–30 min** 

Students solve rate problems using rate tables and per-unit rates. Note that in Problem 5, students need to convert gallons to pints.

8.2 Solving Rate Problems with Proportions

OBJECTIVE **To use proportions to model and solve rate problems.**

summaries	materials
1 Teaching the Lesson	
Students use simplified rate tables to write open proportions (proportions containing a variable). Students also solve simple rate problems by setting up and solving proportions. [Patterns, Functions, and Algebra]	☐ *Math Journal 2,* pp. 290 and 291 ☐ Study Link 8.1 ☐ slate
2 Ongoing Learning & Practice	
Students divide a whole number by a whole number to a given decimal place. [Operations and Computation] Students practice and maintain skills through Math Boxes and Study Link activities.	☐ *Math Journal 2,* pp. 292 and 293 ☐ Study Link Masters (*Math Masters,* pp. 341 and 342) ☐ Geometry Template
3 Options for Individualizing	
Extra Practice Students solve "What's My Rule?" rate problems. [Patterns, Functions, and Algebra] **Reteaching** Students read an essay about using proportions to solve rate problems. [Patterns, Functions, and Algebra]	☐ *Student Reference Book,* pp. 114 and 115 ☐ Teaching Master (*Math Masters,* p. 130)

Additional Information

Vocabulary • **open proportion** • **solution of a proportion**

Getting Started

Mental Math and Reflexes

Solve "percent of" problems. Have students share their strategies for solving the problems. *Suggestions:*

- 30% of 60 18
- 53% of 200 106
- 75% of 44 33
- 84% of 50 42
- 46% of 300 138
- 12.5% of 32 4

Math Message

Solve Problems 1–3 on journal page 290.

Study Link 8.1 Follow-Up

Briefly go over the answers to the problems. Collect the nutrition labels that students have brought to class. (See sample below.) Ask a volunteer to assemble them into a bulletin-board display. Encourage students to continue bringing nutrition labels to class.

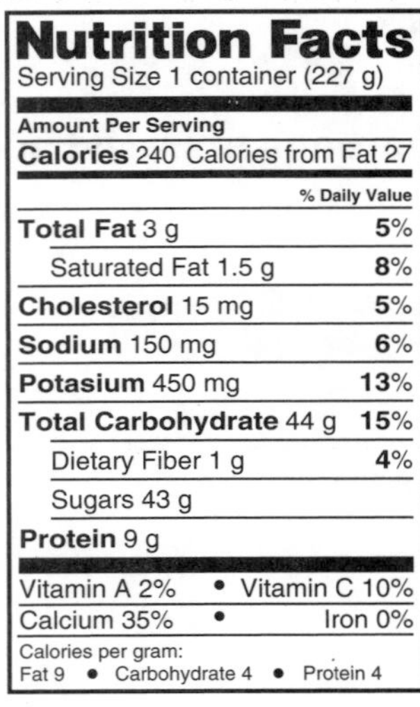

Nutrition Facts
Serving Size 1 container (227 g)

Amount Per Serving
Calories 240 Calories from Fat 27

	% Daily Value
Total Fat 3 g	**5%**
Saturated Fat 1.5 g	**8%**
Cholesterol 15 mg	**5%**
Sodium 150 mg	**6%**
Potasium 450 mg	**13%**
Total Carbohydrate 44 g	**15%**
Dietary Fiber 1 g	**4%**
Sugars 43 g	
Protein 9 g	

Vitamin A 2% • Vitamin C 10%
Calcium 35% • Iron 0%
Calories per gram:
Fat 9 • Carbohydrate 4 • Protein 4

Teaching the Lesson

Math Message Follow-Up (*Math Journal 2,* p. 290)

WHOLE-CLASS DISCUSSION

Students share solution strategies. Discuss how the proportions students wrote correspond to the problems. Ask them to describe what the proportions stand for and to summarize the solution in words. For example, for the proportion in Problem 1,

$$\frac{8 \text{ miles}}{1 \text{ hour}} = \frac{24 \text{ miles}}{3 \text{ hours}}$$

the left side, $\frac{8 \text{ miles}}{1 \text{ hour}}$, is the original rate given in the problem. The right side, $\frac{24 \text{ miles}}{3 \text{ hours}}$, is an equivalent rate that gives the number of miles that Robin rode in 3 hours—24 miles. You can summarize the solution as follows: At the rate of 8 miles per hour, Robin can ride 24 miles in 3 hours.

Until now, students have used proportions only to *summarize* solutions after they have been found by some other method. In this lesson and the next, students will learn how to use proportions to *solve* rate problems.

Introducing Simplified Rate Tables and Open Proportions

WHOLE-CLASS ACTIVITY

Use the following problem to show students how to set up a proportion: *Hannah can type at the rate of 40 words per minute. How long would it take her to type a 200-word essay?* Most students will probably be able to solve this problem mentally, but explain that you are using it to introduce a method that can be used on all rate problems, no matter how complicated they are.

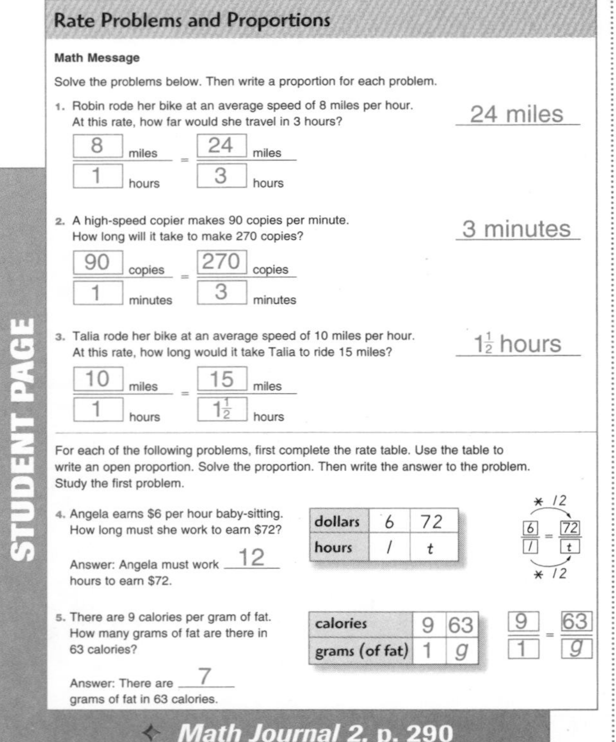

STUDENT PAGE

Rate Problems and Proportions

Math Message

Solve the problems below. Then write a proportion for each problem.

1. Robin rode her bike at an average speed of 8 miles per hour. At this rate, how far would she travel in 3 hours? 24 miles

$\frac{8 \text{ miles}}{1 \text{ hours}} = \frac{24 \text{ miles}}{3 \text{ hours}}$

2. A high-speed copier makes 90 copies per minute. How long will it take to make 270 copies? 3 minutes

$\frac{90 \text{ copies}}{1 \text{ minutes}} = \frac{270 \text{ copies}}{3 \text{ minutes}}$

3. Talia rode her bike at an average speed of 10 miles per hour. At this rate, how long would it take Talia to ride 15 miles? $1\frac{1}{2}$ hours

$\frac{10 \text{ miles}}{1 \text{ hours}} = \frac{15 \text{ miles}}{1\frac{1}{2} \text{ hours}}$

For each of the following problems, first complete the rate table. Use the table to write an open proportion. Solve the proportion. Then write the answer to the problem. Study the first problem.

4. Angela earns $6 per hour baby-sitting. How long must she work to earn $72?

dollars	6	72
hours	1	t

$\frac{6}{1} = \frac{72}{t}$ (∗ 12)

Answer: Angela must work 12 hours to earn $72.

5. There are 9 calories per gram of fat. How many grams of fat are there in 63 calories?

calories	9	63
grams (of fat)	1	g

$\frac{9}{1} = \frac{63}{g}$

Answer: There are 7 grams of fat in 63 calories.

Math Journal 2, p. 290

Draw the following simplified rate table on the board and ask students to help you complete it. Use t to represent the time that it would take Hannah to type the essay.

words	40	200
minutes	1	t

Ask students to use this rate table to write a proportion for the problem on their slates, using t in place of the unknown number of minutes. Students should write the following proportion:

$$\frac{40 \text{ words}}{1 \text{ minute}} = \frac{200 \text{ words}}{t \text{ minutes}}$$

Explain that this is an **open proportion;** that is, it is neither true nor false. For most values of *t,* the proportion is false. For one specific value of *t,* however, the proportion is true. The value of t that makes the proportion true is called the **solution of the proportion.**

Ask students to solve the proportion. You might show with "times 5" arrows that both the numerator and denominator must be multiplied by 5. The solution is 5, so Hannah would need 5 minutes to type the essay.

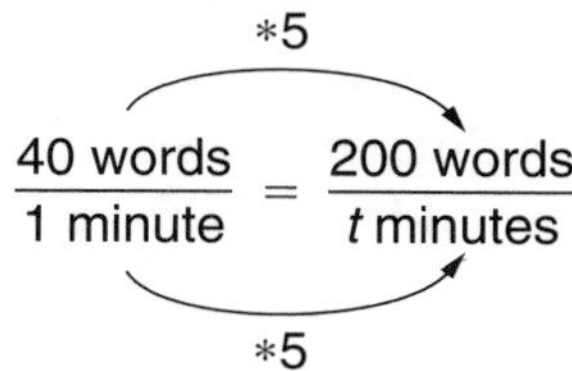

Work through one or two more problems with the class. (Suggested problems appear on the next page.) For each problem, follow these steps:

Step 1: Complete a simplified rate table, using a letter for the unknown quantity.

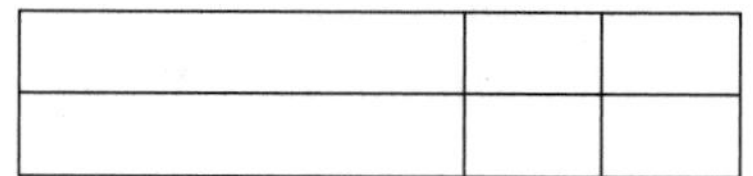

Step 2: Use the rate table to write an open proportion.

$$\frac{\square \text{ (unit)}}{\square \text{ (unit)}} = \frac{\square \text{ (unit)}}{\square \text{ (unit)}}$$

Step 3: Solve the proportion.

Step 4: State the answer in words.

NOTE: The last step, stating the answer in words, is very important. It encourages students to check whether their solutions make sense.

Adjusting the Activity For some students, the unit labels in the proportion may get in the way when trying to solve the proportion. The labels can be omitted, as long as they appear in the rate table. For example, in the given problem, students need write only $\frac{40}{1} = \frac{200}{t}$. Later, they may want to omit the rate table altogether. If so, it is important that they show the labels next to the proportion.

$$\frac{(\text{words})\ 40}{(\text{minutes})\ 1} = \frac{200}{t}$$

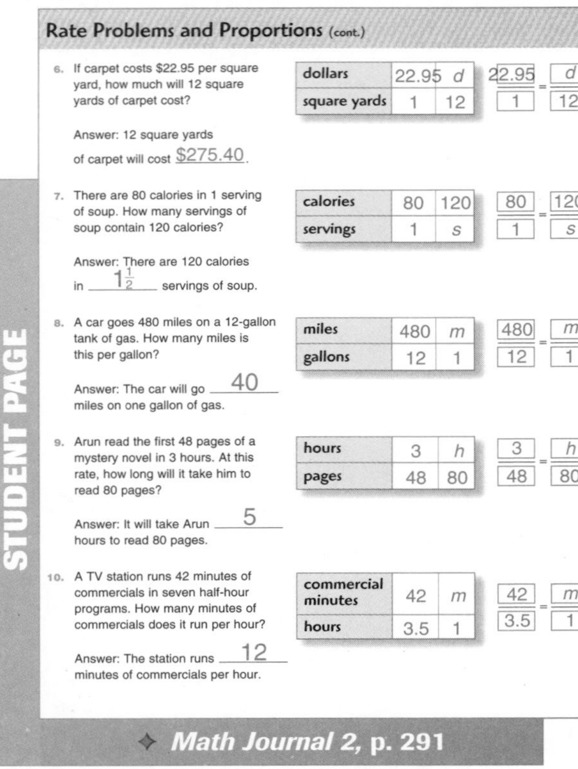

Rate Problems and Proportions (cont.)

6. If carpet costs $22.95 per square yard, how much will 12 square yards of carpet cost?

dollars	22.95	d
square yards	1	12

$\frac{22.95}{1} = \frac{d}{12}$

Answer: 12 square yards of carpet will cost $275.40.

7. There are 80 calories in 1 serving of soup. How many servings of soup contain 120 calories?

calories	80	120
servings	1	s

$\frac{80}{1} = \frac{120}{s}$

Answer: There are 120 calories in $1\frac{1}{2}$ servings of soup.

8. A car goes 480 miles on a 12-gallon tank of gas. How many miles is this per gallon?

miles	480	m
gallons	12	1

$\frac{480}{12} = \frac{m}{1}$

Answer: The car will go 40 miles on one gallon of gas.

9. Arun read the first 48 pages of a mystery novel in 3 hours. At this rate, how long will it take him to read 80 pages?

hours	3	h
pages	48	80

$\frac{3}{48} = \frac{h}{80}$

Answer: It will take Arun 5 hours to read 80 pages.

10. A TV station runs 42 minutes of commercials in seven half-hour programs. How many minutes of commercials does it run per hour?

commercial minutes	42	m
hours	3.5	1

$\frac{42}{3.5} = \frac{m}{1}$

Answer: The station runs 12 minutes of commercials per hour.

STUDENT PAGE

Math Journal 2, p. 291

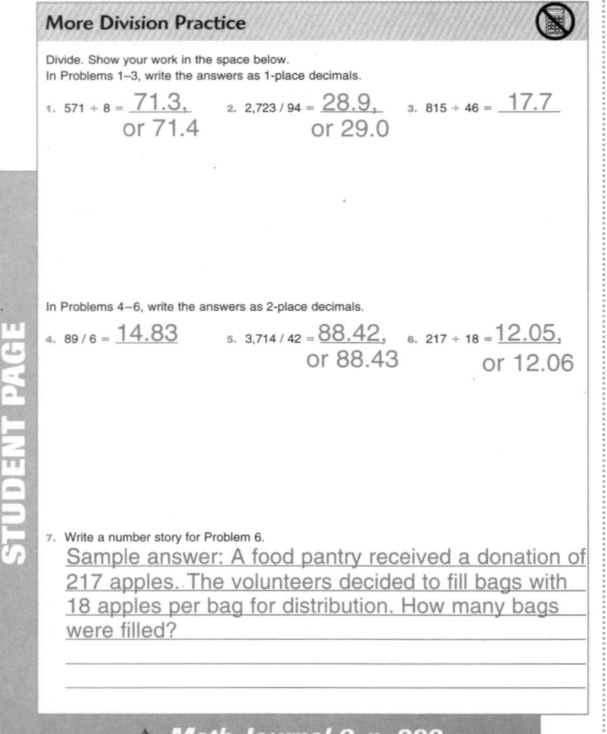

More Division Practice

Divide. Show your work in the space below.
In Problems 1–3, write the answers as 1-place decimals.

1. 571 ÷ 8 = 71.3, or 71.4
2. 2,723 / 94 = 28.9, or 29.0
3. 815 ÷ 46 = 17.7

In Problems 4–6, write the answers as 2-place decimals.

4. 89 / 6 = 14.83
5. 3,714 / 42 = 88.42, or 88.43
6. 217 ÷ 18 = 12.05, or 12.06

7. Write a number story for Problem 6.
Sample answer: A food pantry received a donation of 217 apples. The volunteers decided to fill bags with 18 apples per bag for distribution. How many bags were filled?

STUDENT PAGE

Math Journal 2, p. 292

Suggested problems:

1. Alex ran 200 meters in 45 seconds. At this pace, how long would it take him to run 1,600 meters?

meters	200	1,600
seconds	45	s

$\frac{200}{45} = \frac{1{,}600}{s}$ Solution: 360

Possible solution strategy: $200 * 8 = 1{,}600$. Therefore, multiply 45 by 8. Answer: It would take Alex 360 seconds, or 6 minutes, to run 1,600 meters.

2. A recipe that makes 48 oatmeal cookies calls for 2 eggs. How many cookies can be made with 3 eggs?

cookies	48	c
eggs	2	3

$\frac{48}{2} = \frac{c}{3}$ Solution: 72

Possible solution strategy: Find how many cookies can be made with one egg. 24 Then add that number of cookies to 48 for the total number of cookies. Answer: 72 cookies can be made with 3 eggs.

3. In March 2000, the Big Dig construction project in Boston was spending about $4 million a day. At this rate, how long would it take to spend $100 million?

dollars	4 million	100 million
days	1	d

$\frac{4{,}000{,}000}{1} = \frac{100{,}000{,}000}{d}$ Solution: 25

Answer: It would take 25 days to spend 100 million dollars.

4. In the first 8 games of the basketball season, Sandra scored 48 points. At this rate, how many points would she score in 24 games?

points	48	p
games	8	24

$\frac{48}{8} = \frac{p}{24}$ Solution: 144

Answer: She would score 144 points in 24 games.

Adjusting the Activity To extend Problem 4 above, have students continue the rate table with numbers of games that are not multiples of 8. For example, how many points would Sandra score in 10 games? 60 In 18 games? 108 In 30 games? 180 In 15 games? 90

 Using Proportions to Solve Rate Problems (*Math Journal 2,* pp. 290 and 291)

PARTNER ACTIVITY

Most of the problems on journal pages 290 and 291 are relatively easy, so students can focus on setting up proportions to solve rate problems without being distracted by complex calculations. They will solve more complicated problems in Lesson 8.3. Tell students to use proportions to solve the problems, even if they can solve them using other methods. Circulate and assist as needed.

Adjusting the Activity It may help some students to think of equivalent fractions when finding missing numbers in the simplified rate tables.

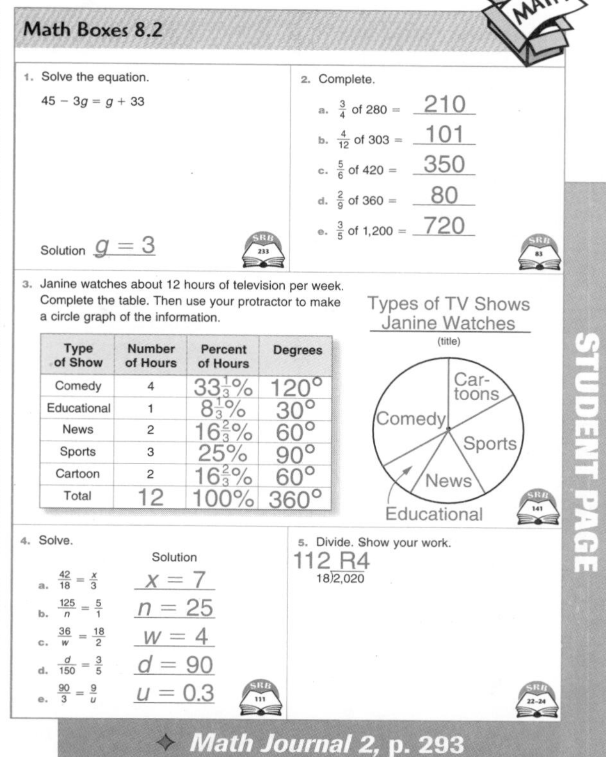

Math Boxes 8.2

1. Solve the equation.
$45 - 3g = g + 33$
Solution $g = 3$

2. Complete.
a. $\frac{3}{4}$ of 280 = 210
b. $\frac{4}{12}$ of 303 = 101
c. $\frac{5}{6}$ of 420 = 350
d. $\frac{2}{9}$ of 360 = 80
e. $\frac{3}{5}$ of 1,200 = 720

3. Janine watches about 12 hours of television per week. Complete the table. Then use your protractor to make a circle graph of the information.

Type of Show	Number of Hours	Percent of Hours	Degrees
Comedy	4	$33\frac{1}{3}\%$	120°
Educational	1	$8\frac{1}{3}\%$	30°
News	2	$16\frac{2}{3}\%$	60°
Sports	3	25%	90°
Cartoon	2	$16\frac{2}{3}\%$	60°
Total	12	100%	360°

4. Solve.

		Solution
a.	$\frac{42}{18} = \frac{x}{3}$	$x = 7$
b.	$\frac{125}{n} = \frac{5}{1}$	$n = 25$
c.	$\frac{36}{w} = \frac{18}{2}$	$w = 4$
d.	$\frac{d}{150} = \frac{3}{5}$	$d = 90$
e.	$\frac{90}{3} = \frac{9}{u}$	$u = 0.3$

5. Divide. Show your work.
112 R4
18)2,020

◆ *Math Journal 2,* p. 293

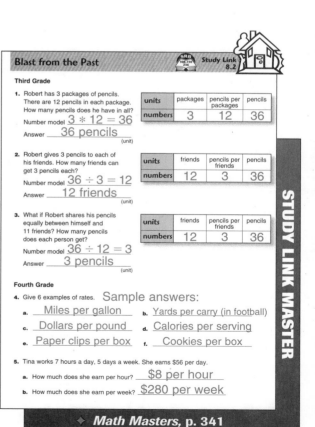

2 Ongoing Learning & Practice

◆ Expressing Division Remainders to a Given Decimal Place (*Math Journal 2,* p. 292)

INDEPENDENT ACTIVITY 

Students divide whole numbers by whole numbers. In Problems 1–3, they find the quotients to one decimal place. In Problems 4–6, they find the quotients to two decimal places.

ONGOING ASSESSMENT
Use this page to assess students' ability to adjust the dividend in order to get a quotient with the required number of decimal places.

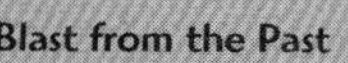

Blast from the Past Study Link 8.2

Third Grade

1. Robert has 3 packages of pencils. There are 12 pencils in each package. How many pencils does he have in all?
Number model $3 * 12 = 36$
Answer 36 pencils (unit)

units	packages	pencils per packages	pencils
numbers	3	12	36

2. Robert gives 3 pencils to each of his friends. How many friends can get 3 pencils each?
Number model $36 \div 3 = 12$
Answer 12 friends (unit)

units	friends	pencils per friends	pencils
numbers	12	3	36

3. What if Robert shares his pencils equally between himself and 11 friends? How many pencils does each person get?
Number model $36 \div 12 = 3$
Answer 3 pencils (unit)

units	friends	pencils per friends	pencils
numbers	12	3	36

Fourth Grade

4. Give 6 examples of rates. Sample answers:
a. Miles per gallon
b. Yards per carry (in football)
c. Dollars per pound
d. Calories per serving
e. Paper clips per box
f. Cookies per box

5. Tina works 7 hours a day, 5 days a week. She earns $56 per day.
a. How much does she earn per hour? $8 per hour
b. How much does she earn per week? $280 per week

◆ *Math Masters,* p. 341

◆ Math Boxes 8.2 (*Math Journal 2,* p. 293)

INDEPENDENT ACTIVITY 

Mixed Review Math Boxes in this lesson are paired with Math Boxes in Lesson 8.4. The skill in Problem 1 is a prerequisite for Unit 9.

STUDY LINK MASTER

Blast from the Past (cont.) — Study Link 8.2

6. The Davis family drove 280 miles to visit relatives. It took 5 hours. At that rate, how many miles did the family drive in 3 hours? 168 miles

Fill in the rate table, if needed.

hours	1	2	3	4	5	6
miles	56	112	168	224	280	336

7. A store charges $1.49 for a 20-ounce box of Puff Flakes cereal and $1.72 for a 24-ounce box of the same cereal. Which is the better buy? The 24-oz box

Explain. $1.49 / 20 oz = $0.0745 per ounce; $1.72 / 24 oz = $0.0717 per ounce. The 24-oz box costs slightly less per ounce.

Fifth Grade

8. Complete the table below. Then graph the data. Connect the points.

Andy earns $8 per hour. *Rule:* Earnings = $8 * number of hours worked

Time (hr) (*h*)	Earnings ($) (8 * *h*)
1	8
2	16
3	24
5	40
7	56

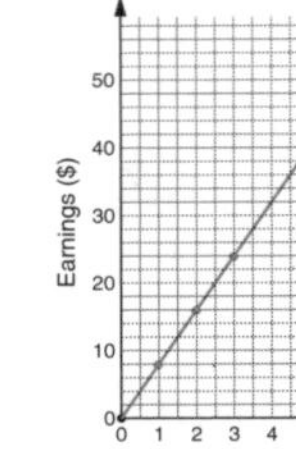

Plot a point to show Andy's earnings for $5\frac{1}{2}$ hours. How much will he earn? $44

◆ *Math Masters*, p. 342

TEACHING MASTER

"What's My Rule?"

Complete the tables and find the missing rules. State the rules in words.

1. *Rule:* Marge walks 3 miles per hour.

Time (hr) *h*	Distance (mi) 3 * *h*
2	6
5	15
1	3
3	9
12	36
Answers vary.	

2. *Rule:* Mike earns $5 per hour.

Time (hr)	Earnings ($)
1	5
7	35
15	75
20	100
6.5	32.50
22	110
Answers vary.	

3. *Rule:* A car gets 25 miles per gallon.

Gasoline (gal)	Distance (mi)
1	25
7	175
12	300
18	450
25	625
Answers vary.	

Challenge

4. *Rule:* Roger reads 8 pages in 10 minutes.

Time (min) *m*	Pages $\frac{8}{10} * m$
20	16
15	12
20	16
45	36
Answers vary.	

◆ *Math Masters*, p. 130

◆ **Study Link 8.2** (*Math Masters,* pp. 341 and 342)

Home Connection This "Blast from the Past" reviews students' past experiences with rates.

3 Options for Individualizing

◆ **EXTRA PRACTICE Solving "What's My Rule?" Rate Problems** (*Math Masters,* p. 130)

INDEPENDENT ACTIVITY  **5–15 min** 

Students solve a set of "What's My Rule?" problems that involve rates. These are similar to problems they solved in fifth grade.

Adjusting the Activity To extend this activity, have students rewrite the tables as a sequence of equivalent rates. For example, in Problem 1, the table can be rewritten as: $\frac{2}{6} = \frac{5}{15} = \frac{1}{3} = \frac{3}{9} = \frac{12}{36}$.

◆ **RETEACHING Reading an Essay about Using Proportions to Solve Rate Problems** (*Student Reference Book,* pp. 114 and 115)

INDEPENDENT ACTIVITY  **5–15 min** 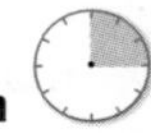

Students read an essay about using proportions to solve rate problems in the *Student Reference Book*. They also complete the Check Your Understanding problem set.

8.3 Solving Proportions by Cross Multiplication

OBJECTIVES **To introduce cross multiplication as a way to test whether two fractions are equivalent; and to use cross multiplication to solve proportions.**

summaries	materials
1 Teaching the Lesson	
Students develop the rule that two fractions are equivalent if their cross products are equal. [Numeration] Students use the cross-products rule to solve proportions by cross multiplication. Students solve rate problems by writing proportions and then using cross multiplication. [Patterns, Functions, and Algebra]	□ *Math Journal 2,* pp. 294, 296, and 297 □ Study Link 8.2 □ Assessment Master (*Math Masters,* p. 478; optional)
2 Ongoing Learning & Practice	
Students divide decimals by whole numbers. [Operations and Computation] Students practice and maintain skills through Math Boxes and Study Link activities.	□ *Math Journal 2,* pp. 295 and 298 □ Study Link Masters (*Math Masters,* pp. 343 and 344) ***See* Advance Preparation**
3 Options for Individualizing	
Extra Practice From a recipe, students calculate the ingredients needed to make various amounts of peanut butter fudge. [Patterns, Functions, and Algebra] **Enrichment** Students find examples of rates in the story *Math Curse*. [Patterns, Functions, and Algebra]	□ Teaching Master (*Math Masters,* p. 131) □ *Math Curse* ***See* Advance Preparation**

Additional Information

Advance Preparation Study Link 8.4 asks students to visit a grocery store to collect data about the cost and weight of various items. It should be assigned along with Study Link 8.3 to give students enough time to plan their visit to the grocery store. Review the instructions for the activity with the class. Suggest that students collect the data as soon as possible. They may postpone the calculations of unit price until after Lesson 8.4 has been completed. If a grocery store posts a unit price, ask students to check that the information is accurate.

For the optional Enrichment activity in Part 3, you will need a copy of *Math Curse* by Jon Scieszka (Viking, 1995).

Vocabulary • **cross products** • **cross multiplication**

Getting Started

Mental Math and Reflexes

Have students solve equations and share their solution strategies. *Suggestions:*

- $3 * x = 18$ 6
- $64 = p * 8$ 8
- $72 = 9 * r$ 8
- $b * 7 = 14 * 2$ 4
- $12 * 3 = m * 4$ 9
- $5 * 4 = 10 * a$ 2

Math Message

Complete the problems on journal page 294.

Study Link 8.2 Follow-Up

Briefly go over the answers.

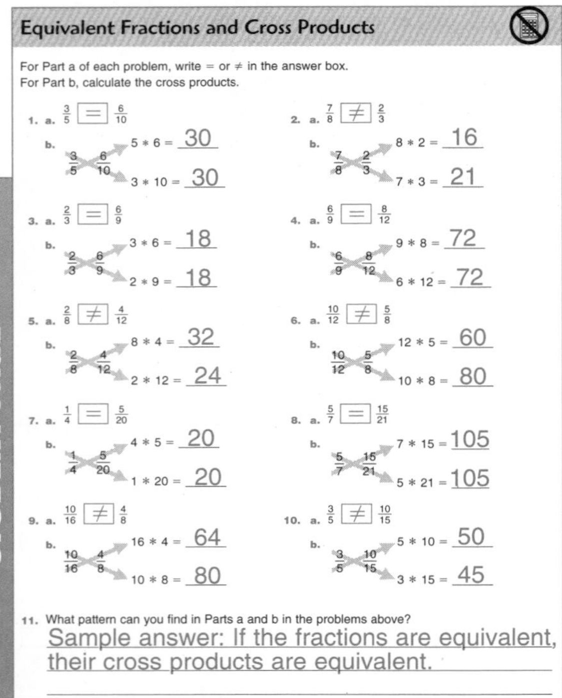

Equivalent Fractions and Cross Products

For Part a of each problem, write = or ≠ in the answer box.
For Part b, calculate the cross products.

1. a. $\frac{3}{5}$ = $\frac{6}{10}$
   b. $5 * 6 =$ 30; $3 * 10 =$ 30
2. a. $\frac{7}{8}$ ≠ $\frac{2}{3}$
   b. $8 * 2 =$ 16; $7 * 3 =$ 21
3. a. $\frac{2}{3}$ = $\frac{6}{9}$
   b. $3 * 6 =$ 18; $2 * 9 =$ 18
4. a. $\frac{6}{9}$ = $\frac{8}{12}$
   b. $9 * 8 =$ 72; $6 * 12 =$ 72
5. a. $\frac{2}{8}$ ≠ $\frac{4}{12}$
   b. $8 * 4 =$ 32; $2 * 12 =$ 24
6. a. $\frac{10}{12}$ ≠ $\frac{5}{8}$
   b. $12 * 5 =$ 60; $10 * 8 =$ 80
7. a. $\frac{1}{4}$ = $\frac{5}{20}$
   b. $4 * 5 =$ 20; $1 * 20 =$ 20
8. a. $\frac{5}{7}$ = $\frac{15}{21}$
   b. $7 * 15 =$ 105; $5 * 21 =$ 105
9. a. $\frac{10}{16}$ ≠ $\frac{4}{8}$
   b. $16 * 4 =$ 64; $10 * 8 =$ 80
10. a. $\frac{3}{5}$ ≠ $\frac{10}{15}$
    b. $5 * 10 =$ 50; $3 * 15 =$ 45
11. What pattern can you find in Parts a and b in the problems above?
    Sample answer: If the fractions are equivalent, their cross products are equivalent.

STUDENT PAGE

✦ *Math Journal 2,* p. 294

Adjusting the Activity Students who are having trouble multiplying the numbers mentally can use pencil and paper or a calculator if they wish. However, most students should be able to find the products mentally.

1 Teaching the Lesson

✦ Math Message Follow-Up
(*Math Journal 2,* p. 294)

WHOLE-CLASS DISCUSSION

Go over the answers to Problems 1–10. Clarify the terms *cross products* and *cross multiplication:*

> **Cross products** are found by multiplying the numerator of each fraction by the denominator of the other fraction. **Cross multiplication** is the process of finding cross products.

Then discuss Problem 11. While there are several possible patterns, the one that stands out is that if the fractions in Part a are equivalent, then the cross products in Part b are equal; if the fractions in Part a are not equivalent, then the cross products in Part b are not equal.

Finally, point out that this pattern provides a way to test whether two fractions are equivalent: If the cross products are equal, the fractions are equivalent; if the cross products are not equal, the fractions are not equivalent. Have students use this rule to test several pairs of fractions for equivalence. *Suggestions:*

- $\frac{3}{4}$ __?__ $\frac{9}{12}$ Cross products: $3 * 12 = 36$; $4 * 9 = 36$. The cross products are equal; therefore, the fractions are equivalent.
- $\frac{5}{6}$ __?__ $\frac{8}{9}$ Cross products: $5 * 9 = 45$; $6 * 8 = 48$. The cross products are not equal; therefore, the fractions are not equivalent.
- $\frac{3}{8}$ __?__ $\frac{1}{4}$ Not equivalent
- $\frac{16}{20}$ __?__ $\frac{12}{15}$ equivalent

Pose additional problems as needed.

✦ Using Cross Products to Solve Proportions

WHOLE-CLASS ACTIVITY

If checking fractions for equivalence were the only application of cross products, they wouldn't be very important. What makes cross products especially useful is that they can be used to solve proportions.

Write the following proportion on the board: $\frac{5}{6} = \frac{x}{18}$. Ask students how they can solve the proportion, using cross products.

Many students probably solved the proportion by applying the multiplication rule for finding equivalent fractions, as was done in Lessons 8.1 and 8.2. If so, praise them but remind them that they are to find a solution using cross products. If no one is able to do so, demonstrate the following approach:

Step 1: Cross multiply. Note that the cross product of 6 and x is written as $6 * x$.

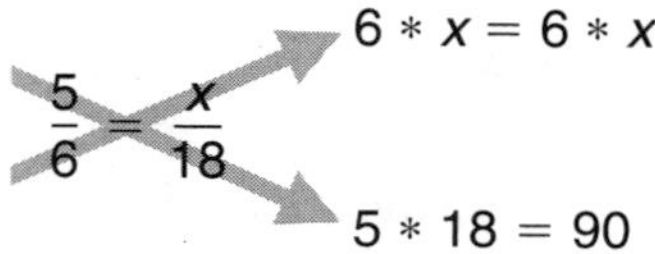

Step 2: Since we want the two fractions in the proportion to be equivalent, we also want the two cross products to be equal; that is, we want $6 * x$ to be equal to $5 * 18$.

Step 3: Solve the equation from Step 2.

$$6 * x = 5 * 18$$
$$6 * x = 90$$
$$x = 90 / 6$$
$$x = 15$$

Step 4: Write 15 in place of x in the proportion: $\frac{5}{6} = \frac{15}{18}$. Check by cross multiplication that the two fractions are equivalent. $6 * 15 = 5 * 18 = 90$

Guide students in solving a few more proportions using cross products. Suggested problems appear on the next page.

NOTE: The answer to this proportion and many other problems can be found more easily using other methods. The advantage of the cross-products method, however, is that it works for all proportions, not just those with convenient numbers. You may need to point this fact out to students who question the need to practice the cross-products method.

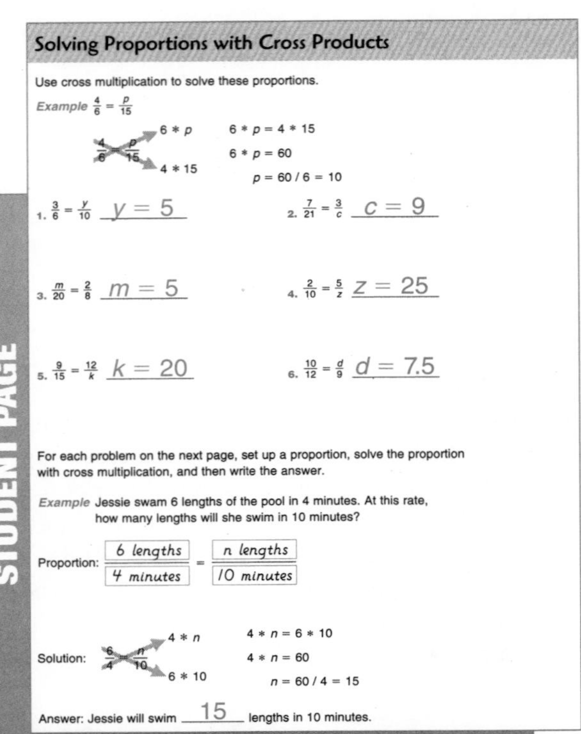

Solving Proportions with Cross Products

Use cross multiplication to solve these proportions.

Example $\frac{4}{6} = \frac{p}{15}$

$6 * p$ $\quad$ $6 * p = 4 * 15$

$4 * 15$ $\quad$ $6 * p = 60$

$p = 60 / 6 = 10$

1. $\frac{3}{6} = \frac{y}{10}$ $y = 5$
2. $\frac{7}{21} = \frac{3}{c}$ $c = 9$
3. $\frac{m}{20} = \frac{2}{8}$ $m = 5$
4. $\frac{2}{10} = \frac{5}{z}$ $z = 25$
5. $\frac{9}{15} = \frac{12}{k}$ $k = 20$
6. $\frac{10}{12} = \frac{d}{9}$ $d = 7.5$

For each problem on the next page, set up a proportion, solve the proportion with cross multiplication, and then write the answer.

Example Jessie swam 6 lengths of the pool in 4 minutes. At this rate, how many lengths will she swim in 10 minutes?

Proportion: $\frac{6 \text{ lengths}}{4 \text{ minutes}} = \frac{n \text{ lengths}}{10 \text{ minutes}}$

Solution: $4 * n$, $6 * 10$ $\quad$ $4 * n = 6 * 10$ $\quad$ $4 * n = 60$ $\quad$ $n = 60 / 4 = 15$

Answer: Jessie will swim 15 lengths in 10 minutes.

STUDENT PAGE

Math Journal 2, p. 296

Solving Proportions with Cross Products *(cont.)*

7. Belle bought 8 yards of ribbon for $6. How many yards could she buy for $9?

$\frac{8 \text{ yards}}{\$6} = \frac{n \text{ yards}}{\$9}$

Solution: $8 * 9 = 6n$; $72 = 6n$; $72 / 6 = 6n / 6$; $12 = n$

Answer: Belle could buy 12 yards of ribbon for $9.

8. Before going to France, Maurice exchanged $25 for 125 French francs. At that exchange rate, how many French francs could he get for $80?

$\frac{\$25}{125 \text{ francs}} = \frac{\$80}{x \text{ francs}}$

Solution: $25x = 80 * 125$; $25x = 10{,}000$; $25x / 25 = 10{,}000 / 25$; $x = 400$

Answer: Maurice could get 400 French francs for $80.

9. One gloomy day, 4 inches of rain fell in 6 hours. At this rate, how many inches of rain had fallen after 4 hours?

$\frac{4 \text{ inches}}{6 \text{ hours}} = \frac{p \text{ inches}}{4 \text{ hours}}$

Solution: $4 * 4 = 6p$; $16 = 6p$; $16 / 6 = 6p / 6$; $2.\overline{6} = p$

Answer: $2.\overline{6}$ inches of rain had fallen in 4 hours.

10. Ben's apartment building has 9 flights of stairs. To climb to the top floor, he must go up 144 steps. How many steps must he climb to get to the fifth floor?

$\frac{9 \text{ flights}}{144 \text{ steps}} = \frac{5 \text{ flights}}{s \text{ steps}}$

Solution: $9s = 144 * 5$; $9s = 720$; $9s / 9 = 720 / 9$; $s = 80$

Answer: Ben must climb 80 steps.

11. At sea level, sound travels 0.62 mile in 3 seconds. What is the speed of sound in miles per hour? (*Hint:* First find the number of seconds in 1 hour.)

$\frac{0.62 \text{ mile}}{3 \text{ sec}} = \frac{d \text{ miles}}{3{,}600 \text{ sec}}$

Solution: $0.62 * 3{,}600 = 3d$; $2{,}232 = 3d$; $2{,}232 / 3 = 3d / 3$; $744 = d$

Answer: Sound travels at the rate of 744 miles per hour.

STUDENT PAGE

Math Journal 2, p. 297

Problem:	$\frac{6}{48} = \frac{8}{n}$	$\frac{6}{9} = \frac{x}{12}$
Cross multiply:	$6 * n = 48 * 8$	$6 * 12 = 9 * x$
Solve:	$6 * n = 384$ $n = 384 / 6$ $n = 64$	$72 = 9 * x$ $72 / 9 = x$ $8 = x$
Replace the variable:	$\frac{6}{48} = \frac{8}{64}$	$\frac{6}{9} = \frac{8}{12}$
Check:	$6 * 64 = 48 * 8$	$6 * 12 = 9 * 8$

Problem:	$\frac{15}{20} = \frac{9}{r}$	$\frac{z}{3} = \frac{1}{5}$
Cross multiply:	$15 * r = 20 * 9$	$z * 5 = 3 * 1$
Solve:	$15 * r = 180$ $r = 180 / 15$ $r = 12$	$z * 5 = 3$ $z = 3 / 5$ $z = 0.6$
Replace the variable:	$\frac{15}{20} = \frac{9}{12}$	$\frac{0.6}{3} = \frac{1}{5}$
Check:	$15 * 12 = 20 * 9$	$0.6 * 5 = 3 * 1$

Adjusting the Activity You might want to demonstrate the relationship between cross multiplication and the renaming of pairs of fractions with a common denominator. Use $\frac{3}{4}$ and $\frac{1}{6}$ to illustrate this relationship.

1. Find the QCD of $\frac{3}{4}$ and $\frac{1}{6}$: $4 * 6 = 24$.
2. Convert $\frac{3}{4}$ and $\frac{1}{6}$ to 24ths:

$\frac{3}{4} = \frac{\square}{24}$ $\qquad$ $\frac{1}{6} = \frac{\square}{24}$

$\frac{3 * 6}{4 * 6} = \frac{18}{24}$ $\qquad$ $\frac{1 * 4}{6 * 4} = \frac{4}{24}$

Solving Proportions and Rate Problems Using Cross Multiplication

(*Math Journal 2,* pp. 296 and 297)

PARTNER ACTIVITY

Assign Problems 1–6 on journal page 296. When most students have completed the problems, bring the class together and go over the answers.

Work through the second example on page 296 with the class. Then students work with partners to solve the problems on journal page 297. Point out that although students should usually feel free to use whichever method they wish to solve problems, for these problems they are to write proportions and then solve them using cross multiplication.

ONGOING ASSESSMENT

On an Exit Slip (*Math Masters,* page 478) have students explain which of Problems 1–6 they could have solved easily by using a method *other* than cross multiplication.

2 Ongoing Learning & Practice

✦ Dividing Decimals by Whole Numbers (*Math Journal 2,* p. 298)

INDEPENDENT ACTIVITY 

Students practice finding the quotient of decimals and whole numbers. Review the procedure for dividing a decimal by a whole number.

1. Estimate the quotient.
2. Divide, ignoring the decimal point.
3. Use the estimate in Step 1 to place the decimal point in the answer.

ONGOING ASSESSMENT

Use this journal page to check how well students are able to make magnitude estimates.

✦ Math Boxes 8.3 (*Math Journal 2,* p. 295)

INDEPENDENT ACTIVITY 

Mixed Review Math Boxes in this lesson are paired with Math Boxes in Lesson 8.1. The skill in Problem 1 is a prerequisite for Unit 9.

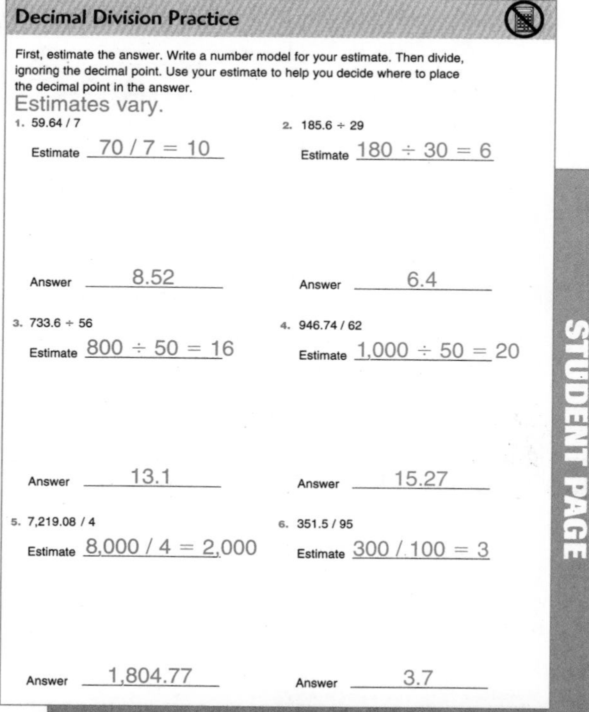

Decimal Division Practice

First, estimate the answer. Write a number model for your estimate. Then divide, ignoring the decimal point. Use your estimate to help you decide where to place the decimal point in the answer.

Estimates vary.

1. 59.64 / 7
   Estimate 70 / 7 = 10
   Answer 8.52
2. 185.6 ÷ 29
   Estimate 180 ÷ 30 = 6
   Answer 6.4
3. 733.6 ÷ 56
   Estimate 800 ÷ 50 = 16
   Answer 13.1
4. 946.74 / 62
   Estimate 1,000 ÷ 50 = 20
   Answer 15.27
5. 7,219.08 / 4
   Estimate 8,000 / 4 = 2,000
   Answer 1,804.77
6. 351.5 / 95
   Estimate 300 / 100 = 3
   Answer 3.7

STUDENT PAGE

✦ *Math Journal 2,* p. 298

Math Boxes 8.3

1. Insert parentheses to make each number sentence true.
   a. 0.01 ∗ (7 + 9) / 4 = 0.04
   b. ($\frac{4}{5}$ ∗ 25) − (10 / 2) = 15
   c. [$\sqrt{64}$ / (5 + 3)] ∗ 3 = 3
   d. 5 ∗ (10^2 + 10^2) ∗ 2 = 2,000
   e. (5 ∗ 10^2) + (10^2 ∗ 2) = 700
2. Insert the decimal point in the product.
   a. 3.6 ∗ 5.35 = 1 9.2 6
   b. −299 ∗ −0.03 = 8.9 7
   c. 218 ∗ 2.15 = 4 6 8.7
   d. −6.56 ∗ 3.03 = − 1 9.8 7 6 8
   e. 25 ∗ −0.025 = −.6 2 5
3. Without using a protractor, find the measure in degrees of each numbered angle. Write each measure on the drawing. (Lines *a* and *b* are parallel.)

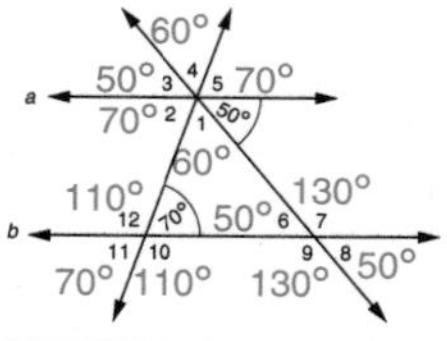

4. Fill in the blanks. (*Hint:* For decimals, think fractions.)
   a. $\frac{3}{5}$ ∗ $\frac{5}{3}$ = 1
   b. $\frac{8}{9}$ ∗ $\frac{9}{8}$ = 1
   c. $\frac{7}{3}$ ∗ $\frac{3}{7}$ = 1
   d. 0.01 ∗ $\frac{100}{1}$ = 1
   e. 0.5 ∗ $\frac{10}{5}$ = 1
5. Cherie made a deal with her mother. If Cherie could mow the lawn in 1 hour or less, she would get paid double. In 45 minutes, she mowed $\frac{7}{10}$ of the lawn. If she continues to mow at the same rate, will she finish mowing the lawn in time to be paid double?
   no Explain. $\frac{1}{10}$ of the lawn took $6\frac{3}{7}$ min. $\frac{3}{10}$ will take more than 18 min.

STUDENT PAGE

✦ *Math Journal 2,* p. 295

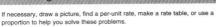

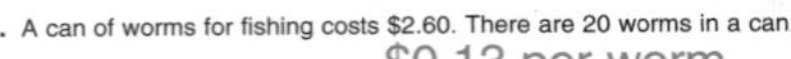

Calculating Rates

Study Link 8.3

If necessary, draw a picture, find a per-unit rate, make a rate table, or use a proportion to help you solve these problems.

1. A can of worms for fishing costs $2.60. There are 20 worms in a can.
   a. What is the cost per worm? $0.13 per worm
   b. At this rate, how much would 26 worms cost? $3.38
2. An 11-ounce bag of chips costs $1.99.
   a. What is the cost per ounce, rounded to the nearest cent? $0.18 per ounce
   b. What is the cost per pound, rounded to the nearest cent? $2.88
3. Just 1 gram of venom from a king cobra snake can kill 150 people. At this rate, about how many people would 1 kilogram kill? 150,000 people
4. A good milking cow produces nearly 6,000 quarts of milk each year. At this rate, about how many gallons of milk will a cow produce in 5 months? 625 gallons
5. A dog-walking service costs $117 for 6 months. What is the cost for 2 months? $39 For 3 years? $702

Challenge

6. A 1-pound bag of candy, containing 502 pieces, costs 16.8 cents per ounce. What is the cost of 1 piece of candy? Circle the best answer.
   1.86 cents   2.99 cents   0.33 cent   ($\frac{1}{2}$ cent)
7. Mr. Rainier's car uses about 1.6 fluid ounces of gas per minute when the engine is idling. One night, he parked his car but forgot to turn off the motor. He had just filled his tank. His tank holds 12 gallons.
   About how many hours will it take before his car runs out of gas? 16 hours
   Explain what you did to find the answer. Sample answer: 128 oz = 1 gal; 12 gal = 1,536 oz; 1,536 oz / 1.6 oz per min = 960 min; 960 min / 60 min per hour = 16 hr

Sources: 2201 Fascinating Facts; Everything Has Its Price

STUDY LINK MASTER

◆ Math Masters, p. 343

Ingredients for Peanut Butter Fudge

1. The list at the right shows the ingredients used to make peanut butter fudge, but not how much of each ingredient is needed. Use the following clues to calculate the amount of each ingredient needed to make 1 pound of peanut butter fudge. Record each amount in the ingredient list.

Clues

- Use 20 cups of sugar to make 10 pounds of fudge.
- You need $3\frac{3}{4}$ cups of milk to make 5 pounds of fudge.
- You need 15 cups of peanut butter to make 48 pounds of fudge. (*Hint:* 1 cup = 16 tablespoons)
- An 8-pound batch of fudge uses 1 cup of corn syrup.
- Use 6 teaspoons of vanilla for each 4 pounds of fudge.
- Use $\frac{1}{2}$ teaspoon of salt for each 4 pounds of fudge.

Peanut Butter Fudge (makes 1 pound)
2 cups of sugar
$\frac{3}{4}$ cup of milk
5 tablespoons of peanut butter
2 tablespoons of corn syrup
$1\frac{1}{2}$ teaspoons of vanilla
$\frac{1}{8}$ teaspoon of salt

2. Suppose you wanted to make an 80-pound batch of fudge. Record how much of each ingredient you would need.

Ingredient List for 80 Pounds of Peanut Butter Fudge	
160 cups of sugar	160 tablespoons of corn syrup
60 cups of milk	120 teaspoons of vanilla
400 tablespoons of peanut butter	10 teaspoons of salt

More on Measuring Food

Some foods have their own special units of measure. Have you ever heard of a *hand* of bananas (a small bunch)? Other special units are a *cran* of fresh herring (45 gallons), a *firkin* of butter (56 pounds), a *frail* of raisins (50 pounds), and a *clove* of cheese (8 to 10 pounds).

Source: Numbers

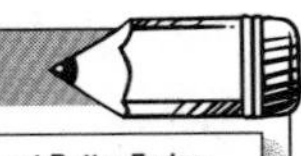

TEACHING MASTER

◆ Math Masters, p. 131

◆ Study Link 8.3 (*Math Masters,* pp. 343 and 344)

Home Connection Students solve rate problems on Study Link 8.3. Also assign Study Link 8.4. Students will need time to plan a trip to the grocery store.

3 Options for Individualizing

◆ EXTRA PRACTICE Calculating Amounts of Ingredients for Making Peanut Butter Fudge (*Math Masters,* p. 131)

INDEPENDENT ACTIVITY  **15–30 min**

Students use a recipe for peanut butter fudge to calculate how much of each ingredient is needed to make 1 pound and 80 pounds.

◆ ENRICHMENT Finding Rates in the Story *Math Curse*

PARTNER ACTIVITY  **15–30 min**

Literature Link *Math Curse* by Jon Scieszka is the story of a young girl whose teacher proclaims that "... you can think of almost anything as a math problem." Beginning the next morning, the girl lives through the story problems. Students work with a partner to find rates in the story. Have them share the rates they found. 5 students per bus stop; fingers at a rate of 10 per person; ears at a rate of 2 per person; carrot sticks 3 at a time; a batting average as the rate of "hits" to "at bats"; 60 minutes per hour, 24 hours per day, 365 days per year. You may want students to try writing their own rate problems based on ideas in the story.

PLANNING AHEAD

Remind students to collect and bring to school nutrition labels from containers of food, such as cans of soup, cups of yogurt, and cereal boxes. These labels will be discussed in Lesson 8.5.

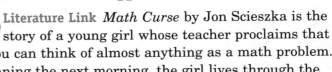

8.4 Calorie Use

OBJECTIVES **To estimate students' calorie use per day; and to practice solving rate problems.**

summaries	materials
1 Teaching the Lesson	
Students refer to a calorie-use chart to estimate their calorie use in a typical 24-hour day. [Operations and Computation]	☐ *Math Journal 2,* pp. 299–301 ☐ Study Link 8.3 ☐ calculator ***See*** **Advance Preparation**
2 Ongoing Learning & Practice	
Given a fractional part of a whole, students find the whole. [Patterns, Functions, and Algebra] Students practice and maintain skills through Math Boxes and Study Link activities.	☐ *Math Journal 2,* pp. 302 and 303 ☐ Study Link Master (*Math Masters,* p. 344) ☐ Geometry Template
3 Options for Individualizing	
Extra Practice Students calculate how many calories a sixth grader uses in a triathlon. [Operations and Computation]	☐ *Math Journal 2,* p. 300 ☐ Teaching Master (*Math Masters,* p. 132) ☐ calculator

Additional Information

Advance Preparation Continue adding the nutrition labels that students bring to school to the bulletin-board display.

Vocabulary • **calorie**

Getting Started

Mental Math and Reflexes

Students solve simple rate problems on their slates. They share solution strategies. *Suggestions:*

- 6 candy bars cost $3. How much does 1 candy bar cost? $0.50
- A car goes 316 miles on 10 gallons of gas. How far does it go on 1 gallon? 31.6 miles
- A plant grows 30 inches a week. On average, how much does it grow each day? $4\frac{2}{7}$ inches
- Jack reads 72 pages in 60 minutes. At that rate, how many pages does he read in 5 minutes? 6 pages
- Melinda runs 5 miles in $47\frac{1}{2}$ minutes. What is her average time per mile? $9\frac{1}{2}$ minutes

Math Message

Solve Problems 1–5 on page 299 in your journal.

Study Link 8.3 Follow-Up

See Part 1 for the Study Link 8.3 Follow-Up discussion.

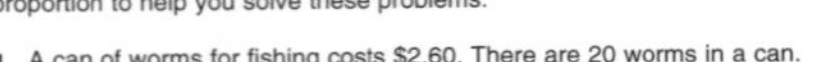

STUDY LINK MASTER

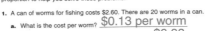

If necessary, draw a picture, find a per-unit rate, make a rate table, or use a proportion to help you solve these problems.

SRB 114 115

1. A can of worms for fishing costs \$2.60. There are 20 worms in a can.
   a. What is the cost per worm? \$0.13 per worm
   b. At this rate, how much would 26 worms cost? \$3.38
2. An 11-ounce bag of chips costs \$1.99.
   a. What is the cost per ounce, rounded to the nearest cent? \$0.18 per ounce
   b. What is the cost per pound, rounded to the nearest cent? \$2.88
3. Just 1 gram of venom from a king cobra snake can kill 150 people. At this rate, about how many people would 1 kilogram kill? 150,000 people
4. A good milking cow produces nearly 6,000 quarts of milk each year. At this rate, about how many gallons of milk will a cow produce in 5 months? 625 gallons
5. A dog-walking service costs \$117 for 6 months. What is the cost for 2 months? \$39 For 3 years? \$702

Challenge

6. A 1-pound bag of candy, containing 502 pieces, costs 16.8 cents per ounce. What is the cost of 1 piece of candy? Circle the best answer.
   1.86 cents 2.99 cents 0.33 cent ($\frac{1}{2}$ cent) (circled)
7. Mr. Rainier's car uses about 1.6 fluid ounces of gas per minute when the engine is idling. One night, he parked his car but forgot to turn off the motor. He had just filled his tank. His tank holds 12 gallons.
   About how many hours will it take before his car runs out of gas? 16 hours
   Explain what you did to find the answer. Sample answer: 128 oz = 1 gal; 12 gal = 1,536 oz; 1,536 oz / 1.6 oz per min = 960 min; 960 min / 60 min per hour = 16 hr

Sources: 2201 Fascinating Facts; Everything Has Its Price

Math Masters, p. 343

1 Teaching the Lesson

✦ Study Link 8.3 Follow-Up (*Math Masters,* p. 343)

WHOLE-CLASS DISCUSSION

Discuss the answers to the problems. Make sure that students understand how to solve Problems 1 and 2 because Study Link 8.4 involves finding unit costs. Pose additional unit cost problems if students need more practice.

Ask students who chose the correct answer in Problem 6 to defend their choices. This is a two-step problem. First, find the cost per pound by multiplying 16.8 cents by 16 (ounces per pound). \$2.688 per pound Second, divide the cost of 1 pound by 502, the number of pieces. \$0.0054; a little more than $\frac{1}{2}$ cent

A strategy for solving Problem 7: Since corresponding parts of a proportion must have the same unit, convert 12 gallons to fluid ounces. Then set up and solve a proportion. Finally, convert minutes to hours, and then answer the question.

1. 1 gal = 128 fl oz; so 12 gal = 12 ∗ 128 fl oz = 1,536 fl oz
2. $\frac{\text{fl ounces}}{\text{minutes}} = \frac{1.6}{1} = \frac{1{,}536}{x}$ Use cross multiplication:
   $1.6 * x = 1 * 1{,}536$
   $x = 1{,}536 / 1.6 = 960$ (min)
3. 960 min / 60 min per hr = 16 (hr)
4. The car will run out of gas in 960 minutes, or 16 hours.

A second strategy: Calculate the number of fluid ounces of gasoline used in 1 hour. Then, using the number of fluid ounces in 12 gallons, calculate the number of hours before the car runs out of gas. (*See Strategy 2 in the margin.*)

A third strategy: Express fluid ounces used per hour (see strategy above) as a fraction of a gallon. Then, calculate the number of hours before the car runs out of gas. (*See Strategy 3 in the margin.*)

Strategy 2:

1. $\frac{\text{fl ounces}}{\text{minutes}} = \frac{1.6}{1} = \frac{n}{60}$ Use cross multiplication:
   $1.6 * 60 = 1 * n$
   $1.6 * 60 = 96$ (fl oz)
2. $\frac{\text{fl ounces}}{\text{minutes}} = \frac{96}{1} = \frac{1{,}536}{h}$ Use cross multiplication:
   $96 * h = 1 * 1{,}536$
   $h = 1{,}536 / 96 = 16$ (hours)

Strategy 3:

1. $\frac{96 \text{ fl oz}}{128 \text{ fl oz}} = \frac{3}{4}$ gal
2. $\frac{\text{gal}}{\text{hr}} = \frac{\frac{3}{4}}{1} = \frac{12}{h}$ Use cross multiplication:
   $\frac{3}{4} * h = 1 * 12$
   $h = 12 \div \frac{3}{4} = 16$ (hr)

✦Math Message Follow-Up
(*Math Journal 2,* p. 299)

WHOLE-CLASS DISCUSSION

Students should have had little difficulty solving the problems on the journal page. Ask students to share their number models. Spend a few minutes comparing different number models for the same problem.

All of the problems on journal page 299 involve rates of distance over time. Students may have written number models of the form $r * t = d$, where r is the given rate, t is the given time, and d is the unknown distance. This is fine. They should be made aware that such number models are based on proportions. For example, the proportion for Problem 1 is $\frac{60}{1} = \frac{n}{4}$. Using cross multiplication, $60 * 4 = 1 * n$. Students should understand that proportions are also number models. Note that in Problem 5, they must convert inches to feet.

In the previous two lessons, they have been using proportions to solve rate problems. The problems in this lesson can be modeled by equations of the form $r * t = d$, although they involve calorie use over time rather than distance over time.

ONGOING ASSESSMENT

Use students' answers on this page to assess their ability to construct and use a rate table. For additional information, you may want to have students explain in writing how constructing a rate table can help to solve the problems on this page.

✦Examining a Table of Calorie Use
(*Math Journal 2,* p. 300)

WHOLE-CLASS DISCUSSION

Health Link Tell the class that nutrition will be the theme for several upcoming lessons, including this one. Briefly discuss nutrition and ask students to define *calorie.* Make sure that the following points are mentioned:

▷ The body uses the materials in food to produce energy—energy to keep the body warm and moving and to build and repair muscles and tissues.

▷ A **calorie** is a unit for measuring the amount of energy a food will produce when it is digested.

▷ Calories are not *substances* in food. They are *units* for measuring the amount of energy in food.
(Points continue on next page.)

STUDENT PAGE

Rate * Time = Distance

For each problem, make a rate table. Then write a number model and solve it. Write the answer.

1. Ms. Riley drove her car at 60 miles per hour for 4 hours. How far did she travel?
Number model $60 * 4 = m$
Answer: She traveled 240 miles in 4 hours.

miles	60	240
hours	1	4

2. A bamboo plant grows 8 inches per day. How tall will it be after 7 days?
Number model $8 * 7 = i$
Answer: The plant will be 56 inches tall.

inches	8	56
days	1	7

3. A rocket is traveling at 40,000 miles per hour. How far will it travel in 168 hours?
Number model $40{,}000 * 168 = m$
Answer: The rocket will travel 6,720,000 miles in 168 hours.

miles	40,000	6,720,000
hours	1	168

4. Chelsea can ride her bicycle at 9 miles per hour. At this rate, how long will it take her to ride 30 miles?
Number model $9 * n = 30$
Answer: It will take her $3\frac{1}{3}$ hours to ride 30 miles.

miles	9	30
hours	1	$3\frac{1}{3}$

5. Australia is moving about 3 inches per year with respect to the southern Pacific Ocean. How many *feet* will it move in 50 years?
Number model $3 * 50 = i$; $i / 12 = f$
Answer: Australia will move 12.5 feet in 50 years.

inches	3	150
years	1	50

✦ *Math Journal 2,* p. 299

STUDENT PAGE

How Many Calories Do You Use Per Day?

Your body needs food. It uses the materials in food to produce energy—energy to keep your body warm and moving, to live and grow, and to build and repair muscles and tissues.

The amount of energy a food will produce when it is digested by the body is measured in a unit called the **calorie.** A calorie is not a substance in food.

1. The following table shows the number of calories per minute and per hour used by the average sixth grader for various activities. Complete the table. Round your answers for calories per minute to the nearest tenth and calories per hour to the nearest ten.

Calorie Use by Average 6th Graders

Activity	Calories/Minute	Calories/Hour
Sleeping	0.7	40
Studying, writing, sitting	1.2	70
Eating, talking, sitting in class	1.2	70
Standing	1.3	80
Dressing, undressing	1.5	90
Walking (slowly, at 2 mph)	2.2	130
Walking (briskly, at 3.5 mph)	3.0	180
Doing housework, gardening	2.0	120
Vacuuming	2.7	160
Raking leaves	3.7	220
Shoveling snow	5.0	300
Bicycling (6 mph)	2.8	170
Bicycling (13 mph)	4.5	270
Bicycling (20 mph)	8.3	500
Running (5 mph)	6.0	360
Running (7.5 mph)	9.3	560
Swimming (20 yards/minute)	3.3	200
Swimming (40 yards/minute)	5.8	350
Basketball, soccer (vigorous)	9.7	580
Volleyball	4.0	240
Aerobic dancing (vigorous)	6.0	360
Square dancing	4.0	240

✦ *Math Journal 2,* p. 300

NOTE: The calorie used in talking about food is actually a unit scientists call the *kilocalorie,* or *Calorie.* It is 1,000 times as large as the metric unit called the "calorie."

Language Arts Link

Write the following three words on the board: French, *calorie;* Czech, *kalorie;* Spanish, *caloria.* Students should recognize their meanings without prompting. Explain that the word is so similar in these languages because scientists from every country share knowledge through scientific publications.

STUDENT PAGE

How Many Calories Do You Use Per Day? (cont.)

2. Think of all of the things you do during a typical 24-hour school day.

   a. List your activities in the table below.

   b. Record your estimate of the time you spend on each activity (to the nearest fifteen minutes). Be sure that the times add up to 24 hours.

   c. For each activity, record the number of calories used per minute or per hour. Then calculate the number of calories you use for the activity.

Example
Suppose you spend 8 hours and 15 minutes sleeping.
Choose the per-hour rate: Sleeping uses 40 calories per hour.
Multiply: 8.25 hours * 40 calories per hour = 330 calories

Answers vary.

My Activities During a Typical 24-Hour School Day

Activity	Time Spent on Activity	Calorie Rate (cal/min or cal/hr)	Calories Used for Activity

3. When you have completed the table, find the total number of calories you use in a typical 24-hour day.

In a typical 24-hour school day, I use about Answers vary. calories.

Math Journal 2, p. 301

▷ The average adult should consume about 2,000 calories a day, but individuals may need more or fewer. Calorie information on nutrition labels assumes that an average adult eats food that supply about 2,000 calories per day. Larger people, for example, need to take in more calories than smaller people do.

▷ Active people need to take in more calories than less active people do.

▷ Some people use up (metabolize) energy more quickly than others.

Take a few minutes to discuss the calorie-use table on journal page 300. Note that calorie use is reported in two ways—calories per minute and calories per hour. Make sure the discussion answers the following two questions:

- How do you convert a number of calories per minute to a number of calories per hour? Multiply the number of calories per minute by 60.
- How do you convert a number of calories per hour to a number of calories per minute? Divide the number of calories per hour by 60.

To ensure that students know how to convert between the two rates, ask them to use calculators to find the missing numbers in the table. They should round their answers for calories per minute to the nearest tenth and for calories per hour to the nearest ten. Discuss the wide range in calorie use for various activities. Ask: *Are you surprised by any of the data?*

Point out that walking, running, bicycling, and swimming are each listed more than once. For these activities, the calorie use varies, depending on the speed. Mention also that the data in the table are for *average* sixth graders. The number of calories used during an activity depends on the weight of a person, so the number of calories used during a given activity is greater for adults than it is for sixth graders.

✦ Estimating the Total Number of Calories Used in One Day

(*Math Journal 2,* pp. 300 and 301)

PARTNER ACTIVITY

Briefly go over journal page 301. Students list all of their activities and indicate how long they engage in each during a typical 24-hour school day. Then they refer to the table on journal page 300 to calculate the number of calories used for each activity and the total number of calories used in a day.

Students' estimates need not be precise: Suggest that they round their times to the nearest 15 minutes. In filling out the Calorie Rate column, students should choose the rate that is appropriate for the duration of the activity. For example, if they swim for 15 minutes, they should record the rate as a *per-minute* rate; if they sit for 4 hours, they should record a *per-hour* rate.

If an activity is not listed in the calorie-use table, students should use the calorie rate for a similar activity. For example, playing a musical instrument, which is not listed in the table, perhaps requires about the same amount of energy as eating or talking. When most students have completed journal page 301, bring the class together to compare results.

Adjusting the Activity If students have difficulty dealing with rates given both as calories per minute and calories per hour, suggest that they use calories per minute throughout.

Extend the activity by having students do research on rates of calorie consumption for favorite activities not listed on journal page 300.

Using Unit Fractions to Find a Whole

Example 1

Alex collects sports cards. Seventy of the cards feature basketball players. These 70 cards are $\frac{2}{3}$ of Alex's collection. How many sports cards does Alex have?

- If $\frac{2}{3}$ of the collection is 70 cards, then $\frac{1}{3}$ is 35 cards.
- Alex has all of the cards—that's $\frac{3}{3}$ of the cards.
- Therefore, Alex has 3 * 35, or 105 cards.

Example 2

Barb's mother baked cookies. She gave Barb 12 cookies, which were $\frac{2}{5}$ of the total number she baked. How many cookies did Barb's mother bake?

- If $\frac{2}{5}$ of the total is 12 cookies, then $\frac{1}{5}$ is 6 cookies.
- Barb's mother baked all the cookies—that's $\frac{5}{5}$ of the cookies.
- She baked 5 * 6, or 30 cookies.

1. Six jars are filled with cookies. The number of cookies in each jar is not known. For each clue given in the table, find the number of cookies in the jar.

Clue	Number of Cookies in Jar
$\frac{1}{2}$ jar contains 31 cookies.	62 cookies
$\frac{2}{8}$ jar contains 10 cookies.	40 cookies
$\frac{3}{5}$ jar contains 36 cookies.	60 cookies
$\frac{3}{8}$ jar contains 21 cookies.	56 cookies
$\frac{4}{7}$ jar contains 64 cookies.	112 cookies
$\frac{3}{11}$ jar contains 45 cookies.	165 cookies

2. Alan is walking to a friend's house. He has gone $\frac{6}{10}$ of the distance in 48 minutes. If he continues at the same speed, about how long will the entire walk take? 80 minutes

3. A candle burned $\frac{3}{8}$ of the way down in 36 minutes. If it continues to burn at the same rate, about how many more minutes will the candle burn before it is used up? 60 minutes

STUDENT PAGE

Math Journal 2, p. 302

2 Ongoing Learning & Practice

Using Unit Fractions to Find the Whole
(*Math Journal 2,* p. 302)

INDEPENDENT ACTIVITY 

Students solve problems in which they find the whole when a fractional part is given. Spend a few minutes introducing the assignment. Then pose a few problems, such as the following:

- If 12 counters are $\frac{1}{5}$ of a set, how many counters are in the set? $5 * 12 = 60$
- If 30 pages are $\frac{3}{8}$ of a book, how many pages are in the book? $\frac{1}{8}$ of the book = 30 / 3, or 10; then the whole book ($\frac{8}{8}$ of the book) = 8 * 10 = 80.

Discuss the two examples at the top of the journal page with the class. The examples illustrate the two-step solution method on the next page.

Math Boxes 8.4

MATH

1. Solve the equation.

$(18 \div 2)C = 56 + C$

Solution $C = 7$

2. Complete.

a. $\frac{1}{3}$ of 216 = 72

b. $\frac{5}{8}$ of 160 = 100

c. $\frac{9}{10}$ of 300 = 270

d. $\frac{3}{20}$ of 420 = 63

e. $\frac{5}{7}$ of 777 = 555

3. Peabody's Bookstore had a sale. Complete the table. Then use your protractor to make a circle graph of the information.

Book Category	Number Sold	Percent of Total	Degrees
Fiction	280	28%	101°
Sports	283	28.3%	102°
Children's	125	12.5%	45°
Travel	212	21.2%	76°
Computer	100	10%	36°
Total	1,000	100%	360°

Book Sale Results
(title)

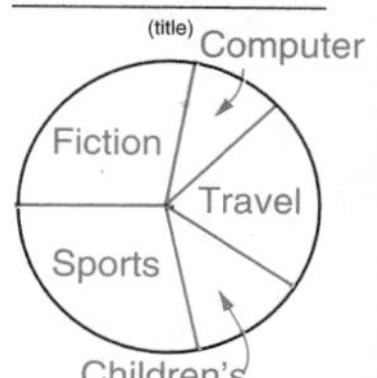

4. Solve.

		Solution
a.	$\frac{3}{4} = \frac{m}{28}$	$m = 21$
b.	$\frac{12}{16} = \frac{p}{32}$	$p = 24$
c.	$\frac{14}{1} = \frac{42}{g}$	$g = 3$
d.	$\frac{5}{14} = \frac{f}{28}$	$f = 10$
e.	$\frac{250}{20} = \frac{2.5}{u}$	$u = 0.2$

5. Divide. Show your work.

107 R21
38)4,087

STUDENT PAGE

Math Journal 2, p. 303

Food Costs as Unit Rates

Study Link 8.4

STUDY LINK MASTER

SRB 109 110

Visit a grocery store in the next day or two. Select 10 different items and record the cost and weight of each item in the table below.

- Select items that include a wide range of weights—from very light to very heavy.
- Select only items whose containers list weights in pounds, ounces, or a combination of pounds and ounces (such as 2 lb 6 oz).
- Do not choose produce items (fruits and vegetables).
- Do not choose milk, ice cream, soft drinks, juices, or other liquid items. Liquid items are usually sold by volume, not by weight. Their containers list volumes (gallons, quarts, liters, or fluid ounces).

Item	Cost	Weight Shown	Weight in Ounces	Cents per Ounce	Weight in Pounds	Dollars per Pound

1. Convert each weight to ounces. Calculate the unit cost in cents per ounce.
2. Convert each weight to pounds. Calculate the unit cost in dollars per pound.

Example A jar of pickles weighs 1 lb 5 oz and costs $2.39.

Convert weight	Calculate cost
to ounces: 1 lb 5 oz = 21 oz	in cents per ounce: $\frac{\$2.39}{21 \text{ oz}} = \frac{11.4 \text{ cents}}{1 \text{ oz}}$
to pounds: 1 lb 5 oz = $1\frac{5}{16}$ lb = 1.31 lb	in dollars per pound: $\frac{\$2.39}{1.31 \text{ lb}} = \frac{\$1.82}{1 \text{ lb}}$

Math Masters, p. 344

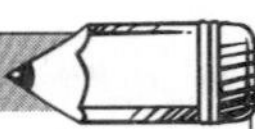

Calorie Use for a Triathlon

TEACHING MASTER

In a triathlon, athletes compete in swimming, cycling, and running races. In a "short-course" triathlon, athletes go the distances shown in the table below. Alan is a fit sixth grader who plans to compete in the short-course triathlon. He estimates his rate of speed for each event to be as shown.

Event	Miles	Alan's Estimated Times
Swimming	1	40 yards per minute
Cycling	25	20 miles per hour
Running	6.2	7.5 miles per hour

Refer to the information above and the table on journal page 300 to answer these questions.

1. a. About how long will it take Alan to swim the mile? About 44 minutes
   (*Hint:* Find the number of yards in a mile.)
   b. About how many calories will he use? About 255 calories
2. a. About how long will it take Alan to cycle the 25 miles? About 1 hour 15 minutes
   b. About how many calories will he use? About 625 calories
3. a. About how long will it take Alan to run the 6.2 miles? About 50 minutes
   b. About how many calories will he use? About 465 calories
4. About how many calories will Alan use to complete the triathlon? About 1,345 calories

Healthy Hearts

Some scientists theorize that most mammals live for about 800 million heartbeats. Since a mouse's heart beats at a rate of about 650 times per minute, it would live about $\frac{1}{10}$ as long as a giraffe, which has a heart rate of about 60 beats per minute. Humans are a notable exception to this rule, living about three times as long as they should according to the 800-million-heartbeats-per-lifetime rule.

Source: *Numbers*

Math Masters, p. 132

Step 1: Find the number of objects in $\frac{1}{nth}$ of the whole.

Step 2: Find the number of objects in the whole by multiplying the number of objects in $\frac{1}{nth}$ of the whole by n.

When most students have completed the page, bring the class together and go over the answers and solution strategies.

✦ Math Boxes 8.4 (*Math Journal 2,* p. 303)

INDEPENDENT ACTIVITY 

Mixed Review Math Boxes in this lesson are paired with Math Boxes in Lesson 8.2. The skill in Problem 1 is a prerequisite for Unit 9.

✦ Study Link 8.4 (*Math Masters,* p. 344)

Home Connection Students compare prices of items from the grocery store. The assignment of this Study Link was suggested in Lesson 8.3 to allow students time for gathering data.

3 Options for Individualizing

✦ EXTRA PRACTICE Solving Calorie Use Problems (*Math Journal 2,* p. 300; *Math Masters,* p. 132)

PARTNER ACTIVITY  **15–30 min**

Physical Education Link Students calculate how many calories a sixth grader uses in a triathlon.

PLANNING AHEAD

Remind students to bring nutrition labels to school and to complete Study Link 8.4 before the start of Lesson 8.5.

8.5 Using Nutrition Information

OBJECTIVE **To use nutrition information to plan a healthful meal.**

summaries	materials
1 Teaching the Lesson	
Students discuss some of the elements of a balanced diet. [Data and Chance] Students convert quantities of carbohydrate and protein from grams to calories. They calculate the percents of calories in their lunches that come from fat, carbohydrate, and protein. Then they plan a lunch that meets the recommended guidelines for fat, carbohydrate, and protein calories. [Operations and Computation]	□ *Math Journal 2,* pp. 304, 306, and 307 □ Study Link 8.4 □ Assessment Master (*Math Masters,* p. 478; optional) □ calculator □ *World Almanac for Kids,* health books (optional) ***See* Advance Preparation**
2 Ongoing Learning & Practice	
Given a percent of the whole, students find the whole. [Operations and Computation] Students practice and maintain skills through Math Boxes and Study Link activities.	□ *Math Journal 2,* pp. 305 and 308 □ Study Link Master (*Math Masters,* p. 345)
3 Options for Individualizing	
Language Diversity Students discuss the nature of technical language. [Patterns, Functions, and Algebra] **Enrichment** Students make up a menu for a meal and calculate the calories for each item on the menu. Then they make a circle graph to display the percents of calories from fat, carbohydrate, and protein. [Operations and Computation; Data and Chance] **Extra Practice** Students solve rate problems. [Patterns, Functions, and Algebra]	□ *Math Journal 2,* p. 306 □ Teaching Masters (*Math Masters,* pp. 133 and 134) □ Geometry Template □ computer with Internet access (optional) □ nutrition labels

Additional Information

Advance Preparation The bulletin-board display of nutrition labels should be completed before the start of this lesson.

Vocabulary • **balanced diet** • **fat** • **carbohydrate** • **protein**

Getting Started

Mental Math and Reflexes

Convert linear measurements from one unit to another. *Suggestions:*

- How many inches in 5 feet? 60 inches
- How many feet in 42 inches? $3\frac{1}{2}$ feet
- How many feet in 12 yards? 36 feet
- How many inches in $2\frac{1}{2}$ yards? 90 inches
- How many yards in 126 feet? 42 yards

Math Message

Look at the nutrition labels on the bulletin board and study the top of journal page 304.

Study Link 8.4 Follow-Up

Ask volunteers to share some of the information they collected, especially for similar items. To compare unit costs, ask questions such as the following: *What were their unit costs? Did the size of an item affect the unit cost? If so, in what ways? Were any of the per-unit costs surprising? For example, the unit cost of certain spices is very high.*

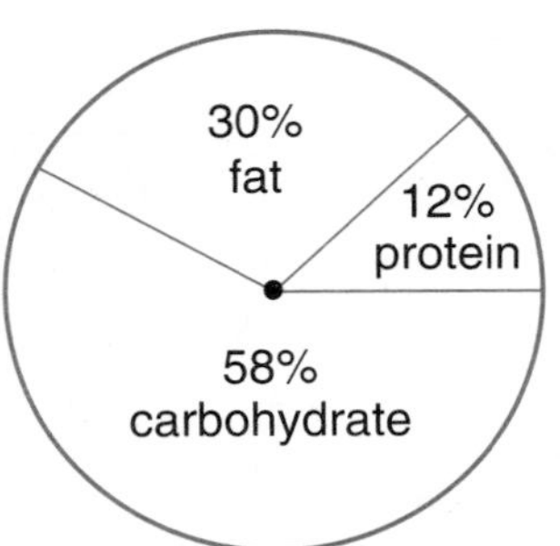

Recommended balance of fat, carbohydrate, and protein

1 Teaching the Lesson

✦ Math Message Follow-Up (*Math Journal 2,* p. 304)

WHOLE-CLASS DISCUSSION 

Health Link Spend some class time discussing **balanced diets,** the focus of this lesson. The discussion should include the following information:

- ▷ Food contains six types of materials that the body needs: **fat, carbohydrate, protein,** vitamins, minerals, and water. Of these, only fat, carbohydrate, and protein supply calories.
- ▷ A balanced diet gives the body all the food materials it needs in the right amounts. A balanced diet provides the appropriate total number of calories per day in the recommended balance of fat, carbohydrate, and protein.
- ▷ Foods that are pure fat, pure carbohydrate, or nearly pure protein include oil (fat), sugar (carbohydrate), and egg white (protein).
- ▷ Weights on food labels are given in grams rather than ounces.
- ▷ One tablespoon of oil, sugar, or water weighs about 15 grams.
- ▷ One large egg white is equivalent to approximately 2 tablespoons.

A complete discussion of a healthful diet focuses on recommended total calorie intake and recommended distribution of the calorie intake among sources. You might also ask students to calculate the approximate recommended number of calories from each source (about 10% of total calories from protein, 30% from fat, about 60% from carbohydrate), assuming a recommended diet of 2,000 calories per day. 200 calories from protein; 600 calories from fat; 1,200 calories from carbohydrate

Adjusting the Activity To extend the activity, review the food pyramid for a healthful diet. (It appears in books such as *World Almanac for Kids* and health books.) Discuss the recommended numbers of servings from the different food groups.

✦ Discussing Food Labels and Calculating Calories (*Math Journal 2,* p. 304)

WHOLE-CLASS ACTIVITY

Discuss the yogurt label on journal page 304, making sure that the following points are mentioned:

▷ Both the total number of calories and the number of calories from fat per serving are given on the label.

▷ For carbohydrate and protein, the label gives the grams per serving but not the number of calories.

▷ The information at the bottom of the label can be used to find the numbers of calories per serving that come from carbohydrate and protein.

NOTE: The bottom row on the label shows that 1 gram of fat generates more than twice as many calories (9) as 1 gram of protein or carbohydrate (4).

Go over the calculations for finding the number of calories from carbohydrate (44 ∗ 4) and protein (9 ∗ 4) in a serving of yogurt. If time permits, you might have students do similar calculations with food labels from the bulletin-board display. Since calories from fat are given on the label, there is no need to calculate them.

Partners use the data on food labels to verify the total number of calories in a single serving. This involves converting the number of grams per serving of carbohydrate and protein to calories. Circulate and assist as needed.

In the follow-up discussion, students may point out a discrepancy between the total number of calories per serving given on the food label and their calculated totals. These differences may be the result of rounding: The weights given on the labels have been rounded to the nearest gram, and the number of calories is often rounded to the nearest multiple of 5 calories.

Food Nutrition Labels

Study the food label at the right for a container of low-fat yogurt.

- There are 240 calories per serving. There are 3 grams of fat per serving.
- There are 44 grams of carbohydrate per serving. The label does not indicate how many calories come from carbohydrate, but it does provide the information you need to calculate the number of calories from carbohydrate. One gram of carbohydrate generates 4 calories of energy. So 44 grams generates 44 grams ∗ 4 calories per gram, or 176 calories.
- There are 9 grams of protein per serving. One gram of protein generates 4 calories. So 9 grams generates 9 grams ∗ 4 calories per gram, or 36 calories.

Nutrition Facts
Serving Size 1 container (227 g)

Amount Per Serving	
Calories 240	Calories from Fat 27
	% Daily Value
Total Fat 3 g	5%
Saturated Fat 1.5 g	8%
Cholesterol 15 mg	5%
Sodium 150 mg	6%
Potassium 450 mg	13%
Total Carbohydrate 44 g	15%
Dietary Fiber 1 g	4%
Sugars 43 g	
Protein 9 g	
Vitamin A 2% •	Vitamin C 10%
Calcium 35% •	Iron 0%

Calories per gram:
Fat 9 • Carbohydrate 4 • Protein 4

For each food label below, record the number of calories from fat. Then calculate the numbers of calories from carbohydrate and from protein. Add to find the total calories per serving.

Nutrition Facts
Serving Size 1 slice (23 g)
Servings Per Container 20

Amount Per Serving	
Calories 65	Calories from Fat 9
	% Daily Value
Total Fat 1 g	2%
Total Carbohydrate 12 g	4%
Protein 2 g	

White bread

Nutrition Facts
Serving Size 1 link (45 g)
Servings Per Container 10

Amount Per Serving	
Calories 150	Calories from Fat 120
	% Daily Value
Total Fat 13 g	20%
Total Carbohydrate 1 g	<1%
Protein 7 g	

Hot dog

1. Calories
   From fat 9
   From carbohydrate 48
   From protein 8
   Total calories 65

2. Calories
   From fat 117
   From carbohydrate 4
   From protein 28
   Total calories 149

3. Does the total number of calories per serving shown on each food label agree with the total calories you calculated? Answers vary.

STUDENT PAGE

✧ *Math Journal 2,* p. 304

STUDENT PAGE

Plan Your Own Lunch

1. Choose 5 items you would like to have for lunch from the following menu. Choose your favorite foods—pay no attention to calories. Make a check mark next to each item.

Sample answers:

Food	Total Calories	Calories from Fat	Calories from Carbohydrate	Calories from Protein
Ham sandwich ✓	265	110	110	45
Turkey sandwich	325	70	155	100
Hamburger	330	135	120	75
Cheeseburger	400	200	110	90
Double burger, cheese, sauce	500	225	175	100
Grilled cheese sandwich	380	220	100	60
Peanut butter and jelly sandwich	380	160	170	50
Chicken nuggets (6)	250	125	65	60
Bagel	165	20	120	25
Bagel with cream cheese	265	105	125	35
Hard-boiled egg ✓	80	55	0	25
French fries (small bag) ✓	250	120	115	15
Apple	100	10	90	0
Carrot	30	0	25	5
Orange	75	0	70	5
Cake (slice)	235	65	160	10
Cashews (1 oz)	165	115	30	20
Doughnut	200	100	75	25
Blueberry muffin	110	30	70	10
Apple pie (slice)	250	125	115	10
Frozen-yogurt cone ✓	100	10	75	15
Orange juice (8 fl oz)	110	0	104	8
2% milk (8 fl oz)	145	45	60	40
Skim milk (8 fl oz)	85	0	50	35
Soft drink (8 fl oz)	140	0	140	0
Diet soft drink (8 fl oz) ✓	0	0	0	0

Math Journal 2, p. 306

STUDENT PAGE

Plan Your Own Lunch (cont.)

2. In the table below, record the 5 items you chose. Fill in the rest of the table and write the total number of calories for each column. Sample answers:

Food	Total Calories	Calories from Fat	Calories from Carbohydrate	Calories from Protein
Ham sandwich	265	110	110	45
Hard-boiled egg	80	55	0	25
French fries	250	120	115	15
Frozen-yogurt cone	100	10	75	15
Diet soft drink	0	0	0	0
Total	695	295	300	100

What percent of the total number of calories in your lunch comes from fat? 42%

From carbohydrate? 43% From protein? 14%

3. Nutritionists recommend that, at most, 30% of the total number of calories comes from fat, about 12% of the calories from protein, and at least 58% of the calories from carbohydrate.

Does the lunch you chose meet these recommendations? no

4. Plan another lunch. This time, try to limit the percent of calories from fat to 30% or less, from protein to between 10% and 15%, and from carbohydrate to between 55% and 60%.

Food Sample answers:	Total Calories	Calories from Fat	Calories from Carbohydrate	Calories from Protein
Turkey sandwich	325	70	155	100
Apple	100	10	90	0
Blueberry muffin	110	30	70	10
Frozen-yogurt cone	100	10	75	15
French fries	250	120	115	15
Total	885	240	505	140

What percent of the total number of calories in your lunch comes from fat? 27%

From carbohydrate? 57% From protein? 16%

Math Journal 2, p. 307

✦ Planning a Healthful Lunch
(*Math Journal 2,* pp. 306 and 307)

PARTNER ACTIVITY 

Ask students to examine the total number of calories for various items on the menu on journal page 306. Ask: *Are there any surprises?* Sample answers: A peanut butter and jelly sandwich has more calories than a hamburger. A soft drink and 2% milk have about the same number of calories.

Students choose any five items from the menu they might like for lunch and check them off on the menu. Circulate and assist as they do the following:

1. Copy the five items from the menu to the table in Problem 2 on journal page 307 and enter the number of calories in the appropriate columns.
2. Calculate the total number of calories for each column.
3. Calculate what percents of the total number of calories come from fat, carbohydrate, and protein.
4. Determine whether this is a "healthy" lunch—one in which no more than 30% of calories come from fat and that comes close to the recommended distribution of carbohydrate and protein calories.
5. Plan another lunch in which no more than 30% of calories come from fat and that comes fairly close to meeting the recommended distribution of calories that come from carbohydrate and protein. Enter the items and numbers of calories in the table in Problem 4.
6. Calculate what percents of the total number of calories come from fat, carbohydrate, and protein.

While some students initially may have chosen a healthful lunch, it is likely that most will have chosen a lunch that does *not* meet the recommended distribution of fat, carbohydrate, and protein. Even when focusing on a healthful lunch on their second try, they should choose foods that they like to eat.

After everyone has completed the activity, bring the class together to share menus. During the discussion, ask: *Which foods appear to be especially fatty?* Cashews and hard-boiled eggs both have about 70% of their calories from fat; grilled cheese sandwiches, cheeseburgers, apple pie, and chicken nuggets all have about $\frac{1}{2}$ of their calories from fat.

Discuss how students balanced the second menu. Ask: *What kinds of trade-offs did you make to keep the fat content down while still choosing items you wanted?* Sample answer: I still wanted a hamburger and fries. So to keep the fat content down, I had skim milk and an apple for dessert. That's 35% of calories from fat, compared to 44% just for the hamburger and fries.

ONGOING ASSESSMENT

To assess students' understanding of the concept of proportions, have them complete an Exit Slip (*Math Masters*, page 478) explaining their strategy for designing their "healthy menus."

2 Ongoing Learning & Practice

✦ Using Unit Percents to Find the Whole (*Math Journal 2*, p. 308)

INDEPENDENT ACTIVITY 

Students solve problems in which part of the whole is given as a percent and they are to find the whole. Spend a few minutes introducing the assignment. Pose some problems such as the following:

- If $5.43 is 1% of the cost of a TV, what does the TV cost? $5.43 * 100 = $543
- If 195 marbles are 15% of the marbles in a jar, how many marbles are in the jar? 1% of the total number of marbles = 195 / 15, or 13 marbles; then the total number of marbles (100% of the marbles) = 13 * 100, or 1,300 marbles

Discuss the two examples at the top of the journal page. The examples illustrate the following two-step solution method:

Step 1: Find the number of objects in 1% of the whole.

Step 2: Find the number of objects in the whole by multiplying the number of objects in 1% of the whole by 100.

When most students have finished the page, briefly review the answers.

Unit Percents to Find a Whole

Example 1

The sale price of a CD player is $120, which is 60% of its list price. What is the list price?

- If 60% of the list price is $120, then 1% is $2. (120 / 60 = 2)
- The list price (the whole or 100%) is $200. (100 * 2 = 200)

Example 2

A toaster is on sale for $40, which is 80% of its list price. What is the list price?

- If 80% of the list price is $40, then 1% is $0.50. (40 / 80 = 0.5)
- The list price (100%) is $50. (100 * 0.5 = 50)

Use your percent sense to estimate the list price for each item below. Then calculate the list price. (*Hint:* First use your calculator to find what 1% is worth.) Estimated prices vary.

Sale Price	Percent of List Price	Estimated List Price	Calculated List Price
$120	60%	$180	$200
$100	50%	$200	$200
$8	32%	$20	$25
$255	85%	$285	$300
$77	55%	$140	$140
$80	40%	$200	$200
$9	60%	$15	$15
$112.50	75%	$140	$150
$450	90%	$500	$500

STUDENT PAGE

Math Journal 2, p. 308

STUDENT PAGE

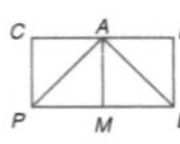

Math Boxes 8.5

1. The area of Square *CAMP* is 25 cm². Squares *CAMP* and *MADE* are congruent. What is the area of Triangle *APE*?
25 cm²

Explain how you found the area of Triangle *APE*.

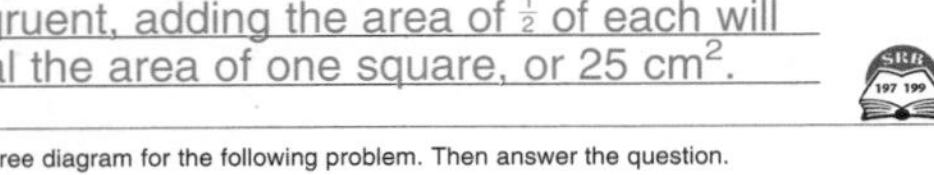
Sample answer: Since the squares are congruent, adding the area of $\frac{1}{2}$ of each will equal the area of one square, or 25 cm².

2. Draw a tree diagram for the following problem. Then answer the question.

A bag contains one red counter, two blue counters, and one white counter. You take out one counter. Then you take out a second counter without replacing the first counter. What is the probability of taking out one red counter and one white counter (in either order)?
$\frac{2}{12}$, or $\frac{1}{6}$

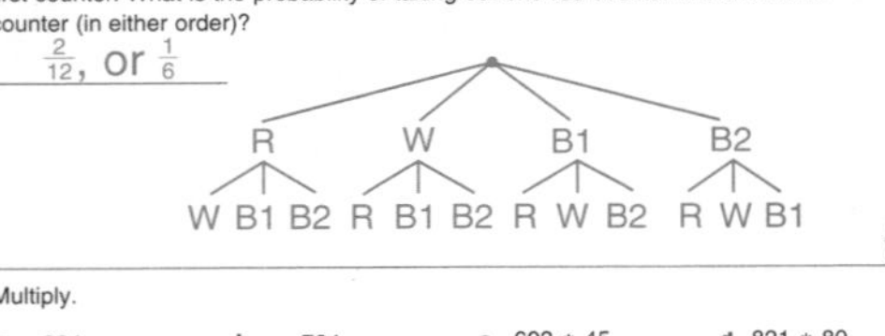

3. Multiply.

a. 234 × 15 = 3,510
b. 784 × 129 = 101,136
c. 603 ∗ 45 = 27,135
d. 821 ∗ 80 = 65,680

Math Journal 2, p. 305

Math Boxes 8.5 (*Math Journal 2*, p. 305)

INDEPENDENT ACTIVITY 

Mixed Review Math Boxes in this lesson are paired with Math Boxes in Lesson 8.7. The skill in Problem 1 is a prerequisite for Unit 9.

Study Link 8.5 (*Math Masters*, p. 345)

Home Connection Students choose what they would like for breakfast from a chart showing the number of calories from fat and the total number of calories for various items. Their goal is to limit the percent of calories from fat to 30% or less. Then they calculate the percent of calories from fat.

STUDY LINK MASTER

Calculating Calories from Fat — Study Link 8.5

1. Choose 5 items from the following menu that you would like to have for breakfast. Choose your favorite foods. Pay no attention to total calories, but try to limit the percent of calories from fat to 30% or less. Put a check mark next to each item.

Sample answers:

Food	Total Calories	Calories from Fat
Toast (1 slice)	70	10
Corn flakes (8 oz) ✓	95	trace
Oatmeal (8 oz)	130	20
Butter (1 pat) ✓	25	25
Doughnut	205	105
Jam (1 tbs)	55	trace
Pancakes (butter, syrup)	180	60
Bacon (2 slices)	85	65
Yogurt	240	25
Sugar (1 tsp)	15	0
Scrambled eggs (2)	140	90
Fried eggs (2)	175	125
Hash browns	130	65
Skim milk (8 fl oz) ✓	85	0
2% milk (8 fl oz)	145	45
Blueberry muffin ✓	110	30
Orange juice (8 fl oz) ✓	110	0
Bagel	165	20
Bagel with cream cheese	265	105

2. Record the 5 items you chose in the table. Fill in the rest of the table, and then find the total number of calories for each column.

Food	Total Calories	Calories from Fat
Corn flakes	95	trace
Butter	25	25
Skim milk	85	0
Blueberry muffin	110	30
Orange juice	110	0
Total	425	55

3. What percent of the total number of calories comes from fat? About 13%

Math Masters, p. 345

3 Options for Individualizing

LANGUAGE DIVERSITY Recognizing Technical Language

SMALL-GROUP ACTIVITY  **5–15 min** 

Group a few proficient English speakers with students learning English. Work with the group for a few minutes, discussing the nature of the vocabulary on nutrition labels used in the lesson. Guide students to see that the vocabulary belongs to a specialized subject area (chemistry) and that many of the words (such as *saturated, potassium, dietary*) are not commonly used even by native English speakers.

Distribute nutrition labels that students brought in with Study Link 8.3. Have them highlight the total number of calories and calories from fat on each label. If possible, encourage them to bring in labels in other languages so that they can compare the label vocabulary in different languages.

✦ ENRICHMENT Making a Circle Graph to Represent a Meal (*Math Journal 2,* p. 306; *Math Masters,* p. 133)

INDEPENDENT ACTIVITY  **15–30 min** 

Health Link Students can choose items from the menu on journal page 306, from the class bulletin board of nutrition labels, or from other sources. Their goal is to construct a menu of foods they enjoy for one meal of the day: breakfast, lunch, or dinner.

Have students make a table for the meal on *Math Masters,* page 133. When they have completed the table, they should make a circle graph to display what percents of the total number of calories come from fat, carbohydrate, and protein. Consider making a bulletin board of the student-selected meals and corresponding circle graphs.

Adjusting the Activity Challenge students to write number stories based on the circle-graph display.

NOTE: Currently, you can find information about the calorie content of foods at the following Web sites:

For fast foods: www.olen.com/food/book.html
www.olen.com/food/index.html

For all foods: www.ntwrks.com/~mikev/chart1.html

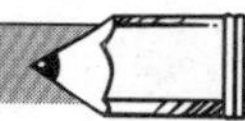

Planning a Meal

Plan a menu of foods that you would enjoy for one meal of the day—breakfast, lunch, or dinner. In the table below, record nutrition label information for the foods you chose. Fill in the rest of the table and find the total number of calories for each column. Then find the total percent for each column. (*Note:* The percents from fat, carbohydrate, and protein should total about 100%.) Answers vary.

Meal ______________

Food	Total Number of Calories	Calories from Fat	Calories from Carbohydrate	Calories from Protein
Total Number of Calories				
Percent of Calories	100%			

In the space to the right, make a circle graph to show the percentages of calories from fat, carbohydrate, and protein in the meal you planned. Be sure to label each section of the circle graph and write the percent of the total number of calories. Title your graph.

______________ (title)

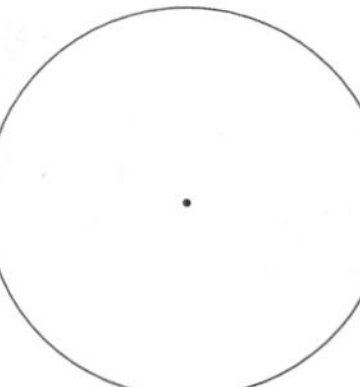

TEACHING MASTER

✦ *Math Masters,* p. 133

✦ EXTRA PRACTICE Solving Rate Problems (*Math Masters,* p.134)

INDEPENDENT ACTIVITY  **15–30 min** 

Students solve the problems on *Math Masters,* page 134. Encourage students who are having difficulty to draw pictures, make rate tables, or use proportions.

For Problem 1, the times for the 800-meter and 1,500-meter runs are given in minutes and seconds. Students must first convert these times to seconds. For Problem 3, students use the height of the stack to set up a proportion to find the per-centimeter rate.

After most students have finished the page, go over the answers. Have students share their strategies.

Rate Problems

1. Find the average speed (in meters per second) for each running event.

Event	Time (minutes and seconds)	Time (seconds)	Average Speed (meters per second)
100 meters	0 min 10.94 sec	10.94 sec	9.14 m/sec
200 meters	0 min 22.12 sec	22.12 sec	9.04 m/sec
400 meters	0 min 48.25 sec	48.25 sec	8.29 m/sec
800 meters	1 min 57.73 sec	117.73 sec	6.80 m/sec
1,500 meters	4 min 0.83 sec	240.83 sec	6.23 m/sec

2. Why do you think the average speed is different for each event?
Sample answer: Speed decreases as distance increases because most runners' endurance wears down in longer races.

The picture at the right shows a stack of 50 pennies, drawn to actual size.

Stack of 50 pennies (actual size)

3. Carefully measure the height of the stack. Use your measurement to calculate about how many pennies there would be in a stack 1 centimeter high.
About 7 pennies (unit)

4. About how many pennies would there be in a 50-foot stack of pennies? (1 inch is about 2.5 centimeters.)
About 10,500 pennies (unit)

5. To determine the temperature in degrees Fahrenheit, you can count the number of times a cricket chirps in 14 seconds and then add 40.
   a. What is the temperature if a cricket chirps 3 times per second? 82°F (unit)
   b. At a temperature of 61°F, how many times does a cricket chirp per second? 1.5 times (unit)

Source: The Handy Science Answer Book

TEACHING MASTER

✦ *Math Masters,* p. 134

8.6 Ratios

OBJECTIVES **To review notations for and meanings of ratios; and to solve problems involving part-to-part and part-to-whole ratios.**

summaries	materials
1 Teaching the Lesson	
Students use playing cards to model and solve problems involving part-to-part and part-to-whole ratios. [Patterns, Functions, and Algebra] Students review the notations for and meanings of ratios and share real-life examples of ratios. [Numeration] Students solve ratio number stories by setting up and solving proportions. [Patterns, Functions, and Algebra]	□ *Math Journal 2,* pp. 309–311 □ Study Link 8.5 □ Per partnership: deck of playing cards (from the Everything Math Deck, if available)
2 Ongoing Learning & Practice	
Students solve fraction and mixed-number computation problems. [Operations and Computation] Students practice and maintain skills through Math Boxes and Study Link activities.	□ *Math Journal 2,* pp. 312 and 313 □ Study Link Master (*Math Masters,* p. 346)
3 Options for Individualizing	
Enrichment Students solve challenging ratio problems. [Patterns, Functions, and Algebra] **Reteaching** Students read an essay on ratios. [Patterns, Functions, and Algebra] **Language Diversity** English language learners and English-proficient students work together to write and solve ratio number stories. [Patterns, Functions, and Algebra]	□ *Math Journal 2,* p. 309 □ *Student Reference Book,* pp. 116–118 □ Per partnership: deck of playing cards (from the Everything Math Deck, if available)

Additional Information

Vocabulary • **ratio** • **equivalent ratios** • **part-to-whole ratio** • **part-to-part ratio**

Getting Started

Mental Math and Reflexes

What number am I? (If students are able, have them write a number model for each problem.) Discuss how the number models can be solved using either the "cover up" method (see Lesson 6.8) or a systematic approach (see Lesson 6.11).

- Double me and add 10; you get 110. 50; $2 * x + 10 = 110$
- Take half of me and divide by 20; you get 2. 80; $(\frac{1}{2} * y) / 20 = 2$
- Triple me and multiply by 7; you get 0. 0; $(3 * z) * 7 = 0$
- Double me and subtract 80; you get 100. 90; $(2 * w) - 80 = 100$
- Take one-third of me and then one-half of the result; you get 40. 240; $\frac{1}{2} * (\frac{1}{3} * v) = 40$

Math Message

Solve Problems 1–6 on page 309 in your journal.

Study Link 8.5 Follow-Up

Make a stem-and-leaf plot of the class results to find the median percent of the total number of calories from fat for the whole class (Problem 3).

1 Teaching the Lesson

✦ Math Message Follow-Up
(*Math Journal 2,* p. 309)

WHOLE-CLASS DISCUSSION

Discuss students' solutions to Problem 1. To illustrate the solution, draw groups of cards on the board, each group having 2 facedown cards and 1 faceup card, until there are 6 faceup cards in all. There should be 6 such groups having a total of 12 facedown cards.

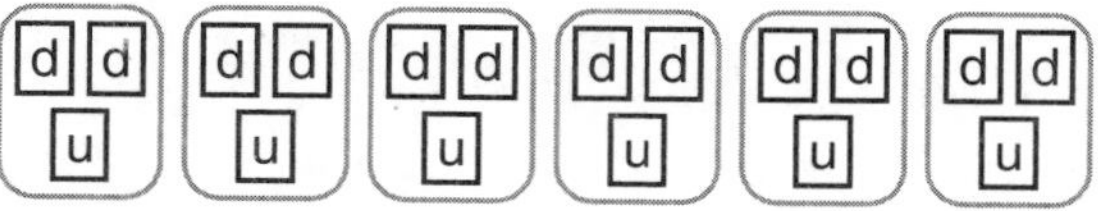

Explain that the statement "there are 2 facedown cards for every faceup card" is an example of a **ratio.** Another way to describe this ratio is to say: "The ratio of facedown cards to faceup cards is 2 to 1."

Ratios are similar to rates. They are different in that rates are comparisons of quantities that have different units (such as miles and hours), whereas ratios are comparisons of quantities that have the same units (such as cards and cards).

Just as we did with rates, we can write proportions to model solutions of ratio problems. The proportion for the solution to Problem 1 is:

$$\frac{\text{facedown}}{\text{faceup}} \quad \frac{2}{1} = \frac{12}{6}$$

When setting up a proportion, it is important to start by recording the two key labels (such as *facedown* and *faceup*). These are helpful in keeping track of where to write a number—in the numerator or denominator of a fraction. (The discussion continues on the next page.)

Ratios

Math Message

Work with a partner. You may use a deck of cards to help you with these problems.

1. There are 2 facedown cards for every faceup card. If 6 of the cards are faceup, how many cards are facedown? 12 cards
2. You have 12 cards. One out of every 4 cards is faceup. The rest are facedown. How many cards are faceup? 3 cards
3. There are 4 facedown cards for every 3 faceup cards. If 8 of the cards are facedown, how many cards are faceup? 6 cards
4. Three out of every 5 cards are faceup. If 12 cards are faceup, how many cards are there in all? 20 cards
5. There are 2 faceup cards for every 5 facedown. If there are 21 cards in all, how many cards are faceup? 6 cards
6. The table at the right shows the average number of wet days in selected cities for the month of October.
   a. How many more wet days does Moscow have than Beijing? 12 days
   b. Moscow has how many times as many wet days as Beijing? 5 times
   c. The number of wet days in Beijing is what fraction of the number of wet days in Sydney? $\frac{1}{4}$

City	Wet Days
Beijing, China	3
Boston, United States	9
Frankfurt, Germany	14
Mexico City, Mexico	13
Moscow, Russia	15
Sydney, Australia	12

Challenge

7. You have 5 faceup cards and no facedown cards. You add some facedown cards so that 1 in every 3 cards is faceup. How many cards are there now? 15 cards
8. You have 5 faceup cards and 12 facedown cards. You add some faceup cards so that 2 out of every 5 cards are faceup. How many cards are there now? 20 cards
9. You have 8 faceup cards and 12 facedown cards. You add some faceup cards so that $\frac{2}{3}$ of the cards are faceup.
   How many cards are faceup? 24 cards Facedown? 12 cards

STUDENT PAGE

✧ *Math Journal 2,* p. 309

Ratios that can be named by equivalent fractions are called **equivalent ratios.** The ratios 2 to 1 and 12 to 6 are equivalent because $\frac{2}{1}$ and $\frac{12}{6}$ are equivalent fractions. Ask students to name other ratios equivalent to the ratio of 2 to 1. 4 to 2, 6 to 3, and so on

Next, illustrate the solution to Problem 2 by drawing groups of cards, each having 1 faceup card and 3 facedown cards, until there are 12 cards in all. There should be 3 such groups with 3 facedown cards in each group.

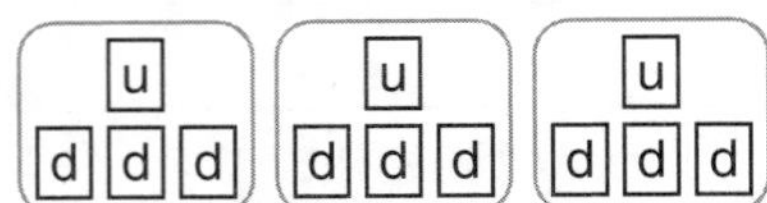

Point out how this problem is different from Problem 1: Here we are comparing a number of cards to the total number of cards. This is called a **part-to-whole ratio.** In Problem 1, we were comparing one kind of card (facedown) to another kind of card (faceup), that is, one part of the whole to another part of the whole number of cards. This is called a **part-to-part ratio.**

Again, write a proportion to model the solution to the problem:

$$\frac{\text{faceup}}{\text{whole}} \quad \frac{1}{4} = \frac{3}{12}$$

As we did earlier with rates, we can write and solve open proportions to solve ratio problems. Use Problems 3–5 to illustrate how to write open proportions to model such situations.

Problem 3:

Step 1: Write the key words and the given ratio.

$$\frac{\text{facedown}}{\text{faceup}} \quad \frac{4}{3}$$

Step 2: Write an equivalent fraction with a variable for the unknown quantity.

$$\frac{\text{facedown}}{\text{faceup}} \quad \frac{4}{3} = \frac{8}{n}$$

Adjusting the Activity If students are having trouble with Step 2, suggest that they first translate "4 facedown cards for every 3 faceup cards" into a number model $\frac{4}{3} = \frac{\text{down}}{\text{up}}$. Then substitute "8" for "down" resulting in $\frac{4}{3} = \frac{8}{\text{up}}$.

Step 3: Solve the proportion.

$$\frac{\text{facedown}}{\text{faceup}} \quad \frac{4}{3} = \frac{8}{n}$$

$4 * n = 3 * 8$

$4 * n = 24$

$n = 24 / 4 = 6$

There are 6 faceup cards.

STUDENT PAGE

Ratios

Math Message

Work with a partner. You may use a deck of cards to help you with these problems.

1. There are 2 facedown cards for every faceup card. If 6 of the cards are faceup, how many cards are facedown? 12 cards
2. You have 12 cards. One out of every 4 cards is faceup. The rest are facedown. How many cards are faceup? 3 cards
3. There are 4 facedown cards for every 3 faceup cards. If 8 of the cards are facedown, how many cards are faceup? 6 cards
4. Three out of every 5 cards are faceup. If 12 cards are faceup, how many cards are there in all? 20 cards
5. There are 2 faceup cards for every 5 facedown. If there are 21 cards in all, how many cards are faceup? 6 cards
6. The table at the right shows the average number of wet days in selected cities for the month of October.

City	Wet Days
Beijing, China	3
Boston, United States	9
Frankfurt, Germany	14
Mexico City, Mexico	13
Moscow, Russia	15
Sydney, Australia	12

a. How many more wet days does Moscow have than Beijing? 12 days

b. Moscow has how many times as many wet days as Beijing? 5 times

c. The number of wet days in Beijing is what fraction of the number of wet days in Sydney? $\frac{1}{4}$

Challenge

7. You have 5 faceup cards and no facedown cards. You add some facedown cards so that 1 in every 3 cards is faceup. How many cards are there now? 15 cards
8. You have 5 faceup cards and 12 facedown cards. You add some faceup cards so that 2 out of every 5 cards are faceup. How many cards are there now? 20 cards
9. You have 8 faceup cards and 12 facedown cards. You add some faceup cards so that $\frac{2}{3}$ of the cards are faceup. How many cards are faceup? 24 cards Facedown? 12 cards

Math Journal 2, p. 309

Problem 4:

$$\frac{\text{faceup}}{\text{cards in all}} \qquad \frac{3}{5} = \frac{12}{x}$$

$$x = 20$$

Problem 5:

$$\frac{\text{faceup}}{\text{cards in all}} \qquad \frac{2}{7} = \frac{z}{21}$$

$$z = 6$$

For Problem 5, some students may have written the proportion $\frac{2}{5} = \frac{z}{21}$. Point out that the 5 refers to facedown cards and the 21 to the total number of cards. The ratios in a proportion must compare the same kinds of things. To put the idea another way, the ratio we are dealing with is a part-to-whole ratio—the ratio of faceup cards to the total number of cards, whereas the ratio $\frac{2}{5}$ is a part-to-part ratio—the ratio of faceup cards to facedown cards.

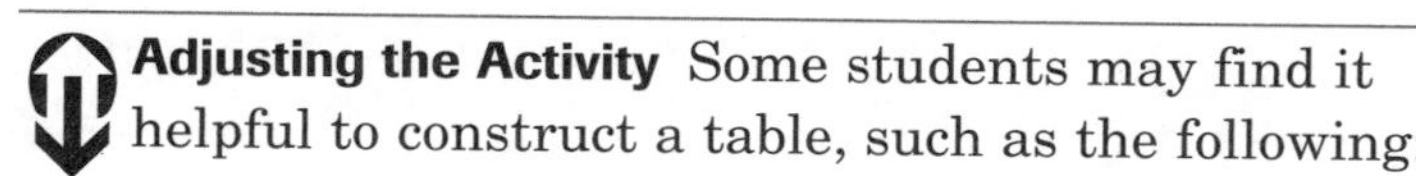

Adjusting the Activity Some students may find it helpful to construct a table, such as the following:

faceup cards	2	4	6
facedown cards	5	10	15
total number of cards	7	14	21

Finally, discuss the answers to Problem 6. Parts a and b illustrate that there are two ways of comparing quantities with the same units. In Part a, we find how much more one quantity is than another (difference comparison); in Part b, we see how many times greater one quantity is than another (ratio comparison). In Part a, we use subtraction to find the difference between two quantities; in Part b, we use division to find the ratio of one quantity to another.

The Challenge problems at the bottom of journal page 309 are for students who might benefit from an optional Enrichment activity. (See Part 3, page 640.)

✦ Solving Ratio Problems

(Math Journal 2, pp. 310 and 311)

PARTNER ACTIVITY

Before assigning journal pages 310 and 311, ask students to give real-life examples of ratios. Encourage them to find examples of both part-to-part and part-to-whole ratios. (See next page for examples.)

Ratio Number Stories

For each problem, write and solve a proportion.

1. A spinner lands on blue 4 times for every 6 times it lands on green. How many times does it land on green if it lands on blue 12 times?
   a. $\frac{\text{lands on blue}}{\text{lands on green}} = \frac{4}{6} = \frac{12}{n}$ b. It lands on green 18 times.
2. It rained 2 out of 5 days in the month of April. On how many days did it rain that month?
   a. $\frac{\text{days with rain}}{\text{days}} = \frac{2}{5} = \frac{n}{30}$ b. It rained 12 days in April.
3. Of the 42 animals in the Children's Zoo, 3 out of 7 are mammals. How many mammals are there in the Children's Zoo?
   a. $\frac{\text{mammals}}{\text{animals}} = \frac{3}{7} = \frac{n}{42}$ b. Answer 18 mammals
4. Last week, Charles spent 2 hours doing homework for every 3 hours he watched TV. If he spent 6 hours doing homework, how many hours did he spend watching TV?
   a. $\frac{\text{homework}}{\text{television}} = \frac{2}{3} = \frac{6}{n}$ b. Answer 9 hours
5. Five out of 8 students at Lane Junior High School play a musical instrument. 140 students play an instrument. How many students attend Lane School?
   a. $\frac{\text{musicians}}{\text{students}} = \frac{5}{8} = \frac{140}{n}$ b. Answer 224 students
6. A choir has 50 members. Twenty members are sopranos. How many sopranos are there for every 5 members of the choir?
   a. $\frac{\text{choir members}}{\text{sopranos}} = \frac{50}{20} = \frac{5}{n}$ b. Answer 2 sopranos

STUDENT PAGE

Math Journal 2, p. 310

Ratio Number Stories *(cont.)*

STUDENT PAGE

7. Mr. Dexter sells subscriptions to a magazine for $18 each. For each subscription he sells, he earns $8. One month, he sold $900 in subscriptions. How much did he earn?

   a. $\frac{\text{profit}}{\text{subscriptions}} = \frac{8}{18} = \frac{n}{900}$ b. Answer $400

8. At Kozminski School, the ratio of weeks of school to weeks of vacation is 9 to 4. How many weeks of vacation do students at the school get in one year?

   a. Complete the table.

Weeks of school	9	18	27	36	
Weeks of vacation	4	8	12	16	
Total weeks	13	26	39	52	

   b. Write a proposition. c. Answer 16 weeks

   $\frac{\text{vacation weeks}}{\text{total weeks}} = \frac{4}{13} = \frac{n}{52}$

9. The class library has 3 fiction books for every 4 nonfiction books. If the library has a total of 63 books, how many fiction books does it have?

   a. $\frac{\text{fiction books}}{\text{total books}} = \frac{3}{7} = \frac{n}{63}$ b. Answer 27 fiction books

Challenge

10. There are 48 students in the sixth grade at Robert's school. Three out of 8 sixth graders read two books last month. One out of 3 students read just one book. The rest of the students read no books at all. How many books in all did the sixth graders read last month? 52 books

    Tell what you did to solve the problem. Sample answer: I used the proportion $\frac{3}{8} = \frac{n}{48}$ to find the number of students who read 2 books: 18 students read 36 books. Then I used a proportion $\frac{1}{3} = \frac{n}{48}$ to find how many students read only 1 book: 16 students read 16 books. 16 + 36 = 52 books

◇ *Math Journal 2*, p. 311

For example, suppose the Lions win 5 games and lose 15 games. Then all of the comparisons below are ratios.

Part-to-part ratios

ratio of wins to losses: 5 to 15
ratio of losses to wins: 15 to 5

Part-to-whole ratios

ratio of wins to all games: 5 out of 20
ratio of losses to all games: 15 out of 20

Other examples of ratios:

- ▷ In May, the ratio of cloudy days to clear days was 2 to 5.
- ▷ For every hour Jacob listened to music, he spent 2 hours reading.
- ▷ Marcy sleeps 8 hours a day (8 hours out of every 24 hours).
- ▷ Jean played soccer for 12 minutes out of every 15-minute quarter.
- ▷ The ratio of the cost of premium grade gasoline to regular gasoline is 1.25 to 1.
- ▷ The ratio of calories generated by 1 gram of fat to 1 gram of protein is 9 to 4.

Point out that the last two ratios are neither part-to-part nor part-to-whole ratios. They compare the same kinds of things (cost of gasoline, calories), but they are not parts of the same whole.

NOTE: At times, different words are needed for similar mathematical situations. For example, the ratio "boys to class" can be expressed as "the number of boys out of the number of students in the class." However, the ratio "boys to girls" would not be expressed as "the number of boys out of the number of girls." The wording "ratio of *a* out of *b*" fits part-to-whole ratio comparisons, while "ratio of *a* to *b*" fits all ratio comparisons.

Work through one or two problems on journal page 310 with students. Make sure that they know how to set up and solve a proportion. Students complete the rest of the problems on pages 310 and 311 on their own as you circulate and assist as needed.

Expect that part-to-part problems will be more difficult for most students. Watch for students who have a strategy for solving the problems but who have a difficult time writing number models.

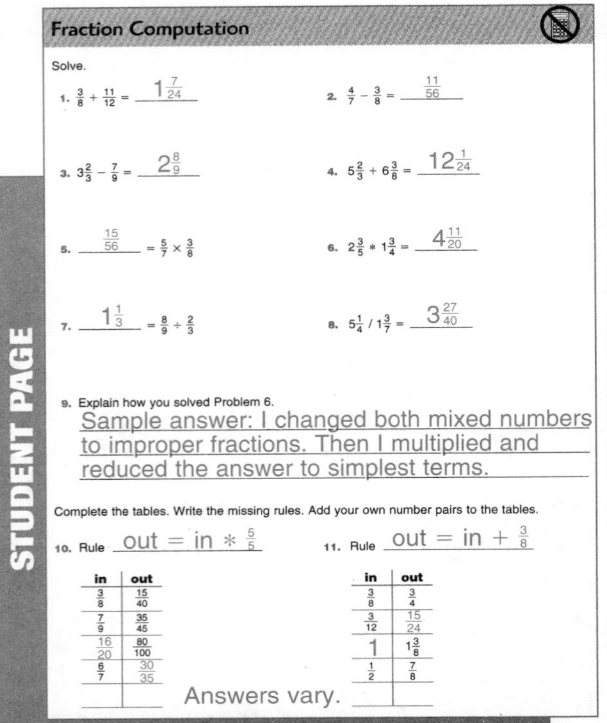

Fraction Computation

STUDENT PAGE

Solve.

1. $\frac{3}{8} + \frac{11}{12} = 1\frac{7}{24}$
2. $\frac{4}{7} - \frac{3}{8} = \frac{11}{56}$
3. $3\frac{2}{3} - \frac{7}{9} = 2\frac{8}{9}$
4. $5\frac{2}{3} + 6\frac{3}{8} = 12\frac{1}{24}$
5. $\frac{15}{56} = \frac{5}{7} \times \frac{3}{8}$
6. $2\frac{3}{5} * 1\frac{3}{4} = 4\frac{11}{20}$
7. $1\frac{1}{3} = \frac{8}{9} \div \frac{2}{3}$
8. $5\frac{1}{4} / 1\frac{3}{7} = 3\frac{27}{40}$
9. Explain how you solved Problem 6.
   Sample answer: I changed both mixed numbers to improper fractions. Then I multiplied and reduced the answer to simplest terms.

Complete the tables. Write the missing rules. Add your own number pairs to the tables.

10. Rule out = in $* \frac{5}{5}$

in	out
$\frac{3}{8}$	$\frac{15}{40}$
$\frac{7}{9}$	$\frac{35}{45}$
$\frac{16}{20}$	$\frac{80}{100}$
$\frac{6}{7}$	$\frac{30}{35}$

11. Rule out = in + $\frac{3}{8}$

in	out
$\frac{3}{8}$	$\frac{3}{4}$
$\frac{3}{12}$	$\frac{15}{24}$
1	$1\frac{3}{8}$
$\frac{1}{2}$	$\frac{7}{8}$

Answers vary.

▷ *Math Journal 2*, p. 312

Expect that in Problem 9, students may have difficulty translating the story into a useful number model. Note that the given comparison is a part-to-part ratio (3 fiction to 4 nonfiction) but that the answer to the problem results from a part-to-whole ratio. Thus, the correct proportion is $\frac{3}{7} = \frac{n}{63}$, which compares part to whole.

When most students have completed the assignment, bring the class together to share solution strategies.

ONGOING ASSESSMENT

Use journal page 310 to assess students' understanding of ratios. Use their answers to Problem 1 for part-to-part problems and their answers to Problem 2 for part-to-whole problems.

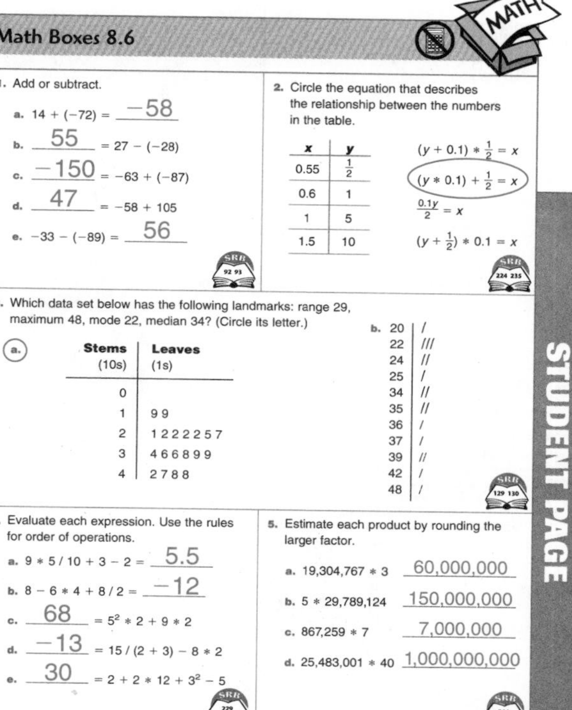

Math Boxes 8.6

1. Add or subtract.
   a. $14 + (-72) =$ −58
   b. 55 $= 27 - (-28)$
   c. −150 $= -63 + (-87)$
   d. 47 $= -58 + 105$
   e. $-33 - (-89) =$ 56

2. Circle the equation that describes the relationship between the numbers in the table.

x	y
0.55	$\frac{1}{2}$
0.6	1
1	5
1.5	10

$(y + 0.1) * \frac{1}{2} = x$

(circled) $(y * 0.1) + \frac{1}{2} = x$

$\frac{0.1y}{2} = x$

$(y + \frac{1}{2}) * 0.1 = x$

3. Which data set below has the following landmarks: range 29, maximum 48, mode 22, median 34? (Circle its letter.)

(a.) (circled)

Stems (10s)	Leaves (1s)
0	
1	9 9
2	1 2 2 2 2 5 7
3	4 6 6 8 9 9
4	2 7 8 8

b.

20	/
22	///
24	//
25	/
34	//
35	//
36	/
37	/
39	//
42	/
48	/

4. Evaluate each expression. Use the rules for order of operations.
   a. $9 * 5 / 10 + 3 - 2 =$ 5.5
   b. $8 - 6 * 4 + 8 / 2 =$ −12
   c. 68 $= 5^2 * 2 + 9 * 2$
   d. −13 $= 15 / (2 + 3) - 8 * 2$
   e. 30 $= 2 + 2 * 12 + 3^2 - 5$

5. Estimate each product by rounding the larger factor.
   a. 19,304,767 ∗ 3 60,000,000
   b. 5 ∗ 29,789,124 150,000,000
   c. 867,259 ∗ 7 7,000,000
   d. 25,483,001 ∗ 40 1,000,000,000

STUDENT PAGE

✧ Math Journal 2, p. 313

Ongoing Learning & Practice

✦Solving Mixed-Number and Fraction Computation Problems (*Math Journal 2,* p. 312)

INDEPENDENT ACTIVITY 

Students complete a page of mixed-number and fraction computation problems.

✦Math Boxes 8.6 (*Math Journal 2,* p. 313)

INDEPENDENT ACTIVITY 

Mixed Review Math Boxes in this lesson are paired with Math Boxes in Lesson 8.8. The skill in Problem 1 is a prerequisite for Unit 9.

✦Study Link 8.6 (*Math Masters,* p. 346)

Home Connection Students solve a set of ratio problems.

Solving Ratio Problems Study Link 8.6

Solve the following problems. Use coins or two-color counters to help you. If you need to draw pictures, use the back of this page.

1. You have 45 coins. Five out of every 9 are HEADS up and the rest are TAILS up. How many coins are HEADS up? 25 coins

2. You have 36 coins. The ratio of HEADS-up coins to TAILS-up coins is 3 to 1. How many coins are HEADS up? 27 coins

3. You have 16 coins that are HEADS up and 18 coins that are TAILS up. After you add some coins that are TAILS up, the ratio of HEADS-up coins to TAILS-up coins is 1 to 1.5. How many coins are TAILS up? 24 coins How many coins in all? 40 coins

4. At Richards Middle School, there are 448 students and 32 teachers. The San Miguel Middle School has 234 students and 18 teachers. Which school has a better ratio of students to teachers, that is, fewer students per teacher? San Miguel Middle School
   Explain how you found your answer. Sample answer: I wrote a ratio comparing the number of students to the number of teachers for each school. Then I reduced each ratio to its simplest form. Richards Middle School has a ratio of $\frac{14}{1}$; San Miguel, $\frac{13}{1}$.

5. There are six shelves for books. Numbers of books are listed in the table. The ratio of mystery books to adventure books to humor books is the same on each shelf. Complete the table.

Shelf	Mystery Books	Adventure Books	Humor Books
1	4	10	18
2	6	15	27
3	8	20	36
4	10	25	45
5	12	30	54
6	14	35	63

Challenge

6. You have a number of coins. The ratio of HEADS-up coins to TAILS-up coins is 2 to 5. Fewer than 10 coins are HEADS up, and more than 15 coins are TAILS up.
   a. How many coins are HEADS up? 8 coins
   b. How many coins are there in all? 28 coins

STUDY LINK MASTER

✧ Math Masters, p. 346

3 Options for Individualizing

✦ ENRICHMENT Solving Challenging Ratio Problems (*Math Journal 2,* p. 309)

PARTNER ACTIVITY  **15–30 min**

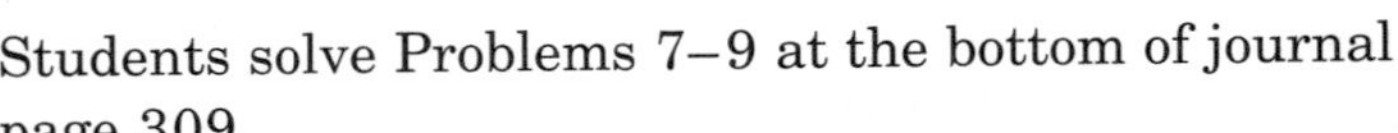

Students solve Problems 7–9 at the bottom of journal page 309.

✦ RETEACHING Reading an Essay about Ratios (*Student Reference Book,* pp. 116–118)

INDEPENDENT ACTIVITY  **15–30 min**

Students read an essay about ratios in the *Student Reference Book.* They also complete the Check Your Understanding problems.

✦ LANGUAGE DIVERSITY Writing Ratio Number Stories

PARTNER ACTIVITY  **15–30 min** 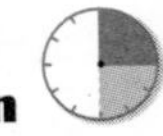

Pair a student proficient in English with a student who is learning English. Students work together to write, illustrate, and solve ratio number stories.

STUDENT PAGE

Rates, Ratios, and Proportions

Ratios

In her monthly report, the manager of a grocery store wrote: "We sold three times as many quarts of ice cream as quarts of frozen yogurt." This statement is an example of a comparison of two like quantities called a **ratio.** You can say that the ratio of quarts of ice cream to quarts of frozen yogurt is 3 to 1. This means that for every 3 quarts of ice cream the store sold, it sold 1 quart of frozen yogurt.

> NOTE: **Like quantities** are numbers with the same unit. For example, 5 inches and 8 inches are like quantities since they have the same unit, inches.

All of the following are statements of ratios:

- It is estimated that by 2020, there will be *5 times as many* people at least 100 years old as there were in 1990.
- Elementary school students make up about *14%* of the United States population.
- On an average evening, about $\frac{1}{3}$ of the United States population watches TV.
- The chances of winning a prize in a lottery can be less than *1 in 1 million.*
- A common scale for dollhouses is *1 inch to 12 inches.*

Percent notation is especially useful for comparing ratios. When ratios are renamed as percents, they are given the number 100 as their common denominator. For example, if Cindy got 14 out of 25 votes in the fifth grade class election, this is the same as getting 56 out of 100 votes, or 56% of the votes. If Bruce got 18 out of 30 votes in the sixth grade class election, this is the same as getting 60 out of 100 votes, or 60% of the votes. Once each ratio is renamed in percent form, it is easy to see that Bruce got a larger portion of votes than Cindy did.

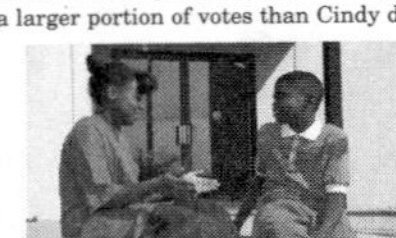

Cindy got 14 out of 25 votes in the fifth grade class election. $\frac{14}{25} = \frac{56}{100} = 56\%$

Bruce got 18 out of 30 votes in the sixth grade class election. $\frac{18}{30} = \frac{60}{100} = 60\%$

SRB 116 one hundred sixteen

✧ *Student Reference Book,* p. 116

STUDENT PAGE

Rates, Ratios, and Proportions

Some ratios compare quantities that involve a whole and its parts.

EXAMPLES In a class of 20 students, there are 12 girls and 8 boys.

You can think of the 20 students as the **whole** and the 12 girls and 8 boys as **parts of the whole.**

A **part-to-whole** ratio compares a part of the whole to the whole. The statements, "8 out of 20 students are boys" and "12 out of 20 students are girls," each express a part-to-whole ratio.

A **part-to-part** ratio compares a part of the whole to another part of the whole. The statement, "There are 8 boys for every 12 girls," expresses a part-to-part ratio.

Ratios can be expressed in a number of ways. For the above example, the ratio of girls to the total number of students can be expressed—

In *words:* Twelve out of 20 students are girls.
Twelve in 20 students are girls.
There are 12 girls for every 20 students.
The ratio of girls to all students is 12 to 20.

With a *fraction*: $\frac{12}{20}$, or $\frac{3}{5}$, of the students are girls.

With a *percent:* 60% of the students are girls.

With a *colon* between the two numbers being compared: The ratio of girls to all students is 12:20 (12 to 20).

In a *proportion:* $\frac{\text{number of girls}}{\text{number of students}} = \frac{12 \text{ girls}}{20 \text{ students}}$.

> NOTE: When ratios are made up of smaller numbers, such as the ratio 3 to 2, they are usually easier to understand.

Equivalent Ratios

Ratios that can be named by equivalent fractions are called **equivalent ratios.** The ratios 12 to 20, 6 to 10, and 3 to 5 are equivalent, because $\frac{12}{20}$, $\frac{6}{10}$, and $\frac{3}{5}$ are equivalent fractions. If 12 out of 20 students are girls, then you can also say that 6 out of 10 students are girls, or 3 out of 5 students are girls. Similarly, the ratios 12 girls to 8 boys, 6 girls to 4 boys, and 3 girls to 2 boys are equivalent, because $\frac{12}{8}$, $\frac{6}{4}$, and $\frac{3}{2}$ are equivalent fractions.

: girl
: boy

The ratio of girls to boys is 3 to 2.

one hundred seventeen SRB 117

✧ *Student Reference Book,* p. 117

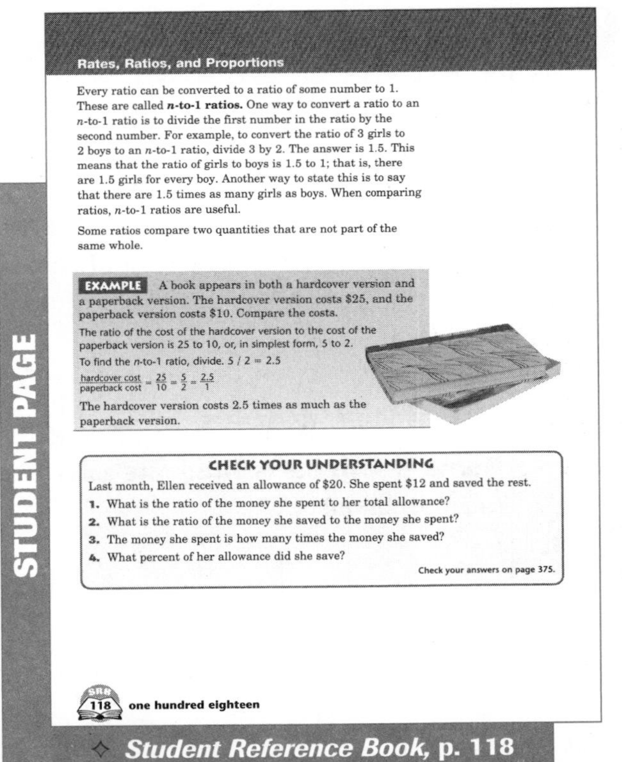

STUDENT PAGE

Rates, Ratios, and Proportions

Every ratio can be converted to a ratio of some number to 1. These are called ***n*-to-1 ratios.** One way to convert a ratio to an *n*-to-1 ratio is to divide the first number in the ratio by the second number. For example, to convert the ratio of 3 girls to 2 boys to an *n*-to-1 ratio, divide 3 by 2. The answer is 1.5. This means that the ratio of girls to boys is 1.5 to 1; that is, there are 1.5 girls for every boy. Another way to state this is to say that there are 1.5 times as many girls as boys. When comparing ratios, *n*-to-1 ratios are useful.

Some ratios compare two quantities that are not part of the same whole.

EXAMPLE A book appears in both a hardcover version and a paperback version. The hardcover version costs $25, and the paperback version costs $10. Compare the costs.

The ratio of the cost of the hardcover version to the cost of the paperback version is 25 to 10, or, in simplest form, 5 to 2.

To find the *n*-to-1 ratio, divide. 5 / 2 = 2.5

$\frac{\text{hardcover cost}}{\text{paperback cost}} = \frac{25}{10} = \frac{5}{2} = \frac{2.5}{1}$

The hardcover version costs 2.5 times as much as the paperback version.

CHECK YOUR UNDERSTANDING

Last month, Ellen received an allowance of $20. She spent $12 and saved the rest.

1. What is the ratio of the money she spent to her total allowance?
2. What is the ratio of the money she saved to the money she spent?
3. The money she spent is how many times the money she saved?
4. What percent of her allowance did she save?

Check your answers on page 375.

SRB 118 one hundred eighteen

✧ *Student Reference Book,* p. 118

8.7 Using Proportions to Solve Percent Problems

OBJECTIVE **To solve percent problems by writing and solving proportions.**

summaries	materials
1 Teaching the Lesson	
Students set up and use proportions as an alternate method for solving percent problems. They use this method to solve problems in which the percent is unknown, the part is unknown, or the whole is unknown. [Patterns, Functions, and Algebra]	☐ *Math Journal 2,* pp. 314 and 315 ☐ Study Link 8.6
2 Ongoing Learning & Practice	
Students make a stem-and-leaf plot, based on a set of data landmarks. [Data and Chance] Students practice and maintain skills through Math Boxes and Study Link activities.	☐ *Math Journal 2,* pp. 316 and 317 ☐ Study Link Master (*Math Masters,* p. 347) ☐ blank overhead transparency (optional)
3 Options for Individualizing	
Extra Practice Students solve a variety of percent problems, some of which involve percents of increase or decrease. [Patterns, Functions, and Algebra]	☐ Teaching Master (*Math Masters,* p. 135)

Getting Started

Mental Math and Reflexes

Students show "thumbs up" if the answer is a positive number and "thumbs down" if the answer is a negative number.

Suggestions

- 24 + (−38) down
- (−73) + 12 down
- (−28) − (−50) up
- 16 − (−25) up
- (−45) − (−30) down
- (−19) − 36 down

Math Message

Solve Problems 1–4 at the top of page 314 in your journal.

Study Link 8.6 Follow-Up

Students share solution strategies. Problems 1, 2, 3, and 5 are fairly straightforward and can be easily solved by setting up proportions. One strategy for solving Problem 4 is to change each ratio to an *n*-to-1 ratio (a ratio with 1 in the denominator). A rate table probably works best for Problem 6.

1 Teaching the Lesson

◆ Math Message Follow-Up
(*Math Journal 2,* p. 314)

WHOLE-CLASS DISCUSSION

Discuss students' solutions for each problem. Possible solution strategies:

Problem 1: The team made $\frac{6}{15}$ of its three-point shots. Rename $\frac{6}{15}$ as $\frac{2}{5}$, which is equal to 40%. Another approach is to divide 6 by 15. This yields 0.40, or 40%. The team made 40% of its three-point shots.

Problem 2: $45\% = \frac{45}{100} = 0.45$. Since 45% of 20 = $0.45 * 20 = 9$, the team made 9 two-point shots. Another approach is to rename $\frac{45}{100}$ as $\frac{9}{20}$ and to multiply $\frac{9}{20} * 20$.

Problem 3: Since 16 free throws are 80% of the total, 10% is $\frac{1}{8}$ of 16, or 2. Then 100% is $10 * 2$, or 20. The team attempted 20 free throws.

Problem 4: The team took 15 three-point shots, 20 two-point shots, and 20 free throws for a total of 55 shots. They made 6 three-point shots ($6 * 3 = 18$ points), 9 two-point shots ($9 * 2 = 18$ points), and 16 free throws ($16 * 1 = 16$ points) for a total of 52 points.

◆ Using Proportions to Solve Percent Problems
(*Math Journal 2,* p. 314)

WHOLE-CLASS DISCUSSION

Students may have solved the Math Message problems by using a variety of methods: renaming a fraction as an equivalent fraction or decimal; dividing the numerator of a fraction by its denominator; finding a unit percent or a multiple of a unit percent; making a simplified table; or setting up and solving a proportion.

The Math Message problems were simple enough so that students did not need to get bogged down in calculations. However, some students may have had some difficulty deciding how to solve the problems. Which method should they use? Should they multiply? Divide?

The first three problems could have been solved by using proportions. The advantage of the proportion method is that it can be used to solve almost any percent problem. That is not to say that students should solve all percent problems this way; students should be encouraged to use whichever method is easiest for a particular problem.

STUDENT PAGE

Using Proportions to Solve Percent Problems

Math Message

1. In a recent game, the Mansfield School basketball team took 15 three-point shots and made 6 shots. What percent of its shots did the team make? 40%
2. The team also took 20 two-point shots and made 45% of them. How many two-point shots did the players make? 9 two-point shots
3. The team made 80% of its free throws (one-point shots). If players made 16 free throws, how many free throws did they attempt? 20 free throws
4. How many shots did the team take in all? 55 shots
   How many points did the team score in all? 52 points
   If your answers are 55 shots and 52 points, then your answers to Problems 2 and 3 are correct.

For each problem, write and solve a proportion.

5. The 12 girls in Ms. Arnold's class make up 40% of the class. How many students are in Ms. Arnold's class?
   a. $\frac{\text{girls}}{\text{total}} = \frac{12}{n} = \frac{40}{100}$
   b. There are 30 students in Ms. Arnold's class.
6. A sow had a litter with 3 female piglets and 5 male piglets. What percent of piglets are female?
   a. $\frac{\text{female}}{\text{total}} = \frac{3}{8} = \frac{n}{100}$
   b. 37.5% of the piglets are female.
7. Matt bought his favorite movie on video for 40% off the regular price. He paid only $18. What was the regular price?
   a. $\frac{\text{sale price}}{\text{regular price}} = \frac{18}{n} = \frac{60}{100}$
   b. The regular price was $ 30. He saved $ 12.
8. In Illinois in 2000, people paid 3% of their income for state tax. What was the tax on an income of $65,000?
   a. $\frac{\text{tax paid}}{\text{income}} = \frac{3}{100} = \frac{n}{65{,}000}$
   b. The tax on an income of $65,000 was $ 1,950.

◇ *Math Journal 2,* p. 314

Demonstrate how to use proportions to solve the Math Message problems. The key is to think of a percent as a ratio with 100 in the denominator.

In Problem 1, the number of three-point shots the team made and the number of shots the team took are known. The ratio of the number of shots made to the number of shots taken can be written as the ratio:

$$\frac{\text{shots made}}{\text{total shots}} = \frac{6}{15}$$

To complete the proportion, it may help to think of the problem as follows: *If the team made 6 out of the 15 shots it took, how many shots would it have made if it had taken 100 shots?* We don't know the answer; therefore, in completing the proportion, we use a variable to show how many out of 100:

$$\frac{\text{shots made}}{\text{total shots}} = \frac{6}{15} = \frac{m}{100}$$

Students can solve this proportion by using cross multiplication or by renaming the ratio $\frac{6}{15}$ as $\frac{2}{5}$ and using the multiplication rule (multiply $\frac{2}{5}$ by $\frac{20}{20}$). Point out that in Problem 1, *the part* and *the whole* are known, and *the percent* is *unknown.*

In Problem 2, the *whole* and the *percent* are known, and the *part is unknown.* You can think of the problem as follows: *If the team made 45% of its two-point shots, this means that players made 45 shots for every 100 shots they took. If they took 20 shots, how many shots did they make?* Stated as a proportion:

$$\frac{\text{shots made}}{\text{total shots}} = \frac{45}{100} = \frac{x}{20}$$

Students can solve this proportion by using either cross multiplication or the division rule (divide numerator and denominator by 5).

In Problem 3, the number of free throws the team made and the percent are known; the *total number of shots is unknown.* You can think of the problem as follows: *If players made 80 shots for every 100 shots they took, how many shots did they take if they made 16 shots?*

Stated as a proportion:

$$\frac{\text{shots made}}{\text{total shots}} = \frac{80}{100} = \frac{16}{y}$$

Using Proportions to Solve Percent Problems (cont.)

9. In the 2000 presidential election, California had 54 electoral votes out of a total of 538. What percent of the electoral votes did California have?

   a. $\frac{\text{California's votes}}{\text{total electoral votes}} = \frac{54}{538} = \frac{n}{100}$

   b. California had 10.04 % of the electoral votes.

10. Female college graduates earn only about 70% as much as male college graduates. If the average female graduate earns about $40,000 a year, how much does the average male graduate earn?

   a. $\frac{\text{female earnings}}{\text{male earnings}} = \frac{40{,}000}{n} = \frac{70}{100}$

   b. The average male graduate earns about $ 57,143.

11. In 1999, about 75% of airline flights arrived on time. About how many of the 8.3 million flights arrived on time?

   a. $\frac{\text{on-time flights}}{\text{total flights}} = \frac{n}{8{,}300{,}000} = \frac{75}{100}$

   b. About 6,225,000 flights were on time. About 2,075,000 flights were late.

12. In 1997, about 9% of eighth grade students smoked daily. About how many of the 3,500,000 eighth graders smoked?

   a. $\frac{\text{smokers}}{\text{non-smokers}} = \frac{n}{3{,}500{,}000} = \frac{9}{100}$

   b. About 315,000 eighth graders smoked.

13. 32% of 50 = 16

   $\frac{\text{part}}{\text{whole}} = \frac{32}{100} = \frac{n}{50}$

14. 15 is 30% of 50.

   $\frac{\text{part}}{\text{whole}} = \frac{15}{n} = \frac{30}{100}$

15. 24 is what percent of 60? 40%

   $\frac{\text{part}}{\text{whole}} = \frac{24}{60} = \frac{n}{100}$

16. 36 is what percent of 80? 45%

   $\frac{\text{part}}{\text{whole}} = \frac{36}{80} = \frac{n}{100}$

STUDENT PAGE

◇ *Math Journal 2,* p. 315

Stem-and-Leaf Plot

1. Construct a stem-and-leaf plot with the following data landmarks. There should be at least 12 data entries in your plot.

median: 57
minimum: 42
maximum: 78
mode: 60

Sample answer:

Stems (10s)	Leaves (1s)
0	
1	
2	
3	
4	2 3 8
5	1 5 7 7
6	0 0 0
7	2 8
8	
9	

2. Explain how you chose the numbers for your data set.
Sample answer: The minimum and maximums are given. Then I wrote two 57s to be sure it would be the median since the set has an even number of entries. I wrote three 60s to be sure 60 would be the mode. That left 5 more numbers to place to get at least 12 data entries. I placed them to keep 57 as the median—4 numbers smaller than 57 and 1 number larger than 57.

3. Describe a data set that your stem-and-leaf plot could represent.
Sample answer: It could represent the number of people who visited a roadside vegetable stand over the course of 12 days.

STUDENT PAGE

◇ *Math Journal 2,* p. 316

Math Boxes 8.7

1. The area of Triangle *FOG* is 12 cm². What is the perimeter of Rectangle *FROG*?
22 cm

R O F G — 8 cm

Explain how you found the perimeter of Rectangle *FROG*.
Sample answer: For a triangle, $A = \frac{1}{2}bh$, so $12 \text{ cm}^2 = \frac{1}{2}(8 * h)$ and $h = 3$. $P = 2l + 2w$, so $P = 16 + 6 = 22$ cm.

2. Draw a tree diagram for the following problem. Then answer the two questions.
The cafeteria is serving spaghetti, hamburgers, and hot dogs for lunch. The drinks are milk, soda, and juice. If you choose your meal and drink at random, what is the probability of having
a. a hot dog? $\frac{1}{3}$
b. a hot dog and juice? $\frac{1}{9}$

spaghetti — milk, soda, juice
hamburger — milk, soda, juice
hot dog — milk, soda, juice

3. Multiply.
a. 473 × 95 = 44,935
b. 847 × 103 = 87,241
c. 624 * 215 = 134,160
d. 704 * 425 = 299,200

STUDENT PAGE

◇ *Math Journal 2,* p. 317

✦ Solving Percent Problems Using Proportions
(*Math Journal 2,* pp. 314 and 315)

PARTNER ACTIVITY 

Consumer Education Link Students use proportions to solve percent problems. Circulate and assist as needed.

Problem 7 may confuse some students. If an item is on sale for 40% off, then the sale price is 60% of the regular price. Students need to read very carefully: "40% *of* the regular price" is not the same as "40% *off* the regular price."

Students can use fraction equivalents to help them solve the problem. For example, \$18 is 60%, which is the same as $\frac{3}{5}$ of the total. So $\frac{1}{5}$ of the total is $18 \div 3$ or \$6. Then $\frac{5}{5}$ of the total is $6 * 5$, or \$30.

Adjusting the Activity If students are having difficulty writing proportions for the problems, help them verbalize the situations. For example, for Problem 5, you might say: "Twelve students in Ms. Arnold's class are girls. If there were 100 students in her class, 40 students would be girls. How many students are in her class?" Encourage students to construct rate tables to help them solve the problems.

ONGOING ASSESSMENT
Use Problems 6–10 to help you assess students' understanding of how to set up and use proportions to solve percent problems. Expect that these tasks will be difficult for some students.

2 Ongoing Learning & Practice

✦ Constructing a Stem-and-Leaf Plot
(*Math Journal 2,* p. 316)

INDEPENDENT ACTIVITY 

Given landmarks for an unknown data set, students construct a stem-and-leaf plot that is consistent with the landmarks. Then, they describe a real-life situation that might be represented by their stem-and-leaf plot.

You may want to ask a volunteer who finishes early to record his or her data on an overhead transparency. As most students finish, have the volunteer share the data and describe the situation in which the data might occur. Examples include weights of a group of dogs, amount of money sixth graders have saved, or average age of retirement.

ONGOING ASSESSMENT

Use this page to assess students' understanding of the organization of stem-and-leaf plots, as well as their knowledge of data landmarks and their ability to interpret data.

◆ Math Boxes 8.7 (*Math Journal 2,* p. 317)

INDEPENDENT ACTIVITY 

Mixed Review Math Boxes in this lesson are paired with Math Boxes in Lesson 8.5. The skill in Problem 1 is a prerequisite for Unit 9.

◆ Study Link 8.7 (*Math Masters,* p. 347)

Home Connection Students use proportions to solve a set of percent problems.

3 Options for Individualizing

◆ EXTRA PRACTICE Solving Percent Problems (*Math Masters,* p. 135)

INDEPENDENT ACTIVITY  **15–30 min** 

Students solve percent problems, some of which involve percents of increase or decrease.

Body Composition by Weight Study Link 8.7

Solve.

1. About 1 out of every 5 pounds of the body weight of an average adult is fat. What percent of body weight is fat? 20%
2. Muscles make up about 40% of the body weight of an average adult. About how many pounds do the muscles of a 160-pound adult weigh? 64 lb
3. About 18% of the total body weight of an adult is bone. The rest is mostly water and other fluids. If an adult weighs 150 pounds, about how many pounds are bone? 27 lb
4. The human body contains a number of different elements. The table gives the percents of various elements in the human body. Fill in the missing number in the table.

Element	%
Carbon	50%
Oxygen	20%
Hydrogen	10%
Nitrogen	8.5%
Calcium	4%
Phosphorus	2.5%
Potassium	1%
Other	4%

Use the information in the table to set up proportions and solve the following problems.

5. a. If the weight of all of the oxygen in an adult's body is about 25 pounds, what is the total weight of this adult? About 125 lb
   $\frac{25}{n} = \frac{20}{100}$
   b. What is the approximate weight of the carbon in that adult's body? About 62.5 lb
   $\frac{n}{125} = \frac{50}{100}$
6. a. If the weight of the calcium in an adult's body is about 8 pounds, what is the total weight of this adult? About 200 lb
   $\frac{8}{n} = \frac{4}{100}$
   b. What is the approximate weight of the potassium? About 2 lb
   $\frac{n}{200} = \frac{1}{100}$

Source: Numbers: How Many, How Far, How Long, How Much

STUDY LINK MASTER

◆ *Math Masters,* p. 347

The World of Percents

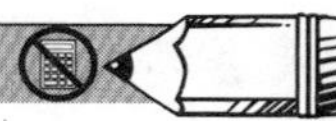

Solve.

1. If reduced-fat hot dogs have 8 fewer grams of fat than regular hot dogs, how much fat do the regular hot dogs have? 20 grams

Reduced-Fat Hot Dogs with 40% Less Fat!

2. If the public transportation system is currently collecting about $28,000 per day, what will it collect per day if it reaches its goal? $35,000

Public Transportation Authority Aims to Increase Ridership by 25%

3. If there are 420 fewer people attending the concert series, what was the total attendance for the previous year? 3,500 people

Attendance at Music Hall Down 12% Over Previous Year for 10-Concert Series

4. Reginald read 168 pages of his book. He has 42 pages left. What percent of the book has he read? 80%
5. Last year, Maria's insect collection had 250 insects in it. She added 60 more to her collection this summer. By what percent did she increase her collection? 24%
6. Jackie had a batting average of .250 for the season. If she went to bat 52 times during the season, how many hits did she get? (*Hint:* 0.250 = 0.25 = ___%.) 13 hits
7. Make up and solve your own problem. Write it on the back of this page. Answers vary.

TEACHING MASTER

◆ *Math Masters,* p. 135

8.8 Calculating the Fat Content of Foods

OBJECTIVES **To estimate percent equivalents for fractions; and to calculate what percent of total calories comes from fat, protein, and carbohydrate.**

summaries	materials
1 Teaching the Lesson	
Students develop mental computation and estimation skills for converting fractions to percents. They convert fractions to percents with a calculator, using division. [Operations and Computation] Students use information from food labels to estimate and then calculate the percents of total calories that come from fat, protein, and carbohydrate. [Patterns, Functions, and Algebra]	□ *Math Journal 2,* pp. 318 and 319 □ Study Link 8.7 □ Assessment Master (*Math Masters,* p. 478; optional) □ calculator □ slate
2 Ongoing Learning & Practice	
Students convert percents and fractions to degree measures on circle graphs. [Data and Chance] Students practice and maintain skills through Math Boxes and Study Link activities.	□ *Math Journal 2,* pp. 320 and 321 □ Study Link Masters (*Math Masters,* pp. 348 and 349) □ protractor ***See* Advance Preparation**
3 Options for Individualizing	
Extra Practice Students estimate the percent equivalents of fractions. [Operations and Computation]	□ Teaching Master (*Math Masters,* p. 136) ***See* Advance Preparation**

Additional Information

Advance Preparation The Study Link in Part 2 of this lesson consists of two pages. For Part 3, make one copy of *Math Masters,* page 136 for every two students. Cut the copies in half.

Getting Started

Mental Math and Reflexes

Have students rename "easy" fractions as percents. *Suggestions:*

- $\frac{1}{2}$ 50%
- $\frac{2}{8}$ 25%
- $\frac{1}{4}$ 25%
- $\frac{3}{5}$ 60%
- $\frac{1}{5}$ 20%
- $\frac{4}{25}$ 16%
- $\frac{1}{20}$ 5%
- $\frac{3}{10}$ 30%
- $\frac{9}{12}$ 75%
- $\frac{7}{50}$ 14%
- $\frac{1}{3}$ $33\frac{1}{3}$%
- $\frac{6}{9}$ $66\frac{2}{3}$%

Math Message

The Dress-Rite men's clothing store is having a sale. The price of every sale item is $\frac{4}{5}$ of its regular price. What percent of the regular price must you pay for a sale item?

Study Link 8.7 Follow-Up
Students share answers and solution strategies.

1 Teaching the Lesson

✦ Math Message Follow-Up

WHOLE-CLASS DISCUSSION

Point out that the problem is about a part-to-whole comparison. The fraction $\frac{4}{5}$ expresses the ratio of the sale price of an item to its regular price.

$$\frac{\text{sale price}}{\text{regular price}} = \frac{4}{5}$$

Remind students that a part-to-whole ratio may be expressed as a percent. Review the two methods for converting fractions to percents.

1. Setting up and solving a proportion

$$\frac{4}{5} = \frac{n}{100}$$

$$n = 80$$

Therefore, $\frac{4}{5} = \frac{80}{100} = 80\%$.

2. Division

Divide the numerator of the fraction by the denominator; then rename the resulting decimal as a percent by multiplying it by 100.

$$\frac{4}{5} = 4 / 5 = 0.8$$

$$0.8 = (0.8 * 100)\% = 80\%$$

Both methods work with any fractions. With a fraction whose denominator is a factor of 100, as in the above example, the problem may be solved more easily mentally, using a proportion. When converting difficult fractions like $\frac{3}{7}$ to percents, the division method is more useful, especially if a calculator is used for the computation.

Pose a few problems (*see margin*) for students to solve with their calculators using the division method. Have them rename each fraction as a percent, rounded to the nearest percent.

Example $\frac{9}{16} = 9 / 16 = 0.5625$

$0.5625 = (0.5625 * 100)\% = 56.25\%$, or 56%, rounded to the nearest percent

Suggested problems

- $\frac{4}{7}$ 57%
- $\frac{5}{8}$ 63%
- $\frac{4}{11}$ 36%
- $\frac{8}{9}$ 89%
- $\frac{18}{31}$ 58%
- $\frac{9}{26}$ 35%

✦Estimating Percent Equivalents for Fractions

WHOLE-CLASS ACTIVITY

Estimation is useful when there is no need to find an exact answer or when one needs simply to check that an exact answer is reasonable. Students have already developed techniques for estimating sums, differences, products, and quotients. The focus of the activity in this lesson is on *estimating* percent equivalents of fractions that are not "easy" fractions. Here are two estimation methods.

1. Estimate by finding an equivalent fraction whose denominator is "about 100."

Remind students that most fractions cannot be renamed as fractions with 100 in the denominator. But many fractions can be renamed as fractions with denominators "close to 100." *For example:*

$$\frac{7}{9} = \frac{7 * 11}{9 * 11} = \frac{77}{99}$$

This is close to $\frac{77}{100}$, so $\frac{7}{9}$ is about 77%.

2. Estimate with reference to easy fractions.

For example, to estimate the percent equivalent of $\frac{4}{9}$, think: *$\frac{4}{9}$ is between the easy fractions $\frac{4}{8}$ and $\frac{4}{10}$. Since $\frac{4}{8} = \frac{1}{2} = 50\%$ and $\frac{4}{10} = 40\%$, $\frac{4}{9}$ is between 40% and 50%.*

Have students practice estimating percent equivalents on their slates. Ask them to share their reasoning after each problem. Then have them find the actual percents with their calculators.

NOTE: Keep in mind as you work with students that there are many different ways to arrive at an estimate. The strategies discussed here should be viewed as suggestions. Encourage students to use any reasonable strategies that make sense to them.

Suggestions

▷ Decide whether the following fractions are closest to 0%, 25%, 50%, 75%, or 100%.

- $\frac{3}{7}$ $\frac{3}{7}$ is a little less than $\frac{1}{2}$, or 50%; $\frac{4}{7}$ is a little more than $\frac{1}{2}$; therefore, $\frac{3}{7}$ is closest to 50%.
  Or: $\frac{3}{7}$ is between $\frac{3}{6}$ and $\frac{3}{8}$; $\frac{3}{6} = \frac{1}{2} = 50\%$; $\frac{3}{8}$ is between $\frac{2}{8}$ (25%) and $\frac{4}{8}$ (50%); therefore, $\frac{3}{8}$ must be closer to 50% than to 25%.

- $\frac{1}{6}$ $\frac{1}{6}$ is half of $\frac{2}{6}$, or $\frac{1}{3}$; $\frac{1}{3}$ is more than 30%, so $\frac{1}{6}$ is more than 15%; therefore, $\frac{1}{6}$ is closest to 25%.

- $\frac{7}{9}$ $\frac{1}{9}$ is slightly larger than $\frac{1}{10}$, so $\frac{7}{9}$ is a little more than $\frac{7}{10}$; therefore, $\frac{7}{9}$ is a little more than 70%; therefore, it is closest to 75%.
  Or: If you add $\frac{2}{9}$ to $\frac{7}{9}$, you get 1, or 100%. But $\frac{2}{9}$ is a little less than $\frac{2}{8}$ or $\frac{1}{4}$, so $\frac{7}{9}$ is closest to 75%.

▷ Estimate an equivalent percent name for the following fractions:

- $\frac{2}{9}$ Equivalent to $\frac{22}{99}$; about 22%
- $\frac{2}{11}$ Equivalent to $\frac{18}{99}$; about 18%
- $\frac{20}{24}$ Equivalent to $\frac{40}{48}$ and $\frac{80}{96}$; about 80%
  Is it more or less than 80%? more
- $\frac{8}{13}$ Equivalent to $\frac{16}{26}$; close to $\frac{15}{25}$, which is equal to $\frac{60}{100}$; about 60%
- $\frac{13}{15}$ A little more than $\frac{12}{15}$, which is equal to $\frac{4}{5}$, or $\frac{80}{100}$; a little more than 80%
- $\frac{34}{49}$ Equivalent to $\frac{68}{98}$; about 68%
- $\frac{3}{7}$ Equivalent to $\frac{21}{49}$ and $\frac{42}{98}$; about 42%
- $\frac{15}{33}$ Equivalent to $\frac{45}{99}$; about 45%

If students seem ready for a challenge, try these:

- $\frac{32}{67}$ 32 is a little less than $\frac{1}{2}$ of 67, so $\frac{32}{67}$ is a little less than 50%
- $\frac{18}{115}$ About $\frac{20}{120}$, or $\frac{1}{6}$; near 16%
- $\frac{8}{76}$ Between $\frac{8}{72}$ and $\frac{8}{80}$, so $\frac{8}{76}$ is between $\frac{1}{9}$ and $\frac{1}{10}$ or 10% and 11%

✦ Finding the Fat Content in Foods (*Math Journal 2,* pp. 318 and 319)

PARTNER ACTIVITY

Health Link Have students study the examples of nutrition labels on journal pages 318 and 319. Only the tops of the labels are shown. Point out the following facts to students:

▷ The top of every label shows the same information in the same format (typeface, arrangement of information, use of solid bars, and so on).

▷ The first line under Amount Per Serving gives the total number of calories and the number of calories from fat in a single serving. This is the information needed to answer Problem 1.

Go over steps a, b, and c in the directions for Problem 1 with the class. Use the food label for bologna as an example.

The Fat Content of Foods

1. Use the information about calories on each food label below and on the next page.
   a. Write the ratio of calories that come from fat to the total number of calories as a fraction.
   b. Then estimate the percent of total calories that come from fat. Do not use your calculator.
   c. Finally, use your calculator to find the percent of calories that come from fat. (Round to the nearest whole percent.) Estimates vary.

Food Label	Food	Calories from Fat / Total Calories	Estimated Fat Percent	Calculated Fat Percent
Nutrition Facts Serving Size 1 slice (28 g) Servings Per Container 12 Amount Per Serving Calories 90 Calories from Fat 80	bologna	$\frac{80}{90}$	About 90	89%
Nutrition Facts Serving Size 2 waffles (72 g) Servings Per Container 4 Amount Per Serving Calories 190 Calories from Fat 50	waffle	$\frac{50}{190}$	About 25%	26%
Nutrition Facts Serving Size 2 tablespoons (32 g) Servings Per Container 15 Amount Per Serving Calories 190 Calories from Fat 140	peanut butter	$\frac{140}{190}$	About 75%	74%
Nutrition Facts Serving Size 1 slice (19 g) Servings Per Container 24 Amount Per Serving Calories 70 Calories from Fat 50	American cheese	$\frac{50}{70}$	About 70%	71%
Nutrition Facts Serving Size 1 egg (50 g) Servings Per Container 12 Amount Per Serving Calories 70 Calories from Fat 40	egg	$\frac{40}{70}$	About 60%	57%

STUDENT PAGE

✧ *Math Journal 2,* p. 318

The Fat Content of Foods (cont.)

MATH

Food Label	Food	Calories from Fat / Total Calories	Estimated Fat Percent	Calculated Fat Percent
Nutrition Facts Serving Size 1 cup (60 mL) Servings Per Container 6 Amount Per Serving Calories 110 Calories from Fat 0	orange juice	$\frac{0}{110}$	0%	0%
Nutrition Facts Serving Size 1/2 cup (125 g) Servings Per Container About 3 1/2 Amount Per Serving Calories 90 Calories from Fat 5	corn	$\frac{5}{90}$	About 6%	6%
Nutrition Facts Serving Size 1 package (255 g) Servings Per Container 1 Amount Per Serving Calories 280 Calories from Fat 90	macaroni and cheese	$\frac{90}{280}$	About 30%	32%
Nutrition Facts Serving Size 1/2 cup (106 g) Servings Per Container 4 Amount Per Serving Calories 270 Calories from Fat 160	ice cream	$\frac{160}{270}$	About 60%	59%

2. Compare whole milk to skim (nonfat) milk.

Type of Milk	Total Calories	Calories from Fat	Calories from Carbohydrate	Calories from Protein
1 cup whole milk	160	75	50	35
1 cup skim milk	85	trace	50	35

   a. For whole milk, what percent of the total calories comes from
   fat? 47 % carbohydrate? 31 % protein? 22 %
   b. For skim milk, what percent of the total calories comes from
   fat? 0 % carbohydrate? 59 % protein? 41 %

3. Find the missing percents.
   a. 25% + 30% + 45 % = 100% b. 82% + 9 % + 9% = 100%

STUDENT PAGE

✧ *Math Journal 2,* p. 319

Circle Graphs

1. Convert the following percents to degree measures on a circle graph.
   a. 27% 97.2°
   b. 49% 176.4°
   c. 73% 262.8°
   d. 98% 352.8°
   e. 65% 234°

2. Convert the following fractions to degree measures on a circle graph.
   a. $\frac{3}{8}$ 135°
   b. $\frac{6}{9}$ 240°
   c. $\frac{4}{5}$ 288°
   d. $\frac{8}{12}$ 240°
   e. $\frac{3}{4}$ 270°

3. Use your protractor to divide the circle into three sectors by drawing a 48° sector and a 116° sector.

   What is the degree measure of the third sector? 196°

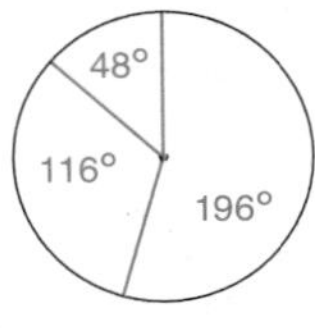

4. Ms. Camponella's sixth graders were having a surprise birthday party for her. The table below shows how many students signed up to bring each kind of treat.
   a. Complete the table.
   b. Use your protractor to make a circle graph that displays the information. Title your graph.

Treat	Number Signed Up	Degree Measure of Sector
Chips	8	115.2°
Cookies	5	72°
Drinks	3	43.2°
Fruit	9	129.6°

Birthday Treats
(title)

STUDENT PAGE

◇ *Math Journal 2,* p. 320

When students have completed Problems 1–3, briefly discuss their answers. You might want to include the following questions in your discussion: *Were there any surprises? Were there foods that you thought would have a greater or smaller fat percent? For Problem 2, do the three percents for each type of milk add to 100%?* Most likely, but there may be a 1% or 2% variation as a result of rounding.

NOTE: Because of the way calories are calculated and rounded, there will sometimes be small discrepancies in the total. The calories in any food come solely from fat, protein, and carbohydrate.

Adjusting the Activity Some students may benefit from recording the "easy" fractions they are using to make their estimates. Suggest that they record these fractions in the Estimated Fat Percent column.

ONGOING ASSESSMENT

Have students complete an Exit Slip (*Math Masters,* page 478) explaining how they made their estimates for the percent of fat in macaroni and cheese.

Math Boxes 8.8

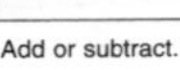

1. Add or subtract.
   a. −303 + (−28) = −331
   b. −273 = 245 − 518
   c. 16 = −73 + 89
   d. 81 = 176 + (−95)
   e. 280 − (−31) = 311

2. Circle the equation that describes the relationship between the numbers in the table.

x	y
1	$\frac{3}{8}$
2	$\frac{3}{4}$
8	3
24	9

$\frac{y}{8} * 3 = x$

$(3 * y) + 8 = x$

(circled) $\frac{x}{8} * 3 = y$

$(3 * x) + 8 = y$

3. Which data set below has the following landmarks: maximum 25, minimum 10, mode 18, median 18? (Circle its letter.)

a.

Stems (10s)	Leaves (1s)
0	
1	0 1 1 5 7
2	0 1 3 3 3 5

(b.) (circled)

10	//
11	//
14	///
17	/
18	~~////~~
22	//
23	/
25	/

4. Evaluate each expression. Use the rules for order of operations.
   a. 3 ∗ 8 / 4 + 7 = 13
   b. 9 + 3 ∗ 5 − 7 = 17
   c. 51 = 6 ∗ 5 + 7 ∗ 3
   d. 26.6 = 8 / (2 + 8) ∗ 3^3 + 5
   e. 30 = 28 − 7 ∗ 4 ∗ 0 + 2

5. Estimate each product by rounding the larger factor to the nearest million.
   a. 65,002,389 ∗ 2 130,000,000
   b. 3 ∗ 300,894,115 903,000,000
   c. 15,224,025 × 5 75,000,000
   d. 501,444 × 70 70,000,000

STUDENT PAGE

◇ *Math Journal 2,* p. 321

2 Ongoing Learning & Practice

✦ Reviewing Circle Graphs (*Math Journal 2,* p. 320)

INDEPENDENT ACTIVITY

Students complete a page of problems reviewing circle graphs.

✦ Math Boxes 8.8 (*Math Journal 2,* p. 321)

INDEPENDENT ACTIVITY

Mixed Review Math Boxes in this lesson are paired with Math Boxes in Lesson 8.6. The skill in Problem 1 is a prerequisite for Unit 9.

✦Study Link 8.8
(*Math Masters,* pp. 348 and 349)

Home Connection Students collect data about a variety of objects. They should have several days to complete the assignment. Information from this Study Link will serve as problem data in Lesson 8.11.

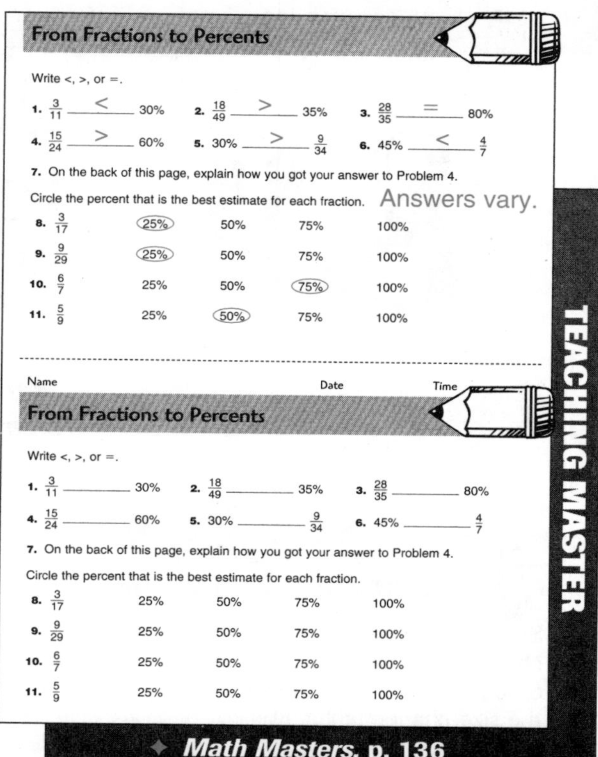

From Fractions to Percents

Write <, >, or =.

1. $\frac{3}{11}$ < 30% 2. $\frac{18}{49}$ > 35% 3. $\frac{28}{35}$ = 80%
4. $\frac{15}{24}$ > 60% 5. 30% > $\frac{9}{34}$ 6. 45% < $\frac{4}{7}$
7. On the back of this page, explain how you got your answer to Problem 4.

Circle the percent that is the best estimate for each fraction. Answers vary.

8. $\frac{3}{17}$ (25%) 50% 75% 100%
9. $\frac{9}{29}$ (25%) 50% 75% 100%
10. $\frac{6}{7}$ 25% 50% (75%) 100%
11. $\frac{5}{9}$ 25% (50%) 75% 100%

Name Date Time

From Fractions to Percents

Write <, >, or =.

1. $\frac{3}{11}$ ______ 30% 2. $\frac{18}{49}$ ______ 35% 3. $\frac{28}{35}$ ______ 80%
4. $\frac{15}{24}$ ______ 60% 5. 30% ______ $\frac{9}{34}$ 6. 45% ______ $\frac{4}{7}$
7. On the back of this page, explain how you got your answer to Problem 4.

Circle the percent that is the best estimate for each fraction.

8. $\frac{3}{17}$ 25% 50% 75% 100%
9. $\frac{9}{29}$ 25% 50% 75% 100%
10. $\frac{6}{7}$ 25% 50% 75% 100%
11. $\frac{5}{9}$ 25% 50% 75% 100%

TEACHING MASTER

✦ *Math Masters,* p. 136

3 Options for Individualizing

✦ EXTRA PRACTICE Estimating Percent Equivalents for Fractions
(*Math Masters,* p. 136)

INDEPENDENT ACTIVITY  **15–30 min** 

Students use a variety of estimation strategies to find percents that are approximately equivalent to fractions.

Home Data Study Link 8.8

1. Record the following data about all of the members of your household. Answers vary.
   a. Total number of people ______ b. Number of males ______
   c. Number of females ______ d. Number of left-handed people ______
   e. Number of right-handed people ______ (For people who are ambidextrous, record the hand most often used for writing.)

For the rectangles in this Study Link, use length as the measure of the longer sides and width as the measure of the shorter sides.

2. Find an American flag or a picture of one. Measure its length and width.
   a. length ______ (unit) b. width ______ (unit)

3. Measure the length and width of a television screen to the nearest $\frac{1}{2}$ inch.
   a. length ______ (unit) b. width ______ (unit)

4. Find three books of different sizes, such as a small paperback, your journal, and a large reference book. Measure the length and width of each book to the nearest $\frac{1}{2}$ inch.
   a. Small book: length ______ (unit) width ______ (unit)
   b. Medium book: length ______ (unit) width ______ (unit)
   c. Large book: length ______ (unit) width ______ (unit)

STUDY LINK MASTER

✦ *Math Masters,* p. 348

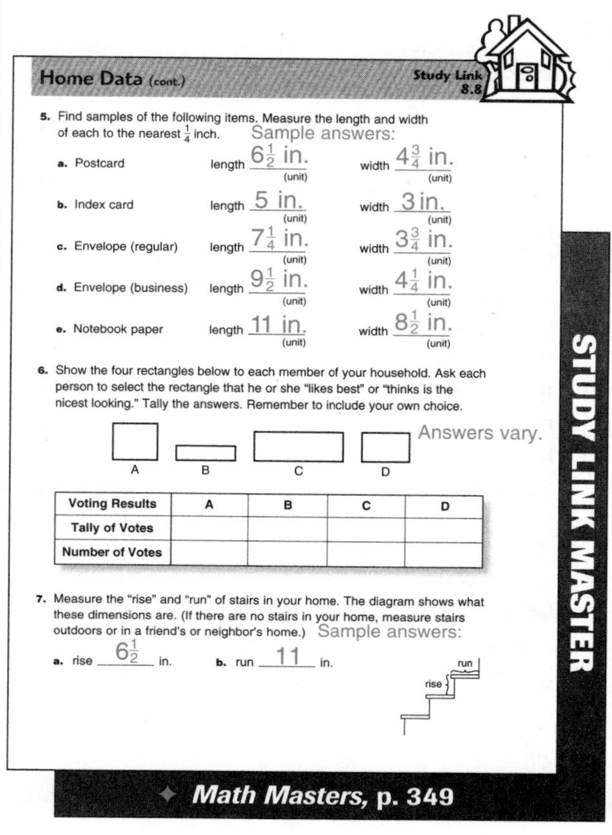

Home Data (cont.) Study Link 8.8

5. Find samples of the following items. Measure the length and width of each to the nearest $\frac{1}{4}$ inch. Sample answers:
   a. Postcard length $6\frac{1}{2}$ in. (unit) width $4\frac{3}{4}$ in. (unit)
   b. Index card length 5 in. (unit) width 3 in. (unit)
   c. Envelope (regular) length $7\frac{1}{4}$ in. (unit) width $3\frac{3}{4}$ in. (unit)
   d. Envelope (business) length $9\frac{1}{2}$ in. (unit) width $4\frac{1}{4}$ in. (unit)
   e. Notebook paper length 11 in. (unit) width $8\frac{1}{2}$ in. (unit)

6. Show the four rectangles below to each member of your household. Ask each person to select the rectangle that he or she "likes best" or "thinks is the nicest looking." Tally the answers. Remember to include your own choice. Answers vary.

A B C D

Voting Results	A	B	C	D
Tally of Votes				
Number of Votes				

7. Measure the "rise" and "run" of stairs in your home. The diagram shows what these dimensions are. (If there are no stairs in your home, measure stairs outdoors or in a friend's or neighbor's home.) Sample answers:
   a. rise $6\frac{1}{2}$ in. b. run 11 in.

STUDY LINK MASTER

✦ *Math Masters,* p. 349

8.9 Using Ratios to Describe Size Changes

OBJECTIVES **To explore the use of ratios to describe size changes; and to use a variety of notations to show the size-change factor.**

summaries	materials
1 Teaching the Lesson	
Students explore the use of ratios to describe size changes—for geometric figures, scale models, and maps. Students also practice using a variety of notations to show the size-change factor. [Patterns, Functions, and Algebra]	□ *Math Journal 2,* pp. 322 and 323 □ *Student Reference Book,* pp. 119–121 □ Study Link 8.8 □ Teaching Master (*Math Masters,* p. 137) □ calculator □ inch ruler □ Geometry Template (optional) ***See* Advance Preparation**
2 Ongoing Learning & Practice	
Students divide decimals by whole numbers, rounding the quotients to the nearest tenth or hundredth. [Operations and Computation] Students practice and maintain skills through Math Boxes and Study Link activities.	□ *Math Journal 2,* pp. 324 and 325 □ Study Link Master (*Math Masters,* p. 350) □ centimeter ruler
3 Options for Individualizing	
Enrichment Students practice interpreting map scales found on the Internet. [Patterns, Functions, and Algebra] **Extra Practice** Students use scale drawings to find the dimensions of the original objects. [Patterns, Functions, and Algebra] **Extra Practice** Students investigate the relationship between the size-change factor in polygons and their perimeters. [Patterns, Functions, and Algebra] **Language Diversity** Students work together to make small posters illustrating enlargements and reductions.	□ Teaching Masters (*Math Masters,* pp. 138 and 139) □ computer with Internet access (optional) □ centimeter and inch ruler

Additional Information

Advance Preparation For the Math Message in Part 1, make one copy of *Math Masters,* page 137 for every two students. Cut the copies in half and place them near the Math Message.

Vocabulary • **size-change factor (or "scale factor" or "scale")** • ***n*-to-1 ratio** • **enlargement** • **reduction** • **scale model**

Getting Started

Mental Math and Reflexes

Have students estimate the percent equivalents for fractions.
Suggestions

- $\frac{8}{9}$ Close to $\frac{88}{99}$, or 88%
- $\frac{5}{7}$ Equals $\frac{35}{49}$, which is close to $\frac{70}{100}$, or 70%
- $\frac{5}{6}$ $\frac{4}{6}$ is about 66%; add $\frac{1}{6}$, or about 16%; result: about 82%
- $\frac{18}{47}$ Close to $\frac{20}{50}$, or 40%
- $\frac{3}{21}$ Close to $\frac{3}{20} = \frac{15}{100}$, or 15%

Math Message

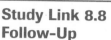

Take a copy of the Math Message and solve the problem. Then read pages 119–121 in your Student Reference Book.

Study Link 8.8 Follow-Up

Remind students that Study Link 8.8 must be completed within the next 2 or 3 days.

Teaching the Lesson

✦ Math Message Follow-Up
(*Math Masters,* p. 137)

WHOLE-CLASS DISCUSSION

Discuss who is correct and why. Address the following points in the discussion:

▷ The diameter of a 12-inch pizza is 50% more than the diameter of an 8-inch pizza. From their reading of the *Student Reference Book* essay, students may be able to state that the size-change factor for this increase is 1.5:

$$\frac{\text{diameter of larger pizza}}{\text{diameter of smaller pizza}} = \frac{12 \text{ inches}}{8 \text{ inches}} = \frac{1.5}{1}$$

▷ Considering only the size-change ratio, $\frac{1.5}{1}$, it appears that a 12-inch pizza is not worth twice as much as an 8-inch pizza. This is what misled Zach. (This issue will be considered again later in the lesson.)

▷ The *area* of a pizza is a better measure of its value than the diameter.

Ask students to use their calculators to find the areas of an 8-inch and a 12-inch pizza. The area of a 12-inch pizza is more than twice as much as the area of an 8-inch pizza.

Area of 8-inch pizza: $\pi * 4^2$ inches is about 50 in.^{2}

Area of 12-inch pizza: $\pi * 6^2$ inches is about 113 in.^{2}

Since its area is more than twice as much as the area of an 8-inch pizza, one 12-inch pizza is a better buy than two 8-inch pizzas.

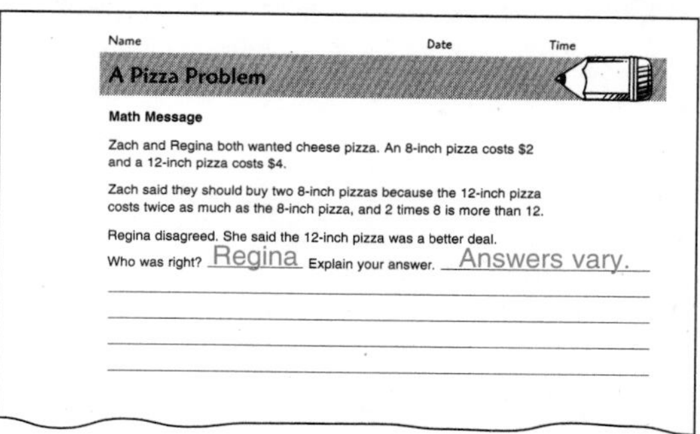

Name Date Time

A Pizza Problem

Math Message

Zach and Regina both wanted cheese pizza. An 8-inch pizza costs $2 and a 12-inch pizza costs $4.

Zach said they should buy two 8-inch pizzas because the 12-inch pizza costs twice as much as the 8-inch pizza, and 2 times 8 is more than 12.

Regina disagreed. She said the 12-inch pizza was a better deal.

Who was right? Regina Explain your answer. Answers vary.

Math Masters, page 137

STUDENT PAGE

Rates, Ratios, and Proportions

Using Ratios to Describe Size Changes

Many situations produce a **size change.** For example, a magnifying glass, a microscope, and an overhead projector all produce size changes that enlarge the original image. Most copying machines can create a variety of size changes—both enlargements and reductions of the original document.

Similar figures are figures that have the same shape but not necessarily the same size. In the examples of size changes above, the enlargement or reduction is **similar** to the original; that is, they have the same shape.

The **size-change factor** is a number that tells the amount of enlargement or reduction that takes place. For example, if you use a copy machine to make a 2X change in size, then every length in the copy is twice the size of the original. The size-change factor is 2. If you make a 0.5X change in size, then every length in the copy is half the size of the original. The size-change factor is $\frac{1}{2}$, or 0.5.

You can think of the size-change factor as a ratio. For a 2X size change, the ratio of a length in the copy to the corresponding length in the original is 2 to 1.

size-change factor 2: $\frac{\text{copy size}}{\text{original size}} = \frac{2}{1}$

For a 0.5X size change, the ratio of a length in the copy to a corresponding length in the original is 0.5 to 1.

size-change factor 0.5: $\frac{\text{copy size}}{\text{original size}} = \frac{0.5}{1}$

If the size-change factor is greater than 1, then the copy is an **enlargement** of the original; if it is less than 1, then the copy is a **reduction** of the original.

Devices That Magnify and Reduce

A photographer uses an enlarger to make prints from negatives. If the size of the image on the negative is 2" by 2" and the size of the image on the print is 4" by 4", then the size-change factor is 2. Binoculars that are 8X, or "8 power," magnify all the lengths you see with the naked eye to 8 times their actual size.

one hundred nineteen SRB 119

✧ *Student Reference Book*, p. 119

STUDENT PAGE

Rates, Ratios, and Proportions

Scale Models

A model that is a careful, reduced copy of an actual object is called a **scale model.** You have probably seen scale models of cars, trains, and airplanes. The size-change factor in scale models is usually called the **scale factor.**

Dollhouses often have a scale factor of $\frac{1}{12}$. You can write this as "$\frac{1}{12}$ of actual size," "scale 1:12," "$\frac{1}{12}$ scale," or as a proportion: "$\frac{\text{dollhouse length}}{\text{real house length}} = \frac{1"}{12"}$."

All the dimensions of an E-scale model railroad are $\frac{1}{96}$ of the actual size. We can write this as "scale 1:96," or "scale: $\frac{1}{8}$ inch represents 1 foot," "scale: 0.125 inch represents 1 foot," or "$\frac{\text{model railroad length}}{\text{real railroad length}} = \frac{1"}{96"}$."

Note: The scale is 1:96 since "$\frac{1}{8}$ inch:12 inches" is the same as "1 inch:96 inches."

Maps

The size-change factor for maps is usually called the **scale.** If a map scale is 1:25,000, then every length on the map is $\frac{1}{25,000}$ of the actual length, and any real distance is 25,000 times the distance shown on the map.

$\frac{\text{map distance}}{\text{real distance}} = \frac{1}{25,000}$

Scale Drawings

The size-change factor for scale drawings is also usually called the **scale.** If an architect's scale drawing shows "scale $\frac{1}{4}$ inch:1 foot" or "scale $\frac{1}{4}$ inch represents 1 foot," then the drawing is $\frac{1}{48}$ of the actual size.

$\frac{\text{drawing length}}{\text{real length}} = \frac{\frac{1}{4}\text{ inch}}{1\text{ foot}}$

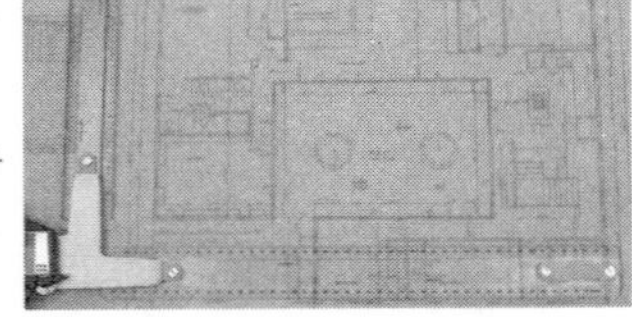

one hundred twenty

✧ *Student Reference Book*, p. 120

Adjusting the Activity To extend the investigation comparing areas of the two pizzas, have students make scale drawings of the pizzas as concentric circles using the scale: 1 centimeter represents 1 inch. The Geometry Template is the perfect tool for creating such a scale drawing.

The inner circle will represent the 8-inch pizza. Students cut off the part of the larger circle that is not covered by the smaller one. Then they cut this rim into pieces and place it inside the smaller circle. They will find that the rim will more than cover the smaller circle, thus proving that the 12-inch pizza has more than twice as much area as the 8-inch pizza.

✦Using Ratios to Describe Size Changes
(*Student Reference Book,* pp. 119–121)

WHOLE-CLASS DISCUSSION 

Discuss the essay on *Student Reference Book,* pages 119–121. Include the following ideas in the discussion:

▷ The **size-change factor** is really an ***n*-to-1 ratio:** a ratio of some number to 1. It tells the amount of enlargement or reduction that occurs in a size-change situation. For example, a size-change factor of 3X describes an **enlargement** in which each length is 3 times the size of the corresponding length in the original object. That is, the ratio of the enlargement to the original is 3 to 1.

$$\frac{\text{enlarged length}}{\text{original length}} = \frac{3}{1}$$

The same size-change factor applies to every length in the original figure. A size-change factor that is less than 1 (such as 0.4X) describes a **reduction** of the original figure.

$$\frac{\text{reduced length}}{\text{original length}} = \frac{0.4}{1}$$

▷ The size-change factor applies to lengths only, not to areas, volumes, or angle sizes. This is what misled Zach in the Math Message: The size-change factor of the diameters from the 8-inch pizza to the 12-inch pizza is 1.5. Zach interpreted this ratio to mean that a 12-inch pizza is only 1.5 times larger than an 8-inch pizza, which is less than the increase in price. But the area changes by a factor of 2.25, more than the increase in price and *considerably* more than the 1.5 size-change factor.

To further emphasize this idea, you might have students draw a 5-by-5 square on a sheet of grid paper. Then ask them to draw a 2X enlargement of the square (a 10-by-10 square). All lengths are multiplied by 2, but the area of the enlargement is 4 times the area of the original. All angles of the square are 90°, in both the original and the enlargement. Students will work with this important concept in Problem 5 on journal page 323 and in Problem 2 on *Math Masters,* page 138.

▷ The size-change factor is often identified by other names, such as "scale factor" or "scale." Many different notations are used to indicate this ratio. The following examples show a variety of notations:

aX	scale 1:a	$\frac{1}{a}$ actual size
0.aX	$\frac{1}{a}$ scale	
a power	a unit 1 = b unit 2	

In practice, any of these notations will serve. But for students, more explicit notations are often preferable since they are easier to understand. For this reason, we use $\frac{\text{changed size}}{\text{original size}} = \frac{a}{1}$ whenever possible, even though it is not the most common.

Each size-change factor has two possible forms, because a ratio may be expressed in either order. Context will always dictate which size-change factor is being used, and students are not likely to be confused in this regard. For example, for 8X binoculars, it is clear that the size-change factor 8 refers to the enlargement of the object viewed and the size-change factor $\frac{1}{8}$ to the size of the object viewed without binoculars compared to the size viewed through the binoculars.

▷ Make a table on the board or overhead and record each new notation (from the essay) as it arises. Then record the size-change factor for this notation. Also enter the reciprocal of the size-change factor. For example, with the binoculars and map examples, you might write the notation from the top table in the margin.

With the copy machine, doll house, and model railroad examples, you might write notation from the second table in the margin.

▷ In cases where two different units are used to convey size-change factor information, caution students to convert one of the quantities, so that both have the same unit, before making a ratio calculation. For example, for the architect's "$\frac{1}{4}$ inch represents 1 foot" scale, converting all units to inches means that 1 inch represents 48 inches, which yields the scale of 1:48.

NOTE: Caution students that at times they may see scales written in this way.

scale: 1 inch = 1 foot

The two measures are obviously not equal. The equal sign is being used as a symbol for the word *represents.*

Size-change	Size-change Factor $\frac{\text{changed length}}{\text{original length}}$
8X	$\frac{8}{1}$
scale 1:25,000	$\frac{1}{25{,}000}$

Size-change	Size-change Factor $\frac{\text{changed length}}{\text{original length}}$
0.5X	$\frac{0.5}{1}$
scale 1:12	$\frac{1}{12}$
scale 1:96	$\frac{1}{96}$

Enlargements

A copy machine was used to make a 2X enlargement of shapes on the Geometry Template.

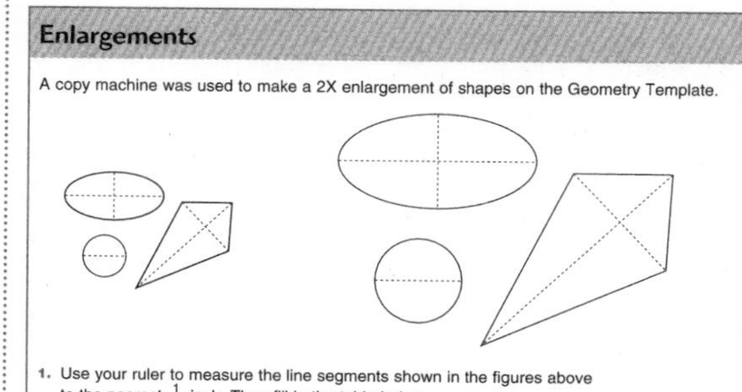

1. Use your ruler to measure the line segments shown in the figures above to the nearest $\frac{1}{16}$ inch. Then fill in the table below.

Line Segment	Length of Original	Length of Enlargement	Ratio of Enlargement to Original
Diameter of circle	$\frac{7}{16}$"	$\frac{7}{8}$"	$\frac{2}{1}$
Longer axis of ellipse	1"	2"	$\frac{2}{1}$
Shorter axis of ellipse	$\frac{1}{2}$"	1"	$\frac{2}{1}$
Longer side of kite	1"	2"	$\frac{2}{1}$
Shorter side of kite	$\frac{1}{2}$"	1"	$\frac{2}{1}$
Longer diagonal of kite	$1\frac{5}{16}$"	$2\frac{5}{8}$"	$\frac{2}{1}$
Shorter diagonal of kite	$\frac{11}{16}$"	$1\frac{3}{8}$"	$\frac{2}{1}$

2. Are the figures in the enlargement similar to the original figures? yes

3. What does a 3.5X enlargement mean? Sample answer: Each length in the enlarged figure is 3.5 times the corresponding length in the original figure.

STUDENT PAGE

Math Journal 2, p. 322

Map Scale

This map shows the downtown area of the city of Chicago. The shaded area shows the part of Chicago that was destroyed in the Chicago fire of 1871.

The map was drawn to a scale of 1:50,000. This means that each 1-inch length on the map represents 50,000 inches (about $\frac{3}{4}$ mile) of actual distance.

$$\frac{\text{map distance}}{\text{actual distance}} = \frac{1}{50{,}000}$$

1. Measure the distance on the map between Fullerton Parkway and Roosevelt Road, to the nearest $\frac{1}{4}$ inch. This is the approximate north-south length of the part that burned.
   Burn length on map = 5 inches

2. Measure the width of the part that burned, along Chicago Avenue, to the nearest $\frac{1}{4}$ inch. This is the approximate east-west length of the part that burned.
   Burn width on map = $1\frac{1}{2}$ inches

3. Use the map scale to find the actual length and width of the part of Chicago that burned.
   a. Actual burn length = 250,000 inches
   b. Actual burn width = 75,000 inches

4. Convert the answers in Problem 3 from inches to miles, to the nearest tenth of a mile.
   a. Actual burn length = 3.9 miles
   b. Actual burn width = 1.2 miles

5. Estimate the area of the part of Chicago that burned, to the nearest square mile.
   Area of part that burned About 5 square miles

STUDENT PAGE

Math Journal 2, p. 323

Solving Size-change Problems (*Math Journal 2,* pp. 322 and 323; *Student Reference Book,* pp. 119–121)

PARTNER ACTIVITY 

Assign the journal pages as partner work. Suggest that students keep the *Student Reference Book* open to pages 119–121 so that they can refer to vocabulary and examples of notation. For Problem 4 on page 323, students may need to look up the number of feet in a mile in the back of the journal or in the *Student Reference Book.* Reserve some time near the end of class for a discussion of answers.

ONGOING ASSESSMENT

Use students' answers to Problem 1 on journal page 322 to assess understanding of the ratios involved in enlarging the dimensions of an object.

2 Ongoing Learning & Practice

Rounding Quotients to the Nearest Tenth or Hundredth (*Math Journal 2,* p. 324)

INDEPENDENT ACTIVITY 

Students divide decimals by whole numbers. They round the quotients to the nearest tenth or hundredth.

ONGOING ASSESSMENT

Use this page to assess students' ability to solve division problems in which the remainder is not 0.

Rounding Quotients

Divide. Show your work in the space below.
In Problems 1–3, round your answers to the nearest tenth.

1. 97.6 ÷ 6 = 16.3
2. 74.9 / 32 = 2.3
3. 864.9 ÷ 15 = 57.7

In Problems 4–6, round your answers to the nearest hundredth.

4. 587.48 / 9 = 65.28
5. 307.4 ÷ 7 = 43.91
6. 696.1 / 68 = 10.24

7. Explain how you rounded the answer in Problem 6.
   Sample answer: I divided so the quotient would have 2 decimal places and then compared the remainder to the divisor. It was more than half, so I rounded the hundredth digit up.

STUDENT PAGE

Math Journal 2, p. 324

Math Boxes 8.9 (*Math Journal 2,* p. 325)

INDEPENDENT ACTIVITY 

Mixed Review Math Boxes in this lesson are paired with Math Boxes in Lesson 8.11. The skill in Problem 1 is a prerequisite for Unit 9.

✦ Study Link 8.9 (*Math Masters,* p. 350)

Home Connection Students calculate the size of original objects shown in scale drawings.

3 Options for Individualizing

✦ ENRICHMENT Investigating Map Scales

PARTNER ACTIVITY **15–30 min**

Social Studies Link Students use one of the available Internet map sites to locate their school. (See below for suggested sites.) Students conduct the search for their school in several different ways and compare results. For each search, students record the following information:

- ▷ How they conducted the search (by state, by city, by ZIP code, by street address, and so on)
- ▷ The map scale of the first map retrieved. (Students may need to measure, because map scale is often displayed on the screen as a bar with a label of miles, kilometers, and so on.)
- ▷ Whether or not they can find the exact location of their school from the initial map retrieved

If they cannot immediately locate the school, they should zoom in and see its location appear. Each time they zoom in, they should record the new map scale.

You might want all students to do the same searches at the same site, or you may want to assign different searches and sites to partnerships for later comparisons. As of this printing, two popular Internet map sites are listed below.

www.webcrawler-maps.excite.com/address/

www.maps.expedia.com/QuickMaps.asp

Students compare the results of their searches and discuss which searches resulted in locating the school. If students found the school by zooming in (not all searches will result in locating the school even with zooming in), ask at what map scale they were first able to locate the school.

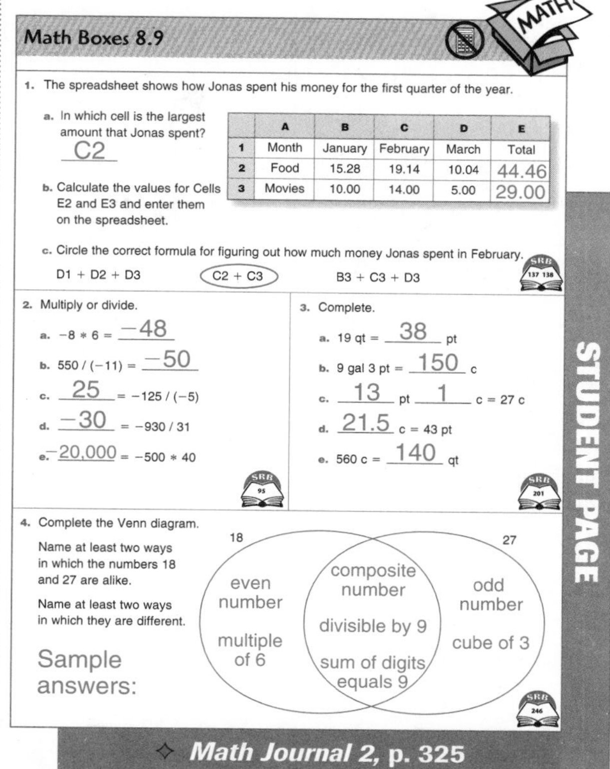

Math Boxes 8.9

1. The spreadsheet shows how Jonas spent his money for the first quarter of the year.

a. In which cell is the largest amount that Jonas spent? C2

b. Calculate the values for Cells E2 and E3 and enter them on the spreadsheet.

	A	B	C	D	E
1	Month	January	February	March	Total
2	Food	15.28	19.14	10.04	44.46
3	Movies	10.00	14.00	5.00	29.00

c. Circle the correct formula for figuring out how much money Jonas spent in February.

D1 + D2 + D3   (C2 + C3)   B3 + C3 + D3

2. Multiply or divide.

a. −8 ∗ 6 = −48

b. 550 / (−11) = −50

c. 25 = −125 / (−5)

d. −30 = −930 / 31

e. −20,000 = −500 ∗ 40

3. Complete.

a. 19 qt = 38 pt

b. 9 gal 3 pt = 150 c

c. 13 pt 1 c = 27 c

d. 21.5 c = 43 pt

e. 560 c = 140 qt

4. Complete the Venn diagram.

Name at least two ways in which the numbers 18 and 27 are alike.

Name at least two ways in which they are different.

Sample answers:

✦ *Math Journal 2,* p. 325

STUDENT PAGE

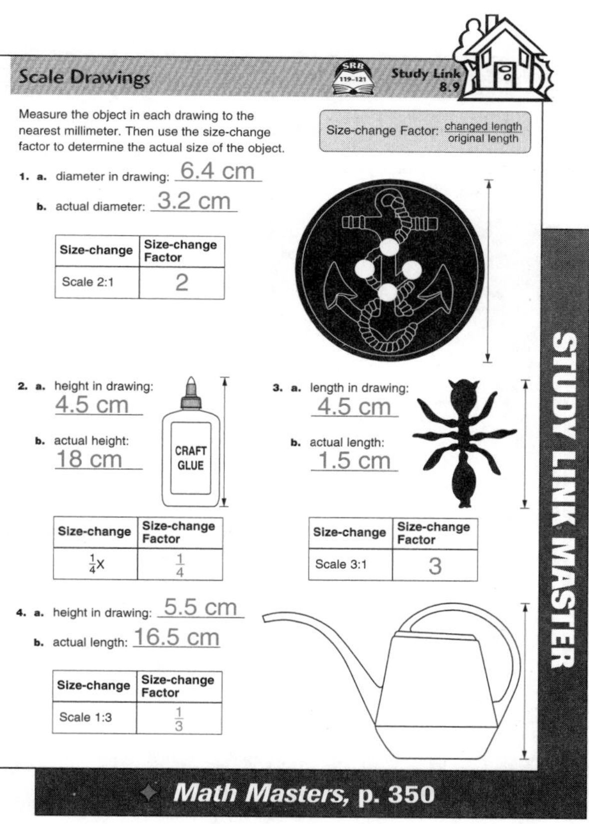

Scale Drawings Study Link 8.9

Measure the object in each drawing to the nearest millimeter. Then use the size-change factor to determine the actual size of the object.

Size-change Factor: $\frac{\text{changed length}}{\text{original length}}$

1. a. diameter in drawing: 6.4 cm

b. actual diameter: 3.2 cm

Size-change	Size-change Factor
Scale 2:1	2

2. a. height in drawing: 4.5 cm

b. actual height: 18 cm

Size-change	Size-change Factor
$\frac{1}{4}$X	$\frac{1}{4}$

3. a. length in drawing: 4.5 cm

b. actual length: 1.5 cm

Size-change	Size-change Factor
Scale 3:1	3

4. a. height in drawing: 5.5 cm

b. actual length: 16.5 cm

Size-change	Size-change Factor
Scale 1:3	$\frac{1}{3}$

✦ *Math Masters,* p. 350

STUDY LINK MASTER

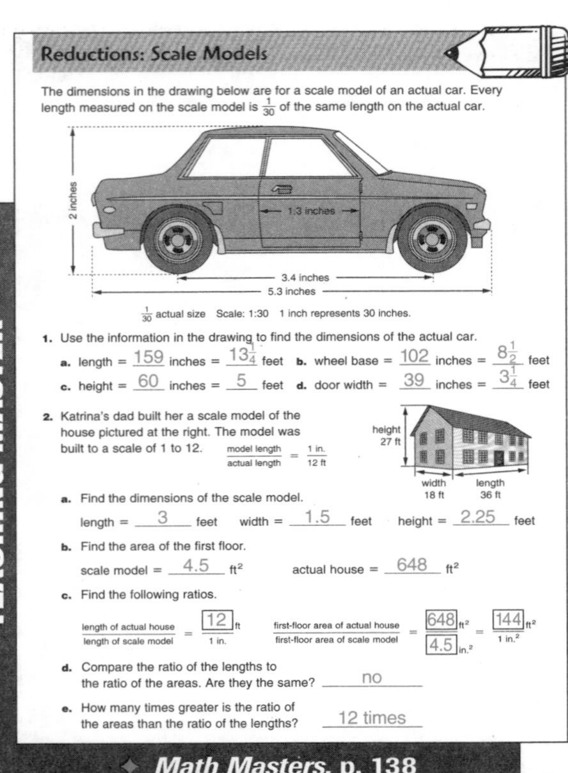

Reductions: Scale Models

The dimensions in the drawing below are for a scale model of an actual car. Every length measured on the scale model is $\frac{1}{30}$ of the same length on the actual car.

$\frac{1}{30}$ actual size Scale: 1:30 1 inch represents 30 inches.

1. Use the information in the drawing to find the dimensions of the actual car.
   a. length = 159 inches = $13\frac{1}{4}$ feet b. wheel base = 102 inches = $8\frac{1}{2}$ feet
   c. height = 60 inches = 5 feet d. door width = 39 inches = $3\frac{1}{4}$ feet
2. Katrina's dad built her a scale model of the house pictured at the right. The model was built to a scale of 1 to 12. $\frac{\text{model length}}{\text{actual length}} = \frac{1 \text{ in.}}{12 \text{ ft}}$

   a. Find the dimensions of the scale model.
      length = 3 feet width = 1.5 feet height = 2.25 feet
   b. Find the area of the first floor.
      scale model = 4.5 ft² actual house = 648 ft²
   c. Find the following ratios.
      $\frac{\text{length of actual house}}{\text{length of scale model}} = \frac{12 \text{ ft}}{1 \text{ in.}}$ $\frac{\text{first-floor area of actual house}}{\text{first-floor area of scale model}} = \frac{648 \text{ ft}^2}{4.5 \text{ in.}^2} = \frac{144 \text{ ft}^2}{1 \text{ in.}^2}$
   d. Compare the ratio of the lengths to the ratio of the areas. Are they the same? no
   e. How many times greater is the ratio of the areas than the ratio of the lengths? 12 times

TEACHING MASTER

Math Masters, p. 138

EXTRA PRACTICE Finding Dimensions of Objects Based on Scale Models

(*Math Masters*, p. 138)

PARTNER ACTIVITY  **15–30 min** 

Students study scale drawings of a car and a house and calculate their actual dimensions. The drawing of the car shows the actual size of the scale model. It can be used to emphasize that a size-change factor applies only to lengths. Every length measured on the scale model is $\frac{1}{30}$ of that same length on the real car. Yet it is obvious that it would take more than thirty model cars of this size to fill the real car. So the size-change factor, which applies to lengths, does not apply to volumes.

EXTRA PRACTICE Investigating the Relationship between Perimeter and Size-change Factor (*Math Masters*, p. 139)

INDEPENDENT ACTIVITY  **5–15 min** 

Students measure the dimensions of polygons and determine the enlargement or reduction factors. This activity is a review of scale factors from *Fifth Grade Everyday Mathematics*.

LANGUAGE DIVERSITY Illustrating Terms

PARTNER ACTIVITY **15–30 min**

Pair a student learning English with a proficient English speaker. Have students work together to make a small poster illustrating the meaning of "enlargement" and "reduction." Direct them to write and place labels on the poster. The poster can then be displayed in the classroom to facilitate vocabulary development.

PLANNING AHEAD

Pattern blocks are used in Lesson 8.10. Each partnership will need at least 16 triangles and 10 trapezoids. Other shapes may be useful but are not required. If you do not have these materials, you might be able to borrow them from a teacher in Grades 1 through 5.

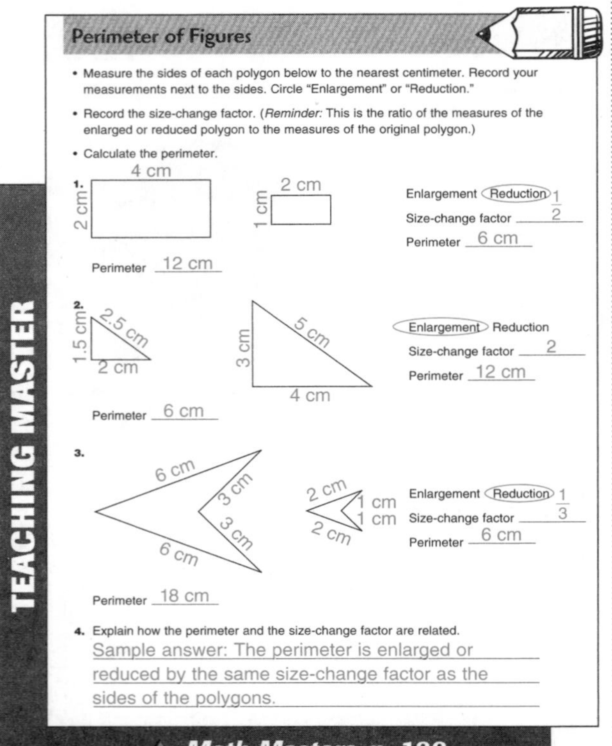

Perimeter of Figures

- Measure the sides of each polygon below to the nearest centimeter. Record your measurements next to the sides. Circle "Enlargement" or "Reduction."
- Record the size-change factor. (*Reminder:* This is the ratio of the measures of the enlarged or reduced polygon to the measures of the original polygon.)
- Calculate the perimeter.

1. 4 cm, 2 cm; 2 cm, 1 cm
   Perimeter 12 cm
   Enlargement (Reduction) Size-change factor $\frac{1}{2}$ Perimeter 6 cm
2. 2.5 cm, 1.5 cm, 2 cm; 5 cm, 3 cm, 4 cm
   Perimeter 6 cm
   (Enlargement) Reduction Size-change factor 2 Perimeter 12 cm
3. 6 cm, 3 cm, 3 cm, 6 cm; 2 cm, 1 cm, 1 cm, 2 cm
   Perimeter 18 cm
   Enlargement (Reduction) Size-change factor $\frac{1}{3}$ Perimeter 6 cm
4. Explain how the perimeter and the size-change factor are related.
   Sample answer: The perimeter is enlarged or reduced by the same size-change factor as the sides of the polygons.

TEACHING MASTER

Math Masters, p. 139

8.10 Similar Polygons

OBJECTIVES **To explore the properties of similar polygons; and to use ratios to find the lengths of corresponding sides of similar polygons.**

summaries	materials
1 Teaching the Lesson	
Students explore the properties of similar polygons by constructing similar polygons out of pattern blocks and by drawing them with drawing and measuring tools. They also use ratios to find the lengths of corresponding sides of similar polygons. [Geometry; Patterns, Functions, and Algebra]	☐ *Math Journal 2,* pp. 326 and 327 ☐ *Student Reference Book,* p. 167 ☐ Study Link 8.9 ☐ Per partnership: 16 green triangle and 10 red trapezoid pattern blocks ☐ overhead pattern blocks (optional) ☐ protractor ☐ compass ☐ ruler ☐ Geometry Template (optional) ***See* Advance Preparation**
2 Ongoing Learning & Practice	
Students use division to rename fractions as decimals. [Operations and Computation] Students play *Spoon Scramble.* [Numeration] Students practice and maintain skills through Math Boxes and Study Link activities.	☐ *Math Journal 2,* pp. 328 and 329 ☐ *Student Reference Book,* p. 305 ☐ Study Link Master (*Math Masters,* p. 351) ☐ Per group of 4 students: 3 spoons ☐ *Spoon Scramble* cards (*Math Journal 1,* Activity Sheets 1 and 2) ☐ 3" × 5" index cards (optional) ***See* Advance Preparation**
3 Options for Individualizing	
Enrichment Students use a grid to draw an enlargement of a picture. [Geometry] **Enrichment** Students use small rubber bands to draw an enlargement of a triangle. [Geometry] **Enrichment** Students reduce a design on a grid and find the scale factor of the reduction. [Geometry]	☐ *Student Reference Book,* p. 317 ☐ Teaching Masters (*Math Masters,* pp. 8, 9, 140, and 141) ☐ 2 identical, small rubber bands ***See* Advance Preparation**

Additional Information

Advance Preparation For Part 1, you will need 16 green triangle and 10 red trapezoid pattern blocks per partnership. You may need to borrow extra blocks from a teacher in a lower grade. If pattern blocks are not available, consider putting off this lesson until you can obtain some, or students can use the pattern-block shapes on their Geometry Templates. For the second activity in Part 2, read the directions for playing *Spoon Scramble* on *Student Reference Book,* page 305. For the first two Enrichment activities in Part 3, make copies of *Math Masters,* pages 8 and 9 available to students who want to make enlargements or reductions of drawings.

Vocabulary • **similar figures** • **congruent figures** • **similar polygons** • **corresponding sides** • **corresponding angles**

Getting Started

Mental Math and Reflexes

How many marbles are in the bag if

- 12 marbles are $\frac{1}{4}$ of the total? 48
- 9 marbles are $\frac{3}{5}$ of the total? 15
- 16 marbles are $\frac{4}{9}$ of the total? 36
- 15 marbles are $\frac{5}{8}$ of the total? 24
- 24 marbles are $\frac{8}{11}$ of the total? 33

Find the total. It might help to find unit ratios as a first step in finding the solution.

- 8 is $\frac{1}{3}$ of what number? 24
- 20 is $\frac{4}{5}$ of what number? 25
- 18 is $\frac{6}{7}$ of what number? 21
- 27 is $\frac{3}{4}$ of what number? 36

Math Message

Read page 167 in your Student Reference Book *and solve the Check Your Understanding problems.*

Study Link 8.9 Follow-Up

Go over the answers with the class.

1 Teaching the Lesson

✦ Math Message Follow-Up (*Student Reference Book,* p. 167)

WHOLE-CLASS DISCUSSION

Discuss page 167 of the *Student Reference Book* with the class. Make sure that the following points are addressed:

- **Similar figures** have the same shape but are not necessarily the same size. **Congruent figures** have the same shape and also the same size. Thus, congruent figures are always similar, but similar figures are not necessarily congruent.
- Use the first example to introduce **similar polygons.** Triangle *HOG* is a 2X enlargement of triangle *BAT*. Side *HO* is a 2X enlargement of side *BA;* sides *HO* and *BA* are called **corresponding sides.** Sides *AT* and *OG* and sides *TB* and *GH* are two other pairs of corresponding sides of the triangles; they have the same size-change factor. Pairs of corresponding sides in pictures of similar polygons are often identified by equal numbers of slash marks.

STUDENT PAGE

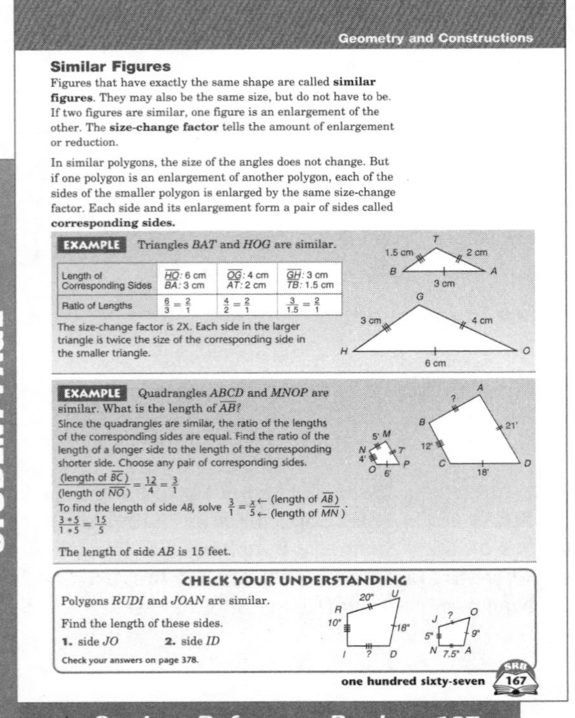

Geometry and Constructions

Similar Figures

Figures that have exactly the same shape are called **similar figures**. They may also be the same size, but do not have to be. If two figures are similar, one figure is an enlargement of the other. The **size-change factor** tells the amount of enlargement or reduction.

In similar polygons, the size of the angles does not change. But if one polygon is an enlargement of another polygon, each of the sides of the smaller polygon is enlarged by the same size-change factor. Each side and its enlargement form a pair of sides called **corresponding sides.**

EXAMPLE Triangles *BAT* and *HOG* are similar.

Length of Corresponding Sides	$\overline{HO}$: 6 cm $\overline{BA}$: 3 cm	$\overline{OG}$: 4 cm $\overline{AT}$: 2 cm	$\overline{GH}$: 3 cm $\overline{TB}$: 1.5 cm
Ratio of Lengths	$\frac{6}{3} = \frac{2}{1}$	$\frac{4}{2} = \frac{2}{1}$	$\frac{3}{1.5} = \frac{2}{1}$

The size-change factor is 2X. Each side in the larger triangle is twice the size of the corresponding side in the smaller triangle.

EXAMPLE Quadrangles *ABCD* and *MNOP* are similar. What is the length of $\overline{AB}$?

Since the quadrangles are similar, the ratio of the lengths of the corresponding sides are equal. Find the ratio of the length of a longer side to the length of the corresponding shorter side. Choose any pair of corresponding sides.

$\frac{(\text{length of } \overline{BC})}{(\text{length of } \overline{NO})} = \frac{12}{4} = \frac{3}{1}$

To find the length of side *AB*, solve $\frac{3}{1} = \frac{x}{5}$ ← (length of $\overline{AB}$) ← (length of $\overline{MN}$).

$\frac{3 * 5}{1 * 5} = \frac{15}{5}$

The length of side *AB* is 15 feet.

CHECK YOUR UNDERSTANDING

Polygons *RUDI* and *JOAN* are similar.

Find the length of these sides.

1. side *JO*
2. side *ID*

Check your answers on page 378.

one hundred sixty-seven SRB 167

✧ *Student Reference Book,* p. 167

- ▷ The ratio of the lengths of the corresponding sides of similar polygons is the same for each pair of corresponding sides.
- ▷ **Corresponding angles** are formed by pairs of corresponding sides that meet at a vertex. Point out that the size of corresponding angles does not change—pairs of corresponding angles are congruent.
- ▷ If the ratio of the lengths of each pair of corresponding sides of two polygons is 1 to 1 and all corresponding angles are congruent, then the polygons are congruent.

Go over the method shown in the second example for finding the lengths of the sides of similar polygons. This method involves finding the ratio to express the size-change factor and then determining the appropriate equivalent ratio. Check that students were able to solve the Check Your Understanding problems.

✦Using Pattern Blocks to Explore Similar Polygons

WHOLE-CLASS ACTIVITY

Each partnership will need at least 16 green triangle pattern blocks. Place one green triangle pattern block on the overhead projector. Tell students that the length of each side of the triangle is 1 unit.

Ask students to use only green pattern-block triangles to construct a similar triangle whose sides are twice as long as the corresponding sides of a single pattern-block triangle. (If no pattern blocks are available, students can use the shapes on their Geometry Templates.) This task should take no more than a couple of minutes; ask a volunteer to display the figure on the overhead.

Ask: *What is the ratio of the length of each side of the larger triangle to the corresponding side of the smaller triangle?* 2 to 1 *Of the length of each side of the smaller triangle to the corresponding side of the larger triangle?* $\frac{1}{2}$ to 1

Students should note that each angle of the new triangle is formed by an angle of the original triangle; thus, pairs of corresponding angles are congruent.

Ask: *How many times larger is the area of the large triangle than the area of the small triangle?* 4 times larger Ask students to explain how they figured out the answer.

(Activity continues on the next page.)

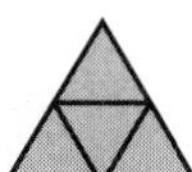

When the sides of a triangle are twice the length of the sides of the original triangle, the area of the larger triangle is 4 times the area of the original.

When the sides of a triangle are 3 times the length of the sides of the original triangle, the area of the larger triangle is 3^2, or 9 times the area of the original.

When the sides of a triangle are 4 times the length of the sides of the original triangle, the area of the larger triangle is 4^2, or 16 times the area of the original.

Now ask students to construct two additional triangles similar to the original green triangle—one whose corresponding sides are three times as long and one whose corresponding sides are four times as long. Again, students may use only pattern-block triangles. Have volunteers display their solutions on the overhead, and pose the same questions as asked on page 661. Discuss the following observations:

- ▷ The ratio of the lengths of corresponding sides is 3 to 1. The area of the new triangle is 9 times the area of the original.
- ▷ The ratio of the lengths of corresponding sides is 4 to1. The area of the new triangle is 16 times the area of the original.
- ▷ Ask students how many triangles would be needed to construct a triangle with sides 5 times as long as a small green triangle? 25 triangles

Conclusion

Each triangle constructed of pattern-block triangles is similar to each of the others (and to a single pattern-block triangle), because the ratios of the lengths of pairs of corresponding sides are equal.

Adjusting the Activity To extend the activity, have students explain or show why the area is 2 squared as large (or 4 times as large) when the length is two times as large and 3 squared as large (or 9 times as large) when the length is tripled. Students might think about the answer as a general pattern:

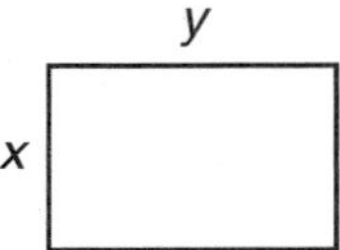

- ▷ The area of the original rectangle is $x * y$ or xy.
- ▷ The area of the doubled rectangle is $2x * 2y$ or 2^2xy or $4xy$.
- ▷ The area of the tripled rectangle is $3x * 3y$ or 3^2xy or $9xy$, and so on.

Have students predict what happens if the length is five times as large. The area is 5 squared as large, or 25 times as large.

✦ Investigating Similar Polygons Using Pattern Blocks and Drawing and Measuring Tools
(*Math Journal 2,* p. 326)

PARTNER ACTIVITY

In Problem 1, partners use a red pattern-block trapezoid to construct a trapezoid twice the size of a single pattern-block trapezoid. In Problem 2, they use drawing and measuring tools of their choice to draw an enlargement of the pattern-block trapezoid. Problem 3 is quite challenging. Do not expect everyone to find a solution.

Adjusting the Activity Some students may find it easier to trace pattern blocks than to use their templates to record their answers.

When students have completed at least the first two problems, bring the class together to demonstrate solutions on the overhead. You might want to postpone discussion of Problem 3 so that interested students who have not yet found a solution can work on it in their spare time.

To solve Problem 2, copy some of the angles of the original trapezoid and draw sides that are three times as long as the sides in the original trapezoid. This can be done in several ways. The angles can be measured with a protractor, or the corners of the pattern-block trapezoid or trapezoid template can be used to trace the angles. The sides can also be measured with a ruler, or a compass can be used to mark off sides that are triple the length of the sides of the original trapezoid. Encourage students to propose alternative strategies.

✦ Solving Problems Involving Similar Figures
(*Math Journal 2,* p. 327)

INDEPENDENT ACTIVITY 

Students complete journal page 327 independently, using techniques for working with ratios from previous lessons. Circulate and assess student progress.

Similar Polygons

1. Use pattern-block trapezoids to construct a trapezoid whose sides are twice the length of the corresponding sides of a single pattern-block trapezoid. Then use your Geometry Template to record what you did. Sample answer:

2. Draw a trapezoid whose sides are 3 times the length of a single pattern-block trapezoid. You may use any drawing or measuring tools you wish, such as a compass, a ruler, a protractor, the trapezoid on your Geometry Template, or a trapezoid pattern block.

Which tools did you use? Answers vary.

3. Cover the trapezoid you drew in Problem 2 with pattern-block trapezoids. Then use your Geometry Template to record the way you covered the trapezoid.

Sample answer:

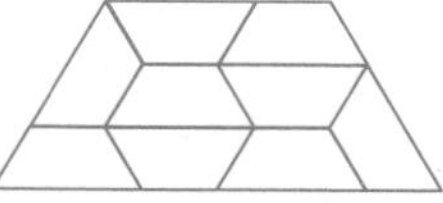

STUDENT PAGE

✧ *Math Journal 2,* p. 326

Similar Polygons (cont.)

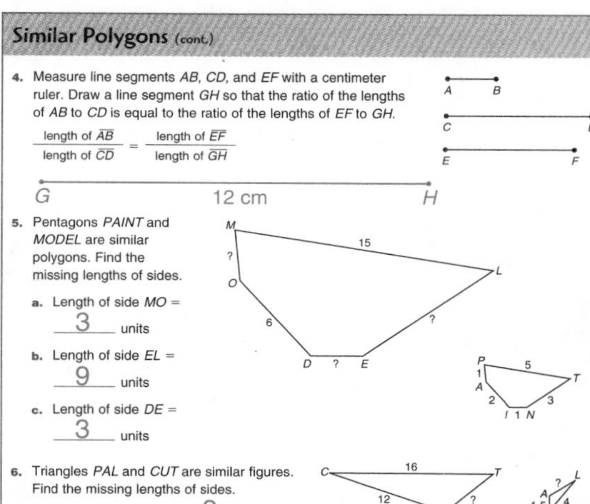

4. Measure line segments *AB*, *CD*, and *EF* with a centimeter ruler. Draw a line segment *GH* so that the ratio of the lengths of *AB* to *CD* is equal to the ratio of the lengths of *EF* to *GH*.

$\frac{\text{length of } \overline{AB}}{\text{length of } \overline{CD}} = \frac{\text{length of } \overline{EF}}{\text{length of } \overline{GH}}$

5. Pentagons *PAINT* and *MODEL* are similar polygons. Find the missing lengths of sides.

a. Length of side *MO* = 3 units

b. Length of side *EL* = 9 units

c. Length of side *DE* = 3 units

6. Triangles *PAL* and *CUT* are similar figures. Find the missing lengths of sides.

a. Length of side *AL* = 3 units

b. Length of side *UT* = 6 units

7. Alexi is looking at a map of his town. The scale given on the map is 1 inch represents $\frac{1}{2}$ mile. Alexi measures the distance from his home to school on the map—it's $3\frac{3}{4}$ inches. What is the actual distance from his home to school?

$1\frac{7}{8}$ miles

8. For a school fair in the cafeteria, Nina wants to construct a scale model of the 984-foot-tall Eiffel Tower. She plans to use a scale of 1 to 6—every length of the scale model will be $\frac{1}{6}$ of the actual size of the Eiffel Tower. Does this scale seem reasonable? If yes, explain why. If no, suggest a more reasonable scale.

Sample answer: No. A more reasonable scale would be 200 to 1. The model would then be about 5 feet tall.

STUDENT PAGE

✧ *Math Journal 2,* p. 327

STUDENT PAGE

Renaming Fractions as Decimals

Rename each fraction as a decimal, rounded to the nearest hundredth, by dividing the numerator by the denominator.

Example $\frac{3}{7} = ?$

Step 1 Estimate the quotient: $\frac{3}{7}$ is a little less than $\frac{1}{2}$; so $\frac{3}{7}$ is a little less than 0.50.

Step 2 To get two decimals places in the quotient, rewrite 3 as 3.00; $\frac{3}{7} = \frac{3.00}{7}$

Step 3 Divide, ignoring the decimal point.

Step 4 Use the estimate to place the decimal point in your quotient: 0.42

$$\begin{array}{r|l} 7\overline{)300} & \\ -\ 280 & 40 \\ 20 & \\ -\ 14 & 2 \end{array}$$

Step 5 Round the answer: Since the remainder, 6, is more than half of the dividend, 7, round up: 0.43

Estimates vary.

1. $\frac{5}{7}$ a. Estimate A little more than 0.70
   b. Answer 0.71
2. $\frac{8}{9}$ a. Estimate About 0.90
   b. Answer 0.89
3. $\frac{5}{6}$ a. Estimate A little more than 0.80
   b. Answer 0.83
4. $\frac{2}{15}$ a. Estimate A little more than 0.10
   b. Answer 0.13

Challenge

5. $\frac{15}{16}$ a. Estimate A little more than 0.90
   b. Answer 0.94
6. Explain what you would do to find the decimal equivalent for $\frac{3}{7}$ to the thousandths place (three decimal places).
   Sample answer: I would add another zero to the end of the dividend.

◇ *Math Journal 2,* p. 328

NOTE: In Lesson 8.11, decimal divisors are introduced with the partial-quotients algorithm, a skill that can be postponed until later if students are still struggling with the algorithms.

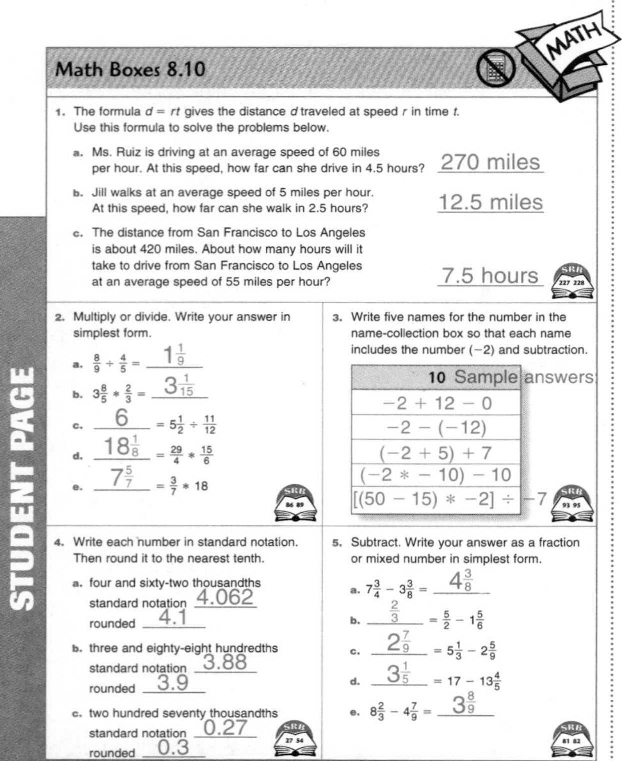

STUDENT PAGE

Math Boxes 8.10

1. The formula $d = rt$ gives the distance d traveled at speed r in time t. Use this formula to solve the problems below.
   a. Ms. Ruiz is driving at an average speed of 60 miles per hour. At this speed, how far can she drive in 4.5 hours? 270 miles
   b. Jill walks at an average speed of 5 miles per hour. At this speed, how far can she walk in 2.5 hours? 12.5 miles
   c. The distance from San Francisco to Los Angeles is about 420 miles. About how many hours will it take to drive from San Francisco to Los Angeles at an average speed of 55 miles per hour? 7.5 hours
2. Multiply or divide. Write your answer in simplest form.
   a. $\frac{8}{9} \div \frac{4}{5} = 1\frac{1}{9}$
   b. $3\frac{8}{5} * \frac{2}{3} = 3\frac{1}{15}$
   c. $6 = 5\frac{1}{2} \div \frac{11}{12}$
   d. $18\frac{1}{8} = \frac{29}{4} * \frac{15}{6}$
   e. $7\frac{5}{7} = \frac{3}{7} * 18$
3. Write five names for the number in the name-collection box so that each name includes the number (−2) and subtraction.

10 Sample answers:
−2 + 12 − 0
−2 − (−12)
(−2 + 5) + 7
(−2 ∗ − 10) − 10
[(50 − 15) ∗ −2] ÷ −7

4. Write each number in standard notation. Then round it to the nearest tenth.
   a. four and sixty-two thousandths
      standard notation 4.062
      rounded 4.1
   b. three and eighty-eight hundredths
      standard notation 3.88
      rounded 3.9
   c. two hundred seventy thousandths
      standard notation 0.27
      rounded 0.3
5. Subtract. Write your answer as a fraction or mixed number in simplest form.
   a. $7\frac{3}{4} - 3\frac{3}{8} = 4\frac{3}{8}$
   b. $\frac{2}{3} = \frac{5}{2} - 1\frac{5}{6}$
   c. $2\frac{7}{9} = 5\frac{1}{3} - 2\frac{5}{9}$
   d. $3\frac{1}{5} = 17 - 13\frac{4}{5}$
   e. $8\frac{2}{3} - 4\frac{7}{9} = 3\frac{8}{9}$

◇ *Math Journal 2,* p. 329

2 Ongoing Learning & Practice

✦ Renaming Fractions as Decimals Using Division (*Math Journal 2,* p. 328)

PARTNER ACTIVITY

Students use division to rename fractions as decimals. Pose a problem, such as, "Rename the fraction $\frac{2}{7}$ to two decimal places." Go over the following steps with the class.

Step 1: Estimate.

$\frac{2}{7}$ is a little more than $\frac{2}{8}$. Since $\frac{2}{8} = \frac{1}{4} = 0.25$, $\frac{2}{7}$ is a little more than 0.25.

Step 2: Rewrite the numerator with a 0 for each decimal place needed. $\frac{2}{7} = \frac{2.00}{7}$

Step 3: Divide 2.00 by 7. Remember to ignore the decimal point for now and divide 200 by 7.

$$\begin{array}{r|l} 7\overline{)200} & \\ -\ 140 & 20 \\ 60 & \\ -\ 56 & 8 \\ 4 & 28 \end{array}$$

Step 4: Use the estimate to place the decimal point in the quotient. Since the estimate was a little more than 0.25, the decimal point should be placed before the 2. Thus, $\frac{2}{7}$ is 0.28 to 2 decimal places.

Check the answer with a calculator. Ask: *How would you round the answer to the nearest hundredth?* The remainder, 4, is more than half of the divisor, 7. Therefore, round the answer up to 0.29.

Pose a few similar problems. Have students rename each fraction as a decimal to the nearest hundredth. *Suggestions:* $\frac{3}{8}$ 0.38; $\frac{5}{6}$ 0.83; $\frac{4}{9}$ 0.44; $\frac{5}{7}$ 0.71; $\frac{9}{13}$ 0.69

ONGOING ASSESSMENT

Use the problems on this page to assess students' comfort with decimal dividends and with estimating answers to decimal division problems.

If students need more practice, consider adding two division problems to the back of their Study Links for extra practice.

✦ Playing *Spoon Scramble* (*Student Reference Book,* p. 305; *Spoon Scramble* cards)

SMALL-GROUP ACTIVITY

Students play *Spoon Scramble* to practice finding equivalent fraction expressions. The game was suggested in Lesson 4.12.

Students could create their own set of cards. Each student cuts two index cards in half. Each student chooses a number and writes four different expressions for it, one on each card. Make sure that everyone is using the same writing tool and writes the expression in the same place on the card.

Students check one another's cards to make sure that all four expressions are equivalent. Have groups trade cards so that they cannot look for their own sets of cards once the game begins.

✦ Math Boxes 8.10 (*Math Journal 2,* p. 329)

INDEPENDENT ACTIVITY 

Mixed Review Math Boxes in this lesson are paired with Math Boxes in Lesson 8.12. The skill in Problem 1 is a prerequisite for Unit 9.

✦ Study Link 8.10 (*Math Masters,* p. 351)

Home Connection Students find the lengths of sides of similar polygons. They determine whether the size-change factor for an enlargement or reduction applies to the perimeter of a polygon.

3 Options for Individualizing

✦ ENRICHMENT Using a Grid to Draw an Enlargement of a Picture (*Student Reference Book,* p. 317; *Math Masters,* p. 8)

INDEPENDENT ACTIVITY  **15–30 min**

Page 317 of the *Student Reference Book* describes a procedure for creating an enlargement of a simple drawing. Students might want to pursue this project at home or during free time in class. If so, they will need copies of 1-inch grids (*Math Masters,* page 8).

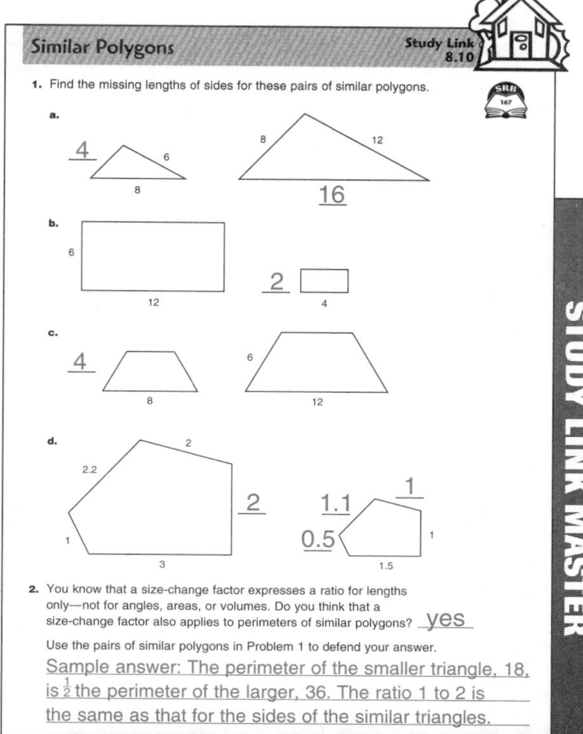

STUDY LINK MASTER

Similar Polygons — Study Link 8.10

1. Find the missing lengths of sides for these pairs of similar polygons.

a. Smaller triangle: 4, 6, 8; larger triangle: 8, 12, 16

b. Larger rectangle: 6, 12; smaller rectangle: 2, 4

c. Smaller trapezoid: 4, 8; larger trapezoid: 6, 12

d. Larger polygon: 2.2, 2, 2, 3, 1; smaller polygon: 1.1, 1, 1, 1.5, 0.5

2. You know that a size-change factor expresses a ratio for lengths only—not for angles, areas, or volumes. Do you think that a size-change factor also applies to perimeters of similar polygons? yes

Use the pairs of similar polygons in Problem 1 to defend your answer.

Sample answer: The perimeter of the smaller triangle, 18, is $\frac{1}{2}$ the perimeter of the larger, 36. The ratio 1 to 2 is the same as that for the sides of the similar triangles.

✧ *Math Masters,* p. 351

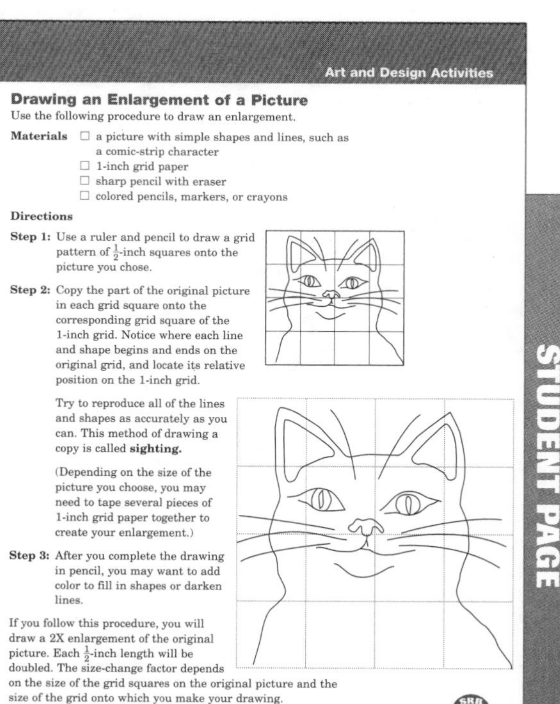

STUDENT PAGE

Art and Design Activities

Drawing an Enlargement of a Picture

Use the following procedure to draw an enlargement.

Materials
- ☐ a picture with simple shapes and lines, such as a comic-strip character
- ☐ 1-inch grid paper
- ☐ sharp pencil with eraser
- ☐ colored pencils, markers, or crayons

Directions

Step 1: Use a ruler and pencil to draw a grid pattern of $\frac{1}{2}$-inch squares onto the picture you chose.

Step 2: Copy the part of the original picture in each grid square onto the corresponding grid square of the 1-inch grid. Notice where each line and shape begins and ends on the original grid, and locate its relative position on the 1-inch grid.

Try to reproduce all of the lines and shapes as accurately as you can. This method of drawing a copy is called **sighting.**

(Depending on the size of the picture you choose, you may need to tape several pieces of 1-inch grid paper together to create your enlargement.)

Step 3: After you complete the drawing in pencil, you may want to add color to fill in shapes or darken lines.

If you follow this procedure, you will draw a 2X enlargement of the original picture. Each $\frac{1}{2}$-inch length will be doubled. The size-change factor depends on the size of the grid squares on the original picture and the size of the grid onto which you make your drawing.

three hundred seventeen 317

✧ *Student Reference Book,* p. 317

✦ ENRICHMENT Enlarging a Triangle with Rubber Bands (*Math Masters,* p. 140)

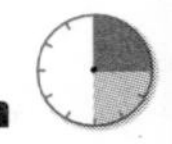

PARTNER ACTIVITY **15–30 min**

Students use knotted rubber bands of equal size to double the size of a triangle. Extend this activity by asking students to guess how they might triple the size of a triangle.

✦ ENRICHMENT Reducing Designs (*Math Masters,* pp. 9 and 141)

INDEPENDENT ACTIVITY  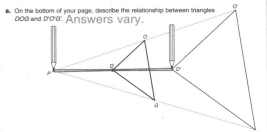 **15–30 min**

Portfolio Ideas

Students reduce the design shown on *Math Masters,* page 141. Then they determine the scale factor of their reductions. As an extension, students can create their own designs on a centimeter grid (*Math Masters,* page 9) and then enlarge or reduce them. You might want to collect students' work in a class book.

PLANNING AHEAD

The data students collected for Study Link 8.8 will be needed for the next lesson.

TEACHING MASTER

Enlarging a Triangle with Rubber Bands

Materials

- ❑ 2 rubber bands of the same size, knotted as shown
- ❑ 2 pencils
- ❑ a large piece of paper

1. Draw a triangle. Label the vertices *D, O,* and *G.*
2. Draw a point *P* straight out from point *D.* Make the distance between points *P* and *D* greater than the length of *one unstretched* rubber band.
3. Partner A puts his or her pencil point through one end of the knotted rubber bands and places the pencil on point *P.*
4. Partner B puts his or her pencil through the other end of the knotted rubber bands and stretches the rubber bands until the knot between them is directly over point *D.* Partner B makes a pencil mark with his or her pencil at that point. Partner B labels the point *D'.*
5. Repeat Steps 2 and 3 for points *O* and *G.* Label the new points *O'* and *G'.*
6. Connect points *D', O',* and *G'.*
7. Measure the sides of Triangles *DOG* and *D'O'G'.* Record your measurements underneath your drawing.
8. On the bottom of your page, describe the relationship between triangles *DOG* and *D'O'G'.* Answers vary.

P D D' O O' G G'

✦ *Math Masters,* p. 140

TEACHING MASTER

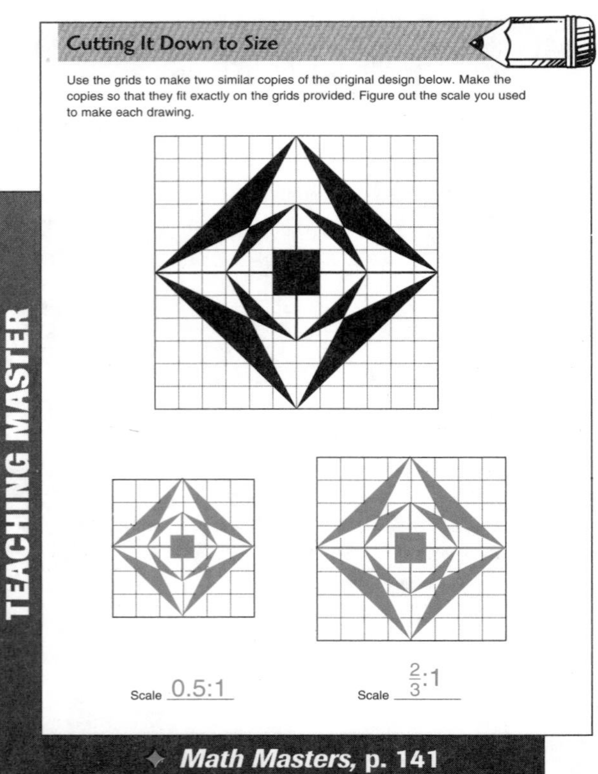

Cutting It Down to Size

Use the grids to make two similar copies of the original design below. Make the copies so that they fit exactly on the grids provided. Figure out the scale you used to make each drawing.

Scale 0.5:1 Scale $\frac{2}{3}$:1

✦ *Math Masters,* p. 141

8.11 Comparing Ratios

OBJECTIVES **To compare ratios by renaming them as *n*-to-1 ratios; and to introduce the Golden Ratio.**

summaries	materials
1 Teaching the Lesson	
Students rename ratios as *n*-to-1 ratios by dividing the first number by the second. They also compare ratios for the home data they collected on Study Link 8.8 by converting them to *n*-to-1 ratios. [Patterns, Functions, and Algebra]	☐ *Math Journal 2,* pp. 330–332 ☐ Study Links 8.8 and 8.10 ☐ Teaching Master (*Math Masters,* p. 142) ☐ calculator ***See* Advance Preparation**
2 Ongoing Learning & Practice	
Students solve division problems with decimal divisors. [Operations and Computation] Students practice and maintain skills through Math Boxes and Study Link activities.	☐ *Math Journal 2,* pp. 333 and 334 ☐ Study Link Master (*Math Masters,* p. 352)
3 Options for Individualizing	
Extra Practice Students collect equivalent ratios in name-collection boxes. [Numeration, Operations and Computation] **Language Diversity** Students practice reading ratios. [Patterns, Functions, and Algebra]	☐ posterboard (or chart paper) and markers ☐ calculator (optional)

Additional Information

Advance Preparation This lesson offers many opportunities for discussion and practice of ratio skills, so plan to spend more than one class period on the material. For the Math Message, make one copy of *Math Masters,* page 142 for every 8 students. Cut each copy apart into 8 slips. Place a box and the slips near the Math Message.

Vocabulary • **Golden Rectangle**

Getting Started

Mental Math and Reflexes

Suggest that students think of fraction equivalents for the percents to solve the problems.

- \$9 is 50% of \$_____? \$18
- \$80 is 50% of \$_____? \$160
- \$30 is 25% of \$_____? \$120
- \$5 is $33\frac{1}{3}$% of \$_____? \$15
- \$10 is $66\frac{2}{3}$% of \$_____? \$15
- \$8 is 20% of \$_____? \$40
- \$75 is 25% of \$_____? \$300
- \$15 is 75% of \$_____? \$20
- \$8 is 40% of \$_____? \$20

Math Message

Take a slip of paper. On the slip, record the number of females and the number of males in your household. Then put the slip into the box.

(*Note:* You may want to have students work on Math Boxes while you tabulate the total numbers of females and males in all students' households.)

Study Link 8.10 Follow-Up

Briefly go over the answers for Problem 1. The similar polygons in the problem demonstrate that the size-change factor for sides also applies to perimeters. Ask students whether they think the size-change factor for sides also applies to diagonals. yes Then have them measure to verify that the size-change factor does indeed apply to diagonals. Thinking of diagonals as sides of triangles may help students understand why this is: If two pairs of sides of similar triangles have a certain size-change factor, then the third pair of sides will, too.

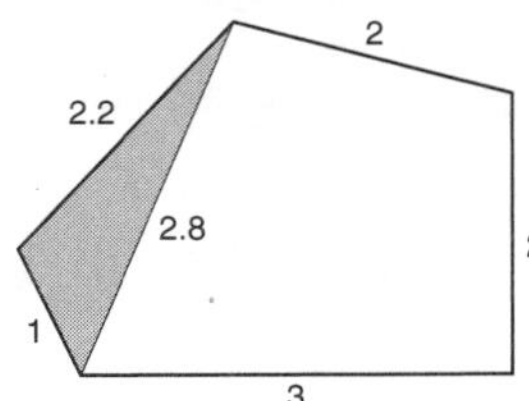

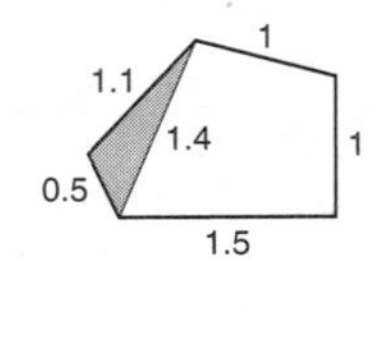

1 Teaching the Lesson

✦ Math Message Follow-Up
(*Math Masters,* p. 142)

WHOLE-CLASS DISCUSSION

Social Studies Link Write the total numbers of females and males in students' households on the board and ask students to express these numbers as a ratio of females to males. For example, if the class ratio of females to males is 53 to 49, write on the board:

$$\frac{\text{household females}}{\text{household males}} = \frac{53}{49}$$

Tell the class that, according to the 2000 U.S. census estimates, there were about 140,752,000 females and 134,554,000 males living in the United States in 2000. Write these numbers on the board as a ratio of females to males.

$$\frac{\text{U.S. females}}{\text{U.S. males}} = \frac{140{,}752{,}000}{134{,}554{,}000}$$

Then ask: *Does the ratio of females to males in all of our class's households appear to be close to the same ratio in the total U.S. population? How can you decide?*

TEACHING MASTER

Survey Slips

People in Your Household	People in Your Household
Number of males ______ Number of females ______	Number of males ______ Number of females ______
People in Your Household Number of males ______ Number of females ______	**People in Your Household** Number of males ______ Number of females ______
People in Your Household Number of males ______ Number of females ______	**People in Your Household** Number of males ______ Number of females ______
People in Your Household Number of males ______ Number of females ______	**People in Your Household** Number of males ______ Number of females ______

✧ *Math Masters,* p. 142

After students have expressed their opinions, suggest that it would be very easy to compare the two ratios if each were converted to an n-to-1 ratio, that is, to a ratio of the number of females to 1.

Suppose the ratio of females to males for the class is 53 to 49. To convert this ratio to an n-to-1, you can write and solve the following proportion:

$$\frac{53}{49} = \frac{n}{1}$$

$$49 * n = 53 * 1$$

$n = 53 / 49 = 1.08$, rounded to the nearest hundredth

Thus, the class's n-to-1 ratio of females to males is about 1.08 to 1.

$$\frac{\text{household females}}{\text{household males}} = \frac{53}{49} \approx \frac{1.08}{1}$$

NOTE: The symbol $\approx$ means "is about equal to."

Point out that to find the n-to-1 ratio, we divided the first number (53) by the second number (49). You can always find an n-to-1 ratio by dividing the first number by the second.

Next, use division to convert the ratio for the total U.S. population to an n-to-1. Divide the number of females in the U.S. by the number of males and round to the nearest hundredth.

$140{,}752{,}000 / 134{,}554{,}000 = 1.05$, rounded to the nearest hundredth

So, according to the 2000 census estimates, the ratio of females to males was about 1.05 to 1.

$$\frac{\text{U.S. females}}{\text{U.S. males}} = \frac{140{,}752{,}000}{134{,}554{,}000} \approx \frac{1.05}{1}$$

Now compare the two unit ratios. The ratio 1.08 to 1 means that for every male in the class, there are about 1.08 females. The ratio 1.05 to 1 for the U.S. population means that for every male, there are about 1.05 females. Thus, the ratio of females to males is greater for the class than for the U.S. population.

Renaming and Comparing Ratios

Use the data you collected on Study Link 8.8. Use your calculator. Answers vary.
Round to the nearest tenth.

1. The ratio of left-handed to right-handed people in my household — left-handed / right-handed = ☐/☐ is about ☐/1
2. The ratio of the length of the American flag I found to its width — flag length / flag width = ☐/☐ is about ☐/1
3. The ratio of the length of the screen of my TV set to its width — TV length / TV width = ☐/☐ is about ☐/1
4. a. The ratio of the length of a small book to its width — small book length / small book width = ☐/☐ is about ☐/1
   b. The ratio of the length of a medium book to its width — medium book length / medium book width = ☐/☐ is about ☐/1
   c. The ratio of the length of a large book to its width — large book length / large book width = ☐/☐ is about ☐/1
   d. What is the shape of a book with a length to width ratio of 1 to 1? square
5. a. The ratio of the length of a postcard to its width — postcard length / postcard width = ☐/☐ is about ☐/1
   b. The ratio of the length of an index card to its width — index card length / index card width = ☐/☐ is about ☐/1
   c. The ratio of the length of a regular-size envelope to its width — envelope length / envelope width = ☐/☐ is about ☐/1
   d. The ratio of the length of a business envelope to its width — business envelope length / business envelope width = ☐/☐ is about ☐/1
   e. The ratio of the length of a sheet of notebook paper to its width — notebook paper length / notebook paper width = ☐/☐ is about ☐/1

STUDENT PAGE

Math Journal 2, p. 330

Renaming and Comparing Ratios (cont.)

6. Measure the length and width of each rectangle in Problem 6 on Study Link 8.8. to the nearest tenth of a centimeter. Find the ratio of length to width for each rectangle.
   a. $\frac{\text{length of A}}{\text{width of A}} = \frac{1.5}{1.3} = \frac{1.15}{1}$ b. $\frac{\text{length of B}}{\text{width of B}} = \frac{2}{0.5} = \frac{4}{1}$
   c. $\frac{\text{length of C}}{\text{width of C}} = \frac{3}{1} = \frac{3}{1}$ d. $\frac{\text{length of D}}{\text{width of D}} = \frac{1.6}{1} = \frac{1.6}{1}$
   e. Which of the four rectangles was the most popular? Answers vary.
7. The ratio of the rise to the run of my stairs is rise / run = ☐/☐ = ☐/1

Share the data you recorded in Problems 1–7 with the other members of your group. Use these data to answer the following questions.

8. Which group member has the largest ratio of left-handed people to right-handed people at home? ______ What is this ratio? Answers vary.
9. By law, the length of an official United States flag must be 1.9 times its width.
   a. Did the flag you measured meet this standard? Answers vary.
   b. What percent of the flags measured by your group meets this standard? ______
   c. Why do you think such a law exists? ______
   d. One of the largest United States flags was displayed at the J.L. Hudson store in Detroit, Michigan. The flag was 235 feet by 104 feet. Does this flag meet the legal requirements? no
   e. How can you tell? Sample answer: The ratio is greater than 1.9 to 1; it's about 2.26 to 1.
10. a. For most television sets, the ratio of the length to the width of the screen is about 4 to 3. Is this true of the television sets in your group? Answers vary.
    b. Why do you think it is important to have similar ratios of length to width for TV screens? Sample answer: The shape of the screen must conform to the shape of the picture being transmitted.

STUDENT PAGE

Math Journal 2, p. 331

✦ Comparing Ratios Based on Data Collected for Study Link 8.8 (*Math Journal 2,* pp. 330–332; Study Link 8.8)

SMALL-GROUP ACTIVITY

Divide the class into groups of 6 students. Briefly explain the two parts of the activity. In the first part (Problems 1 through 7, starting on journal page 330), students record the data they collected for Study Link 8.8 as n-to-1 ratios. In the second part (Problems 8 through 13, starting on page 331), they compare and interpret these ratios. Some of the problems involve combining the data collected by all members of each group.

Tell the class that after the groups have completed the problems, each group will report its results. Suggest that each member of the group be responsible for reporting the results for at least *one* of the 6 items on pages 331 and 332. Circulate and assist as needed.

✦ Sharing the Ratio Comparisons (*Math Journal 2,* pp. 331 and 332)

WHOLE-CLASS DISCUSSION

Bring the class together to share results. Some discussion notes and suggestions follow.

Problem 8: It is likely that most if not all ratios will be ratios of a number less than 1 to 1. For example, in a family of 5, if 1 out of 5 people is left-handed, the ratio of left-handed people to right-handed people is 1 to 4, or 0.25 to 1. If every ratio is expressed as some number to 1, it becomes easy to compare the ratios. If, in a family of 5, 3 people are left-handed, what would be the ratio of left-handed to right-handed people? 3 to 2, or 1.5 to 1

Problem 9: Ask students to raise their hands if their flags have a length between 1.8 and 2 times their width. Record that number on the board. What percent of the total number of flags is that?

Problem 10: Again, ask students to raise their hands if the ratio of the length to the width of their TV screens is close to 4 to 3. What percent of students raised their hands? Most if not all students will probably have raised their hands, since most TV manufacturers use standard dimensions for TV screens. Ask: *What might happen if these ratios varied?* On some screens, the picture might not fill the screen, or some of the picture would be cut off. The shape of the screen must conform to the shape of the picture being transmitted.

NOTE: Students may be aware of the letter-box format used when movies made for wide screens are shown on television. To accommodate the full length of the picture, the width must be reduced.

Problem 12: Ask students to calculate what percent of people surveyed by the class chose the **Golden Rectangle**—Rectangle D. It has a length to width ratio of 8 to 5.

To draw a Golden Rectangle with shorter sides of 2 centimeters (Problem 12c), students needed to calculate the length of the longer side. One way to do this is to start with $\frac{8}{5}$ as the length to width ratio:

$$\frac{\text{length}}{\text{width}} = \frac{8}{5}$$

Since the shorter side measures 2 centimeters, this becomes $\frac{\text{length}}{\text{width}} = \frac{8}{5} = \frac{l}{2}$.

This proportion is easier to solve if $\frac{8}{5}$ is replaced by the equivalent unit ratio $\frac{1.6}{1}$:

$$\frac{\text{length}}{\text{width}} = \frac{1.6}{1} = \frac{l}{2}$$

$$1 * l = 2 * 1.6$$

$$l = 3.2$$

Thus, the length of the longer side is 3.2 centimeters.

Ask: *Are any of the books in Problem 4 on journal page 330 shaped like a Golden Rectangle? Are any of the items in Problem 5 on page 330 shaped like a Golden Rectangle?*

Adjusting the Activity Some students may find it easier to use patterns in a table to find lengths.

Length	8	16	1.6	3.2
Width	5	10	1	2

To find the length when the width is 2, start with the ratio $\frac{8}{5}$. Find an equivalent ratio by doubling. Next, divide the length and width by 10 to get the length when the width is 1. Finally, double the table entries to find the length.

Problem 13: Discuss how the ratio of rise to run of stairs affects how steep the stairs are. Students may notice that the ratio of rise to run probably varies more than the ratio of length to width for television screens but not nearly as much as for book lengths to widths.

Renaming and Comparing Ratios (cont.)

11. Compare the ratios for small, medium, and large books measured by your group.
    Which size books tends to have the largest ratio of length to width? Answers vary.
    Which size tends to have the smallest ratio? ______

12. It is often claimed that the "nicest looking" rectangular shapes have a special ratio of length to width. Such rectangles are called **Golden Rectangles.** In a Golden Rectangle, the ratio of length to width is about 8 to 5.

    A B C D

    a. Which of the four rectangles—A, B, C, or D—is closest to having the shape of a Golden Rectangle? D
    b. Did most people in your family choose the Golden Rectangle? Answers vary.
    c. Draw a Golden Rectangle whose shorter sides are 2 centimeters long.
    d. Are any of the items in Problem 5 on page 330 Golden Rectangles? ______
       If so, which ones are they? Answers vary.

13. Most stairs in homes have a rise of about 7 inches and a run of about $10\frac{1}{2}$ inches. Therefore, the rise is about $\frac{2}{3}$ of the run. Answers vary.
    a. Is this true of your stairs? ______
    b. Which stairs would be steeper, stairs with a rise-to-run ratio of 2:3 or 3:2? 3:2
    c. Which member of your group has the steepest stairs? ______
       What is the ratio of rise to run? ______
    d. On the grid at the right, draw stairs whose rise is $\frac{2}{5}$ of the run.

    Sample answer:

STUDENT PAGE

✧ Math Journal 2, p. 332

NOTE: The Golden Rectangle is investigated further in Lesson 8.12.

NOTE: Strictly defined, *run* is the width of a step as shown in the diagram below. If there is an overhang at the front of the step, the total width is called the *tread.* However, this distinction does not need to be made at this time.

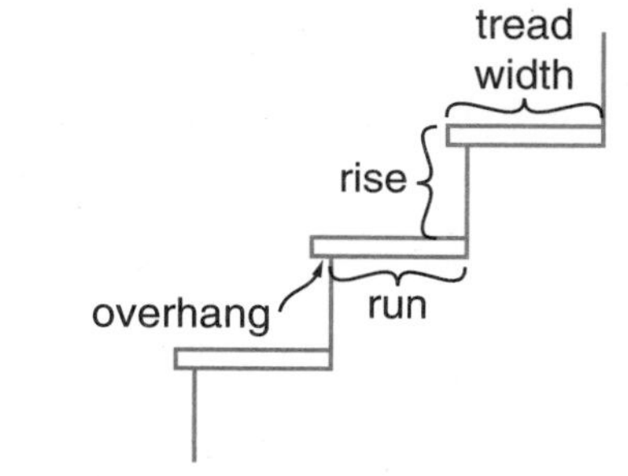

Decimal Divisors

First, estimate the answer. Write a number model for the estimate. Then divide, ignoring the decimal points. Finally, use your estimate to place the decimal point in the answer. Show your work in the space below each problem. Estimates vary.

1. 18.86 ÷ 2.3
   Estimate 18 ÷ 2 = 9
   Answer 8.2

2. 326.86 ÷ 5.9
   Estimate 300 ÷ 6 = 50
   Answer 55.4

3. 28.81 / 4.3
   Estimate 28 ÷ 4 = 7
   Answer 6.7

4. 23.033 ÷ 3.1
   Estimate 21 ÷ 3 = 7
   Answer 7.43

5. 15.5 / 0.5
   Estimate 15 ÷ $\frac{1}{2}$ = 30
   Answer 31

6. 378 ÷ 2.4
   Estimate 380 ÷ 2 = 190
   Answer 157.5

STUDENT PAGE

Math Journal 2, p. 333

$$\begin{array}{r|l} 54\overline{)2754} & \\ -\ 2700 & 50 \\ 54 & \\ -\ 54 & 1 \\ \hline 0 & 51 \end{array}$$

Adjusting the Activity Extend this activity by having students do research on other objects that have standard ratios. Begin by brainstorming a list of possibilities, such as the height of chairs to the height of tables or the length of a paper clip to its width. Add all suggestions to the list, even if they do not seem to have a standard ratio. Students can measure the dimensions to find out whether or not there is actually a standard ratio.

2 Ongoing Learning & Practice

✦ Dividing a Decimal by a Decimal

(*Math Journal 2,* p. 333)

INDEPENDENT ACTIVITY 

Ask students to solve the following problem:

27.54 ÷ 5.4 = ?

After a few minutes, ask a volunteer to demonstrate the solution at the board. Make sure that the following procedure is discussed:

Step 1: Estimate.

Since 27.54 is close to 25 and 5.5 is close to 5, the answer must be close to 25 ÷ 5 = 5.

Step 2: Divide, ignoring the decimal point.

Step 3: Use the estimate to place the decimal point in the quotient. Since the estimate was about 5, the decimal point should be placed between the 5 and the 1. Thus, 27.54 ÷ 5.4 = 5.1.

Check the answer on the calculator. Have students complete journal page 333.

ONGOING ASSESSMENT

Although this is the first time students are solving division problems in which the divisor is a decimal, the procedure is the same as the one for a whole number divisor. As before, students' success will depend in part on whether they are skilled at estimating the quotient. If they need more practice, consider adding two division problems to the back of their Study Links.

✦ Math Boxes 8.11 (*Math Journal 2,* p. 334)

INDEPENDENT ACTIVITY 

Mixed Review Math Boxes in this lesson are paired with Math Boxes in Lesson 8.9. The skill in Problem 1 is a prerequisite for Unit 9.

✦ Study Link 8.11 (*Math Masters,* p. 352)

Home Connection Students practice solving ratio and rate number stories.

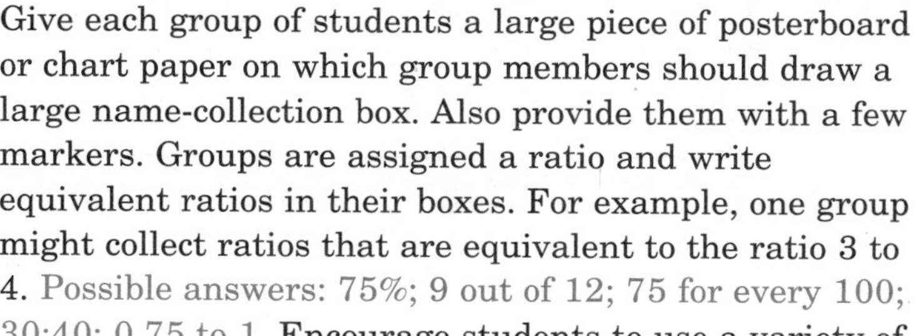

3 Options for Individualizing

✦ EXTRA PRACTICE Finding Equivalent Ratios

SMALL-GROUP ACTIVITY  **5–15 min**

Give each group of students a large piece of posterboard or chart paper on which group members should draw a large name-collection box. Also provide them with a few markers. Groups are assigned a ratio and write equivalent ratios in their boxes. For example, one group might collect ratios that are equivalent to the ratio 3 to 4. Possible answers: 75%; 9 out of 12; 75 for every 100; 30:40; 0.75 to 1. Encourage students to use a variety of notations.

These posters can be displayed in the class for a few days. You might want to laminate the posterboard before students write on it. If they use water-soluble markers, the posters can be washed off and reused for other name-collection boxes.

✦ LANGUAGE DIVERSITY Reading Ratios

PARTNER ACTIVITY **5–15 min**

Pair students who are learning English with proficient English speakers. Students take turns reading to each other the ratios generated in the Extra Practice activity above. Have them make their own name-collection boxes for their portfolios.

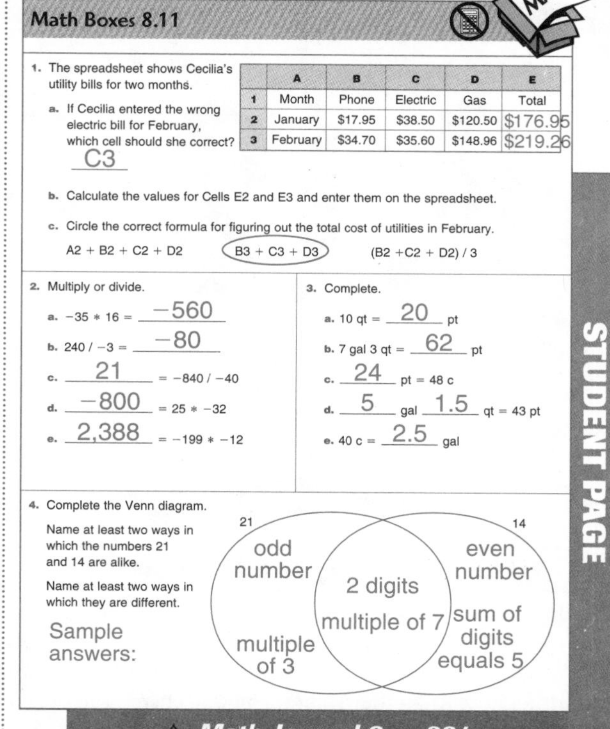

Math Boxes 8.11

1. The spreadsheet shows Cecilia's utility bills for two months.

	A	B	C	D	E
1	Month	Phone	Electric	Gas	Total
2	January	$17.95	$38.50	$120.50	$176.95
3	February	$34.70	$35.60	$148.96	$219.26

a. If Cecilia entered the wrong electric bill for February, which cell should she correct? C3

b. Calculate the values for Cells E2 and E3 and enter them on the spreadsheet.

c. Circle the correct formula for figuring out the total cost of utilities in February.

A2 + B2 + C2 + D2   (B3 + C3 + D3)   (B2 + C2 + D2) / 3

2. Multiply or divide.

a. −35 ∗ 16 = −560

b. 240 / −3 = −80

c. 21 = −840 / −40

d. −800 = 25 ∗ −32

e. 2,388 = −199 ∗ −12

3. Complete.

a. 10 qt = 20 pt

b. 7 gal 3 qt = 62 pt

c. 24 pt = 48 c

d. 5 gal 1.5 qt = 43 pt

e. 40 c = 2.5 gal

4. Complete the Venn diagram.

Name at least two ways in which the numbers 21 and 14 are alike.

Name at least two ways in which they are different.

Sample answers:

21: odd number; multiple of 3

Both: 2 digits; multiple of 7

14: even number; sum of digits equals 5

STUDENT PAGE

✦ *Math Journal 2,* p. 334

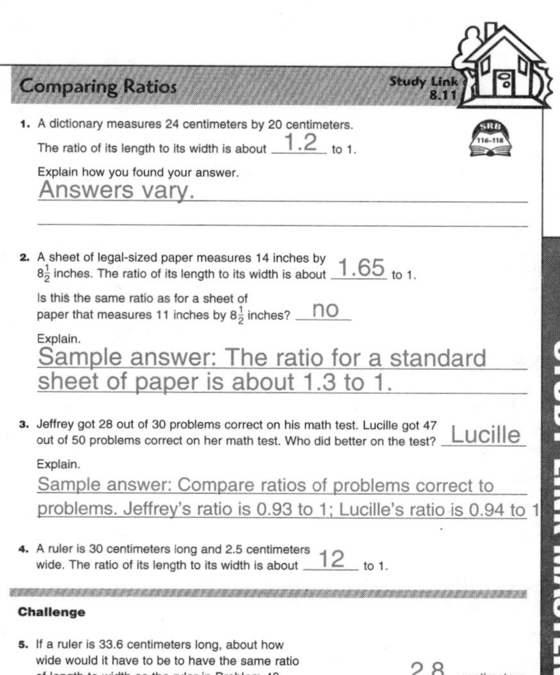

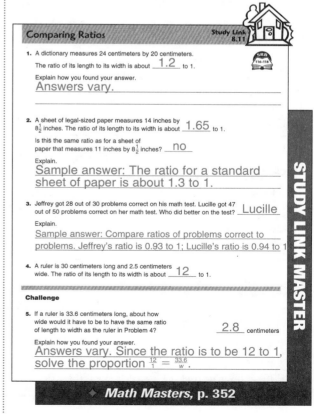

Comparing Ratios Study Link 8.11

SRB 116–118

1. A dictionary measures 24 centimeters by 20 centimeters. The ratio of its length to its width is about 1.2 to 1.

Explain how you found your answer. Answers vary.

2. A sheet of legal-sized paper measures 14 inches by $8\frac{1}{2}$ inches. The ratio of its length to its width is about 1.65 to 1.

Is this the same ratio as for a sheet of paper that measures 11 inches by $8\frac{1}{2}$ inches? no

Explain. Sample answer: The ratio for a standard sheet of paper is about 1.3 to 1.

3. Jeffrey got 28 out of 30 problems correct on his math test. Lucille got 47 out of 50 problems correct on her math test. Who did better on the test? Lucille

Explain. Sample answer: Compare ratios of problems correct to problems. Jeffrey's ratio is 0.93 to 1; Lucille's ratio is 0.94 to 1

4. A ruler is 30 centimeters long and 2.5 centimeters wide. The ratio of its length to its width is about 12 to 1.

Challenge

5. If a ruler is 33.6 centimeters long, about how wide would it have to be to have the same ratio of length to width as the ruler in Problem 4? 2.8 centimeters

Explain how you found your answer. Answers vary. Since the ratio is to be 12 to 1, solve the proportion $\frac{12}{1} = \frac{33.6}{w}$.

STUDY LINK MASTER

✦ *Math Masters,* p. 352

8.12 The Golden Ratio

OBJECTIVE **To explore Golden Rectangles and the Golden Ratio.**

summaries	materials
1 Teaching the Lesson	
Students explore length to width ratios for various rectangles. They find that certain rectangles, known as Golden Rectangles, have a very special length to width ratio, known as the Golden Ratio. [Patterns, Functions, and Algebra; Geometry]	☐ *Math Journal 2,* pp. 335 and 336 ☐ Study Link 8.11 ☐ Transparency (*Math Masters,* p. 143; optional) ☐ compass and yardstick for demonstration purposes ☐ compass ☐ ruler ☐ calculator ***See* Advance Preparation**
2 Ongoing Learning & Practice	
Students practice and maintain skills through Math Boxes and Study Link activities.	☐ *Math Journal 2,* p. 337 ☐ Study Link Masters (*Math Masters,* pp. 353 and 354)
3 Options for Individualizing	
Enrichment Students read an essay about the Golden Ratio. [Geometry; Patterns, Functions, and Algebra] **Enrichment** Students learn about the connection between the Golden Ratio and the Fibonacci numbers. [Patterns, Functions, and Algebra] **Enrichment** Students read and recite the poem "The Golden Mean." [Patterns, Functions, and Algebra]	☐ *Student Reference Book,* pp. 318–320 ☐ Teaching Master (*Math Masters,* p. 144) ☐ calculator ☐ *Math Talk: Mathematical Ideas in Poems for Two Voices* ***See* Advance Preparation**

Additional Information

Advance Preparation For Part 1, try the construction on journal page 335. For the third optional Enrichment activity in Part 3, obtain the book *Math Talk: Mathematical Ideas in Poems for Two Voices* by Theoni Pappas (Wide World Publishing/Tetra, 1991).

Vocabulary • **Golden Ratio** • **Golden Rectangle**

Getting Started

Mental Math and Reflexes

Tell whether the answer is more than 200 (thumbs up), less than 200 (thumbs down), or exactly 200 (stand up).

- 2,000 / 10 Stand up
- 299 − 88 Thumbs up
- 299 − 107 Thumbs down
- 20 ∗ 100 Thumbs up
- 200,000 / 100 Thumbs up
- 2,000,000 / 100,000 Thumbs down

Math Message

Complete Problems 1–6 on page 335 in your journal. Do not draw a square for Problem 1.

(*Note:* If a student draws a square in Problem 1, the ratio in Problem 5 will be $\frac{0}{0}$.)

Study Link 8.11 Follow-Up

Students share answers and solution strategies.

1 Teaching the Lesson

◆ Math Message Follow-Up
(*Math Journal 2,* p. 335)

WHOLE-CLASS DISCUSSION

Ask students to share the ratios they calculated for their rectangles. Record them in a table like the one below.

Problem 2 $\frac{\text{length}}{\text{width}}$	Problem 5 $\frac{\text{length}}{\text{width}}$

Point out that in most cases, the ratios will not be equal. The focus of this lesson is on special rectangles in which these ratios are equal.

◆ Introducing the Golden Ratio
(*Math Journal 2,* p. 336; *Math Masters,* p. 143)

WHOLE-CLASS DISCUSSION

Assign partners to work on journal page 336. When students have finished, discuss the page. The key result is that the ratio of length to width for the small rectangle (*XBCY*) is equal to the length to width ratio for the large rectangle (*ABCD*).

The exact value of this length to width ratio is an irrational number that begins 1.618.... This number, like π, has been studied for thousands of years. Mathematicians today use the Greek letter phi (ϕ) to denote this number, which is known as the **Golden Ratio.** Because of measurement

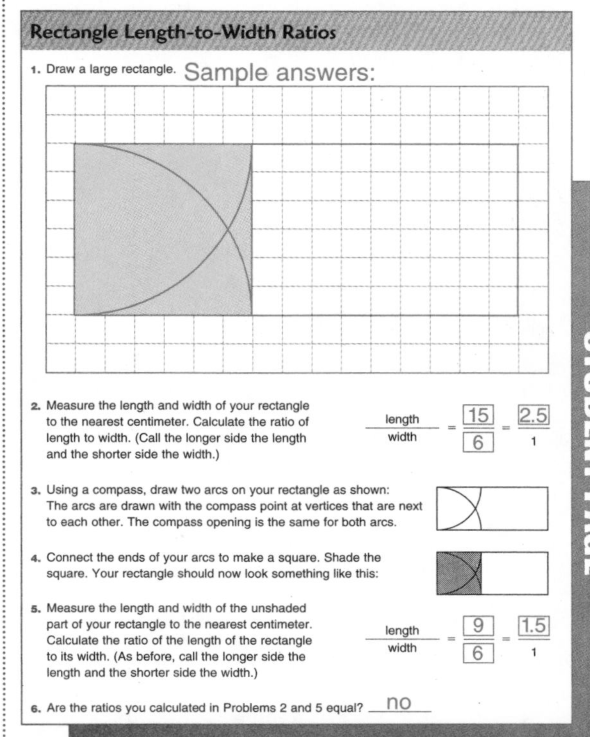

Rectangle Length-to-Width Ratios

1. Draw a large rectangle. Sample answers:

2. Measure the length and width of your rectangle to the nearest centimeter. Calculate the ratio of length to width. (Call the longer side the length and the shorter side the width.) $\frac{\text{length}}{\text{width}} = \frac{15}{6} = \frac{2.5}{1}$

3. Using a compass, draw two arcs on your rectangle as shown: The arcs are drawn with the compass point at vertices that are next to each other. The compass opening is the same for both arcs.

4. Connect the ends of your arcs to make a square. Shade the square. Your rectangle should now look something like this:

5. Measure the length and width of the unshaded part of your rectangle to the nearest centimeter. Calculate the ratio of the length of the rectangle to its width. (As before, call the longer side the length and the shorter side the width.) $\frac{\text{length}}{\text{width}} = \frac{9}{6} = \frac{1.5}{1}$

6. Are the ratios you calculated in Problems 2 and 5 equal? no

STUDENT PAGE

◆ *Math Journal 2,* p. 335

STUDENT PAGE

Length-to-Width Ratios in a Golden Rectangle

1. Measure the length and width of Rectangle *ABCD* to the nearest tenth of a centimeter. (Call the longer side the length and the shorter side the width.) Calculate the length to width ratio to the nearest tenth.

$\frac{\text{length}}{\text{width}} = \frac{12.4}{7.7} = \frac{1.6}{1}$

A X B

D Y C

2. Measure the sides of Rectangle *AXYD*. What kind of rectangle is *AXYD*? square

3. Measure the length and width of Rectangle *XBCY*. (Call the longer side the length and the shorter side the width.) Calculate the length to width ratio.

$\frac{\text{length}}{\text{width}} = \frac{7.7}{4.7} = \frac{1.6}{1}$

4. What do you notice about the ratios you calculated in Problems 1 and 3? Sample answer: They are about the same.

Math Journal 2, p. 336

error, students' values for the Golden Ratio will probably vary slightly from 1.618.... This is unavoidable, though if students measured carefully, they should be in the range 1.5 to 1.75 or so.

Any rectangles whose ratio of length to width is the Golden Ratio, 1.618..., are called **Golden Rectangles.** Rectangle *ABCD* is a Golden Rectangle. Probably none of the rectangles that students drew for the Math Message were Golden Rectangles, though some may have been close.

Ask students whether Rectangle *XBCY* on journal page 336 is also a Golden Rectangle. yes You may use a transparency of *Math Masters,* page 143 to show that it is by repeating the construction from the Math Message on Rectangle *XBCY.* Work through the following steps with the class:

1. Inside Rectangle *XBCY,* construct a square with side *XB*.
2. Measure the length and width of the resulting smaller rectangle.
3. Compute the length to width ratio for the smaller rectangle.

Once again, within measurement error, the length to width ratio should equal the Golden Ratio, 1.618....

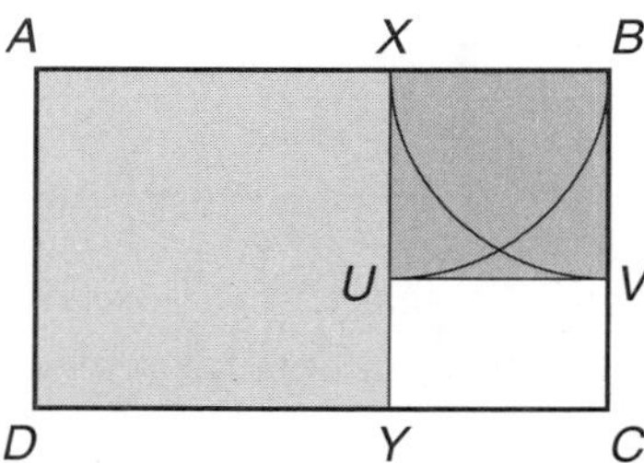

Rectangles *ABCD, XBCY,* and *UVCY* are all Golden Rectangles.

Point out that this process can be continued: Since Rectangle *UVCY* is a Golden Rectangle, it can, in turn, be divided into a square and another, smaller, Golden Rectangle.

NOTE: For centuries, the Golden Rectangle has been an important and intriguing idea in art, architecture, and mathematics. The basic ideas are accessible to students and are presented in a variety of encyclopedia articles and books (such as *Zero to Lazy Eight: The Romance of Numbers,* by Alexander Humez, Nicholas Humez, and Joseph Maguire. Simon and Schuster, 1993).

2 Ongoing Learning & Practice

✦Math Boxes 8.12 (*Math Journal 2,* p. 337)

INDEPENDENT ACTIVITY 

Mixed Review Math Boxes in this lesson are paired with Math Boxes in Lesson 8.10. The skill in Problem 1 is a prerequisite for Unit 9.

✦Study Link 8.12 (*Math Masters,* pp. 353 and 354)

Home Connection Students solve problems that review some of the concepts in this unit. This Study Link consists of two pages.

Math Boxes 8.12

1. The formula $d = rt$ gives the distance d traveled at speed r in time t. Use this formula to solve the problems below.
   a. The distance from Chicago to Los Angeles is about 2,190 miles. About how many hours will it take to drive from Chicago to Los Angeles at an average speed of 55 miles per hour? About 40 hours
   b. About how long will an airplane flying at an average speed of 500 miles per hour take to travel this distance? About 4.5 hours
   c. Circle the formula that is equivalent to $d = rt$.
   (circled) $r = d / t$ $\quad r = d - t \quad r = t / d \quad r = t + d$

2. Multiply or divide. Write your answer in simplest form.
   a. $\frac{3}{8} \div \frac{6}{7} = \frac{7}{16}$
   b. $1\frac{2}{3} * \frac{4}{5} = 1\frac{1}{3}$
   c. $3\frac{2}{3} = \frac{6}{2} \div \frac{9}{11}$
   d. $\frac{20}{33} = 3\frac{3}{9} * \frac{2}{11}$
   e. $41\frac{3}{5} = 5\frac{1}{5} * 8$

3. Write five names for the number in the name-collection box so that each name contains the fraction $\frac{1}{3}$ and includes multiplication.

   Sample answers:

8
$24 * \frac{1}{3}$
$(4 * 6) * \frac{1}{3}$
$(\frac{1}{3} * 3) + (7 * 1)$
$288 * \frac{1}{3} * \frac{1}{12}$
$[(400 \div 10) - 16] * \frac{1}{3}$

4. Write each number in standard notation. Then round to the nearest tenth.
   a. six and twenty-nine hundredths
   standard notation 6.29
   rounded 6.3
   b. four and thirteen ten-thousandths
   standard notation 4.0013
   rounded 4.0
   c. fourteen and sixty-two hundredths
   standard notation 14.62
   rounded 14.6

5. Subtract. Write your answer as a fraction or mixed number in simplest form.
   a. $\frac{3}{2} - \frac{5}{8} = \frac{7}{8}$
   b. $3\frac{1}{6} = 4\frac{2}{3} - 1\frac{1}{2}$
   c. $1\frac{5}{12} = 3\frac{1}{4} - 1\frac{5}{6}$
   d. $5\frac{8}{9} - \frac{25}{25} = 4\frac{8}{9}$

STUDENT PAGE

✧ *Math Journal 2,* p. 337

Rate and Ratio Review Study Link 8.12

1. Match each ratio on the left with one of the ratios on the right.

a. Circumference to diameter of a circle	b.	1.6 to 1
b. Length to width of a Golden Rectangle	e.	3 to 5
c. Diameter to radius of a circle	c.	2 to 1
d. Length of one side of a square to another	a.	3.14 to 1
e. 12 correct answers out of 20 problems	d.	1 to 1

2. Refer to the following numbers to answer the questions below.
   1 2 3 4 5 6 7 8 9 10
   a. What percent of the numbers are prime numbers? 40%
   b. What is the ratio of the numbers divisible by 3 to the numbers divisible by 2? 3:5 or $\frac{3}{5}$

3. A 12-pack of Chummy Cola costs $3 at Stellar Supermart.
   a. Complete the rate table below to find the per-unit rates.

dollars	0.25	3.00	1.00
cans	1	12	4

   b. At this price, how much would 30 cans of Chummy Cola cost? $7.50
   c. How many cans could you buy for $2.00? 8 cans

4. Complete or write a proportion for each problem. Then solve the problem.
   a. Only $\frac{4}{9}$ of the club members voted in the last election. There are 54 members in the club. How many members voted?
   Proportion $\frac{4}{9} = \frac{x}{54}$ Answer 24 members
   b. During basketball practice, Christina made 3 out of every 5 free throws she attempted. If she made 12 free throws, how many free throws did she attempt in all?
   Proportion $\frac{3}{5} = \frac{12}{n}$ Answer 20 free throws

STUDY LINK MASTER

✧ *Math Masters,* p. 353

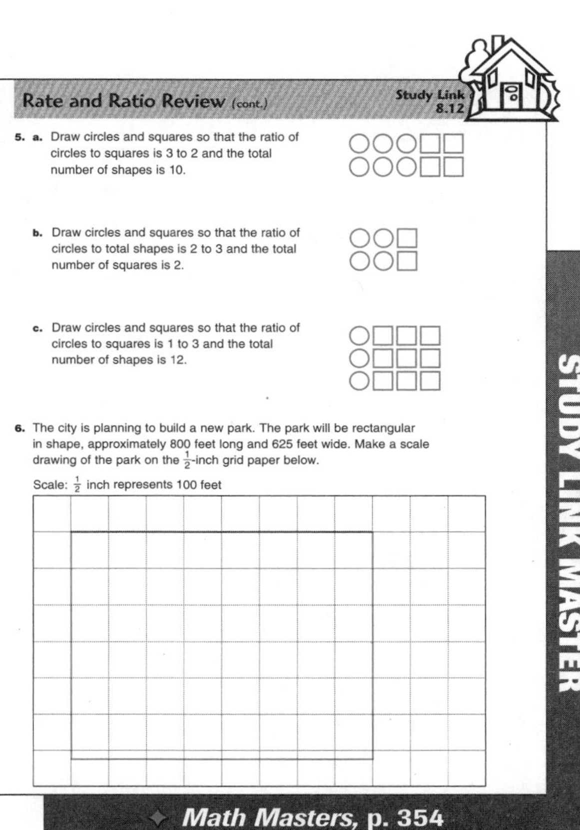
Rate and Ratio Review (cont.) Study Link 8.12

5. a. Draw circles and squares so that the ratio of circles to squares is 3 to 2 and the total number of shapes is 10.
   b. Draw circles and squares so that the ratio of circles to total shapes is 2 to 3 and the total number of squares is 2.
   c. Draw circles and squares so that the ratio of circles to squares is 1 to 3 and the total number of shapes is 12.

6. The city is planning to build a new park. The park will be rectangular in shape, approximately 800 feet long and 625 feet wide. Make a scale drawing of the park on the $\frac{1}{2}$-inch grid paper below.
   Scale: $\frac{1}{2}$ inch represents 100 feet

STUDY LINK MASTER

✧ *Math Masters,* p. 354

STUDENT PAGE

Art and Design Activities

The Golden Ratio

Which of the following rectangles do you like best?

A B C D

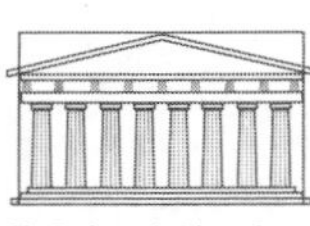

The Parthenon in Athens, Greece

It has been shown that Rectangle D, called the **Golden Rectangle**, is chosen more often than any other rectangle. In a Golden Rectangle, the ratio of the length of the longer side to the length of the shorter side is about 1.618 to 1. This ratio is known as the **Golden Ratio.**

The popularity of the Golden Ratio dates back to the ancient Greeks who used it in many of their works of art and architecture. For example, the front of the Parthenon in Athens fits almost exactly into a Golden Rectangle.

The symbol for the Golden Ratio is the Greek letter ϕ (pronounced "phi"), perhaps chosen for the name of the famous Athenian sculptor Phidias (about 490–430 B.C.).

St. Jerome by Leonardo da Vinci

Throughout the ages, many artists have found that they could create a feeling of order in their works by using the Golden Ratio. For example, in the picture of St. Jerome, painted about the year 1483 by Leonardo da Vinci, the figure of St. Jerome fits perfectly into a Golden Rectangle. It is believed that this was not just a coincidence, but that da Vinci used the Golden Ratio because of his great interest in mathematics.

The mask shown at the right was made in the Benin Kingdom in western Africa in the early sixteenth century. It was worn by the Oba, which means "king." The Oba was a sacred figure, and many ceremonies took place in his honor. If you measure the sides of the rectangles that frame some of the features in the mask, you will find that the ratio of the length of the longer side to the length of the shorter side is the Golden Ratio, about 1.618 to 1. Notice also that the mask is perfectly symmetric.

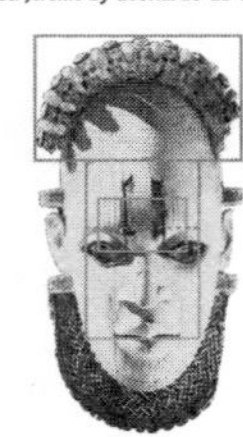

West African mask

SRB 318 three hundred eighteen

◇ *Student Reference Book,* p. 318

3 Options for Individualizing

✦ ENRICHMENT Reading about the Golden Ratio (*Student Reference Book,* pp. 318–320)

INDEPENDENT ACTIVITY  **5–15 min** 

Art Link Students read about the use of the Golden Ratio in works of art. Interested students might try following the directions on page 320 for constructing a Golden Rectangle.

STUDENT PAGE

Art and Design Activities

A Classical Face

The Golden Ratio can be found in many of the sculptures that were made during the classical period of Greek art (about 480–350 B.C.). The picture at the right is a good example of a "classical Greek" face. It shows a sculpture of the head of the Greek goddess Hera. According to Greek mythology, Hera was queen of the Olympian gods and the wife of the god Zeus. The sculpture was found in a temple in Argos, a city of which Hera was a patron. It was probably completed about 420 B.C. The sculpture is currently owned by the National Museum in Athens.

Nine different parts of the face are indicated on the picture shown below. By measuring various parts of the face, you will find many examples of the Golden Ratio in the sculpture.

- a = total width of head (including hair)
- b = top of hair to pupils
- c = top of eye to bottom of chin
- d = top of hair to bottom of chin
- e = distance from ear to ear
- f = peak of hairline to bottom of chin
- g = distance between outsides of eyes
- h = pupil to chin
- i = from inside of one eye to inside of other eye

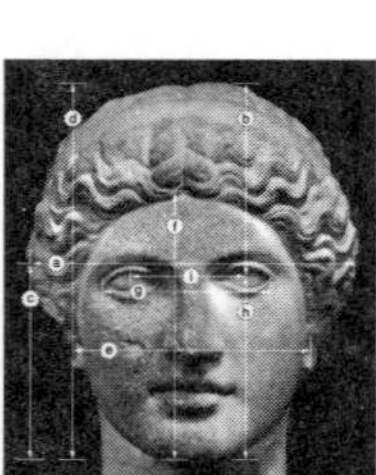

three hundred nineteen  SRB 319

◇ *Student Reference Book,* p. 319

STUDENT PAGE

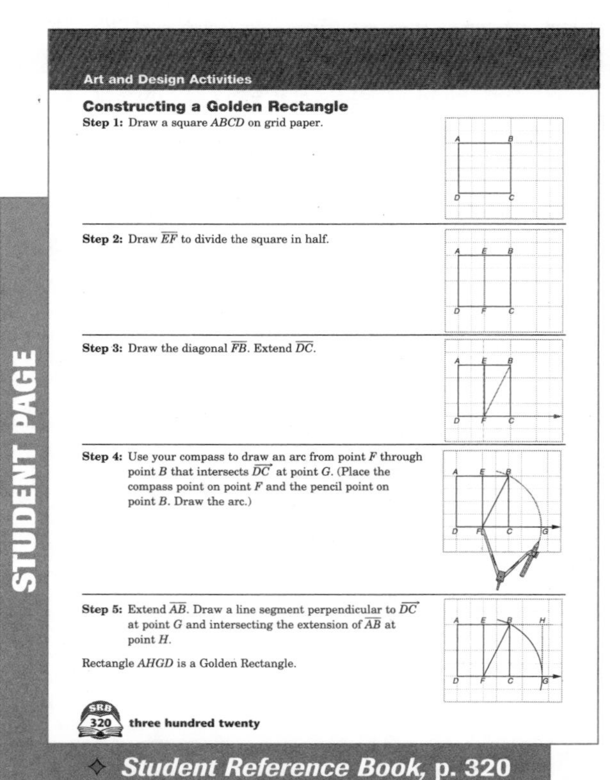

Art and Design Activities

Constructing a Golden Rectangle

Step 1: Draw a square *ABCD* on grid paper.

Step 2: Draw $\overline{EF}$ to divide the square in half.

Step 3: Draw the diagonal $\overline{FB}$. Extend $\overline{DC}$.

Step 4: Use your compass to draw an arc from point *F* through point *B* that intersects $\overline{DC}$ at point *G*. (Place the compass point on point *F* and the pencil point on point *B*. Draw the arc.)

Step 5: Extend $\overline{AB}$. Draw a line segment perpendicular to $\overline{DC}$ at point *G* and intersecting the extension of $\overline{AB}$ at point *H*.

Rectangle *AHGD* is a Golden Rectangle.

SRB 320 three hundred twenty

◇ *Student Reference Book,* p. 320

✦ ENRICHMENT Exploring the Relationship between the Fibonacci Sequence and the Golden Ratio (*Math Masters,* p. 144)

INDEPENDENT ACTIVITY  **15–30 min** 

Assign *Math Masters,* page 144 to students who are interested in exploring other examples of the Golden Ratio. After they have completed the page, ask them to calculate the ratio of pairs of consecutive Fibonacci numbers.

$\frac{1}{1} = 1$

$\frac{2}{1} = 2$

$\frac{3}{2} = 1.5$

$\frac{5}{3} = 1.666...$

$\frac{8}{5} = 1.6$

$\frac{13}{8} = 1.625$

$\frac{21}{13} = 1.61538...$

$\frac{34}{21} = 1.61904...$ and so on

Students will find that the ratio of consecutive Fibonacci numbers gets closer and closer to the Golden Ratio as the sequence continues.

NOTE: After the first two numbers, each Fibonacci number is the sum of the two prior Fibonacci numbers: $2 = 1 + 1$, $3 = 2 + 1$, $5 = 3 + 2$, $8 = 5 + 3$, and so on. The Fibonacci sequence was investigated by the great medieval mathematician, Leonardo de Pisa, who is also known as Fibonacci.

✦ ENRICHMENT Reading the Poem "The Golden Mean"

PARTNER ACTIVITY **5–15 min** 

Literature Link *Math Talk: Mathematical Ideas in Poems for Two Voices* presents mathematical topics through poetic dialogues to be read by two people. "The Golden Mean" is an ideal selection to share at this time. Some students may be interested in memorizing the poem in their spare time and then presenting it to the class.

Leonardo's Rabbits

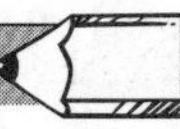

In January, Leonardo began with 1 pair of baby rabbits. He kept track of his rabbits in a table. The row for January shows 1 pair of baby rabbits. In February, the baby rabbits grew to be adolescents. Leonardo still had 1 pair of rabbits. He recorded this information for February. In March, Leonardo's pair of rabbits became parents—they had a pair of baby rabbits. He now had a total of 2 pairs of rabbits. In April, the baby rabbits born in March became adolescents. The parent pair also had another pair of baby rabbits. Leonardo now had 3 pairs of rabbits. The rabbits kept multiplying in this way.

Month	Parent Pairs	Adolescent Pairs	Baby Pairs	Total Number of Pairs
January	0	0	1	1
February	0	1	0	1
March	1	0	1	2
April	1	1	1	3
May	2	1	2	5
June	3	2	3	8
July	5	3	5	13
August	8	5	8	21
September	13	8	13	34
October	21	13	21	55
November	34	21	34	89
December	55	34	55	144

1. Use these rules to fill in the table.
   - Every month, the babies from the month before become adolescents.
   - Every month, the adolescents from the month before become parents. The rabbits that were already parents become parents again.
   - Every month, each pair of parents has a pair of baby rabbits.
2. Continue this number sequence. Each number is the sum of the two numbers before it.
   1 1 2 3 5 8 13 21 34 55 89
3. The numbers in Problem 2 are called the "Fibonacci numbers." Where are the Fibonacci numbers in the table above?
   Each column is a sequence of Fibonacci numbers.

TEACHING MASTER

✦ *Math Masters,* p. 144

8.13 Unit 8 Review and Assessment

OBJECTIVE **To review and assess students' progress on the material covered in Unit 8.**

1 Assess Progress

learning goals	activities
8a **Developing Goal** Write open proportions to model problems. **(Lessons 8.1, 8.2, and 8.6)**	❑ Written Assessment, Problems 12–17
8b **Developing Goal** Solve percent problems. **(Lessons 8.5, 8.7, and 8.8)**	❑ Slate Assessment, Problem 3 ❑ Written Assessment, Problems 16–19 and 23
8c **Developing Goal** Solve problems that involve a size-change factor. **(Lessons 8.9 and 8.10)**	❑ Written Assessment, Problems 26–29
8d **Developing/Secure Goal** Use cross multiplication to solve open proportions. **(Lessons 8.3, 8.6, and 8.7)**	❑ Written Assessment, Problems 8–13
8e **Developing/Secure Goal** Solve rate number stories. **(Lessons 8.1–8.4)**	❑ Written Assessment, Problems 1–4 and 12–15
8f **Developing/Secure Goal** Solve ratio number stories. **(Lessons 8.6 and 8.9–8.12)**	❑ Written Assessment, Problems 16, 17, and 20–29
8g **Developing/Secure Goal** Estimate equivalent percents for fractions. **(Lesson 8.8)**	❑ Slate Assessment, Problem 4 ❑ Written Assessment, Problems 18 and 19
8h **Developing/Secure Goal** Solve division problems that involve decimals. **(Lessons 8.9 and 8.11)**	❑ Written Assessment, Problems 30 and 31
8i **Secure Goal** Use rate tables to solve problems. **(Lessons 8.1 and 8.2)**	❑ Written Assessment, Problems 1, 2, 12, and 13

materials

- ☐ *Math Journal 2,* p. 338
- ☐ Study Link 8.12
- ☐ *Student Reference Book,* p. 317
- ☐ Teaching Master (*Math Masters,* p. 8)
- ☐ Assessment Masters (*Math Masters,* pp. 410–413)
- ☐ recipes

2 Build Background for Unit 9

summaries

Students practice and maintain skills through Math Boxes and Study Link activities.

materials

- ☐ *Math Journal 2,* p. 339
- ☐ Study Link Masters (*Math Masters,* pp. 355–358)

Each **learning goal** listed above indicates a level of performance that might be expected at this point in the *Everyday Mathematics* K–6 curriculum. For a variety of reasons, the levels indicated may not accurately portray your class's performance.

Additional Information

For additional information on assessment for Unit 8, see the *Assessment Handbook,* pages 61–63. For assessment checklists, see *Math Masters,* pages 448, 449, and 468–470.

Getting Started

Math Message
Complete the Time to Reflect *questions on journal page 338.*

Study Link 8.12 Follow-Up
Go over students' answers.

1 Assess Progress

✦ Math Message Follow-Up
(*Math Journal 2,* p. 338)

WHOLE-CLASS DISCUSSION

Students share their answers to the first question.

✦ Oral and Slate Assessments

WHOLE-GROUP ACTIVITY

If the suggested problems below are not appropriate for your class's level of performance, adjust the numbers or the problems themselves to better assess your students' abilities.

Oral Assessment Suggestions

1. Students show thumbs up if the fraction and decimal are equivalent and thumbs down if they are not. (Students may want to write each fraction and decimal on their slates.) *Suggestions:*
   - $\frac{3}{4}$ and 0.75 up
   - $\frac{9}{12}$ and 0.66 down
   - $\frac{4}{5}$ and 0.08 down
   - $\frac{22}{25}$ and 0.88 up
   - $\frac{17}{20}$ and 0.34 down
2. Students show thumbs up if ratios are equivalent and thumbs down if they are not equivalent. *Suggestions:*
   - 3 to 8 and 6 to 10 down
   - 4 out of 9 and 2 out of 18 down
   - 15 for every 20 and 3 for every 4 up
   - 6 out of 8 and 8 out of 12 down
   - 7 to 1 and 21 to 3 up

Time to Reflect

1. Name at least four ways we use ratios or rates in everyday life.
   Answers vary.
2. How would you explain the word *ratio* to a new student who had not studied ratios before?
3. Describe the most difficult thing about solving rate and ratio problems.

STUDENT PAGE

✧ *Math Journal 2,* p. 338

NOTE: Some of these assessment suggestions relate to learning goals that have been addressed in previous units. Now is a good time to evaluate students' progress toward those goals.

Slate Assessment Suggestions

1. Find the reciprocal. (Remind students to think: "What times the number equals 1?") *Suggestions:*
   - $\frac{1}{9}$ 9
   - 6 $\frac{1}{6}$
   - $-\frac{5}{6}$ $-1\frac{1}{5}$
   - $2\frac{3}{4}$ $\frac{4}{11}$
   - $\frac{9}{100}$ $11\frac{1}{9}$
   - 0.4 $2\frac{1}{2}$
2. Given a fraction of a set, find the whole set. *Suggestions:*

   How many marbles are in the bag if
   - $\frac{3}{4}$ of a bag of marbles has 18 marbles? 24
   - $\frac{3}{7}$ of a bag of marbles has 33 marbles? 77
   - $\frac{12}{24}$ of a bag of marbles has 43 marbles? 86
   - $\frac{24}{25}$ of a bag of marbles has 48 marbles? 50
   - $\frac{40}{100}$ of a bag of marbles has 32 marbles? 80
3. Given the sale price and the percent of discount, find the regular price. *Suggestions:*
   - $40 is 80% of the regular price. What is the regular price? $50
   - $28 is the price of a camera that is discounted 20%. What is the regular price? $35
   - A coat is marked down 10%. The sale price is $54. What is the regular price? $60
   - A bicycle is 30% off. The sale price is $210. What is the regular price? $300

   Goal 8b
4. Estimate equivalent percents for fractions. Have students share strategies. *Suggestions:* Sample answers:
   - $\frac{5}{9}$ Just over 50%
   - $\frac{7}{22}$ Just under $33\frac{1}{3}\%$
   - $\frac{32}{41}$ Just under 80%
   - $\frac{12}{17}$ Just under 75%
   - $\frac{19}{94}$ Just over 20%

   Goal 8g
5. Find the product of fractions. *Suggestions:*
   - $\frac{2}{3} * \frac{3}{4}$ $\frac{6}{12}$, or $\frac{1}{2}$
   - $\frac{4}{9} * \frac{2}{7}$ $\frac{8}{63}$
   - $\frac{8}{10} * \frac{6}{7}$ $\frac{48}{70}$, or $\frac{24}{35}$
   - $\frac{4}{5} * \frac{2}{9}$ $\frac{8}{45}$
   - $\frac{7}{11} * \frac{2}{3}$ $\frac{14}{33}$

✦Written Assessment
(*Math Masters,* pp. 410–413)

INDEPENDENT ACTIVITY 

Depending on the needs of students, you may want to work through an example together, reading a problem aloud, discussing it, and providing additional examples as necessary before students work the problem independently.

Each of the problems is listed below and paired with one or more of this unit's learning goals.

- Use rate tables to solve problems. (Problems 1, 2, 12, and 13) **Goals 8e and 8i**
- Write and solve open proportions. (Problems 8–11 and 14–17) **Goals 8a and 8d**
- Solve percent problems. (Problems 16–19 and 23) **Goal 8b**
- Set up and solve ratio problems. (Problems 20–22, 24, and 25) **Goal 8f**
- Use a size-change factor to solve problems. (Problems 26–29) **Goal 8c**
- Divide with decimals. (Problems 30 and 31) **Goal 8h**
- Find unit rates. (Problems 3 and 4) **Goal 8e**
- Use cross multiplication to determine equivalent fractions. (Problems 5–7) **Goal 8d**

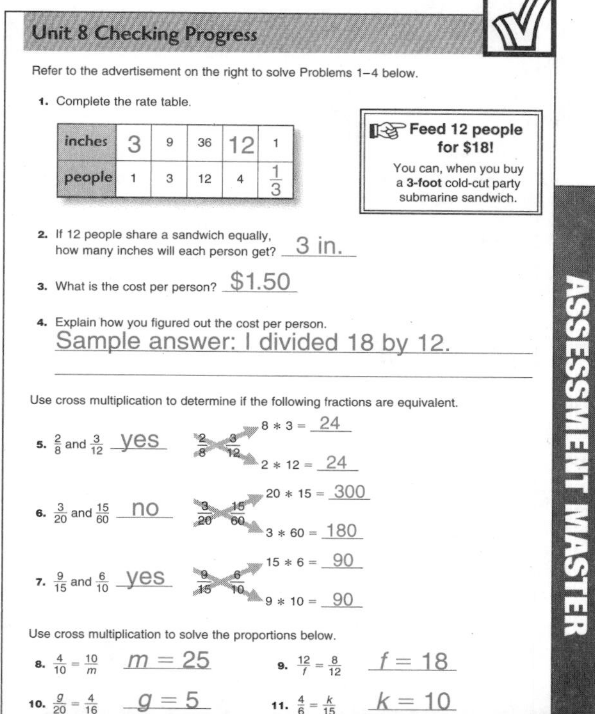

Unit 8 Checking Progress

Refer to the advertisement on the right to solve Problems 1–4 below.

1. Complete the rate table.

inches	3	9	36	12	1
people	1	3	12	4	$\frac{1}{3}$

Feed 12 people for $18!
You can, when you buy a **3-foot** cold-cut party submarine sandwich.

2. If 12 people share a sandwich equally, how many inches will each person get? 3 in.
3. What is the cost per person? $1.50
4. Explain how you figured out the cost per person. Sample answer: I divided 18 by 12.

Use cross multiplication to determine if the following fractions are equivalent.

5. $\frac{2}{8}$ and $\frac{3}{12}$ yes — $8 * 3 = 24$; $2 * 12 = 24$
6. $\frac{3}{20}$ and $\frac{15}{60}$ no — $20 * 15 = 300$; $3 * 60 = 180$
7. $\frac{9}{15}$ and $\frac{6}{10}$ yes — $15 * 6 = 90$; $9 * 10 = 90$

Use cross multiplication to solve the proportions below.

8. $\frac{4}{10} = \frac{10}{m}$ $m = 25$
9. $\frac{12}{f} = \frac{8}{12}$ $f = 18$
10. $\frac{g}{20} = \frac{4}{16}$ $g = 5$
11. $\frac{4}{6} = \frac{k}{15}$ $k = 10$

ASSESSMENT MASTER

✧ *Math Masters,* p. 410

✦ALTERNATIVE ASSESSMENT OPTION
Calculate Amounts of Ingredients

INDEPENDENT ACTIVITY 

Portfolio Ideas

Use this activity, similar to the one in Part 3 of Lesson 8.3, to assess students' ability to use rates to solve problems. Students should bring in a favorite recipe (or you can supply one of your own). They figure out what amounts of ingredients they would need to make 100 servings. Have students rewrite the recipe with the new amounts. They should explain the process they used to make the calculations. Have students attach the original recipe to the paper and collect their work.

NOTE: You may need to vary the amount to be made. If a recipe makes 12 servings, for example, you may want students to make calculations for 240 servings.

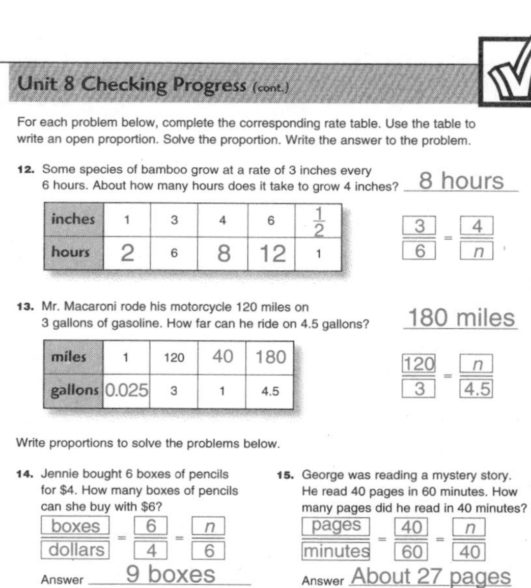

Unit 8 Checking Progress (cont.)

For each problem below, complete the corresponding rate table. Use the table to write an open proportion. Solve the proportion. Write the answer to the problem.

12. Some species of bamboo grow at a rate of 3 inches every 6 hours. About how many hours does it take to grow 4 inches? 8 hours

inches	1	3	4	6	$\frac{1}{2}$
hours	2	6	8	12	1

$\frac{3}{6} = \frac{4}{n}$

13. Mr. Macaroni rode his motorcycle 120 miles on 3 gallons of gasoline. How far can he ride on 4.5 gallons? 180 miles

miles	1	120	40	180
gallons	0.025	3	1	4.5

$\frac{120}{3} = \frac{n}{4.5}$

Write proportions to solve the problems below.

14. Jennie bought 6 boxes of pencils for $4. How many boxes of pencils can she buy with $6?
$\frac{\text{boxes}}{\text{dollars}} = \frac{6}{4} = \frac{n}{6}$
Answer 9 boxes

15. George was reading a mystery story. He read 40 pages in 60 minutes. How many pages did he read in 40 minutes?
$\frac{\text{pages}}{\text{minutes}} = \frac{40}{60} = \frac{n}{40}$
Answer About 27 pages

16. Shawn missed 40% of the questions on the last science test. How many questions did he miss if there were 20 questions on the test?
$\frac{\text{questions missed}}{\text{number of questions}} = \frac{40}{100} = \frac{n}{20}$
Answer 8 questions

17. Melinda went to bat 48 times last season. She had 16 hits. What percent of the time did she make a hit?
$\frac{\text{hits}}{\text{times at bat}} = \frac{16}{48} = \frac{n}{100}$
Answer $33\frac{1}{3}\%$

ASSESSMENT MASTER

✧ *Math Masters,* p. 411

Unit 8 Checking Progress (cont.)

18. The table below shows the calorie and fat content in 1 cup of two kinds of yogurt. Complete the table.

Food Label	Food	Calories from Fat / Total Calories	Estimated Fat Percent
Nutrition Facts: Serving Size 1 cup (225 g); Servings Per Container 1; Amount Per Serving; Calories 260, Calories from Fat 73	strawberry yogurt	$\frac{73}{260}$	About 28%
Nutrition Facts: Serving Size 1 cup (225 g); Servings Per Container 1; Amount Per Serving; Calories 220, Calories from Fat 42	vanilla yogurt	$\frac{42}{220}$	About 19%

19. Explain how you estimated the percent of fat for vanilla yogurt.
Answers vary.

20. Three out of every 5 cards are faceup. If 20 cards are facedown, how many cards are there in all?
50 cards

21. The ratio of facedown to faceup cards is 2 to 3. If there are 25 cards altogether, how many cards are facedown?
10 cards

22. Shade $\frac{4}{5}$ of the circles below.

23. What percent of the circles is shaded?
80%

24. What is the ratio of shaded circles to unshaded circles?
8 to 2, or 8:2

25. How many more unshaded circles would you have to draw so that the ratio of shaded circles to unshaded circles would be 2 to 1?
2 more circles

ASSESSMENT MASTER

◆ *Math Masters*, p. 412

Unit 8 Checking Progress (cont.)

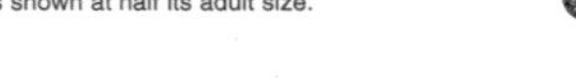

The praying mantis pictured at the right is shown at half its adult size.

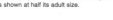

26. The length of the wing in the picture is about 3 centimeters long. What is the actual length of the wing? 6 cm

27. For their science-fiction play, *The Attack of the Bodacious Bugs,* Jaimé and Teresita are making a giant praying mantis that is 10 times its actual size. Circle the best estimate of its length.

1 mm 1 cm 10 cm (1 meter) 1 km

Triangles *ABC* and *ADE* are similar triangles. Sides *AB* and *AE* are each 3 feet long.

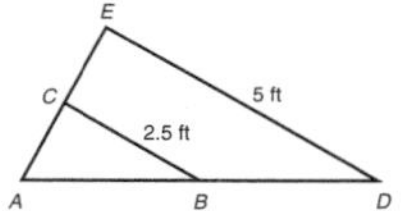

28. What is the length of side *AD*? 6 ft

29. What is the length of side *CA*? 1.5 ft

Divide. Show your work in the space below.

30. 142.72 ÷ 16 = 8.92

31. 32.48 ÷ 2.8 = 11.6

ASSESSMENT MASTER

◆ *Math Masters*, p. 413

◆ ALTERNATIVE ASSESSMENT OPTION
Write Ratio Number Stories

INDEPENDENT ACTIVITY 

Portfolio Ideas

Use this activity from Part 3 of Lesson 8.6 to assess students' understanding of ratios. Students write ratio number stories. Have them include a number model showing how the problem can be solved. Collect students' problems. You may want to refer to the sample rubric given on page 48 of the *Assessment Handbook.*

◆ ALTERNATIVE ASSESSMENT OPTION
Enlarge a Picture (*Student Reference Book,* p. 317; *Math Masters,* p. 8)

INDEPENDENT ACTIVITY 

Portfolio Ideas

Use this first activity from Part 3 of Lesson 8.10 to assess students' understanding of how a size-change factor enlarges a picture. Have students choose a simple picture that is no larger than $\frac{1}{4}$ of an $8\frac{1}{2}$"-by-11" piece of paper. They draw a $\frac{1}{2}$-inch grid on the picture. They should enlarge the part of the picture in each $\frac{1}{2}$-inch square to fill a 1-inch square. (To vary the activity, you might have students draw a $\frac{1}{4}$-inch grid and then enlarge the picture to fill a 1-inch square.)

On the back of their enlarged drawings, ask students to write a brief report explaining the size-change factor they used. To demonstrate that they used the recorded size-change factor, have students make three measurements in the original picture and the corresponding measurements in the enlarged picture.

2 Build Background for Unit 9

✦ Math Boxes 8.13 (*Math Journal 2*, p. 339)

INDEPENDENT ACTIVITY 

Mixed Review The skills in Problems 1 through 5 are prerequisites for Unit 9.

STUDENT PAGE

Math Boxes 8.13

1. Insert parentheses to make each equation true.
   a. $\frac{1}{2} * (18 + 2) * 15 = 150$
   b. $(\frac{1}{2} * 18) + (2 * 15) = 39$
   c. $5 / (3 + 3) * 5 = 4\frac{1}{6}$
   d. $(0.8 * 20) + (10 * 0.7) = 23$
   e. $4 / (9 + 3) * 6 = 2$

2. The circumference of a circle is given by the formula $C = \pi * d$, where C is the circumference and d is the diameter. Circle an equivalent formula.
   $d = C / \pi$ (circled) $d = C * \pi$
   $d = \pi / C$ $d = \pi + C$

   Find the circumference for a circle with a diameter of 5 cm.
   15.7 cm

3. Mr. and Mrs. Gauss keep a record of their expenses on a spreadsheet.

	A	B	C
1	Total of Expense	June	July
2	Rent and Utilities	\$755	\$723
3	Food	\$125	\$189
4	Car Expenses	\$179	\$25
5	Clothing	\$65	\$0
6	Miscellaneous	\$45	\$23
7	Total	\$1,169	\$960

   a. If the Gausses entered the wrong amount for car expenses in July, which cell should they correct? C4
   b. In which month were the total expenses greater? June
   How much greater? \$209
   c. Circle the correct formula for the total for June.
   A7 + B7 + C7 (B2 + B3 + B4 + B5 + B6 circled) (B2 + B3 + B4 + B5 + B6) / 5

4. Solve the equation.
   $-47 + 6z = 3z - 2$
   Solution $z = 15$

5. Add or subtract.
   a. $235 + (-150) =$ 85
   b. $-76 - 24 =$ −100
   c. −115 $= 143 - 258$
   d. 68 $= -99 + 167$
   e. 439 $= 380 - (-59)$

✦ *Math Journal 2*, p. 339

✦ Study Link 8.13: Unit 9 Family Letter (*Math Masters*, pp. 355–358)

Home Connection This Study Link is a four-page newsletter that introduces parents and guardians to Unit 9's topics and terms. The letter also offers ideas for mathematics activities that are supportive of classroom work and can be done at home.

STUDY LINK MASTERS

Family Letter

Study Link 8.13

Unit 9: More about Variables, Formulas, and Graphs

You may be surprised at some of the topics that are covered in Unit 9. Several of them would be traditionally introduced in a first-year algebra course. If you are assisting your child, you might find it useful to refer to the *Student Reference Book* to refresh your memory about topics you have not studied for a number of years.

Your child has been applying many mathematical properties, starting as early as first grade. In Unit 9, the class will explore and apply one of these properties, the distributive property, which can be stated as follows:

For any numbers a, b, and c, $a * (b + c) = (a * b) + (a * c)$.

Students will use this property to simplify algebraic expressions. They will use these simplification procedures, together with the equation-solving methods that were presented in Unit 6, to solve more difficult equations that contain parentheses or like terms on at least one side of the equal sign. Here is an example:

To solve the equation $5(b + 3) - 3b + 5 = 4(b - 1)$,

1. Use the distributive property to remove the parentheses. $5b + 15 - 3b + 5 = 4b - 4$
2. Combine like terms. $2b + 20 = 4b - 4$
3. Solve the equation. $20 = 2b - 4$
   $24 = 2b$
   $b = 12$

Much of Unit 9 also focuses on applying formulas—in computer spreadsheets and in calculating the areas of circles, rectangles, triangles, and parallelograms, the perimeters of polygons, and the circumferences of circles. Formulas for calculating the volumes of rectangular prisms, cylinders, and spheres will also be used to solve a variety of interesting problems.

Finally, your child will be introduced to the Pythagorean Theorem, which states that if a and b are the lengths of the legs of a right triangle and c is the length of the hypotenuse, then $a^2 + b^2 = c^2$. By applying this theorem, students will learn how to calculate long distances indirectly—that is, without actually measuring them.

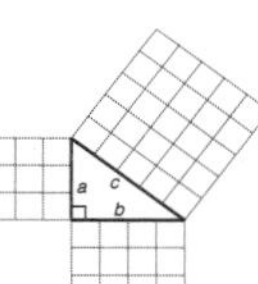

Please keep this Family Letter for reference as your child works through Unit 9.

✦ *Math Masters*, pp. 355–358

Unit 9
More about Variables, Formulas, and Graphs

overview

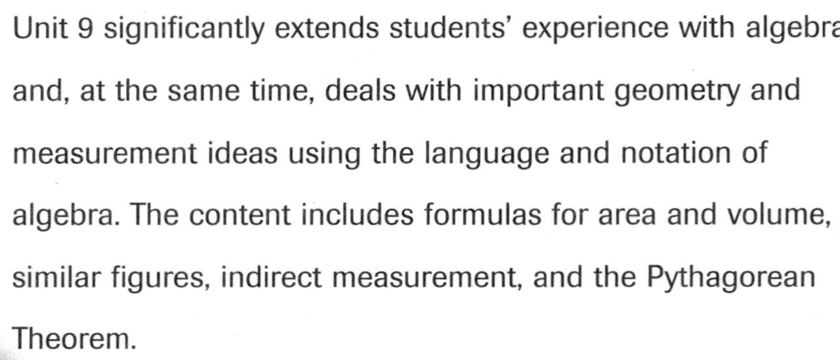

Unit 9 significantly extends students' experience with algebra and, at the same time, deals with important geometry and measurement ideas using the language and notation of algebra. The content includes formulas for area and volume, similar figures, indirect measurement, and the Pythagorean Theorem.

None of the concepts or ideas in Unit 9 are beyond the capabilities of most sixth graders, but some of the problems in the unit are fairly challenging. Most students who do well with Unit 9 can probably handle an algebra course in seventh grade. This does not necessarily mean that they *should* do so. There is much to be gained from taking a pre-algebra course instead, in order to begin algebra in eighth grade with increased maturity and confidence.

contents

Lesson	Objective	Page
9.1	**Area Models for the Distributive Property** *To explore the distributive property of multiplication over addition and over subtraction using area models.*	700
9.2	**The Distributive Property** *To recognize the general patterns used to write the distributive property; and to apply the distributive property to simplify numerical and algebraic expressions.*	704
9.3	**Simplifying Expressions: Combining Like Terms** *To simplify algebraic expressions by combining like terms.*	710
9.4	**Simplifying Expressions: Removing Parentheses** *To simplify expressions by first eliminating parentheses, and then combining like terms.*	715
9.5	**Simplifying and Solving Equations** *To simplify and solve equations.*	720
9.6	**Using Equations to Solve Mobile Problems** *To write and solve equations based on a given formula.*	725
9.7	**Computer Spreadsheets** *To learn how data are entered and displayed in a computer spreadsheet program.*	732
9.8	**Area Formulas with Applications** *To review and use formulas for perimeter, circumference, and area.*	738
9.9	**Volume Formulas with Applications** *To review volume formulas for rectangular prisms, cylinders, and spheres.*	743
9.10	**Solving Equations by Trial and Error** *To approximate the solutions of equations using a trial-and-error method.*	749
9.11	**Formula Equations** *To use formulas to solve problems by substituting for the variables and solving the resulting equations.*	755
9.12	**The Pythagorean Theorem** *To explore the relationship between the square of a number and its square root; and to verify and apply the Pythagorean Theorem.*	761
9.13	**Indirect Measurement Problems** *To find missing lengths in similar figures using a size-change factor.*	768
9.14	**Unit 9 Review and Assessment** *To review and assess students' progress on the material covered in Unit 9.*	773

UNIT 9

learning goals in perspective

	learning goals	links to the past	links to the future
9a	**Developing Goal** Simplify expressions and equations with parentheses. **(Lessons 9.4 and 9.5)**	Grade 4: Review use of parentheses in number sentences. Insert parentheses to make true number sentences. Grade 5: Understand and apply order of operations to evaluate expressions and solve number sentences. Rename fractions and mixed numbers in simplest form. Grade 6: Review the rules for order of operations; evaluate number expressions using order of operations (Unit 6).	Grade 6: Application and maintenance. After Grade 6: Convert expressions and equations to equivalent forms to solve problems.
9b	**Developing/Secure Goal** Apply the distributive property. **(Lessons 9.1, 9.2, 9.4, and 9.5)**	Grades 3–5: Solve problems with parentheses. Grade 6: Understand and apply the commutative and associative properties for addition and multiplication (Unit 6).	After Grade 6: Properties of operations are important in algebra and other mathematics courses.
9c	**Developing/Secure Goal** Combine like terms to simplify expressions and equations. **(Lessons 9.3–9.5)**	See Goals 9a and 9b.	See Goals 9a and 9b.
9d	**Developing/Secure Goal** Solve equations. **(Lessons 9.5, 9.6, and 9.10)**	Grades 4 and 5: Review number sentences, open sentences, and variables; solve addition/subtraction number stories by modeling with open sentences. Grade 6: Solve equations (Unit 6).	Grade 6: Applications and maintenance. After Grade 6: Convert equations to equivalent forms to solve problems.
9e	**Developing/Secure Goal** Write and identify equivalent expressions and equivalent equations. **(Lessons 9.3–9.5)**	See Goals 9a–9c.	See Goals 9a–9c.
9f	**Developing/Secure Goal** Write and solve equations that represent problem situations. **(Lessons 9.1, 9.5, 9.6, and 9.11)**	Grade 4: Develop and apply formulas for area and volume. Grade 5: Write algebraic expressions to represent situations described in words and to express rules for "What's My Rule?" tables. Evaluate expressions. Develop and apply formulas for rates, area, and so on.	Grade 6; Applications and maintenance. After Grade 6: Representing situations with equations and other mathematical models, and using formulas to solve problems, are key elements of mathematics and science.
9g	**Developing/Secure Goal** Use formulas to solve problems. **(Lessons 9.8, 9.9, and 9.11)**		
9h	**Secure Goal** Evaluate expressions and formulas. **(Lessons 9.3, 9.4, 9.8, 9.9, 9.11, and 9.12)**	See Goals 9f and 9g.	See Goals 9f and 9g.

assessment

ongoing • product • periodic

Informal Assessment

Math Boxes These *Math Journal* pages provide opportunities for cumulative review or assessment of concepts and skills.

Ongoing Assessment: Kid Watching Use the Ongoing Assessment suggestions in the following lessons to make quick, on-the-spot observations about students' understanding of:
- Operations and Computation **(Lesson 9.6, Part 2)**
- Patterns, Functions, and Algebra **(Lesson 9.3, Part 1; Lesson 9.4, Part 1; Lesson 9.5, Part 1; Lesson 9.6, Part 1; Lesson 9.10, Part 1; Lesson 9.11, Part 1)**
- Measurement and Reference Frames **(Lesson 9.8, Part 1; Lesson 9.13, Part 1)**

Portfolio Ideas Samples of students' work may be obtained from the following assignments:
- Finding the Area of Rectangles **(Lesson 9.1)**
- Interpreting an Algebra Cartoon **(Lesson 9.3)**
- Using Formulas to Complete a Spreadsheet **(Lesson 9.7)**
- Calculating Floor Space **(Lesson 9.8)**
- Write Volume and Area Number Stories **(Lesson 9.11)**
- Investigating the Pythagorean Theorem **(Lesson 9.12)**
- Solving an Indirect Measurement Problem **(Lesson 9.13)**
- Write Number Stories Involving the Distributive Property; Interpret an Algebra Cartoon; Explore the Area of Parallelograms and Triangles **(Lesson 9.14)**

Unit 9 Review and Assessment

Math Message Use Time to Reflect Problem 2 in Lesson 9.14 to assess students' progress toward the following learning goals: **Goals 9g and 9h**

Oral and Slate Assessments Use oral or slate assessments during Lesson 9.14 to assess students' progress toward the following learning goals: **Goals 9b, 9c, 9e, and 9h**

Written Assessment Use a written review during Lesson 9.14 to assess students' progress toward the following learning goals: **Goals 9a–9h**

Alternative Assessment Options Use independent alternative assessments in Lesson 9.14 to assess students' progress toward the following learning goals: **Goals 9a and 9c–9g**

assessment handbook

For more information on how to use different types of assessment in Unit 9, see the Assessment Overview on pages 64–67 in the *Assessment Handbook*. The following Assessment Masters can be found in the *Math Masters* book:
- Unit 9 Checking Progress, pp. 414–417
- Unit 9 Individual Profile of Progress, p. 451
- Unit 9 Class Checklist, p. 450
- Class Progress Indicator, p. 470
- Math Logs, pp. 473 and 474
- Self-Assessment Forms, pp. 476 and 477
- Interest Inventories, pp. 471 and 472

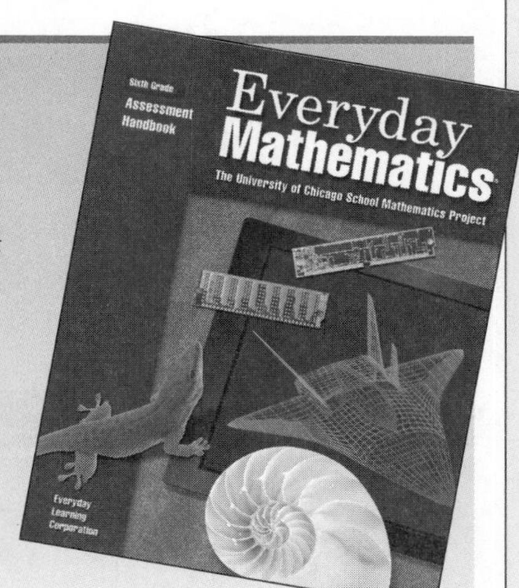

problemsolving

A process of modeling everyday situations using tools from mathematics

Encourage students to use a variety of strategies when attacking a given problem—and to explain those strategies. *Strategies students might use in this unit:*

- Write a number sentence
- Use computation
- Write a number story
- Use a formula
- Use a table (spreadsheet)
- Use a picture/diagram
- Use a graph
- Try and check
- Use physical models

Four Problem-Solving REPRESENTATIONS

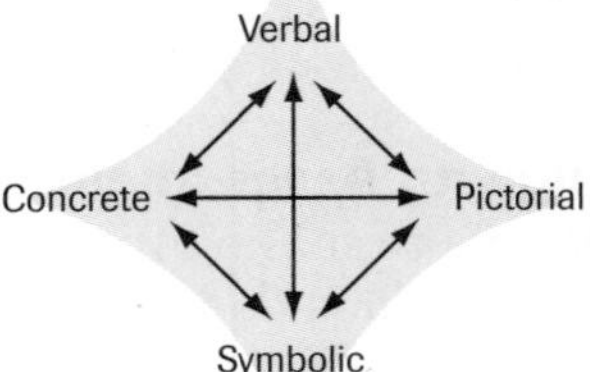

Lessons that teach *through* problem solving, not just *about* problem solving

Lesson	Activity	Lesson	Activity
9.1, 9.4	Find the areas of rectangles partitioned into two parts.	**9.9**	Estimate the volume of the human body by using rectangular prisms, cylinders, and spheres.
9.2, 9.5	Solve number stories using the distributive property.	**9.9**	Solve problems involving data landmarks, step graphs, and mystery graphs.
9.3	Write an explanation to show how a cartoon relates to algebra.	**9.10**	Find approximate solutions for equations; given an 8-inch square, find the dimensions of an open box with the greatest possible volume.
9.6	Find the weights of objects and their distances from the fulcrum to solve mobile problems.	**9.11**	Solve problems involving a variety of formulas.
9.7	Solve problems about the class picnic budget, about circumferences/areas of circles, and about the stopping distance for an automobile.	**9.12**	Verify the Pythagorean Theorem and use it to solve problems.
9.8	Calculate the open area of the classroom floor; solve perimeter, circumference, and area problems.	**9.13**	Solve indirect measurement problems.

For more information about problem solving in *Everyday Mathematics,* see the *Teacher's Reference Manual.*

cross-curricularlinks

art

- Students research mobiles, possibly those of Alexander Calder, a famous artist whose work may be at your local art museum. **(Lesson 9.6)**

science

- Students estimate the volume of the human body. **(Lesson 9.9)**

technology

- Students enter data and formulas into a spreadsheet. They experiment with changing the values of columns that do not involve formulas. **(Lesson 9.7)**
- Students use calculators to solve square root problems. **(Lesson 9.12)**

language arts

- Students read *G Is for Googol,* an alphabet book in which math concepts are humorously discussed. **(Lesson 9.4)**

literature

- Students experiment with perimeters through the book *Sir Cumference and the First Round Table,* a fanciful tale about the knights of Camelot. **(Lesson 9.11)**

meeting INDIVIDUAL needs

UNIVERSAL ACCESS

✦ RETEACHING

The following features provide additional instructional support:

Adjusting the Activity

- **Lesson 9.2, Part 1**
- **Lesson 9.3, Part 1**
- **Lesson 9.5, Part 1**
- **Lesson 9.6, Part 1**
- **Lesson 9.7, Part 1**
- **Lesson 9.8, Part 1**
- **Lesson 9.13, Part 1**

Options for Individualizing

- **Lesson 9.1** Playing *Multiplication Wrestling*
- **Lesson 9.2** Using the Distributive Property
- **Lesson 9.3** Playing *Algebra Election*
- **Lesson 9.5** Solving Pan-Balance Problems
- **Lesson 9.7** Playing *Hidden Treasure*
- **Lesson 9.8** Exploring the Areas of Parallelograms and Triangles
- **Lesson 9.10** Playing *Getting to One*

✦ ENRICHMENT

The following features suggest enrichment and extension activities:

Adjusting the Activity

- **Lesson 9.2, Part 1**
- **Lesson 9.3, Part 1**
- **Lesson 9.4, Part 1**
- **Lesson 9.7, Part 1**
- **Lesson 9.10, Part 1**
- **Lesson 9.11, Part 1**

Options for Individualizing

- **Lesson 9.2** Writing Number Stories
- **Lesson 9.3** Interpreting an Algebra Cartoon
- **Lesson 9.4** Reading a Math Dictionary
- **Lesson 9.6** Researching Mobiles
- **Lesson 9.6** Balancing a Complicated Mobile
- **Lesson 9.7** Using Formulas to Complete a Spreadsheet
- **Lesson 9.9** Comparing Capacities
- **Lesson 9.10** Maximizing the Volume of a Rectangular Prism
- **Lesson 9.11** Solving Perimeter Problems
- **Lesson 9.12** Investigating the Pythagorean Theorem

✦ LANGUAGE DIVERSITY

The following features suggest ways to support students who are acquiring proficiency in English:

Adjusting the Activity

- **Lesson 9.2, Part 3**
- **Lesson 9.4, Part 3**
- **Lesson 9.8, Part 1**
- **Lesson 9.11, Part 3**

Options for Individualizing

- **Lesson 9.2** Building Background for Mathematics Words

✦ MULTIAGE CLASSROOM

The following chart lists related lessons from Grade 5 that can help you meet your instructional needs:

Grade 5								8.6 9.4– 9.7 10.9	9.8 9.9 11.3– 11.5				
Grade 6	9.1	9.2	9.3	9.4	9.5	9.6	9.7	9.8	9.9	9.10	9.11	9.12	9.13

materials

lesson	math masters pages	manipulative kit items	other items
9.1	Study Link Master, p 359 Teaching Masters, pp. 7, 145, and 146	number cards (from the Everything Math Deck, if available)	Geometry Template protractor
9.2	Study Link Master, p. 360 Teaching Masters, pp. 89, 90 (*Polygon Capture* cards); and 147 ***See* Advance Preparation, p. 704**		slate dictionary
9.3	Study Link Master, p. 361 Teaching Masters, pp. 102 and 103 (Electoral Vote Map); and 148 Assessment Master, p. 478 (optional) ***See* Advance Preparation, p. 710**	six-sided die	slate; calculator; protractor 4 pennies or counters *Algebra Election* cards (See Lesson 6.7) Geometry Template
9.4	Study Link Master, p. 362 Teaching Master, p. 149 ***See* Advance Preparation, p. 715**		*G Is for Googol* ***See* Advance Preparation, p. 715**
9.5	Study Link Master, p. 363 Teaching Master, p. 150 ***See* Advance Preparation, p. 720**		Geometry Template protractor
9.6	Study Link Master, p. 364 Teaching Master, p. 151 Assessment Master, p. 473 or 474 (optional)		calculator Geometry Template
9.7	Study Link Master, p. 365 Teaching Masters, pp. 44, 152, 154, and 155 transparency of Teaching Master, p. 153 (optional) ***See* Advance Preparation, p. 732**	compass	calculator red coloring pencil or crayon computer with spreadsheet software cm ruler
9.8	Study Link Master, p. 366 Teaching Masters, pp. 156-158		cm ruler; calculator; Geometry Template scissors; transparent tape At least one each per group: builder's (long) tape measure ruler, yardstick
9.9	Study Link Master, p. 367 Teaching Masters, pp. 160 and 161 transparency of Teaching Master, p. 159 (optional)	compass	centimeter ruler; calculator; cylinder or food can Per partnership: tape; rice or beans; a tray or tub container for the rice or beans; 2 pieces of $8\frac{1}{2}$"-by-11" paper; measuring cup or graduated cylinder ***See* Advanced Preparation p. 743**
9.10	Study Link Master, p. 368 Teaching Master, p. 162		calculator; 8-in. square paper; pan balance and metric weights (optional) ***See* Advanced Preparation p. 749**
9.11	Study Link Master, p. 369		calculator; *Sir Cumference and the First Round Table;* protractor ***See* Advanced Preparation p. 755**
9.12	Study Link Master, p. 370 Teaching Masters, pp. 7, 163, and 164		calculator; cm ruler; blank sheet of paper with square corners scissors; glue or tape
9.13	Study Link Master, p. 371 Teaching Masters, pp. 165 and 166 Assessment Master, p. 478 (optional)		calculator; Geometry Template protractor Per group of 4: 2 metersticks; tape measure
9.14	Study Link Masters, pp. 372-375 Teaching Masters, pp. 148 and 156-158 Assessment Masters, pp. 414-417		slate; Geometry Template

planningtips

Pacing

Pacing depends on a number of factors, such as students' individual needs and how long your school has been using *Everyday Mathematics.* At the beginning of Unit 9, review your Content by Strand Poster to help you set a monthly pace.

APRIL	MAY	JUNE
← MOST CLASSROOMS →		

Using the Projects

Use Project 8, Mathematics and Poetry, during or after Unit 9, to explore poetical use of patterns, systems of rules, and abstract forms. The projects can be found at the back of the *Teacher's Lesson Guide.*

Home Communication

Share Study Links 9.1–9.13 with families to help them understand the content and procedures in this unit. At the end of the unit, use Study Link 9.14 to introduce Unit 10. Supplemental information can be found in the *Home Connection Handbook*.

NCTM Standards

Standard	1	2	3	4	5	6	7	8	9	10
Unit 9 Lessons	9.1, 9.2, 9.4–9.7, 9.10, 9.12	9.1–9.12	9.2, 9.12, 9.13	9.1, 9.3, 9.7–9.11, 9.13	9.7, 9.9	9.1–9.14	9.1–9.14	9.1–9.14	9.1–9.14	9.1–9.14

Content Standards
1 Number and Operations
2 Algebra
3 Geometry
4 Measurement
5 Data Analysis and Probability

Process Standards
6 Problem Solving
7 Reasoning and Proof
8 Communication
9 Connections
10 Representation

PRACTICE *through* Games

Everyday Mathematics uses games to help students develop good fact power and other math skills.

- *Name That Number* to practice writing number sentences using order of operations **(Lesson 9.1)**
- *Multiplication Wrestling* to practice using the distributive property **(Lesson 9.1)**
- *Polygon Capture* to practice identifying the properties of polygons **(Lesson 9.2)**
- *Algebra Election* to practice solving problems involving variables **(Lesson 9.3)**
- *Hidden Treasure* to practice plotting and naming points with ordered number pairs **(Lesson 9.7)**
- *Getting to One* to practice estimation and using trial-and-error to find mystery numbers **(Lesson 9.10)**
- *3-D Shape Sort* to practice with attributes of 3-dimensional shapes **(Lesson 9.12)**

unit 9 content highlights

NOTE: You may choose to skip part or all of this unit, administer the end-of-year assessment to help you identify the concepts and skills students need to review and practice, and/or combine review sessions with the lessons of Unit 10 and with other independent projects.

The discussion below highlights the major content ideas presented in Unit 9 and may help you establish instructional priorities.

The Distributive Property (Lessons 9.1 and 9.2)

Students in *Everyday Mathematics* have been exposed to the distributive property in previous grades—in inventing mental arithmetic procedures (for example: "To find 15 times 6, I take 10 sixes and add 5 sixes"); in playing *Multiplication Wrestling*; and in using the partial-products multiplication algorithm, the lattice method of multiplication, and the partial-quotients division algorithm. The purpose of Lessons 9.1 and 9.2 is to summarize the various forms of the distributive property in preparation for the work with simplifying algebraic expressions and equations beginning in Lesson 9.3.

Partial-Products Algorithm

$$\begin{array}{r} 27 \\ \underline{*\ 32} \\ 600 \\ 210 \\ 40 \\ \underline{+\ 14} \\ 864 \end{array}$$

Multiplication Wrestling

$$\begin{aligned} 27 * 32 &= (20 + 7) * (30 + 2) \\ &= (20 * 30) + (20 * 2) + (7 * 30) + (7 * 2) \\ &= 600 + 40 + 210 + 14 \\ &= 864 \end{aligned}$$

$$(a + b)(c + d) = ac + ad + bc + bd$$

The distributive property is usually applied to the product of two factors, in which one of the factors is a single number and the other factor the sum or difference of two numbers. The single factor is "distributed" over the parts that make up the other factor. For example, $3 * (5 + 7) = (3 * 5) + (3 * 7)$ and $3 * (12 - 7) = (3 * 12) - (3 * 7)$. The distributive property is illustrated in Lesson 9.1 by an area model. Lesson 9.2 presents a more formal treatment of the distributive property and provides practice in its application.

Area = $5 * (3 + 7) = 50$

Area = $(5 * 3) + (5 * 7)$

Area = 50

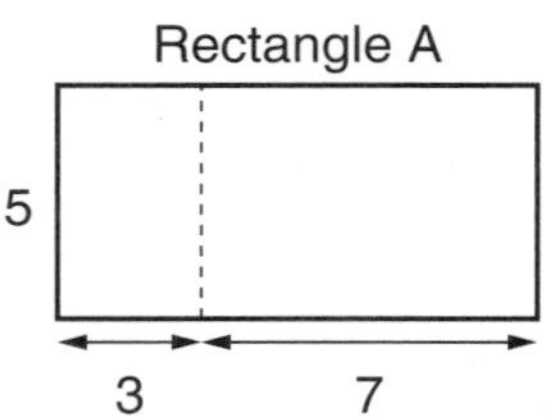

The distributive property also applies to products where both the factors are sums (or differences) or where the sums (or differences) involve more than two terms. The principle is always the same: Every part of one factor is multiplied by every part of the other factor, and then the products are added (or subtracted).

The distributive property may also be used to isolate a common factor in the numbers that make up a sum or difference (for example, $21 + 35 = (7 * 3) + (7 * 5) = 7 * (3 + 5)$). This "factoring" procedure is commonly used in certain algebraic manipulations.

Simplifying Algebraic Expressions and Solving Equations (Lessons 9.3-9.6)

In Unit 6, students learned to solve relatively simple equations, containing at most one variable term on each side of the equal sign. In Lesson 9.5, they learn to solve more complex equations; these may contain several like variable terms on one or both sides of the equal sign and/or expressions in parentheses. Such equations must first be "simplified" by combining like terms and/or eliminating parentheses.

The simplification procedures, which are based on the distributive property, are presented in Lessons 9.3 and 9.4 and applied to the solution of equations in Lesson 9.5.

In Lesson 9.6, students explore the mathematics of balanced mobiles made of a rod and objects suspended from the rod. They write and solve equations to find the weight of these objects and their distances from the fulcrum (the balancing point) of the rod.

Simplifying Expressions

$9x + 3 - 2x + 5 = 7x + 8$

Solving Equations

$9x + 3 - 2x + 5 = 22$

1. Simplify: $7x + 8 = 22$

2. Solve: $7x = 14$

$x = 2$

Computer Spreadsheets (Lesson 9.7)

This is an optional lesson on a favorite business tool. When done by hand on ledger paper, spreadsheets were a practical way of organizing data, but their usefulness was limited. In the early days of the personal computer, a computer program was created that made it possible to work with spreadsheets efficiently by linking entries so that a change in one entry was automatically reflected in all related entries. As one of the first practical applications of microcomputers in business, spreadsheet programs were an instant success. They put the microcomputer revolution into high gear and revolutionized business practice. Over the years, spreadsheet programs, such as Lotus 1-2-3™ and Microsoft Excel™, have become increasingly sophisticated; they can solve complex financial problems and create wonderfully informative graphs and charts. Most of your students will probably use some form of computer spreadsheet in their adult lives.

Class Picnic ($)

	A	B	C	D
1		budget for class picnic		
2				
3	quantity	food items	unit price	cost
4	6	packages of hamburgers	2.79	16.74
5	5	packages of hamburger buns	1.29	6.45
6	3	bags of potato chips	3.12	9.36
7	3	quarts of macaroni salad	4.50	13.50
8	4	bottles of soft drinks	1.69	6.76
9			subtotal	52.81
10			8% tax	4.23
11			total	57.04

Students were introduced to spreadsheets in Lessons 3.7 and 3.8. Lesson 9.7 reviews and extends this first experience by illustrating how various kinds of data (labels, numbers, and formulas) are entered and displayed with a computer spreadsheet program. Students practice using formulas to complete a spreadsheet and use spreadsheet data to draw graphs.

Formulas (Lessons 9.8, 9.9, and 9.11)

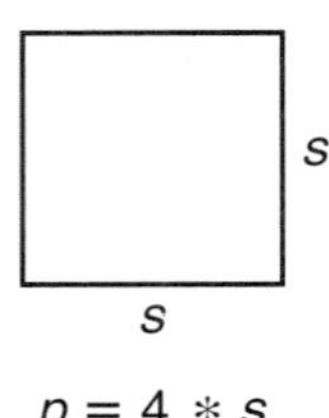

$p = 4 * s$

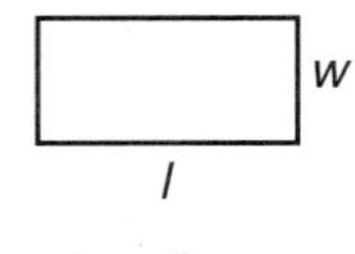

$A = l * w$

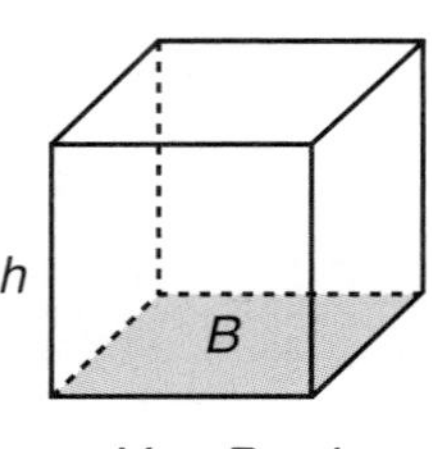

$V = B * h$

Variables are found in equations, formulas, and expressions of functions. In the world of mathematics, algebra is associated primarily with the solving of equations; but in the real world, formulas are often the source from which equations and expressions of functions are derived. Thus, all these uses of variables are interrelated.

In Lessons 9.8, 9.9, and 9.11, students use formulas to review and extend their knowledge of the perimeter and area of polygons, the circumference and area of circles, and the volume of 3-dimensional figures.

In Lesson 9.9, students approximate the volume of an "average" person by modeling the head as a sphere and most other parts of the body as cylinders. This procedure involves quite a bit of rounding, so there may be a variety of equally valid approximations.

A good way to check the validity of an answer is to use units analysis, a technique frequently taught in science courses. For example, in an area problem, if the dimensions of a figure are given in centimeters, then the unit of area will be centimeters * centimeters, or square centimeters; in a volume problem, the unit will be centimeters * centimeters * centimeters, or cubic centimeters. If the product of the units is different from the expected result, then it is likely that a mistake was made in finding the number part of the answer (for example, a step may have been omitted, or the wrong operation may have been chosen).

A word of caution: Some products and quotients of numbers give answers that are more precise than could actually be the case. All measures should be rounded to a degree of accuracy that is appropriate for that context. Answers should conform to the precision of the given dimensions. In some problems, measures must be converted from one unit to another so that calculations are performed on dimensions that have the same unit (for example, one does not multiply feet by inches). Some guidance is provided in the problems in these lessons, but the development of measure sense is more a matter of experience and discussion than of specific rules.

Solving Equations by Trial and Error (Lesson 9.10)

A trial-and-error approach to solving equations was introduced in *Fourth Grade Everyday Mathematics,* but only for equations with relatively "easy" solutions. The same method is used in this lesson, but the equations are considerably more difficult. Indeed, it is the only method for solving these equations available to students at this time. The idea is to zero in on the solution through a series of approximations, until an approximation of the solution is obtained that is very close to the actual solution. Algorithms for solving equations are taught in high school and college mathematics, but even there, successive approximations that often exploit the speed and power of computers may be the preferred, and sometimes the only, way of solving a problem. This is especially true of many applications in science and industry.

An optional activity in this lesson serves as an introduction to a large class of problems, in which the largest (or smallest) possible answer is sought under specified conditions. Students try to find the maximum volume of an open box made from grid paper, with given dimensions, using trial and error.

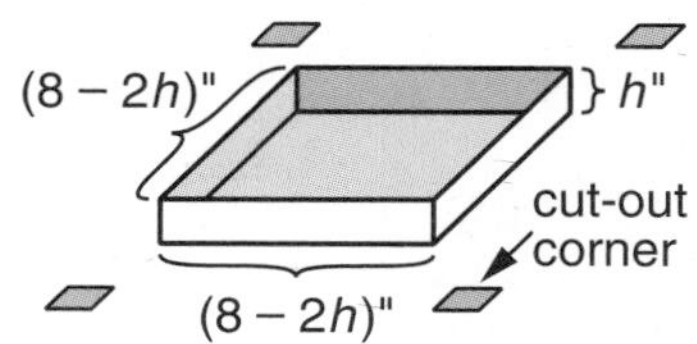

Box made by cutting square corners and folding up sides

This lesson reviews concepts and skills from preceding lessons. Probably the best way to handle this lesson is to put partners to work on the problems.

The Pythagorean Theorem (Lesson 9.12)

This lesson begins with a review of squares and square roots as a prerequisite to the main part of the lesson on the Pythagorean Theorem. A square root of a number a is a number b, which, when squared, is equal to the original number a. For example, a square root of 25 is 5, because 5 squared is equal to 25. Every positive number has two square roots—a positive and a negative square root. Thus, the negative square root of 25 is -5, because $-5 * (-5) = 25$.

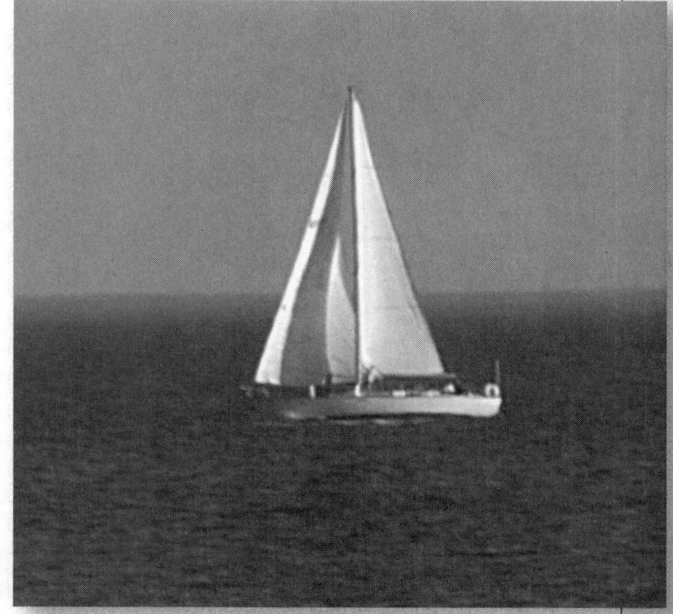

In mathematics, a function expresses a relationship between two sets of values so that for every valid input value, there is a *single* output value. Thus, the *square root function* is defined to give only one result, the positive square root. The square root function is written with the "radical" symbol, $\sqrt{\ }$. Explain to your students that whenever they see this symbol, they are to find *only* the positive square root of the number.

The calculators used in your class will show the distinction between the definition of *square root* and the definition of the *square-root function*—both 5^2 and $(-5)^2$ will show 25 in the display, but [$\sqrt{\ }$] 25 will display only 5.

The Pythagorean Theorem is considered one of humankind's foremost intellectual accomplishments, even apart from its usefulness in many situations. The essay on page 155 of the *Student Reference Book* deals with both its substance and its importance, and the authors suggest that you read it before teaching the lesson. Plan to spend more than one day on the lesson.

Indirect Measurement (Lesson 9.13)

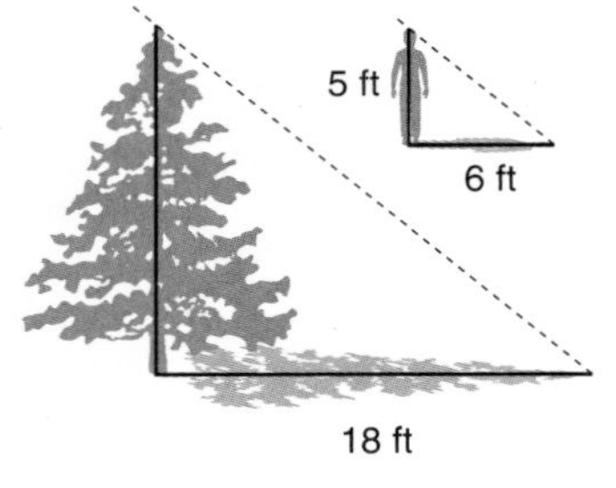

As you may remember from your own geometry course in school, similar figures are an important part of geometry and have many applications in the real world. Similar figures have exactly the same shape but may not be the same size. The size difference is defined by a ratio, or size-change factor, that converts any length in one figure into a corresponding length in the other figure. This makes it possible to measure lengths and distances that are physically inaccessible. For example, one can use the size-change factor to find the dimensions of a larger, similar figure.

This lesson lends itself to interesting projects, in which students suggest physically inaccessible measures they would like to determine and then find ways to do so indirectly.

Review and Assessment (Lesson 9.14)

The Unit 9 assessment in Lesson 9.14 includes oral, slate, and written assessments of the following concepts and skills:

- ▷ applying the distributive property
- ▷ simplifying expressions and equations
- ▷ writing and identifying equivalent expressions and equations
- ▷ evaluating expressions and formulas
- ▷ solving equations
- ▷ writing and solving equations that represent problem situations
- ▷ using formulas to solve problems

For additional information on the following topics, see the *Teacher's Reference Manual:*

- calculators
- reading and writing number sentences
- solving open sentences
- uses of variables

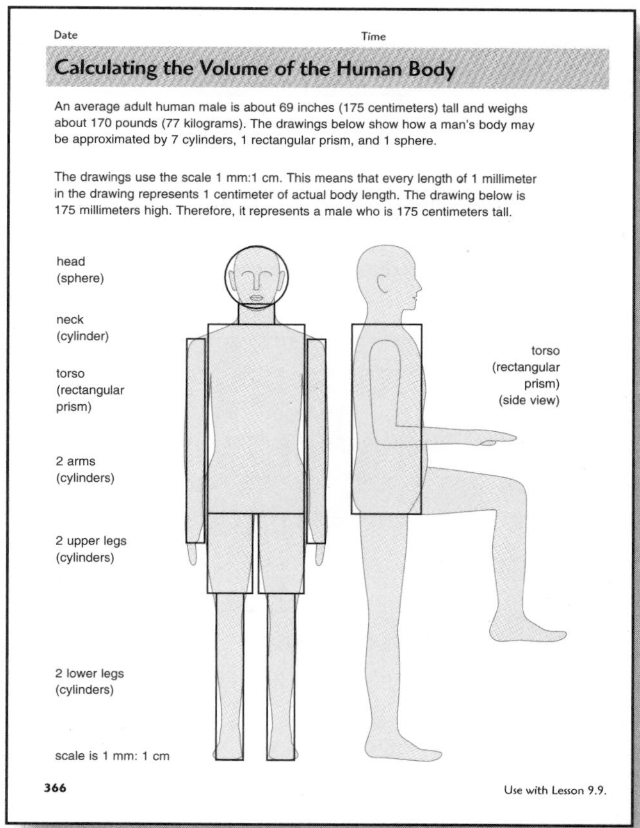
Date Time

Calculating the Volume of the Human Body

An average adult human male is about 69 inches (175 centimeters) tall and weighs about 170 pounds (77 kilograms). The drawings below show how a man's body may be approximated by 7 cylinders, 1 rectangular prism, and 1 sphere.

The drawings use the scale 1 mm:1 cm. This means that every length of 1 millimeter in the drawing represents 1 centimeter of actual body length. The drawing below is 175 millimeters high. Therefore, it represents a male who is 175 centimeters tall.

366 Use with Lesson 9.9.

9.1 Area Models for the Distributive Property

OBJECTIVE **To explore the distributive property of multiplication over addition and over subtraction using area models.**

summaries	materials
1 Teaching the Lesson	
Students write number sentences to represent two methods of finding the areas of rectangles partitioned into two parts. [Patterns, Functions, and Algebra; Measurement and Reference Frames]	☐ *Math Journal 2,* pp. 340 and 341
2 Ongoing Learning & Practice	
Students play *Name That Number* to practice order of operations, computation, and problem solving. [Operations and Computation] Students practice and maintain skills through Math Boxes and Study Link activities.	☐ *Math Journal 2,* p. 342 ☐ *Student Reference Book,* p. 301 ☐ Study Link Master (*Math Masters,* p. 359) ☐ number cards (from the Everything Math Deck, if available) ☐ protractor
3 Options for Individualizing	
Reteaching Students play *Multiplication Wrestling* to practice using the distributive property. [Operations and Computation] **Extra Practice** Students draw rectangles on grid paper and find the areas using the distributive property. [Patterns, Functions, and Algebra; Measurement and Reference Frames]	☐ Teaching Masters (*Math Masters,* pp. 7, 145, and 146) ☐ 4 each of number cards 0–9 (from the Everything Math Deck, if available) ***See* Advance Preparation**

Additional Information

Advance Preparation For the optional Reteaching activity in Part 3, review the rules for *Multiplication Wrestling* if necessary.

Getting Started

Mental Math and Reflexes

Write improper fractions on the board. Students write equivalent mixed numbers or whole numbers on their slates. *Suggestions:*

- $\frac{24}{3}$ 8
- $\frac{30}{6}$ 5
- $\frac{27}{5}$ $5\frac{2}{5}$
- $\frac{19}{8}$ $2\frac{3}{8}$
- $\frac{29}{9}$ $3\frac{2}{9}$
- $\frac{34}{7}$ $4\frac{6}{7}$

Math Message

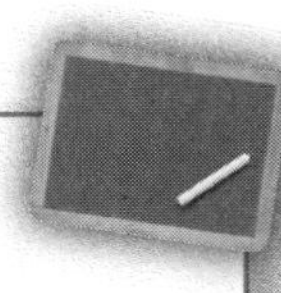

Complete Problem 1 on journal page 340.

Teaching the Lesson

✦ Math Message Follow-Up
(*Math Journal 2,* p. 340)

WHOLE-CLASS DISCUSSION

Draw a picture of Rectangle A on the board and ask students to explain how they solved the problem. Make sure that both of the following methods are mentioned and write the number sentences shown in the margin to represent each method.

▷ Method 1: Find the length of the longer side by adding 3 and 7. Multiply the result by 5.

▷ Method 2: Multiply 5 by 3 to find the area of one part of the rectangle. Multiply 5 by 7 to find the area of the other part of the rectangle. Add the results.

Ask students to look for patterns in the number sentences. *For example:*

- *The numbers on the left sides of the sentences under each method have been "turned around."*
- *The number outside the parentheses in Method 1 appears inside both parentheses in Method 2.*
- *To find the answer in Method 1, you add first and then you multiply. To find the answer in Method 2, you multiply first and then you add.*

Write an example of the partial-products algorithm on the board. *For example:*

```
   52
 *  8
  400
+  16
  416
```

Ask: *Does this algorithm use Method 1 or Method 2?* Method 2

Pose one or two more problems like the Math Message problem. With the help of the class, find the area of the rectangle using both methods and write number sentences on the board to represent each solution.

Example

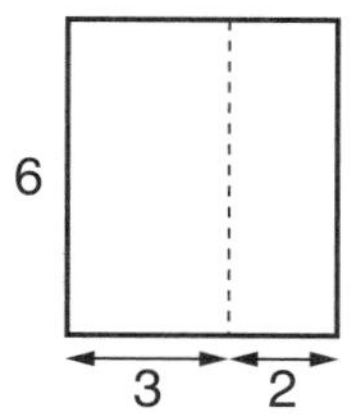

Method 1	Method 2
$6 * (3 + 2) = 30$	$(6 * 3) + (6 * 2) = 30$
$(3 + 2) * 6 = 30$	$(3 * 6) + (2 * 6) = 30$

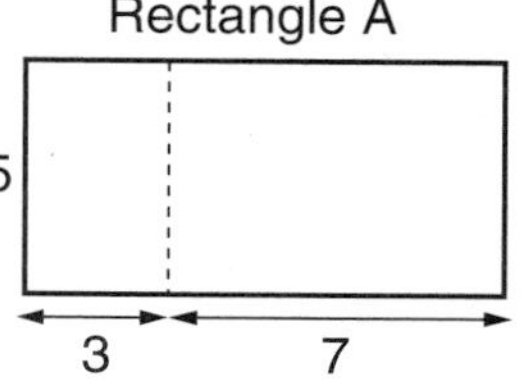

Area = $5 * (3 + 7) = 50$
Area = $(5 * 3) + (5 * 7) = 50$

Method 1	Method 2
$5 * (3 + 7) = 50$	$(5 * 3) + (5 * 7) = 50$
$(3 + 7) * 5 = 50$	$(3 * 5) + (7 * 5) = 50$

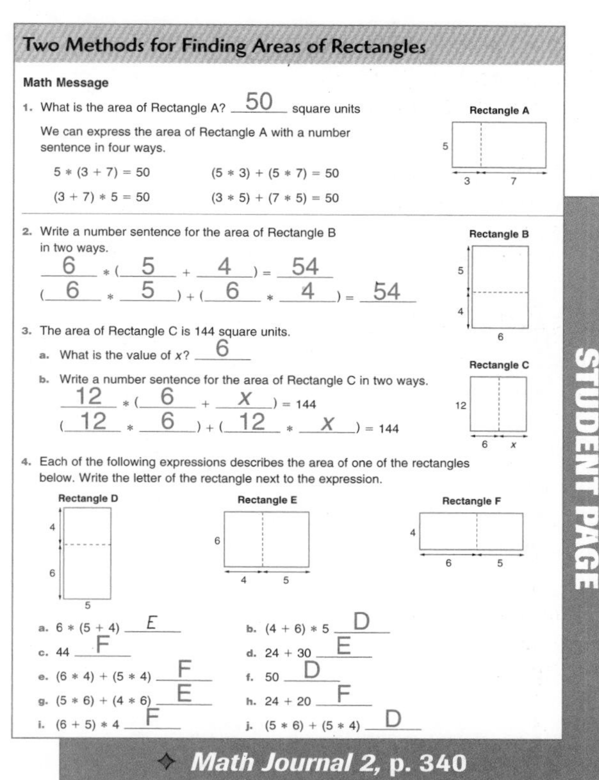

Two Methods for Finding Areas of Rectangles

Math Message

1. What is the area of Rectangle A? 50 square units

   We can express the area of Rectangle A with a number sentence in four ways.

   $5 * (3 + 7) = 50$ $(5 * 3) + (5 * 7) = 50$

   $(3 + 7) * 5 = 50$ $(3 * 5) + (7 * 5) = 50$

2. Write a number sentence for the area of Rectangle B in two ways.

   6 * (5 + 4) = 54

   (6 * 5) + (6 * 4) = 54

3. The area of Rectangle C is 144 square units.

   a. What is the value of *x*? 6

   b. Write a number sentence for the area of Rectangle C in two ways.

   12 * (6 + X) = 144

   (12 * 6) + (12 * X) = 144

4. Each of the following expressions describes the area of one of the rectangles below. Write the letter of the rectangle next to the expression.

   a. $6 * (5 + 4)$ E b. $(4 + 6) * 5$ D
   c. 44 F d. $24 + 30$ E
   e. $(6 * 4) + (5 * 4)$ F f. 50 D
   g. $(5 * 6) + (4 * 6)$ E h. $24 + 20$ F
   i. $(6 + 5) * 4$ F j. $(5 * 6) + (5 * 4)$ D

✦ *Math Journal 2,* p. 340

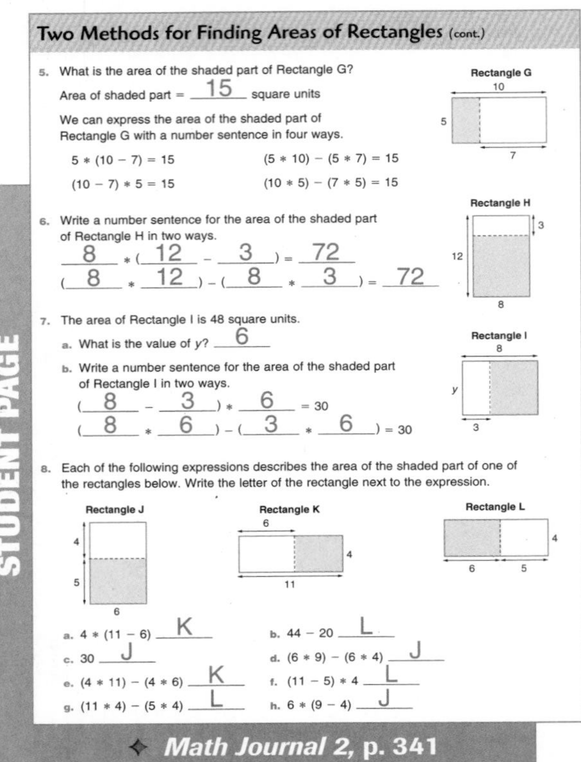
STUDENT PAGE

Two Methods for Finding Areas of Rectangles (cont.)

5. What is the area of the shaded part of Rectangle G?
   Area of shaded part = 15 square units
   We can express the area of the shaded part of Rectangle G with a number sentence in four ways.
   $5 * (10 - 7) = 15$ $(5 * 10) - (5 * 7) = 15$
   $(10 - 7) * 5 = 15$ $(10 * 5) - (7 * 5) = 15$

6. Write a number sentence for the area of the shaded part of Rectangle H in two ways.
   $8 * (12 - 3) = 72$
   $(8 * 12) - (8 * 3) = 72$

7. The area of Rectangle I is 48 square units.
   a. What is the value of y? 6
   b. Write a number sentence for the area of the shaded part of Rectangle I in two ways.
   $(8 - 3) * 6 = 30$
   $(8 * 6) - (3 * 6) = 30$

8. Each of the following expressions describes the area of the shaded part of one of the rectangles below. Write the letter of the rectangle next to the expression.
   a. $4 * (11 - 6)$ K
   b. $44 - 20$ L
   c. 30 J
   d. $(6 * 9) - (6 * 4)$ J
   e. $(4 * 11) - (4 * 6)$ K
   f. $(11 - 5) * 4$ L
   g. $(11 * 4) - (5 * 4)$ L
   h. $6 * (9 - 4)$ J

✦ *Math Journal 2,* p. 341

✦ Representing Area Problems with Number Sentences (*Math Journal 2,* pp. 340 and 341)

PARTNER ACTIVITY

Assign Problems 2–5. Circulate and assist. When most students have completed the problems, discuss Problem 5. If necessary, pose another problem like it, or do Problem 6 as a class. Partners then complete the rest of journal page 341 on their own. When most students have completed the problems, bring the class together to discuss the answers.

2 Ongoing Learning & Practice

✦ Playing *Name That Number* (*Student Reference Book,* p. 301)

PARTNER ACTIVITY

Students play this game, introduced in Lesson 1.3, to practice writing number sentences and using order of operations.

✦ Math Boxes 9.1 (*Math Journal 2,* p. 342)

INDEPENDENT ACTIVITY 

Mixed Review Math Boxes in this lesson are paired with Math Boxes in Lessons 9.3 and 9.5. The skill in Problem 1 is a prerequisite for Unit 10.

✦ Study Link 9.1 (*Math Masters,* p. 359)

Home Connection Students solve number stories, some of which may be solved mentally by applying the distributive property.

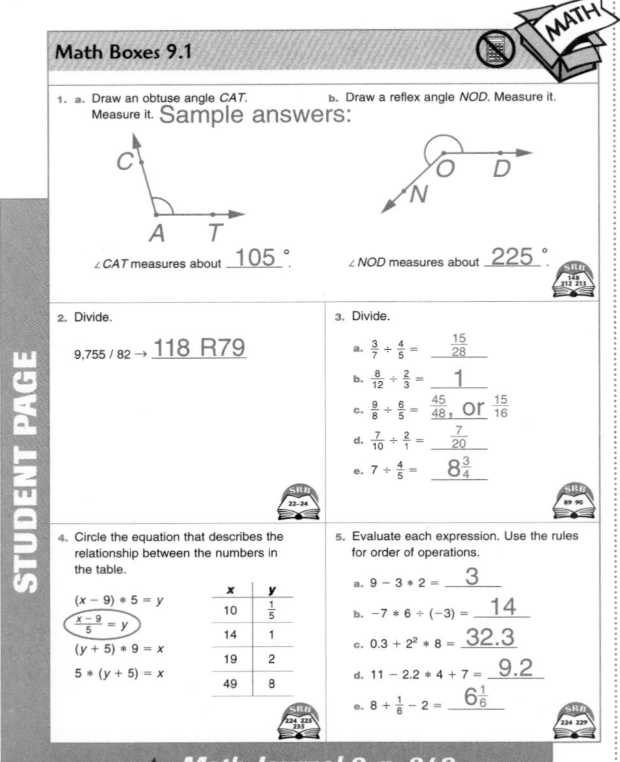
STUDENT PAGE

Math Boxes 9.1

1. a. Draw an obtuse angle CAT. Measure it. Sample answers:
   $\angle CAT$ measures about 105°.
   b. Draw a reflex angle NOD. Measure it.
   $\angle NOD$ measures about 225°.

2. Divide.
   9,755 / 82 → 118 R79

3. Divide.
   a. $\frac{3}{7} \div \frac{4}{5} = \frac{15}{28}$
   b. $\frac{8}{12} \div \frac{2}{3} = 1$
   c. $\frac{9}{8} \div \frac{6}{5} = \frac{45}{48}$, or $\frac{15}{16}$
   d. $\frac{7}{10} \div \frac{2}{1} = \frac{7}{20}$
   e. $7 \div \frac{4}{5} = 8\frac{3}{4}$

4. Circle the equation that describes the relationship between the numbers in the table.
   $(x - 9) * 5 = y$
   $\frac{x - 9}{5} = y$ (circled)
   $(y + 5) * 9 = x$
   $5 * (y + 5) = x$

x	y
10	$\frac{1}{5}$
14	1
19	2
49	8

5. Evaluate each expression. Use the rules for order of operations.
   a. $9 - 3 * 2 = 3$
   b. $-7 * 6 \div (-3) = 14$
   c. $0.3 + 2^2 * 8 = 32.3$
   d. $11 - 2.2 * 4 + 7 = 9.2$
   e. $8 + \frac{1}{6} - 2 = 6\frac{1}{6}$

✦ *Math Journal 2,* p. 342

Options for Individualizing

✦ RETEACHING Playing *Multiplication Wrestling* (*Math Masters,* pp. 145 and 146)

PARTNER ACTIVITY  **5–15 min**

Students play this game, introduced in *Fourth Grade Everyday Mathematics,* to practice using the distributive property.

✦ EXTRA PRACTICE Finding the Area of Rectangles (*Math Masters,* p. 7)

PARTNER ACTIVITY **15–30 min**

Students draw three or four rectangles on grid paper. They divide their rectangles into two parts with a line parallel to one of the sides (vertical or horizontal), and assign values to the sides. They might shade one part to indicate that the area of only one part is to be found. (Students who want an extra challenge might use a variable for one of the values.) Partners exchange papers. They write at least two different number models to represent the area of each of their partner's rectangles.

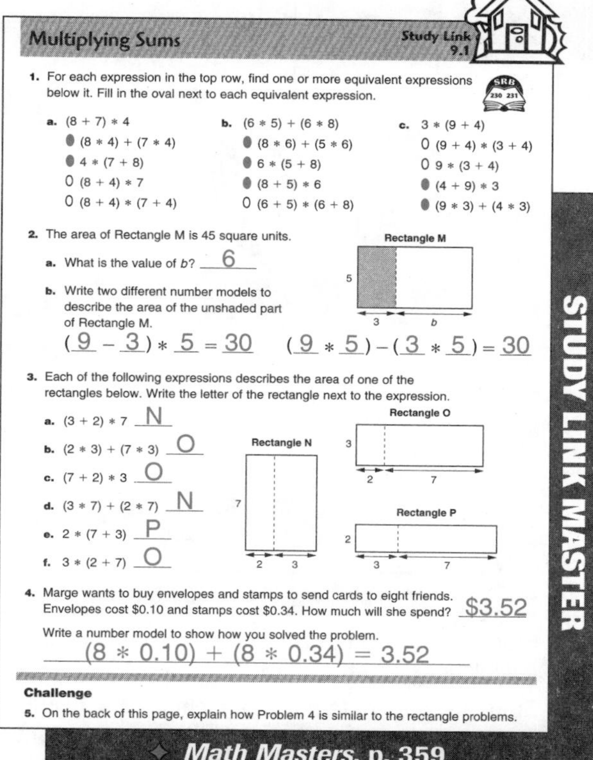

Multiplying Sums — Study Link 9.1

1. For each expression in the top row, find one or more equivalent expressions below it. Fill in the oval next to each equivalent expression.

a. (8 + 7) * 4	b. (6 * 5) + (6 * 8)	c. 3 * (9 + 4)
● (8 * 4) + (7 * 4)	● (8 * 6) + (5 * 6)	O (9 + 4) * (3 + 4)
● 4 * (7 + 8)	● 6 * (5 + 8)	O 9 * (3 + 4)
O (8 + 4) * 7	● (8 + 5) * 6	● (4 + 9) * 3
O (8 + 4) * (7 + 4)	O (6 + 5) * (6 + 8)	● (9 * 3) + (4 * 3)

2. The area of Rectangle M is 45 square units.
   a. What is the value of *b*? 6
   b. Write two different number models to describe the area of the unshaded part of Rectangle M.
   (9 – 3) * 5 = 30 (9 * 5) – (3 * 5) = 30

3. Each of the following expressions describes the area of one of the rectangles below. Write the letter of the rectangle next to the expression.
   a. (3 + 2) * 7 N
   b. (2 * 3) + (7 * 3) O
   c. (7 + 2) * 3 O
   d. (3 * 7) + (2 * 7) N
   e. 2 * (7 + 3) P
   f. 3 * (2 + 7) O

4. Marge wants to buy envelopes and stamps to send cards to eight friends. Envelopes cost $0.10 and stamps cost $0.34. How much will she spend? $3.52
   Write a number model to show how you solved the problem.
   (8 * 0.10) + (8 * 0.34) = 3.52

Challenge

5. On the back of this page, explain how Problem 4 is similar to the rectangle problems.

STUDY LINK MASTER

✦ *Math Masters,* p. 359

Multiplication Wrestling

Materials 4 each of number cards 0–9 (from the Everything Math Deck, if available)

Players 2

Directions

Shuffle the deck of cards and place it facedown. Each player draws 4 cards and forms two 2-digit numbers. There are many possible ways to form 2-digit numbers using the four cards. Each player should form his or her two numbers so that the product of the numbers is as large as possible. The object of the game is to get the largest product of two 2-digit numbers.

Example: *Player 1:* Draws 4, 5, 7, 8 Forms 75 and 84 *Player 2:* Draws 1, 4, 6, 9 Forms 64 and 91

Each player creates two "wrestling teams" by writing each number as a sum of tens and ones.

Player 1: 75 * 84		*Player 2:* 64 * 91	
Team 1	Team 2	Team 1	Team 2
(70 + 5)	* (80 + 4)	(60 + 4)	* (90 + 1)

Next, each player's two teams wrestle. Each member of Team 1 (for example, 70 and 5) is multiplied by each member of Team 2 (for example, 80 and 4). Then the four products are added.

Player 1:		*Player 2:*	
Teams (70 + 5) * (80 + 4)		Teams (60 + 4) * (90 + 1)	
Products:	70 * 80 = 5,600	Products:	60 * 90 = 5,400
	70 * 4 = 280		60 * 1 = 60
	5 * 80 = 400		4 * 90 = 360
	5 * 4 = 20		4 * 1 = 4
Total (add 4 products)	5,000	Total (add 4 products)	5,000
	1,200		700
	+ 100		120
			+ 4
	6,300		5,824

Scoring

The player with the largest product wins the round and receives 1 point. To begin a new round, each player draws 4 new cards to form two new numbers. A game consists of 3 rounds.

TEACHING MASTER

✦ *Math Masters,* p. 145

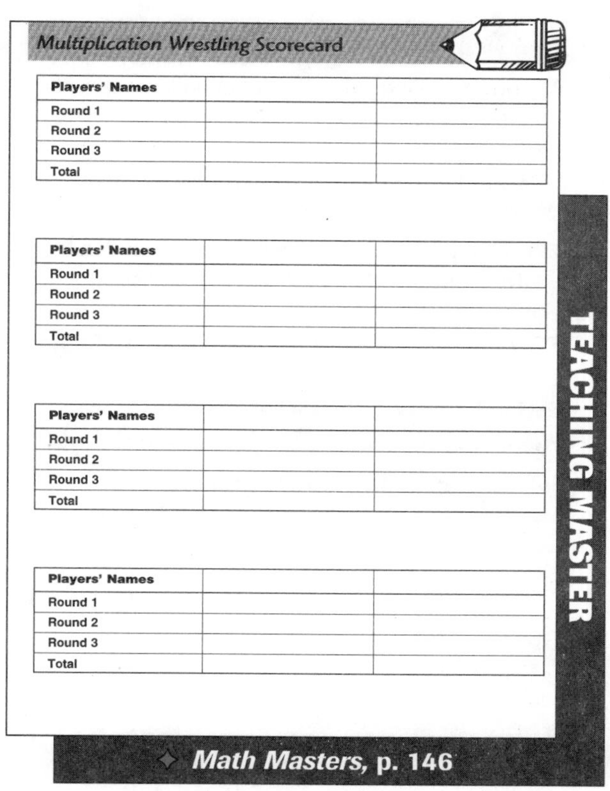

Multiplication Wrestling Scorecard

Players' Names		
Round 1		
Round 2		
Round 3		
Total		

Players' Names		
Round 1		
Round 2		
Round 3		
Total		

Players' Names		
Round 1		
Round 2		
Round 3		
Total		

Players' Names		
Round 1		
Round 2		
Round 3		
Total		

TEACHING MASTER

✦ *Math Masters,* p. 146

9.2 The Distributive Property

OBJECTIVES **To recognize the general patterns used to write the distributive property; and to apply the distributive property to simplify numerical and algebraic expressions.**

summaries	materials
1 Teaching the Lesson	
Students use distributive strategies to make mental calculations. [Operations and Computation] Students write different statements of the distributive property for numerical and algebraic expressions. [Operations and Computation; Patterns, Functions, and Algebra]	☐ *Math Journal 2,* p. 343 ☐ *Student Reference Book,* pp. 230 and 231 ☐ Study Link 9.1 ☐ slate
2 Ongoing Learning & Practice	
Students play *Polygon Capture* to practice identifying the properties of polygons. [Geometry] Students practice and maintain skills through Math Boxes and Study Link activities.	☐ *Math Journal 2,* p. 344 ☐ *Student Reference Book,* p. 302 ☐ Study Link Master (*Math Masters,* p. 360) ☐ *Polygon Capture* cards (*Math Masters,* pp. 89 and 90) ***See* Advance Preparation**
3 Options for Individualizing	
Language Diversity Students build background for the mathematics word *distributive.* [Patterns, Functions, and Algebra] **Reteaching** Students solve problems by using the distributive property. [Patterns, Functions, and Algebra] **Enrichment** Students write number stories that can be solved with the distributive property. [Patterns, Functions, and Algebra]	☐ *Math Journal 2,* p. 343 ☐ Teaching Master (*Math Masters,* p. 147) ☐ dictionary

Additional Information

Advance Preparation For Part 2, students will need the *Polygon Capture* cards they cut out in Lesson 5.9.

Vocabulary • **distributive property**

Getting Started

Mental Math and Reflexes

Give students the number of objects in a fractional part of a set. On their slates, students record the number of objects in the whole set.

Suggestions

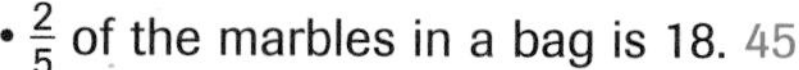

- $\frac{2}{5}$ of the marbles in a bag is 18. 45
- $\frac{7}{8}$ of the crayons in a box is 56. 64
- $\frac{4}{9}$ of the books on a shelf is 12. 27
- $\frac{6}{7}$ of the questions on a test is 66. 77
- $\frac{4}{15}$ of the pages in a book is 40. 150

Math Message

Be ready to explain how to find the following products mentally:

$4 * 36 = ?$ $\quad 99 * 8 = ?$ $\quad \$11.50 * 5 = ?$

Study Link 9.1 Follow-Up

Briefly review the answers. For Problem 1, be sure that students have filled in all of the circles for equivalent expressions. For Problem 5, have a volunteer explain how solving the number story and finding the area of the rectangle are alike. The number model in both cases can be written in the same form.

Teaching the Lesson

✦ Math Message Follow-Up

WHOLE-CLASS DISCUSSION

Students share their solution strategies. Help them record their strategies as number sentences. Be sure to include distributive strategies as you record solutions.

Examples

$$4 * 36 = 4 * (30 + 6) = (4 * 30) + (4 * 6) = 120 + 24 = 144, \text{ or}$$

$$4 * 36 = 4 * (40 - 4) = (4 * 40) - (4 * 4) = 160 - 16 = 144$$

$$99 * 8 = (100 - 1) * 8 = (100 * 8) - (1 * 8) = 800 - 8 = 792, \text{ or}$$

$$99 * 8 = (90 + 9) * 8 = (90 * 8) + (9 * 8) = 720 + 72 = 792$$

$$\$11.50 * 5 = (\$12.00 - \$0.50) * 5 = (\$12.00 * 5) - (\$0.50 * 5) = \$60.00 - \$2.50 = \$57.50, \text{ or}$$

$$\$11.50 * 5 = (\$11.00 + \$0.50) * 5 = (\$11.00 * 5) + (\$0.50 * 5) = \$55.00 + \$2.50 = \$57.50$$

Adjusting the Activity To extend the activity, you may want to initially write the expressions without parentheses. This will give you an opportunity to review the order of operations.

STUDENT PAGE

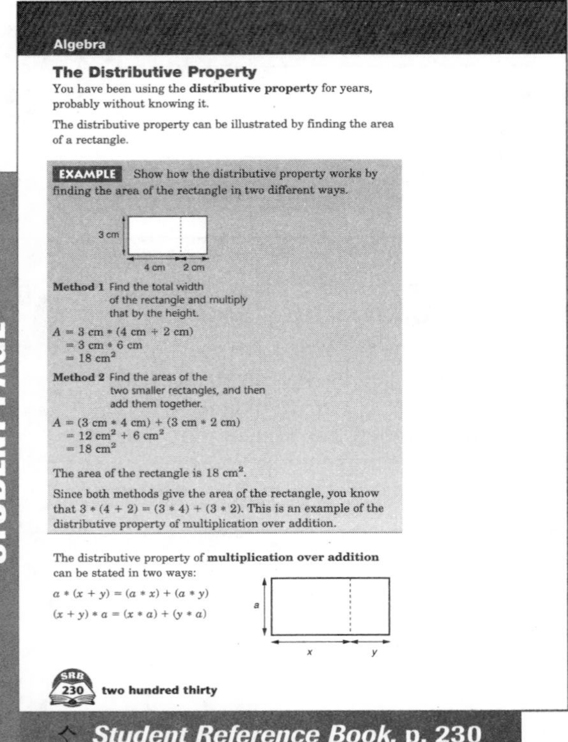
Algebra

The Distributive Property

You have been using the **distributive property** for years, probably without knowing it.

The distributive property can be illustrated by finding the area of a rectangle.

EXAMPLE Show how the distributive property works by finding the area of the rectangle in two different ways.

Method 1 Find the total width of the rectangle and multiply that by the height.

$A = 3 \text{ cm} * (4 \text{ cm} + 2 \text{ cm})$
$= 3 \text{ cm} * 6 \text{ cm}$
$= 18 \text{ cm}^2$

Method 2 Find the areas of the two smaller rectangles, and then add them together.

$A = (3 \text{ cm} * 4 \text{ cm}) + (3 \text{ cm} * 2 \text{ cm})$
$= 12 \text{ cm}^2 + 6 \text{ cm}^2$
$= 18 \text{ cm}^2$

The area of the rectangle is 18 cm^2.

Since both methods give the area of the rectangle, you know that $3 * (4 + 2) = (3 * 4) + (3 * 2)$. This is an example of the distributive property of multiplication over addition.

The distributive property of **multiplication over addition** can be stated in two ways:

$a * (x + y) = (a * x) + (a * y)$

$(x + y) * a = (x * a) + (y * a)$

SRB 230 two hundred thirty

Student Reference Book, p. 230

STUDENT PAGE

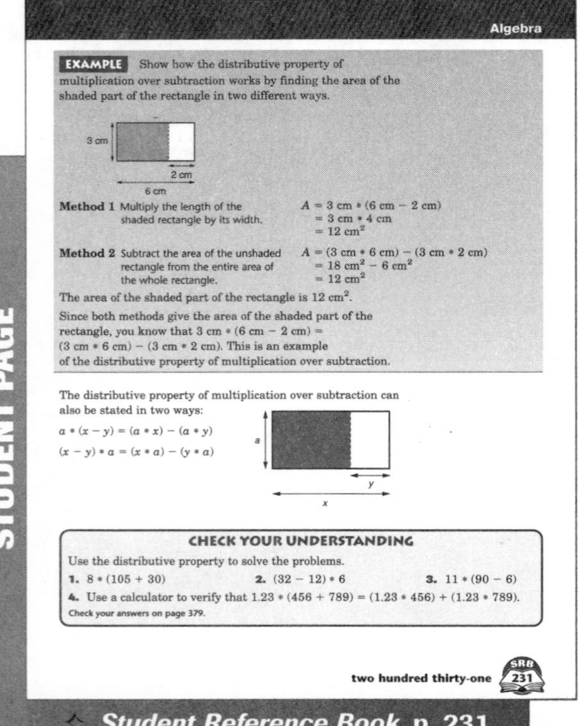
Algebra

EXAMPLE Show how the distributive property of multiplication over subtraction works by finding the area of the shaded part of the rectangle in two different ways.

Method 1 Multiply the length of the shaded rectangle by its width.

$A = 3 \text{ cm} * (6 \text{ cm} - 2 \text{ cm})$
$= 3 \text{ cm} * 4 \text{ cm}$
$= 12 \text{ cm}^2$

Method 2 Subtract the area of the unshaded rectangle from the entire area of the whole rectangle.

$A = (3 \text{ cm} * 6 \text{ cm}) - (3 \text{ cm} * 2 \text{ cm})$
$= 18 \text{ cm}^2 - 6 \text{ cm}^2$
$= 12 \text{ cm}^2$

The area of the shaded part of the rectangle is 12 cm^2.

Since both methods give the area of the shaded part of the rectangle, you know that $3 \text{ cm} * (6 \text{ cm} - 2 \text{ cm}) = (3 \text{ cm} * 6 \text{ cm}) - (3 \text{ cm} * 2 \text{ cm})$. This is an example of the distributive property of multiplication over subtraction.

The distributive property of multiplication over subtraction can also be stated in two ways:

$a * (x - y) = (a * x) - (a * y)$

$(x - y) * a = (x * a) - (y * a)$

CHECK YOUR UNDERSTANDING

Use the distributive property to solve the problems.

1. $8 * (105 + 30)$ **2.** $(32 - 12) * 6$ **3.** $11 * (90 - 6)$

4. Use a calculator to verify that $1.23 * (456 + 789) = (1.23 * 456) + (1.23 * 789)$.

Check your answers on page 379.

two hundred thirty-one SRB 231

Student Reference Book, p. 231

Ask students to look for patterns in the number sentences. Be sure to discuss the following points:

- One of the factors is rewritten as a sum (or difference) of two numbers that can be easily multiplied by the other factor.
- Parentheses are useful for keeping track of this sum (or difference) when it is rewritten.
- The original product becomes the sum (or difference) of two simple products.

This strategy for making mental calculations is based on the general property of operations called the **distributive property.** The property gets its name because it "distributes" the factor that is outside the parentheses over the two terms within the parentheses.

✦Summarizing the General Patterns of the Distributive Property (*Student Reference Book,* pp. 230 and 231)

WHOLE-CLASS DISCUSSION

Use the two examples on pages 230 and 231 of the *Student Reference Book* to discuss how the distributive property summarizes students' work in Lesson 9.1. Remind students that, as with other equations, the left and right sides can be interchanged. *For example:*

$a * (x + y) = (a * x) + (a * y)$

can be written as

$(a * x) + (a * y) = a * (x + y)$.

Review the four different general patterns for the distributive property on pages 230 and 231 of the *Student Reference Book*.

Distributive Property of Multiplication over Addition

$a * (x + y) = (a * x) + (a * y)$

$(x + y) * a = (x * a) + (y * a)$

Distributive Property of Multiplication over Subtraction

$a * (x - y) = (a * x) - (a * y)$

$(x - y) * a = (x * a) - (y * a)$

Make sure students understand that these general statements do not show four different properties, but are different ways of stating the *same* general property. Demonstrate this by solving 7 * 35 using each of the following four statements:

$a * (x + y) = (a * x) + (a * y)$
$7 * (30 + 5) = (7 * 30) + (7 * 5) = 245$

$(x + y) * a = (x * a) + (y * a)$
$(30 + 5) * 7 = (30 * 7) + (5 * 7) = 245$

$a * (x - y) = (a * x) - (a * y)$
$7 * (40 - 5) = (7 * 40) - (7 * 5) = 245$

$(x - y) * a = (x * a) - (y * a)$
$(40 - 5) * 7 = (40 * 7) - (5 * 7) = 245$

Pose additional mental calculation problems. Ask students to show on their slates how they solved each problem, using one of the statements of the distributive property. Encourage alternate strategies. *Suggestions:*

6 * 57 342	99 * 80 7,920	14 * 10.5 147
$1\frac{1}{2}$ * 42 63	103 * 31 3,193	998 * 201 200,598

✦Using the Distributive Property
(*Math Journal 2,* p. 343)

PARTNER ACTIVITY

The problems on journal page 343 provide practice with different statements of the distributive property.

For most problems, there are many ways to fill in the blanks to obtain true sentences. Each problem, however, has a unique solution in the form of the distributive property. For example, in Problem 1, 4 * (70 + 8) = (4 * 50) + (4 * 28) is a true sentence, but 4 * (70 + 8) = (4 * 70) + (4 * 8) is the only solution in the form of the distributive property. When students have finished, go over the answers.

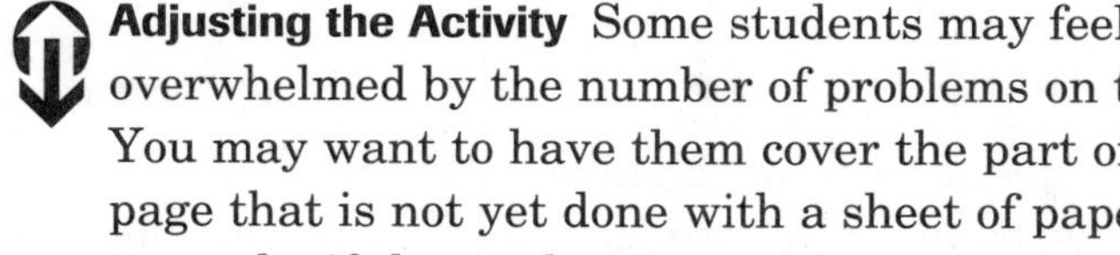

Adjusting the Activity Some students may feel overwhelmed by the number of problems on the page. You may want to have them cover the part of the page that is not yet done with a sheet of paper. For example, if the student is working on Problem 4, Problems 5–16 are covered.

After Problem 4, some problems contain variables. If some students need more practice with problems that do not have variables, use the Reteaching activity in Part 3 of this lesson.

The Distributive Property

The distributive property is a number property that combines multiplication with addition or multiplication with subtraction. The distributive property can be stated in four different ways.

Multiplication over Addition	Multiplication over Subtraction
For any numbers *a*, *x*, and *y*:	For any numbers *a*, *x*, and *y*:
$a * (x + y) = (a * x) + (a * y)$	$a * (x - y) = (a * x) - (a * y)$
$(x + y) * a = (x * a) + (y * a)$	$(x - y) * a = (x * a) - (y * a)$

Use the distributive property to fill in the blanks.

1. 4 * (70 + 8) = (4 * 70) + (4 * 8)
2. 6 * 34 = (6 * 30) + (6 * 4)
3. (6 * 70) − (6 * 4) = 6 * (70 − 4)
4. (40 + 6) * 8 = (40 * 8) + (6 * 8)
5. *y* * (90 + 3) = (*y* * 90) + (*y* * 3)
6. (50 * 7) + (8 * 7) = (50 + 8) * 7
7. 9 * (20 − 7) = (9 * 20) − (9 * 7)
8. (18 − 4) * *r* = (18 * *r*) − (4 * *r*)
9. 7 * (*w* − 6) = (7 * *w*) − (7 * 6)
10. 4 * (5 + 6) = (4 * 5) + (4 * 6)
11. (41 + 19) * 7 = (41 * 7) + (19 * 7)
12. *n* * (13 − 27) = (*n* * 13) − (*n* * 27)
13. (*f* − 8) * 15 = (*f* * 15) − (8 * 15)
14. (29 * *x*) + (12 * *x*) = (29 + 12) * *x*
15. 6 * (*d* − 7) = (6 * *d*) − (6 * 7)
16. 5 * (12 − *h*) = (5 * 12) − (5 * *h*)

STUDENT PAGE

Math Journal 2, p. 343

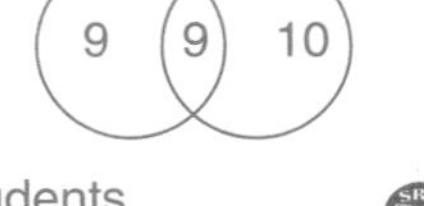

STUDENT PAGE

Math Boxes 9.2

1. Mr. Wilson's 28 sixth graders had to read at least one nonfiction book—either a biography or a science book. At the end of the grading period, Mr. Wilson tallied the number of students who had read each kind of book. Nineteen had read at least one biography, and 18 had read at least one science book.

   Draw a Venn diagram to represent the number of students who read each kind of book.

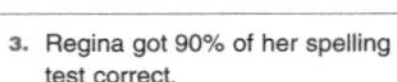

   How many students read at least one biography and one science book? 9 students

   SRB 246

2. Write >, <, or =.
   a. $28 + (-15)$ **>** $36 \div (-2)$
   b. $\frac{1}{2} + (-\frac{3}{4})$ **<** $\frac{2}{3} * \frac{7}{8}$
   c. $-400 * -3$ **>** 20^2
   d. $2 + 15 / 3$ **>** $7 * 10^{-1}$
   e. $\frac{3}{7} + 6\frac{2}{3}$ **<** $\frac{12}{2} \div \frac{7}{9}$

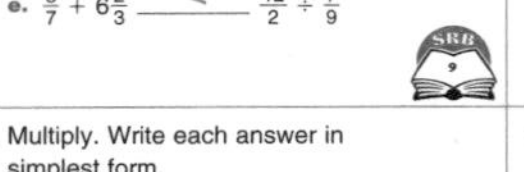

   SRB 9

3. Regina got 90% of her spelling test correct.
   a. How many questions did she get right out of 50? 45 questions
   b. Write a proportion to solve the problem. $\frac{x}{50} = \frac{90}{100}$

   SRB 59 60

4. Multiply. Write each answer in simplest form.
   a. $7\frac{1}{5} * \frac{3}{8} = 2\frac{7}{10}$
   b. $2\frac{14}{15} = 2\frac{4}{9} * 1\frac{1}{5}$
   c. $1\frac{13}{36} = 1\frac{1}{6} * \frac{7}{6}$
   d. $24\frac{1}{12} = 5\frac{2}{3} * 4\frac{1}{4}$
   e. $9 * \frac{8}{7} = 10\frac{2}{7}$

   SRB 86

5. Complete.
   a. $33\frac{1}{3}\%$ of 222 = 74
   b. 25% of 648 = 162
   c. 210 = 40% of 525
   d. 9 = 12.5% of 72
   e. 77 = 70% of 110

   SRB 57

Math Journal 2, p. 344

2 Ongoing Learning & Practice

Playing *Polygon Capture*

(*Student Reference Book,* p. 302; *Math Masters,* pp. 89 and 90)

PARTNER ACTIVITY 

Students play this game, introduced in Lesson 5.9, to practice identifying polygon attributes.

Math Boxes 9.2 (*Math Journal 2,* p. 344)

INDEPENDENT ACTIVITY 

Mixed Review Math Boxes in this lesson are paired with Math Boxes in Lesson 9.4. The skill in Problem 1 is a prerequisite for Unit 10.

Study Link 9.2 (*Math Masters,* p. 360)

Home Connection Students practice using the distributive property.

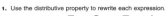

STUDY LINK MASTER

Using the Distributive Property

Study Link 9.2

Reminder: $a * (x + y) = (a * x) + (a * y)$
$a * (x - y) = (a * x) - (a * y)$

SRB 230 231

1. Use the distributive property to rewrite each expression.
   a. $7 * (3 + 4) = (7 * 3) + (7 * 4)$
   b. $7 * (3 + \pi) = (7 * 3) + (7 * \pi)$
   c. $7 * (3 + y) = (7 * 3) + (7 * y)$
   d. $7 * (3 + (2 * 4)) = (7 * 3) + (7 * (2 * 4))$
   e. $7 * (3 + (2 * \pi)) = (7 * 3) + (7 * (2 * \pi))$
   f. $7 * (3 + (2 * y)) = (7 * 3) + (7 * (2 * y))$
2. Use the distributive property to solve each problem. Study the first one.
   a. $7 * (110 + 25) = (7 * 110) + (7 * 25) = 770 + 175 = 945$
   b. $20 * (42 - 19) = (20 * 42) - (20 * 19) = 840 - 380 = 460$
   c. $(32 + 50) * 40 = (32 * 40) + (50 * 40) = 1{,}280 + 2{,}000 = 3{,}280$
   d. $(90 - 8) * 11 = (90 * 11) - (8 * 11) = 990 - 88 = 902$
   e. $9 * (15 + 25) = (9 * 15) + (9 * 25) = 135 + 225 = 360$
3. Circle the statements that are examples of the distributive property.
   a. $(80 * 5) + (120 * 5) = (80 + 120) * 5$ (circled)
   b. $6 * (3 - 0.5) = (6 * 3) - 0.5$
   c. $12(d - t) = 12d - 12t$ (circled)
   d. $(a + c) * n = a * n + c * n$ (circled)
   e. $(16 + 4m) + 9.7 = 16 + (4m + 9.7)$
   f. $\left(9 * \frac{1}{2}\right) - \left(\frac{1}{3} * \frac{1}{2}\right) = \left(9 - \frac{1}{3}\right) * \frac{1}{2}$ (circled)

Math Masters, p. 360

3 Options for Individualizing

LANGUAGE DIVERSITY Building Background for Mathematics Words

PARTNER ACTIVITY  **5–15 min** 

Pair a student learning English with a proficient English speaker. Have students look up the meaning of the word *distribute* in a dictionary. Guide the pair to identify examples of *distributing*. Discuss why the property we are studying in this lesson is called the "distributive property."

✦ RETEACHING Using the Distributive Property
(*Math Masters,* p. 147)

INDEPENDENT ACTIVITY  **5–15 min** 

Students complete a page of problems that require using the distributive property. These problems do not have variables and some are presented in context to help students understand how the distributive property works.

✦ ENRICHMENT Writing Number Stories
(*Math Journal 2,* p. 343)

INDEPENDENT ACTIVITY  **15–30 min** 

Students choose expressions on journal page 343 and make up number stories that fit the expressions.

Example: $4 * (70 + 8)$

> Four friends shared a pile of coins. They each received 7 dimes and 8 pennies. How much money was originally in the pile?

You might want to display the stories. Students will have fun reading and solving each other's problems.

Adjusting the Activity Pair a student learning English with a proficient English speaker. The student who is learning English can illustrate a story and tell the story to the proficient English speaker. The English speaker records the story and reads it back to his or her partner.

Using the Distributive Property

1. Ricky and 5 of his friends are buying lunch. Each person gets a hamburger and a soda. How much money will they spend in all?

Write a number model to show how you solved the problem. Sample answer: $(6 * 1.10) + (6 * 0.90) = c$

Answer $12.00

Explain how the distributive property can help you solve Problem 1.
Sample answer: The distributive property shows how to make the computation easier by using the 6 two times (multiplying it by each item's cost).

2. Maureen signed her new book at a local bookstore. In the morning she signed 36 books, and in the afternoon she signed 51 books. It took her 5 minutes to sign each. How much time did she spend signing books?

Write a number model to show how you solved the problem. Sample answer: $(36 + 51) * 5 = t$

Answer 7 hours and 15 minutes

3. Ms. Hays bought fabric for the school musical chorus. She bought 4 yards each of one kind for 30 costumes and 4 yards each of another kind for 6 soloists. How many yards did she buy in all?

Write a number model to show how you solved the problem. Sample answer: $(30 * 4) - (6 * 4) = y$

Answer 144 yards

4. Mr. Katz gave a party because all of the students got 100% on their math test. He had budgeted $1.15 per student. It turned out that he saved $0.25 per student. If there are 30 students, how much did he spend?

Write a number model to show how you solved the problem. Sample answer: $(30 * 1.15) - (30 * 0.25) = n$

Answer $27.00

Fill in the missing numbers according to the distributive property.

5. $28 * 6 = (\underline{20} + \underline{8}) * 6$
6. $(\underline{20} * 6) + (\underline{8} * 6) = (20 + 8) * 6$

TEACHING MASTER

✦ *Math Masters,* p. 147

9.3 Simplifying Expressions: Combining Like Terms

OBJECTIVE **To simplify algebraic expressions by combining like terms.**

summaries	materials
1 Teaching the Lesson	
Students use the distributive property to combine like terms. Students simplify expressions containing one kind of term, and more than one kind of term. [Patterns, Functions, and Algebra]	☐ *Math Journal 2,* pp. 346 and 347 ☐ Study Link 9.2 ☐ Assessment Master (*Math Masters,* p. 478; optional) ☐ slate
2 Ongoing Learning & Practice	
Students review angle measures. [Measurement and Reference Frames] Students practice and maintain skills through Math Boxes and Study Link activities.	☐ *Math Journal 2,* pp. 345 and 348 ☐ Study Link Master (*Math Masters,* p. 361) ☐ protractor
3 Options for Individualizing	
Reteaching Students play *Algebra Election* to practice substituting values for variables in expressions. [Patterns, Functions, and Algebra] **Enrichment** Students interpret an algebra cartoon. [Patterns, Functions, and Algebra]	☐ *Student Reference Book,* pp. 276 and 277 ☐ Teaching Master (*Math Masters,* p. 148) ☐ *Algebra Election* cards (*Math Journal 2,* Activity Sheets 5 and 6) ☐ Electoral Vote Map (*Math Masters,* pp. 102 and 103) ☐ six-sided die ☐ 4 pennies or counters ☐ calculator ***See* Advance Preparation**

Additional Information

Advance Preparation For the optional Reteaching activity in Part 3, students will need the *Algebra Election* cards they cut out in Lesson 6.7.

Vocabulary • **like terms** • **combine like terms** • **simplify an expression**

Getting Started

Mental Math and Reflexes

Write expressions like the following on the board or overhead. Have students write the value of each expression for $x = 2$.

- $3x + 7$ 13
- $4x + 8x$ 24
- $x + 2x + 3x + 4x$ 20
- $6 + x - (\frac{1}{2})x$ 7
- $x * 2x - 9$ −1
- $-(2x) - (-9)$ 5

Math Message

These expressions have 2 terms.
Rewrite each expression as a single term.

$4y + 7y$ $4y - 7y$

Study Link 9.2 Follow-Up

Briefly review answers.

1 Teaching the Lesson

✦ Math Message Follow-Up

WHOLE-CLASS DISCUSSION 

Discuss students' answers and explanations. Some students may use illustrations based on objects or amounts to justify their answers. *For example:*

▷ Think of $4y + 7y$ as 4 oranges + 7 oranges. That's 11 oranges, so $4y + 7y = 11y$.

▷ 4 dollars minus 7 dollars is 3 dollars owed. So $4y - 7y$ is $-3y$.

Remind students that the multiplication symbol ($*$ or $\times$) is frequently omitted. For example, $7y$ means $7 * y$, and $5(2y + 3)$ means $5 * (2y + 3)$.

✦ Combining Like Terms

(*Math Journal 2,* pp. 346 and 347)

WHOLE-CLASS ACTIVITY

Read the first two paragraphs on journal page 346 as a class. Terms are what are added and subtracted in expressions. **Like terms** are either "number" terms or terms that contain the same variables raised to the same power. Example 1 shows how to use the distributive property to **combine like terms,** which means to rewrite the sum or difference of like terms as a single term.

During the discussion, you might also need to remind students that to subtract a negative number, add the opposite of that number.

Redo the Math Message problems, using the distributive property to combine like terms.

▷ To simplify $4y + 7y$, think:

$$\begin{aligned} 4y + 7y &= (4 * y) + (7 * y) \\ &= (4 + 7) * y \\ &= 11 * y = 11y \end{aligned}$$

Thus, $4y + 7y = (4 + 7)y = 11y$.

▷ To simplify $4y - 7y$, think:

$$\begin{aligned} 4y - 7y &= (4 * y) - (7 * y) \\ &= (4 - 7) * y \\ &= -3 * y = -3y \end{aligned}$$

Thus, $4y - 7y = (4 - 7)y = -3y$.

Combining Like Terms

Algebraic expressions contain **terms.** For example, the expression $4y + 2x - 7y$ contains the terms $4y$, $2x$, and $7y$. The terms $4y$ and $7y$ are called **like terms** because they are multiples of the same variable, y. To **combine like terms** means to rewrite the sum or difference of like terms as a single term. For example, $4y + 7y$ can be rewritten as $11y$.

To **simplify an expression** means to write the expression in a simpler form. Combining like terms is one way to do that. *Reminder:* The multiplication symbol ($*$) is often not written. For example, $4 * y$ is often written as $4y$, and $(x + 3) * 5$ as $(x + 3)5$.

Example 1 Simplify the expression $5x - (-8)x$. Use the distributive property.

$$\begin{aligned} 5x - (-8)x &= (5 * x) - (-8 * x) \\ &= (5 - (-8)) * x \\ &= (5 + 8) * x \\ &= 13 * x, \text{ or } 13x \end{aligned}$$

Check your answer by substituting several values for the variable.

Check: Substitute 5 for the variable.

$$\begin{aligned} 5x - (-8)x &= 13x \\ (5 * 5) - (-8 * 5) &= 13 * 5 \\ 25 - (-40) &= 65 \\ 65 &= 65 \end{aligned}$$

Check: Substitute 2 for the variable.

$$\begin{aligned} 5x - (-8)x &= 13x \\ (5 * 2) - (-8 * 2) &= 13 * 2 \\ 10 - (-16) &= 26 \\ 26 &= 26 \end{aligned}$$

If there are more than two like terms, you can add or subtract the terms in the order in which they occur and keep a running total.

Example 2 Simplify the expression $2n - 7n + 3n - 4n$.

$2n - 7n = -5n$

$-5n + 3n = -2n$

$-2n - 4n = -6n$

Therefore, $2n - 7n + 3n - 4n = -6n$

Simplify each expression by rewriting it as a single term.

1. $6y + 13y =$ <u>$19y$</u>
2. $7g - 12g =$ <u>$-5g$</u>
3. <u>$4x$</u> $= 5\frac{1}{2}x - 1\frac{1}{2}x$
4. $3c - (-5)c =$ <u>$8c$</u>
5. $5y - 3y + 11y =$ <u>$13y$</u>
6. $6g - 8g + 5g - 4g =$ <u>$-g$</u>
7. $n + n + n + n + n =$ <u>$5n$</u>
8. $n + 3n + 5n - 7n =$ <u>$2n$</u>
9. $2x + 4x - (-9)x =$ <u>$15x$</u>
10. $-7x + 2x + 3x =$ <u>$-2x$</u>

STUDENT PAGE

✦ *Math Journal 2,* p. 346

To **simplify an expression** means to write the expression in a simpler form. Combining like terms is one way to simplify an expression. (Removing parentheses is another way. This method will be the focus of Lesson 9.4.)

Example 2 shows how the method of Example 1 may be extended in order to combine more than two like terms. The first two terms are combined. The result is then combined with the next term, and so on.

Adjusting the Activity You might illustrate at the board a "factoring" procedure for combining like terms. Write the expression $2n - 7n + 3n - 4n$. Enclose the expression in parentheses and cross out (or erase) each occurrence of the variable n. Then write the variable n to the right of the parentheses, saying that you have "undistributed" the variable. Then evaluate the numerical expression within parentheses. The simplified expression is $-6n$.

$$\begin{aligned} 2n - 7n + 3n - 4n &= (2\not{n} - 7\not{n} + 3\not{n} - 4\not{n})n \\ &= (2 - 7 + 3 - 4)n \\ &= -6n \end{aligned}$$

Partners complete the problems on journal page 346. Circulate and assist. When most of the class have finished, briefly go over the answers.

Adjusting the Activity Before continuing to the next journal page, students may need more practice combining like terms when the expression contains only one kind of term. If so, write several more expressions on the board or overhead and have students simplify them on their slates.

Read the paragraphs at the top of journal page 347 and go over Example 3, which shows how to combine like terms when there is *more* than one kind of term.

In the expression $2y + 6 + 4y - 8 - 9y + (-3)$

- ▷ the variable terms $2y$, $4y$, and $9y$ are one set of like terms.
- ▷ the numbers 6, 8, and -3 are a second set of like terms.
- ▷ each set of like terms is combined separately.
- ▷ the variable terms are combined into one single term.
- ▷ the number terms are combined into a second single term.

STUDENT PAGE

Combining Like Terms (cont.)

An expression like $2y + 6 + 4y - 8 - 9y + (-3)$ is difficult to work with because it is made up of six different terms that are added and subtracted.

There are two sets of like terms in the expression. The terms $2y$, $4y$, and $9y$ are like terms. The number terms in the expression—6, 8, and (-3)—are a second set of like terms. Each set of like terms can be combined into a single term. To simplify an expression that has more than one set of like terms, you must combine each set of like terms into a single term.

Example 3 Simplify $2y + 6 + 4y - 8 - 9y + (-3)$ by combining like terms.

Step 1 Combine the y terms. $2y + 4y - 9y = 6y - 9y = -3y$

Step 2 Combine the number terms. $6 - 8 + (-3) = -2 + (-3) = -5$

Final result: $2y + 6 + 4y - 8 - 9y + (-3) = -3y + (-5) = -3y - 5$

Check: Substitute 2 for y in both the original expression and the simplified expression.

$$\begin{aligned} 2y + 6 + 4y - 8 - 9y + (-3) &= -3y - 5 \\ (2 * 2) + 6 + (4 * 2) - 8 - (9 * 2) + (-3) &= (-3 * 2) - 5 \\ 4 + 6 + 8 - 8 - 18 + (-3) &= -6 - 5 \\ -11 &= -11 \end{aligned}$$

Simplify each expression by combining like terms. Check each answer by substituting several values for the variable.

11. $4 + 7y + 20 =$ $7y + 24$
12. $5x - 3x + 8 =$ $2x + 8$
13. $5n + 6 - 8n - 2 - 3n =$ $-6n + 4$
14. $n + \pi + 2n - \frac{1}{2}\pi =$ $3n + \frac{1}{2}\pi$
15. $-2.5x + 9 + 1.4x + 0.6 =$ $-1.1x + 9.6$
16. $9d + 2a - (-6a) + 3d - 15d =$ $-3d + 8a$

✧ Math Journal 2, p. 347

Assign the problems on journal page 347. Circulate and assist. When most of the class have finished, briefly go over the answers. Note that an instruction to check the answers is included with the problem set. Students should be reminded to check their answers by substituting at least two *different* values for the variable in each expression of the problems.

ONGOING ASSESSMENT

Have students complete an Exit Slip (*Math Masters,* page 478) explaining to someone how to simplify the expression in Problem 5. Consider having students explain how to simplify the more difficult Problem 13 instead, if they are able.

Ongoing Learning & Practice

◆ Drawing and Measuring Angles
(*Math Journal 2,* p. 348)

INDEPENDENT ACTIVITY 

Students use a protractor to measure angles, as well as draw and label specified types of angles.

◆ Math Boxes 9.3 (*Math Journal 2,* p. 345)

INDEPENDENT ACTIVITY 

Mixed Review Math Boxes in this lesson are paired with Math Boxes in Lessons 9.1 and 9.5. The skill in Problem 1 is a prerequisite for Unit 10.

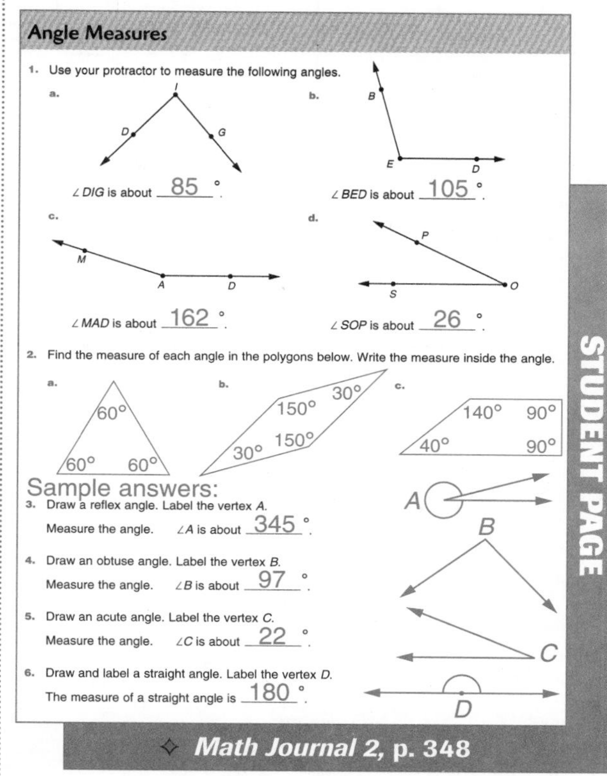

Angle Measures

1. Use your protractor to measure the following angles.
   a. ∠*DIG* is about 85 °.
   b. ∠*BED* is about 105 °.
   c. ∠*MAD* is about 162 °.
   d. ∠*SOP* is about 26 °.
2. Find the measure of each angle in the polygons below. Write the measure inside the angle.
   a. 60°, 60°, 60°
   b. 150°, 30°, 30°, 150°
   c. 140°, 90°, 40°, 90°

Sample answers:

3. Draw a reflex angle. Label the vertex *A*. Measure the angle. ∠*A* is about 345 °.
4. Draw an obtuse angle. Label the vertex *B*. Measure the angle. ∠*B* is about 97 °.
5. Draw an acute angle. Label the vertex *C*. Measure the angle. ∠*C* is about 22 °.
6. Draw and label a straight angle. Label the vertex *D*. The measure of a straight angle is 180 °.

STUDENT PAGE

◇ *Math Journal 2,* p. 348

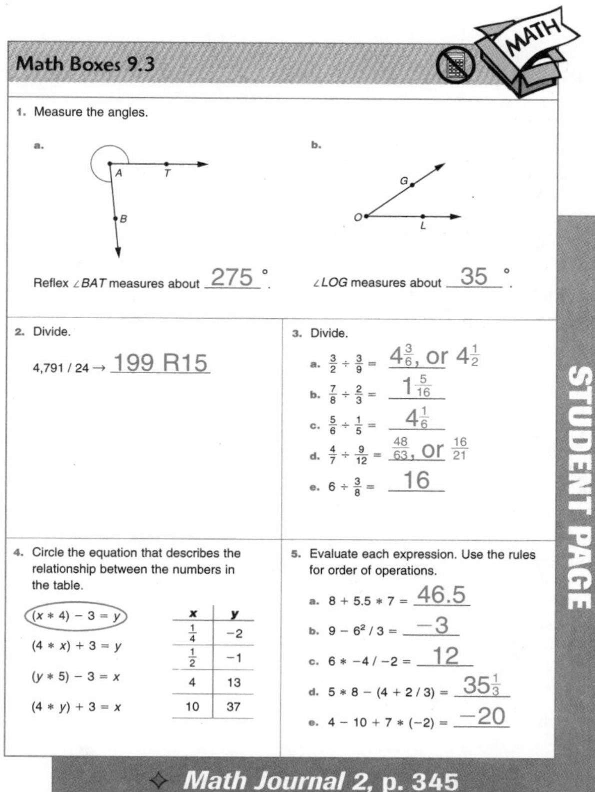

Math Boxes 9.3

1. Measure the angles.
   a. Reflex ∠*BAT* measures about 275 °.
   b. ∠*LOG* measures about 35 °.
2. Divide.
   4,791 / 24 → 199 R15
3. Divide.
   a. $\frac{3}{2} \div \frac{3}{9} =$ $4\frac{3}{6}$, or $4\frac{1}{2}$
   b. $\frac{7}{8} \div \frac{2}{3} =$ $1\frac{5}{16}$
   c. $\frac{5}{6} \div \frac{1}{5} =$ $4\frac{1}{6}$
   d. $\frac{4}{7} \div \frac{9}{12} =$ $\frac{48}{63}$, or $\frac{16}{21}$
   e. $6 \div \frac{3}{8} =$ 16
4. Circle the equation that describes the relationship between the numbers in the table.
   (x ∗ 4) − 3 = y (circled)
   (4 ∗ x) + 3 = y
   (y ∗ 5) − 3 = x
   (4 ∗ y) + 3 = x

x	y
$\frac{1}{4}$	−2
$\frac{1}{2}$	−1
4	13
10	37

5. Evaluate each expression. Use the rules for order of operations.
   a. 8 + 5.5 ∗ 7 = 46.5
   b. $9 - 6^2 / 3 =$ −3
   c. 6 ∗ −4 / −2 = 12
   d. 5 ∗ 8 − (4 + 2 / 3) = $35\frac{1}{3}$
   e. 4 − 10 + 7 ∗ (−2) = −20

STUDENT PAGE

◇ *Math Journal 2,* p. 345

STUDY LINK MASTER

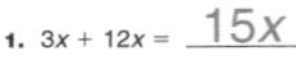

Combining Like Terms — Study Link 9.3

Simplify each expression by rewriting it as a single term.

1. $3x + 12x =$ $15x$
2. $(1\frac{3}{5})y - (1\frac{3}{10})y =$ $\frac{3}{10}y$
3. $-(5t) - 6t =$ $-11t$
4. $4d + (-3d) =$ d

Complete each equation.

5. $15k = (9 -$ -6 $)k$
6. $3.6p - p =$ $3p$ $- 0.4p$
7. $(8 +$ -3 $) * m = 5m$
8. 8.3 $j - 4.5j = 3.8j$

Simplify each expression by combining like terms. Check your answers by substituting the given values for the variables. Show your work.

Example $18 + 6m + 2m + 26$
Combine the *m* terms. $6m + 2m = 8m$
Combine the number terms. $18 + 26 = 44$
So, $18 + 6m + 2m + 26 = 8m + 44$

Check: Substitute 5 for *m*.
$18 + (6 * 5) + (2 * 5) + 26 = (8 * 5) + 44$
$18 + 30 + 10 + 26 = 40 + 44$
$84 = 84$

9. $8b + 9 + 4b - 3b + (-2b) - (-5) =$ $7b + 14$
Check for: $b = -6$

10. $\frac{1}{2}a + \frac{3}{4}t + \frac{2}{3}a + \left(-\frac{1}{2}t\right) =$ $1\frac{1}{6}a + \frac{1}{4}t$
Check for: $a = 2$ and $t = -2$

◆ *Math Masters,* p. 361

TEACHING MASTER

An Algebra Cartoon

x+2=5
x=3

"Just a minute! Yesterday, you said x equals 2!"

Explain how this cartoon is related to the algebra you have been studying.
Sample answer: The cartoon reflects a common misconception that variables stand for one number only. In our work with variables, we have learned that they can stand for any unknown quantity.

Do you think the cartoon is funny? Answers vary.

Why or why not?

◆ *Math Masters,* p. 148

◆ Study Link 9.3 (*Math Masters,* p. 361)

Home Connection Students simplify algebraic expressions by combining like terms.

3 Options for Individualizing

◆ RETEACHING Playing *Algebra Election* (*Student Reference Book,* pp. 276 and 277; Electoral Vote Map; *Algebra Election* cards)

PARTNER ACTIVITY  **15–30 min**

Students play this game, introduced in Lesson 6.7, to practice making substitutions for variables in equations.

◆ ENRICHMENT Interpreting an Algebra Cartoon (*Math Masters,* p. 148)

INDEPENDENT ACTIVITY  **5–15 min**

Students interpret a cartoon to demonstrate their understanding of variables. The value of a variable depends on the number sentence in which it is used.

When most students have completed their explanations, have volunteers share their interpretation of the cartoon humor.

9.4 Simplifying Expressions: Removing Parentheses

OBJECTIVE **To simplify expressions by first eliminating parentheses, and then combining like terms.**

summaries	materials
1 Teaching the Lesson	
Students use the distributive property to remove parentheses in expressions and simplify algebraic expressions and equations by removing parentheses and combining like terms. [Patterns, Functions, and Algebra; Operations and Computation]	□ *Math Journal 2,* pp. 349 and 350 □ Study Link 9.3 □ Teaching Master (*Math Masters,* p. 149) ***See* Advance Preparation**
2 Ongoing Learning & Practice	
Students practice and maintain skills through Math Boxes and Study Link activities.	□ *Math Journal 2,* p. 351 □ Study Link Master (*Math Masters,* p. 362)
3 Options for Individualizing	
Extra Practice Students write and simplify expressions. [Patterns, Functions, and Algebra] **Enrichment** The teacher or students read an alphabet book of mathematical terms. [Patterns, Functions, and Algebra]	□ *G Is for Googol* ***See* Advance Preparation**

Additional Information

Advance Preparation Make one copy of *Math Masters,* page 149 for every two students. Cut the copies apart and place them near the Math Message. For the optional Enrichment activity in Part 3, obtain a copy of *G Is for Googol* by David M. Schwartz (Tricycle Press, 1998).

Vocabulary • **simplify an equation**

Getting Started

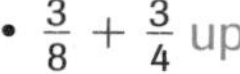

Mental Math and Reflexes

Pose fraction addition problems. Students show "thumbs up" if the sum is greater than 1 and "thumbs down" if the sum is less than 1. *Suggestions:*

- $\frac{3}{8} + \frac{3}{4}$ up
- $\frac{7}{9} + \frac{1}{3}$ up
- $\frac{4}{7} + \frac{5}{9}$ up
- $\frac{2}{5} + \frac{6}{12}$ down
- $\frac{5}{6} + \frac{1}{8}$ down
- $\frac{10}{12} + \frac{2}{3}$ up

Math Message

Take a copy of the Math Message and follow the instructions.

Study Link 9.3 Follow-Up

Go over the answers with the class. Resolve disagreements by asking students to substitute at least two different values for the variable in the original expression and in the simplified expression. Encourage students to try numbers other than whole numbers, using calculators.

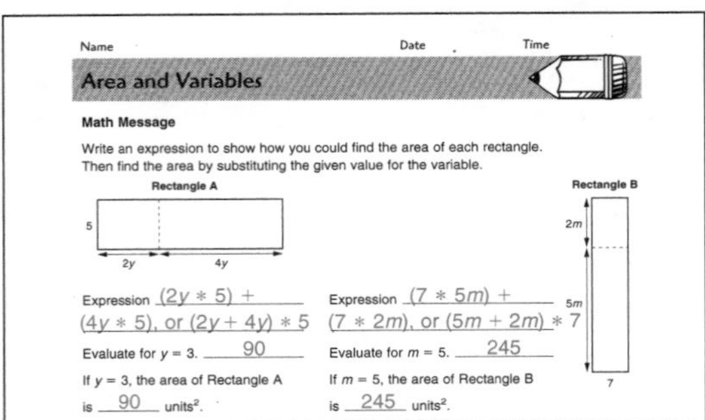

Name Date Time

Area and Variables

Math Message

Write an expression to show how you could find the area of each rectangle. Then find the area by substituting the given value for the variable.

Expression $(2y * 5) + (4y * 5)$, or $(2y + 4y) * 5$

Evaluate for $y = 3$. 90

If $y = 3$, the area of Rectangle A is 90 units².

Expression $(7 * 5m) + (7 * 2m)$, or $(5m + 2m) * 7$

Evaluate for $m = 5$. 245

If $m = 5$, the area of Rectangle B is 245 units².

Math Masters, page 149

1 Teaching the Lesson

✦ Math Message Follow-Up (*Math Masters,* p. 149)

WHOLE-CLASS DISCUSSION 

Review student expressions for each rectangle. Make sure to obtain more than one expression for each rectangle. Compare the expressions. Check to see that they are equivalent by substituting the given values.

✦ Simplifying Algebraic Expressions (*Math Journal 2,* p. 349)

INDEPENDENT ACTIVITY 

In Lesson 9.3, students simplified expressions by combining like terms. In this lesson, students remove parentheses, as well as combine like terms, to simplify expressions.

Read the paragraph at the top of journal page 349. Then go over the example. The example shows how to **simplify an expression** in which a factor must be distributed over a sum or difference before like terms can be combined.

Emphasize that it is important to remove parentheses in an expression *before* combining like terms. Work several additional examples, and continue to remind students to "take care of the parentheses first." *Suggestions:*

1. $10(2n + 3) + 6 = (10 * 2n) + (10 * 3) + 6$
$= 20n + 30 + 6$
$= 20n + 36$

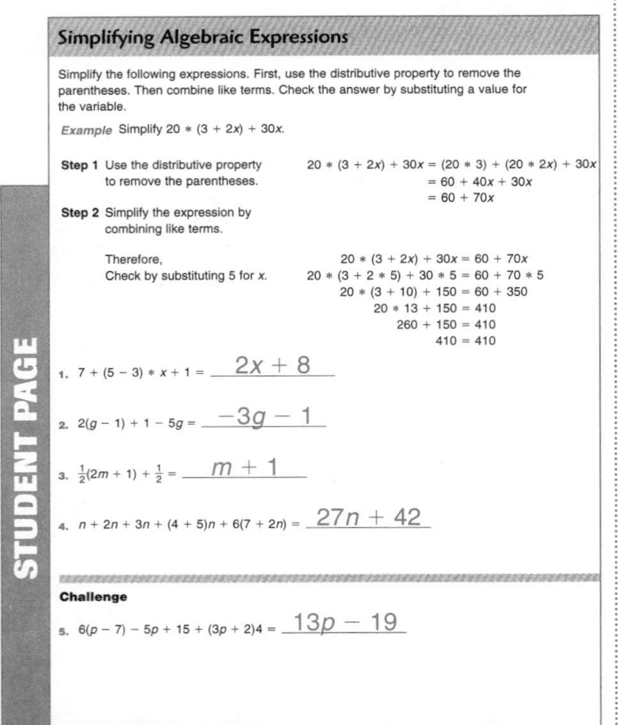

STUDENT PAGE

Simplifying Algebraic Expressions

Simplify the following expressions. First, use the distributive property to remove the parentheses. Then combine like terms. Check the answer by substituting a value for the variable.

Example Simplify $20 * (3 + 2x) + 30x$.

Step 1 Use the distributive property to remove the parentheses.
$20 * (3 + 2x) + 30x = (20 * 3) + (20 * 2x) + 30x$
$= 60 + 40x + 30x$
$= 60 + 70x$

Step 2 Simplify the expression by combining like terms.

Therefore, $20 * (3 + 2x) + 30x = 60 + 70x$

Check by substituting 5 for x.
$20 * (3 + 2 * 5) + 30 * 5 = 60 + 70 * 5$
$20 * (3 + 10) + 150 = 60 + 350$
$20 * 13 + 150 = 410$
$260 + 150 = 410$
$410 = 410$

1. $7 + (5 - 3) * x + 1 =$ $2x + 8$
2. $2(g - 1) + 1 - 5g =$ $-3g - 1$
3. $\frac{1}{2}(2m + 1) + \frac{1}{2} =$ $m + 1$
4. $n + 2n + 3n + (4 + 5)n + 6(7 + 2n) =$ $27n + 42$

Challenge

5. $6(p - 7) - 5p + 15 + (3p + 2)4 =$ $13p - 19$

✦ *Math Journal 2,* p. 349

2. $(3 + 4)y + 9 = 3y + 4y + 9$
$= 7y + 9$, or
$(3 + 4)y + 9 = (7)y + 9$

3. $2(4x + 5x) + x = (2 * 4x) + (2 * 5x) + x$
$= 8x + 10x + x$
$= 18x + x$
$= 19x$, or
$2(4x + 5x) + x = 2(9x) + x$
$= 18x + x$
$= 19x$

For Problems 2 and 3 above, some students may not need to use the distributive property to remove the parentheses. This is fine. In Problem 2, both terms in the parentheses are number terms that can be easily added. In Problem 3, both terms in parentheses are like x-terms that can be easily combined.

Assign the problems on journal page 349. Circulate and assist. When most of the class have finished, briefly go over the answers. Note that an instruction to check the answers is included with the problem set. Students should be reminded to check their answers by substituting at least two *different* values for the variable in each problem.

ONGOING ASSESSMENT

Watch for students who simply remove the parentheses in an expression and do not correctly use the distributive property. For example, some students may remove the parentheses in $7(n + 3) + 6$ by writing $7n + 3 + 6$. Expect that some students may struggle with simplifying these expressions.

✦ Simplifying Equations (*Math Journal 2,* p. 350)

INDEPENDENT ACTIVITY 

Assign the problems on journal page 350. Students are to simplify an equation, but NOT solve it. Remind them that simplifying means removing parentheses and combining like terms on each side of the equation. Students can simplify the expression on each side of the equal sign as though it were a separate problem.

Adjusting the Activity To extend the activity, have students simplify the equations and then *solve* them. But solutions are not *expected* here. Lesson 9.5 will focus on solving equations.

Simplifying Equations

Simplify both sides of the following equations. Don't solve them.

Example $2b + 5 + 3b = 8 - b + 21$
$(2b + 3b) + 5 = 8 - b + 21$
$5b + 5 = 8 - b + 21$
$5b + 5 = -b + 21 + 8$
$5b + 5 = -b + 29$

1. $5h + 13h = 20 - 2$
$18h = 18$

2. $2 + x + 2x + 4 = x + 16$
$3x + 6 = x + 16$

3. $2(y + 2) = 4(y + 3)$
$2y + 4 = 4y + 12$

4. $(4 - 1)m - m = (m - 1) * 4$
$2m = 4m - 4$

5. $4y + 6 = 8(1 + y)$
$4y + 6 = 8 + 8y$

6. $5(x + 3) - 2x = 35 + x$
$3x + 15 = 35 + x$

7. $3 * (3.2 - 2c) = 4.6 + 4c$
$9.6 - 6c = 4.6 + 4c$

8. $4(2z - 5) = z + 1$
$8z - 20 = z + 1$

STUDENT PAGE

✦ *Math Journal 2,* p. 350

Math Boxes 9.4

1. Frederick and Lucille conducted a survey to find out how many of their classmates had brothers and sisters. They surveyed 31 students and learned that 18 had at least one sister and 21 had at least one brother.

   Draw a Venn diagram to represent the results of Frederick and Lucille's survey.

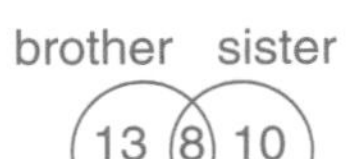

   How many students had at least one brother and one sister? 8 students

2. Write >, <, or =.
   a. $12 - (-3)$ < $\frac{7}{8} + \frac{1}{20}$
   b. $5^2 + 3^2$ > $5\frac{20}{3} + 10\frac{50}{10}$
   c. $3\frac{6}{7} + 2\frac{3}{5}$ > $\frac{100}{18}$
   d. $0.48 * 2.5$ > $3 * 0.26$
   e. $-7 * -6$ > $-7 * 6$

3. Larry was reading a biography of Abraham Lincoln. He read 30 pages in 40 minutes.
   a. How many pages did he read in 60 minutes? 45 pages
   b. Write a proportion to solve the problem. $\frac{30}{40} = \frac{x}{60}$

4. Multiply. Write each answer in simplest form.
   a. $4\frac{3}{7} * \frac{6}{5} =$ $5\frac{11}{35}$
   b. $\frac{16}{11} * 4\frac{2}{3} =$ $6\frac{26}{33}$
   c. $\frac{25}{4} * \frac{10}{6} =$ $10\frac{5}{12}$
   d. $3\frac{1}{7} * 5\frac{8}{9} =$ $18\frac{32}{63}$
   e. $7 * \frac{6}{15} =$ $2\frac{4}{5}$

5. Complete.
   a. 64 = 80% of 80
   b. 96 = 75% of 128
   c. 126 = $66\frac{2}{3}$% of 189
   d. 60% of 255 = 153
   e. 37.5% of 480 = 180

STUDENT PAGE

✦ *Math Journal 2,* p. 351

Simplifying Expressions

Study Link 9.4

Simplify each expression by removing parentheses and combining like terms. Check by substituting the given values for the variables. Show your work.

1. $5(y - b) + 3b - 6y + 4(6 + b) =$ $-y + 2b + 24$
   Check: Substitute 1 for y and $\frac{2}{3}$ for b.

2. $(12 - 3 + 5k)6 + 4k - 2(k + 5) =$ $64 + 32k$
   Check: Substitute 0.5 for k.

3. $3(4 + 5s) - 12 + (-3s) =$ $12s$
   Check: Substitute $\frac{1}{3}$ for s.

STUDY LINK MASTER

✦ *Math Masters,* p. 362

2 Ongoing Learning & Practice

✦ Math Boxes 9.4 (*Math Journal 2,* p. 351)

INDEPENDENT ACTIVITY 

Mixed Review Math Boxes in this lesson are paired with Math Boxes in Lesson 9.2. The skill in Problem 1 is a prerequisite for Unit 10.

✦ Study Link 9.4 (*Math Masters,* p. 362)

Home Connection Students practice simplifying algebraic expressions.

3 Options for Individualizing

✦ EXTRA PRACTICE Writing Expressions to Simplify

PARTNER ACTIVITY

Students write five expressions like those on journal page 349. They exchange papers with a partner and then simplify each other's expressions.

Adjusting the Activity Pair a student learning English with a proficient English speaker. After they have simplified each other's expressions, they should read aloud the original and the simplified expressions.

✦ ENRICHMENT Reading a Math Dictionary

WHOLE-CLASS ACTIVITY  5–15 min

Language Arts Link *G Is for Googol* is an alphabet book of mathematical terms. Each letter of the alphabet is connected to a math concept that is humorously defined and discussed.

Turn to the page titled "X is for *x*". Read this page aloud, or have a student read it. Students may want to try to solve the equation in this description of variables.

Using the illustrations and examples from these pages as a springboard, have students brainstorm ways to use variables besides in mathematical expressions. For example, George Washington is reported to have said, "I cannot tell an *X*." You may want to have students record and illustrate interesting uses of variables that they come up with. These could make a good display.

9.5 Simplifying and Solving Equations

OBJECTIVE **To simplify and solve equations.**

summaries	materials
1 Teaching the Lesson	
Students review procedures for solving equations. They simplify equations by eliminating parentheses and combining like terms. They then solve the simplified equations using the equivalent-equations method learned in Lesson 6.11. [Patterns, Functions, and Algebra]	□ *Math Journal 2,* pp. 352 and 353 □ *Student Reference Book,* pp. 233 and 234 □ Study Link 9.4
2 Ongoing Learning & Practice	
Students use the distributive property to solve number stories. [Patterns, Functions, and Algebra; Operations and Computation] Students practice and maintain skills through Math Boxes and Study Link activities.	□ *Math Journal 2,* pp. 354 and 355 □ Study Link Master (*Math Masters,* p. 363) □ protractor
3 Options for Individualizing	
Extra Practice Students solve Check Your Understanding problems in the *Student Reference Book.* [Patterns, Functions, and Algebra] **Reteaching** Students solve pan-balance problems to review the process of solving equations. [Patterns, Functions, and Algebra]	□ *Student Reference Book,* pp. 233 and 234 □ Teaching Master (*Math Masters,* p. 150) ***See* Advance Preparation**

Additional Information

Advance Preparation For the optional Reteaching activity in Part 3, fill in problems on *Math Masters,* page 150 before making copies. Problems are suggested on page 724.

Vocabulary • **equivalent equations** • **simplify an equation**

Getting Started

Mental Math and Reflexes

Students tell whether fractions are closest to 0, 0.25, 0.5, 0.75, or 1. Have them share their strategies.
Suggestions

- $\frac{3}{16}$ 0.25
- $\frac{17}{20}$ 0.75
- $\frac{4}{7}$ 0.5
- $\frac{11}{25}$ 0.5
- $\frac{31}{50}$ 0.5
- $\frac{1}{12}$ 0
- $\frac{3}{12}$ 0.25
- $\frac{7}{8}$ 0.75, or 1

Math Message

Read pages 233 and 234 in the Student Reference Book.

Study Link 9.4 Follow-Up

Go over the answers with the class. Resolve disagreements by asking students to substitute at least two *different* values for each of the variables. Encourage students to try numbers other than whole numbers, using calculators.

1 Teaching the Lesson

✦ Math Message Follow-Up (*Student Reference Book,* pp. 233 and 234)

WHOLE-CLASS DISCUSSION

Remind students that **equivalent equations** are equations having the same solution. For example, $2 + m = 4$ and $10 = 5m$ are equivalent equations. The solution of both is 2.

Compare the equations in the examples in the *Student Reference Book.* The equation in the example on page 233 has one variable term and one number term on each side of the equal sign. Remind students that the solution shown uses the equivalent-equations method they learned in Unit 6.

The equation in the example on page 234 appears to be more complicated. It contains expressions in parentheses, and it has more than one variable term and number term on the left side of the equal sign.

Go over the example on page 234. Discuss the general outline of the solution strategy. The equation must be transformed into an equivalent equation that looks like the equations students have been solving. Only then can they use the solution method they have learned previously.

STUDENT PAGE

Algebra

A Systematic Method for Solving Equations

Many equations with just one unknown can be solved using only addition, subtraction, multiplication, and division. If the unknown appears on both sides of the equal sign, you must change the equation to an equivalent equation with the unknown appearing on one side. You may also have to change the equation to one with all the constants on the other side of the equal sign.

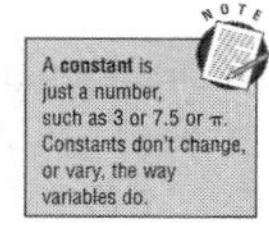

NOTE: A **constant** is just a number, such as 3 or 7.5 or π. Constants don't change, or vary, the way variables do.

EXAMPLE Solve $3y + 10 = 7y - 6$.

Step	Equation
1. Subtract 3y from each side. (S 3y)	$3y + 10 = 7y - 6$ $-3y \quad\quad - 3y$ $10 = 4y - 6$
2. Add 6 to both sides. (A 6)	$10 = 4y - 6$ $+6 \quad\quad +6$ $16 = 4y$
3. Divide both sides by 4. (D 4)	$16 / 4 = 4y / 4$ $4 = y$

Check: Substitute the solution, 4, for y in the original equation:

$3y + 10 = 7y - 6$
$3 * 4 + 10 = 7 * 4 - 6$
$12 + 10 = 28 - 6$
$22 = 22$

Since $22 = 22$ is true, the solution, 4, is correct.
So, $y = 4$.

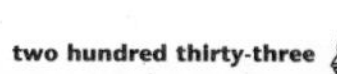

two hundred thirty-three

✧ *Student Reference Book,* p. 233

STUDENT PAGE

Algebra

Like terms are terms that have exactly the same unknown or unknowns. The terms $4x$ and $2x$ are like terms because they both contain x. The terms 6 and 15 are like terms because they both contain no variables; 6 and 15 are both constants.

If an equation has parentheses, or if the unknown or constants appear on both sides of the equal sign, here is how you can **simplify** it.

- If an equation has parentheses, use the distributive property or other properties to write an equivalent equation without parentheses.
- If an equation has two or more like terms on one side of the equal sign, combine the like terms.
- If an equation has more than one constant on one side of the equal sign, combine the constants.

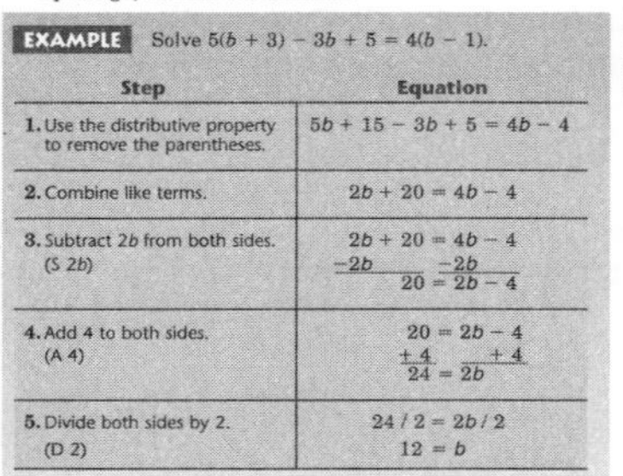

EXAMPLE Solve $5(b + 3) - 3b + 5 = 4(b - 1)$.

Step	Equation
1. Use the distributive property to remove the parentheses.	$5b + 15 - 3b + 5 = 4b - 4$
2. Combine like terms.	$2b + 20 = 4b - 4$
3. Subtract $2b$ from both sides. (S $2b$)	$2b + 20 = 4b - 4$ $-2b \quad -2b$ $20 = 2b - 4$
4. Add 4 to both sides. (A 4)	$20 = 2b - 4$ $+4 \quad +4$ $24 = 2b$
5. Divide both sides by 2. (D 2)	$24 / 2 = 2b / 2$ $12 = b$

Reminder: $5(b + 3)$ means the same as $5 * (b + 3)$.

CHECK YOUR UNDERSTANDING

1. Check that 12 is the solution of the equation in the example above.

Solve.

2. $5x - 7 = 1 + 3x$
3. $5 * (s + 12) = 10 * (3 - s)$
4. $3(9 + b) = 6(b+3)$

Check your answers on page 380.

SRB 234 two hundred thirty-four

Student Reference Book, **p. 234**

Review the procedure that students used in Lesson 9.4 to **simplify an equation:**

1. All parentheses must be eliminated. The simplified equation must not contain any terms in parentheses.
2. The like terms on each side of the equal sign must be combined. There must not be more than one variable term and one number term on each side of the equal sign.
3. When parentheses are removed and like terms are combined, the expression on each side of the equal sign can be treated as though it were a separate problem.

Remind students that they should always remove parentheses first, before combining like terms. Demonstrate how the distributive property is used to remove the parentheses.

$$5(b + 3) = 5 * (b + 3) = (5 * b) + (5 * 3) = 5b + 15$$

$$4(b - 1) = 4 * (b - 1) = (4 * b) - (4 * 1) = 4b - 4$$

✦ Simplifying and Solving Equations
(*Math Journal 2,* pp. 352 and 353)

INDEPENDENT ACTIVITY 

Do Problems 1 and 2 on journal page 352 as a class. Ask one volunteer to simplify an equation, and a second volunteer to solve the simplified equation. Remind students to record the operations they use to obtain equivalent equations (as shown in the *Student Reference Book*).

Adjusting the Activity It has been some time since students first learned a procedure for solving simple equations in Lessons 6.8–6.11. If they are having difficulty, solve several additional equations on the board.

Assign the remaining problems on journal pages 352 and 353. All of the equations must be simplified before they can be solved. Allow plenty of time to go over the answers to the problems with the class.

In Problems 15 and 16, students determine whether pairs of equations are equivalent. In Problem 15, they may notice that $4(1 + 3y) = 4 + 12y$, by the distributive property. Therefore, the equations are equivalent. They are actually the same equation, with two different versions for the right-hand side.

An efficient way to determine that the equations in Problem 16 are equivalent is to solve $f - 1 = 3$. The solution is 4. And if 4 is substituted for the variable in

STUDENT PAGE

Simplifying and Solving Equations

Simplify each equation. Then solve it. Record the operations you used for each step.

1. $6y - 2y = 40$ Solution $y = 10$
2. $5p + 28 = 88 - p$ Solution $p = 10$
3. $8d - 3d = 65$ Solution $d = 13$
4. $12e - 19 = 7 - e$ Solution $e = 2$
5. $3n + \frac{1}{2}n = 42$ Solution $n = 12$
6. $3m - 1 + m + 6 = 2 - 9$ Solution $m = -3$
7. $3(1 + 2y) = y + 2y + 4y$ Solution $y = 3$
8. $8 - 12x = 6 * (1 + x)$ Solution $x = \frac{1}{9}$
9. $-4.8 + b + 0.6b = 1.8 + 3.6b$ Solution $b = -3.3$
10. $4t - 5 = t + 7$ Solution $t = 4$

Math Journal 2, **p. 352**

the first equation, it is clearly the solution of that equation, too.

The challenge problem may be confusing. Point out that parentheses are implied in the expression $\frac{2z + 4}{5}$ even if they are not actually written. This expression may be written as the division expression $(2z + 4) \div 5$ or as the multiplication expression $\frac{1}{5} * (2z + 4)$. One way to start is to multiply both sides of the equation by 5.

ONGOING ASSESSMENT

Use student explanations for Problems 15 and 16 to assess their ability to simplify equations and their understanding of equivalent equations. Expect that some students may still struggle with simplifying equations.

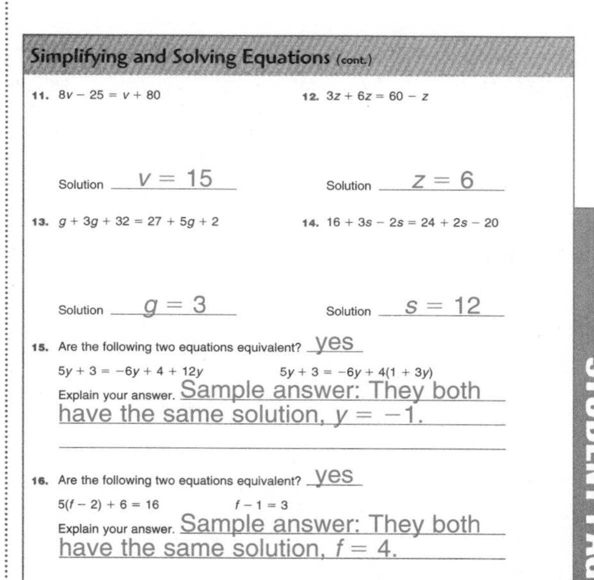

Simplifying and Solving Equations (cont.)

11. $8v - 25 = v + 80$ Solution $v = 15$

12. $3z + 6z = 60 - z$ Solution $z = 6$

13. $g + 3g + 32 = 27 + 5g + 2$ Solution $g = 3$

14. $16 + 3s - 2s = 24 + 2s - 20$ Solution $s = 12$

15. Are the following two equations equivalent? yes

$5y + 3 = -6y + 4 + 12y$ $\quad$ $5y + 3 = -6y + 4(1 + 3y)$

Explain your answer. Sample answer: They both have the same solution, $y = -1$.

16. Are the following two equations equivalent? yes

$5(f - 2) + 6 = 16$ $\quad$ $f - 1 = 3$

Explain your answer. Sample answer: They both have the same solution, $f = 4$.

Challenge

17. Solve $\frac{2z + 4}{5} = z - 1$ $\quad$ $z = 3$

(*Hint:* Multiply both sides by 5.)

STUDENT PAGE

Math Journal 2, p. 353

Ongoing Learning & Practice

✦Applying the Distributive Property (*Math Journal 2,* p. 354)

INDEPENDENT ACTIVITY 

Students use the distributive property to solve number stories.

Number Stories and the Distributive Property 

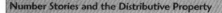

Solve the problems in your head. Do not use a calculator. For each problem, record the number model you used.

1. A carton of milk costs \$0.60. John bought 3 cartons of milk one day and 4 cartons the next day.

How much did he spend in all? \$4.20

Number model $0.60(3 + 4) = n$, or $(0.60 * 3) + (0.60 * 4) = n$

2. During a typical week, Karen runs 16 miles, and Jacob runs 14 miles.

About how many miles in all do Karen and Jacob run in 8 weeks? About 240 miles

Number model $(8 * 16) + (8 * 14) = m$, or $8(16 + 14) = m$

3. Mark bought 6 CDs that cost \$12 each. He returned 2 of them.

How much did he spend in all? \$48

Number model $(6 * 12) - (2 * 12) = c$, or $(6 - 2) * 12 = c$

4. Max collects stamps. He had 9 envelopes, each containing 25 stamps. He sold 3 envelopes to another collector.

How many stamps did he have left? 150 stamps

Number model $(9 * 25) - (3 * 25) = s$, or $(9 - 3) * 25 = s$

5. Jean is sending party invitations to her friends. She has 8 boxes with 12 invitations in each box. She has already mailed 5 boxes of invitations.

How many invitations are left? 36 invitations

Number model $(8 * 12) - (5 * 12) = p$, or $(8 - 5) * 12 = p$

STUDENT PAGE

Math Journal 2, p. 354

✦Math Boxes 9.5 (*Math Journal 2,* p. 355)

INDEPENDENT ACTIVITY 

Mixed Review Math Boxes in this lesson are paired with Math Boxes in Lessons 9.1 and 9.3. The skill in Problem 1 is a prerequisite for Unit 10.

✦Study Link 9.5 (*Math Masters,* p. 363)

Home Connection Students solve equations and find pairs of equivalent equations.

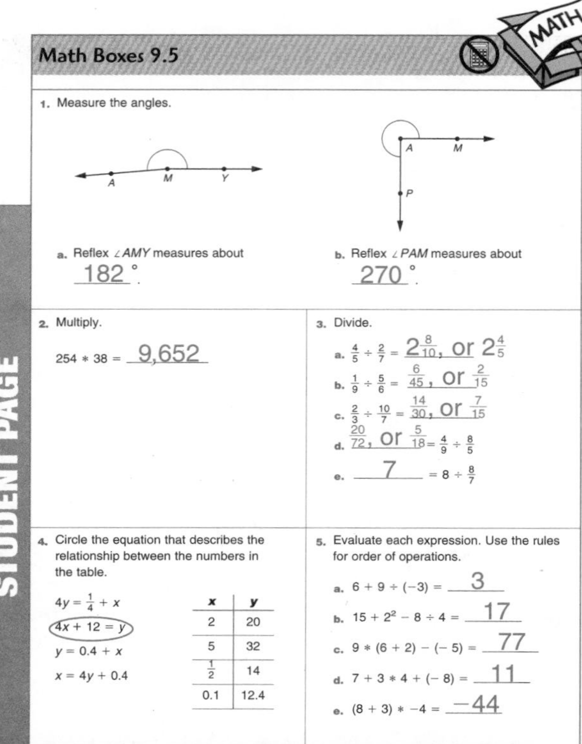

STUDENT PAGE

Math Boxes 9.5

1. Measure the angles.

a. Reflex ∠AMY measures about 182°.

b. Reflex ∠PAM measures about 270°.

2. Multiply.

$254 * 38 =$ 9,652

3. Divide.

a. $\frac{4}{5} \div \frac{2}{7} = 2\frac{8}{10}$, or $2\frac{4}{5}$

b. $\frac{1}{9} \div \frac{5}{6} = \frac{6}{45}$, or $\frac{2}{15}$

c. $\frac{2}{3} \div \frac{10}{7} = \frac{14}{30}$, or $\frac{7}{15}$

d. $\frac{20}{72}$, or $\frac{5}{18} = \frac{4}{9} \div \frac{8}{5}$

e. $7 = 8 \div \frac{8}{7}$

4. Circle the equation that describes the relationship between the numbers in the table.

$4y = \frac{1}{4} + x$

$4x + 12 = y$ (circled)

$y = 0.4 + x$

$x = 4y + 0.4$

x	y
2	20
5	32
$\frac{1}{2}$	14
0.1	12.4

5. Evaluate each expression. Use the rules for order of operations.

a. $6 + 9 \div (-3) =$ 3

b. $15 + 2^2 - 8 \div 4 =$ 17

c. $9 * (6 + 2) - (-5) =$ 77

d. $7 + 3 * 4 + (-8) =$ 11

e. $(8 + 3) * -4 =$ −44

Math Journal 2, p. 355

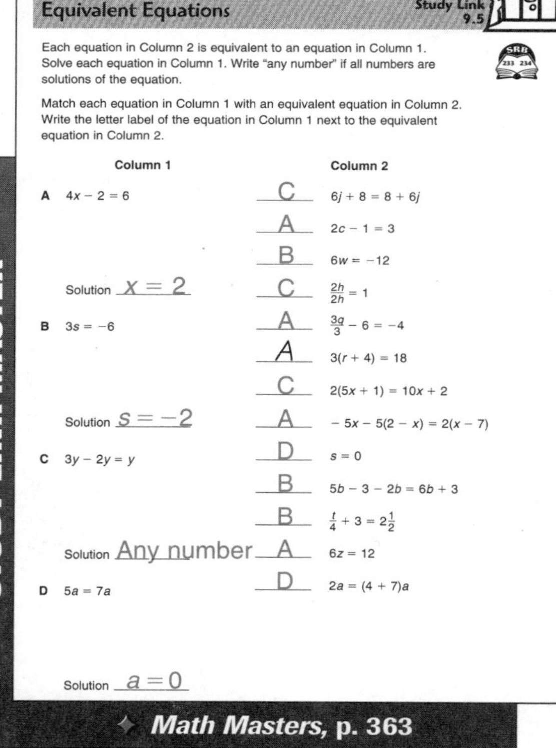

STUDY LINK MASTER

Equivalent Equations — Study Link 9.5

Each equation in Column 2 is equivalent to an equation in Column 1. Solve each equation in Column 1. Write "any number" if all numbers are solutions of the equation.

Match each equation in Column 1 with an equivalent equation in Column 2. Write the letter label of the equation in Column 1 next to the equivalent equation in Column 2.

Column 1

A $4x - 2 = 6$ — Solution $x = 2$

B $3s = -6$ — Solution $s = -2$

C $3y - 2y = y$ — Solution Any number

D $5a = 7a$ — Solution $a = 0$

Column 2

C $6j + 8 = 8 + 6j$

A $2c - 1 = 3$

B $6w = -12$

C $\frac{2h}{2h} = 1$

A $\frac{3q}{3} - 6 = -4$

A $3(r + 4) = 18$

C $2(5x + 1) = 10x + 2$

A $-5x - 5(2 - x) = 2(x - 7)$

D $s = 0$

B $5b - 3 - 2b = 6b + 3$

B $\frac{t}{4} + 3 = 2\frac{1}{2}$

A $6z = 12$

D $2a = (4 + 7)a$

Math Masters, p. 363

3 Options for Individualizing

✦ EXTRA PRACTICE Solving Equations
(*Student Reference Book,* pp. 233 and 234)

INDEPENDENT ACTIVITY  **5–15 min** 

Students review the information on pages 233 and 234 of the *Student Reference Book* and answer the Check Your Understanding questions at the bottom of page 234.

✦ RETEACHING Solving Pan-Balance Problems
(*Math Masters,* p. 150)

INDEPENDENT ACTIVITY  **15–30 min** 

To revisit the step-by-step process for solving equations, prepare a page of pan-balance problems on *Math Masters*, page 150 for students to solve. *Suggestions:*

$8y + (-5) = 5y + 13$

$16f - 24 = 8f$

$11 + 9k = 71 - 3k$

$4r + 37 = 100 - 5r$

TEAACHING MASTER

Revisiting Pan Balances

Solve the equations. For each step, record the operation you use and the equation that results.

Check your solution by substituting it for the variable in the original equation.

1. Original equation ________ = ________
Operation
________ ________ = ________
________ ________ = ________
________ ________ = ________

2. Original equation ________ = ________
Operation
________ ________ = ________
________ ________ = ________
________ ________ = ________

3. Original equation ________ = ________
Operation
________ ________ = ________
________ ________ = ________
________ ________ = ________

4. Original equation ________ = ________
Operation
________ ________ = ________
________ ________ = ________
________ ________ = ________

Math Masters, p. 150

9.6 Using Equations to Solve Mobile Problems

OBJECTIVE **To write and solve equations based on a given formula.**

summaries	materials
1 Teaching the Lesson	
Students explore the mathematics of balanced mobiles made of a rod and objects suspended from the rod. They write and solve equations to find the weights of the objects and their distances from the fulcrum (balancing point) of the rod. [Patterns, Functions, and Algebra]	□ *Math Journal 2,* p. 356 □ *Student Reference Book,* pp. 334 and 335 □ Study Link 9.5 □ Assessment Master (*Math Masters,* p. 473 or 474; optional) ***See* Advance Preparation**
2 Ongoing Learning & Practice	
Students divide using the partial-quotients division algorithm; they use the algorithm to rename remainders as decimals. [Operations and Computation] Students practice and maintain skills through Math Boxes and Study Link activities.	□ *Math Journal 2,* pp. 357 and 358 □ Study Link Master (*Math Masters,* p. 364) □ calculator □ Geometry Template
3 Options for Individualizing	
Enrichment Students research mobiles as art. [Patterns, Functions, and Algebra] **Enrichment** Students figure out how to rearrange an unbalanced mobile so that it will balance. [Patterns, Functions, and Algebra]	□ Teaching Master (*Math Masters,* p. 151)

Additional Information

Advance Preparation If your school has a seesaw, consider a trip to the playground to demonstrate the principles of a lever, or mobile, referred to in Part 1 of this lesson.

Vocabulary • **mobile** • **fulcrum**

Getting Started

Mental Math and Reflexes

Students use "friendly numbers" and mental math to solve division problems. They record their answers on their slates. *Suggestions:*

- 284 ÷ 4 71
- 444 ÷ 6 74
- 369 ÷ 9 41
- 378 ÷ 7 54
- 576 ÷ 8 72
- 279 ÷ 3 93

Math Message

Read pages 334 and 335 of the Student Reference Book.

Study Link 9.5 Follow-Up

As you discuss the answers with the class, encourage students to propose alternative solution strategies. For example, to find the equation in Column 1 that is equivalent to $2c - 1 = 3$, solve the equation by adding 1 to both sides and then dividing both sides by 2. The solution is 2. Another approach is to multiply both sides by 2 to obtain the equation $4c - 2 = 6$, which is the same as Equation A in Column 1 except for the variable.

Several other equations may be matched with an equation in Column 1, without actually solving the equation. *For example:*

▷ If you remove the parentheses in the equation $2(5x + 1) = 10x + 2$, you obtain $10x + 2 = 10x + 2$, which must be true for all numbers.

▷ The equation $\frac{2h}{2h} = 1$ must be true for all numbers (except 0), since any fraction that has the same numerator and denominator is equal to 1.

Teaching the Lesson

✦Math Message Follow-Up
(*Student Reference Book,* pp. 334 and 335)

WHOLE-CLASS DISCUSSION

Discuss the essay on pages 334 and 335 of the *Student Reference Book*. These are some of the points you should cover:

▷ The simplest **mobile** consists of a single suspended rod, from which two objects are hung. (All mobiles in the lesson are of this type.)

▷ The **fulcrum** of the mobile is the point at which the single rod is suspended.

▷ Before the two objects are hung from the rod, the rod will be in balance if the fulcrum is at the center of the rod.

▷ The two objects hung from the rod need not have the same weight, nor must they be the same distance from the fulcrum.

A mobile whose fulcrum is at the center will remain balanced if, when the weight of each object is multiplied by its distance from the fulcrum, the products are equal. If they are not equal, the mobile tilts. This relationship is expressed by the formula $W * D = w * d$, where the variables W and w represent the weights of the two objects and the variables D and d their distances from the fulcrum.

STUDENT PAGE

Art and Design Activities

How to Balance a Mobile

A **mobile** is a piece of sculpture constructed of rods and other objects that are suspended by wire, twine, or thread in midair. The rods and objects are connected in such a way that the sculpture is balanced when it is suspended.

The point at which the rod is suspended is called the fulcrum. The **fulcrum** may be the center point of the rod or some other point on the rod. The objects may be hung at the ends of the rods or at points between the ends of the rod and the fulcrum.

Suppose the fulcrum is the center point of a rod and you hang two objects from points on the rod, one on each side of the fulcrum.

Let W = the weight of one object
D = the distance of this object, W, from the fulcrum
w = the weight of the second object
d = the distance of this object, w, from the fulcrum

The mobile will balance if $W * D = w * d$.

This mobile, titled *Sea Scape, 1947,* was made by Alexander Calder (1898–1976). It is made of painted wood, sheet metal, string, and wire; it is 60 inches wide.

fulcrum (at center of rod)
D d
W w

EXAMPLE In the mobile at the right, what is the missing distance?

Replace the variables in the formula $W * D = w * d$ with the values shown in the diagram. Then, solve the equation.

$W = 6$ $D = 7$ $w = 10$ $d = x$

Solution: $W * D = w * d$
$6 * 7 = 10 * x$
$42 = 10 * x$
$4.2 = x$

Therefore, the distance, x, to the fulcrum is 4.2 units.

7 7 x 6 10

CHECK YOUR UNDERSTANDING

Decide whether the mobiles are in balance.

1. 10 10 6 8 12 9

2. 8 8 4 6 11 7

Check your answers on page 380.

SRB 334 three hundred thirty-four

< *Student Reference Book,* p. 334

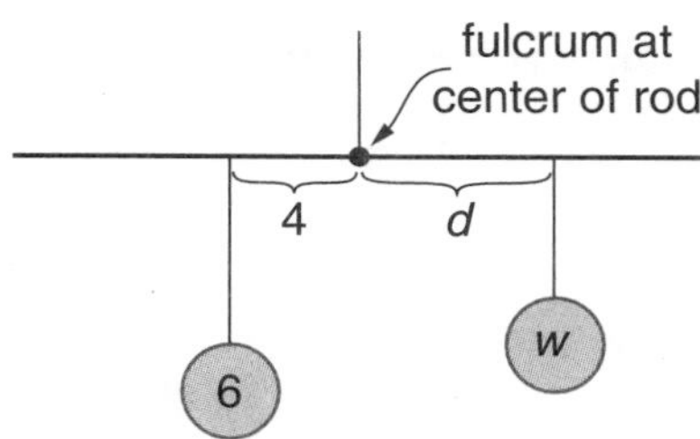

Sketch the mobile shown above on the board and ask students to give possible replacements for the variables w and d that will make the mobile balance. Sample answers: $w = 6$ and $d = 4$; $w = 4$ and $d = 6$; $w = 8$ and $d = 3$; $w = 2.4$ and $d = 10$; and so on.

Adjusting the Activity It may help some students to compare a mobile (with the fulcrum at the center of the rod) to a seesaw. A seesaw is a plank that is balanced in the middle. When two children of approximately the same weight sit at opposite ends, they can easily move the seesaw alternately up and down. If one child is much heavier than the other, the seesaw will not move up and down unless the heavier child sits closer to the center than the lighter child. The formula $W * D = w * d$ also applies to the seesaw. If your playground has a seesaw, you may want to demonstrate how to balance the seesaw by moving students closer to and farther from the fulcrum. Be sure to use appropriate vocabulary throughout the exercise.

Go over the example on *Student Reference Book,* page 334. Point out that when solving problems in which numbers are substituted for variables in a formula, it is best to list the values of the variables before substituting them in the formula. This way of organizing the data will be reinforced in the problems on the journal pages.

Give the class time to solve the Check Your Understanding problems at the bottom of the page. Then have students share their solutions.

Adjusting the Activity You may want to make a poster of the simple mobile used in this lesson with the parts labeled *fulcrum, rod, center, weights,* and *distance.*

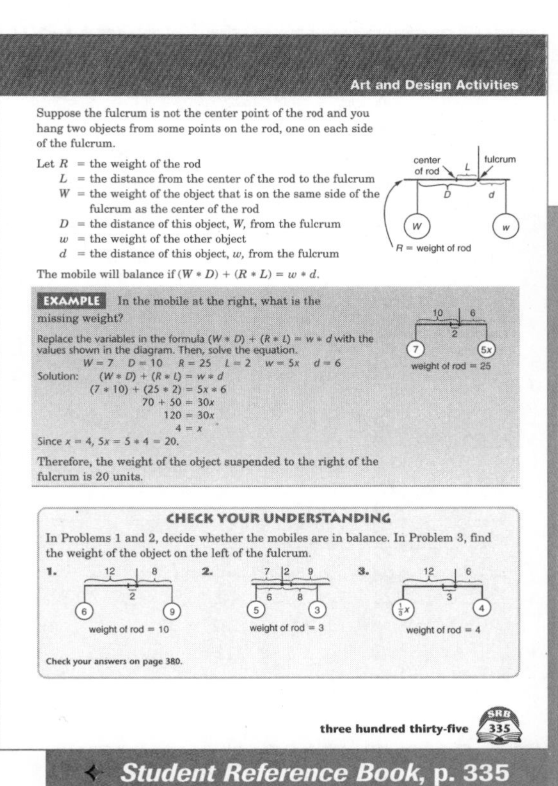

Art and Design Activities

Suppose the fulcrum is not the center point of the rod and you hang two objects from some points on the rod, one on each side of the fulcrum.

Let R = the weight of the rod
L = the distance from the center of the rod to the fulcrum
W = the weight of the object that is on the same side of the fulcrum as the center of the rod
D = the distance of this object, W, from the fulcrum
w = the weight of the other object
d = the distance of this object, w, from the fulcrum

The mobile will balance if $(W * D) + (R * L) = w * d$.

EXAMPLE In the mobile at the right, what is the missing weight?

Replace the variables in the formula $(W * D) + (R * L) = w * d$ with the values shown in the diagram. Then, solve the equation.

$W = 7$ $D = 10$ $R = 25$ $L = 2$ $w = 5x$ $d = 6$

Solution:
$$(W * D) + (R * L) = w * d$$
$$(7 * 10) + (25 * 2) = 5x * 6$$
$$70 + 50 = 30x$$
$$120 = 30x$$
$$4 = x$$

Since $x = 4$, $5x = 5 * 4 = 20$.

Therefore, the weight of the object suspended to the right of the fulcrum is 20 units.

CHECK YOUR UNDERSTANDING

In Problems 1 and 2, decide whether the mobiles are in balance. In Problem 3, find the weight of the object on the left of the fulcrum.

1.

2.

3.

Check your answers on page 380.

three hundred thirty-five SRB 335

STUDENT PAGE

Student Reference Book, p. 335

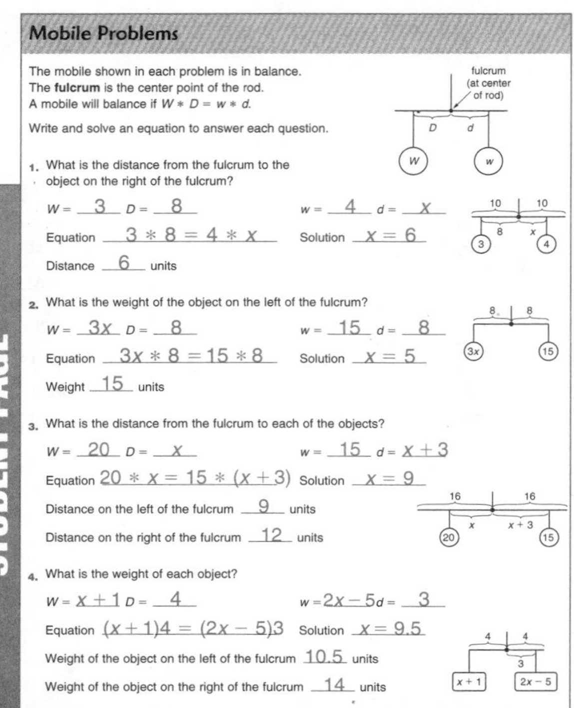

Mobile Problems

The mobile shown in each problem is in balance.
The **fulcrum** is the center point of the rod.
A mobile will balance if $W * D = w * d$.

Write and solve an equation to answer each question.

1. What is the distance from the fulcrum to the object on the right of the fulcrum?
   $W =$ 3 $D =$ 8 $w =$ 4 $d =$ x
   Equation $3 * 8 = 4 * x$ Solution $x = 6$
   Distance 6 units

2. What is the weight of the object on the left of the fulcrum?
   $W =$ $3x$ $D =$ 8 $w =$ 15 $d =$ 8
   Equation $3x * 8 = 15 * 8$ Solution $x = 5$
   Weight 15 units

3. What is the distance from the fulcrum to each of the objects?
   $W =$ 20 $D =$ x $w =$ 15 $d =$ $x + 3$
   Equation $20 * x = 15 * (x + 3)$ Solution $x = 9$
   Distance on the left of the fulcrum 9 units
   Distance on the right of the fulcrum 12 units

4. What is the weight of each object?
   $W =$ $x + 1$ $D =$ 4 $w =$ $2x - 5$ $d =$ 3
   Equation $(x + 1)4 = (2x - 5)3$ Solution $x = 9.5$
   Weight of the object on the left of the fulcrum 10.5 units
   Weight of the object on the right of the fulcrum 14 units

STUDENT PAGE

Math Journal 2, p. 356

Solving Mobile Problems
(*Math Journal 2,* p. 356)

PARTNER ACTIVITY

Partners solve the problems on journal page 356 as you circulate and assist. When most of the students have finished, bring the class together to share solution strategies.

ONGOING ASSESSMENT

Have students complete a Math Log page (*Math Masters,* page 473 or 474) explaining the relationship between mobile problems and the lessons on solving equations.

Weekly Math Log

1. What did you study in math this week?

2. Many ideas in math are related to other ideas within math. Think about how the topic(s) you studied in class this week relate to other topics you learned before.

   Your reflection can include what you learned in previous years.

TEACHING MASTER

Math Masters, p. 473

2 Ongoing Learning & Practice

Renaming a Remainder as a Decimal

WHOLE-CLASS DISCUSSION

A remainder is a fractional part of a dividend. Instead of expressing a remainder as a fraction, the following technique can be used to rename remainders as decimals. In most cases, such problems are best solved with a calculator, but some students might enjoy the challenge of solving them with paper and pencil.

Pose a problem such as, "Find 7.5 divided by 3.5, to two decimal places." Students might be able to work out a solution on their own. If not, show them the following solution.

Step 1 Estimate. $7.5 \div 3.5$ will be about 2.

Step 2 Find an equivalent problem without decimals.

$7.5 \div 3.5 = 75 \div 35$

Step 3 Divide.

```
35)75  |
 - 70  |2
    5   2
```

Step 4 Estimate the remainder as a decimal. The partial-quotient division algorithm shows that $75 \div 35 = 2\frac{5}{35}$.

To rename $\frac{5}{35}$ as a 2-place decimal, first estimate the answer:

$\frac{5}{35} = \frac{1}{7}$

$\frac{1}{7}$ is close to $\frac{1}{8}$, or 0.125

So $\frac{5}{35}$ is about 0.1.

Step 5 Rename the remainder as a decimal. Write $\frac{5}{35} = \frac{5.00}{35}$. Use partial-quotient division algorithm to find $500 \div 35$.

$$\begin{array}{r|l} 35\overline{)500} & \\ -\ 350 & 10 \\ 150 & \\ -\ 140 & 4 \\ 10 & 14 \end{array}$$

Round the answer to the nearest whole number: $500 \div 35 = 14\frac{10}{35}$, or about 14.

Since the estimate was that $\frac{5}{35}$ is about 0.1, the decimal point should be placed before the 1 in 14; write 0.14.

Step 6 Combine the whole-number quotient with the decimal expression of the remainder.

$$\begin{aligned} 75 / 35 &= 2\tfrac{5}{35} \\ &= 2 + \tfrac{5}{35} \\ &= 2 + 0.14 \\ &= 2.14 \end{aligned}$$

Thus, $7.5 \div 3.5 = 2.14$, correct to two decimal places.

Pose similar problems. Students can use a calculator to check their work.

✦ Solving Division Problems
(*Math Journal 2,* p. 357)

INDEPENDENT ACTIVITY 

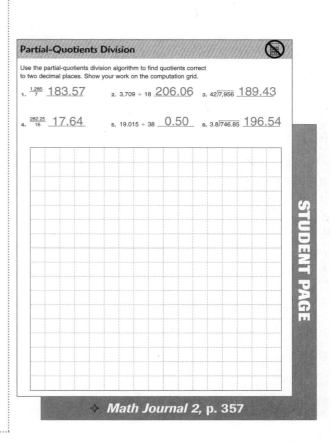

Students find quotients correct to two decimal places.

ONGOING ASSESSMENT

Use this page to assess students' facility with the partial-quotients division algorithm. Expect that most students should be good at using the algorithm with whole numbers, but that some will still have difficulty with division of decimals. Remind them to make an estimate of the answer before performing the algorithm.

Partial-Quotients Division

Use the partial-quotients division algorithm to find quotients correct to two decimal places. Show your work on the computation grid.

1. $\frac{1,285}{7}$ 183.57
2. $3,709 \div 18$ 206.06
3. $42\overline{)7,956}$ 189.43
4. $\frac{282.25}{16}$ 17.64
5. $19.015 \div 38$ 0.50
6. $3.8\overline{)746.85}$ 196.54

STUDENT PAGE

✧ *Math Journal 2,* p. 357

Math Boxes 9.6

1. Find a kite on your Geometry Template. Use the template to draw a kite in the space to the right.

How would you describe a kite?
Sample answer: A quadrilateral with exactly two pairs of adjacent, congruent sides

2. Solve.

		Solution
a.	$\frac{15}{2} = \frac{y}{6}$	$y = 45$
b.	$\frac{x}{99} = \frac{10}{11}$	$x = 90$
c.	$\frac{144}{3} = \frac{x}{1}$	$x = 48$
d.	$\frac{24}{x} = \frac{80}{100}$	$x = 30$
e.	$\frac{50}{x} = \frac{18}{72}$	$x = 200$

3. Seven out of nine cards are faceup. If 16 cards are facedown, how many cards are there altogether? 72 cards

Explain how you found your answer.
Sample answer: I used a ratio comparing facedown cards to total cards. $\frac{2}{9} = \frac{16}{x}$

4. The table at the right shows how much a person weighing 100 pounds on Earth would weigh on each of the planets in the solar system.

a. On which planet would a person weigh about $\frac{1}{6}$ as much as on Mercury? Pluto

b. On which planet would a person weigh about 3 times as much as on Mars? Neptune, or Saturn

c. On which planet would a person weigh about $2\frac{1}{2}$ times as much as on Earth? Jupiter

Planet	Weight (lb)
Mercury	37
Venus	88
Earth	100
Mars	38
Jupiter	264
Saturn	115
Uranus	93
Neptune	122
Pluto	6

STUDENT PAGE

✦ *Math Journal 2,* p. 358

✦ Math Boxes 9.6 (*Math Journal 2,* p. 358)

INDEPENDENT ACTIVITY 

Mixed Review Math Boxes in this lesson are paired with Math Boxes in Lesson 9.8. The skill in Problem 1 is a prerequisite for Unit 10.

✦ Study Link 9.6 (*Math Masters,* p. 364)

Home Connection Students review simplifying and solving equations. The Challenge problem involves a mobile.

3 Options for Individualizing

✦ ENRICHMENT Researching Mobiles

INDEPENDENT ACTIVITY  **30+ min** 

Art Link Have students research mobiles. Alexander Calder is a famous artist who has produced a well-known collection of mobiles. You may have a Calder mobile at your local art museum.

Expressions and Equations Study Link 9.6

Solve.

1. $3x + 9 = 30$ $x =$ 7
2. $73 = \frac{1}{2}(108 + e)$ $e =$ 38
3. $55 = (9 - d) * 11$ $d =$ 4
4. $(m * 15) + (m * 6) = 42$ $m =$ 2

Simplify these expressions by combining like terms.

5. $8y + 27 + 6y + (-4)$ $23 + 14y$
6. $7b + 17 - 9b + 15$ $-2b + 32$
7. $3f - 80 + 25 - 10e$ $3f - 55 - 10e$
8. $240 + 5g + 3(10g - 5)$ $225 + 35g$

Circle all expressions that are equivalent to the original. There may be more than one. Check your answer by substituting values for the variable.

9. Original: $3r + 17 - 2r + 6$
$5r + 23$ $23 - r$ 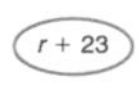 $r + 23$ (circled) $13 + r$

10. Original: $8(9 + b) - 4b$
$89 - 3b$ $72 - 3b$  $4b + 72$ (circled)   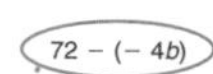 $72 - (-4b)$ (circled)

Challenge

11. The top mobile is in balance. The fulcrum is in the center of the rod. A mobile will balance when $W * D = w * d$.
Look at the bottom mobile. What is the weight of the object on the left?

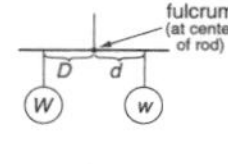

Write and solve an equation to answer the question.
$W =$ 5b $D =$ 4 $w =$ 30 $d =$ 12
Equation $5b * 4 = 30 * 12$ Solution $b = 18$
Weight of the object on the left 90 units

STUDY LINK MASTER

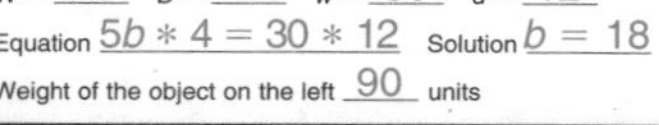
✦ *Math Masters,* p. 364

✦ ENRICHMENT Balancing a Complicated Mobile (*Math Masters*, p. 151)

PARTNER ACTIVITY **30+ min** 

Give each student a copy of *Math Masters*, page 151. The master shows a mobile made from 3 rods and suspended weights. All weights and distances are given, including the weights of the rods. Students are asked to discover which of the rods is not balanced. They are then asked how to move one of the wires so that the mobile will balance.

This is a challenging problem. You may want to give the following hint: For each smaller mobile suspended from the main (top) rod, the total weight is the sum of the 2 weights suspended from it, PLUS the weight of the rod itself. Ask students to share solution strategies. One possible strategy:

▷ The lower rod on the left side is balanced, since $15.3 * 3\frac{1}{3} = 8.5 * 6 = 51$.

▷ The lower rod on the right side is also balanced, since $9.5 * 8 = 7.6 * 10 = 76$.

▷ To calculate $W * D$ for the left side of the main rod, multiply the weight of the objects suspended from that side by 17.

$$15.3 + 6 + 3 = 24.3;\ 24.3 * 17 = 413.1$$

▷ To calculate $w * d$ for the right side of the main rod, first calculate $w * d$ for the lower mobile.

$$9.5 + 7.6 + 3 = 20.1;\ 20.1 * 15 = 301.5$$

To this, add $w * d$ for the 10-weight.

$$10 * 10 = 100;\ 301.5 + 100 = 401.5$$

Then compare the two results. Since they are not equal, the main rod of the mobile is not balanced.

▷ The difference of weight $*$ distance between the two sides of the main rod is 11.6.

$$413.1 - 401.5 = 11.6$$

If the 10-weight on the right side is moved 1.16 units to the right, the main rod will be balanced, since this will add $10 * 1.16 = 11.6$ units to the right side.

Challenge: Balancing a Mobile 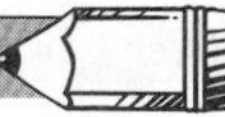

In the mobile shown below, each rod is suspended at its center.

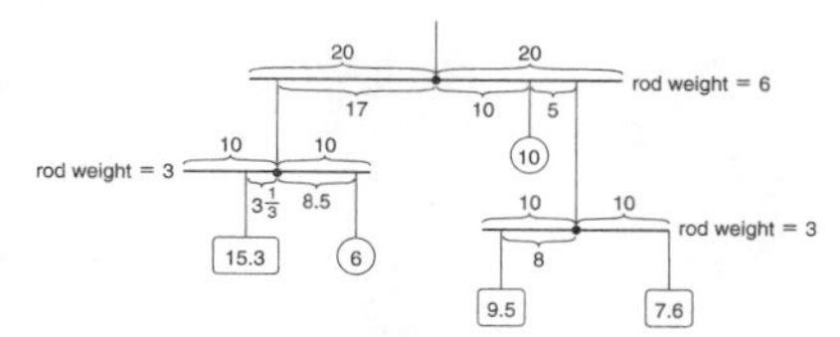

1. Is each of the rods in perfect balance? no

If not, which of the rods is not balanced? The main (top) rod

Explain how you found the answer. Sample answer: Using the formula $W * D = w * d$, I determined that the two lower rods are balanced. Then I used the same formula to determine that weight $*$ distance on the left side of the main rod is 413.1 units, and weight $*$ distance on the right side is 401.5 units.

2. If you found that a rod in the mobile shown above is not balanced, how would you move exactly one of the suspending wires so that the rod would be in balance?
Sample answer: The weight $*$ distance difference between the two sides of the main rod is 11.6 units. So I would move the 10-weight 1.16 units to the right.

TEACHING MASTER

✦ *Math Masters*, p. 151

9.7 Computer Spreadsheets

OBJECTIVE **To learn how data are entered and displayed in a computer spreadsheet program.**

summaries	materials
1 Teaching the Lesson	
Students identify the parts of a spreadsheet and learn how labels, numbers, and formulas are entered and displayed in a spreadsheet. Students solve spreadsheet problems. [Patterns, Functions, and Algebra]	□ *Math Journal 2,* p. 359 □ *Student Reference Book,* pp. 137 and 138 □ Study Link 9.6 □ Teaching Master (*Math Masters,* p. 152) □ Transparency (*Math Masters,* p. 153; optional) □ calculator ***See* Advance Preparation**
2 Ongoing Learning & Practice	
Students review ratios. [Numeration] Students practice and maintain skills through Math Boxes and Study Link activities.	□ *Math Journal 2,* pp. 360 and 361 □ Study Link Master (*Math Masters,* p. 365) □ compass □ cm ruler
3 Options for Individualizing	
Reteaching Students play *Hidden Treasure* to practice locating addresses on a grid. [Measurement and Reference Frames] **Extra Practice** Students create spreadsheets on a computer. [Patterns, Functions, and Algebra] **Enrichment** Students practice using formulas to complete a spreadsheet. They use the spreadsheet data to draw graphs. [Patterns, Functions, and Algebra; Data and Chance]	□ *Math Journal 2,* p. 359 □ *Student Reference Book,* p. 296 □ Teaching Masters (*Math Masters,* pp. 44, 154, and 155) □ red coloring pencil or crayon □ computer with spreadsheet software

Additional Information

Advance Preparation For Part 1, make one copy of *Math Masters,* page 152 for every 4 students. Cut the copies apart and put them near the Math Message.

Vocabulary • **spreadsheet program** • **cell** • **address of a cell** • **address box** • **display bar** • **labels** • **number** • **formulas**

Getting Started

Mental Math and Reflexes

Students identify equivalent ratios. Remind students that simplifying a ratio will sometimes help answer the question. *Suggestions:*

- The ratio 2 to 3 is the same as the ratio 8 to what number? 12
- The ratio 4 out of 10 is the same as the ratio 20 out of what number? 50
- The ratio 3 for 18 is the same as 4 for how many? 24
- The ratio 5 to −30 is the same as 7 to what number? −42
- The ratio $\frac{1}{2}$ out of 7 is the same as 2 out of what number? 28

Math Message

Take a copy of the Math Message. Follow the directions.

Study Link 9.6 Follow-Up

Briefly review answers.
Have volunteers share their solutions to the Challenge problem.

Teaching the Lesson

✦ Math Message Follow-Up (*Math Masters,* p. 152)

WHOLE-CLASS DISCUSSION 

Briefly go over the answers.

Name ____________

Math Message

Evaluate the expression $(b^2 * 4) + k$ for the following values:

1. $b = 3$ and $k = 5$ 41
2. $b = \frac{1}{2}$ and $k = \frac{3}{4}$ $1\frac{3}{4}$
3. $b = -2$ and $k = -10$ 6
4. $b = 5$ and $k = 115$ 215

Math Masters, page 152

✦ Discussing Computer Spreadsheets (*Student Reference Book,* pp. 137 and 138; *Math Masters,* p. 153)

WHOLE-CLASS ACTIVITY 

Read pages 137 and 138 of the *Student Reference Book* as a class. You may want to use an overhead transparency of *Math Masters*, page 153 to illustrate how a **spreadsheet program** works. This page shows the same spreadsheet that appears at the bottom of page 137 in the *Student Reference Book.*

Adjusting the Activity To help students with the vocabulary of spreadsheets, consider drawing a large spreadsheet on the board or on a poster. Label the address box and the display bar. Write a formula in one of the cells and label it *formula*. Write a cell address in a different cell and label it *cell address*. If you make a poster, consider listing at the bottom examples of labels, numbers, and formulas, clearly categorized. Examples of labels: *budget, food items, 8% tax.*

address box
cancel
accept
display bar

Supplies ($)

D3 | x | ✓ | = B3 ∗ C3

	A	B	C	D
1	item name	unit price	quantity	totals
2				
3	pencils	0.29	6	1.74
4	graph paper	1.19	2	2.38
5	ruler	0.50	1	0.50
6	book	5.95	1	5.95
7				
8	Subtotal			10.57
9	tax 7%			0.74
10	Total			$11.31

Math Masters, page 153

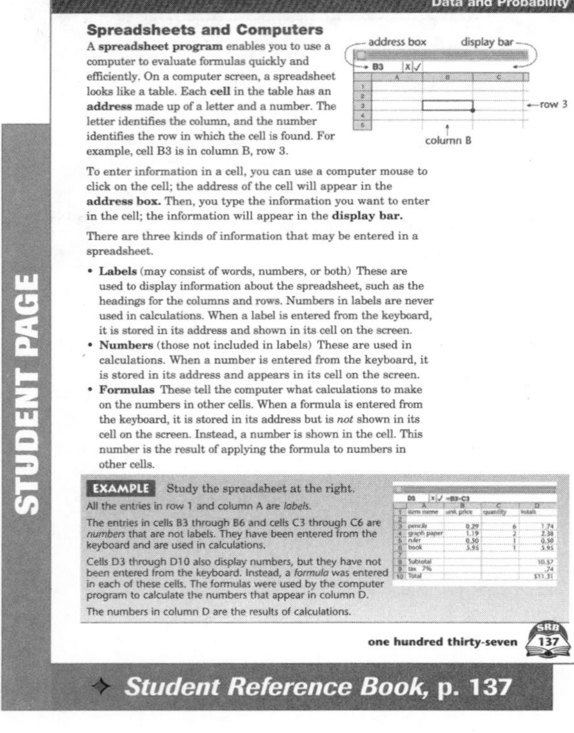

Data and Probability

Spreadsheets and Computers

A **spreadsheet program** enables you to use a computer to evaluate formulas quickly and efficiently. On a computer screen, a spreadsheet looks like a table. Each **cell** in the table has an **address** made up of a letter and a number. The letter identifies the column, and the number identifies the row in which the cell is found. For example, cell B3 is in column B, row 3.

To enter information in a cell, you can use a computer mouse to click on the cell; the address of the cell will appear in the **address box.** Then, you type the information you want to enter in the cell; the information will appear in the **display bar.**

There are three kinds of information that may be entered in a spreadsheet.

- **Labels** (may consist of words, numbers, or both) These are used to display information about the spreadsheet, such as the headings for the columns and rows. Numbers in labels are never used in calculations. When a label is entered from the keyboard, it is stored in its address and shown in its cell on the screen.
- **Numbers** (those not included in labels) These are used in calculations. When a number is entered from the keyboard, it is stored in its address and appears in its cell on the screen.
- **Formulas** These tell the computer what calculations to make on the numbers in other cells. When a formula is entered from the keyboard, it is stored in its address but is *not* shown in its cell on the screen. Instead, a number is shown in the cell. This number is the result of applying the formula to numbers in other cells.

EXAMPLE Study the spreadsheet at the right.

All the entries in row 1 and column A are *labels*.

The entries in cells B3 through B6 and cells C3 through C6 are *numbers* that are not labels. They have been entered from the keyboard and are used in calculations.

Cells D3 through D10 also display numbers, but they have not been entered from the keyboard. Instead, a *formula* was entered in each of these cells. The formulas were used by the computer program to calculate the numbers that appear in column D.

The numbers in column D are the results of calculations.

D3 =B3*C3

	A	B	C	D
1	item name	unit price	quantity	totals
2				
3	pencils	0.29	6	1.74
4	graph paper	1.19	2	2.38
5	ruler	0.50	1	0.50
6	book	5.95	1	5.95
7				
8	Subtotal			10.57
9	tax 7%			.74
10	Total			$11.31

one hundred thirty-seven SRB 137

✦ Student Reference Book, p. 137

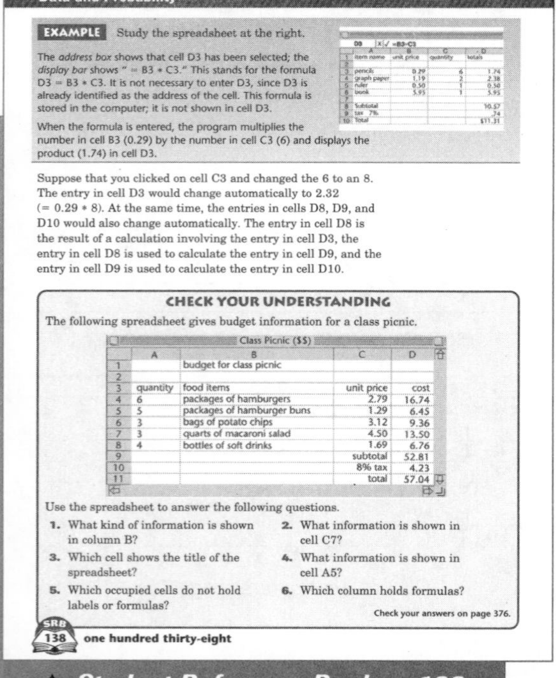

Data and Probability

EXAMPLE Study the spreadsheet at the right.

The *address box* shows that cell D3 has been selected; the *display bar* shows " = B3 * C3." This stands for the formula D3 = B3 * C3. It is not necessary to enter D3, since D3 is already identified as the address of the cell. This formula is stored in the computer; it is not shown in cell D3.

When the formula is entered, the program multiplies the number in cell B3 (0.29) by the number in cell C3 (6) and displays the product (1.74) in cell D3.

D3 =B3*C3

	A	B	C	D
1	item name	unit price	quantity	totals
2				
3	pencils	0.29	6	1.74
4	graph paper	1.19	2	2.38
5	ruler	0.50	1	0.50
6	book	5.95	1	5.95
7				
8	Subtotal			10.57
9	tax 7%			.74
10	Total			$11.31

Suppose that you clicked on cell C3 and changed the 6 to an 8. The entry in cell D3 would change automatically to 2.32 (= 0.29 * 8). At the same time, the entries in cells D8, D9, and D10 would also change automatically. The entry in cell D8 is the result of a calculation involving the entry in cell D3, the entry in cell D8 is used to calculate the entry in cell D9, and the entry in cell D9 is used to calculate the entry in cell D10.

CHECK YOUR UNDERSTANDING

The following spreadsheet gives budget information for a class picnic.

Class Picnic ($$)

	A	B	C	D
1		budget for class picnic		
2				
3	quantity	food items	unit price	cost
4	6	packages of hamburgers	2.79	16.74
5	5	packages of hamburger buns	1.29	6.45
6	3	bags of potato chips	3.12	9.36
7	3	quarts of macaroni salad	4.50	13.50
8	4	bottles of soft drinks	1.69	6.76
9			subtotal	52.81
10			8% tax	4.23
11			total	57.04

Use the spreadsheet to answer the following questions.

1. What kind of information is shown in column B?
2. What information is shown in cell C7?
3. Which cell shows the title of the spreadsheet?
4. What information is shown in cell A5?
5. Which occupied cells do not hold labels or formulas?
6. Which column holds formulas?

Check your answers on page 376.

SRB 138 one hundred thirty-eight

✦ Student Reference Book, p. 138

Refer to the empty spreadsheet at the top of *Student Reference Book* page 137 to identify the parts of a spreadsheet:

- **cell:** One of the rectangular parts that make up the spreadsheet. Cells are selected with the keyboard or mouse.
- **address of a cell:** A letter and a number that identify a cell. Every cell is located at the intersection of a column—identified by a letter; and a row—identified by a number.
- **address box:** A box that shows the address of a selected cell.
- **display bar:** A bar that shows data for a selected cell. Data are entered from the keyboard.

Ask students to describe the information in the spreadsheet example at the bottom of page 137 of the *Student Reference Book.* The spreadsheet program calculates the total cost of a number of items. The numbers in Column B show the cost of one of each item. The numbers in Column C show how many of each item were purchased. Column D shows the total cost of the items purchased, the total cost of all the items before tax, the tax on the items, and the total cost, including the tax.

Discuss the three kinds of information stored in the cells and how the information appears in the cells:

- **labels:** Words, numbers, or both. For example, the cells in row 1 and in column A contain labels. Point out that the label in cell A9 contains both a word (tax) and a number (7%).
- **numbers:** Figures used in calculations. Numbers are entered from the keyboard or calculated by the computer.
- **formulas:** Rules for calculation, entered from the keyboard. Formulas are shown in the display bar at the top of the spreadsheet but *not in the cell.* What does appear in the cell is the result obtained by applying the formula. The address box and display bar show that "= B3 ∗ C3" has been stored in Cell D3. The number shown in D3 (1.74) is the product of the number in B3 (0.29) and the number in C3 (6).

Make sure students understand the difference between the numbers in Columns B and C and the numbers in Column D: The numbers in Columns B and C are entered from the keyboard and are used to *generate* the numbers in Column D. The numbers in Column D are not entered from the keyboard, but are the result of applying the formulas stored in Column D to the numbers stored in Columns B and C.

Ask students to name the formulas that are stored in the following cells:

- D4 = B4 ∗ C4
- D8 = D3 + D4 + D5 + D6
- D9 = 0.07 ∗ D8
- D10 = D8 + D9

When any number in Column B or C is changed, the spreadsheet program will change the numbers in Column D accordingly. Ask students to explain why. Have them use their calculators to find out what happens if

- the number in Cell B4 is changed to 1.25. The number in Cell D4 is changed to 2.50, the number in D8 to 10.69, the number in D9 to 0.75, and the number in D10 to 11.44.
- the number in Cell C6 is changed to 2. The number in Cell D6 is changed to 11.90, the number in D8 to 16.52, the number in D9 to 1.16, and the number in D10 to 17.68.

Point out that, had a spreadsheet program been used instead of a calculator, all of these numbers would have been changed automatically by the program once the new number in Cell B4 (or C6) was entered from the keyboard.

✦Solving Spreadsheet Problems

(*Math Journal 2,* p. 359; *Student Reference Book,* p. 138)

PARTNER ACTIVITY

Give the class a few minutes to answer the Check Your Understanding questions on page 138 of the *Student Reference Book.* Briefly go over students' answers.

Assign the problems on journal page 359. The budget spreadsheet on the journal page is the same as the spreadsheet on page 138 of the *Student Reference Book.* When most students have finished, discuss their answers.

Adjusting the Activity To extend the activity, have students figure out how to write the formulas using variables instead of cell addresses. They should list what each variable represents. For example, let h equal the quantity of hamburgers. The total cost of hamburgers would equal $h * 2.79$.

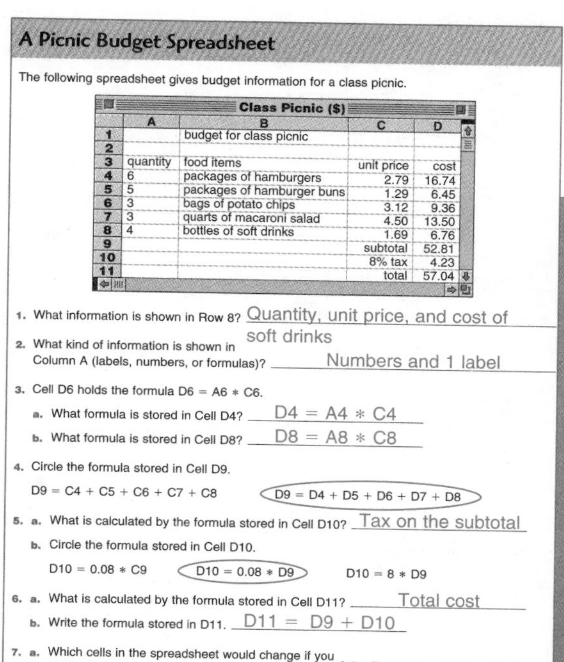

A Picnic Budget Spreadsheet

The following spreadsheet gives budget information for a class picnic.

Class Picnic ($)

	A	B	C	D
1		budget for class picnic		
2				
3	quantity	food items	unit price	cost
4	6	packages of hamburgers	2.79	16.74
5	5	packages of hamburger buns	1.29	6.45
6	3	bags of potato chips	3.12	9.36
7	3	quarts of macaroni salad	4.50	13.50
8	4	bottles of soft drinks	1.69	6.76
9			subtotal	52.81
10			8% tax	4.23
11			total	57.04

1. What information is shown in Row 8? Quantity, unit price, and cost of soft drinks
2. What kind of information is shown in Column A (labels, numbers, or formulas)? Numbers and 1 label
3. Cell D6 holds the formula D6 = A6 ∗ C6.
   a. What formula is stored in Cell D4? D4 = A4 ∗ C4
   b. What formula is stored in Cell D8? D8 = A8 ∗ C8
4. Circle the formula stored in Cell D9.
   D9 = C4 + C5 + C6 + C7 + C8 (D9 = D4 + D5 + D6 + D7 + D8)
5. a. What is calculated by the formula stored in Cell D10? Tax on the subtotal
   b. Circle the formula stored in Cell D10.
   D10 = 0.08 ∗ C9 (D10 = 0.08 ∗ D9) D10 = 8 ∗ D9
6. a. What is calculated by the formula stored in Cell D11? Total cost
   b. Write the formula stored in D11. D11 = D9 + D10
7. a. Which cells in the spreadsheet would change if you changed the number of bags of potato chips to 4? A6, D6, D9, D10, D11
   b. Calculate the number that would be shown in each of these cells.
   A6 = 4; D6 = $12.48; D9 = $55.93; D10 = $4.47; D11 = $60.40

STUDENT PAGE

Math Journal 2, p. 359

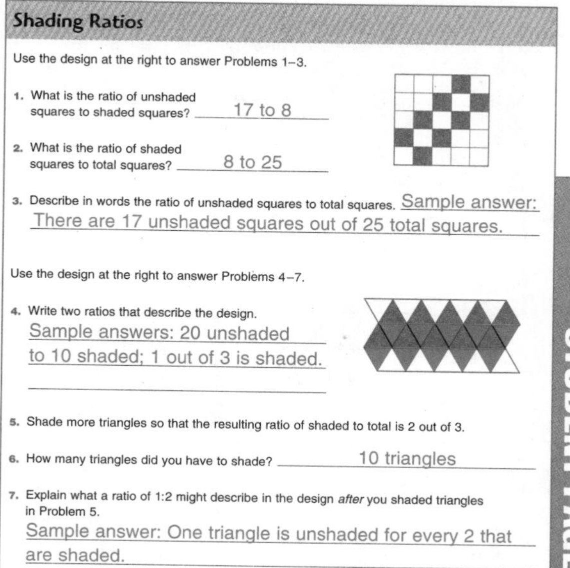

Shading Ratios

Use the design at the right to answer Problems 1–3.

1. What is the ratio of unshaded squares to shaded squares? 17 to 8
2. What is the ratio of shaded squares to total squares? 8 to 25
3. Describe in words the ratio of unshaded squares to total squares. Sample answer: There are 17 unshaded squares out of 25 total squares.

Use the design at the right to answer Problems 4–7.

4. Write two ratios that describe the design. Sample answers: 20 unshaded to 10 shaded; 1 out of 3 is shaded.
5. Shade more triangles so that the resulting ratio of shaded to total is 2 out of 3.
6. How many triangles did you have to shade? 10 triangles
7. Explain what a ratio of 1:2 might describe in the design *after* you shaded triangles in Problem 5. Sample answer: One triangle is unshaded for every 2 that are shaded.

STUDENT PAGE

Math Journal 2, p. 360

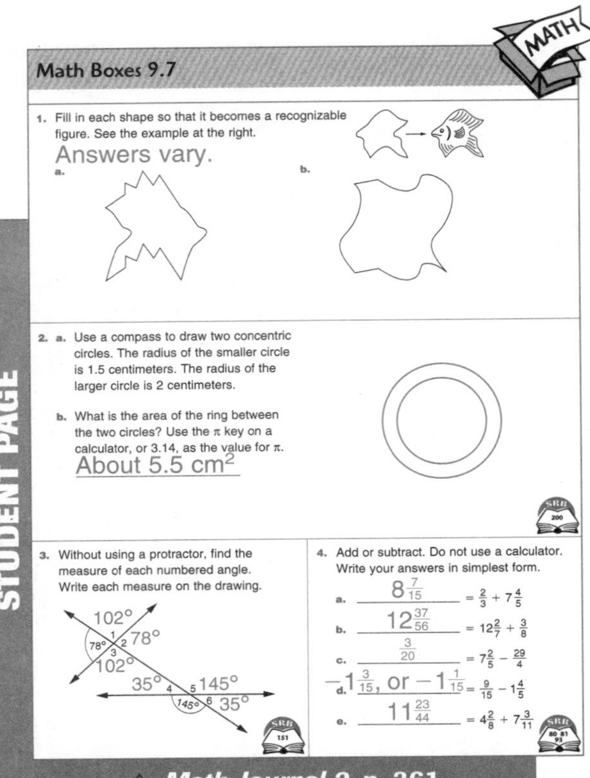

Math Boxes 9.7

1. Fill in each shape so that it becomes a recognizable figure. See the example at the right.
Answers vary.
a.
b.

2. a. Use a compass to draw two concentric circles. The radius of the smaller circle is 1.5 centimeters. The radius of the larger circle is 2 centimeters.

b. What is the area of the ring between the two circles? Use the π key on a calculator, or 3.14, as the value for π.
About 5.5 cm^2

3. Without using a protractor, find the measure of each numbered angle. Write each measure on the drawing.

4. Add or subtract. Do not use a calculator. Write your answers in simplest form.

a. $8\frac{7}{15}$ = $\frac{2}{3} + 7\frac{4}{5}$

b. $12\frac{37}{56}$ = $12\frac{2}{7} + \frac{3}{8}$

c. $\frac{3}{20}$ = $7\frac{2}{5} - \frac{29}{4}$

d. $-1\frac{3}{15}$, or $-1\frac{1}{15}$ = $\frac{9}{15} - 1\frac{4}{5}$

e. $11\frac{23}{44}$ = $4\frac{2}{8} + 7\frac{3}{11}$

STUDENT PAGE

Math Journal 2, p. 361

2 Ongoing Learning & Practice

✦ Interpreting Ratios (*Math Journal 2,* p. 360)

INDEPENDENT ACTIVITY 

Students identify ratios for designs, and they create designs with given ratios of shaded to unshaded squares.

✦ Math Boxes 9.7 (*Math Journal 2,* p. 361)

INDEPENDENT ACTIVITY 

Mixed Review Math Boxes in this lesson are paired with Math Boxes in Lesson 9.9. The skill in Problem 1 is a prerequisite for Unit 10.

✦ Study Link 9.7 (*Math Masters,* p. 365)

Home Connection Students practice using the formulas for circumference and area of a circle to complete a spreadsheet. They use the spreadsheet data to draw graphs.

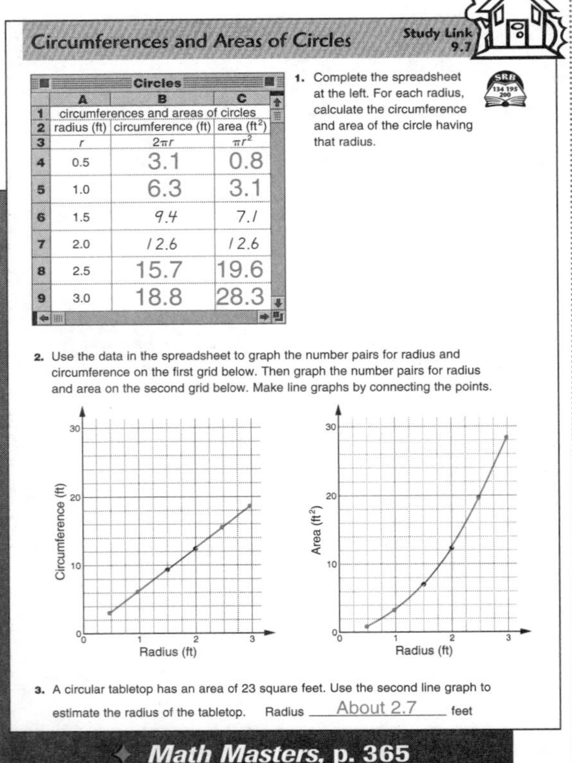

Circumferences and Areas of Circles — Study Link 9.7

1. Complete the spreadsheet at the left. For each radius, calculate the circumference and area of the circle having that radius.

Circles

	A	B	C
1	circumferences and areas of circles		
2	radius (ft)	circumference (ft)	area (ft^2)
3	r	$2\pi r$	πr^2
4	0.5	3.1	0.8
5	1.0	6.3	3.1
6	1.5	9.4	7.1
7	2.0	12.6	12.6
8	2.5	15.7	19.6
9	3.0	18.8	28.3

2. Use the data in the spreadsheet to graph the number pairs for radius and circumference on the first grid below. Then graph the number pairs for radius and area on the second grid below. Make line graphs by connecting the points.

3. A circular tabletop has an area of 23 square feet. Use the second line graph to estimate the radius of the tabletop. Radius About 2.7 feet

STUDY LINK MASTER

Math Masters, p. 365

3 Options for Individualizing

✦ RETEACHING Playing *Hidden Treasure* (*Student Reference Book,* p. 296; *Math Masters,* p. 44)

PARTNER ACTIVITY  **5–15 min**

If students struggle with locating and naming cells in a spreadsheet, have them play this game introduced in Lesson 3.10, which uses a coordinate grid as the gameboard.

✦ EXTRA PRACTICE Using a Computer Spreadsheet (*Math Journal 2,* p. 359)

PARTNER ACTIVITY **15–30 min**

Technology Link If you have access to computers and a spreadsheet program, have your students enter data and formulas for the class-picnic spreadsheet into the computer. Experiment with changing the values of columns that do not involve formulas.

Students might want to organize other information into spreadsheets. They could enter their spelling test scores for a grading period and use a formula in the spreadsheet to calculate their averages.

✦ ENRICHMENT Using Formulas to Complete a Spreadsheet (*Math Masters,* pp. 154 and 155)

PARTNER ACTIVITY  **15–30 min**

Students complete a spreadsheet, answer questions about the data, and make graphs based on the data in the spreadsheet.

Before students begin working, call attention to the formulas in Cells B4, C4, and D4. These are entered as labels, not as spreadsheet formulas. The spreadsheet formulas have been stored in Cells B5 through B11, C5 through C11, and D5 through D11. For example, if one were to click on B5, the display bar would show the formula used to calculate B5 as "= 1.1 ∗ A5." Similarly, clicking on C10 would display "= 0.06 ∗ A10 ∗ A10."

The graphs in Problem 7 will not look alike. The graph for reaction-time distance is a straight line. It is easy to see that the reaction-time distance increases by 11 feet for every 10-mile-per-hour increase in speed. The graph for braking distance is a curved line. As vehicle speed increases, the braking distance increases very rapidly. Problem 9 asks students to make an observation regarding speeds of 50 miles per hour or more. For example, the braking distance is at least 150 feet and is more than twice the reaction-time distance.

Stopping Distance for an Automobile

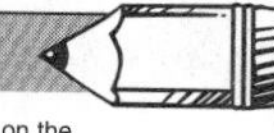

A driver may need to stop quickly. The time it takes to stop depends on the car's speed. It takes the driver about $\frac{3}{4}$ second to react before actually stepping on the brake pedal. Once the brake has been depressed, it takes additional time before the car comes to a complete stop.

The spreadsheet below shows the minimum stopping distances for various vehicle speeds.

1. The spreadsheet is not completely filled in. Calculate and record the numbers for the cells in Rows 9, 10, and 11. (*Hint:* Use the formulas in Cells B4, C4, and D4.)

Stopping Distances

	A	B	C	D
1	minimum stopping distance on a dry, level, concrete surface			
2				
3	speed (mph)	reaction-time distance (ft)	braking distance (ft)	total stopping distance (ft)
4		distance = 1.1 ∗ speed	distance = 0.06 ∗ speed²	distance = 1.1 ∗ speed + 0.06 ∗ speed²
5	10	11	6	17
6	20	22	24	46
7	30	33	54	87
8	40	44	96	140
9	50	55	150	205
10	60	66	216	282
11	70	77	294	371

2. Circle the cell(s) that contain labels. D4 B10 C6 (A3)

3. Circle the cell(s) that contain numbers used in calculations but not in formulas. B4 (A5) D5 C10

4. Circle the cell(s) in which formulas are stored. (D9) (B5) A11 C4

5. Write the formula stored in each cell.
B7 = 1.1 ∗ A7 D11 = (1.1 ∗ A11) + (0.06 ∗ (A11)²)

6. If you change the number in Cell A7 to 35, will the numbers in any other cells change?
yes If so, which cells? B7, C7, D7

TEACHING MASTER

✦ **Math Masters, p. 154**

Stopping Distance for an Automobile (cont.)

7. Use the data in the spreadsheet on *Math Masters,* page 154.
   a. Graph the number pairs for speed and reaction-time distance on the first grid below. Make a line graph by connecting the points.
   b. Graph the number pairs for speed and braking distance on the second grid below. Make a line graph by connecting the points.

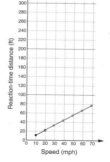

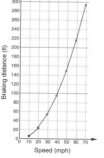

Reaction-Time Distance — Reaction-time distance (ft) (0–300) vs. Speed (mph) (0–70)

Braking Distance — Braking distance (ft) (0–300) vs. Speed (mph) (0–70)

8. How are the two graphs different?
Sample answer: The second graph is much steeper. The reaction-time-distance graph is a straight line.

9. Complete the statement. At speeds of 50 miles per hour or more,
Sample answer: the braking distance is at least 150 feet.

TEACHING MASTER

✦ **Math Masters, p. 155**

9.8 Area Formulas with Applications

OBJECTIVE **To review and use formulas for perimeter, circumference, and area.**

summaries	materials
1 Teaching the Lesson	
Students apply the area formulas for a circle, rectangle, parallelogram, and triangle, measuring any lengths needed to calculate the areas. Students use perimeter, circumference, and area formulas to solve for missing lengths and areas. [Patterns, Functions, and Algebra; Measurement and Reference Frames]	□ *Math Journal 2,* pp. 362, 364, and 365 □ *Student Reference Book,* pp. 197–200 □ Study Link 9.7 □ cm ruler □ calculator
2 Ongoing Learning & Practice	
Students practice and maintain skills through Math Boxes and Study Link activities.	□ *Math Journal 2,* p. 363 □ Study Link Master (*Math Masters,* p. 366) □ Geometry Template
3 Options for Individualizing	
Extra Practice Students calculate the open area of their classroom floor that is available for storage. [Patterns, Functions, and Algebra; Measurement and Reference Frames] **Reteaching** Students derive the area formulas for parallelograms and triangles. [Patterns, Functions, and Algebra; Measurement and Reference Frames]	□ Teaching Masters (*Math Masters,* pp. 156–158) □ scissors □ transparent tape At least one of each per group: □ builder's (long) tape measure □ ruler, yardstick

Getting Started

Mental Math and Reflexes

Students rewrite numbers with exponents in standard notation.

Suggestions

- 5^2 25
- 3^3 27
- 2^4 16
- 50^2 2,500
- 30^3 27,000
- 20^4 160,000
- 100^2 10,000
- 300^3 27,000,000
- 200^4 1,600,000,000

Math Message

Complete the problems on journal page 362.

Study Link 9.7 Follow-Up

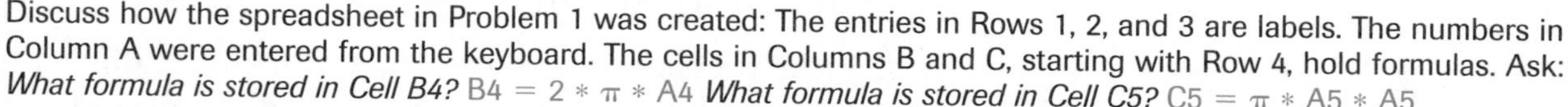

Discuss how the spreadsheet in Problem 1 was created: The entries in Rows 1, 2, and 3 are labels. The numbers in Column A were entered from the keyboard. The cells in Columns B and C, starting with Row 4, hold formulas. Ask: *What formula is stored in Cell B4?* B4 = 2 * π * A4 *What formula is stored in Cell C5?* C5 = π * A5 * A5

Compare the two graphs in Problem 2. The first graph is a straight line; this shows that as the radius increases, the circumference also increases at a uniform rate. The second graph is curved; this shows that area increases at a faster rate than the radius.

To solve Problem 3, find the point on the second graph to the right of 23 on the vertical axis, and from that point, move straight down to the horizontal axis, where it can be seen that the radius is between $2\frac{1}{2}$ and $2\frac{3}{4}$ feet.

1 Teaching the Lesson

✦Math Message Follow-Up

(*Math Journal 2,* p. 362; *Student Reference Book,* pp. 197–200)

WHOLE-CLASS DISCUSSION

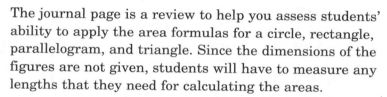

The journal page is a review to help you assess students' ability to apply the area formulas for a circle, rectangle, parallelogram, and triangle. Since the dimensions of the figures are not given, students will have to measure any lengths that they need for calculating the areas.

The figures deliberately exclude dashed lines to indicate heights. For Problems 4 and 5, students must draw a reasonably correct height and measure it. Remind students to measure each length to the nearest tenth of a centimeter (that is, to the nearest millimeter). Areas should be given to the nearest square centimeter.

Students should refer to pages 197 to 200 of the *Student Reference Book* for area formulas and examples of applications of the formulas.

When most students have completed at least Problems 1–5, bring the class together to discuss solutions.

One strategy for finding the area in Problem 6 is to divide the trapezoid into a rectangle and a triangle and find the sum of their areas.

ONGOING ASSESSMENT

Watch for students who are having difficulties with Problem 4. Remind them that the height of a triangle is the shortest distance between any base and the vertex opposite that base. The height may have to be drawn outside the triangle. For Problem 5, the height must be drawn at right angles to the bases.

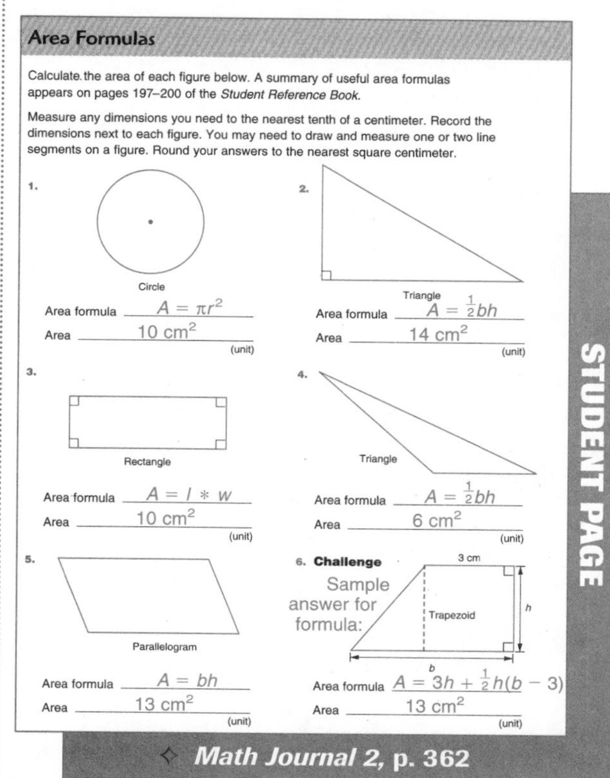

Area Formulas
Calculate the area of each figure below. A summary of useful area formulas appears on pages 197–200 of the Student Reference Book.
Measure any dimensions you need to the nearest tenth of a centimeter. Record the dimensions next to each figure. You may need to draw and measure one or two line segments on a figure. Round your answers to the nearest square centimeter.
1. Circle
Area formula A = πr²
Area 10 cm² (unit)
2. Triangle
Area formula A = ½bh
Area 14 cm² (unit)
3. Rectangle
Area formula A = l * w
Area 10 cm² (unit)
4. Triangle
Area formula A = ½bh
Area 6 cm² (unit)
5. Parallelogram
Area formula A = bh
Area 13 cm² (unit)
6. Challenge
3 cm
Sample answer for formula:
Trapezoid
h
b
Area formula A = 3h + ½h(b − 3)
Area 13 cm² (unit)
STUDENT PAGE

✧ *Math Journal 2,* p. 362

STUDENT PAGE

Perimeter, Circumference, and Area

Solve each problem. Explain your answers.

1. Rectangle *PERK* has a perimeter of 40 feet.

Length of side *PE* 12 ft (unit)

Area of Rectangle *PERK* 96 ft^2 (unit)

Sample answer: $p = 2l + 2w$; $40 = 2l + 16$; $24 = 2l$; $12 = l$. $A = lw$; $A = 12 * 8$; $A = 96$

2. The area of Triangle *ABC* is 300 $meters^2$. What is the length of side *AB*?

Length of side *AB* 40 m (unit)

Sample answer: $A = \frac{1}{2}bh$; $300 = (\frac{1}{2}) * b * 15$; $600 = 15b$; $40 = b$

3. The area of Parallelogram *KLMN* is 72 square inches. The length of side $\overline{LX}$ is 6 inches, and the length of side $\overline{KY}$ is 3 inches. What is the length of $\overline{LY}$?

Length of $\overline{LY}$ 8 in. (unit)

Sample answer: $A = bh$; $72 = (6 + 3)h$; $72 = 9h$; $8 = h$

Math Journal 2, p. 364

STUDENT PAGE

Perimeter, Circumference, and Area (cont.)

4. The area of Triangle *ACE* is 42 square yards. What is the area of Rectangle *BCDE*?

Area of Rectangle *BCDE* 240 yd^2

Sample answer: $A = \frac{1}{2}bh$; $42 = \frac{1}{2} * 7 * h$; $84 = 7h$; $12 = h$. $A = bh$; $A = (13 + 7) * 12$; $A = 240$

5. To the nearest percent, about what percent of the area of the square is covered by the area of the circle?

Answer 20%

Sample answer: Square: $A = s^2$; $A = 20^2 = 400$. Circle: $A = \pi r^2$; $A = \pi (5^2) = 79$. $79 / 400 = 0.1975$; $(0.1975 * 100)\% = 19.75\%$

6. Which path is longer: once around the figure 8—from *A*, to *B*, to *C*, to *B*, and back to *A*—or once around the large circle?

Answer: They are the same distance around. Sample answer: Large circle: $C = \pi d$; $C = \pi(40 \text{ ft})$; $C = 126$ ft. Smaller circle: $C = \pi d$; $C = \pi * 20$ ft $= 63$ ft. Figure eight: 63 ft $*$ 2 ft $= 126$ ft

Math Journal 2, p. 365

✦Using Perimeter, Circumference, and Area Formulas (*Math Journal 2,* pp. 364 and 365)

INDEPENDENT ACTIVITY 

Assign the problems on journal pages 364 and 365. Circulate and assist. Reserve time for a discussion of students' solutions. Expect that they will adopt a variety of strategies. The numbers in all problems are relatively "easy" numbers. This may encourage some students to attempt trial-and-error solutions. When most students have completed the problems, bring the class together to share solutions.

Adjusting the Activity You might want to write the relevant formulas on the board. The list should include the formulas for the area and circumference of a circle and for the areas of a square, rectangle, parallelogram, and triangle. Follow the format and notation used in the *Student Reference Book.*

Pair a student learning English with a proficient English speaker to share their strategies. Have the proficient English speaker read his or her explanation aloud and guide the English learner to ask for clarification where necessary. Then direct the English learner to explain his or her solution, while the partner records it and then reads it back.

Many students are likely to quote or write the relevant formula, substitute the given values in the formula, and then solve for the missing length or area. Students may or may not reduce the problem to an equation. For example, in Problem 3:

Student A: *The area of the parallelogram is base times height. The base is 6 + 3, or 9 inches. Since 9 times 8 is 72, the height must be 8 inches.*

Student B: *The formula I used is 'Area is equal to base times height.' I know the area is 72 square inches, and I figured out the base is 9 inches. If I substitute these numbers in the formula, I get 72 = 9 ∗ height. So the height has to be 8 inches.*

In Problem 6, some students might figure out that the paths are the same length without actually calculating the circumferences. The circumference of the large circle is 40π, and the circumference of the two smaller circles is 20π each, or 40π together.

2 Ongoing Learning & Practice

✦ Math Boxes 9.8 (*Math Journal 2*, p. 363)

INDEPENDENT ACTIVITY 

Mixed Review Math Boxes in this lesson are paired with Math Boxes in Lesson 9.6. The skill in Problem 1 is a prerequisite for Unit 10.

✦ Study Link 9.8 (*Math Masters*, p. 366)

Home Connection Students solve area problems. For some problems, the lengths are given as variables. In several cases, extraneous information is given.

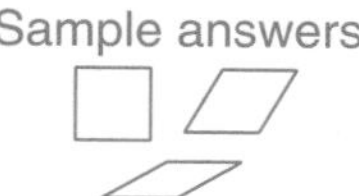

Math Boxes 9.8

1. Find a rhombus on your Geometry Template. Use the template to draw a rhombus in the space below.

   How would you describe a rhombus? Sample answer: A parallelogram whose sides are all the same length

   Sample answers:

2. Solve.

	Solution
a. $24 * f = 12$	$f = 0.5$, or $\frac{1}{2}$
b. $\frac{y}{15} = 3$	$y = 45$
c. $n - 136 = 65$	$n = 201$
d. $\frac{36}{q} = 3$	$q = 12$
e. $\frac{2{,}000}{y} = 50$	$y = 40$

3. The ratio of facedown to faceup cards is 5:4. If there are 72 cards altogether, how many cards are faceup? 32 cards

   Explain how you found your answer. Sample answer: I used a ratio comparing faceup cards to total cards. $\frac{4}{9} = \frac{x}{72}$

4. The table at the right shows how many calories per hour a person weighing 150 pounds uses for various activities.

   a. For which activity does the person use about $\frac{1}{6}$ of the number of calories used in running? sitting

   b. For which activity does the person use about 2.5 times as many calories as when sleeping? driving

   c. For which activity does the person use about $\frac{2}{3}$ of the number of calories used in walking? driving

Activity	Calories Per Hour
Sleeping	60
Sitting	100
Standing	140
Driving	150
Walking	225
Volleyball	350
Basketball	500
Running	600

STUDENT PAGE

✧ *Math Journal 2*, p. 363

3 Options for Individualizing

✦ EXTRA PRACTICE Calculating Floor Space

SMALL-GROUP ACTIVITY  **30+ min**

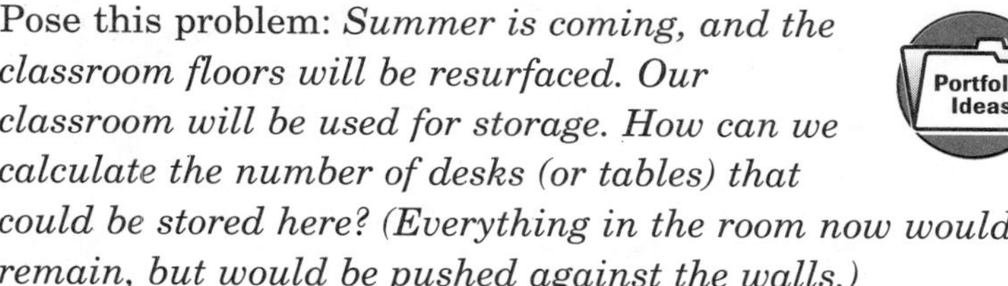

Pose this problem: *Summer is coming, and the classroom floors will be resurfaced. Our classroom will be used for storage. How can we calculate the number of desks (or tables) that could be stored here? (Everything in the room now would remain, but would be pushed against the walls.)*

Portfolio Ideas

Give students time to formulate a plan for calculating the available area in the classroom and the number of desks (or tables) that could be stored. Objects will not be stacked. Each object stored will take up floor space.

One possible strategy:

1. Calculate the total floor area by measuring the length and width of the classroom.
2. Measure objects in the classroom—desks, bookcases, computer carts, and so on.
3. Calculate the floor area each object takes up. (It may help to make a drawing of the room, recording the area of objects on the drawing.)

(*Strategy continues on next page.*)

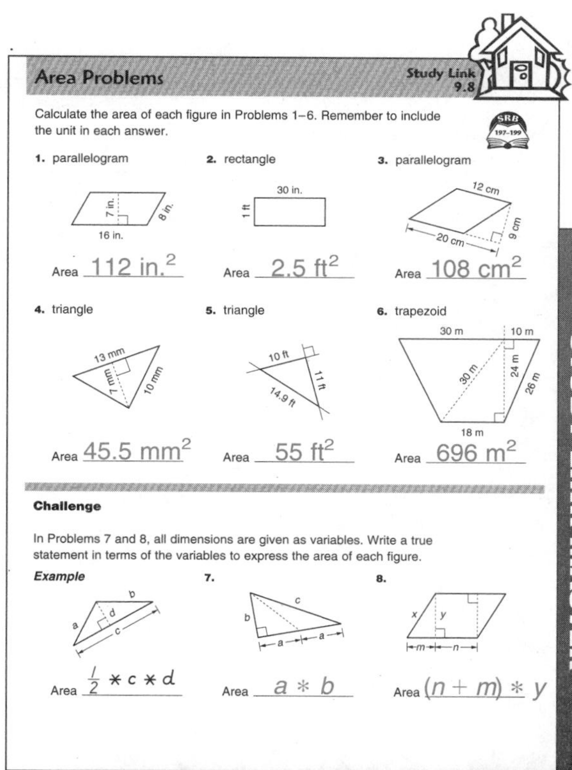
Area Problems — Study Link 9.8

Calculate the area of each figure in Problems 1–6. Remember to include the unit in each answer.

1. parallelogram — Area 112 in.^{2}
2. rectangle — Area 2.5 ft^2
3. parallelogram — Area 108 cm^2
4. triangle — Area 45.5 mm^2
5. triangle — Area 55 ft^2
6. trapezoid — Area 696 m^2

Challenge

In Problems 7 and 8, all dimensions are given as variables. Write a true statement in terms of the variables to express the area of each figure.

Example Area $\frac{1}{2} * c * d$

7. Area $a * b$

8. Area $(n + m) * y$

STUDY LINK MASTER

✧ *Math Masters*, p. 366

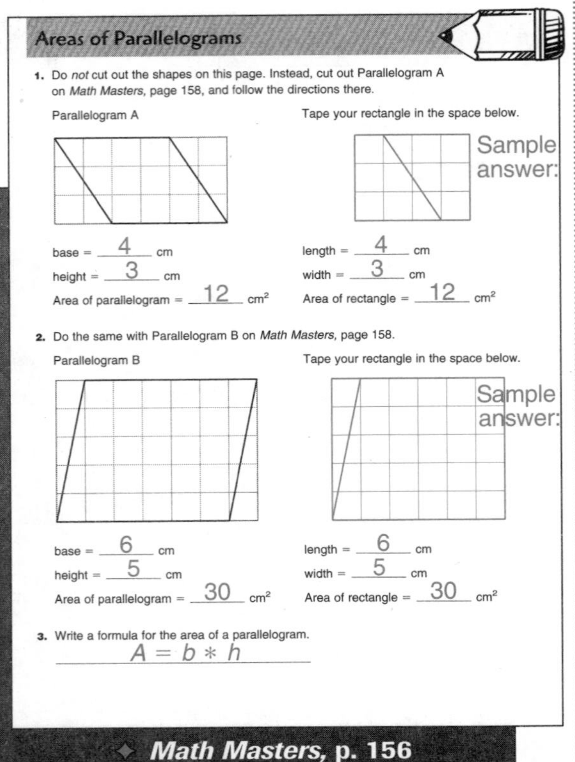
TEACHING MASTER

Areas of Parallelograms

1. Do *not* cut out the shapes on this page. Instead, cut out Parallelogram A on *Math Masters,* page 158, and follow the directions there.

Parallelogram A — Tape your rectangle in the space below. Sample answer:

base = 4 cm — length = 4 cm
height = 3 cm — width = 3 cm
Area of parallelogram = 12 cm² — Area of rectangle = 12 cm²

2. Do the same with Parallelogram B on *Math Masters,* page 158.

Parallelogram B — Tape your rectangle in the space below. Sample answer:

base = 6 cm — length = 6 cm
height = 5 cm — width = 5 cm
Area of parallelogram = 30 cm² — Area of rectangle = 30 cm²

3. Write a formula for the area of a parallelogram.
$A = b * h$

✦ *Math Masters,* p. 156

4. Subtract the total area of the objects from the area of the classroom floor to find the available area.
5. Based on available area, calculate how many desks (or tables) could be stored in the classroom in addition to the existing furniture.

You might want to have students record their proposed plans and then solve the problem. If more than one group of students solves the problem, have them compare strategies and solutions.

✦ RETEACHING Exploring the Areas of Parallelograms and Triangles
(*Math Masters,* pp. 156–158)

INDEPENDENT ACTIVITY  **15–30 min** 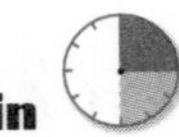

This activity is for students who need more experience to help them understand how the area formulas for parallelograms and triangles are derived. Students transform parallelograms into rectangles to derive the area formula for parallelograms. They combine two identical triangles to derive the area formula for triangles.

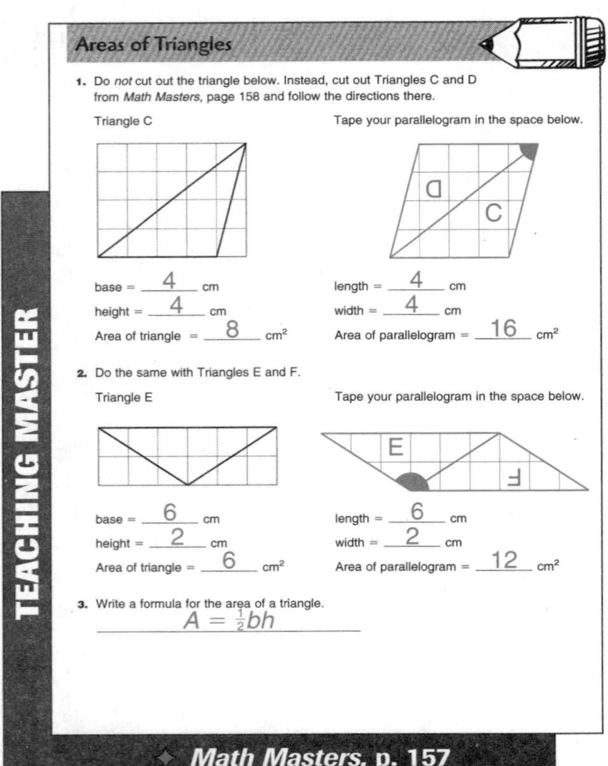
TEACHING MASTER

Areas of Triangles

1. Do *not* cut out the triangle below. Instead, cut out Triangles C and D from *Math Masters,* page 158 and follow the directions there.

Triangle C — Tape your parallelogram in the space below.

base = 4 cm — length = 4 cm
height = 4 cm — width = 4 cm
Area of triangle = 8 cm² — Area of parallelogram = 16 cm²

2. Do the same with Triangles E and F.

Triangle E — Tape your parallelogram in the space below.

base = 6 cm — length = 6 cm
height = 2 cm — width = 2 cm
Area of triangle = 6 cm² — Area of parallelogram = 12 cm²

3. Write a formula for the area of a triangle.
$A = \frac{1}{2}bh$

✦ *Math Masters,* p. 157

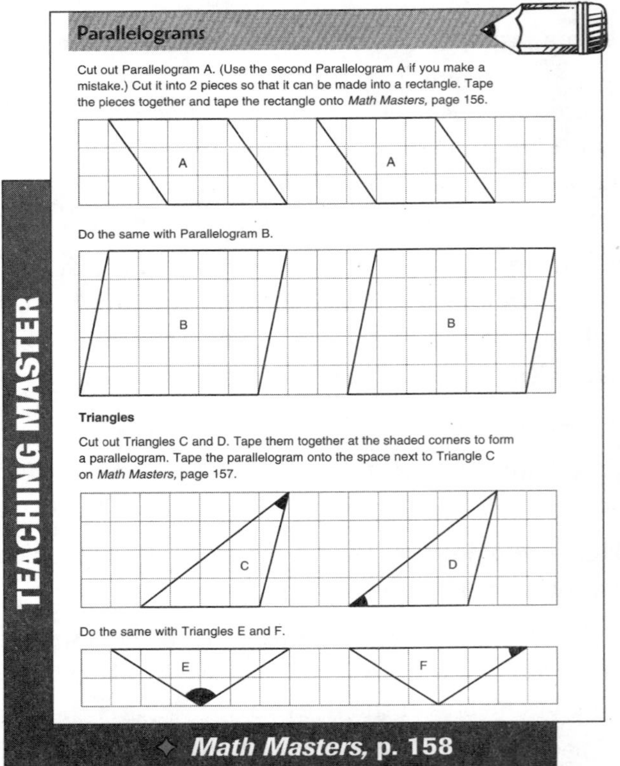
TEACHING MASTER

Parallelograms

Cut out Parallelogram A. (Use the second Parallelogram A if you make a mistake.) Cut it into 2 pieces so that it can be made into a rectangle. Tape the pieces together and tape the rectangle onto *Math Masters,* page 156.

Do the same with Parallelogram B.

Triangles

Cut out Triangles C and D. Tape them together at the shaded corners to form a parallelogram. Tape the parallelogram onto the space next to Triangle C on *Math Masters,* page 157.

Do the same with Triangles E and F.

✦ *Math Masters,* p. 158

9.9 Volume Formulas with Applications

OBJECTIVE **To review volume formulas for rectangular prisms, cylinders, and spheres.**

summaries	materials
1 Teaching the Lesson	
Students estimate the volume of the human body. They use cylinders, a rectangular prism, and a sphere to represent parts of the body; and then calculate the volumes of these geometric solids. [Patterns, Functions, and Algebra; Measurement and Reference Frames]	☐ *Math Journal 2,* pp. 366 and 367 ☐ Study Link 9.8 ☐ *Student Reference Book,* pp. 203, 204, and 206 ☐ Transparency (*Math Masters,* p. 159; optional) ☐ cm ruler ☐ calculator ☐ cylinder, like a food can
2 Ongoing Learning & Practice	
Students review data landmarks, step graphs, and mystery graphs. [Data and Chance] Students practice and maintain skills through Math Boxes and Study Link activities.	☐ *Math Journal 2,* pp. 368 and 369 ☐ Study Link Master (*Math Masters,* p. 367) ☐ compass ☐ cm ruler
3 Options for Individualizing	
Extra Practice Students solve perimeter and area problems using formulas. [Patterns, Functions, and Algebra; Measurement and Reference Frames] **Enrichment** Students solve a capacity problem, either in a hands-on experiment or by using formulas for area, circumference, and volume. [Patterns, Functions, and Algebra; Measurement and Reference Frames]	☐ Teaching Masters (*Math Masters,* pp. 160 and 161) Per partnership (Using a Model): ☐ tape ☐ calculator ☐ a tray or tub ☐ container for rice or beans ☐ rice or beans ☐ 2 pieces of $8\frac{1}{2}$-by-11-inch paper ☐ measuring cup or graduated cylinder ***See* Advance Preparation**

Additional Information

Advance Preparation If you do the optional Enrichment activity in Part 3, decide whether to have students do the Using a Model activity, the Formula Solution, or both. Form a cylinder by curving an $8\frac{1}{2}$-by-11-inch piece of sturdy paper and taping it where the 11-inch edges meet (as exactly as possible). Form a second cylinder by curving another $8\frac{1}{2}$-by-11-inch piece of sturdy paper and taping it where the $8\frac{1}{2}$-inch edges meet. (See the illustration in Part 3 on page 748.)

Getting Started

Mental Math and Reflexes

Answer the following questions for a circle or sphere. (Note: r stands for *radius,* and d stands for *diameter.*)

- If $r = 5$ inches, what is d? 10 in.
- If $d = 8.6$ centimeters, what is r? 4.3 cm
- If $r = 6$ yards, what is r^2? 36 yd^2
- If $r = 2.3$ inches, what is d? 4.6 in.
- If $d = 2\frac{1}{2}$ centimeters, what is r? $1\frac{1}{4}$ cm
- If $r = \frac{1}{2}$ yard, what is r^2? $\frac{1}{4}$ yd^2
- If $r = 3\frac{1}{2}$ feet, what is d? 7 ft
- If $d = 12$ centimeters, what is r? 6 cm
- If $d = 4$ yards, what is r^2? 4 yd^2

Math Message

The formula for the volume of a sphere is $V = \frac{4}{3}\pi r^3$, where V = volume and r = radius. Use your calculator to find the volume of a ball whose radius is 2 inches. Record your answer to the nearest tenth of a cubic inch.

Study Link 9.8 Follow-Up

See the Study Link 9.8 Follow-Up discussion in Part 1 below.

1 Teaching the Lesson

✦ Study Link 9.8 Follow-Up

Review answers. Note that in Problems 1 to 6, some dimensions are given that are not needed to find the area of the figure. In Problem 2, the dimensions have unlike units, so that one dimension must be converted to the unit of the other dimension. In Problem 5, the figure is a right triangle, because the vertical angle outside the triangle is a right angle.

There are several ways to solve Problem 6. One is to find the areas of the three triangles and add them. Students may also use the area formula for a trapezoid, which is $A = \frac{1}{2}$ (length of base 1 + length of base 2) ∗ height, where the bases are the parallel line segments in the trapezoid and the height is measured on a line segment perpendicular to the bases.

The area of the triangle in Problem 7 is $\frac{1}{2} * b * (a + a)$, or $\frac{1}{2} * b * 2a$, which can be simplified as $a * b$. The solution to Problem 8 can be used to demonstrate the distributive property. If you think of the area as base times height, then the area is $(n + m) * y$. If you think of the area as the sum of the areas of the rectangle in the middle and the two right triangles, then the area is $(n * y) + (2 * (\frac{1}{2} * m * y))$. This can be simplified as $(n * y) + (m * y)$, or $(n + m) * y$.

✦ Math Message Follow-Up

WHOLE-CLASS DISCUSSION 

Briefly go over the solution. 33.5 in.^{3} The formula for finding the volume of a sphere will be used in estimating the volume of the human body.

✦ Estimating the Volume of the Human Body
(*Math Journal 2*, pp. 366 and 367; *Math Masters*, p. 159)

PARTNER ACTIVITY

Science Link Introduce the activity to make sure that students know what they are to do. You might want to use a transparency of *Math Masters*, page 159 as a visual aid. Discuss the figures on journal page 366 and go over the instructions and table in Problem 1 on journal page 367.

Emphasize the following points:

- ▷ While the familiar solids used to approximate the human body are imperfect, they are reasonable approximations. The final estimate for total body volume will likely be within 10% of the true volume for an average adult male.
- ▷ The scale for the figures on journal page 366 is 1 mm:1 cm. That is, a 1 mm length in the drawing represents 1 cm of actual body length. Students should measure lengths to the nearest *millimeter* but then report these measures in *centimeters*.
- ▷ All seven cylinders outlined on journal page 366 are in an upright position. Some students may not realize that the rectangles shown for neck, arms, and legs do, in fact, represent cylinders. Use a food can or other cylinder to demonstrate as follows:

  Ask students to stand 5 to 10 feet away from the cylinder and look at it at eye level. The outline of the cylinder will appear to be a rectangle. The *width* of this rectangle is the *diameter* of the cylinder.

  Students will measure diameters, not radii, for the cylinders and the sphere. Remind them to divide their measures of the diameters by 2, because the table on journal page 367 asks for radii.
- ▷ Have students round the calculated volume for each body part to the nearest 1,000 cubic centimeters. The body dimensions are estimates and are subject to measurement error, so it would be misleading to report volume calculations that are too precise.

NOTE: The volume formulas students need can be found on pages 203, 204, and 206 of the *Student Reference Book*. The formula for the volume of the sphere was reviewed in the Math Message.

Calculating the Volume of the Human Body

An average adult human male is about 69 inches (175 centimeters) tall and weighs about 170 pounds (77 kilograms). The drawings below show how a man's body may be approximated by 7 cylinders, 1 rectangular prism, and 1 sphere.

The drawings use the scale 1 mm:1 cm. This means that every length of 1 millimeter in the drawing represents 1 centimeter of actual body length. The drawing below is 175 millimeters high. Therefore, it represents a male who is 175 centimeters tall.

STUDENT PAGE

✧ *Math Journal 2*, p. 366

Calculating the Volume of the Human Body (cont.)

1. a. Use a centimeter ruler to estimate the diameters of the cylinders and sphere and the dimensions of the rectangular prism shown on page 366. Record your estimates on the drawing. Then record the radius of each cylinder and the sphere and the dimensions of the rectangular prism in the table below. (To find the radius, divide the diameter by 2.) Be sure to record the actual body dimensions. For example, if you measure the length of an arm as 72 millimeters, record this as 72 centimeters, because the scale of the drawings is 1 mm:1 cm.

   b. Calculate the volume of each body part and record it in the table. You will find a summary of useful volume formulas on pages 203, 204, and 206 in your *Student Reference Book*.

   For the arm, upper leg, and lower leg, multiply the volume by 2. Add to find the total volume of an average adult male's body. Your answer will be in cubic centimeters.

Sample answers:

Body Part and Shape	Actual Body Dimensions (cm)	Volume (Round to the nearest 1,000 cm³.)
head (sphere)	radius: 10	* 1 = 4,000
neck (cylinder)	radius: 6 height: 7	* 1 = 1,000
torso (rectangular prism)	length: 23 width: 32 height: 64	* 1 = 47,000
arm (cylinder)	radius: 3 height: 69	* 2 = 4,000
upper leg (cylinder)	radius: 7.5 height: 27	* 2 = 10,000
lower leg (cylinder)	radius: 4.5 height: 57	* 2 = 7,000
	Total Volume:	About 73,000

2. One liter is equal to 1,000 cubic centimeters. Use this fact to complete the following statement: I estimate that the total volume of an average adult male's body is about 73 liters.
3. John weighs about 136 pounds. What is the ratio of John's weight to the average adult male's weight of about 170 pounds? Ratio 0.8 to 1

   Use the ratio to estimate the volume of John's body.

   The volume of John's body is about 60,000 cm^3, or about 60 liters.

STUDENT PAGE

✧ *Math Journal 2*, p. 367

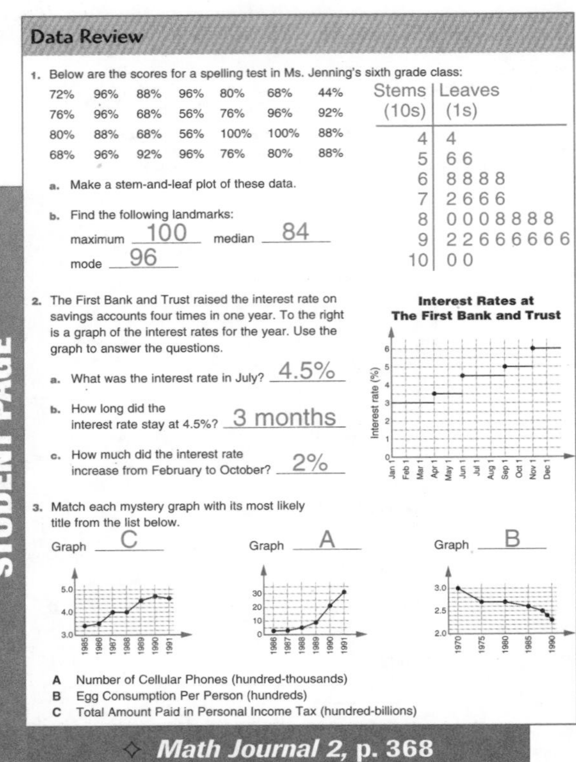
STUDENT PAGE

Data Review

1. Below are the scores for a spelling test in Ms. Jenning's sixth grade class:

72%	96%	88%	96%	80%	68%	44%
76%	96%	68%	56%	76%	96%	92%
80%	88%	68%	56%	100%	100%	88%
68%	96%	92%	96%	76%	80%	88%

a. Make a stem-and-leaf plot of these data.

Stems (10s)	Leaves (1s)
4	4
5	6 6
6	8 8 8 8
7	2 6 6 6
8	0 0 0 8 8 8 8
9	2 2 6 6 6 6 6 6
10	0 0

b. Find the following landmarks:

maximum 100 median 84

mode 96

2. The First Bank and Trust raised the interest rate on savings accounts four times in one year. To the right is a graph of the interest rates for the year. Use the graph to answer the questions.

a. What was the interest rate in July? 4.5%

b. How long did the interest rate stay at 4.5%? 3 months

c. How much did the interest rate increase from February to October? 2%

3. Match each mystery graph with its most likely title from the list below.

Graph C Graph A Graph B

A Number of Cellular Phones (hundred-thousands)
B Egg Consumption Per Person (hundreds)
C Total Amount Paid in Personal Income Tax (hundred-billions)

✧ *Math Journal 2,* p. 368

When most students have completed the journal pages, bring the class together to share students' results from journal page 367.

Problems 1 and 2: Expect that most students' estimates for total body volume will fall in the range of 65,000 to 80,000 cm^3. Volumes in cubic centimeters may be converted to more understandable units. For example, a body volume of 70,000 cm^3 is the same as 70 liters and nearly equivalent to 80 quarts (20 gallons), or 2.5 cubic feet.

Problem 3: John's weight is about $\frac{8}{10}$ of an average adult male's weight. Therefore, John's body volume is $\frac{8}{10}$ of the volume of an average adult male.

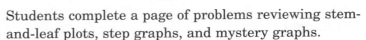

2 Ongoing Learning & Practice

✦ Reviewing Data (*Math Journal 2,* p. 368)

PARTNER ACTIVITY

Students complete a page of problems reviewing stem-and-leaf plots, step graphs, and mystery graphs.

✦ Math Boxes 9.9 (*Math Journal 2,* p. 369)

INDEPENDENT ACTIVITY 

Mixed Review Math Boxes in this lesson are paired with Math Boxes in Lesson 9.7. The skill in Problem 1 is a prerequisite for Unit 10.

NOTE: For Problem 2, the circle drawn by students should have a radius of about 2.5 centimeters.

STUDENT PAGE

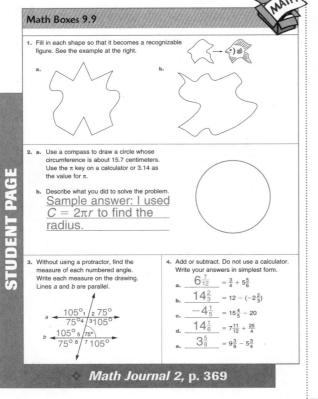

Math Boxes 9.9

1. Fill in each shape so that it becomes a recognizable figure. See the example at the right.

a.

b.

2. a. Use a compass to draw a circle whose circumference is about 15.7 centimeters. Use the π key on a calculator or 3.14 as the value for π.

b. Describe what you did to solve the problem.
Sample answer: I used $C = 2\pi r$ to find the radius.

3. Without using a protractor, find the measure of each numbered angle. Write each measure on the drawing. Lines *a* and *b* are parallel.

105° 1, 2 75°, 75° 4, 3 105°, 105° 5, 75°, 75° 6, 7 105°

4. Add or subtract. Do not use a calculator. Write your answers in simplest form.

a. $6\frac{7}{12} = \frac{3}{4} + 5\frac{5}{6}$

b. $14\frac{2}{3} = 12 - (-2\frac{2}{3})$

c. $-4\frac{1}{5} = 15\frac{4}{5} - 20$

d. $14\frac{1}{6} = 7\frac{11}{12} + \frac{25}{4}$

e. $3\frac{5}{8} = 9\frac{3}{8} - 5\frac{3}{4}$

✧ *Math Journal 2,* p. 369

✦ Study Link 9.9 (*Math Masters,* p. 367)

Home Connection Students solve area and volume problems for which all dimensions are given. In Problem 2, the volume of the globe is 904.32 $in.^3$ when 3.14 is used as the value of π; the volume is 904.78 $in.^3$ when the π key on a calculator is used.

Options for Individualizing

✦ EXTRA PRACTICE Solving Perimeter and Area Problems (*Math Masters,* p. 160)

INDEPENDENT ACTIVITY  **15–30 min** 

Give a copy of *Math Masters*, page 160 to each student. Students solve problems in which at least one dimension is given as an algebraic expression. They substitute the dimensions in a formula and solve the resulting equation.

Go over the example with the class. Point out that the answer to the problem is not 2, the solution of the equation, but the value of $3x + 1$ for $x = 2$, or 7. You may want to do Problem 1 as a class. Circulate and assist.

✦ ENRICHMENT Comparing Capacities (*Math Masters,* p. 161)

PARTNER ACTIVITY  **15–30 min** 

Pose the following problem:

- A farmer wants to make a storage bin for grain. The farmer has an $8\frac{1}{2}$-foot by 11-foot sheet of plastic that can be formed into a cylinder for the wall of the bin. Which cylinder will hold more grain—one that it is $8\frac{1}{2}$ feet tall or one that is 11 feet tall?

Ask whether students can think of a way to model this problem. (If no one suggests a piece of paper, ask them to think of something in the classroom that is $8\frac{1}{2}$ inches by 11 inches). Show the students an $8\frac{1}{2}$-inch by 11-inch piece of paper. Say that it can provide a model for the problem, with a scale of 1 inch:1 foot.

Ask whether the way the cylinder is formed will affect the capacity (volume) of the cylinder. Have them predict which cylinder—taller or shorter—will hold more. Remind them that the piece of material is the same size in both cylinders. Once they have made their initial predictions, show them the cylinders you made. *(See next page.)*

▷ Ask whether the surface areas of the two cylinders are the same. The curved surfaces of the cylinders are the same, but the bases are different.

▷ Ask whether anyone would like to change their predictions before testing them.

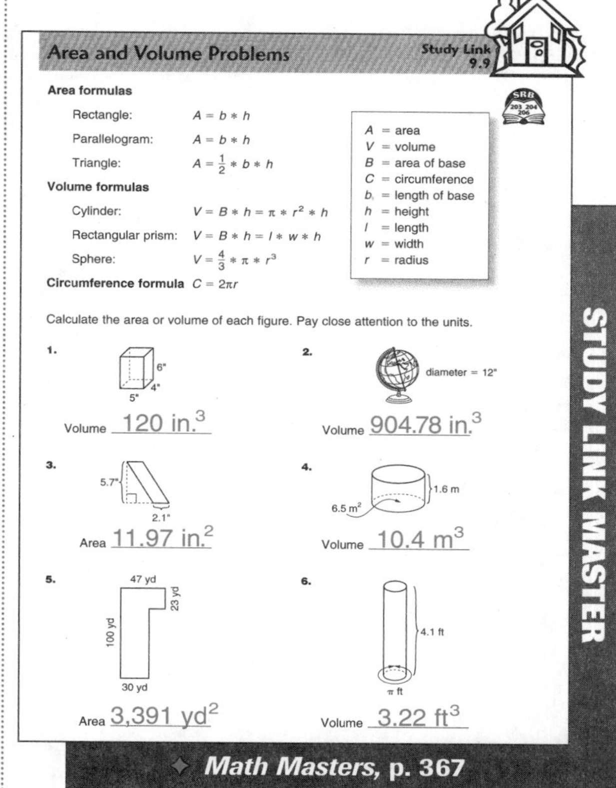

Area and Volume Problems Study Link 9.9

Area formulas

Rectangle: $A = b * h$

Parallelogram: $A = b * h$

Triangle: $A = \frac{1}{2} * b * h$

Volume formulas

Cylinder: $V = B * h = \pi * r^2 * h$

Rectangular prism: $V = B * h = l * w * h$

Sphere: $V = \frac{4}{3} * \pi * r^3$

Circumference formula $C = 2\pi r$

A = area, V = volume, B = area of base, C = circumference, b = length of base, h = height, l = length, w = width, r = radius

Calculate the area or volume of each figure. Pay close attention to the units.

1. Volume 120 in.^{3}
2. Volume 904.78 in.^{3}
3. Area 11.97 in.^{2}
4. Volume 10.4 m^3
5. Area 3,391 yd^2
6. Volume 3.22 ft^3

STUDY LINK MASTER

✦ *Math Masters,* p. 367

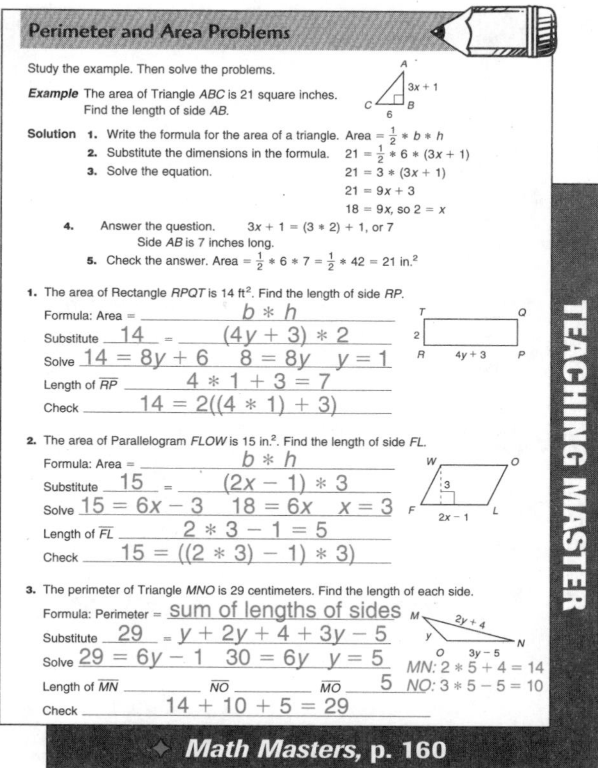

Perimeter and Area Problems

Study the example. Then solve the problems.

Example The area of Triangle *ABC* is 21 square inches. Find the length of side *AB*.

Solution
1. Write the formula for the area of a triangle. Area $= \frac{1}{2} * b * h$
2. Substitute the dimensions in the formula. $21 = \frac{1}{2} * 6 * (3x + 1)$
3. Solve the equation. $21 = 3 * (3x + 1)$; $21 = 9x + 3$; $18 = 9x$, so $2 = x$
4. Answer the question. $3x + 1 = (3 * 2) + 1$, or 7. Side *AB* is 7 inches long.
5. Check the answer. Area $= \frac{1}{2} * 6 * 7 = \frac{1}{2} * 42 = 21$ in.^{2}

1. The area of Rectangle *RPQT* is 14 ft^2. Find the length of side *RP*.
   Formula: Area = $b * h$
   Substitute $14 = (4y + 3) * 2$
   Solve $14 = 8y + 6$ $8 = 8y$ $y = 1$
   Length of $\overline{RP}$ $4 * 1 + 3 = 7$
   Check $14 = 2((4 * 1) + 3)$

2. The area of Parallelogram *FLOW* is 15 in.^{2}. Find the length of side *FL*.
   Formula: Area = $b * h$
   Substitute $15 = (2x - 1) * 3$
   Solve $15 = 6x - 3$ $18 = 6x$ $x = 3$
   Length of $\overline{FL}$ $2 * 3 - 1 = 5$
   Check $15 = ((2 * 3) - 1) * 3)$

3. The perimeter of Triangle *MNO* is 29 centimeters. Find the length of each side.
   Formula: Perimeter = sum of lengths of sides
   Substitute $29 = y + 2y + 4 + 3y - 5$
   Solve $29 = 6y - 1$ $30 = 6y$ $y = 5$
   Length of $\overline{MN}$ ____ $\overline{NO}$ ____ $\overline{MO}$ 5
   Check $14 + 10 + 5 = 29$
   MN: $2 * 5 + 4 = 14$
   NO: $3 * 5 - 5 = 10$

TEACHING MASTER

✦ *Math Masters,* p. 160

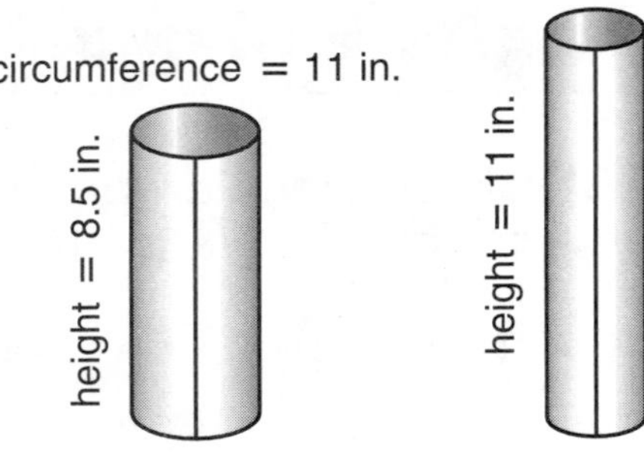

Using a Model

Students work with a partner or in groups to make a taller cylinder and a shorter cylinder. They should tape the edges so that they just meet. Then they follow these steps:

1. Stand one cylinder vertically in the tub and fill it with rice or small beans. Fill it to the top—as close to level as possible.
2. Lift the cylinder out of the tub, leaving the rice or beans behind.
3. Pour the rice or beans into another container.
4. Stand the other cylinder vertically in the tub. Pour the contents from the first cylinder into the second cylinder.
5. Record the results: *Did the contents fill the cylinder or not? Was there some rice left over?*

Once students have determined which cylinder holds more, The shorter one have them figure out a way to measure how *much* more. For example, fill the taller cylinder. Remove it. Pour the contents into the shorter cylinder. Slowly pour rice or beans from a measuring cup to fill the shorter cylinder, and note how much was poured.

Formula Solution

Once students have finished modeling the problem, consider allowing time for them to work out a "theoretical" solution using a formula (*Math Masters,* page 161). Please note that answers may vary, depending on rounding and the value used for π. The shorter cylinder holds almost 30% more than the taller cylinder.

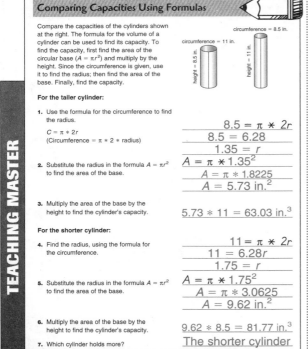

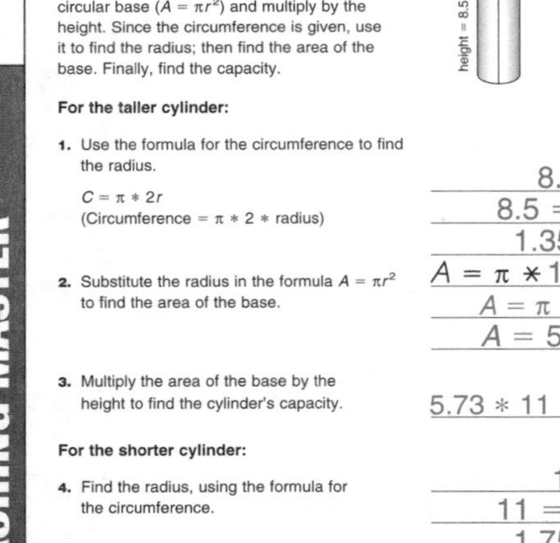

TEACHING MASTER

Comparing Capacities Using Formulas

Compare the capacities of the cylinders shown at the right. The formula for the volume of a cylinder can be used to find its capacity. To find the capacity, first find the area of the circular base ($A = \pi r^2$) and multiply by the height. Since the circumference is given, use it to find the radius; then find the area of the base. Finally, find the capacity.

For the taller cylinder:

1. Use the formula for the circumference to find the radius.
   $C = \pi * 2r$
   (Circumference = π * 2 * radius)
   $8.5 = \pi * 2r$
   $8.5 = 6.28$
   $1.35 = r$
2. Substitute the radius in the formula $A = \pi r^2$ to find the area of the base.
   $A = \pi * 1.35^2$
   $A = \pi * 1.8225$
   $A = 5.73 \text{ in.}^2$
3. Multiply the area of the base by the height to find the cylinder's capacity.
   $5.73 * 11 = 63.03 \text{ in.}^3$

For the shorter cylinder:

4. Find the radius, using the formula for the circumference.
   $11 = \pi * 2r$
   $11 = 6.28r$
   $1.75 = r$
5. Substitute the radius in the formula $A = \pi r^2$ to find the area of the base.
   $A = \pi * 1.75^2$
   $A = \pi * 3.0625$
   $A = 9.62 \text{ in.}^2$
6. Multiply the area of the base by the height to find the cylinder's capacity.
   $9.62 * 8.5 = 81.77 \text{ in.}^3$
7. Which cylinder holds more? The shorter cylinder

Math Masters, p. 161

9.10 Solving Equations by Trial and Error

OBJECTIVE **To approximate the solutions of equations using a trial-and-error method.**

summaries	materials
1 Teaching the Lesson	
Students substitute a sequence of test numbers for the variable in an equation. As successive test numbers are used, students "close in" on the exact solution. [Patterns, Functions, and Algebra]	□ *Math Journal 2,* pp. 370 and 371 □ Study Link 9.9 □ calculator □ pan balance (optional) □ metric weights (optional) ***See* Advance Preparation**
2 Ongoing Learning & Practice	
Students practice evaluating formulas by completing "What's My Rule?" tables and graphing the table values. [Patterns, Functions, and Algebra; Operations and Computation] Students practice and maintain skills through Math Boxes and Study Link activities.	□ *Math Journal 2,* pp. 372 and 373 □ Study Link Master (*Math Masters,* p. 368)
3 Options for Individualizing	
Reteaching Students play *Getting to One* to practice the trial-and-error method in simple problem situations. [Patterns, Functions, and Algebra] **Enrichment** Students use a trial-and-error method to find the maximum capacity (volume) of a box. They use a spreadsheet to record their results. [Patterns, Functions, and Algebra; Measurement and Reference Frames]	□ *Student Reference Book,* p. 295 □ Teaching Master (*Math Masters,* p. 162) □ calculator □ 8-inch square of paper ***See* Advance Preparation**

Additional Information

Advance Preparation Check that the calculators used by your students have the keys suggested for the Mental Math and Reflexes problems.

For the optional Enrichment activity in Part 3, cut out an 8-inch square of paper. Draw lines parallel to the edges, 2 inches from the edges. Fold along these lines. Then use this paper square to introduce the problem on *Math Masters,* page 162 by cutting out the square corners, folding the sides, and taping them to form a box.

Vocabulary • **trial-and-error method** • **test number**

Getting Started

Mental Math and Reflexes

Students use special calculator keys to simplify numerical expressions. *Suggestions:*

- (−): $-8 + 5$ -3
  $87 - (-43)$ 130
  $70 + (-16)$ 54
- (^): 27^2 729
  0.48^2 0.2304
  $(-18)^3$ $-5{,}832$
- (√): $\sqrt{3{,}136}$ 56
  $\sqrt{2.25}$ 1.5
  $\sqrt{0.25}$ 0.5

Math Message

Find the value of the expression $\frac{1}{n}$ as a decimal, for any number n except 0. Use your calculator. Record the key sequence that you use.

Study Link 9.9 Follow-Up

Go over the answers. For each problem, have students name the steps in the solution while you or a student writes them on the board. For example, for Problem 1:

Formula: $V = l * w * h$
Substitute: $V = 4 * 5 * 6$
Solve: $V = 120$ in.^{3}

1 Teaching the Lesson

✦Math Message Follow-Up

WHOLE-CLASS DISCUSSION

Have students share the key sequences they used. If they thought of the expression as a fraction, the following key sequence would be used on the TI-15 for whole number values of n:

1 (n) n (d) (Enter) (F↔D)

They could also see the expression as division and use the key sequence:

1 (÷) n (Enter)

Ask students why both key sequences yield the same answer for *any* non-zero value. Have them use both key sequences for a few values of n. *Suggestions:*
$n = 20$ 0.05, $n = 5.4$ $0.1\overline{85}$, $n = -4$ -0.25

✦Exploring the Trial-and-Error Method of Solving an Equation (*Math Journal 2,* p. 370)

WHOLE CLASS ACTIVITY

Before students turn to the journal page, introduce the activity by writing the equation $\frac{1}{x} + x = 4$ on the board. Ask students to brainstorm a solution, using any possible method.

Some students may try simplifying the equation:

- ▷ Multiply both sides of the equation by x to get the equation $\frac{x}{x} + x^2 = 4x$, or $1 + x^2 = 4x$.
- ▷ Transform $1 + x^2 = 4x$ into $x^2 - 4x + 1 = 0$ or $x * (x - 4) + 1 = 0$.

The resulting equations will not allow these students to proceed any further, and will not yield a solution.

Some students may suggest making a table and graphing the results:

- ▷ Construct a table of number pairs, where the number in the first column is a value of x and the number in the second column is the corresponding value of $\frac{1}{x} + x$.
- ▷ Graph the number pairs in the table on a coordinate grid. Then connect the points to form a line graph.
- ▷ Find the point on the line graph that is 4 units above the horizontal axis, and then read the x-coordinate for this point.

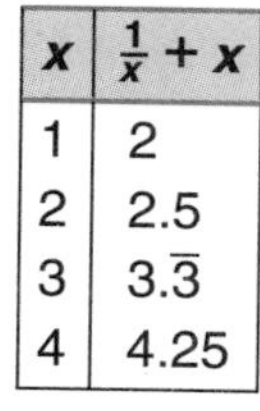

x	$\frac{1}{x} + x$
1	2
2	2.5
3	$3.\overline{3}$
4	4.25

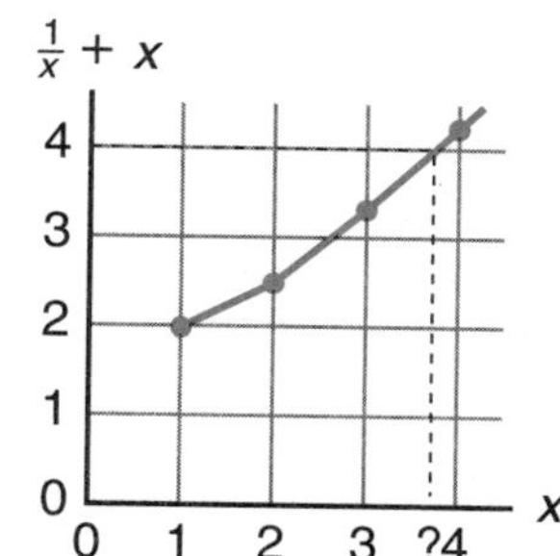

Praise any student who suggests this approach, but do not pursue it further.

Some students may propose the **trial-and-error method** described below. This method is the focus of this lesson.

Have students turn to the example on journal page 370. Use a pan-balance analogy to introduce the method. Suppose that there is an object to be weighed in the right-hand pan and that you place a set of known weights in the left-hand pan, trying to balance the object. If your known weights were heavier than the object, you would remove some weights from the left-hand pan to try to make it balance; if your weights were lighter, you would add some weights to the left-hand pan. Continuing in this way, you could "zero in" on the object's weight. After a number of adjustments, the weights in the left-hand pan would balance, or nearly balance, the object in the right-hand pan.

Adjusting the Activity If you have a pan balance and a set of metric weights available, ask a volunteer to show how to weigh an object. You can refer to this process in your discussion.

In the example, different **test numbers** are substituted for x on the left side of the equation, and this result is compared to the number 4 on the right side. Read through the example as a class. Mention the facts on the following page:

Solving Equations by Trial and Error

If you substitute a number for the variable in an equation and the result is a true number sentence, then that number is a solution of the equation. One way to solve an equation is to try several **test numbers** until you find the solution. Each test number can help you "close in" on the exact solution. Using this **trial-and-error method** for solving equations, you may not find the exact solution, but you can come very close to the exact solution.

Example Find a solution of the equation $\frac{1}{x} + x = 4$ by trial and error. If you can't find an exact solution, try to find a number that is very close to an exact solution.

The table shows the results of substituting several test numbers for x.

x	$\frac{1}{x}$	$\frac{1}{x} + x$	Compare $(\frac{1}{x} + x)$ to 4
1	1	2	less than 4
2	0.5	2.5	still less than 4, but closer
3	0.3	3.3	less than 4, but even closer
4	0.25	4.25	greater than 4

These results suggest that we try testing numbers for x that are between 3 and 4.

x	$\frac{1}{x}$	$\frac{1}{x} + x$	Compare $(\frac{1}{x} + x)$ to 4
3.9	0.256...	4.156...	>4
3.6	$0.2\overline{7}$	$3.8\overline{7}$	<4

We're getting closer. Now it's your turn. Try other test numbers. See how close you can get to 4 for the value of $\frac{1}{x} + x$. Sample answers:

x	$\frac{1}{x}$	$\frac{1}{x} + x$	Compare $(\frac{1}{x} + x)$ to 4
3.7	$0.2\overline{702}$	$3.\overline{702}$	<4
3.8	0.263...	4.063...	>4
3.75	$0.2\overline{6}$	$4.01\overline{6}$	>4
3.73	0.268...	3.998...	<4

My closest solution 3.73

STUDENT PAGE

✧ Math Journal 2, p. 370

▷ A test number that makes the value of $\frac{1}{x} + x$ equal to 4 is a solution of the equation.

▷ A test number that makes the value of $\frac{1}{x} + x$ close to 4 is close to a solution.

▷ If one test number makes the value of $\frac{1}{x} + x$ greater than 4, and a second test number makes it less than 4, then the solution will be a number between these two test numbers.

Ask students to use their calculators to check the values in the first two tables. For example, for $x = 2$ they enter the following key sequence:

1 (÷) 2 (+) 2 (Enter)

Now ask students to try several additional test numbers to see how close they can get to the solution of the equation. Compare their final answers.

One solution to $\frac{1}{x} + x = 4$ is 3.732050… . It is unlikely that any student will find a test number this close to the solution. Point out that close-but-not-exact solutions are legitimate, useful, and often the best that can be achieved in real-world situations. A second solution, which the example does not attempt to find, is 0.267949… .

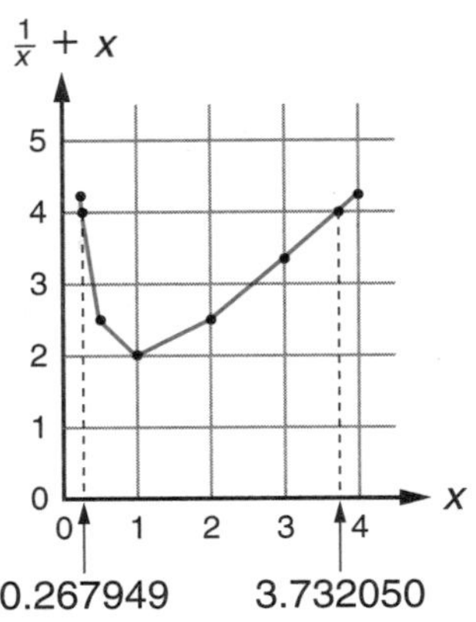

✦ Using the Trial-and-Error Method to Approximate Solutions (*Math Journal 2,* p. 371)

PARTNER ACTIVITY

Students use their calculators to approximate the solutions of the equations. Do not expect anyone to find an exact solution to either equation. Students should, however, be able to find good approximations to the exact solutions, within 0.1 of the exact solutions. Solutions: Problem 1: 7.2984379… ; Problem 2: 4.7015621… .

ONGOING ASSESSMENT

To assess students' understanding of the process of trial and error to solve equations, watch to see that they are making appropriate new guesses based on the results for each previous guess. The intervals they use will also provide some assessment information about students' proportional reasoning.

STUDENT PAGE

Solving Equations by Trial and Error (cont.)

Find the numbers that are closest to the solutions of the equations.
Use the suggested test numbers to get started.

1. Equation: $\sqrt{y} + y = 10$ Sample answers:

y	$\sqrt{y}$	$\sqrt{y} + y$	Compare ($\sqrt{y} + y$) to 10
0	0	0	<10
5	2.24	7.24	<10
9	3	12	>10
8	2.828	10.828	>10
7	2.646	9.646	<10
7.5	2.739	10.239	>10
7.4	2.72	10.12	>10
7.3	2.702	10.002	>10

My closest solution 7.3

2. Equation: $x^2 - 3x = 8$

x	x^2	$3x$	$x^2 - 3x$	Compare ($x^2 - 3x$) to 8
4	16	12	4	<8
6	36	18	18	>8
5	25	15	10	>8
4.5	20.25	13.5	6.75	<8
4.6	21.16	13.8	7.36	<8
4.7	22.09	14.1	7.99	<8
4.71	22.18	14.13	8.05	>8

My closest solution 4.7

✧ *Math Journal 2,* p. 371

2 Ongoing Learning & Practice

✦ Reviewing Formulas, Tables, and Graphs
(*Math Journal 2,* p. 372)

INDEPENDENT ACTIVITY 

Students complete "What's My Rule?" tables with formulas for the rule. They then make a graph of the values in the table.

✦ Math Boxes 9.10 (*Math Journal 2,* p. 373)

INDEPENDENT ACTIVITY 

Mixed Review Math Boxes in this lesson are paired with Math Boxes in Lesson 9.12. The skill in Problem 1 is a prerequisite for Unit 10.

✦ Study Link 9.10 (*Math Masters,* p. 368)

Home Connection Students approximate the solutions to two equations using the trial-and-error method. Note that if students do not have calculators, this is a good opportunity for them to practice computation skills with decimals.

Solving Equations by Trial and Error — Study Link 9.10

Find numbers that are close to the solution of each equation. Use the suggested test numbers to get started.

SRB 225–226

1. Equation: $r^2 + r = 15$ Answers vary.

r	r^2	$r^2 + r$	Compare $r^2 + r$ to 15
3	9	12	< 15
4	16	20	> 15
3.5	12.25	15.75	> 15

My closest solution Answers vary.

2. Equation: $x^2 - 2x = 23$

x	x^2	$2x$	$x^2 - 2x$	Compare $x^2 - 2x$ to 23
6	36	12	24	> 23
5	25	10	15	< 23
5.5	30.25	11	19.25	< 23

My closest solution Answers vary.

STUDY LINK MASTER

✦ *Math Masters,* p. 368

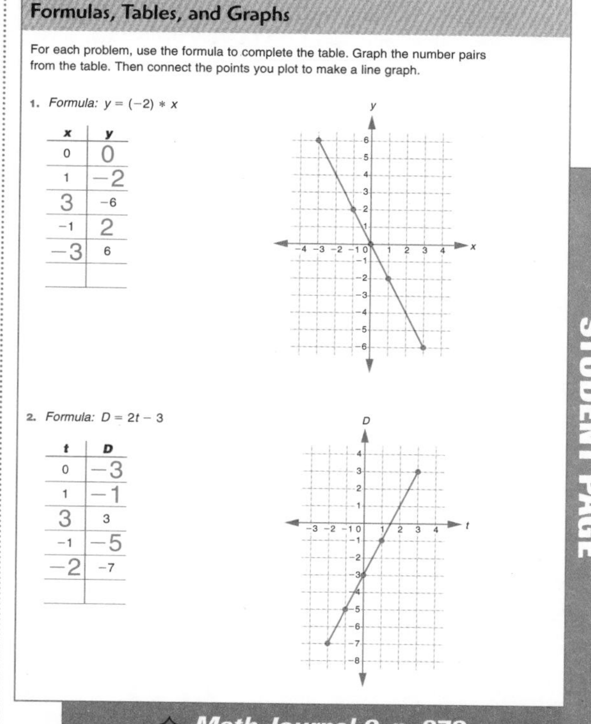
Formulas, Tables, and Graphs

For each problem, use the formula to complete the table. Graph the number pairs from the table. Then connect the points you plot to make a line graph.

1. Formula: $y = (-2) * x$

x	y
0	0
1	−2
3	−6
−1	2
−3	6

2. Formula: $D = 2t - 3$

t	D
0	−3
1	−1
3	3
−1	−5
−2	−7

STUDENT PAGE

✦ *Math Journal 2,* p. 372

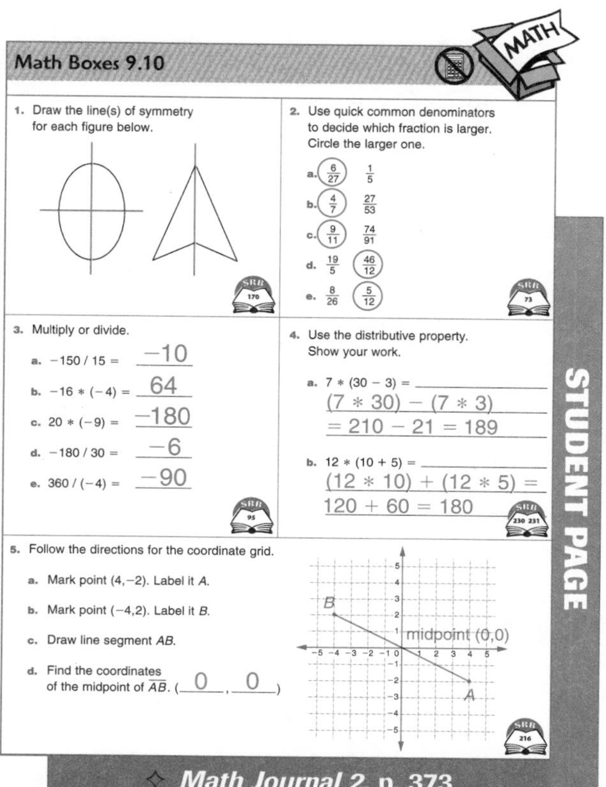
Math Boxes 9.10

1. Draw the line(s) of symmetry for each figure below.

2. Use quick common denominators to decide which fraction is larger. Circle the larger one.

a. $\frac{6}{27}$ (circled) $\frac{1}{5}$

b. $\frac{4}{7}$ (circled) $\frac{27}{53}$

c. $\frac{9}{11}$ (circled) $\frac{74}{91}$

d. $\frac{19}{5}$ $\frac{46}{12}$ (circled)

e. $\frac{8}{26}$ $\frac{5}{12}$ (circled)

3. Multiply or divide.

a. −150 / 15 = −10

b. −16 ∗ (−4) = 64

c. 20 ∗ (−9) = −180

d. −180 / 30 = −6

e. 360 / (−4) = −90

4. Use the distributive property. Show your work.

a. 7 ∗ (30 − 3) = (7 ∗ 30) − (7 ∗ 3) = 210 − 21 = 189

b. 12 ∗ (10 + 5) = (12 ∗ 10) + (12 ∗ 5) = 120 + 60 = 180

5. Follow the directions for the coordinate grid.

a. Mark point (4,−2). Label it *A*.

b. Mark point (−4,2). Label it *B*.

c. Draw line segment *AB*.

d. Find the coordinates of the midpoint of $\overline{AB}$. (0, 0)

midpoint (0,0)

STUDENT PAGE

✦ *Math Journal 2,* p. 373

Games

Getting to One

Materials □ calculator
Players 2

Object of the game To guess a mystery number in as few tries as possible.

Directions

1. Player A chooses a mystery number that is less than 100. Suppose the mystery number is 65.
2. Player B guesses the mystery number.
3. Player A uses a calculator to divide the guessed number by the mystery number. Player A then reads the answer that appears in the calculator display. If the answer has more than two decimal places, only the first two decimal places are read.
4. Player B continues to guess until the result is 1. Player B keeps track of the number of guesses.
5. When Player B has guessed the mystery number, players trade roles and follow Steps 1–4. The player who guesses the mystery number in the fewest number of guesses wins the round. The first player to win three rounds wins the game.

EXAMPLE Player A chooses the mystery number 65.

Player B guesses: 55. Player A keys in: 55 ÷ 65 Enter. Answer: 0.846153 Too small.
Player B guesses: 70. Player A keys in: 70 ÷ 65 Enter. Answer: 1.076923 Too big.
Player B guesses: 65. Player A keys in: 65 ÷ 65 Enter. Answer: 1 Just right!

Advanced Version Allow mystery numbers up to 1,000.

two hundred ninety-five 

STUDENT PAGE

✧ *Student Reference Book,* p. 295

A Box Problem

Suppose you have a square piece of cardboard that measures 8 inches along each side. To construct an open box out of the cardboard, you can cut same-sized squares from the 4 corners of the cardboard and then turn up and tape the sides.

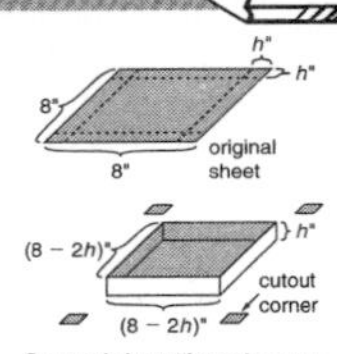

Box made by cutting out square corners and folding up sides

1. John cut small squares to make his box. Amy cut large squares to make her box.
   a. Whose box was taller? Amy's 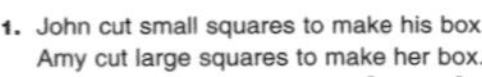
   b. Whose box had a greater area of the base? John's 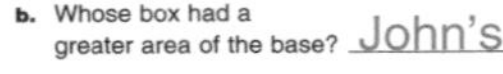

The volume of the box depends on the size of the squares cut from the corners.

2. Find the dimensions of a box with the greatest possible volume. Use trial-and-error to solve the problem. Keep a record of your results in the spreadsheet below.
   a. Three test values for h (the height of the box) are listed in Column A. Complete Rows 4, 5, and 6.

Boxes

	A	B	C	D
1	Problem: Find the length that maximizes the box volume.			
2	box height (in.)	box length, width (in.)	base area of box (in.^{2})	volume of box (in.^{3})
3	h	$8 - 2h$	$(8 - 2h)^2$	$(8 - 2h)^2 * h$
4	1	6	36	36
5	2	4	16	32
6	3	2	4	12
7				
8				
9				

   b. Use the results in your spreadsheet to select new test values for h that are likely to give a box of greater volume. Sample answers:

The box that I found with the greatest volume has a height of 1.25 inches and a volume of 37.8 cubic inches.

TEACHING MASTER

✧ *Math Masters,* p. 162

3 Options for Individualizing

✦ RETEACHING Playing *Getting to One* (*Student Reference Book,* p. 295)

PARTNER ACTIVITY  5–15 min 

Students play this game, introduced in *Fourth Grade Everyday Mathematics,* to practice using trial-and-error for guessing mystery numbers. This game also helps strengthen proportional reasoning skills.

✦ ENRICHMENT Maximizing the Volume of a Rectangular Prism (*Math Masters,* p. 162)

PARTNER ACTIVITY 15–30 min 

Use the square sheet of paper you prepared to introduce the problem. (See Advance Preparation.) Cut out the corners and assemble a box to illustrate the figures at the top of *Math Masters,* page 162.

The master gives the dimensions and volume of a box that has been made by cutting h-inch squares from the corners. The bottom of the box is a square, measuring $(8 - 2h)$ inches on each side. The height of the box is h inches. The volume of the box is $(8 - 2h)^2 * h$ cubic inches.

For the box you assembled, $h = 2$ inches. Have students examine the spreadsheet shown on *Math Masters,* page 162 and fill in line 5. Verify that the students' entries on line 5 are correct for the box you assembled.

Ask students to complete lines 4 and 6 of the spreadsheet on their own. They should then use the results in the spreadsheet to select new test values for h. They are looking for a value of h that gives a box with the greatest possible volume.

9.11 Formula Equations

OBJECTIVE **To use formulas to solve problems by substituting for the variables and solving the resulting equations.**

summaries	materials
1 Teaching the Lesson	
Students solve problems using formulas with one unknown. They substitute known quantities for variables, and solve the resulting equation for the unknown variable. [Patterns, Functions, and Algebra] Students solve volume, angle, perimeter, and area problems. They first express given information in a formula or equation. [Measurement and Reference Frames; Patterns, Functions, and Algebra]	□ *Math Journal 2,* pp. 374–376 □ Study Link 9.10 □ calculator
2 Ongoing Learning & Practice	
Students practice and maintain skills through Math Boxes and Study Link activities.	□ *Math Journal 2,* p. 377 □ Study Link Master (*Math Masters,* p. 369) □ protractor □ calculator
3 Options for Individualizing	
Extra Practice Students write volume and area number stories. [Measurement and Reference Frames] **Enrichment** Students explore a problem about seating arrangements in a story. [Patterns, Functions, and Algebra]	□ *Sir Cumference and the First Round Table* ***See* Advance Preparation**

Additional Information

Advance Preparation For the optional Enrichment activity in Part 3, obtain a copy of the book *Sir Cumference and the First Round Table* by Cindy Neuschwander and Wayne Greehan (Charlesbridge, 1997).

Getting Started

Mental Math and Reflexes

Pose questions that students answer with algebraic expressions. *Suggestions:*

- Bart is 6 years older than Samantha. Samantha is *y* years old. How old is Bart? $y + 6$ years old
- Jeff walked *m* miles yesterday. Today he walked 5 miles farther than yesterday. How many miles did he walk in the two days? $m + m + 5$, or $2m + 5$ miles
- Lucy has *b* baseball cards. Gerard has 2 times as many baseball cards as Lucy. How many baseball cards does Gerard have? $2b$ cards
- Franklin talked on the phone for *h* hours last week. If he talked to 3 people for equal lengths of time, how long did he talk to each person? $h \div 3$ hours

Math Message

Jenny calculated that she could fit exactly 48 cm cubes into the box she had built. Her box was 5 cm long, 7 cm wide, and 4 cm high. Explain Jenny's mistake.

Study Link 9.10 Follow-Up

Briefly review answers. Have students share efficient strategies for finding a good approximation of the answer.

1 Teaching the Lesson

✦ Math Message Follow-Up

WHOLE-CLASS DISCUSSION

Have students share their explanations of Jenny's mistake. Jenny added the length and width instead of multiplying to find the area of the base.

✦ Using Formulas to Solve Problems (*Math Journal 2,* p. 374)

WHOLE-CLASS ACTIVITY

Work through the example on journal page 374 with the class. As the example shows, substituting for a variable in a formula may lead to two types of situations:

▷ When a value is substituted for a variable, the value of the other variable can be calculated directly.

Example: Substitute 30 for C in the formula $F = 1.8C + 32$. You can then calculate the value of F directly, without having to rewrite the equation. $F = (1.8 * 30) + 32 = 86$.

▷ When a value is substituted for a variable, the resulting equation needs to be rewritten before calculating the value of the other variable.

Example: Substitute 50 for F in the formula $F = (1.8 * C) + 32$. Then solve the resulting equation. $50 = 1.8C + 32$. $C = 10$

The problems on journal page 374 include both types of situations. Suggestions for follow-up discussion:

▷ In Problem 1, the words-to-age formula applies loosely to children ages 2 through 8. The formula indicates that 2-year-olds know an average of about 300 words.

STUDENT PAGE

Using Formulas to Solve Problems

To solve a problem using a formula, you can substitute the known quantities for variables in the formula and solve the resulting equation.

Example A formula for converting between Celsius and Fahrenheit temperatures is $F = 1.8C + 32$, where C represents the Celsius temperature and F the Fahrenheit temperature.

- Use the formula to convert 30°C to degrees Fahrenheit.

	$F = 1.8C + 32$
Substitute 30 for C in the formula:	$F = (1.8 * 30) + 32$
Solve the equation:	$F = 86$
Answer:	30°C = 86°F

- Use the formula to convert 50°F to degrees Celsius.

	$F = 1.8C + 32$
Substitute 50 for F in the formula:	$50 = (1.8 * C) + 32$
Solve the equation:	$10 = C$
Answer:	50°F = 10°C

1. The formula $W = 570A - 850$ expresses the relationship between the average number of words small children know and their ages (for ages 2 to 8). The variable W represents the number of words known, and A represents the age in years.
   a. About how many words might a $3\frac{1}{4}$-year-old child know? 1,000 words
   b. About how old might a child be who knows about 1,700 words? $4\frac{1}{2}$ years old
2. A bowler whose average score is less than 200 is given a handicap. The **handicap** is a number of points that is added to a bowler's score for each game. A common handicap formula is $H = 0.8 * (200 - A)$, where H is the handicap and A is the average score.
   a. What is the handicap of a bowler whose average score is 160? 32
   b. What is the average score of a bowler whose handicap is 68? 115
3. An adult human female's height can be estimated from the length of her tibia (shinbone) by using the formula $H = 2.4 * T + 75$, where H is the height in centimeters and T is the length of the tibia in centimeters.
   a. Estimate the height of a female whose tibia is 31 centimeters long. 149.4 cm
   b. Estimate the length of a female's tibia if she is 175 centimeters tall. 41.7 cm

✧ *Math Journal 2,* p. 374

Adjusting the Activity To extend Problem 1, ask students why the formula cannot be applied to children younger than 2. For example, substituting 1 for A in the formula gives $570 - 850$, or -280 words, as the number of words that 1-year-olds know. This makes no sense. Nor is the formula reliable for ages greater than 8.

▹ In Problem 2, the bowler's handicap formula applies only to bowlers whose averages are less than 200. They are given handicaps.

Adjusting the Activity To extend Problem 2, ask students to consider what would happen if the handicap formula applied to all bowlers, even those who average 200 or more. For a bowler with an average of 200, $H = 0$. A bowler whose average is greater than 200 would receive a negative handicap score. For example, a bowler who averages 220 would receive the following handicap:

$0.8 * (200 - 220) = 0.8 * (-20) = -16$

▹ In Problem 3, the tibia-to-height formula applies specifically to adult females. A different tibia-to-height formula applies to adult males. The formula that applies to children is different from each of the adult formulas.

✦ Solving Volume Problems
(*Math Journal 2,* p. 375)

PARTNER ACTIVITY

Assign the problems on journal page 375. Circulate and assist.

ONGOING ASSESSMENT

Use students' answers to Problems 1 and 2 to assess their understanding of how to substitute known values in the appropriate formula, and how to solve the resulting equation. Expect that most students should have no difficulty with these problems.

For Problem 3, ask students to figure out what percent the volume of the ball is of the volume of the box. Volume of ball = 382 in.^{3}; volume of box = 729 in.^{3}; 382 / 729 is about 0.52, or 52%

Volume Problems

Solve each problem. You may need to look up formulas in your *Student Reference Book.* Check your answers.

1. The capacity (volume) of the desk drawer is 1,365 in.^{3}. Find the depth (d) of the drawer.

   Formula $V = l * w * h$
   Substitute $1,365 = d * 10 * 6.5$
   Solve $1,365 = 65d$
   $21 = d$

   Depth of drawer = 21 inches

   6.5 in. 10 in. d

2. The cylindrical can has a capacity of 4 liters (4 liters = 4,000 cm^3). Find the height (h) of the can, to the nearest centimeter.

   Formula $V = \pi r^2 h$
   Substitute $4,000 = \pi(8^2)h$
   Solve $4,000 = 201h$
   $19.9 = h$

   Height is about 20 cm.

   8 cm h

3. A soccer ball has a 9-inch diameter.

   9 in.

   a. What is the shape of the smallest box that will hold the ball? A cube

   b. What are the dimensions of the box? 9 in. $*$ 9 in. $*$ 9 in.

   c. Compare the volume of the box to the volume of the ball. Is the volume of the box more or less than twice the volume of the ball? less
   (*Reminder:* A formula for finding the volume of a sphere is $V = \frac{4}{3} * \pi * r^3$.)

   Explain your answer. Sample answer:
   (sphere) $V = \frac{4}{3}\pi r^3$ (cube) $V = Bh$
   $V = 382$ in.^{3} $V = 729$ in.^{3}
   $382 * 2 = 764$ $764 > 729$

STUDENT PAGE

✧ *Math Journal 2,* p. 375

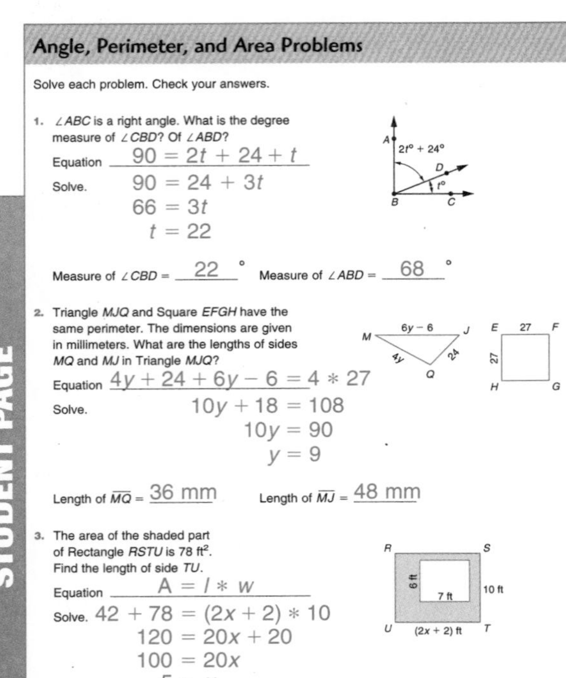
STUDENT PAGE

Angle, Perimeter, and Area Problems

Solve each problem. Check your answers.

1. $\angle ABC$ is a right angle. What is the degree measure of $\angle CBD$? Of $\angle ABD$?

   Equation $90 = 2t + 24 + t$

   Solve. $90 = 24 + 3t$
   $66 = 3t$
   $t = 22$

   Measure of $\angle CBD$ = 22° Measure of $\angle ABD$ = 68°

2. Triangle *MJQ* and Square *EFGH* have the same perimeter. The dimensions are given in millimeters. What are the lengths of sides *MQ* and *MJ* in Triangle *MJQ*?

   Equation $4y + 24 + 6y - 6 = 4 * 27$

   Solve. $10y + 18 = 108$
   $10y = 90$
   $y = 9$

   Length of $\overline{MQ}$ = 36 mm Length of $\overline{MJ}$ = 48 mm

3. The area of the shaded part of Rectangle *RSTU* is 78 ft^2. Find the length of side *TU*.

   Equation $A = l * w$

   Solve. $42 + 78 = (2x + 2) * 10$
   $120 = 20x + 20$
   $100 = 20x$
   $5 = x$

   Length of side *TU* = 12 ft

✧ *Math Journal 2*, p. 376

✦ Solving Angle, Perimeter, and Area Problems
(*Math Journal 2,* p. 376)

PARTNER ACTIVITY

Assign the problems on journal page 376. Circulate and assist. Reserve some time for a discussion of students' answers. To solve each problem, students must first express the information in the number story and in the figure, as an equation. Then they solve the equation.

▷ In Problem 1, the measure of $\angle ABC$ is 90°. Therefore, the sum of the measures of $\angle ABD$ and $\angle CBD$ must be 90°, that is, $(2t° + 24°) + t° = 90°$.

▷ In Problem 2, the perimeter of the square is 108 mm ($4 * 27$ mm). Therefore, the perimeter of the triangle can be expressed by the equation $4y + (6y - 6) + 24 = 108$.

▷ In Problem 3, the area of the larger rectangle is the sum of the area of the smaller rectangle and the shaded area, that is, $(6 * 7) + 78 = 120 \text{ ft}^2$. The area of the larger rectangle can be expressed by the equation $10 * (2x + 2) = 120 \text{ ft}^2$.

2 Ongoing Learning & Practice

✦ Math Boxes 9.11 (*Math Journal 2,* p. 377)

INDEPENDENT ACTIVITY 

Mixed Review Math Boxes in this lesson are paired with Math Boxes in Lesson 9.13. The skill in Problem 1 is a prerequisite for Unit 10.

✦ Study Link 9.11 (*Math Masters,* p. 369)

Home Connection Students practice solving problems by substituting known values in formulas.

Math Boxes 9.11

1. Circle all the regular polygons.

Explain why the circled figures are regular polygons. Sample answer: All sides are the same length, and all angles are the same size.

2. Solve.

	Solution
a. $\frac{22}{m} = \frac{1}{2}$	$m = 44$
b. $0.25 * s = 64$	$s = 256$
c. $d * 10^2 = 420.5$	$d = 4.205$
d. $f * \frac{1}{8} = \frac{3}{16}$	$f = 1\frac{1}{2}$
e. $\sqrt{h} = 20$	$h = 400$

3. When Marlene removed her dinner from the freezer, the temperature of the dinner was −10°C. She heated the dinner in the oven, and then put it on the table. It cooled to room temperature, 23°C, while she was talking on the phone.

How many degrees warmer was the dinner at room temperature than it was when removed from the freezer? 33°C warmer

Write a number model to show how you found your answer. Sample answer: $-10 + x = 23$, or $-10 + 33 = 23$

4. The table shows the results of a survey that asked people where they keep their computers at home. Fill in the missing information in the table. Use a protractor to make a circle graph of the results. Do not use the Percent Circle.

Where People Keep Their Computers (title)

Family room, Basement, Kitchen, Home office, Living room, Bed-room

Location	Number of People	Percent of Total
Family room	20	40%
Bedroom	10	20%
Living room	8	16%
Home office	8	16%
Kitchen	2	4%
Basement	2	4%
Total	50	100%

STUDENT PAGE

✧ *Math Journal 2,* p. 377

3 Options for Individualizing

✦ EXTRA PRACTICE Writing Volume and Area Number Stories

PARTNER ACTIVITY  **15–30 min** 

Students work together to write, illustrate, and solve volume and area number stories. You may want to display the number stories, so that students can enjoy solving each other's problems.

Adjusting the Activity Pair a student learning English with a proficient English speaker. Allow the English language learner to dictate his or her number story and have the partner record it. The partner should read it back so the English learner can make corrections if needed.

Using Formulas Study Link 9.11

Each problem below states a formula and gives the values of all but one of the variables in the formula. Substitute the known values for the variables in the formula and solve the equation.

1. The formula $C = \frac{5}{9} * (F - 32)$ may be used to convert between Fahrenheit and Celsius temperatures.

a. Convert 77°F to degrees C.
Equation $C = \frac{5}{9} * (77 - 32)$
Solve.
77°F = 25 °C

b. Convert 50°C to degrees F.
Equation $50 = \frac{5}{9} * (F - 32)$
Solve.
50°C = 122 °F

2. The formula for the area of a trapezoid is $A = \frac{1}{2} * (a + b) * h$.

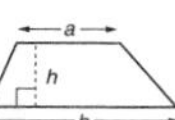

a. Find the area (A) of a trapezoid if a = 7 cm, b = 10 cm, and h = 5 cm.
Equation $A = \frac{1}{2} * 17 * 5$
Solve.
Area 42.5 cm²

b. Find the height (h) of a trapezoid if a = 6.5 inches, b = 5.5 inches, and A = 90 inches².
Equation $90 = \frac{1}{2} * 12 * h$
Solve.
Height 15 in.

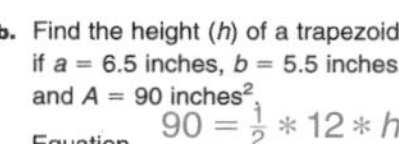

3. The formula for the volume of a cone is $V = \frac{1}{3} * \pi * r^2 * h$.

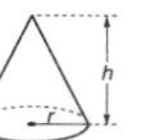

a. Find the volume (V) of a cone if r = 2 inches and h = 9 inches.
Equation $V = \frac{1}{3} * \pi * 4 * 9$
Solve.
Volume 37.68 in.³

b. Find the height (h) of a cone if r = 3 cm and V = 94.2 cm³.
Equation $94.2 = \frac{1}{3} * \pi * 9 * h$
Solve.
Height 10 cm

STUDY LINK MASTER

✧ *Math Masters,* p. 369

✦ ENRICHMENT Solving Perimeter Problems

SMALL-GROUP ACTIVITY  **15–30 min** 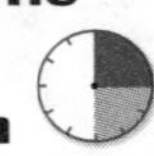

Literature Link The book *Sir Cumference and the First Round Table* is a fanciful tale about how the knights of Camelot ended up with a round table. After much experimenting with perimeters, they finally realize that they will all fit comfortably if the table is round.

After reading the story to the class, you may want to have students calculate the various perimeters from the story (the first three configurations). Note that for the hexagon, they may need to get creative—the length between two parallel sides of the hexagon is 10 feet based on the past configurations. By measuring, they will see that the scale is about 1 cm : 2 ft. Since the small sides measure about 2 cm, they are about 4 feet long.

You might want to skip the oval table or assign it as a challenge problem (note that the ellipse is 10 feet long). For the final circular table, students should estimate the circumference based on the fact that the diameter is the length of Lady Di's height plus her reach. A good estimate of the final circumference is probably between 26 and 27 square feet (assuming Lady Di is about $5\frac{1}{2}$ feet tall).

9.12 The Pythagorean Theorem

OBJECTIVES **To explore the relationship between the square of a number and its square root; and to verify and apply the Pythagorean Theorem.**

summaries	materials
1 Teaching the Lesson	
Students review squares and square roots of numbers. They solve problems that focus on both the algebraic and geometric character of square roots. [Operations and Computation] Students verify the Pythagorean Theorem through a measurement activity. Students examine a simple proof of the theorem, and apply it to find missing lengths in right triangles. [Geometry; Patterns, Functions, and Algebra]	☐ *Math Journal 2,* pp. 378–380 ☐ *Student Reference Book,* p. 155 ☐ Study Link 9.11 ☐ calculator ☐ centimeter ruler ☐ blank sheet of paper with square corners
2 Ongoing Learning & Practice	
Students play *3-D Shape Sort* to practice with attributes of 3-dimensional shapes. [Geometry] Students practice and maintain skills through Math Boxes and Study Link activities.	☐ *Math Journal 2,* p. 381 ☐ *Student Reference Book,* p. 307 ☐ Teaching Masters (*Math Masters,* pp. 163 and 164) ☐ Study Link Master (*Math Masters,* p. 370)
3 Options for Individualizing	
Enrichment Students construct a visual model that verifies the Pythagorean Theorem. [Geometry; Patterns, Functions, and Algebra]	☐ Teaching Master (*Math Masters,* p. 7) ☐ scissors ☐ glue or tape

Additional Information

Advance Preparation Plan on spending two days on this lesson, possibly covering squares and square roots and introducing the Pythagorean Theorem on the first day, and continuing with the Pythagorean Theorem on the second day.

Vocabulary • **square of a number** • **square root of a number** • **legs of a right triangle** • **hypotenuse** • **Pythagorean Theorem** • **right triangle** • **theorem**

Getting Started

Mental Math and Reflexes

Students use their calculators. *Suggestions:*

- Use the [∧] key to find the following squares:
  18^2 324　　5.2^2 27.04　　$(\frac{2}{3})^2$ $\frac{4}{9}$, or 0.444...　　25^2 625　　0.06^2 0.0036
- Use the [√] and [)] keys to find the following square roots. Round answers to the nearest hundredth.
  $\sqrt{27}$ 5.20　　$\sqrt{172}$ 13.11　　$\sqrt{3.258}$ 1.80　　$\sqrt{3.258^2}$ 3.26　　$\sqrt{\frac{9}{64}}$ $\frac{3}{8}$, or 0.38

Math Message

Read the top of journal page 378 and do the first 3 problems.

Study Link 9.11 Follow-Up

Students share their solution strategies.

1 Teaching the Lesson

✦ Math Message Follow-Up
(*Math Journal 2,* p. 378)

WHOLE-CLASS DISCUSSION 

Review the definition of square of a number and square root of a number. The **square of a number** n is that number multiplied by itself: $n * n$, or n^2. A **square root of a number** n is a number whose square is n. We use the symbol $\sqrt{n}$ to write the square root of the number n.

NOTE: The square root of a number can also be defined as: The square root of a number n is a number that when multiplied by itself, gives the number n. For example, 4 is the square root of 16 because $4 * 4 = 16$.

Help students to verbalize the solutions to Problem 1. *For example:*

- $\sqrt{100} =$? What number can I square to get 100? 10, because $10 * 10 = 100$. So the square root of 100 is 10. We write $\sqrt{100} = 10$.
- $\sqrt{100^2} =$? What number can I square to get 100^2? 100, because $100 * 100 = 100^2$. So the square root of 100^2 is 100. We write $\sqrt{100^2} = 100$.

Students might experiment with the following routines on their calculators to reinforce the relationship between the square of a number and its square root.

Enter a positive number. Press [^] 2 [Enter]. Record the answer. Then press [√] (answer) [)] [Enter]. The display shows the original number. The square root operation "undoes" the squaring operation that was done first.

Press [√], any positive number, [)] [Enter] [^] 2 [Enter]. The display shows the original number. The squaring operation "undoes" the square root operation that was done first.

In reviewing the answers to Problems 2 and 3, try to cover the following points presented on the next page:

STUDENT PAGE

Squares and Square Roots of Numbers

Math Message

You know that the **square of a number** is equal to the number multiplied by itself. For example, $5^2 = 5 * 5 = 25$.

The **square root** of a number n is a number whose square is n. For example, a square root of 25 is 5, because $5^2 = 5 * 5 = 25$. The square root of 25 is also equal to -5, because $(-5) * (-5) = (-5)^2 = 25$. So every positive number has two square roots, which are opposites of each other.

We use the symbol $\sqrt{\ }$ to write positive square roots. $\sqrt{25}$ is read as *the positive square root of 25.*

1. Write the square root of each number.
   a. $\sqrt{81} =$ 9 b. $\sqrt{100} =$ 10 c. $\sqrt{100^2} =$ 100
2. What is the square root of zero? 0
3. Can a negative number have a square root? no
   Explain. Sample answer: The product of two positive or two negative numbers is always positive.

To find the positive square root of a number with a calculator, use the [√] key. For example, to find the square root of 25, enter [√] 25 [)] [Enter]. The display will show 5.

4. Use a calculator. Round your answers for a. and d. to the nearest hundredth.
   a. $\sqrt{17} =$ 4.12 b. $\sqrt{17} * \sqrt{17} =$ 17 c. $\sqrt{\pi} * \sqrt{\pi} =$ π
   d. $\sqrt{\pi} =$ 1.77 e. $(\sqrt{17})^2 =$ 17 f. $\sqrt{\frac{1}{16}} =$ 0.25, or $\frac{1}{4}$
5. The length of a side of a square is $\sqrt{6.25}$ centimeters. What is the area of the square? 6.25 cm²
6. The area of a square is 21 square inches. What is the length of a side, to the nearest tenth of an inch? 4.6 in.
7. The radius of a circle is $\sqrt{20}$ feet. What is its area, to the nearest hundredth? About 62.83 ft²

✦ *Math Journal 2,* p. 378

- ▷ A positive number has two square roots—a positive number and its opposite. Examples:
  9 and -9 are both square roots of 81, because $9 * 9 = 81$, and $(-9) * (-9) = 81$.
  $\frac{1}{2}$ and $-\frac{1}{2}$ are both square roots of $\frac{1}{4}$, because $\frac{1}{2} * \frac{1}{2} = \frac{1}{4}$, and $(-\frac{1}{2}) * (-\frac{1}{2}) = \frac{1}{4}$.
- ▷ The symbol "$\sqrt{\ }$" refers to the positive square root of a number. Take the opposite of the square root to get the negative square root. Thus $\sqrt{25}$ is equal to 5, and $-\sqrt{25}$ is equal to -5.
- ▷ A negative number cannot have a square root: The square of a number cannot be a negative number, since the square of a positive number is a positive number and the square of a negative number is also a positive number.
- ▷ The square root of zero is zero, since $0^2 = 0$.

✦ Solving Square-Root Problems
(*Math Journal 2,* p. 378)

INDEPENDENT ACTIVITY 

Technology Link Assign Problems 4–7 on journal page 378. Circulate and assist as needed. When most students have finished, discuss their answers.

As you go over Problem 4, review how to use the [√] and [∧] keys on the calculator. A few students may realize that they can solve Problems 4b, 4c, and 4e without doing any calculations. Probably most will use their calculators to find the square roots, only to discover that they will obtain the number inside the square root symbol. Problems like $\sqrt{17} * \sqrt{17}$ and $\sqrt{\pi} * \sqrt{\pi}$ may be confusing to some students. Help students by verbalizing the definition of square root and saying: *$\sqrt{17}$ is a number whose square is 17. So if you square $\sqrt{17}$ (that is, multiply $\sqrt{17}$ by $\sqrt{17}$), the result will be 17.*

Problems 5 and 6 address the geometric characterization of the square root. Some students, recalling that every positive number has both a positive and negative square root, may wonder why -4.6 is not also a solution to Problem 6. Remind them that the length of the side of a square must be a positive number. Similarly, for Problem 7, the negative square root cannot be the length of a radius.

Adjusting the Activity You may want to make a poster showing the square of a number and the square root of a number. *(See below.)* Display it in a prominent place in the classroom.

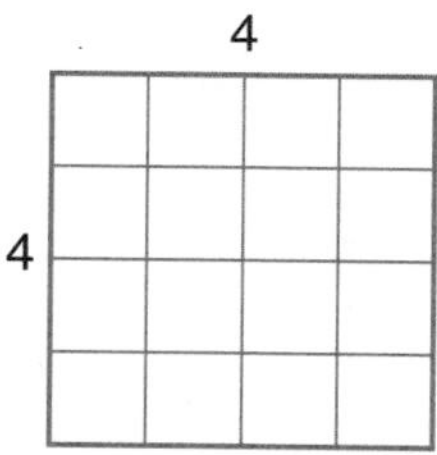

$4 * 4 = 16$
$4^2 = 16$
Four squared is 16.

$\sqrt{16} = 4$
The square root of 16 is 4.

NOTE: For Problem 4f, the calculator will display the answer as a decimal. Use the [F↔D] and [Simp] keys to display the answer as a fraction.

Verifying the Pythagorean Theorem

In a right triangle, the side opposite the right angle is called the **hypotenuse.** The other two sides are called the **legs of the triangle.**

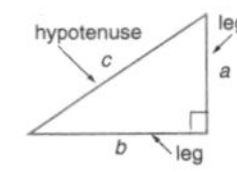

Think about the following statement:
If a and b are the lengths of the legs of a right triangle and c is the length of the hypotenuse, then $a^2 + b^2 = c^2$.

This statement is known as the **Pythagorean Theorem.**

1. To verify that the Pythagorean Theorem is true, use a blank sheet of paper that has square corners. Draw diagonal lines to form 4 right triangles, one at each corner. Then measure the lengths of the legs and the hypotenuse of each right triangle, to the nearest millimeter. Record the lengths in the table below. Then complete the table.

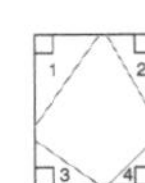

Triangle	Leg (a)	Leg (b)	Hypotenuse (c)	$a^2 + b^2$	c^2
1			Answers	vary.	
2					
3					
4					

2. Compare $(a^2 + b^2)$ to c^2 for each of the triangles you drew. Why might these two numbers be slightly different?
Sample answer: Measurements are always estimates, and there may be differences due to rounding.

3. Use the Pythagorean Theorem to find c^2 for the triangle at the right. Then find the length c.

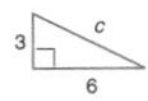

c^2 = 45 units^2 c is about 6.7 units.

STUDENT PAGE

Math Journal 2, **p. 379**

Introducing and Verifying the Pythagorean Theorem (*Math Journal 2,* p. 379)

PARTNER ACTIVITY 

Read the top of journal page 379 as a class. Be sure students can identify the hypotenuse and **legs of a right triangle.**

Draw a right triangle on the board. Define and label the legs and **hypotenuse.** Write the statement of the **Pythagorean Theorem** on the board:

hypotenuse
leg
leg

If a and b are the lengths of the legs of a **right triangle,** and c is the length of the hypotenuse, then $a^2 + b^2 = c^2$.

The statement is credited to the Greek mathematician and philosopher Pythagoras (6th century B.C.E.). A **theorem** is a proposition (statement) that can (or might) be proved.

Partners complete journal page 379 as you circulate and assist.

Problem 1 asks students to draw four right triangles on a blank sheet of paper. The edges of the paper will be the legs. The diagonals that students draw will form the hypotenuses. Encourage students to vary the sizes and shapes of the triangles they draw.

If students measure carefully, they will find that $(a^2 + b^2)$ and c^2 are approximately equal. These two numbers will usually be slightly different because the measurements of a, b, and c cannot be exact. By pooling the class results, students will gain confidence that the theorem is true for every right triangle.

Geometry and Constructions

The Theorem of Pythagoras

A right triangle is a triangle that has a right angle (90°). In a right triangle, the side opposite the right angle is called the **hypotenuse.** The other two sides are called **legs.**

hypotenuse
leg
c
a
b
leg

In the diagram at the right, a and b represent the lengths of the legs, and c represents the length of the hypotenuse.

There is a surprising connection between the lengths of the three sides of any right triangle. It is probably the most useful property in all of geometry and is known as the Pythagorean Theorem. It is stated at the right.

Pythagorean Theorem

If the legs of a right triangle have lengths a and b, and the hypotenuse has length c, then $a^2 + b^2 = c^2$.

Nobody knows when this relationship was first discovered. The Babylonians, Egyptians, and Chinese knew of it before the Greeks. But Pythagoras, a Greek philosopher born about 572 B.C., was the first person to prove that the relationship is true for any right triangle. It is called a **theorem** because it is a statement that has been proved.

A Chinese proof of the Pythagorean Theorem (written about A.D. 40) is shown below. Two identical squares, each with sides of length $a + b$, are partitioned in different ways.

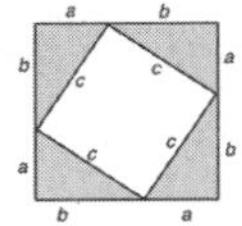
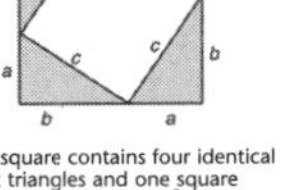

This square contains four identical right triangles and one square whose area is $c * c = c^2$.

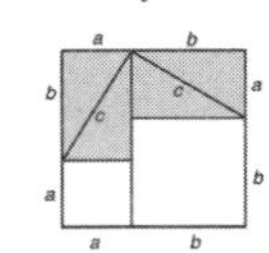

This square contains four identical right triangles and two squares whose areas are a^2 and b^2.

The four right triangles inside each square all have the same area. Therefore, the area of the large square (c^2) inside the first square must be equal to the total area of the two smaller squares ($a^2 + b^2$) that are inside the second square; that is, c^2 must equal $a^2 + b^2$.

one hundred fifty-five 

STUDENT PAGE

Student Reference Book, **p. 155**

Studying a Proof of the Pythagorean Theorem (*Student Reference Book,* p. 155)

PARTNER ACTIVITY

Ask students to read page 155 of the *Student Reference Book* on their own. Then discuss the proof of the theorem.

Since Squares 1 and 2 have the same area, the area of the unshaded part in Square 1 is equal to the area of the unshaded part in Square 2. That is, c^2 is equal to $a^2 + b^2$. Many proofs of the theorem exist, but this version is one of the most visual and one of the simplest.

✦ Using the Pythagorean Theorem to Find Missing Lengths (*Math Journal 2,* p. 380)

PARTNER ACTIVITY

Discuss how the Pythagorean Theorem can be used to find missing lengths in a right triangle. Work several examples, as a class, before assigning the problems on journal page 380. Use Problem 3 on journal page 379 as a first example. Show students how to find the solution:

Formula: $a^2 + b^2 = c^2$

Solve:

$$3^2 + 6^2 = c^2$$
$$9 + 36 = c^2$$
$$45 = c^2$$
$$\sqrt{45} = c$$
$$6.708203933... = c$$

So side c is about 6.7 units long.

Include one or two examples that use the Pythagorean Theorem to solve for the length of a leg. For example, in Problem 3 on journal page 380,

$$b^2 + 7^2 = 25^2$$
$$b^2 + 49 = 625$$
$$b^2 = 625 - 49$$
$$b^2 = 576.$$

Taking the square root of both sides of the equation gives $b = 24$.

Using the Pythagorean Theorem

In Problems 1–6, use the Pythagorean Theorem to find each missing length. Round your answer to the nearest tenth.

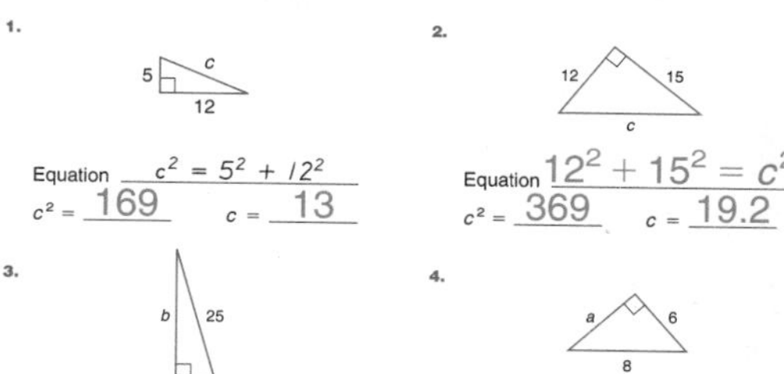

1. Equation $c^2 = 5^2 + 12^2$ $c^2 =$ 169 $c =$ 13

2. Equation $12^2 + 15^2 = c^2$ $c^2 =$ 369 $c =$ 19.2

3. Equation $25^2 = 7^2 + b^2$ $b^2 =$ 576 $b =$ 24

4. Equation $a^2 + 6^2 = 8^2$ $a^2 =$ 28 $a =$ 5.3

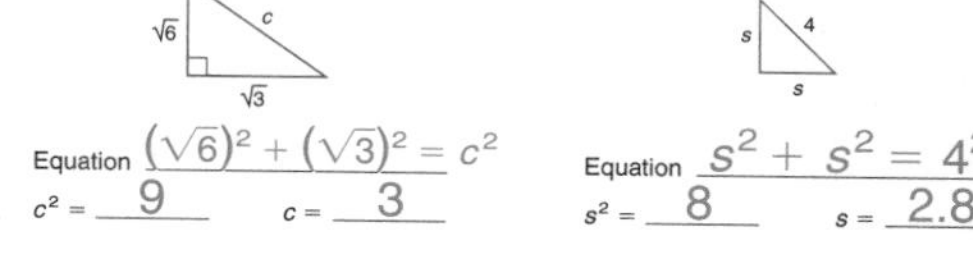

5. Equation $(\sqrt{6})^2 + (\sqrt{3})^2 = c^2$ $c^2 =$ 9 $c =$ 3

6. Equation $s^2 + s^2 = 4^2$ $s^2 =$ 8 $s =$ 2.8

7. Is the triangle shown at the right a right triangle? no

8.5, 3, 8

Explain. Sample answer: $3^2 + 8^2 = 9 + 64 = 73$; but $8.5^2 = 72.25$; so the triangle shown is not quite a right triangle.

STUDENT PAGE

✧ *Math Journal 2,* p. 380

2 Ongoing Learning & Practice

✦ Playing *3-D Shape Sort* (*Student Reference Book,* p. 307; *Math Masters,* pp. 163 and 164)

PARTNER ACTIVITY

Students play this game, introduced in *Fifth Grade Everyday Mathematics,* to practice identifying properties of 3-dimensional shapes.

Math Masters, pages 163 and 164 are shown on page 767.

Games

3-D Shape Sort

Materials □ 1 set of 12 Shape Cards (*Math Masters,* p. 163)
□ 1 set of 16 Property Cards (*Math Masters,* p. 164)

Players 2, or two teams of 2

Object of the game To collect the most Shape Cards.

Directions

1. Spread out the Shape Cards faceup on the playing surface. Shuffle the Property Cards and sort them into VERTEX/EDGE-card and SURFACE-card piles.
2. Players take turns doing the following:
   - Draw the top card from each pile of Property Cards.
   - Take all the Shape Cards that have both of the properties shown on the Property Cards.
   - If there are no Shape Cards with both properties, draw one additional Property Card—either a VERTEX/EDGE Card or a SURFACE Card. Look for Shape Cards that have the new property and one of the properties drawn before. Take those Shape Cards.
   - When all the Property Cards have been drawn, shuffle the deck, and sort them again into two facedown piles. Continue playing.
   - At the end of a turn, if a player has not taken a Shape Card he or she could have taken, the other player may name it.
3. The game ends when there are fewer than three Shape Cards left. The winner is the player with the most Shape Cards.

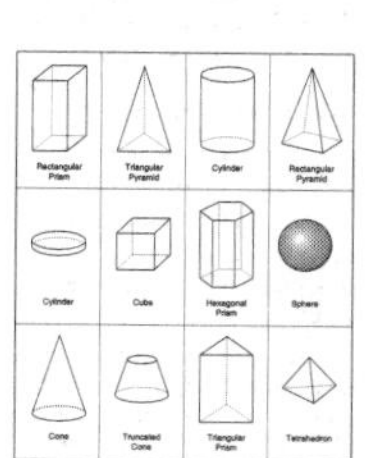

I have an even number of vertices.	I have no vertices.	I have at least 2 edges that are parallel to each other.	I have an odd number of edges.
One of my vertices is formed by an even number of edges.	I have at least one curved edge.	I have fewer than 6 vertices.	I have at least 2 edges that are perpendicular to each other.
All of my surfaces are polygons.	I have at least one face (flat surface).	I have at least one curved surface.	All of my faces are triangles.
All of my faces are regular polygons.	At least one of my faces is a circle.	I have at least one pair of faces that are parallel to each other.	**Wild Card:** Pick your own surface property.

three hundred seven

STUDENT PAGE

✧ *Student Reference Book,* p. 307

STUDENT PAGE

Math Boxes 9.12

1. Draw the line(s) of symmetry for each figure below.

2. Use quick common denominators to decide which fraction is larger. Circle the larger one.
   a. $\frac{2}{15}$ ($\frac{5}{31}$)
   b. $\frac{8}{41}$ ($\frac{5}{22}$)
   c. $\frac{3}{62}$ ($\frac{4}{75}$)
   d. $\frac{12}{39}$ ($\frac{7}{19}$)
   e. ($\frac{3}{16}$) $\frac{1}{6}$

3. Multiply or divide.
   a. $-25 * 8 =$ -200
   b. $-280 / -70 =$ 4
   c. $-40 * -90 =$ $3,600$
   d. $540 \div (-6) =$ -90
   e. $80 * -300 =$ $-24,000$

4. Use the distributive property. Show your work.
   a. $5 * (25 + 40) =$
   $(5 * 25) + (5 * 40) =$
   $125 + 200 = 325$
   b. $11 * (50 - 3) =$
   $(11 * 50) + (11 * 3) =$
   $550 - 33 = 517$

5. Follow the directions for the coordinate grid.
   a. Mark point (−4,3). Label it *M*.
   b. Mark point (5,3). Label it *A*.
   c. Mark point (4,−1). Label it *T*.
   d. Mark point *H* so that the polygon *MATH* is a parallelogram. Draw parallelogram *MATH*.

◆ *Math Journal 2*, p. 381

◆ Math Boxes 9.12 (*Math Journal 2*, p. 381)

INDEPENDENT ACTIVITY 

Mixed Review Math Boxes in this lesson are paired with Math Boxes in Lesson 9.10. The skill in Problem 1 is a prerequisite for Unit 10.

◆ Study Link 9.12 (*Math Masters*, p. 370)

Home Connection Students solve word problems that require applications of the Pythagorean Theorem. One of the problems incorporates simple rate information. These problems are challenging.

STUDY LINK MASTER

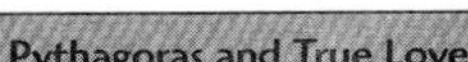

Pythagoras and True Love Study Link 9.12

Pythagoras is a "Mr. Lonelyhearts" columnist for a popular newspaper. He recently received the following letters. How would you solve these lovebirds' problems?

1. Dear Pythagoras: My girlfriend Roma and I want to elope. But we have a problem. She lives in a third-floor apartment. There is a 14-foot-wide moat around the apartment, and Roma's window is 20 feet above the moat. If I throw a rope up to Roma, she could slide down it and escape. How long a rope should I buy?
   Longingly, Jules
   Sample answer: Use the Pythagorean Theorem to calculate the distance: $20^2 + 14^2 = c^2$. The distance is about 24.4 feet. The rope should be at least 29 feet long to allow for rope at each end.

2. Dear Pythagoras: Jack and I have a date. Our meeting spot is 120 miles directly west of Jack's home. Jack will ride his bicycle, and since the trip is all downhill, he should average about 30 miles per hour. I live 160 miles directly south of Jack, and I plan to drive. Suppose that Jack and I both leave home at the same time. What should be my average speed so that we will arrive at the meeting spot at the same time?
   Promptly, Jill
   Sample answer: It will take Jack 4 hours. Jill must travel 200 miles ($120^2 + 160^2 = 200^2$), so she should drive 50 mph to reach the meeting place in 4 hours.

3. Dear Pythagoras: My friend Jules told me that you help out with moat-rescue problems. Well, I've got one. The situation is this: My girlfriend's window is 15 feet above a moat that is 11 feet wide. I have a ladder that is 18 feet long. Can I rescue her, or should I buy a longer ladder?
   Rung out, Igor
   Sample answer: $15^2 + 11^2 = 346$; $18^2 = 324$. Igor should buy a longer ladder. The distance is longer than 18 feet.

◆ *Math Masters*, p. 370

3 Options for Individualizing

◆ ENRICHMENT Investigating the Pythagorean Theorem (*Math Masters*, p. 7)

INDEPENDENT ACTIVITY  **5–15 min**

Students explore a visual model of the Pythagorean Theorem. Each student needs a piece of $\frac{1}{4}$-inch grid paper (*Math Masters*, page 7), scissors, and glue or tape. Have each student cut out a 3-by-3 square, a 4-by-4 square, and a 5-by-5 square. Have them manipulate the three squares so that they form the sides of a triangle. They glue or tape their triangle formation to a separate sheet of paper. *(See the illustration on the next page.)*

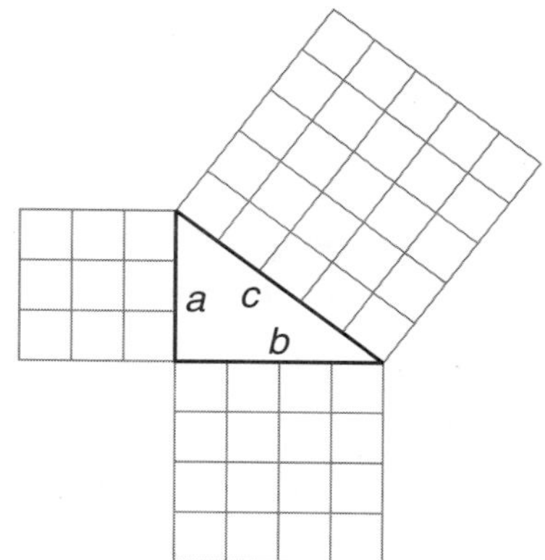

Discuss how this model helps verify the Pythagorean Theorem. One leg of the triangle has a length of 3, the other a length of 4, and the hypotenuse has a length of 5. The square of the lengths of the two legs (9 and 16) add up to the square of the length of the hypotenuse (25).

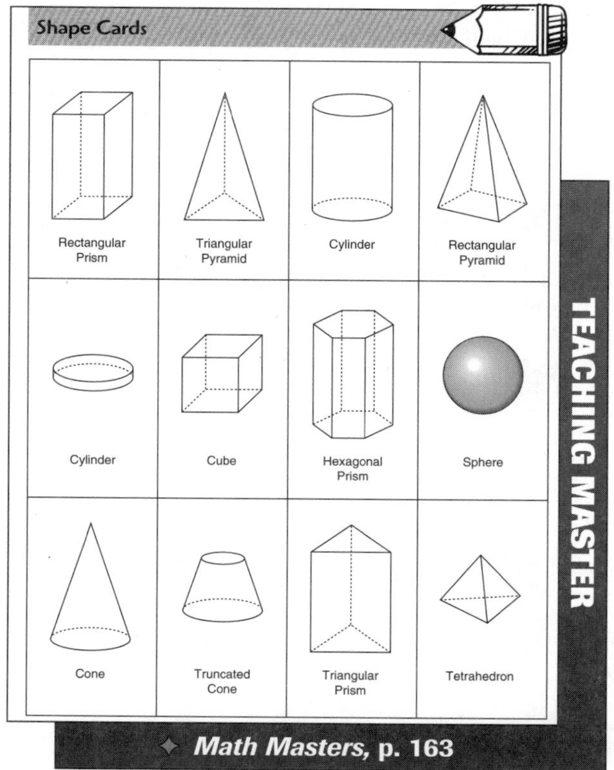

✦ *Math Masters,* p. 163

Property Cards

I have an even number of vertices.	I have no vertices.	I have at least 2 edges that are parallel to each other.	I have an odd number of edges.
One of my vertices is formed by an even number of edges.	I have at least one curved edge.	I have fewer than 6 vertices.	I have at least 2 edges that are perpendicular to each other.
All of my surfaces are polygons.	I have at least one face (flat surface).	I have at least one curved surface.	All of my faces are triangles.
All of my faces are regular polygons.	At least one of my faces is a circle.	I have at least one pair of faces that are parallel to each other.	**Wild Card:** Pick your own surface property.

TEACHING MASTER

✦ *Math Masters,* p. 164

9.13 Indirect Measurement Problems

OBJECTIVE **To find missing lengths in similar figures using a size-change factor.**

summaries	materials
1 Teaching the Lesson	
Students calculate the size-change factor for similar figures and apply this to pairs of corresponding sides to find missing lengths. Students use indirect methods to determine heights and lengths that cannot be measured directly. [Geometry; Measurement and Reference Frames]	☐ *Math Journal 2,* pp. 382 and 383 ☐ *Student Reference Book,* p. 167 ☐ Study Link 9.12 ☐ Assessment Master (*Math Masters,* p. 478; optional) ☐ calculator
2 Ongoing Learning & Practice	
Students practice and maintain skills through Math Boxes and Study Link activities.	☐ *Math Journal 2,* p. 384 ☐ Study Link Master (*Math Masters,* p. 371) ☐ protractor ☐ Geometry Template
3 Options for Individualizing	
Extra Practice Students use sighting measurements and similar triangles to determine the height of a target above the classroom floor. [Geometry; Measurement and Reference Frames]	Per group of 4: ☐ Teaching Masters (*Math Masters,* pp. 165 and 166) ☐ 2 metersticks ☐ 1 tape measure ☐ calculator ***See* Advance Preparation**

Additional Information

Advance Preparation For the optional Extra Practice activity in Part 3, draw a black, circular target, about 1 inch in diameter. Tape the target to a classroom wall, near the ceiling. Measure the height in centimeters of the target above the floor.

Vocabulary • **indirect measurement**

Getting Started

Mental Math and Reflexes

Students show "thumbs up" if a measurement estimate is reasonable and "thumbs down" if it is unreasonable.
Suggestions

- The length of a pencil is about 6 millimeters. down
- The seat of your chair is about 2 meters above the ground. down
- The height of a can of soda is about 6 inches. up
- The area of a regular playing card is about 55 square centimeters. up
- The weight of your journal is about 8 grams. down

Math Message

Read page 167 of the Student Reference Book. *Write one question that can be answered by the information on this page.*

Study Link 9.12 Follow-Up

Students share solution strategies.

1 Teaching the Lesson

Math Message Follow-Up
(*Student Reference Book,* p. 167)

WHOLE-CLASS DISCUSSION

Students share their questions, and the rest of the class answers them. Briefly review the meaning of *similar figures, corresponding sides,* and *size-change factor.* These terms were discussed in Lessons 8.9 and 8.10.

Using a Size-Change Factor to Find Lengths and Volumes in Similar Figures
(*Math Journal 2,* p. 382)

PARTNER ACTIVITY

Assign the problems on journal page 382. Allow about 15 minutes and then gather students to discuss their answers. Include the following points in the discussion:

- ▷ The clamps are similar, because one is an exact enlargement of the other.
- ▷ The size-change factor is 1.5X and may be calculated from the lengths of the tops of the clips (42 / 28 = 1.5). The tops are the only pair of corresponding sides for which lengths are given.
- ▷ The missing lengths a and b may be calculated directly, using the size-change factor. For example, since 18 and a are the lengths for corresponding sections of the clips, $a = 1.5 * 18$. Therefore, $a = 27$ millimeters.
- ▷ The missing lengths x and y are also calculated by applying the size-change factor. However, finding the missing lengths requires solving simple equations. For example, since x and 53 are the lengths for the corresponding openings, $1.5 * x = 53$. To solve the equation, divide both sides by 1.5, getting 35.3 mm.

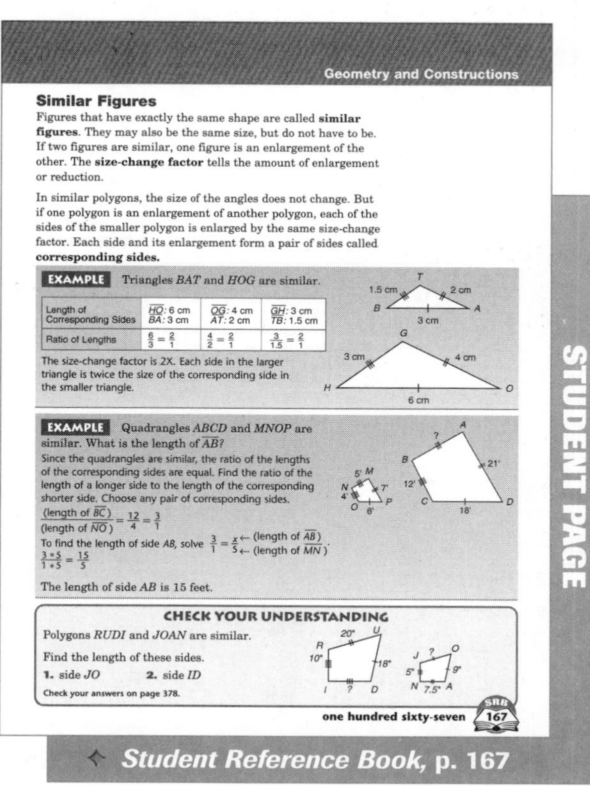

Geometry and Constructions

Similar Figures

Figures that have exactly the same shape are called **similar figures**. They may also be the same size, but do not have to be. If two figures are similar, one figure is an enlargement of the other. The **size-change factor** tells the amount of enlargement or reduction.

In similar polygons, the size of the angles does not change. But if one polygon is an enlargement of another polygon, each of the sides of the smaller polygon is enlarged by the same size-change factor. Each side and its enlargement form a pair of sides called **corresponding sides.**

EXAMPLE Triangles *BAT* and *HOG* are similar.

Length of Corresponding Sides	$\overline{HO}$: 6 cm $\overline{BA}$: 3 cm	$\overline{OG}$: 4 cm $\overline{AT}$: 2 cm	$\overline{GH}$: 3 cm $\overline{TB}$: 1.5 cm
Ratio of Lengths	$\frac{6}{3} = \frac{2}{1}$	$\frac{4}{2} = \frac{2}{1}$	$\frac{3}{1.5} = \frac{2}{1}$

The size-change factor is 2X. Each side in the larger triangle is twice the size of the corresponding side in the smaller triangle.

EXAMPLE Quadrangles *ABCD* and *MNOP* are similar. What is the length of $\overline{AB}$?

Since the quadrangles are similar, the ratio of the lengths of the corresponding sides are equal. Find the ratio of the length of a longer side to the length of the corresponding shorter side. Choose any pair of corresponding sides.

$\frac{(\text{length of } \overline{BC})}{(\text{length of } \overline{NO})} = \frac{12}{4} = \frac{3}{1}$

To find the length of side *AB*, solve $\frac{3}{1} = \frac{x}{5}$ ← (length of $\overline{AB}$) ← (length of $\overline{MN}$).

$\frac{3 * 5}{1 * 5} = \frac{15}{5}$

The length of side *AB* is 15 feet.

CHECK YOUR UNDERSTANDING

Polygons *RUDI* and *JOAN* are similar.

Find the length of these sides.

1. side *JO* 2. side *ID*

Check your answers on page 378.

STUDENT PAGE

Student Reference Book, p. 167

STUDENT PAGE

Similar Figures and the Size-Change Factor

The two butterfly clamps shown below are similar because they each have the same shape. One clamp is an enlargement of the other. The size-change factor tells the amount of enlargement.

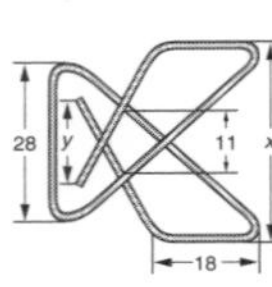

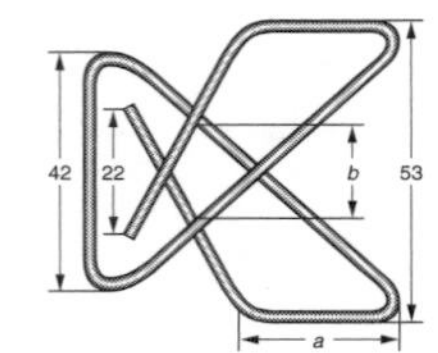

unit: millimeters (mm)

1. The size-change factor for the clamps shown above is 1.5.

In Problems 2–5, use the size-change factor to find the missing lengths.

2. a = 27 mm = 2.7 cm
3. b = 16.5 mm = 1.65 cm
4. x = 35.3 mm = 3.53 cm
5. y = 14.67 mm = 1.467 cm
6. If a butterfly clamp is straightened out, it forms a long, thin cylinder. When the small clamp is straightened out, it is 21 cm long, and the thickness (diameter) of the clamp is 0.15 cm. Its radius is 0.075 cm. Calculate the volume of the small clamp. Use the formula $V = \pi r^2 h$.

   Volume of small clamp = 0.371 cm^3 (to the nearest thousandth cm^3)
7. Find the length, thickness (diameter), and volume of the large clamp.

   Length = 31.5 cm Diameter = 0.225 cm

   Volume of large clamp = 1.252 cm^3 (to the nearest thousandth cm^3)

✧ *Math Journal 2,* p. 382

▹ Most students will have little difficulty applying the formula for the volume of a cylinder to solve Problem 6. (Since the thickness is the diameter of the wire, students need to find the radius before they can substitute in the formula.)

▹ In Problem 7, the large clamp is $1.5 * 21 = 31.5$ cm long, and it has a thickness of $1.5 * 0.15 = 0.225$ cm. The volume is 1.5^3, or 3.375, times the volume of the small clamp.

ONGOING ASSESSMENT

Have students complete an Exit Slip (*Math Masters,* page 478) explaining how they found the length, diameter, and volume of the large butterfly clip in Problem 7. Use their answers to assess students' understanding of size-change factors. Expect that some students may forget that the size-change factor (1.5X) applies to every length—including the thickness and total length of the wire.

STUDENT PAGE

Indirect Measurement Problems

In the problems that follow, you are going to use **indirect methods** to determine the heights and lengths of objects that you cannot measure directly.

1. A tree is too tall to measure, but it casts a shadow that is 18 feet long. Ike is standing near the tree. He is 5 feet tall and casts a shadow that is 6 feet long.

   The light rays, the tree, and its shadow form a triangle that is **similar** to the triangle formed by the light rays, Ike, and his shadow.

   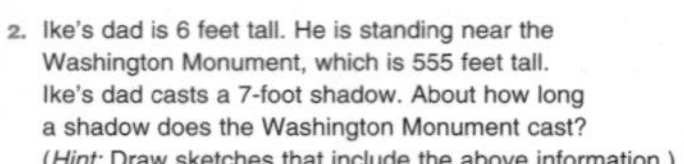

   What is the size-change factor of the triangles? 3

   About how tall is the tree? 15 ft
2. Ike's dad is 6 feet tall. He is standing near the Washington Monument, which is 555 feet tall. Ike's dad casts a 7-foot shadow. About how long a shadow does the Washington Monument cast? (*Hint:* Draw sketches that include the above information.) 647.5 ft

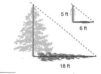

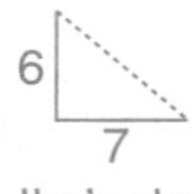

Challenge

3. A surveyor wants to find the distance between points A and B on opposite ends of a lake. He sets a stake at point C so that angle ABC is a right angle. By measuring, he finds that $\overline{AC}$ is 95 meters long and $\overline{BC}$ is 76 meters long.

   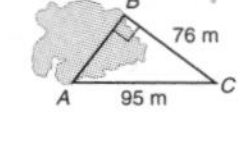

   How far across the lake is it from point A to point B? 57 m

✧ *Math Journal 2,* p. 383

✦ Solving Indirect Measurement Problems

(*Math Journal 2,* p. 383)

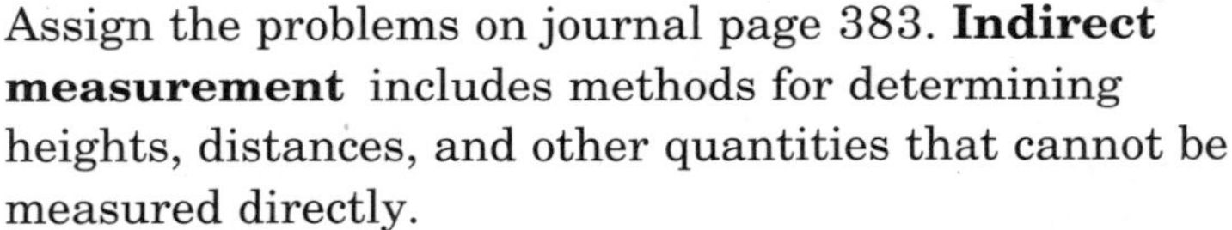

PARTNER ACTIVITY

Assign the problems on journal page 383. **Indirect measurement** includes methods for determining heights, distances, and other quantities that cannot be measured directly.

Problems 1 and 2 make use of similar triangles. In each case, students should calculate the size-change factor and then use the factor to solve the problem. Remind students how they used the size-change factor to find missing lengths for the butterfly clamps.

Note that for Problem 2, students will not be able to draw sketches to scale. Circulate and assist.

Adjusting the Activity If students struggle with Problem 3, you may want to have a volunteer explain how the Pythagorean Theorem can be applied to this problem.

NOTE: Consider rotating the indirect measurement activity in Part 3 among small groups. Assign half of the groups to journal page 383 and the other half to the optional activity in Part 3, *Math Masters,* pages 165 and 166. Then alternate the assignments.

2 Ongoing Learning & Practice

✦ Math Boxes 9.13 (*Math Journal 2,* p. 384)

INDEPENDENT ACTIVITY 

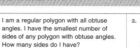

Mixed Review Math Boxes in this lesson are paired with Math Boxes in Lesson 9.11. The skill in Problem 1 is a prerequisite for Unit 10.

✦ Study Link 9.13 (*Math Masters,* p. 371)

Home Connection The Study Link reviews important concepts in Unit 9.

3 Options for Individualizing

✦ EXTRA PRACTICE Solving an Indirect Measurement Problem (*Math Masters,* pp. 165 and 166)

SMALL-GROUP ACTIVITY  **15–30 min** 

Have students work in groups of four. Pass out one copy of *Math Masters,* pages 165 and 166 to each group.

It is recommended that you demonstrate the measurement procedure described and illustrated on *Math Masters,* page 165 before students start work. *(See page 772.)*

STUDENT PAGE

Math Boxes 9.13

1. I am a regular polygon with all obtuse angles. I have the smallest number of sides of any polygon with obtuse angles. How many sides do I have? 5 sides

   Use your Geometry Template to draw me below.

   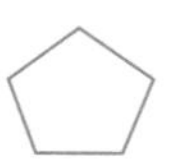

2. Solve.

	Solution
a. $w * 10^{-2} = 28.2$	$w = 2{,}820$
b. $420 * k = 140$	$k = \frac{1}{3}$
c. $\frac{5}{2} - p = \frac{7}{4}$	$p = \frac{3}{4}$
d. $18 / a = -6$	$a = -3$
e. $2^d = 64$	$d = 6$

3. The high temperature in Chicago on January 3 was 38°F, and the low temperature was 24°F. Then a cold front moved in. The low temperature on January 4 was −5°F.

   By how many degrees did the temperature drop from the high on January 3 to the low on January 4? 43°F

   Write a number model to show how you found your answer. $38 + 5 = 43$, or $38 - (-5) = 43$

4. The table shows the results of a survey that asked Internet surfers how they most often find sites to visit. Fill in the missing information in the table. Use a protractor to make a circle graph of the results. Do not use the Percent Circle.

   How People Find Web Sites (title)

   Word-of-mouth; Other; Links; Printed material; Browsing

Method	Number of People	Percent of Total
Word-of-mouth	43	43%
Printed material	26	26%
Browsing	14	14%
Links	9	9%
Other	8	8%
Total	100	100%

✦ *Math Journal 2,* p. 384

STUDY LINK MASTER

Unit 9 Review

Study Link 9.13

1. Simplify the following expressions by combining like terms.
   a. $4x + 3x =$ $7x$
   b. $3x + 7 + x =$ $4x + 7$
   c. $4 * (x + 2) + 2x - 6 =$ $6x + 2$
   d. $(x + 3) * 2 - 2x =$ 6

2. Cindy simplified the expression $8(x + 10)$ as $(8 * x) + 10$. What did she do wrong? Explain her mistake and show how she should have solved the problem.

   Sample answer: Cindy did not multiply 10 by 8. The simplified expression should be $(8 * x) + (8 * 10)$, or $8x + 80$.

3. Solve each equation.
   a. $3x - 4 = 4x + 6$ $x = -10$
   b. $5 * (2 - 6) = 4g$ $g = -5$
   c. $3(2y - 3) = 15$ $y = 4$
   d. $\frac{(2x - 1)}{3} = 9$ $x = 14$

4. The perimeter of Triangle *ABC* is 18 inches. What is the length of each of its sides?

   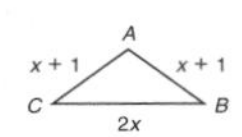

   Length of $\overline{AB}$ 5 in. Length of $\overline{BC}$ 8 in. Length of $\overline{AC}$ 5 in.

5. The perimeter of Right Triangle *GLD* is 12 centimeters.

   What is the area of the triangle? 6 cm^2

   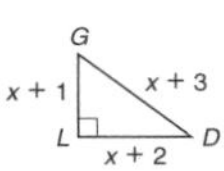

6. Jim often walks to school along Main Street and Elm Street. If he were to take Pythagoras Avenue instead, how many fewer blocks would he walk? 4 blocks

   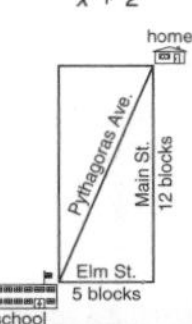

✦ *Math Masters,* p. 371

Problems 1–4 on *Math Masters,* page 166 all make use of similar triangles. In each case, students should calculate the size-change factor and then use the factor to solve the problem. Remind students how they used the size-change factor to find missing lengths for the butterfly clamps.

In Problem 4, you may need to remind students that the length of leg DE in Triangle ADE is not the height of the target above the floor. The target height is the length of $\overline{DE}$ plus the distance from the observer's eye to the floor.

Circulate and assist. Monitor the small-group measurement activity to ensure that students are following the directions and making the correct measurements.

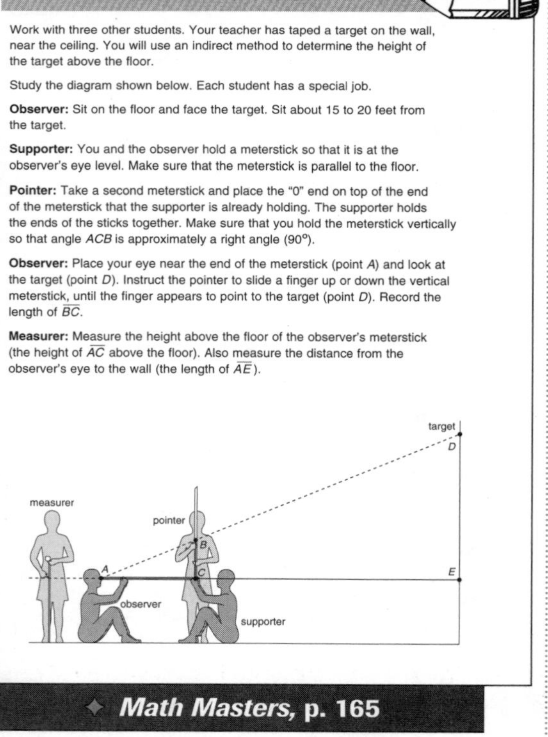

TEACHING MASTER

An Indirect Measurement Problem

Work with three other students. Your teacher has taped a target on the wall, near the ceiling. You will use an indirect method to determine the height of the target above the floor.

Study the diagram shown below. Each student has a special job.

Observer: Sit on the floor and face the target. Sit about 15 to 20 feet from the target.

Supporter: You and the observer hold a meterstick so that it is at the observer's eye level. Make sure that the meterstick is parallel to the floor.

Pointer: Take a second meterstick and place the "0" end on top of the end of the meterstick that the supporter is already holding. The supporter holds the ends of the sticks together. Make sure that you hold the meterstick vertically so that angle ACB is approximately a right angle (90°).

Observer: Place your eye near the end of the meterstick (point A) and look at the target (point D). Instruct the pointer to slide a finger up or down the vertical meterstick, until the finger appears to point to the target (point D). Record the length of $\overline{BC}$.

Measurer: Measure the height above the floor of the observer's meterstick (the height of $\overline{AC}$ above the floor). Also measure the distance from the observer's eye to the wall (the length of $\overline{AE}$).

✦ *Math Masters,* p. 165

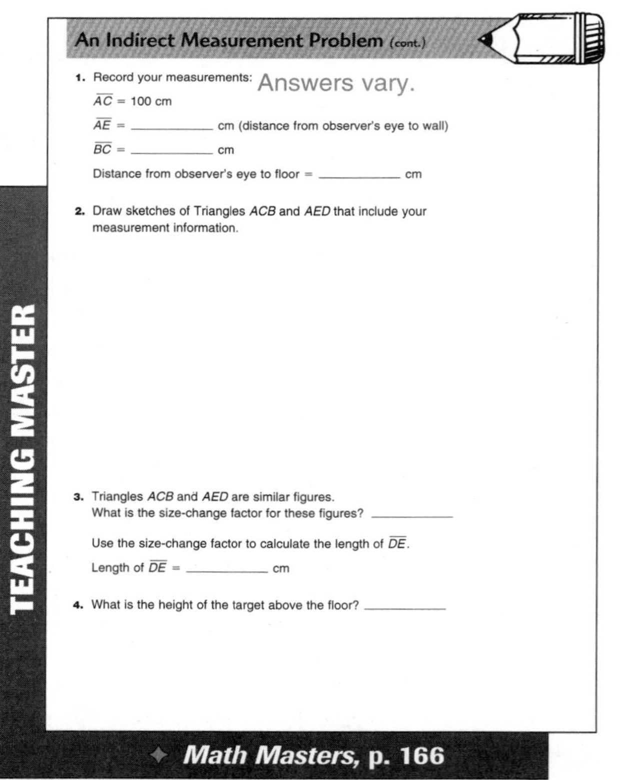

TEACHING MASTER

An Indirect Measurement Problem (cont.)

1. Record your measurements: Answers vary.

   $\overline{AC}$ = 100 cm

   $\overline{AE}$ = ____________ cm (distance from observer's eye to wall)

   $\overline{BC}$ = ____________ cm

   Distance from observer's eye to floor = ____________ cm

2. Draw sketches of Triangles ACB and AED that include your measurement information.

3. Triangles ACB and AED are similar figures. What is the size-change factor for these figures? ____________

   Use the size-change factor to calculate the length of $\overline{DE}$.

   Length of $\overline{DE}$ = ____________ cm

4. What is the height of the target above the floor? ____________

✦ *Math Masters,* p. 166

9.14 Unit 9 Review and Assessment

OBJECTIVE **To review and assess students' progress on the material covered in Unit 9.**

1 Assess Progress

learning goals	activities
9a **Developing Goal** Simplify expressions and equations with parentheses. **(Lessons 9.4 and 9.5)**	❑ Written Assessment, Problems 8, 9, 11, and 12
9b **Developing/Secure Goal** Apply the distributive property. **(Lessons 9.1, 9.2, 9.4, and 9.5)**	❑ Slate Assessment, Problem 4 ❑ Written Assessment, Problems 1, 2, 8, 9, 11, and 12
9c **Developing/Secure Goal** Combine like terms to simplify expressions and equations. **(Lessons 9.3–9.5)**	❑ Slate Assessment, Problem 4 ❑ Written Assessment, Problems 2, 5–10, and 13
9d **Developing/Secure Goal** Solve equations. **(Lessons 9.5, 9.6, and 9.10)**	❑ Written Assessment, Problems 10–13, and 28
9e **Developing/Secure Goal** Write and identify equivalent expressions and equivalent equations. **(Lessons 9.3–9.5)**	❑ Slate Assessment, Problem 4 ❑ Written Assessment, Problems 5–13, and 16
9f **Developing/Secure Goal** Write and solve equations that represent problem situations. **(Lessons 9.1, 9.5, 9.6, and 9.11)**	❑ Written Assessment, Problems 2 and 23–27
9g **Developing/Secure Goal** Use formulas to solve problems. **(Lessons 9.8, 9.9, and 9.11)**	❑ Written Assessment, Problems 2–4, 14, 15, and 17–27
9h **Secure Goal** Evaluate expressions and formulas. **(Lessons 9.3, 9.4, 9.8, 9.9, 9.11, and 9.12)**	❑ Slate Assessment, Problem 2 ❑ Written Assessment, Problems 3, 4, 14, 15, and 17–27

materials

- ☐ *Math Journal 2,* pp. 343 and 385
- ☐ Study Link 9.13
- ☐ Assessment Masters (*Math Masters,* pp. 414–417)
- ☐ Teaching Masters (*Math Masters,* pp. 148 and 156–158)
- ☐ slate

2 Build Background for Unit 10

summaries	materials
Students practice and maintain skills through Math Boxes and Study Link activities.	☐ *Math Journal 2,* p. 386 ☐ Study Link Masters (*Math Masters,* pp. 372–375) ☐ Geometry Template

Each **learning goal** listed above indicates a level of performance that might be expected at this point in the *Everyday Mathematics* K–6 curriculum. For a variety of reasons, the levels indicated may not accurately portray your class's performance.

Additional Information

Advance Preparation For additional information on assessment for Unit 9, see the *Assessment Handbook,* pages 64–67. For assessment checklists, see *Math Masters,* pages 450, 451, and 468–470.

Getting Started

Math Message

Complete the Time to Reflect *questions on journal page 385.*

Study Link 9.13 Follow-Up

Review answers.

1 Assess Progress

✦ Math Message Follow-Up
(*Math Journal 2,* p. 385)

WHOLE-CLASS DISCUSSION

Students share their answers to the first question. Have volunteers share the formulas they wrote for the second question.

NOTE: Some of these assessment suggestions relate to learning goals that have been addressed in previous units. Now is a good time to evaluate students' progress toward those goals.

STUDENT PAGE

Time to Reflect

The following is an excerpt from the beginning of the poem "Mathematics" by Theoni Pappas. It is taken from *Math Talk: Mathematical Ideas in Poems for Two Voices.* This poem is meant to be read by two people. Each person reads one column, speakers alternating between the two columns.

Mathematics	
	the word has been known
to conjure up	
love	**hate**
delight	**despair**
recreation	**anxiety**
joy	**fear**

Answers vary.

1. Which words would you use to describe the mathematics in Unit 9? (Think of the poem as a starting point.)

2. Formulas are used in math to solve problems that always require the same information and steps. Think of something you do often that has several steps. Write a formula and explain what it means.

Example $S + W + B + R = T$

S is the time it takes to squeeze out the toothpaste and put it on the brush.

W is the time it takes to run the water to get the right temperature.

B is the time it takes to brush.

R is the length of time for rinsing my mouth.

T is the total time needed to brush my teeth.

✦ *Math Journal 2,* **p. 385**

✦ Oral and Slate Assessments

WHOLE-CLASS ACTIVITY

If the list of suggested problems below is not appropriate for your class's level of performance, adjust the numbers or the problems themselves to better assess your student's abilities.

Oral Assessment Suggestions

1. Show "thumbs up" if the sum or difference is greater than 1, and "thumbs down" if it is less than 1. Share strategies.
   - $\frac{3}{4} + \frac{5}{8}$ up
   - $\frac{1}{3} + \frac{5}{7}$ up
   - $1\frac{8}{12} - \frac{3}{4}$ down
   - $1\frac{7}{8} - \frac{5}{9}$ up
   - $\frac{13}{16} + \frac{1}{8}$ down
2. Use your arms to model these types of angles: acute, obtuse, right, reflex, straight, adjacent, complementary, supplementary, vertical.

3. Show "thumbs up" if the fraction and mixed number are equivalent, and "thumbs down" if they are not equivalent.

- $\frac{15}{4}$ and $3\frac{1}{4}$ down
- $\frac{20}{3}$ and $5\frac{5}{3}$ up
- $4\frac{4}{5}$ and $\frac{20}{5}$ down
- $\frac{15}{2}$ and $7\frac{1}{2}$ up
- $\frac{33}{8}$ and $5\frac{3}{8}$ down

Slate Assessment Suggestions

1. Find the reciprocal of each number. (Remind students to think, "What times the number equals 1?")

- $\frac{1}{7}$ 7
- 5 $\frac{1}{5}$
- $-\frac{3}{4}$ $-\frac{4}{3}$
- $1\frac{4}{7}$ $\frac{7}{11}$
- $\frac{7}{10}$ $\frac{10}{7}$
- 0.9 $\frac{10}{9}$, or 1.111...
- 0.15 $\frac{100}{15}$, or 6.666...

2. Evaluate each expression for $x = 7$. **Goal 9h**

- $8 + x$ 15
- $5(30 + x)$ 185
- $2x + 4x$ 42
- $\frac{4}{7} * x + 20$ 24
- $2(2x + 6)$ 40

3. Find the whole, given a fraction of the set.

- If $\frac{3}{8}$ of a bag of marbles is 12 marbles, the whole bag is _____ marbles. 32
- If $\frac{4}{5}$ of a bag of marbles is 20 marbles, the whole bag is _____ marbles. 25
- If $\frac{5}{7}$ is 35, the whole is _____. 49
- If $\frac{2}{3}$ is 24, the whole is _____. 36
- If $\frac{7}{10}$ is 56, the whole is _____. 80

4. Find equivalent expressions by combining like terms. **Goals 9b, 9c, and 9e**

- $3y + 5 + 7y$ $10y + 5$
- $4b - 6 - 5b + 8$ $-b + 2$
- $18 - 2m + 9 - 4m$ $27 - 6m$
- $11 + 3(5 + n) + n$ $26 + 4n$
- $7(z + 3) + 8z$ $15z + 21$

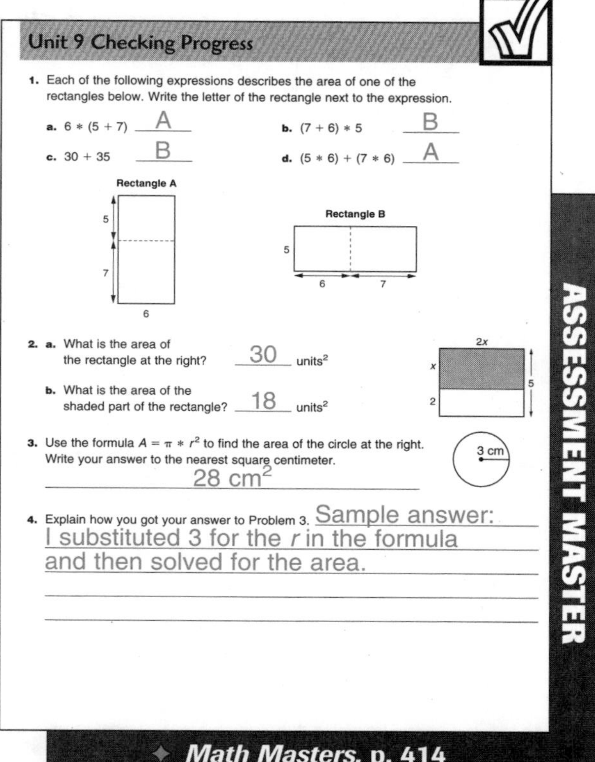

Unit 9 Checking Progress

1. Each of the following expressions describes the area of one of the rectangles below. Write the letter of the rectangle next to the expression.

a. $6 * (5 + 7)$ A b. $(7 + 6) * 5$ B

c. $30 + 35$ B d. $(5 * 6) + (7 * 6)$ A

2. a. What is the area of the rectangle at the right? 30 units²

b. What is the area of the shaded part of the rectangle? 18 units²

3. Use the formula $A = \pi * r^2$ to find the area of the circle at the right. Write your answer to the nearest square centimeter. 28 cm²

4. Explain how you got your answer to Problem 3. Sample answer: I substituted 3 for the *r* in the formula and then solved for the area.

ASSESSMENT MASTER

Math Masters, p. 414

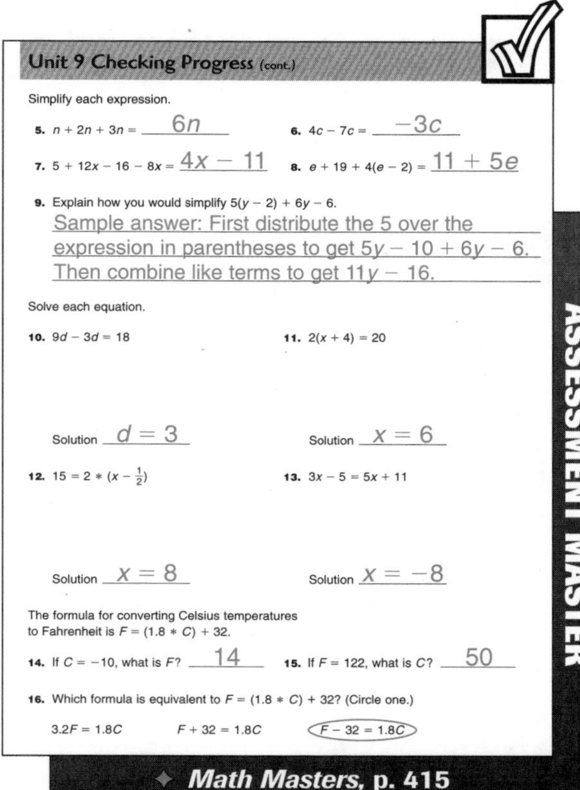

Unit 9 Checking Progress (cont.)

Simplify each expression.

5. $n + 2n + 3n =$ $6n$ 6. $4c - 7c =$ $-3c$

7. $5 + 12x - 16 - 8x =$ $4x - 11$ 8. $e + 19 + 4(e - 2) =$ $11 + 5e$

9. Explain how you would simplify $5(y - 2) + 6y - 6$. Sample answer: First distribute the 5 over the expression in parentheses to get $5y - 10 + 6y - 6$. Then combine like terms to get $11y - 16$.

Solve each equation.

10. $9d - 3d = 18$ Solution $d = 3$

11. $2(x + 4) = 20$ Solution $x = 6$

12. $15 = 2 * (x - \frac{1}{2})$ Solution $x = 8$

13. $3x - 5 = 5x + 11$ Solution $x = -8$

The formula for converting Celsius temperatures to Fahrenheit is $F = (1.8 * C) + 32$.

14. If $C = -10$, what is F? 14 15. If $F = 122$, what is C? 50

16. Which formula is equivalent to $F = (1.8 * C) + 32$? (Circle one.)

$3.2F = 1.8C$ $F + 32 = 1.8C$ ($F - 32 = 1.8C$ circled)

ASSESSMENT MASTER

Math Masters, p. 415

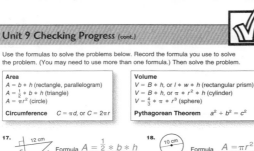

Unit 9 Checking Progress (cont.)

Use the formulas to solve the problems below. Record the formula you use to solve the problem. (You may need to use more than one formula.) Then solve the problem.

Area
$A = b * h$ (rectangle, parallelogram)
$A = \frac{1}{2} * b * h$ (triangle)
$A = \pi r^2$ (circle)

Circumference $C = \pi d$, or $C = 2\pi r$

Volume
$V = B * h$, or $l * w * h$ (rectangular prism)
$V = B * h$, or $\pi * r^2 * h$ (cylinder)
$V = \frac{4}{3} * \pi * r^3$ (sphere)

Pythagorean Theorem $a^2 + b^2 = c^2$

17. (12 cm, 9 cm, 15 cm)
Formula $A = \frac{1}{2} * b * h$
Area 54 cm^2

18.
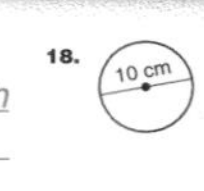

Formula $A = \pi r^2$
Area 78.5 cm^2

19.
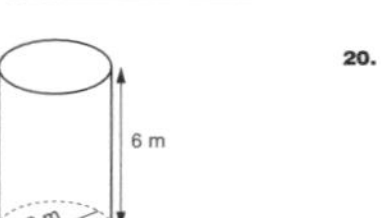

Formula $V = B * h$, or $\pi * r^2 * h$
Volume 381.5 cm^3

20. (9", 4", 5")
Formula $V = B * h$, or $l * w$
Volume 180 $in.^3$

21. (9 in., 7 in., 8 in.)
Formula $A = b * h$
Area 63 $in.^2$

22. (c, 8 ft, 6 ft)
Formula $a^2 + b^2 = c^2$
c = 10 ft

23. The perimeter of Triangle *CRY* is 20 meters. Find the length of each side of the triangle. (R, C, Y; $6x - 4$, $x + 6$, $2x$)
Length of $\overline{CR}$ 8 m   Length of $\overline{RY}$ 8 m
Length of $\overline{CY}$ 4 m

ASSESSMENT MASTER

◆ *Math Masters,* **p. 416**

◆ Written Assessment
(*Math Masters,* pp. 414–417)

INDEPENDENT ACTIVITY 

You may want to go over the questions with students before they complete the pages independently. You may want to work several examples as well.

Depending on the needs of students, you may want to work through an example together, reading a problem aloud, discussing it, and providing additional examples as necessary before students work the problem independently.

Each of the problems is listed below and paired with one or more of this unit's learning goals.

- Use the distributive property. (Problems 1, 2, 8, 9, 11, and 12) **Goals 9a, 9b, 9d, 9e**
- Combine like terms to simplify expressions and equations. (Problems 2, 5–10, and 13) **Goal 9c**
- Solve equations. (Problems 10–13 and 28) **Goal 9d**
- Use formulas to solve for an unknown. (Problems 2–4, 14, 15, and 17–27) **Goals 9g and 9h**
- Identify and write equivalent equations. (Problems 5–13 and 16) **Goal 9e**
- Write equations to solve problems. (Problems 2 and 23–27) **Goal 9f**

Unit 9 Checking Progress (cont.)

Mr. Merlin is a home repairman. He charges $25 per hour and rounds his time to the nearest quarter of an hour. Below is a spreadsheet that shows a record of his last 3 jobs.

	A	B	C	D
1	Customer	Job	Hours	Charge (at $25 per hour)
2	Mrs. Martinez	Window repairs	3.5	87.50
3	Mr. O'Hara	Repair kitchen ceiling	6.25	156.25
4	Ms. Liu	Install ceiling fan	5.5	137.50

24. Circle the formula stored in Cell D2.
C2 + C3   C2 * C3    C2 * 25   D4 * 25

25. Write the formula that belongs in Cell D4. D1 * C4

26. Calculate the amount that should appear in D4 and write it in the cell.

The mobile shown is in balance.

Reminder: $(W * D) = (w * d)$

27. The fulcrum of the mobile at the right is the center point of the rod.
What is the weight of the object to the right of the fulcrum? 6 units

28. Find an approximate solution to the equation $x^2 + 4 = 94$. Use trial and error. Record your results in the table. A first guess is shown. Stop when you get within 1 of 94.
Sample answers:

x	x^2	$x^2 + 4$	Compare $x^2 + 4$ to 94
9	81	85	85 < 94
8	64	68	$x = 8$ is too small.
5	25	29	$x = 5$ is too small.
9.5	90.25	94.25	$x = 9.5$ is slightly too large.

ASSESSMENT MASTER

◆ *Math Masters,* **p. 417**

◆ ALTERNATIVE ASSESSMENT OPTION
Write Number Stories Involving the Distributive Property (*Math Journal 2,* p. 343)

INDEPENDENT ACTIVITY 

Use this activity from Part 3 of Lesson 9.2 to assess students' understanding of the distributive property. Students choose expressions on journal page 343 and make up number stories to fit the expressions. You may want to use the rubric for number stories on page 65 of the *Assessment Handbook.*

Portfolio Ideas

◆ ALTERNATIVE ASSESSMENT OPTION
Interpret an Algebra Cartoon
(*Math Masters,* p. 148)

INDEPENDENT ACTIVITY 

Use this activity from Part 3 of Lesson 9.3 to assess students' understanding of algebra, variables, and solving equations. Students explain the humor in the cartoon. Ask them to address how the cartoon relates to algebra. Algebra uses variables, often letters, to represent unknowns.

Have students explain the humor behind the changing variable. Look for students who understand that a variable may have a single correct value. In the cartoon, the value of x for which the equation is true is 3. The correct value will change, depending on the equation. Sometimes there is not one correct value for the variable. For example, $x > 10$ has many solutions.

✦ ALTERNATIVE ASSESSMENT OPTION

Explore the Area of Parallelograms and Triangles (*Math Masters,* pp. 156–158)

INDEPENDENT ACTIVITY 

Use these masters from Part 3 of Lesson 9.8 to assess students' understanding of the area formulas for rectangles, parallelograms, and triangles. After students have completed the masters, have them explain on the back of the masters why the area formulas for parallelograms $l * w$ and triangles $\frac{1}{2}(b * h)$ work.

Portfolio Ideas

2 Build Background for Unit 10

✦ Math Boxes 9.14 (*Math Journal 2,* p. 386)

INDEPENDENT ACTIVITY 

Mixed Review The skills in Problems 1–5 are prerequisites for Unit 10.

✦ Study Link 9.14: Unit 10 Family Letter (*Math Masters,* pp. 372–375)

Home Connection This Study Link is a four-page newsletter that introduces parents and guardians to Unit 10's topics and terms. The letter also offers ideas for home-based mathematics activities that support classroom work.

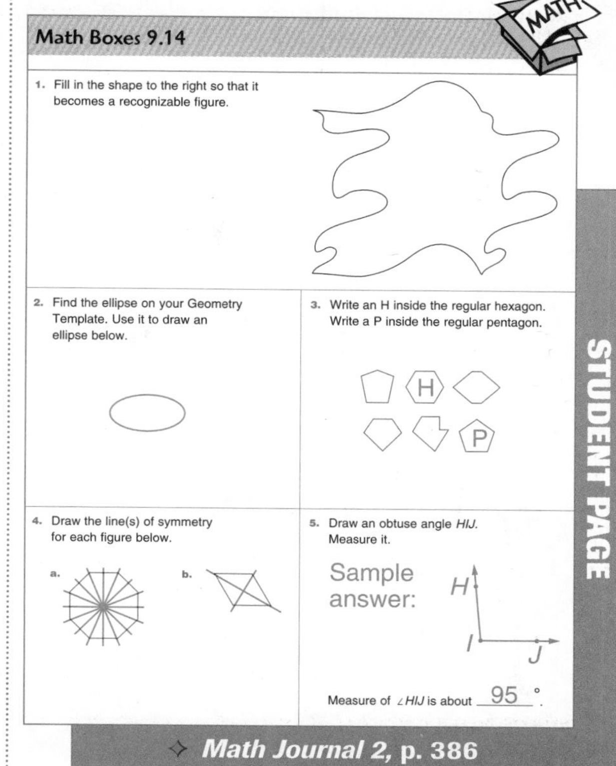

Math Boxes 9.14

1. Fill in the shape to the right so that it becomes a recognizable figure.

2. Find the ellipse on your Geometry Template. Use it to draw an ellipse below.

3. Write an H inside the regular hexagon. Write a P inside the regular pentagon.

4. Draw the line(s) of symmetry for each figure below.

a. b.

5. Draw an obtuse angle *HIJ*. Measure it.

Sample answer:

Measure of ∠*HIJ* is about 95 °.

✦ *Math Journal 2,* p. 386

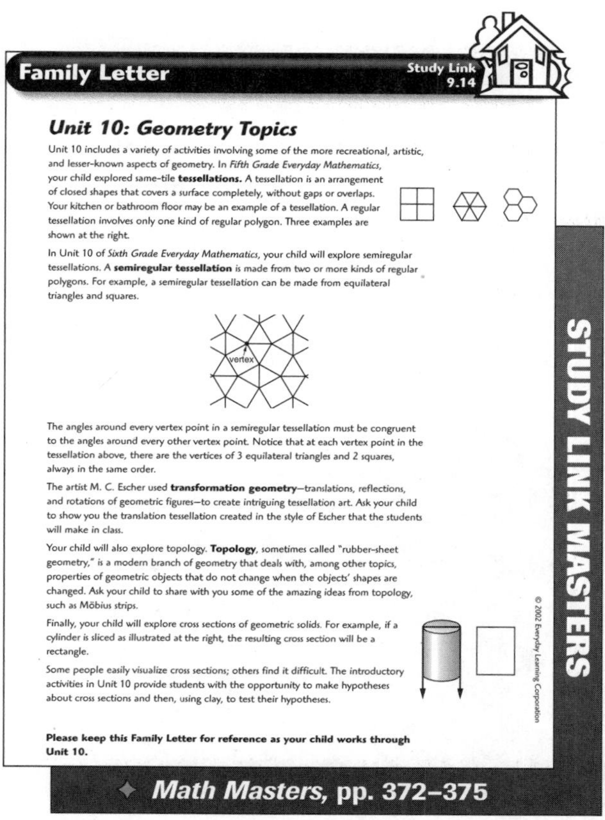

Family Letter Study Link 9.14

Unit 10: Geometry Topics

Unit 10 includes a variety of activities involving some of the more recreational, artistic, and lesser-known aspects of geometry. In *Fifth Grade Everyday Mathematics,* your child explored same-tile **tessellations.** A tessellation is an arrangement of closed shapes that covers a surface completely, without gaps or overlaps. Your kitchen or bathroom floor may be an example of a tessellation. A regular tessellation involves only one kind of regular polygon. Three examples are shown at the right.

In Unit 10 of *Sixth Grade Everyday Mathematics,* your child will explore semiregular tessellations. A **semiregular tessellation** is made from two or more kinds of regular polygons. For example, a semiregular tessellation can be made from equilateral triangles and squares.

The angles around every vertex point in a semiregular tessellation must be congruent to the angles around every other vertex point. Notice that at each vertex point in the tessellation above, there are the vertices of 3 equilateral triangles and 2 squares, always in the same order.

The artist M. C. Escher used **transformation geometry**—translations, reflections, and rotations of geometric figures—to create intriguing tessellation art. Ask your child to show you the translation tessellation created in the style of Escher that the students will make in class.

Your child will also explore topology. **Topology**, sometimes called "rubber-sheet geometry," is a modern branch of geometry that deals with, among other topics, properties of geometric objects that do not change when the objects' shapes are changed. Ask your child to share with you some of the amazing ideas from topology, such as Möbius strips.

Finally, your child will explore cross sections of geometric solids. For example, if a cylinder is sliced as illustrated at the right, the resulting cross section will be a rectangle.

Some people easily visualize cross sections; others find it difficult. The introductory activities in Unit 10 provide students with the opportunity to make hypotheses about cross sections and then, using clay, to test their hypotheses.

Please keep this Family Letter for reference as your child works through Unit 10.

✦ *Math Masters,* pp. 372–375

Unit 10 Geometry Topics

overview

Unit 10 deals with geometric transformations, cross sections of 3-dimensional shapes, and ideas from topology, mainly through projects that encourage individual creativity and a sense of fun. Doing all or part of Unit 10, perhaps along with other projects of interest to you or to students, serves as a relaxed way to end the year.

There are a number of optional projects in the *Student Reference Book,* which interested students may wish to undertake.

contents

Lesson	Objective	Page
10.1	**Semiregular Tessellations** *To review regular tessellations; to introduce semiregular tessellations; to introduce notation for both; and to find the eight semiregular tessellations.*	788
10.2	**Escher-Type Translation Tessellations** *To create nonpolygonal, Escher-type, translation tessellations.*	795
10.3	**Rotation Symmetry** *To explore rotation symmetry and point symmetry.*	800
10.4	**Cross Sections of Clay Solids** *To construct geometric solids out of clay; to visualize what happens when a solid is sliced by a plane; and to describe the shapes of cross sections.*	806
10.5	**Introduction to Topology** *To introduce topology; and to perform topological transformations.*	812
10.6	**Möbius Strips** *To experiment with Möbius strips.*	818
10.7	**Unit 10 Review and Assessment** *To review and assess students' progress on the material covered in Unit 10.*	823

learning goals in perspective

The final unit of Grade 6 "serves as a relaxed way to end the year." No Goals are listed. Following are the lesson titles. The grid shows links for lesson objectives.

Lesson 10.1 Semiregular Tessellations

Lesson 10.2 Escher-Type Translation Tessellations

Lesson 10.3 Rotation Symmetry

Lesson 10.4 Cross Sections of Clay Solids

Lesson 10.5 Introduction to Topology

Lesson 10.6 Möbius Strips

	lesson objectives	links to the past	links to the future
10.1	To review regular tessellations; to introduce semiregular tessellations; to introduce notation for regular and semiregular tessellations; and to find the eight semiregular tessellations.	Grades 1-4: Solve spatial puzzles; create and complete patterns using dot paper, pattern blocks, and a ruler and pattern-block template; tessellate pattern blocks to make large polygons. Grade 5: Define and create tessellations.	After Grade 6: Tessellations are a fascinating topic in geometry and art.
10.2	To create nonpolygonal, Escher-type, translation tessellations.		
10.3	To explore rotation symmetry and point symmetry.	Grades 1-3: Define and demonstrate angles, including right angles; use straws to explore rotations and angles. Grade 3: Explore symmetry with geoboards and pattern blocks; complete symmetric figures; identify symmetric shapes and draw lines of symmetry. Grade 4: Identify lines of symmetry, lines of reflection, reflected figures, and figures with line symmetry.	After Grade 6: Symmetry is an important concept in geometry, art, design, and architecture.
10.4	To construct geometric solids out of clay; to visualize what happens when a solid is sliced by a plane; and to describe the shapes of cross sections of clay solids.	Grade 2: Review names and parts of 3-dimensional objects. Grade 3: Identify five basic 3-dimensional shapes (pyramid, prism, cone, cylinder, and sphere). Construct models of a cube, pyramid, and prism. Grade 4: Describe properties of geometric solids. Solve cube-stacking problems. Grade 5: Know the properties of geometric solids.	After Grade 6: The ability to visualize cross sections of 3-dimensional objects is a useful skill in geometry, biology, industrial design, medicine, and daily life.
10.5	To introduce topology; and to introduce and perform topological transformations.	Grade 5: Explore transformations of polygons using a coordinate grid.	After Grade 6: Transformations are important in geometry and other areas of mathematics. Topology is a major branch of advanced mathematics. Topology as "rubber-sheet geometry" is an intriguing topic in recreational mathematics.
10.6	To experiment with Möbius strips.		

assessment

ongoing • product • periodic

Informal Assessment

Math Boxes These *Math Journal* pages provide opportunities for cumulative review or assessment of concepts and skills.

Ongoing Assessment: Kid Watching Use the Ongoing Assessment suggestions in the following lessons to make quick, on-the-spot observations about students' understanding of:

- Geometry **(Lesson 10.1, Part 1; Lesson 10.3, Part 1; Lesson 10.5, Part 1)**

Portfolio Ideas Samples of students' work may be obtained from the following assignments:

- Exploring Regular Tessellations **(Lesson 10.1)**
- Drawing Shapes with Rotation Symmetry of a Given Order **(Lesson 10.3)**

Unit 10 Review and Assessment

Math Message Use Time to Reflect Problem 3 in Lesson 10.7 to assess students' progress toward the following learning goal: **Goal 10d**

Oral and Slate Assessments Use oral or slate assessments during Lesson 10.7 to assess students' progress toward the following learning goal: **Goal 10e**

Written Assessment Use a written review during Lesson 10.7 to assess students' progress toward the following learning goals: **Goals 10a–10f**

Alternative Assessment Options Use independent alternative assessments in Lesson 10.7 to assess students' progress toward the following learning goals: **Goals 10b and 10c**

assessmenthandbook

For more information on how to use different types of assessment in Unit 10.7, see the Assessment Overview on pages 68–70 in the *Assessment Handbook*. The following Assessment Masters can be found in the *Math Masters* book:

- Unit 10 Checking Progress, pp. 418 and 419
- Unit 10 Individual Profile of Progress, p. 453
- Unit 10 Class Checklist, p. 452
- Class Progress Indicator, p. 470
- Math Logs, pp. 473 and 474
- Self-Assessment Forms, pp. 476 and 477
- Interest Inventories, pp. 471 and 472

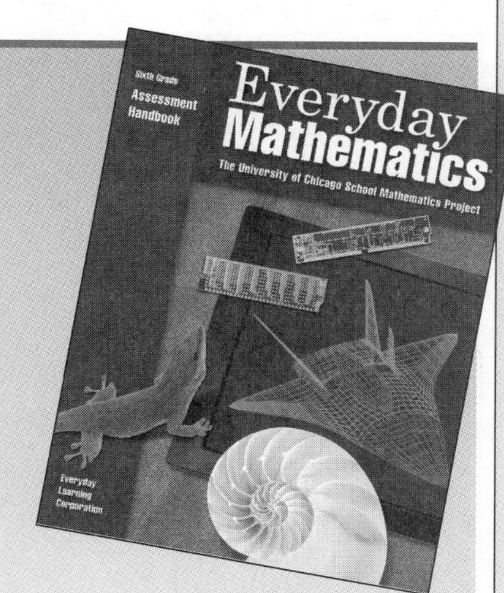

problem solving

A process of modeling everyday situations using tools from mathematics

Encourage students to use a variety of strategies when attacking a given problem—and to explain those strategies. *Strategies students might use in this unit:*

- Draw a picture
- Use a pattern
- Use computation
- Act out the problem
- Use physical models

Four Problem-Solving REPRESENTATIONS

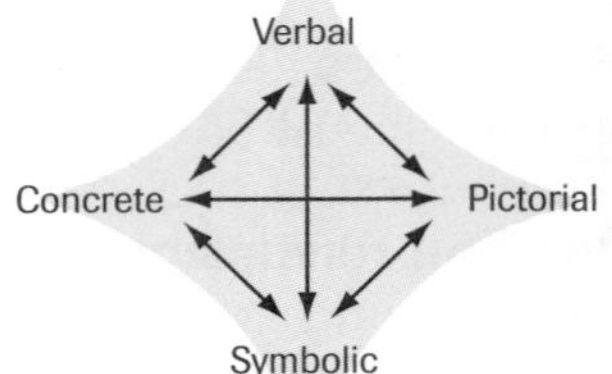

Lessons that teach *through* problem solving, not just *about* problem solving

Lesson	Activity	Lesson	Activity
10.1	Find the eight semiregular tessellations.	**10.4**	Identify shapes formed by cross sections of solid figures.
10.1	Solve problems involving triangular numbers.	**10.5**	Transform a coffee cup into a doughnut; experiment with other examples of topological transformations.
10.2	Create an Escher-type translation: Do all convex quadrangles tessellate? Do all concave quadrangles tessellate?	**10.6**	Describe the results of cutting a Möbius strip into half and into thirds.
10.3	Determine the order of rotation symmetry for 2-dimensional figures.		

For more information about problem solving in *Everyday Mathematics,* see the *Teacher's Reference Manual.*

cross-curricularlinks

art

- Students color polygons within tessellation patterns to make interesting designs. **(Lesson 10.1)**
- Students create an Escher-type translation tessellation. **(Lesson 10.2)**
- Students make and color tessellation designs or designs that use any form of symmetry. **(Lesson 10.7)**

language arts

- Students write about subjects they explored in this unit. **(Lesson 10.7)**

literature

- Students read "Tessellations" in *Math Talk: Mathematical Ideas in Poems for Two Voices.* **(Lesson 10.2)**
- Students read "The Möbius Strip" in *Math Talk: Mathematical Ideas in Poems for Two Voices.* **(Lesson 10.6)**

technology

- Students experiment with *TesselMania!®*, a computer program. **(Lesson 10.1)**

meeting INDIVIDUAL needs

✦ RETEACHING

The following features provide additional instructional support:

Adjusting the Activity

- **Lesson 10.1, Part 1**
- **Lesson 10.4, Part 1**
- **Lesson 10.5, Part 1**
- **Lesson 10.6, Part 1**

Options for Individualizing

- **Lesson 10.1** Creating Tessellating Patterns
- **Lesson 10.1** Exploring Regular Tessellations
- **Lesson 10.2** Exploring Quadrangle Tessellations
- **Lesson 10.3** Reviewing Reflection Symmetry

✦ ENRICHMENT

The following features suggest enrichment and extension activities:

Adjusting the Activity

- **Lesson 10.1, Parts 1 and 2**
- **Lesson 10.2, Parts 1, 2, and 3**
- **Lesson 10.4, Part 1**

Options for Individualizing

- **Lesson 10.1** Using a Computer Program to Explore Tessellations
- **Lesson 10.2** Reading a Poem about Tessellations
- **Lesson 10.3** Performing a Point-Symmetry Magic Trick
- **Lesson 10.4** Solving Cross-Section Problems
- **Lesson 10.6** Reading an Essay about Möbius
- **Lesson 10.6** Reading a Mathematical Poem

✦ LANGUAGE DIVERSITY

The following feature suggests ways to support students who are acquiring proficiency in English:

Adjusting the Activity

- **Lesson 10.1, Part 1**
- **Lesson 10.4, Part 1**

✦ MULTIAGE CLASSROOM

The following chart lists a related lesson from Grade 5 that can help you meet your instructional needs:

Grade 5	5.8					
Grade 6	10.1	10.2	10.3	10.4	10.5	10.6

materials

lesson	math masters pages	manipulative kit items	other items
10.1	Study Link Master, p. 376 Teaching Masters, pp. 167 and 169; and p. 168 (optional) ***See* Advance Preparation, p. 788**	pattern blocks	overhead pattern-block triangles and squares (hexagons optional) Geometry Template; scissors *The Adventures of Penrose the Mathematical Cat* computer program *TesselMania!®* ***See* Advance Preparation, p. 788**
10.2	Study Link Master, p. 377 Teaching Master, p. 170		several squares of cardstock, 3"-by-3" (like an index card, cut to size) scissors; tape; large piece of white construction paper markers, crayons, or color pencils *Every Number Is Special* *Math Talk: Mathematical Ideas in Poems For Two Voices* *Teaching Tessellating Art* ***See* Advance Preparation, p. 795**
10.3	Study Link Master, p. 378 Teaching Masters, pp. 171–173 transparency of Study Link 10.2 (optional) ***See* Advance Preparation, p. 800**	compass	paper fastener; scissors; compass Per partnership: deck of regular playing cards index card or other cardstock protractor; reflective transparent mirror
10.4	Study Link Master, p. 379 Teaching Masters, pp. 174–176 transparency of Study Link 10.3 (optional)		For demonstration purposes: at least 3 carrots orange; sharp knife; cutting board Per partnership: clay or modeling compound dental floss or cheese slicer conical paper cup (optional) slate; quarter *Stephen Biesty's Incredible Cross Sections* and/or *Stephen Biesty's Incredible Explosions* (optional) ***See* Advance Preparation, p. 806**
10.5	Study Link Master, p. 380 Teaching Masters, pp. 110 and 177		Geometry Template; slate Optional items: coffee mug with single handle doughnut with hole juice glass without handle scissors; clay, modeling compound, or Silly Putty® Per partnership: 3 disposable latex gloves; permanent marker pencil; string; large button ***See* Advance Preparation, p. 812**
10.6	Study Link Master, p. 381		marker, crayon, or pencil; tape scissors; sheet of newspaper or adding machine tape *Math Talk: Mathematical Ideas in Poems for Two Voices*
10.7	Study Link Masters, pp. 382–385 Teaching Masters, pp. 7–9 Assessment Masters, pp. 418–419; and pp. 425–432 (optional)	compass	straightedge

planningtips

Pacing

Pacing depends on a number of factors, such as students' individual needs and how long your school has been using *Everyday Mathematics.* At the beginning of Unit 10, review your Content by Strand Poster to help you set a monthly pace.

APRIL	MAY	JUNE

←MOST CLASSROOMS→ (late May to early June)

Using the Projects

Use Project 6, Anthropometry Project: Formulas for Body Height and Neck Circumference, during or after Unit 10, to measure body parts and plot measurements as data pairs. Investigate formulas that relate body measurements. The Projects can be found at the back of this book.

Home Communication

Share Study Links 10.1–10.6 with families to help them understand the content and procedures in this unit. At the end of the unit, use Study Link 10.7 to introduce Grade 7. Supplemental information can be found in the *Home Connection Handbook*.

NCTM Standards

Standard	1	2	3	4	5	6	7	8	9	10
Unit 10 Lessons	10.2	10.1, 10.5	10.1–10.6			10.1–10.7	10.1–10.7	10.1–10.7	10.1–10.7	10.1–10.7

Content Standards
1 Number and Operations
2 Algebra
3 Geometry
4 Measurement
5 Data Analysis and Probability

Process Standards
6 Problem Solving
7 Reasoning and Proof
8 Communication
9 Connections
10 Representation

PRACTICE *through* Games

Everyday Mathematics uses games to help students develop good fact power and other math skills.

- *Solution Search* to practice identifying solutions to inequalities **(Lesson 10.5)**

unit 10 content highlights

The discussion below highlights the major content ideas presented in Unit 10 and may help you establish instructional priorities.

NOTE: The topics covered in Unit 10 are explained in the journal and the *Student Reference Book.* The authors suggest that you review these materials before teaching the lessons.

Geometric Transformations and Their Uses in Art and Design (Lessons 10.1–10.3)

All geometric transformations involve a "before" state (the preimage) and an "after" state (the image). Transformations can be classified by the properties that remain the same from preimage to image. For figures that undergo *isometry transformations,* shape and size are preserved—lengths and angle measures in the preimage equal those in the image, although position or orientation may change. The isometry transformations in these lessons—reflections and rotations—are used in the context of art and design. (In earlier grades, these transformations were nicknamed "flips" and "turns.")

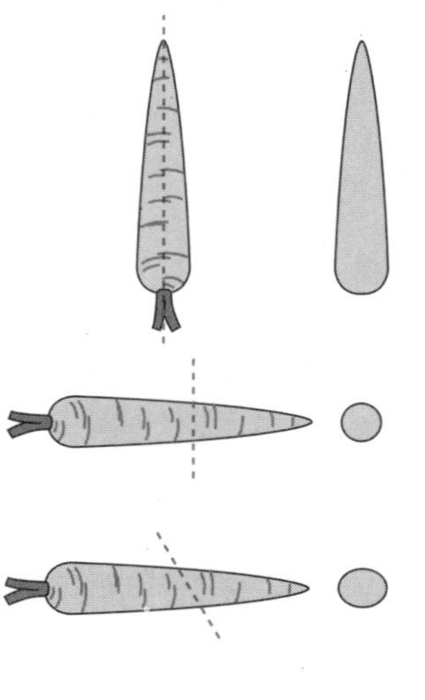

Cross Sections of Solids (Lesson 10.4)

When a 3-dimensional shape is cut by a plane, a cross-sectional trace of the intersection is created, which is one way of transforming a 3-dimensional shape into a 2-dimensional figure (*see margin*). Complicated shapes can be modeled with a series of cross sections. This technique has been used for decades in the design of automobiles, aircraft, and many other industrial products and has been made much easier by computer-assisted design (CAD) programs. Biologists in several specialties prepare very thin cross sections of plant or animal matter and study them in series under a microscope to investigate structure and development. Medical imaging instruments provide valuable information about the body—for example, about possible injuries to the brain. These applications might be interesting for students to investigate.

Topology (Lessons 10.5 and 10.6)

Isometry transformations preserve shape and size. Similarity transformations preserve shape but not size. Other transformations preserve even fewer properties. One of the few properties preserved by *topological transformations* is that points starting out as neighbors remain neighbors. Another is the number of holes in the object. Shape, size, measure, ratios of measures, and almost everything else is lost. Some topological transformations lead to paradoxical results that are interesting re-creations, and those are the projects suggested in Lessons 10.5 and 10.6. The details are in the journal and the *Student Reference Book.* (These re-creations barely scratch the surface of topology, which is a large and active field of research by professional mathematicians.)

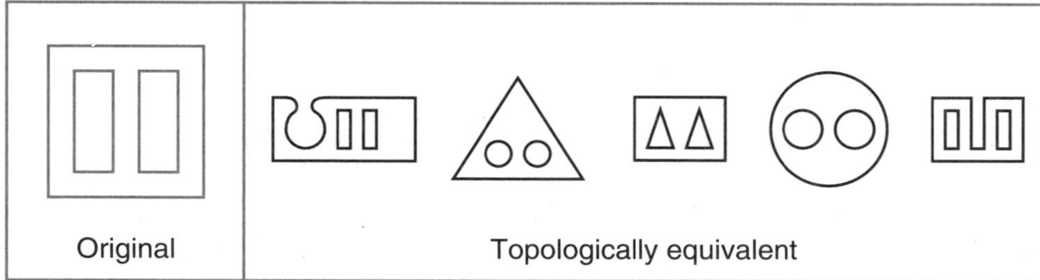

End-of-Year Assessment

Sixth Grade Everyday Mathematics closes with a cumulative written assessment, which covers many, but certainly not all, of the topics presented this year. Concepts and skills tested are taken from Units 1 through 9. You may use all or part of it. The Family Letter that accompanies Lesson 10.7 offers parents ideas for summer math-based reading as well as summer mathematics activities.

> "The whole of mathematics is nothing more than a refinement of everyday thinking."
>
> — Albert Einstein

The End-of-Year Assessment (*Math Masters,* pages 425–433) provides an additional assessment opportunity that you may want to use as part of your balanced assessment plan. This test covers many of the important concepts and skills presented in *Sixth Grade Everyday Mathematics.* It should be used along with ongoing, product, and periodic assessments. Please see the *Assessment Handbook* for further information.

For additional information on the following topics, see the *Teacher's Reference Manual:*

- assessment
- classifying tessellations
- connecting 2-D and 3-D
- other symmetries
- size-change transformations
- slides, flips, and turns
- topology

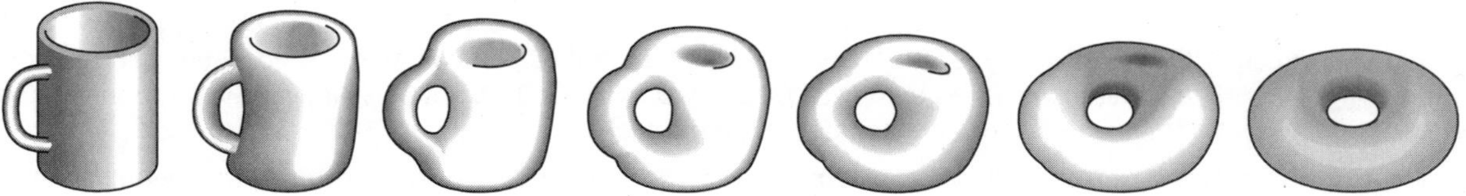

10.1 Semiregular Tessellations

OBJECTIVES **To review regular tessellations; to introduce semiregular tessellations; to introduce notation for both; and to find the eight semiregular tessellations.**

summaries	materials
1 Teaching the Lesson	
Students review what a tessellation is and which regular polygons can be used to make regular tessellations. The teacher introduces notation for regular and semiregular tessellations. Students find all eight possible semiregular tessellations. [Geometry]	□ *Math Journal 2,* pp. 388 and 389 □ *Student Reference Book,* pp. 323 and 324 □ Teaching Master (*Math Masters,* p. 167) □ overhead pattern-block triangles and squares (hexagons optional) □ Geometry Template □ scissors ***See*** **Advance Preparation**
2 Ongoing Learning & Practice	
Students explore triangular numbers. [Patterns, Functions, and Algebra] Students practice and maintain skills through Math Boxes and Study Link activities.	□ *Math Journal 2,* pp. 387 and 390 □ Study Link Master (*Math Masters,* p. 376) □ *The Adventures of Penrose the Mathematical Cat* (optional) ***See*** **Advance Preparation**
3 Options for Individualizing	
Extra Practice Students color the tessellations they made in Part 1 to create designs. [Geometry] **Enrichment** Students use a computer program to explore tessellations. [Geometry] **Reteaching** Students create tessellating patterns. [Geometry] **Reteaching** Students determine whether certain regular polygons tessellate. For those that do, they create a tessellating pattern. [Geometry]	□ *Math Journal 2,* pp. 388 and 389 □ Teaching Masters (*Math Masters,* p. 168, optional; and p. 169) □ computer program *TesselMania!*® □ pattern blocks □ Geometry Template ***See*** **Advance Preparation**

Additional Information

Advance Preparation For Part 1, copy *Math Masters,* page 167, which has 15 regular dodecagon templates, preferably onto cardstock. Cut out the templates or pass copies of the master around and have each student cut one out. For the Adjusting the Activity in Part 2, obtain a copy of *The Adventures of Penrose the Mathematical Cat* by Theoni Pappas (Wide World Publishing/Tetra, 1997). For the optional Enrichment activity in Part 3, you will need a computer and the computer program *TesselMania!* by Kevin Lee, MECC Software, 1994, 1996; also available from Key Curriculum Press. For the second optional Reteaching activity in Part 3, each student needs a copy of *Math Masters,* page 169, but you may also want to make copies of *Math Masters,* page 168 for students who want to use paper pattern blocks.

Vocabulary • **regular polygon** • **tessellation** • **vertex point** • **regular tessellation** • **semiregular tessellation**

Getting Started

Mental Math and Reflexes

Pose "fraction of" problems. *Suggestions:*

- $\frac{2}{3}$ of 15 10
- $\frac{5}{8}$ of 16 10
- $\frac{2}{5}$ of 100 40
- $\frac{2}{3}$ of 60 40
- $\frac{5}{8}$ of 56 35
- $\frac{2}{5}$ of 10 4
- $\frac{2}{3}$ of 21 14
- $\frac{5}{8}$ of 48 30
- $\frac{2}{5}$ of 15 6

Math Message

Which pattern-block shapes (labeled PB) on your Geometry Template are regular polygons? Be prepared to explain your answer.

1 Teaching the Lesson

Math Message Follow-Up

WHOLE-CLASS DISCUSSION

In a **regular polygon,** all sides are the same length and all angles have the same measure. The pattern-block square, triangle, and hexagon on the Geometry Template are regular polygons. (The octagon and the pentagon on the template are also regular, but they are not pattern-block shapes.)

Ask students to explain why the pattern-block trapezoid and two rhombuses are not regular. The sides of the trapezoid are not all the same length, and the angles do not all have the same measure. The angles of the rhombuses do not all have the same measure.

Adjusting the Activity To help students who are not proficient in English, guide them to make a poster of the pattern-block shapes and label each with the name of its shape. You may want to add a pentagon and an octagon, as well as some other names for the square and rhombus (for example, *quadrangle, quadrilateral,* and *parallelogram*).

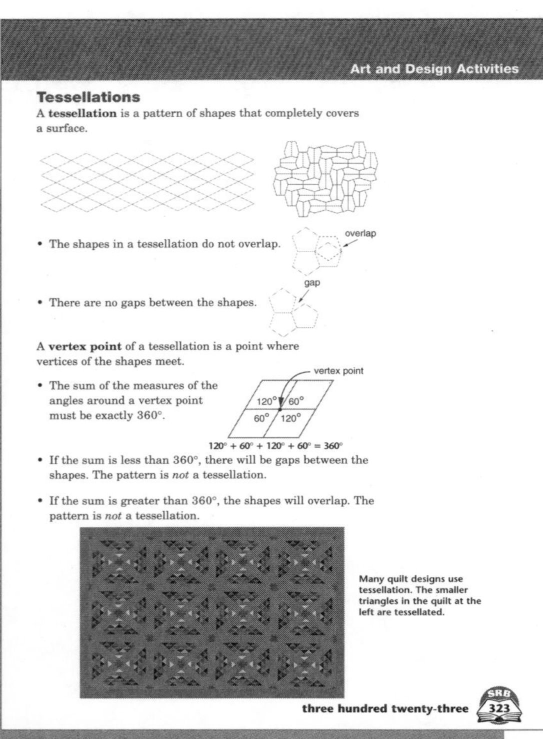

Art and Design Activities

Tessellations

A **tessellation** is a pattern of shapes that completely covers a surface.

- The shapes in a tessellation do not overlap.
- There are no gaps between the shapes.

A **vertex point** of a tessellation is a point where vertices of the shapes meet.

- The sum of the measures of the angles around a vertex point must be exactly 360°.

- If the sum is less than 360°, there will be gaps between the shapes. The pattern is *not* a tessellation.
- If the sum is greater than 360°, the shapes will overlap. The pattern is *not* a tessellation.

Many quilt designs use tessellation. The smaller triangles in the quilt at the left are tessellated.

three hundred twenty-three SRB 323

✦ *Student Reference Book,* p. 323

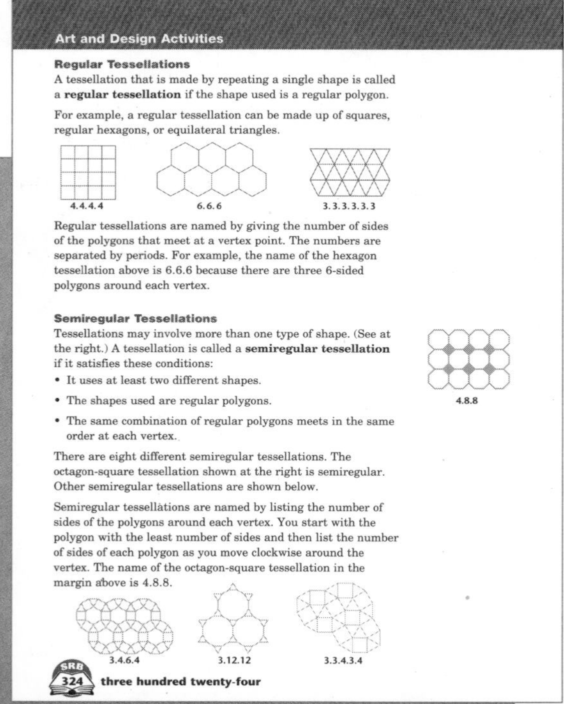

STUDENT PAGE

Art and Design Activities

Regular Tessellations

A tessellation that is made by repeating a single shape is called a **regular tessellation** if the shape used is a regular polygon.

For example, a regular tessellation can be made up of squares, regular hexagons, or equilateral triangles.

Regular tessellations are named by giving the number of sides of the polygons that meet at a vertex point. The numbers are separated by periods. For example, the name of the hexagon tessellation above is 6.6.6 because there are three 6-sided polygons around each vertex.

Semiregular Tessellations

Tessellations may involve more than one type of shape. (See at the right.) A tessellation is called a **semiregular tessellation** if it satisfies these conditions:

- It uses at least two different shapes.
- The shapes used are regular polygons.
- The same combination of regular polygons meets in the same order at each vertex.

There are eight different semiregular tessellations. The octagon-square tessellation shown at the right is semiregular. Other semiregular tessellations are shown below.

Semiregular tessellations are named by listing the number of sides of the polygons around each vertex. You start with the polygon with the least number of sides and then list the number of sides of each polygon as you move clockwise around the vertex. The name of the octagon-square tessellation in the margin above is 4.8.8.

SRB 324 three hundred twenty-four

✦ *Student Reference Book,* p. 324

✦ Defining and Naming Regular and Semiregular Tessellations

(*Student Reference Book,* pp. 323 and 324)

WHOLE-CLASS DISCUSSION

As a class, read the review of tessellations on *Student Reference Book,* page 323. The discussion should stress the following concepts:

- ▷ A **tessellation** is an arrangement of closed shapes that covers a surface.
- ▷ In a tessellation, shapes may not overlap, and no gaps between shapes are allowed.
- ▷ In a tessellation of polygons, the sum of the measures of the angles about any **vertex point** is 360°.

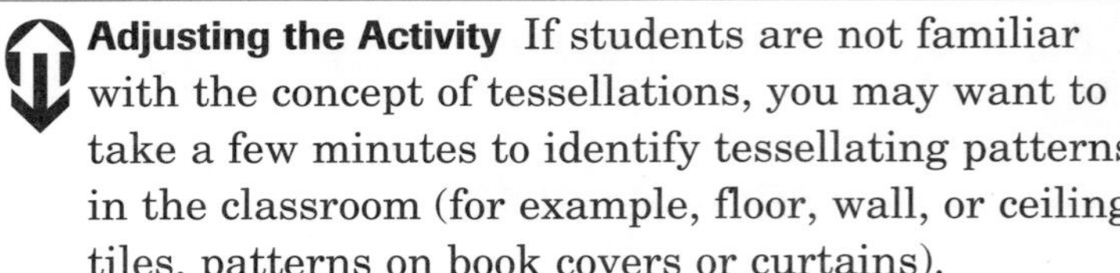

Adjusting the Activity If students are not familiar with the concept of tessellations, you may want to take a few minutes to identify tessellating patterns in the classroom (for example, floor, wall, or ceiling tiles, patterns on book covers or curtains).

NOTE: In *Fifth Grade Everyday Mathematics,* students were introduced to tessellations. They determined which regular polygons would tessellate by finding the sum of the angles at any vertex point. They found that there are only three regular tessellations. Students also constructed an equilateral, but nonregular, pentagon that tessellates.

As a class, read the section on regular tessellations on *Student Reference Book,* page 324. The discussion should stress the following concepts:

- ▷ A **regular tessellation** is made up of one type of regular polygon.
- ▷ In a regular tessellation, the vertices of at least 3 of the regular polygons must meet at each vertex point. There must be at least 3 angles around each vertex point.
- ▷ Regular tessellations are named by giving the number of sides of the polygons that meet at a vertex point. For example, the name of a regular tessellation made up of hexagons is 6.6.6 because three polygons with 6 sides come together at each vertex.

As part of the Math Message problem, students determined that the triangle, square, and hexagon pattern-block shapes are regular polygons. Ask students to use their Geometry Templates to create regular tessellations of triangles, squares, and hexagons. Have volunteers use overhead pattern blocks to share their findings at the overhead projector. Remind students that these three (3.3.3.3.3.3, 4.4.4.4, and 6.6.6) are the only possible regular tessellations.

NOTE: The pattern-block trapezoid and two rhombuses can also be used to form tessellations, but these are not regular tessellations because the polygons are not regular.

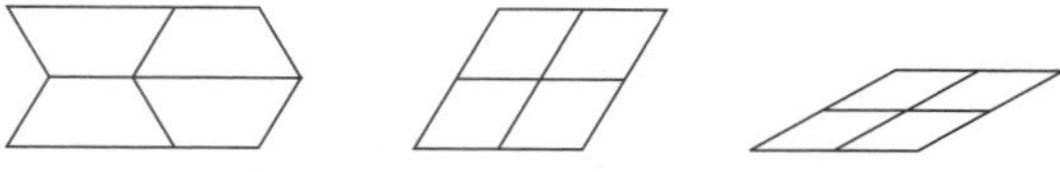

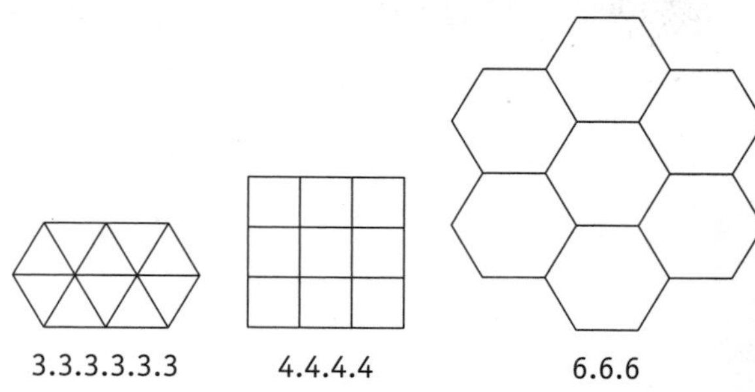

The three regular tessellations

As a class, read the section on **semiregular tessellations** on page 324 of the *Student Reference Book*. The discussion should stress the following concepts:

- ▷ Semiregular tessellations are made up of two or more kinds of regular polygons.
- ▷ In a semiregular tessellation, the angles around any vertex point must be congruent to the angles around any other vertex point. In other words, the arrangement of angles about any vertex point must look the same.
- ▷ Semiregular tessellations, like regular tessellations, are named by giving, in order, the number of sides of the polygons at a vertex point. Begin with the polygon that has the fewest sides. Move clockwise or counterclockwise around the vertex point and write the number of sides of the polygons. If two or more polygons with the fewest sides are adjacent (next to each other), begin with these and take them as a group.

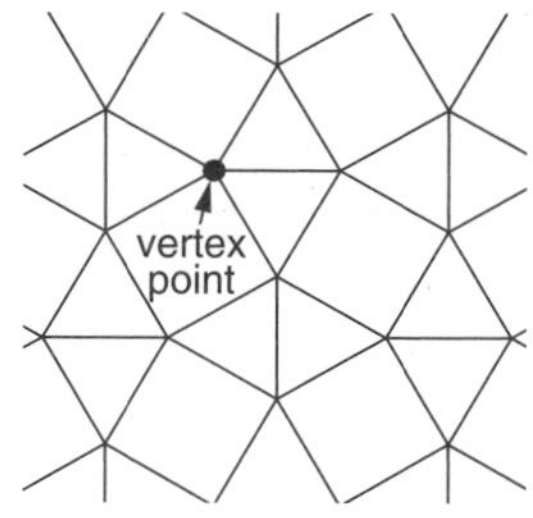

The name of this semiregular tessellation is 3.3.4.3.4.

Adjusting the Activity There are tessellations with regular polygons in which the angles around vertex points are *not* all congruent. These tessellations are called *demiregular*. For example, there are two types of arrangements at vertex points *A* and *B* in the tessellation below. While demiregular tessellations are not covered in *Sixth Grade Everyday Mathematics,* you may want to have students create their own such tessellations.

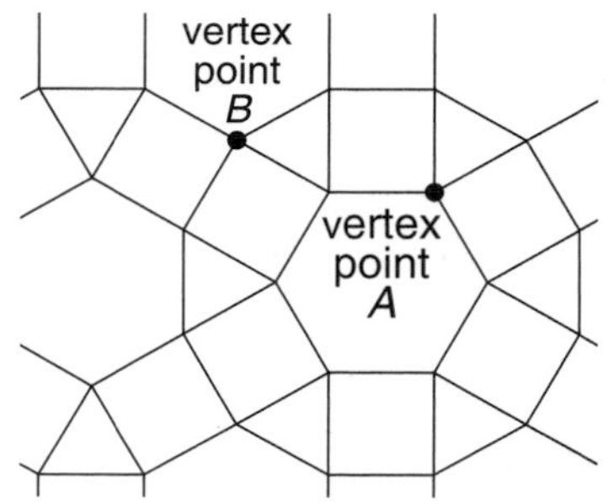

The name of this demiregular tessellation is 3.4.6.4/3.4.4.6.

Semiregular Tessellations

A **semiregular tessellation** is made up of two or more kinds of regular polygons. In a semiregular tessellation, the arrangement of angles about each **vertex point** looks the same. There are exactly eight different semiregular tessellations. One of the eight is shown below.

Find and draw the other seven semiregular tessellations. The only polygons that are possible in semiregular tessellations are equilateral triangles, squares, regular hexagons, regular octagons, and regular dodecagons. Use your Geometry Template and the template of a regular dodecagon that your teacher will provide.

Experiment first on a separate piece of paper. Then draw the tessellations below and on the next page. Write the name of each tessellation.

1.

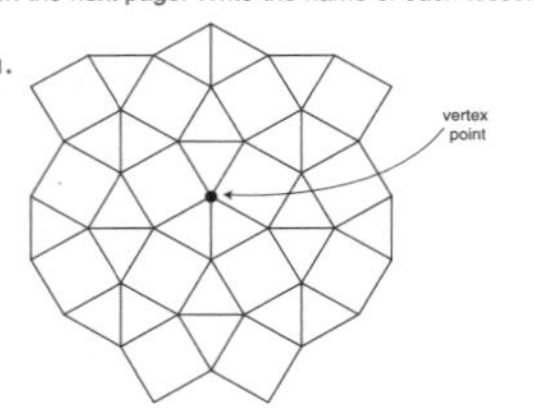

Name 3.3.4.3.4

2.

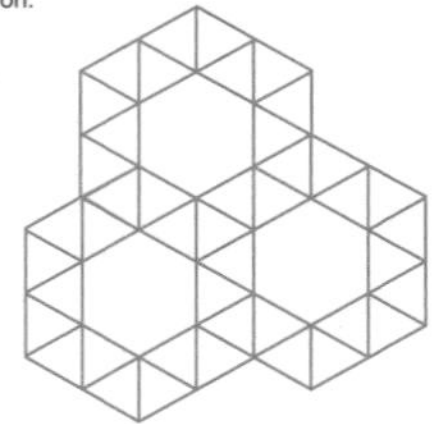

Name 3.3.3.3.6

3.

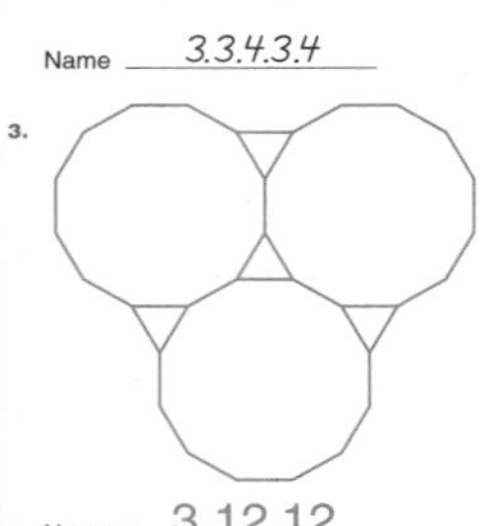

Name 3.12.12

4.

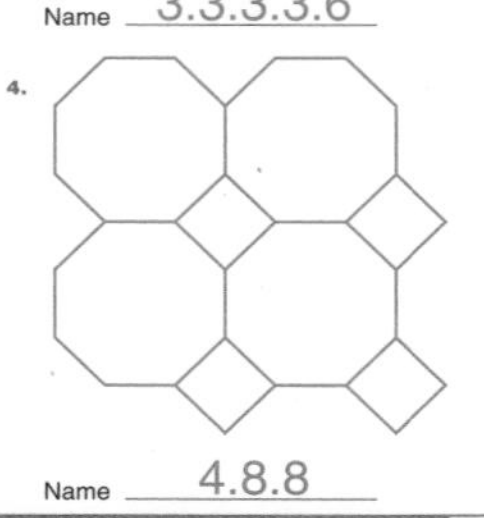

Name 4.8.8

STUDENT PAGE

✧ *Math Journal 2,* p. 388

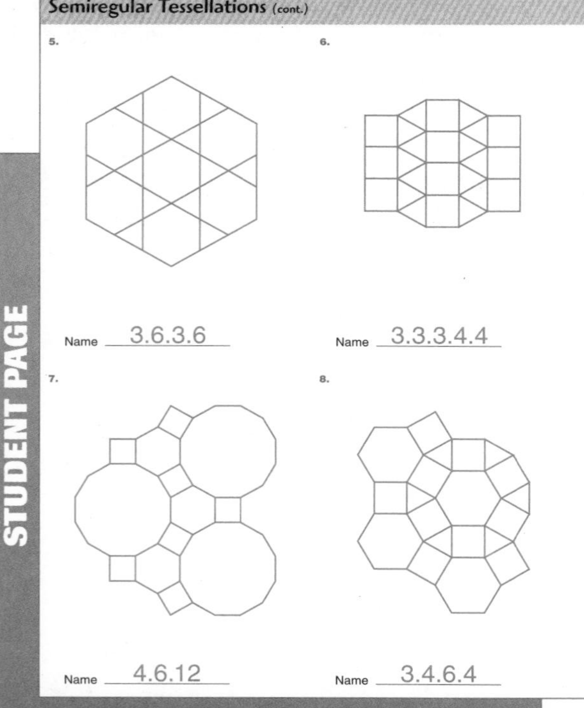

Semiregular Tessellations (cont.)

5. Name 3.6.3.6

6. Name 3.3.3.4.4

7. Name 4.6.12

8. Name 3.4.6.4

STUDENT PAGE

✧ *Math Journal 2,* p. 389

✦ Finding Semiregular Tessellations

(*Math Journal 2,* pp. 388 and 389; *Math Masters,* p. 167)

PARTNER ACTIVITY 

Students work in partnerships to find all eight possible semiregular tessellations. Each student will need a dodecagon template from *Math Masters,* page 167 to complete the activity. Remind students that in order for a tessellation to be classified as semiregular, it must be made of two or more kinds of regular polygons and the arrangement of angles must be the same at each vertex point. Circulate and assist. Hints are provided below for students who may need them.

▷ There are two different semiregular tessellations using only hexagons and triangles. One of these has one hexagon at each vertex point 3.3.3.3.6; the other has two hexagons at each vertex point. 3.6.3.6

▷ Besides 3.3.4.3.4, there is one other semiregular tessellation that uses only squares and triangles. 3.3.3.4.4

▷ There is one semiregular tessellation that is made of equilateral triangles, squares, and hexagons. 3.4.6.4

▷ There is one semiregular tessellation that is made of squares, hexagons, and dodecagons. 4.6.12

▷ There is one semiregular tessellation that has two octagons at each vertex point. 4.8.8

▷ There is one semiregular tessellation that has two dodecagons at each vertex point. 3.12.12

ONGOING ASSESSMENT

Use students' tessellations on journal pages 388 and 389 to evaluate their understanding of semiregular tessellations. Expect that most students will be able to create tessellations, although some students may still be confused about semiregular tessellations.

2 Ongoing Learning & Practice

✦ Exploring Triangular Numbers
(*Math Journal 2,* p. 390)

PARTNER ACTIVITY 

Figurate numbers are numbers that link geometry and arithmetic. Triangular numbers are examples of figurate numbers. Students explore number patterns formed by triangular numbers.

✦ Math Boxes 10.1 (*Math Journal 2,* p. 387)

INDEPENDENT ACTIVITY 

Mixed Review Math Boxes in this lesson are paired with Math Boxes in Lesson 10.4.

✦ Study Link 10.1 (*Math Masters,* p. 376)

Home Connection Students continue their exploration of tessellations and explain possible uses for them.

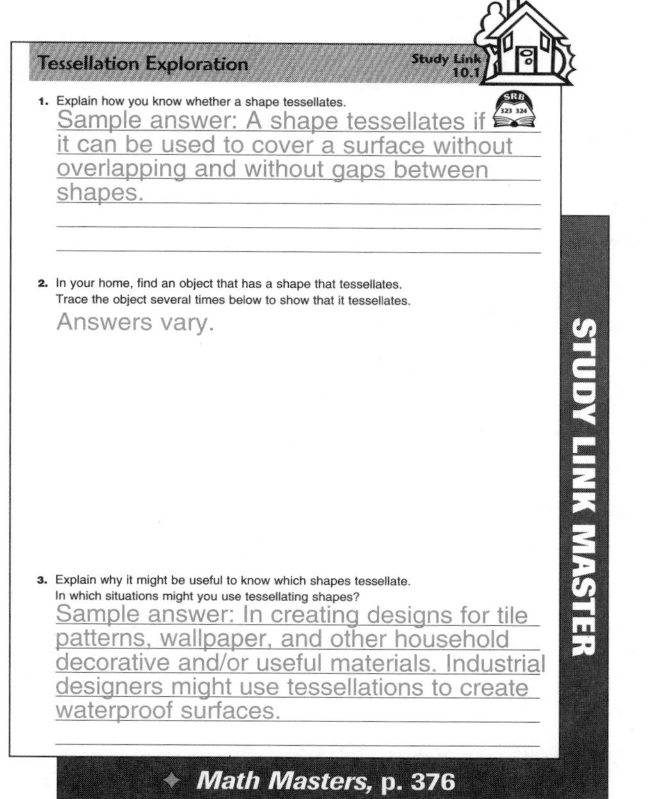

Tessellation Exploration — Study Link 10.1

1. Explain how you know whether a shape tessellates.
Sample answer: A shape tessellates if it can be used to cover a surface without overlapping and without gaps between shapes.

2. In your home, find an object that has a shape that tessellates. Trace the object several times below to show that it tessellates.
Answers vary.

3. Explain why it might be useful to know which shapes tessellate. In which situations might you use tessellating shapes?
Sample answer: In creating designs for tile patterns, wallpaper, and other household decorative and/or useful materials. Industrial designers might use tessellations to create waterproof surfaces.

STUDY LINK MASTER

✦ *Math Masters,* p. 376

Triangular Numbers

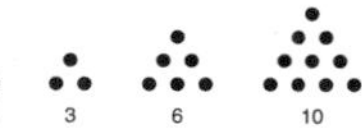

Figurate numbers link geometry and arithmetic. They can be shown by dots arranged in geometric patterns. A triangular number is a figurate number that can be shown by a triangular arrangement of dots.

1. Name the first 15 triangular numbers
1, 3, 6, 10, 15, 21, 28, 36, 45, 55, 66, 78, 91, 105, 120

2. What kind of triangle is used to display triangular numbers? equilateral

3. a. Is the *sum* of two triangular numbers always, sometimes, or never another triangular number? Give examples to support your answer.
Sample answer: Sometimes; $15 + 21 = 36$ (triangular), but $3 + 6 = 9$ (not triangular)

b. Is the *difference* between two triangular numbers always, sometimes, or never another triangular number? Give examples to support your answer.
Sample answer: Sometimes; $55 - 45 = 10$ (triangular), but $15 - 10 = 5$ (not triangular)

c. Is the *product* of two triangular numbers always, sometimes, or never another triangular number? Give examples to support your answer.
Sample answer: Sometimes; $15 * 3 = 45$ (triangular), but $6 * 10 = 60$ (not triangular)

STUDENT PAGE

✦ *Math Journal 2,* p. 390

Adjusting the Activity To extend the activity on journal page 390, read the section "Penrose Discovers the Mystery of the Triangle of Numbers" in *The Adventures of Penrose the Mathematical Cat*. Have students discover other patterns in the triangular numbers.

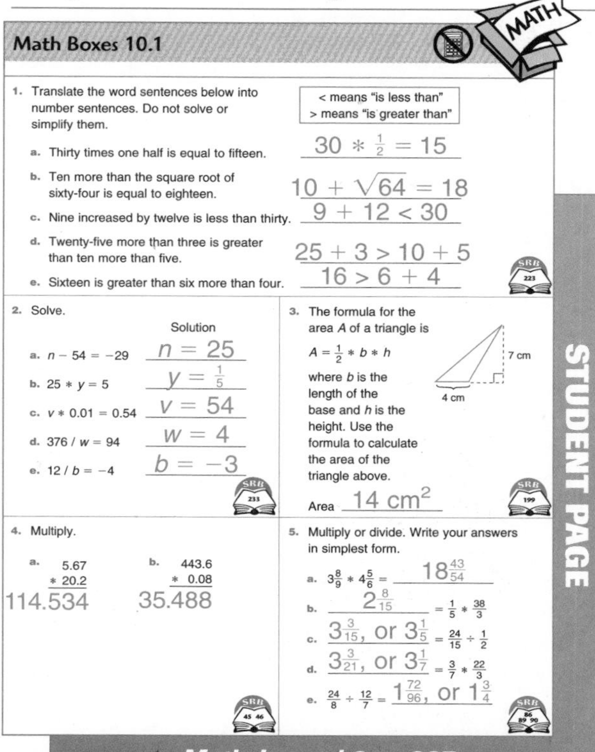

Math Boxes 10.1

1. Translate the word sentences below into number sentences. Do not solve or simplify them.

< means "is less than"
> means "is greater than"

a. Thirty times one half is equal to fifteen. $30 * \frac{1}{2} = 15$

b. Ten more than the square root of sixty-four is equal to eighteen. $10 + \sqrt{64} = 18$

c. Nine increased by twelve is less than thirty. $9 + 12 < 30$

d. Twenty-five more than three is greater than ten more than five. $25 + 3 > 10 + 5$

e. Sixteen is greater than six more than four. $16 > 6 + 4$

2. Solve.

	Solution
a. $n - 54 = -29$	$n = 25$
b. $25 * y = 5$	$y = \frac{1}{5}$
c. $v * 0.01 = 0.54$	$v = 54$
d. $376 / w = 94$	$w = 4$
e. $12 / b = -4$	$b = -3$

3. The formula for the area A of a triangle is $A = \frac{1}{2} * b * h$ where b is the length of the base and h is the height. Use the formula to calculate the area of the triangle above.

7 cm
4 cm

Area 14 cm^2

4. Multiply.

a. $5.67 * 20.2$ = 114.534

b. $443.6 * 0.08$ = 35.488

5. Multiply or divide. Write your answers in simplest form.

a. $3\frac{8}{9} * 4\frac{5}{6} = 18\frac{43}{54}$

b. $2\frac{8}{15} = \frac{1}{5} * \frac{38}{3}$

c. $3\frac{3}{15}$, or $3\frac{1}{5} = \frac{24}{15} \div \frac{1}{2}$

d. $3\frac{3}{21}$, or $3\frac{1}{7} = \frac{3}{7} * \frac{22}{3}$

e. $\frac{24}{8} \div \frac{12}{7} = 1\frac{72}{96}$, or $1\frac{3}{4}$

STUDENT PAGE

✦ *Math Journal 2,* p. 387

3 Options for Individualizing

✦ EXTRA PRACTICE Making Tessellation Designs (*Math Journal 2,* pp. 388 and 389)

INDEPENDENT ACTIVITY  **5–15 min**

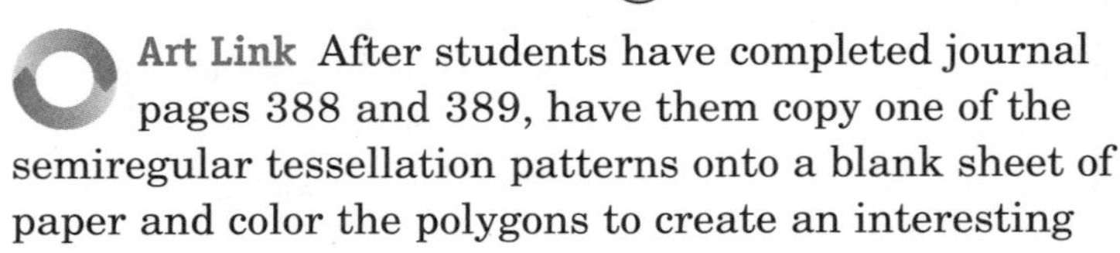

Art Link After students have completed journal pages 388 and 389, have them copy one of the semiregular tessellation patterns onto a blank sheet of paper and color the polygons to create an interesting design.

✦ ENRICHMENT Using a Computer Program to Explore Tessellations

PARTNER ACTIVITY **15–30 min**

Technology Link If you have a computer available for school use, try acquiring the program *TesselMania!*® for students to experiment with.

✦ RETEACHING Creating Tessellating Patterns

PARTNER ACTIVITY **5–15 min**

Students use pattern blocks to create tessellating patterns. Have students record their patterns with their Geometry Templates.

✦ RETEACHING Exploring Regular Tessellations (*Math Masters,* pp. 168 and 169)

PARTNER ACTIVITY **5–15 min**

Students discover which of the regular polygons tessellate. They can use their Geometry Templates to experiment. The template includes an equilateral triangle, a square, a pentagon, a hexagon, and an octagon. You may want to provide students with a copy of *Math Masters,* page 168 so that they can manipulate actual polygons to explore the tessellations. Have volunteers share their results.

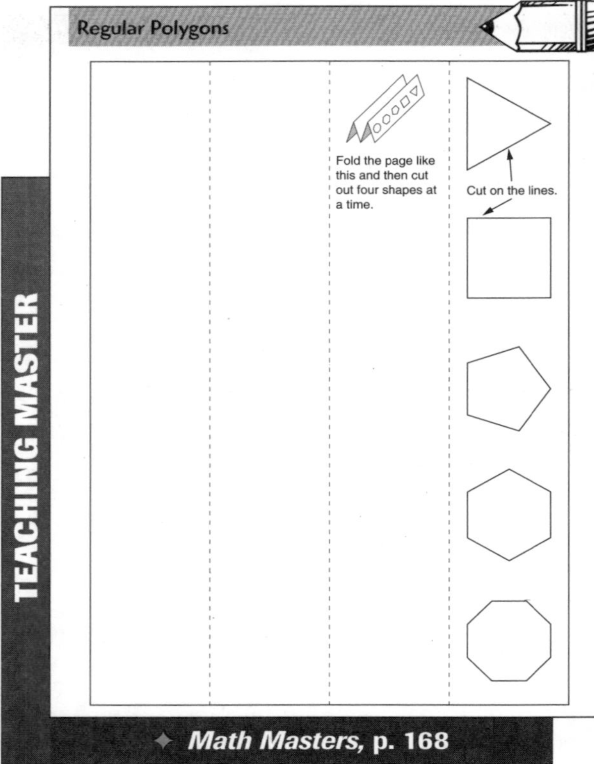

TEACHING MASTER
Regular Polygons
Fold the page like this and then cut out four shapes at a time.
Cut on the lines.

✦ *Math Masters,* p. 168

TEACHING MASTER

Same-Tile Tessellations

Decide whether each polygon can be used to create a same-tile tessellation. Write the name of the polygon. Then record your answers in Column A. In Column B, use your Geometry Template to draw examples illustrating your answers in Column A.

Polygon	A. Tessellation? (Yes or No)	B. Draw an example.
triangle	yes	
square	yes	
pentagon	no	gap
hexagon	yes	
octagon	no	overlap

✦ *Math Masters,* p. 169

10.2 Escher-Type Translation Tessellations

OBJECTIVE **To create nonpolygonal, Escher-type, translation tessellations.**

summaries	materials
1 Teaching the Lesson	
Students create nonpolygonal, Escher-type, translation tessellations. [Geometry]	☐ *Math Journal 2,* p. 391 ☐ *Student Reference Book,* pp. 325 and 326 ☐ Study Link 10.1 ☐ several squares of cardstock, 3-by-3 inches (an index card, cut to size or use blank cardstock page at the back of *Math Journal 2*) ☐ scissors ☐ tape ☐ large piece of white construction paper ☐ markers, crayons, or color pencils ***See* Advance Preparation**
2 Ongoing Learning & Practice	
Students identify special meanings of numbers. [Numeration] Students practice and maintain skills through Math Boxes and Study Link activities.	☐ *Math Journal 2,* pp. 392 and 393 ☐ Study Link Master (*Math Masters,* p. 377) ☐ *Every Number Is Special* (optional) ***See* Advance Preparation**
3 Options for Individualizing	
Enrichment Students read a poem about tessellations. [Geometry] **Extra Practice** Students make Escher-type tessellations. [Geometry] **Reteaching** Students explore quadrangle tessellations. [Geometry]	☐ Teaching Master (*Math Masters,* p. 170) ☐ *Math Talk: Mathematical Ideas in Poems for Two Voices* ☐ *Teaching Tessellating Art* ☐ cardstock ☐ scissors ***See* Advance Preparation**

Additional Information

Advance Preparation For Part 1, locate or have students look for examples of the tessellations and other artwork of M. C. Escher in books and on posters, wrapping paper, and articles of clothing. Students might also search the Internet for *Escher* and *tessellations.* You might want to spend one or two days in class working with Escher-type tessellations to be sure that students understand the procedure. Experimenting with shapes and decorating the tessellations can be done outside of class. You might find it helpful to review page 326 in the *Student Reference Book* before teaching this lesson.

For the Adjusting the Activity in Part 2, obtain *Every Number Is Special* by Henry Boyd (Dale Seymour Publications, 1985). For the optional Enrichment activity in Part 3, obtain *Math Talk: Mathematical Ideas in Poems for Two Voices* by Theoni Pappas (Wide World Publishing/Tetra, 1991). For the optional Extra Practice activity in Part 3, obtain *Teaching Tessellating Art* by Jill Britton (Dale Seymour Publications, 1989).

Vocabulary • **translation tessellation**

Getting Started

Mental Math and Reflexes

Multiply or divide by powers of 10. *Suggestions:*

- 87 / 10 8.7
- 8.7 / 100 0.087
- 334 / 100 3.34
- 0.00067 * 1,000 0.67
- 92 * 0.1 9.2
- 15 * 0.1 1.5
- 940 / 1,000 0.94
- 0.6 * 10 6
- 0.002 * 100 0.2
- 228 * 0.0001 0.0228
- 1.98 / 100 0.0198
- 3 / 1,000 0.003

Math Message

Read page 325 in your Student Reference Book.

Study Link 10.1 Follow-Up

Briefly go over the answers. Ask students to share examples of situations in which tessellating shapes might be used. Floor tiles, windows, brick walls

1 Teaching the Lesson

✦ Math Message Follow-Up (*Student Reference Book,* p. 325)

WHOLE-CLASS DISCUSSION

Discuss any questions or comments that students may have about the information presented on page 325 of the *Student Reference Book.* Invite students to look for and share examples of Escher's tessellations.

Adjusting the Activity Extend the activity by inviting interested students to explore Escher's non-tessellation artwork as well.

✦ Creating an Escher-Type Translation Tessellation (*Student Reference Book,* p. 326; *Math Journal 2,* p. 391)

INDEPENDENT ACTIVITY 

Art Link Students follow the procedure on page 326 of the *Student Reference Book* to create an Escher-type translation tessellation. A **translation tessellation** is created by moving (translating) curves from one side of a shape to the opposite side. In this case, the shape is a square. The template is traced and then slid, or translated, to create the next interlocking piece in the tessellation. In the final tessellation, all figures face in the same direction.

STUDENT PAGE

Art and Design Activities

Escher Translation Tessellations

The graphic artist M. C. Escher (Maurits Cornelius Escher) was born on June 17, 1898, in Leeuwarden, a small town in the Netherlands. He became famous for his drawings that combined realistic details with optical illusions and distorted perspectives. The drawing at the right, *Hand with Reflecting Sphere,* is a self-portrait of Escher.

In 1936, Escher visited the Alhambra, a Moorish palace in Spain that was built in the thirteenth and fourteenth centuries. He was fascinated by the beautiful tiling patterns created from simple geometric shapes that covered the floors and walls. Escher was inspired by these intricate designs to create tessellations such as those at the bottom of this page.

Unlike the Islamic artists who decorated the Alhambra, Escher did not limit himself to purely geometric designs. He built tessellations from representations of objects such as birds, fish, reptiles, and humans. Escher used translations (slides), reflections (flips), and rotations (turns) to create unusual and fantastic designs.

three hundred twenty-five

✦ *Student Reference Book,* p. 325

Circulate and assist. Encourage students not to settle for the first tessellation template they create, but rather, like Escher, to spend some time experimenting until a recognizable figure appears. They record their tessellation templates and their tessellations in their journals.

NOTE: The translation technique described on *Student Reference Book,* page 326 can also be used with parallelograms and regular hexagons. However, because a regular hexagon has three pairs of parallel sides, three sets of opposite curves must be drawn.

Similar procedures exist to create rotation tessellations and reflection tessellations. However, these procedures are more complicated and will not be covered in *Sixth Grade Everyday Mathematics.*

Art and Design Activities

Creating an Escher-Type Translation Tessellation

Materials
- ☐ sharp pencil
- ☐ scissors
- ☐ markers, crayons, or colored pencils
- ☐ 3-inch by 3-inch square cut from card stock (such as an index card)
- ☐ tape
- ☐ large piece of white construction paper

Directions

Step 1: To create a template for your **translation tessellation,** begin with a 3-inch by 3-inch square of card stock.

Step 2: Draw a curve from point *A* to point *B*.

Step 3: Use scissors to cut along curve *AB*. Tape the cut-out edge of the square so that point *A* lines up with point *D* and point *B* lines up with point *C*.

Step 4: Draw a curve from point *A* to point *D*.

Step 5: Use scissors to cut along curve *AD*. Tape the cut-out edge of the square so that point *A* lines up with point *B* and point *D* lines up with point *C*.

Step 6: You now have a template for your tessellation. Begin by tracing your template onto the *center* of the construction paper. Continue tracing, interlocking each new tracing with the previous tracing, until you have filled the entire sheet.

Step 7: Use markers, crayons, or colored pencils to decorate your design.

M. C. Escher worked hard to create shapes that not only tessellated but also looked like birds, reptiles, insects, and other familiar objects. You may want to repeat Steps 1 to 5 several times until you create a recognizable shape.

SRB 326 **three hundred twenty-six**

STUDENT PAGE

Student Reference Book, p. 326

My Tessellation

On a separate piece of paper, create an Escher-type translation tessellation using the procedure described on page 326 of your *Student Reference Book*. Experiment with several tessellations until you create one that you especially like.

Trace your final tessellation template in the space below. Answers vary.

In the space below, use your tessellation template to record what your tessellation looks like. Add details to or color your final design. Answers vary.

STUDENT PAGE

Math Journal 2, p. 391

2 Ongoing Learning & Practice

✦Associating Numbers with Their Applications (*Math Journal 2,* p. 392)

PARTNER ACTIVITY 

Students are given a list of "memorable" numbers and asked to tell why each is memorable.

Adjusting the Activity Extend this activity with the book *Every Number Is Special* by Henry Boyd. This book explores interesting facts about the numbers 0 through 151. Challenge students to find special characteristics for other numbers.

✦Math Boxes 10.2 (*Math Journal 2,* p. 393)

INDEPENDENT ACTIVITY 

Mixed Review Math Boxes in this lesson are paired with Math Boxes in Lesson 10.5.

✦Study Link 10.2 (*Math Masters,* p. 377)

Home Connection Students plot points on a coordinate grid to draw the images of figures resulting from translations.

STUDENT PAGE

"Memorable" Numbers

Below is a list of "memorable" numbers. Explain why each number is memorable. The first one has been done for you. Sample answers:

1. 365 — *Number of days in a year*
2. 3.14159... — Value of π
3. 2.54 — Number of centimeters in an inch
4. 144 — Number of square inches in 1 square foot
5. 4 — Number of quarts in a gallon
6. 52 — Number of weeks in a year
7. 2,000 — Number of pounds in a ton
8. 1492 — Year that Columbus reached America
9. 90 — Degree measure of a right angle
10. 366 — Number of days in a leap year
11. 1.6 — Approximation of the Golden Ratio
12. 12 — Number of items in a dozen

Add two additional numbers to the list of "memorable" numbers, and explain why they are memorable to you. Answers vary.

13. ______ ______________________
14. ______ ______________________

✦ *Math Journal 2,* p. 392

STUDENT PAGE

Math Boxes 10.2

1. Find the following measures for a circle with a radius of 3 cm.

   Diameter 6 cm

   Circumference About 18.85 cm

   Area About 28.27 cm^2

   Explain how you found the area. Sample answer: Square 3 ($3^2 = 3 * 3$), then multiply by π.

   SRB 195 200

2. Evaluate each expression. Use the rules for order of operations. Do not use a calculator.

   a. $15 - 3.3 * 4 =$ 1.8

   b. $\frac{20}{4} * 5 + (-8) * 2 =$ 9

   c. $7 * 3^2 - \frac{10}{2} =$ 58

   d. $8 * (2 + -5) - 4 =$ −28

   e. $0.01 + 0.01 * 10 + 0.01 =$ 0.12

   SRB 229

3. Write each number in scientific notation.

   a. A modern personal computer can perform 10,000,000 mathematical operations, or $1 * 10^7$ operations, in one second.

   b. A fiber-optic wire carries 1,700,000,000 bits per second, or $1.7 * 10^9$ bits per second.

   This is equivalent to 25,000 people, or $2.5 * 10^4$ people, speaking over a wire roughly the width of a human hair.

   c. An ant weighs about 0.00001 kilogram, or $1 * 10^{-5}$ kilogram.

   d. The approximate weight of the ocean is 1,320,000,000,000,000,000,000 kilograms, or $1.32 * 10^{21}$ kilograms.

   e. One grass pollen weighs approximately 0.0000000047 gram, or $4.7 * 10^{-9}$ gram.

Sources: The World Almanac for Kids, 1996; The Sizesaurus

SRB 7 8

✦ *Math Journal 2,* p. 393

3 Options for Individualizing

✦ ENRICHMENT Reading a Poem about Tessellations

PARTNER ACTIVITY  **5–15 min**

Literature Link *Math Talk: Mathematical Ideas in Poems for Two Voices* presents mathematical topics through poetic dialogues to be read by two people. "Tessellations" would be an ideal selection to share at this time. Some students may be interested in memorizing the poem in their spare time and then presenting it to the class.

✦ EXTRA PRACTICE Creating Tessellation Designs

INDEPENDENT ACTIVITY  **15–30 min**

Students can practice making more Escher-type tessellations as well as explore tessellating patterns in art and design by following the instructions in the book *Teaching Tessellating Art*. The book includes both instructions and teaching masters.

✦ RETEACHING Exploring Quadrangle Tessellations (*Math Masters,* p. 170)

PARTNER ACTIVITY  **5–15 min**

Students tessellate convex quadrangles of their own making to try to answer the question: Do all convex quadrangles tessellate? When they have completed this exploration, discuss the results.

Since the sum of the measures of the four angles of a convex quadrangle is 360 degrees, *any* convex quadrangle can be tessellated. When tessellating a quadrangle, make sure that all four angles meet at each vertex (totaling 360°).

Adjusting the Activity Extend the investigation by asking this question: *Do all* concave *quadrangles tessellate?* yes

Translations — Study Link 10.2

Plot and label the vertices of the image that would result from each translation. One vertex of each image has already been plotted and labeled.

1. preimage: A, B, C, D — horizontal translation ← — image: A', B', C', D'

2. preimage: I, J, H, E, G, F — vertical translation ↓ — image: I', J', H', E', G', F'

3. preimage: L, M, N, K, O — diagonal translation ↗ — image: L', M', N', K', O'

STUDY LINK MASTER

✦ *Math Masters,* p. 377

PLANNING AHEAD

For Lesson 10.3 each partnership will need one deck of regular playing cards. Have students ask permission to bring in a deck of cards from home.

An Angle Investigation

Do all convex quadrangles tessellate? (A convex quadrangle is one in which all vertices are "pushed outward.") To find out, do the following:

1. Draw a convex quadrangle on a piece of cardstock paper. Answers vary.
2. Measure the angles of your quadrangle. Write the measure of each angle on the angle.
3. Find the sum of the angles. Write the sum of the angles on your quadrangle.
4. Cut out your quadrangle and try to make a tessellation by tracing your quadrangle repeatedly. Draw your tessellation on the back of this page. (*Hint:* Label your angles *A, B, C,* and *D* so you can be sure that all four angles meet at each vertex.)
5. Repeat Steps 1 through 4 for a different convex quadrangle. Try to tessellate your second quadrangle. Draw your tessellation on the back of this page.
6. Do both of your quadrangles tessellate? yes
7. Do you think that all convex quadrangles will tessellate? yes
   Why or why not? Sample answer: Since the sum of the measures of the four angles of any convex quadrangle equals 360°, the quadrangle can be repeated about a point, with each vertex of the quadrangle meeting at the point, and with no gaps and no overlapping.

TEACHING MASTER

✦ *Math Masters,* p. 170

10.3 Rotation Symmetry

OBJECTIVE **To explore rotation symmetry and point symmetry.**

summaries	materials
1 Teaching the Lesson	
Students explore rotation symmetry by determining how many ways a figure can be rotated about a point so that the image (resulting figure) exactly matches the preimage (original figure). [Geometry]	□ *Math Journal 2,* p. 394 and Activity Sheet 7 □ *Student Reference Book,* p. 171 □ Study Link 10.2 □ Transparency (Study Link 10.2; optional) □ Teaching Masters (*Math Masters,* pp. 171 and 172) □ paper fastener □ scissors □ Per partnership: deck of regular playing cards ***See* Advance Preparation**
2 Ongoing Learning & Practice	
Students practice and maintain skills through Math Boxes and Study Link activities.	□ *Math Journal 2,* p. 395 □ Study Link Master (*Math Masters,* p. 378)
3 Options for Individualizing	
Enrichment Students perform a point-symmetry magic trick. [Geometry] **Reteaching** Students draw the missing half of figures with line symmetry. They draw the lines of symmetry in symmetric figures. [Geometry] **Extra Practice** Students draw shapes with rotation symmetry of a given order. [Geometry]	□ *Student Reference Book,* pp. 321 and 322 □ Teaching Master (*Math Masters,* p. 173) □ Per partnership: deck of regular playing cards □ index card or other cardstock □ protractor □ compass □ reflective transparent mirror

Additional Information

Advance Preparation You might want to make a transparency of Study Link 10.2 to review the problems. For Part 1, make one copy each of *Math Masters,* pages 171 and 172. Copies made on cardstock are preferable for durability, but regular paper will suffice. Cut out square *ABCD* from *Math Masters,* page 172.

Vocabulary • **rotation symmetry** • **order of rotation symmetry** • **point symmetry**

Getting Started

Mental Math and Reflexes

Students close their journals and place them on their desks. They rotate the journals as you direct. After you check each rotation, students return the journals to their original positions. *Suggestions:* clockwise one-half of a complete rotation, counterclockwise one-half turn, clockwise 90 degrees, counterclockwise 180 degrees. Continue as necessary or desired.

Math Message

Carefully tear Activity Sheet 7 from the back of your journal. Cut out the rectangles in the left column along the dashed lines, and then cut out the figures in the right column. Cut only along the dashed lines. Is the parallelogram you cut out symmetric? Be prepared to explain your answer.

Study Link 10.2 Follow-Up

Go over the translations. Students give the ordered number pairs for each vertex in the translations. Alternatively, you could have volunteers draw the translations on a transparency of the Study Link.

1 Teaching the Lesson

✦ Math Message Follow-Up
(*Math Journal 2,* Activity Sheet 7)

WHOLE-CLASS DISCUSSION

Verify that all students have correctly cut out the figures on Activity Sheet 7. Students should put these figures aside until they are needed for the Partner Activity described on page 803.

Briefly discuss whether the parallelogram is symmetric. Expect some disagreement. Some students will probably believe the parallelogram has a line of symmetry, but it does not. There is no fold line that can divide the parallelogram into two matching halves. Nevertheless, the parallelogram is symmetric: it has rotation symmetry, which is the topic of this lesson.

NOTE: This is students' first formal exposure to the vocabulary of rotation symmetry, also known as turn symmetry. However, students who have used previous grades of *Everyday Mathematics* should be familiar with line symmetry (also called reflection symmetry or mirror symmetry). If your students need more exposure to line symmetry, have them do the mirror activity in Part 3 of this lesson.

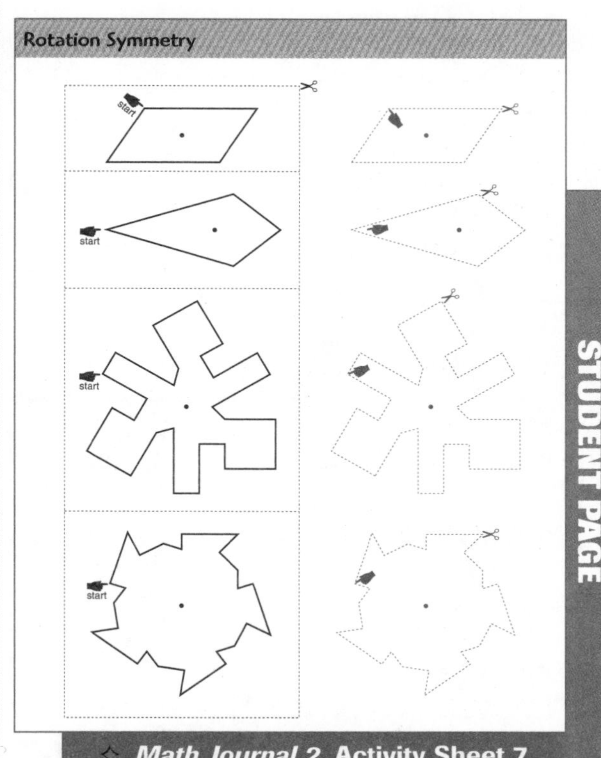

✧ *Math Journal 2,* Activity Sheet 7

STUDENT PAGE

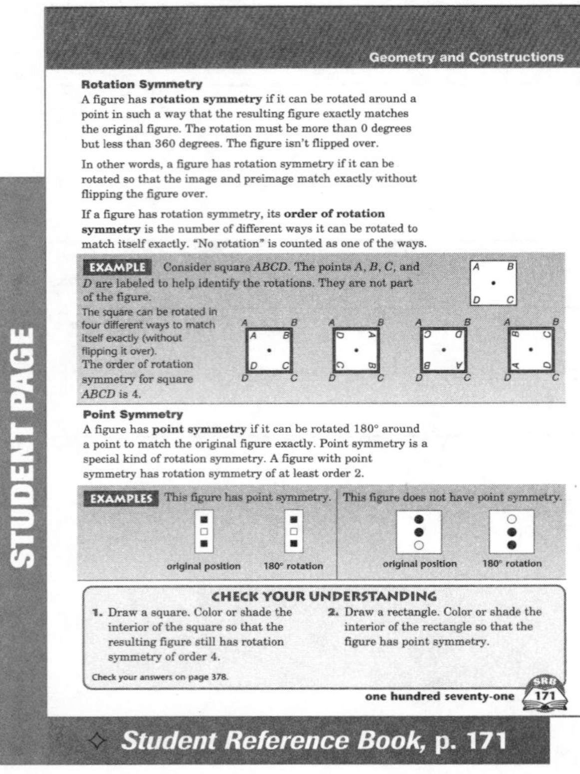
Geometry and Constructions

Rotation Symmetry

A figure has **rotation symmetry** if it can be rotated around a point in such a way that the resulting figure exactly matches the original figure. The rotation must be more than 0 degrees but less than 360 degrees. The figure isn't flipped over.

In other words, a figure has rotation symmetry if it can be rotated so that the image and preimage match exactly without flipping the figure over.

If a figure has rotation symmetry, its **order of rotation symmetry** is the number of different ways it can be rotated to match itself exactly. "No rotation" is counted as one of the ways.

EXAMPLE Consider square *ABCD*. The points *A*, *B*, *C*, and *D* are labeled to help identify the rotations. They are not part of the figure.

The square can be rotated in four different ways to match itself exactly (without flipping it over). The order of rotation symmetry for square *ABCD* is 4.

Point Symmetry

A figure has **point symmetry** if it can be rotated 180° around a point to match the original figure exactly. Point symmetry is a special kind of rotation symmetry. A figure with point symmetry has rotation symmetry of at least order 2.

EXAMPLES This figure has point symmetry. | This figure does not have point symmetry.

original position 180° rotation | original position 180° rotation

CHECK YOUR UNDERSTANDING

1. Draw a square. Color or shade the interior of the square so that the resulting figure still has rotation symmetry of order 4.
2. Draw a rectangle. Color or shade the interior of the rectangle so that the figure has point symmetry.

Check your answers on page 378.

one hundred seventy-one SRB 171

◇ *Student Reference Book*, **p. 171**

STUDENT PAGE

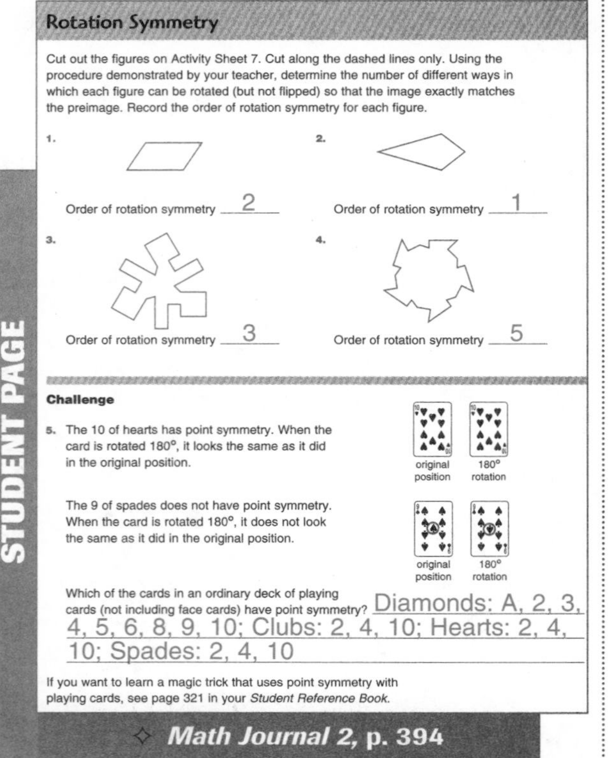
Rotation Symmetry

Cut out the figures on Activity Sheet 7. Cut along the dashed lines only. Using the procedure demonstrated by your teacher, determine the number of different ways in which each figure can be rotated (but not flipped) so that the image exactly matches the preimage. Record the order of rotation symmetry for each figure.

1. Order of rotation symmetry 2
2. Order of rotation symmetry 1
3. Order of rotation symmetry 3
4. Order of rotation symmetry 5

Challenge

5. The 10 of hearts has point symmetry. When the card is rotated 180°, it looks the same as it did in the original position.

original position 180° rotation

The 9 of spades does not have point symmetry. When the card is rotated 180°, it does not look the same as it did in the original position.

original position 180° rotation

Which of the cards in an ordinary deck of playing cards (not including face cards) have point symmetry? Diamonds: A, 2, 3, 4, 5, 6, 8, 9, 10; Clubs: 2, 4, 10; Hearts: 2, 4, 10; Spades: 2, 4, 10

If you want to learn a magic trick that uses point symmetry with playing cards, see page 321 in your *Student Reference Book*.

◇ *Math Journal 2*, **p. 394**

✦ Determining Whether a Figure Has Rotation Symmetry (*Student Reference Book,* p. 171; *Math Masters,* pp. 171 and 172)

WHOLE-CLASS DISCUSSION

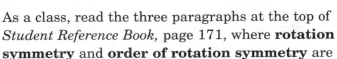

As a class, read the three paragraphs at the top of *Student Reference Book,* page 171, where **rotation symmetry** and **order of rotation symmetry** are defined.

Work through the example. Use *Math Masters,* pages 171 and 172 to demonstrate the procedure that students will follow on journal page 394 to determine whether a figure has rotation symmetry.

▷ Use a sharp pencil, the point of a compass, or a pair of scissors to make a hole in the center of each square.

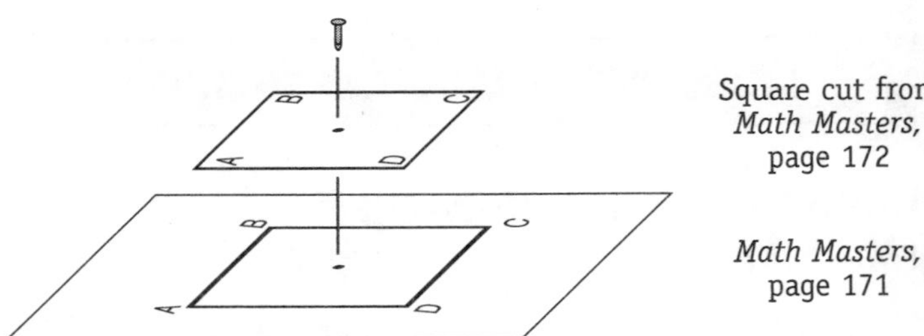

▷ Use a paper fastener to attach square *ABCD* on *Math Masters,* page 172 to the square on *Math Masters,* page 171, as shown above. Explain to students that the paper fastener will represent the point around which the square is rotated.

▷ Demonstrate how the square can be rotated around the paper fastener in the four ways shown on *Student Reference Book,* page 171.

Continue reading the remainder of page 171 in the *Student Reference Book.* Students will use the concept of **point symmetry** to complete the Challenge problem on journal page 394 as well as an optional activity.

✦Determining the Order of Rotation Symmetry
(*Math Journal 2,* p. 394 and Activity Sheet 7)

PARTNER ACTIVITY

Students complete journal page 394, using the figures they cut out from Activity Sheet 7 and the procedure that you modeled with the square. Circulate and assist. Students will need to look at a deck of regular playing cards to solve the Challenge problem. When most students have finished, bring the class together to discuss the answers.

ONGOING ASSESSMENT

Use students' answers to Problems 1–4 on journal page 394 to assess their understanding of rotation symmetry. Since this is their first exposure to rotation symmetry, expect that many students may find the concept confusing.

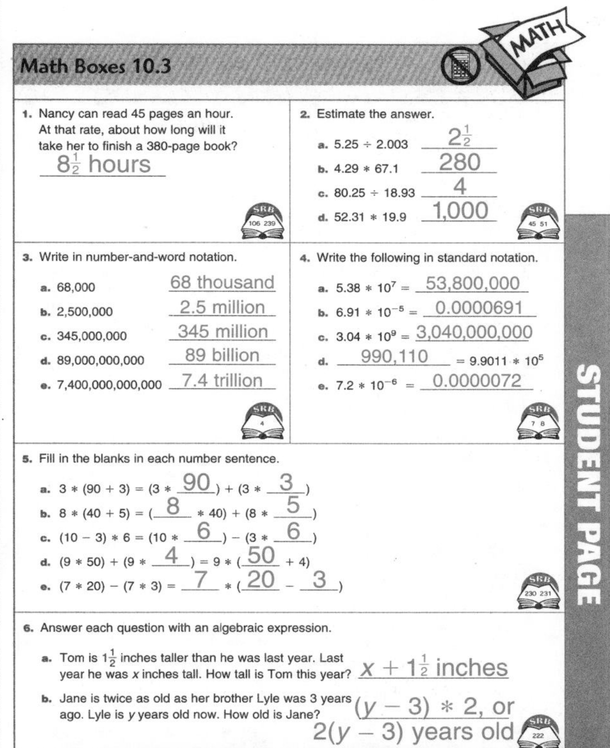

Math Boxes 10.3

1. Nancy can read 45 pages an hour. At that rate, about how long will it take her to finish a 380-page book? $8\frac{1}{2}$ hours

2. Estimate the answer.
   a. 5.25 ÷ 2.003 $2\frac{1}{2}$
   b. 4.29 ∗ 67.1 280
   c. 80.25 ÷ 18.93 4
   d. 52.31 ∗ 19.9 1,000

3. Write in number-and-word notation.
   a. 68,000 68 thousand
   b. 2,500,000 2.5 million
   c. 345,000,000 345 million
   d. 89,000,000,000 89 billion
   e. 7,400,000,000,000 7.4 trillion

4. Write the following in standard notation.
   a. $5.38 * 10^7$ = 53,800,000
   b. $6.91 * 10^{-5}$ = 0.0000691
   c. $3.04 * 10^9$ = 3,040,000,000
   d. 990,110 = $9.9011 * 10^5$
   e. $7.2 * 10^{-6}$ = 0.0000072

5. Fill in the blanks in each number sentence.
   a. 3 ∗ (90 + 3) = (3 ∗ 90) + (3 ∗ 3)
   b. 8 ∗ (40 + 5) = (8 ∗ 40) + (8 ∗ 5)
   c. (10 − 3) ∗ 6 = (10 ∗ 6) − (3 ∗ 6)
   d. (9 ∗ 50) + (9 ∗ 4) = 9 ∗ (50 + 4)
   e. (7 ∗ 20) − (7 ∗ 3) = 7 ∗ (20 − 3)

6. Answer each question with an algebraic expression.
   a. Tom is $1\frac{1}{2}$ inches taller than he was last year. Last year he was *x* inches tall. How tall is Tom this year? $x + 1\frac{1}{2}$ inches
   b. Jane is twice as old as her brother Lyle was 3 years ago. Lyle is *y* years old now. How old is Jane? $(y - 3) * 2$, or $2(y - 3)$ years old

STUDENT PAGE

✧ *Math Journal 2,* p. 395

Ongoing Learning & Practice

✦Math Boxes 10.3 (*Math Journal 2,* p. 395)

INDEPENDENT ACTIVITY 

Mixed Review Math Boxes in this lesson are paired with Math Boxes in Lesson 10.6.

✦Study Link 10.3 (*Math Masters,* p. 378)

Home Connection Students draw lines of reflection symmetry and determine the order of rotation symmetry for given figures.

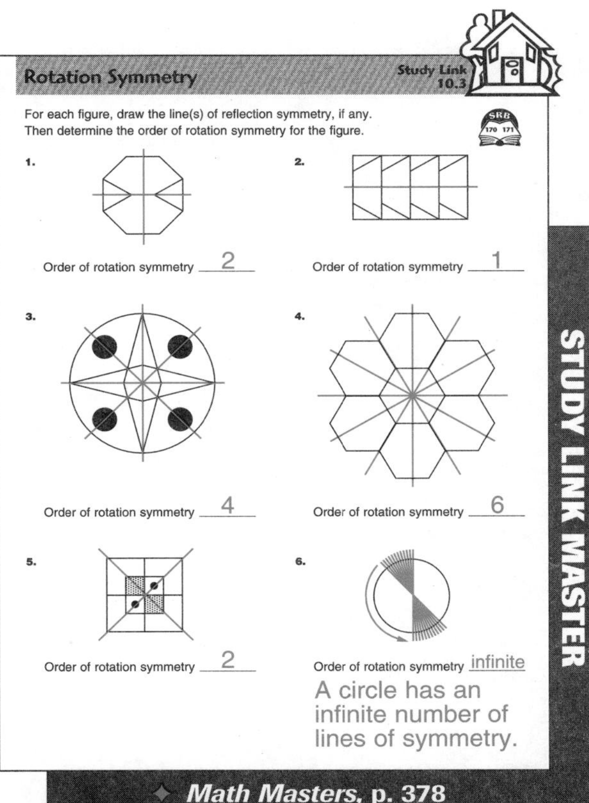

Rotation Symmetry — Study Link 10.3

For each figure, draw the line(s) of reflection symmetry, if any. Then determine the order of rotation symmetry for the figure.

1. Order of rotation symmetry 2
2. Order of rotation symmetry 1
3. Order of rotation symmetry 4
4. Order of rotation symmetry 6
5. Order of rotation symmetry 2
6. Order of rotation symmetry infinite

A circle has an infinite number of lines of symmetry.

STUDY LINK MASTER

✧ *Math Masters,* p. 378

STUDENT PAGE

Art and Design Activities

Rotation Symmetry

A Point-Symmetry Magic Trick

Setting the Stage Tell a friend that you will be able to guess which playing card, from a set of four, she or he turns upside down while you are not looking.

Materials ☐ four cards from a regular deck of playing cards:
- 1 card with point symmetry
- 3 cards without point symmetry

Performing the Trick

Step 1: Place the four playing cards in a row, faceup. Of the cards shown at the right, only the 10 of hearts has point symmetry. The other three cards do not.

Step 2: Turn your back to the four cards, but be sure to study the position of the figures on the cards before you do. Tell your friend to rotate one of the cards 180 degrees (turn it upside down).

Step 3: Turn around, study the cards, and tell which card your friend turned. If your friend has turned one of the three cards without point symmetry, it will be easy to determine that it was rotated. For example:

The middle spade is now pointing toward the bottom of the card.	The middle diamond is now at the bottom of the card.	The stem of the middle club is now pointing toward the bottom of the card.
original position / 180° rotation	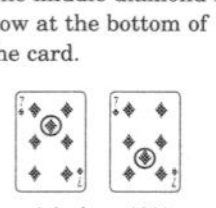 original position / 180° rotation	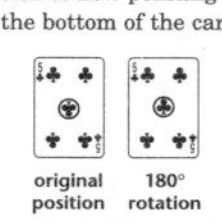 original position / 180° rotation

If none of the cards without point symmetry has been rotated, then the one card with point symmetry must have been rotated.

This may seem like a simple trick, but that's because you know how it works. Many cards look almost the same before and after they have been rotated 180°.

three hundred twenty-one

✧ *Student Reference Book*, p. 321

3 Options for Individualizing

✦ ENRICHMENT Performing a Point-Symmetry Magic Trick (*Student Reference Book*, p. 321)

INDEPENDENT ACTIVITY  **15–30 min** 

Students learn a point-symmetry magic trick. Provide time for those students who learn the trick to perform it for the class.

✦ RETEACHING Reviewing Reflection Symmetry (*Math Masters*, p. 173)

PARTNER ACTIVITY  **5–15 min** 

Students use reflective transparent mirrors to identify and explore lines of symmetry in figures and designs.

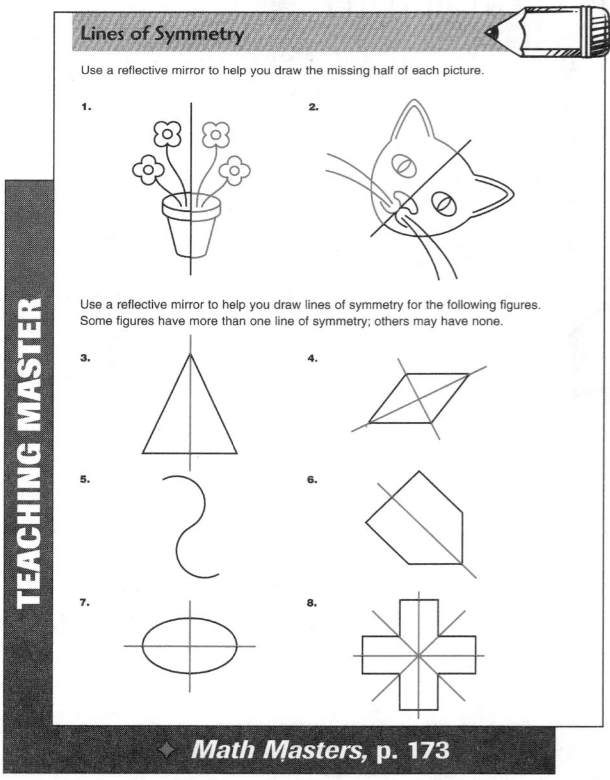

TEACHING MASTER

Lines of Symmetry

Use a reflective mirror to help you draw the missing half of each picture.

1.

2.

Use a reflective mirror to help you draw lines of symmetry for the following figures. Some figures have more than one line of symmetry; others may have none.

3.

4.

5.

6.

7.

8.

✧ *Math Masters*, p. 173

✦ EXTRA PRACTICE Drawing Shapes with Rotation Symmetry of a Given Order

(*Student Reference Book*, p. 322)

INDEPENDENT ACTIVITY  **15–30 min**

Portfolio Ideas

Students follow a procedure to draw a shape with rotation symmetry of order 3. Guide students to discover that it is also possible to draw shapes with rotation symmetry of other orders by using the fact that a complete rotation is 360°. *For example:*

- ▷ To draw a shape with rotation symmetry of order 2, draw two rays from one point, separated by 180°. (The rays form a line.)
- ▷ To draw a shape with rotation symmetry of order 4, draw four rays from one point so that each ray is separated from the next ray by 90°. (The rays form angles of 90°.)
- ▷ To draw a shape with rotation symmetry of order 5, draw five rays from one point, separated by 72°.
- ▷ To draw a shape with rotation symmetry of order 6, draw six rays from one point, separated by 60°.

In general, to draw a shape with rotation symmetry of order *n,* draw *n* rays from one point, separated by 360 / *n* degrees.

STUDENT PAGE

Art and Design Activities

Drawing Shapes with Rotation Symmetry of a Given Order

Materials
- ☐ sharp pencil
- ☐ blank piece of paper
- ☐ protractor
- ☐ compass
- ☐ scissors
- ☐ index card or other card stock

Directions

Step 1: On a blank piece of paper, use a sharp pencil to *lightly* draw three rays coming from one point. The rays should be separated by 120°, forming three 120° angles.

120° 120° 120°

Step 2: Cut out any shape you wish from an index card. The first time that you try this activity, you might want to work with a simple shape. Once you have learned the procedure, you could try a more complicated shape.

Step 3: Draw a line anywhere through the shape.

Step 4: Push the point of your compass through the shape at any point along the line that you drew. Place the compass point on the paper with the three rays at the point where the rays intersect. Match the line on the shape with one of the rays.

Step 5: When the shape is lined up properly, remove the compass. Hold the shape in place, and trace around it. Replace the compass point, and use it to rotate the shape so that the line on the shape matches up with the next ray. Remove the compass, and trace around the shape. Repeat the procedure for the third ray.

Step 6: Erase any interior lines. The outer edges of the three tracings form a shape with rotation symmetry of order 3. You might want to use tracing paper to copy your shape and check if it is symmetric.

Use this procedure to create a shape with a rotation symmetry of order 2. Then create a shape with a rotation symmetry of order 5.

SRB 322 **three hundred twenty-two**

✧ *Student Reference Book*, p. 322

10.4 Cross Sections of Clay Solids

OBJECTIVES **To construct geometric solids out of clay; to visualize what happens when a solid is sliced by a plane; and to describe the shapes of cross sections.**

summaries	materials
1 Teaching the Lesson	
Students attempt to visualize what happens when a solid is sliced at a particular location and angle. They test their visualizations by slicing their clay models. They name or describe the cross sections formed. [Geometry]	☐ *Math Journal 2,* pp. 396–398 ☐ *Student Reference Book,* pp. 152 and 153; optional ☐ Study Link 10.3 ☐ Transparency (Study Link 10.3; optional) For demonstration purposes: ☐ 3 carrots ☐ orange ☐ sharp knife ☐ cutting board Per partnership: ☐ clay or modeling compound ☐ dental floss or cheese slicer ☐ conical paper cup (optional) ☐ slate ☐ *Stephen Biesty's Incredible Cross Sections* and/or *Stephen Biesty's Incredible Explosions* (optional) ***See*** **Advance Preparation**
2 Ongoing Learning & Practice	
Students practice and maintain skills through Math Boxes and Study Link activities.	☐ *Math Journal 2,* p. 399 ☐ Study Link Master (*Math Masters,* p. 379) ☐ quarter
3 Options for Individualizing	
Enrichment Students solve more advanced cross-section problems. [Geometry]	☐ Teaching Masters (*Math Masters,* pp. 174–176) ☐ clay or modeling compound ☐ dental floss or cheese slicer ☐ cutting board

Additional Information

Advance Preparation You might want to make a transparency of Study Link 10.3 to assist in the review of these problems. To construct the clay solids for the second and third activities in Part 1, oil-base clays, such as the colored clays sold at toy stores, work best. Water-base clays dry out quickly if not stored correctly. For slicing the cross sections, a cheese slicer, consisting of a handle and a thin wire, works well. However, dental floss works almost as well and is easy to obtain. Knives and similar cutting tools tend to distort the clay as they move through it. Two books–*Stephen Biesty's Incredible Cross Sections* and *Stephen Biesty's Incredible Explosions*–show colorful cross sections of a variety of subjects, including a castle, a jumbo jet, and the Empire State Building. Both books are illustrated by Stephen Biesty with text by Richard Platt (Random House, 1992, 1996).

Vocabulary • **cross section**

Getting Started

Mental Math and Reflexes

Have students answer each of the following questions on their slates by writing an algebraic expression with one variable.

- Dave has x cents. Amy has 25 cents less than Dave. How much money does Amy have? $x - 25$ cents
- Eric ran M miles this week. Denise ran 3.6 miles farther than Eric. How many miles did Denise run? $M + 3.6$ miles
- Julie ate c apples this week. Scott ate 4 times as many apples as Julie. How many apples did Scott eat? $4 * c$, or $4c$ apples
- Frank has B books about the Civil War. Elaine has $\frac{1}{8}$ as many books about the Civil War as Frank. How many Civil War books does Elaine have? $B / 8$, or $B * \frac{1}{8}$ books

Math Message

Look up the definition of cross section *in the glossary of your* Student Reference Book.

Study Link 10.3 Follow-Up

Review the problems. A transparency of Study Link 10.3 will be helpful for demonstrating the answers.

1 Teaching the Lesson

✦Math Message Follow-Up (*Student Reference Book*)

WHOLE-CLASS DISCUSSION

Have a student read the definition of **cross section** in the *Student Reference Book.* Ask students to try to restate the definition in their own words. If this is difficult for many students, go on to the next activity and then return to the definition.

NOTE: If you were able to obtain either of the cross-section books described in Advance Preparation, now would be a good time to share them with the class.

✦Cutting Fruits and Vegetables to Introduce Cross Sections

WHOLE-CLASS ACTIVITY

Display a carrot to students and ask them to predict answers to the following questions. Consider having students draw a picture of their predictions on their slates, while volunteers share their predictions on the board or overhead projector. After each prediction, make the cut so that students can check their predictions.

- If I slice the carrot straight through, across its width, what will be the shape of the cross section I create? A circle, assuming the carrot is not lopsided

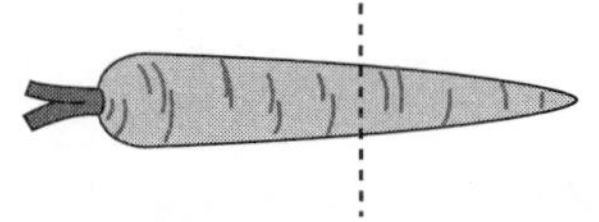

Cross section

STUDENT PAGE

Cross Sections of a Clay Cube

Form a clay cube. Draw your prediction of the shape of the cross section that will be formed by the first cut shown below. After making the cut, draw the actual shape and describe (name) the shape. Re-form the cube and repeat these steps for the other cuts.

Clay Cube	Predicted Shape of Cross Section	Actual Shape of Cross Section	Description of Shape
	Answers vary.		rectangle
			square
			triangle
			rectangle

◇ ***Math Journal 2*, p. 396**

- If the cut is made on a slant instead of straight, what will be the shape of the cross section I create? An oval or ellipse

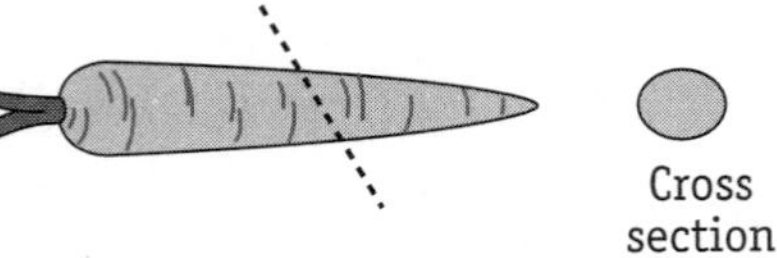

- What shape will I get if the cut is slanted even more? The more slanted the cut, the flatter the ellipse.

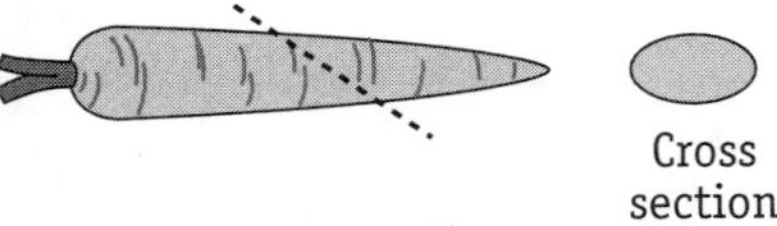

- What will the cross section look like if I cut the carrot lengthwise from tip to top? Something like a thin isosceles triangle with a curved base

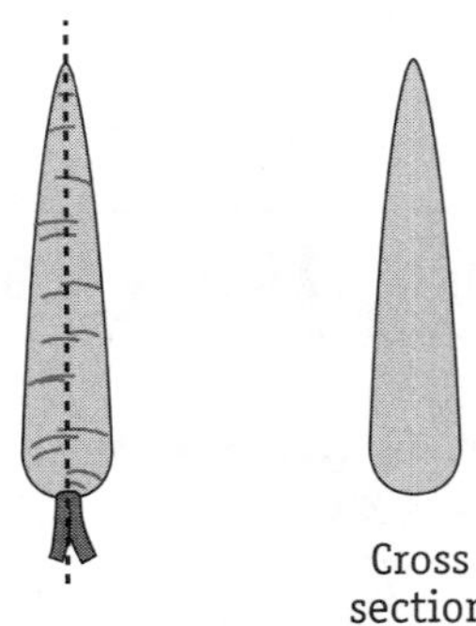

- What will the cross section of an orange look like? A circle, the size of which will vary, depending upon the location of the cut

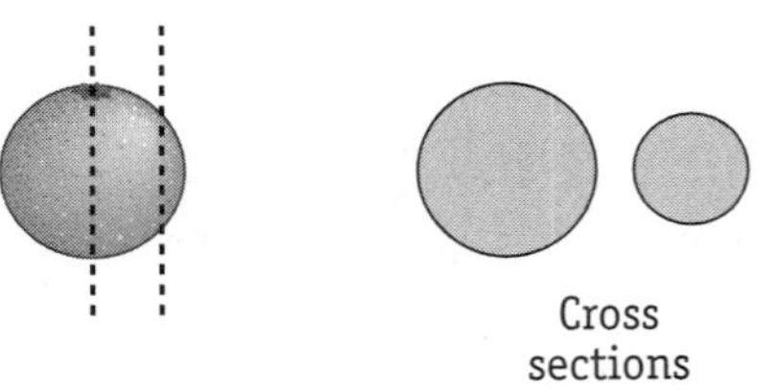

Adjusting the Activity Pair a student learning English with a proficient English speaker. The students draw pictures of their predictions on their slates. Have the less proficient English speaker describe the shapes of the drawings to a partner.

✦ Finding Cross Sections of Clay Solids
(*Math Journal 2,* p. 396)

WHOLE-CLASS ACTIVITY 

For this activity, you will need to construct a clay cube large enough for students to see and for you to work with comfortably. Call students' attention to the cube shown at the top left corner of journal page 396. The dotted lines represent the hidden edges on the opposite sides of the cube.

The first column shows the cube again, with arrows indicating the direction and angle of the cut you will make. In the second column, students make a drawing representing their predictions of the shape of the cross section. Point out that they should draw only the 2-dimensional shape revealed by the cut, not the solid remaining after the cut. After slicing, students draw the actual cross section in the third column. In the last column, students write the name or description of the cross section's shape.

Ask students to predict the shape of the first cross section and to record it in the second column on journal page 396. Then make the cut. When slicing the clay, hold the slicer or dental floss taut and pull it slowly and smoothly through the clay. If the clay is on a cutting board or similar surface, it will be easier to make a clean cut. Ask a student to hold the cube while you cut.

In the third column, students record the actual shape of the cross section. Ask how the actual cross section compares to their predictions. Students should have no trouble describing (in Column 4) the shapes of the first two cross sections on journal page 396 as a rectangle and a square.

Let some students make slices for the third and fourth examples. They may need a little practice in order to make a reasonably straight slice through the clay.

By the time the four examples on journal page 396 have been completed, students will probably be ready to try some cross sections on their own.

Adjusting the Activity Many students may be ready to continue the activity on their own before the class completes all the examples on journal page 396. If so, as soon as they feel comfortable with the the assignment, encourage these students to break into partnerships.

Cross Sections of a Clay Cylinder

Form a clay cylinder. Draw your prediction of the shape of the cross section that will be formed by the first cut shown below. After making the cut, draw the actual shape and describe (name) the shape. Re-form the cylinder and repeat these steps for the other cuts.

Clay Cylinder	Predicted Shape of Cross Section	Actual Shape of Cross Section	Description of Shape
	Answers vary.		rectangle
			Closed parabola
			circle
			ellipse

STUDENT PAGE

✧ Math Journal 2, p. 397

NOTE: Journal pages 397 and 398 are used with the activity described on page 810.

Cross Sections of a Clay Cone

Form a clay cone. Draw your prediction of the shape of the cross section that will be formed by the first cut shown below. After making the cut, draw the actual shape and describe (name) the shape. Re-form the cone and repeat these steps for the other cuts.

Clay Cone	Predicted Shape of Cross Section	Actual Shape of Cross Section	Description of Shape
	Answers vary.		circle
			ellipse
			Closed parabola
			ellipse

STUDENT PAGE

✧ Math Journal 2, p. 398

✦ Finding Cross Sections of Clay Solids (*Math Journal 2,* pp. 397 and 398)

PARTNER ACTIVITY

Students complete journal pages 397 and 398. One partner should hold the solid while the other slices it.

Adjusting the Activity For students who struggle to name the shapes of the cross sections, refer them to *Student Reference Book,* pages 152 and 153.

Making an accurate cone (journal page 398) can be difficult. If conical cups from a water dispenser are available, consider having students fill a cup with clay to form the shape. Don't expect all students to come up with the correct answers even after slicing the solids. Students will vary in their abilities to visualize the cross sections, to form and slice the clay solid, and to name the plane figures formed. For example, on journal pages 397 and 398, a parabola is formed by one of the cuts. It is unlikely that students are familiar with this term. When reviewing the answers to journal pages 397 and 398, suggest that students find the word *parabola* in their *Student Reference Book* glossaries. Remember that this is an introductory experience with cross sections.

2 Ongoing Learning & Practice

✦ Math Boxes 10.4 (*Math Journal 2,* p. 399)

INDEPENDENT ACTIVITY 

Mixed Review Math Boxes in this lesson are paired with Math Boxes in Lesson 10.1.

✦ Study Link 10.4 (*Math Masters,* p. 379)

Home Connection Students attempt to solve the puzzle of passing a quarter through a hole the size of a dime. This Study Link is not related to cross sections but is intended as an introduction to the topic of the next lesson.

STUDENT PAGE

Math Boxes 10.4

1. Translate the word sentences below into number sentences. Do not solve or simplify them.

   < means "is less than"
   > means "is greater than"

   a. Five and one half is less than six. $5\frac{1}{2} < 6$
   b. Eighteen more than twelve is greater than two times seven. $18 + 12 > 2 * 7$
   c. One tenth times forty is equal to four. $\frac{1}{10} * 40 = 4$
   d. Three more than fourteen divided by seven is equal to five. $3 + (14 / 7) = 5$
   e. Nine decreased by four is less than seventeen decreased by two. $9 - 4 < 17 - 2$

2. Solve. (Solution)

   a. $15 * x = 60$ $x = 4$
   b. $\frac{q}{10} = 150$ $q = 1{,}500$
   c. $m + (-28) = -5$ $m = 23$
   d. $\frac{36}{s} + 5 = 9$ $s = 9$
   e. $-1 * t = -15$ $t = 15$

3. The formula for finding the volume of a rectangular prism is

   $V = l * w * h$

   where l is the length of the prism, w is the width, and h is the height. Use the formula to calculate the volume of this rectangular prism.

   (3 in., 2 in., 5 in.)

   Volume 30 in.^3

4. Multiply.

   a. $6.76 * 0.005 = 0.0338$
   b. $14.09 * 2.25 = 31.7025$

5. Multiply or divide. Write your answers in simplest form.

   a. $1\frac{3}{7} * 2\frac{1}{5} =$ $3\frac{5}{35}$, or $3\frac{1}{7}$
   b. $3\frac{6}{8} * \frac{28}{6} =$ $17\frac{24}{48}$, or $17\frac{1}{2}$
   c. $5\frac{1}{10} \div 2\frac{5}{4} =$ $1\frac{74}{130}$, or $1\frac{37}{65}$
   d. $\frac{46}{3} \div 20 =$ $\frac{46}{60}$, or $\frac{23}{30}$
   e. $5\frac{3}{5} * \frac{1}{8} =$ $\frac{28}{40}$, or $\frac{7}{10}$

✧ *Math Journal 2,* p. 399

STUDY LINK MASTER

Shrinking Quarter — Study Link 10.4

1. Cut out the circle in the center of this page. It is about the size of a dime. Try to slip a quarter through the hole left in the page without tearing the paper.

2. Were you able to do this trick? If you were, explain how you did it. If not, explain why you were not able to.

   Sample answer: I was able to do this trick by folding the paper in half, placing the quarter in the fold, and then bending the paper upward as I gripped it at the outer edges of the crease.

✧ *Math Masters,* p. 379

Options for Individualizing

✦ ENRICHMENT Solving Cross-Section Problems (*Math Masters*, pp. 174–176)

INDEPENDENT ACTIVITY  **15–30 min** 

Math Masters, pages 174–176 provide interested students with additional, more advanced cross-section problems.

Cross Sections of a Clay Pyramid

Pyramid with square base

Form a clay pyramid with a square base. Draw your prediction of the shape of the cross section that will be formed by the first cut shown below. After making the cut, draw the actual shape and describe (name) the shape. Re-form the pyramid and repeat these steps for the other cuts.

Clay Pyramid	Predicted Shape of Cross Section	Actual Shape of Cross Section	Description of Shape
	Answers vary.		triangle
			square
			triangle
			trapezoid

TEACHING MASTER

✦ *Math Masters,* p. 174

Cross Sections of a Clay Torus

Torus (doughnut)

Form a clay torus. Draw your prediction of the shape of the cross section that will be formed by the first cut shown below. After making the cut, draw the actual shape and describe (name) the shape. Re-form the torus and repeat these steps for the other cuts.

Clay Torus	Predicted Shape of Cross Section	Actual Shape of Cross Section	Description of Shape
	Answers vary.		Sample answers: Two circles
			A pinched oval
			Two "teardrops"
			A "smile"

TEACHING MASTER

✦ *Math Masters,* p. 175

Cross Sections of a Clay Prism

Triangular prism

Form a clay triangular prism. Draw your prediction of the shape of the cross section that will be formed by the first cut shown below. After making the cut, draw the actual shape and describe (name) the shape. Re-form the triangular prism and repeat these steps for the other cuts.

Clay Prism	Predicted Shape of Cross Section	Actual Shape of Cross Section	Description of Shape
	Answers vary.		rectangle
			rectangle
			triangle
			triangle

TEACHING MASTER

✦ *Math Masters,* p. 176

10.5 Introduction to Topology

OBJECTIVES **To introduce topology; and to perform topological transformations.**

summaries	materials
1 Teaching the Lesson	
Students explore how to transform a coffee mug into a doughnut, without tearing, breaking, or "sticking together." Students use clay and rubber sheets to explore topological transformations. [Geometry]	□ *Math Journal 2,* pp. 400, 402, and 403 □ *Student Reference Book,* pp. 172 and 173 □ Study Link 10.4 □ Geometry Template □ slate Optional items: □ coffee mug with single handle □ doughnut with hole □ juice glass without handle □ scissors □ clay or modeling compound Per partnership: □ 3 disposable latex gloves or Silly Putty® (optional) □ 1 permanent marker ***See* Advance Preparation**
2 Ongoing Learning & Practice	
Students play *Solution Search.* [Patterns, Functions, and Algebra] Students practice and maintain skills through Math Boxes and Study Link activities.	□ *Math Journal 2,* p. 401 □ *Student Reference Book,* p. 304 □ Teaching Master (*Math Masters,* p. 110) □ Study Link Master (*Math Masters,* p. 380)
3 Options for Individualizing	
Extra Practice Students solve topology puzzles. [Geometry]	□ Teaching Master (*Math Masters,* p. 177) □ pencil □ string □ scissors □ large button

Additional Information

Background Information Topology is a modern branch of mathematics dealing with the properties of geometric objects that remain the same when the objects are changed by such means as shrinking, stretching, or twisting. Tearing, breaking, and "sticking together" are not permitted.

Advance Preparation For the first activity in Part 1, you will need to gather enough clay or modeling compound so that everyone can have a handful. If you do not have enough clay, students might complete this activity in partnerships, or you can do a class demonstration. You might also want three latex gloves per partnership for the activities on journal pages 402 and 403. Like the clay, these materials are optional, but the activities are most effective if students have hands-on participation. (Be alert to students who may be allergic to the materials suggested.) Silly Putty® is an expensive but effective alternative to gloves. Encourage students who have this product at home to bring it to school and try the transformations.

Vocabulary • **topology** • **topologically equivalent** • **topological transformation** • **genus** • **rubber-sheet geometry** • **topological property** • **transference of curves**

Getting Started

Mental Math and Reflexes

If a 12-sided die is rolled, what is the probability of getting

- 11? $\frac{1}{12}$
- an odd number? $\frac{6}{12}$, or $\frac{1}{2}$
- a multiple of 3? $\frac{4}{12}$, or $\frac{1}{3}$
- a number that is neither prime nor composite? The number 1, so the probability is $\frac{1}{12}$.
- a factor of 48? The numbers are 1, 2, 3, 4, 6, 8, and 12, so the probability is $\frac{7}{12}$.

Math Message

Complete the problem on page 400 in your journal.

Study Link 10.4 Follow-Up

Ask students to explain how they were able to pass the quarter through the dime-size hole. Sample answer: Fold the paper in half, place the quarter in the fold, and then bend the paper upward as you grip it at the outer edges of the crease. With a little manipulation but no tearing of the paper, the quarter will slip through the dime-size hole.

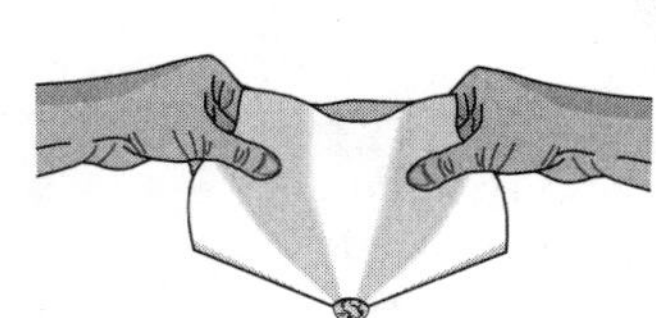

You may wish to return to Study Link 10.4 during the discussion Introducing Topology in Part 1 on page 815. Folding and bending the paper distorts the circle into an ellipse. An ellipse and a circle are topologically equivalent.

1 Teaching the Lesson

✦ Math Message Follow-Up (*Math Journal 2,* p. 400)

WHOLE-CLASS DISCUSSION 

Ask students to share their thoughts regarding the similarities and differences between a coffee mug and a doughnut. Perhaps draw a Venn diagram on the board to record students' responses. Explain to students that today they will learn about a branch of mathematics called **topology.** Topologically speaking, there is no difference between a doughnut and a coffee mug.

NOTE: If you brought a doughnut and a coffee mug to class, refer to them during the discussion of the Math Message problem.

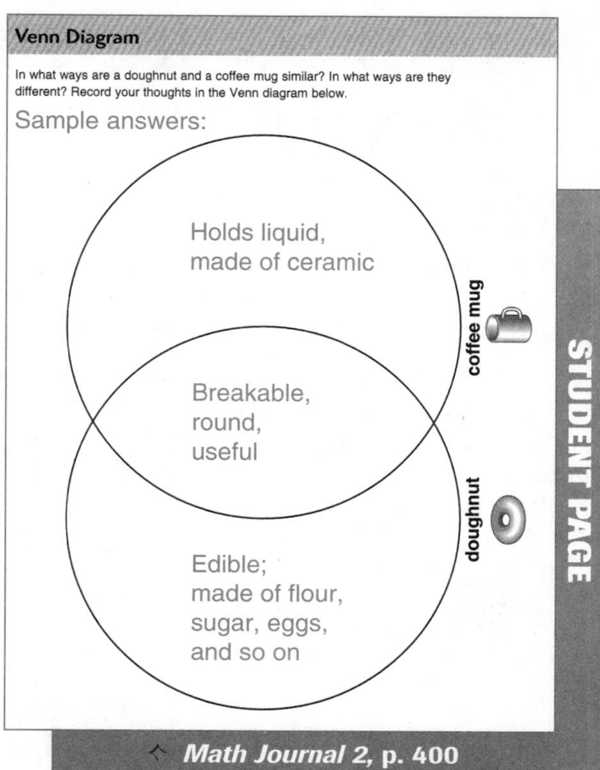

Math Journal 2, p. 400

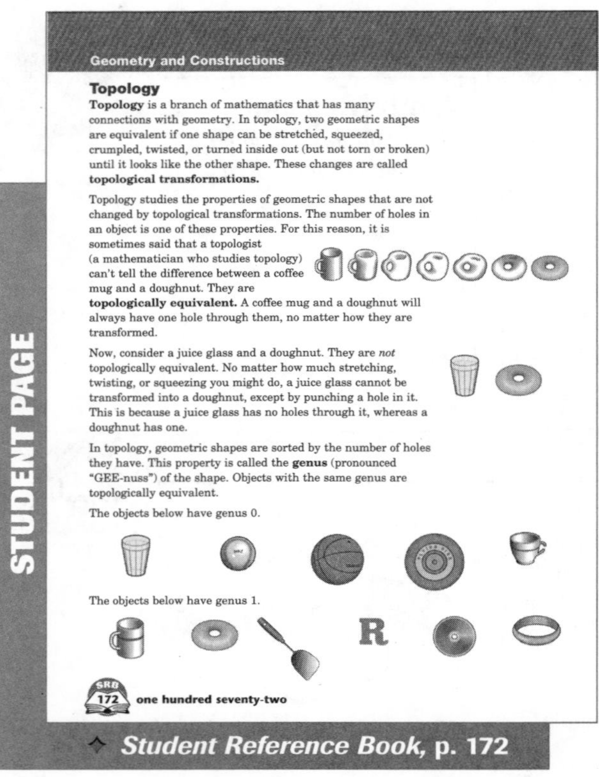
STUDENT PAGE

Geometry and Constructions

Topology

Topology is a branch of mathematics that has many connections with geometry. In topology, two geometric shapes are equivalent if one shape can be stretched, squeezed, crumpled, twisted, or turned inside out (but not torn or broken) until it looks like the other shape. These changes are called **topological transformations.**

Topology studies the properties of geometric shapes that are not changed by topological transformations. The number of holes in an object is one of these properties. For this reason, it is sometimes said that a topologist (a mathematician who studies topology) can't tell the difference between a coffee mug and a doughnut. They are **topologically equivalent.** A coffee mug and a doughnut will always have one hole through them, no matter how they are transformed.

Now, consider a juice glass and a doughnut. They are *not* topologically equivalent. No matter how much stretching, twisting, or squeezing you might do, a juice glass cannot be transformed into a doughnut, except by punching a hole in it. This is because a juice glass has no holes through it, whereas a doughnut has one.

In topology, geometric shapes are sorted by the number of holes they have. This property is called the **genus** (pronounced "GEE-nuss") of the shape. Objects with the same genus are topologically equivalent.

The objects below have genus 0.

The objects below have genus 1.

SRB 172 one hundred seventy-two

Student Reference Book, p. 172

NOTE: The mathematical name for a doughnut-shaped object is *torus*.

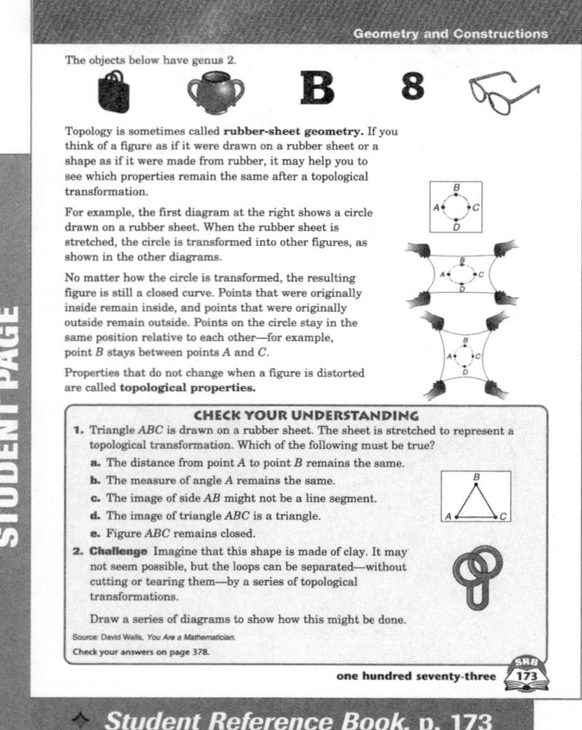
STUDENT PAGE

Geometry and Constructions

The objects below have genus 2.

Topology is sometimes called **rubber-sheet geometry.** If you think of a figure as if it were drawn on a rubber sheet or a shape as if it were made from rubber, it may help you to see which properties remain the same after a topological transformation.

For example, the first diagram at the right shows a circle drawn on a rubber sheet. When the rubber sheet is stretched, the circle is transformed into other figures, as shown in the other diagrams.

No matter how the circle is transformed, the resulting figure is still a closed curve. Points that were originally inside remain inside, and points that were originally outside remain outside. Points on the circle stay in the same position relative to each other—for example, point B stays between points A and C.

Properties that do not change when a figure is distorted are called **topological properties.**

CHECK YOUR UNDERSTANDING

1. Triangle ABC is drawn on a rubber sheet. The sheet is stretched to represent a topological transformation. Which of the following must be true?
   a. The distance from point A to point B remains the same.
   b. The measure of angle A remains the same.
   c. The image of side AB might not be a line segment.
   d. The image of triangle ABC is a triangle.
   e. Figure ABC remains closed.

2. **Challenge** Imagine that this shape is made of clay. It may not seem possible, but the loops can be separated—without cutting or tearing them—by a series of topological transformations.

   Draw a series of diagrams to show how this might be done.

Source: David Wells, *You Are a Mathematician.*

Check your answers on page 378.

one hundred seventy-three SRB 173

Student Reference Book, p. 173

✦ Transforming a Coffee Mug into a Doughnut

WHOLE-CLASS ACTIVITY 

Distribute a handful of clay to each student. (*Note:* This activity may also be done as a class demonstration.) Ask students to form a coffee mug similar to the one illustrated on journal page 400. Expect that these models will be very rough approximations. Next, challenge students to transform the coffee mug into a doughnut. Tell them that while attempting to do so, they may not tear apart, cut and paste together, or poke a hole through any part of the mug. Allow time for students to complete the transformation. When a majority of the class has completed the work, have students share their procedures and results.

Many students may have discovered that they can gradually compress the walls of the mug and distribute that material along the handle. See the illustration on page 172 of the *Student Reference Book.*

ONGOING ASSESSMENT

Expect that students will meet with various levels of success as they work with the clay. This activity is an opportunity for students to experiment with some of the transformations associated with topology. Keep in mind the limits of the material that students are working with. Theoretically, the material should be infinitely malleable.

Now ask students whether they can transform their doughnut into a juice glass. (Display a juice glass if you brought one to class.) Caution students that the same rules still apply—they may not tear apart, cut and paste together, or poke a hole through any part of the figure. After some experimentation, guide students to conclude that the transformation is *not* possible. A juice glass may appear to have a hole, but it is actually just an indentation of the material. If students think they did the transformation, ask them to try to reverse it without poking a hole. It is impossible to turn a figure with one hole into a figure with no holes without breaking the rules of topological transformations.

Ask the class whether it is possible to turn a baseball into a juice glass. Why or why not? It is possible. A baseball has no holes, nor does a juice glass. An indentation in the center of the baseball transforms it into a juice glass. Is it possible to turn a baseball into a single-handle coffee mug? No. The baseball has no holes, but a single-handle coffee mug has one hole. It would be impossible to transform the baseball without making a hole in it and breaking the rules.

✦ Introducing Topology
(*Student Reference Book,* pp. 172 and 173)

WHOLE-CLASS DISCUSSION

As a class, read the essay on pages 172 and 173 of the *Student Reference Book.* Be sure to include the following points in your discussion:

- ▷ Topology has many connections to geometry.
- ▷ Two geometric shapes are said to be **topologically equivalent** if one shape can be stretched, squeezed, crumpled, twisted, or turned inside out (but not torn or broken) until it looks like the other.
- ▷ In topology, the number of holes that an object has and the relative position of points are two properties that remain the same after **topological transformations.**
- ▷ A geometric shape can be classified according to its **genus**—the number of holes it has.

Challenge the class to name other objects that have a genus of 0, 1, or 2. Sample answers: 0: grapefruit, pencil; 1: needle, drinking straw; 2: letter B, figure 8 Name an object with a genus of 3. Pretzel, piece of 3-hole-punched notebook paper Name an object with a genus of 4. button What is the genus of the Geometry Template? 64

NOTE: Although topology is sometimes considered to be a branch of geometry, it includes concepts both from algebra, such as group theory, and from analysis, such as limits and continuity. This lesson introduces only some simple geometric aspects of topology. Students will encounter more rigorous work with topology later in their study of mathematics. Point out that students are familiar with transformations, such as slides, flips, and turns, that leave size and shape unchanged. However, topological transformations may change a figure's size and shape.

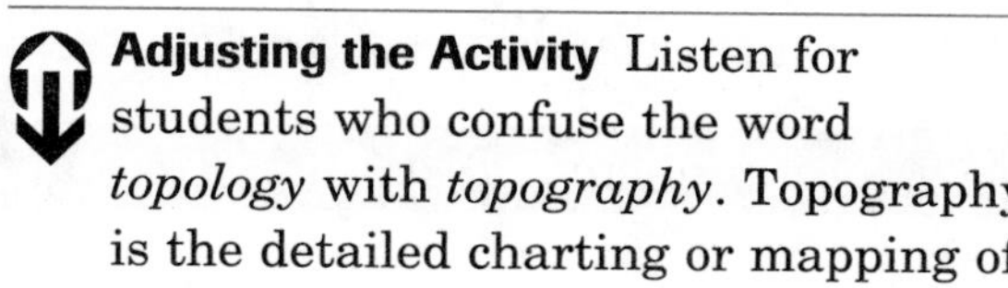

Adjusting the Activity Listen for students who confuse the word *topology* with *topography*. Topography is the detailed charting or mapping of the features of a region.

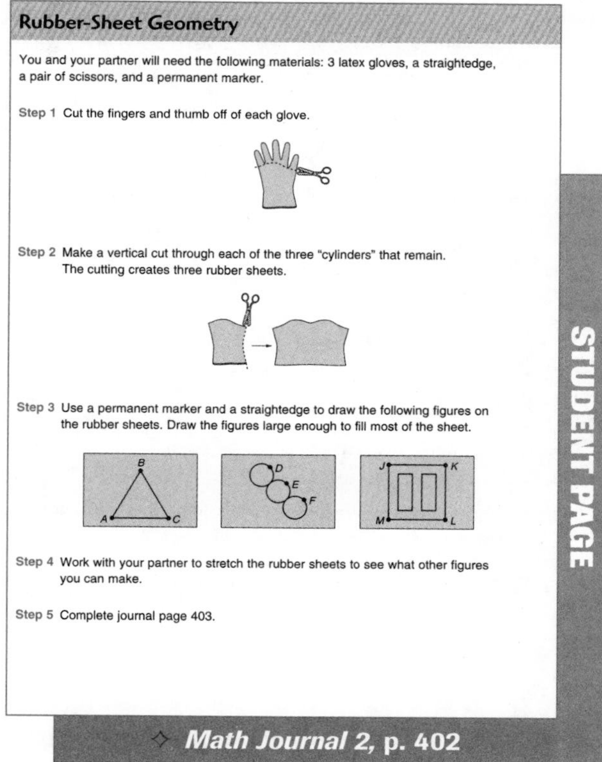

Rubber-Sheet Geometry

You and your partner will need the following materials: 3 latex gloves, a straightedge, a pair of scissors, and a permanent marker.

Step 1 Cut the fingers and thumb off of each glove.

Step 2 Make a vertical cut through each of the three "cylinders" that remain. The cutting creates three rubber sheets.

Step 3 Use a permanent marker and a straightedge to draw the following figures on the rubber sheets. Draw the figures large enough to fill most of the sheet.

Step 4 Work with your partner to stretch the rubber sheets to see what other figures you can make.

Step 5 Complete journal page 403.

STUDENT PAGE

✧ *Math Journal 2,* p. 402

Rubber-Sheet Geometry *(cont.)*

1. Experiment with the figures on your rubber sheets. Circle any of the figures in the right-hand column that are topologically equivalent to the corresponding original figure in the left-hand column.

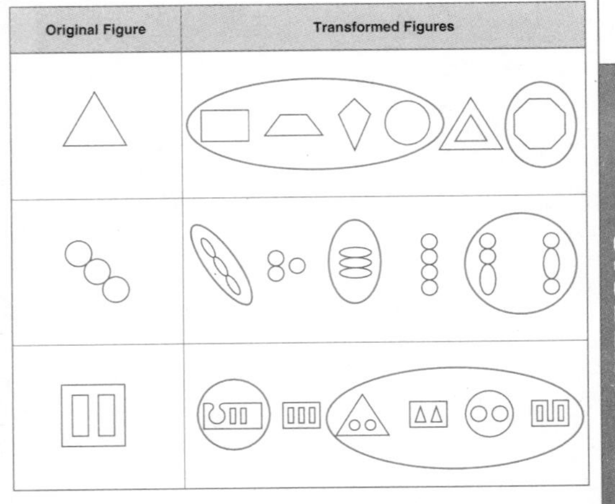

2. Choose one of the above figures that you did not circle and explain why it is not topologically equivalent to its original figure.
Answers vary. The uncircled figures are not topologically equivalent to the originals because they have a different number of holes.

STUDENT PAGE

◇ *Math Journal 2,* p. 403

Math Boxes 10.5

1. Find the following measures for a circle with a radius of 4 cm.
Diameter 8 cm
Circumference About 25.13 cm
Area About 50.27 cm^2
Explain how you found the circumference.
Sample answer: Multiply the diameter (8 cm) times π.

2. Evaluate each expression. Use the rules for order of operations. Do not use a calculator.
a. $4 * \frac{7}{2} + 7 =$ 21
b. $8 + (-15) * 6 =$ −82
c. $\frac{6^2}{9} + 3 * 4 =$ 16
d. $8 + 7 - (-2) * 5 =$ 25
e. $12 / 6 + 9 * 3 =$ 29

3. Write each number in scientific notation.
a. There are about 12,000,000,000 chickens in the world, or $1.2 * 10^{10}$ chickens.
b. A trained tracking dog can follow the sweat scent left by a foot when only 0.00000000004 gram of sweat, or $4 * 10^{-11}$ gram, is present.
c. There are 60,000,000,000,000 cells, or $6 * 10^{13}$ cells, in the body.
d. When a toilet is flushed, between 5,000,000,000 and 10,000,000,000 water droplets, or between $5 * 10^9$ and $1 * 10^{10}$ water droplets, are released into the air.
e. The smallest dust particles are about 0.01 centimeter, or $1 * 10^{-2}$ centimeter, in width.

Sources: The Top Ten of Everything, 1996; The Sizesaurus

STUDENT PAGE

◇ *Math Journal 2,* p. 401

✦Exploring Topological Transformations (*Math Journal 2,* pp. 402 and 403)

PARTNER ACTIVITY

If your class does not have gloves or Silly Putty®, omit the activity on journal page 402 and have partnerships proceed to journal page 403. Students should be able to visualize the transformations on journal page 403 without the use of rubber sheets. However, this activity is most effective if students can actually perform the transformations illustrated.

Circulate and assist. When a majority of the class has completed journal page 403, gather the students together and discuss their experiences.

Students probably noticed that they were able to change line segments into curves, short line segments into longer line segments, and small angles into larger angles. Straightness and length are *not* topological properties. These properties change as a result of a topological transformation.

Some students will notice properties of the figures that did not change when the figures were stretched and distorted—for example, the number of holes and the order of the points along a curve. These are examples of **topological properties**—that is, properties that do *not* change when the figure is distorted.

If you wish, ask students to demonstrate, using their rubber sheets, how one figure can be transformed into another. For example, demonstrate how the rubber sheet can be stretched to transform an equilateral triangle into a kite.

2 Ongoing Learning & Practice

✦Playing *Solution Search* (*Student Reference Book,* p. 304; *Math Masters,* p. 110)

SMALL-GROUP ACTIVITY

Students practice solving open number sentences by playing *Solution Search,* first introduced in Lesson 6.12. Students may create their own sets of *Solution Search* cards to use in place of the ones provided.

✦ Math Boxes 10.5 (*Math Journal 2,* p. 401)

INDEPENDENT ACTIVITY 

Mixed Review Math Boxes in this lesson are paired with Math Boxes in Lesson 10.2.

✦ Study Link 10.5 (*Math Masters,* p. 380)

Home Connection Students learn how to perform a trick that works because of a principle in topology called **transference of curves.**

3 Options for Individualizing

✦ EXTRA PRACTICE Solving Topological Puzzles (*Math Masters,* p. 177)

PARTNER ACTIVITY **15–30 min**

Students solve topological puzzles. To solve Puzzle 1, students thread the pencil through the buttonhole and the loop of string together as in the illustration below. To solve Puzzle 2, students pull the loop back through the scissors holes to pass the button through.

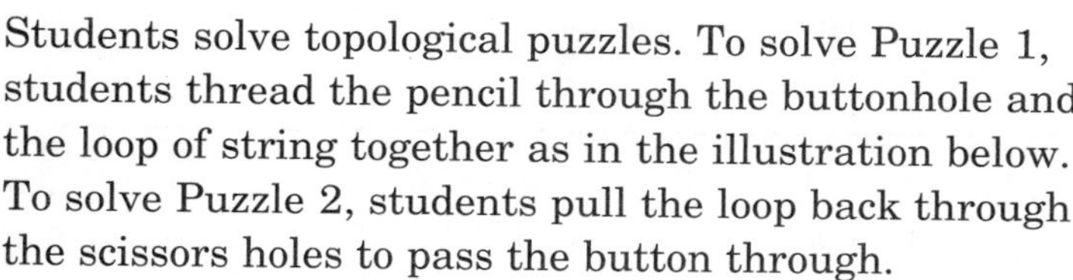

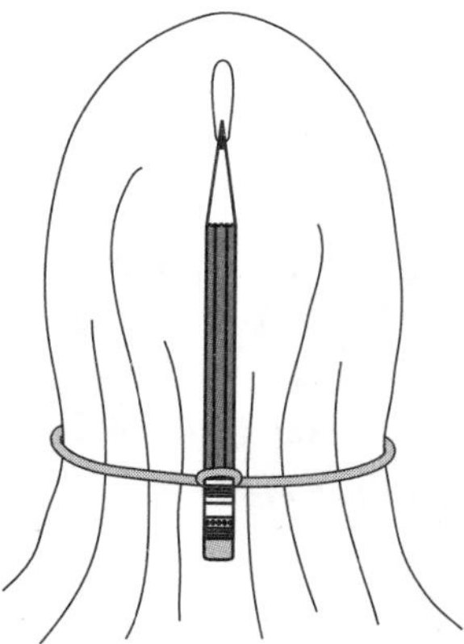

Pull the fabric with the button hole through the loop of string, then thread the pencil through the button hole.

A Topology Trick Study Link 10.5

SRB 172 173

Follow the procedure described below to tie a knot in a piece of string without letting go of the ends.

Step 1 Place a piece of string in front of you on a table or a desk.

Step 2 Fold your arms across your chest.

Step 3 With your arms still folded, grab the left end of the string with your right hand and the right end of the string with your left hand.

Step 4 Hold the ends of the string and unfold your arms. The string should now have a knot in it.

This trick works because of a principle in topology called **transference of curves.** Your arms had a knot in them before you picked up the string. When you unfolded your arms, you transferred the knot from your arms to the string.

STUDY LINK MASTER

✦ *Math Masters,* p. 380

Topology Puzzles

Puzzle #1

Get a pencil and a piece of string. The string should be about $1\frac{1}{2}$ times the length of the pencil. You will also need a shirt or a jacket with a buttonhole.

Tie the two ends of the string together at the top of the pencil so that the string forms a loop, as shown in Figure 1.

Figure out how to attach the pencil to the buttonhole, as shown in Figure 2.

Figure 1

Figure 2

Puzzle #2

Get a pair of scissors, a piece of string, and a large button. The button must be larger than the finger holes in the scissors.

Tie the ends of the string to the holes in the button to form a large loop of string.

Figure out how to attach the button to the scissors as shown in Figure 3.

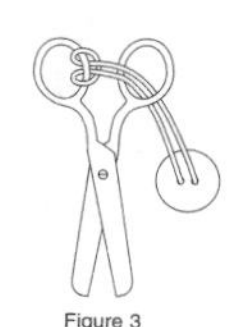

Figure 3

Explain how these puzzles involve topology.

Sample answer: The "shape" of the objects (the way they are attached to each other) change, but the topological properties (the number of holes and the order of points on each object) do not change.

TEACHING MASTER

✦ *Math Masters,* p. 177

10.6 Möbius Strips

OBJECTIVE To experiment with Möbius strips.

summaries	materials
1 Teaching the Lesson	
Students are introduced to the Möbius strip, a topological curiosity that has only one side and one edge. Students experiment with Möbius strips by cutting them in different ways to produce a variety of results. [Geometry]	□ *Math Journal 2,* pp. 404, 406, and 407 □ Study Link 10.5 □ marker, crayon, or pencil □ tape □ scissors □ sheet of newspaper or adding machine tape ***See* Advance Preparation**
2 Ongoing Learning & Practice	
Students complete a Unit 10 review of geometry topics. [Geometry] Students practice and maintain skills through Math Boxes and Study Link activities.	□ *Math Journal 2,* pp. 405 and 408 □ Study Link Master (*Math Masters,* p. 381) ***See* Advance Preparation**
3 Options for Individualizing	
Enrichment Students read an essay about August Ferdinand Möbius. [Geometry] **Enrichment** Students read a poem about Möbius strips. [Geometry]	□ *Student Reference Book,* p. 327 □ *Math Talk: Mathematical Ideas in Poems for Two Voices* ***See* Advance Preparation**

Additional Information

Advance Preparation For Part 1, cut a strip of newspaper about $1\frac{1}{2}$ inches wide and as long as possible or use a strip of adding machine tape about 2 feet long. Save the remaining newspaper for later in the lesson. Tape the ends of the strip together, making sure that there are no twists. Display the strip of paper next to the Math Message.

Note that for the Study Link in Part 2, students will need paper clips, a rubber band, and a strip of paper.

For the second optional Enrichment activity in Part 3, obtain *Math Talk: Mathematical Ideas in Poems for Two Voices* by Theoni Pappas (Wide World Publishing/Tetra, 1991).

Vocabulary • **Möbius strip**

Getting Started

Mental Math and Reflexes

Suggested problems

- If you travel at 60 miles per hour, how far can you go in 3 hours? 180 miles $5\frac{1}{2}$ hours? 330 miles 50 minutes? 50 miles
- If 20 gallons of paint cost $280, what would be the cost of 10 gallons? $140 8 gallons? $112 25 gallons? $350
- Michael walks at an average speed of 2 miles per hour. At this rate, how far would he walk in 30 minutes? 1 mile $2\frac{1}{2}$ hours? 5 miles

Math Message

How many sides does this strip of paper have? How many edges does it have?

Study Link 10.5 Follow-Up

Students briefly share their experiences in performing the topology trick.

1 Teaching the Lesson

✦ Math Message Follow-Up

WHOLE-CLASS DISCUSSION

Students may think that the Math Message question is so easy that there must be a trick. However, it *is* easy—the strip of paper has two sides and two edges. Demonstrate that the strip has two sides by drawing a line with a marker along the inside of the strip as close to the center as possible. It is impossible to get from the inside of the strip to the outside without lifting the marker or crossing an edge. Demonstrate that the strip has two edges by using the marker to color first one edge and then the other.

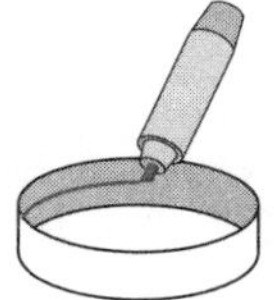

Now ask students what they think the result would be if the strip were cut along the line that you just drew. Perform the cut as illustrated in the margin.

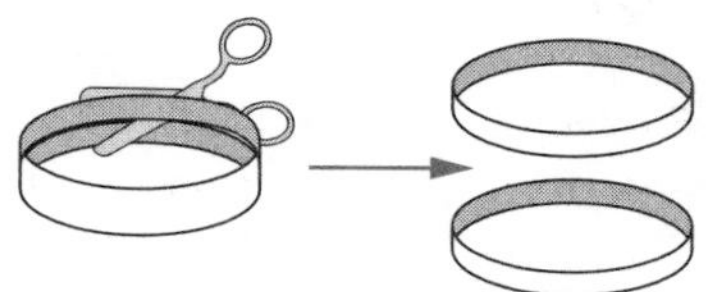

Students will observe that there are now two strips. Each strip is the same length as the original but only one-half the width.

Tell students that in this lesson they will be introduced to a geometric oddity called a **Möbius strip** (mō′•bē•əs). A Möbius strip is curious because it has only *one* side and *one* edge. Interesting results occur when such a strip is cut.

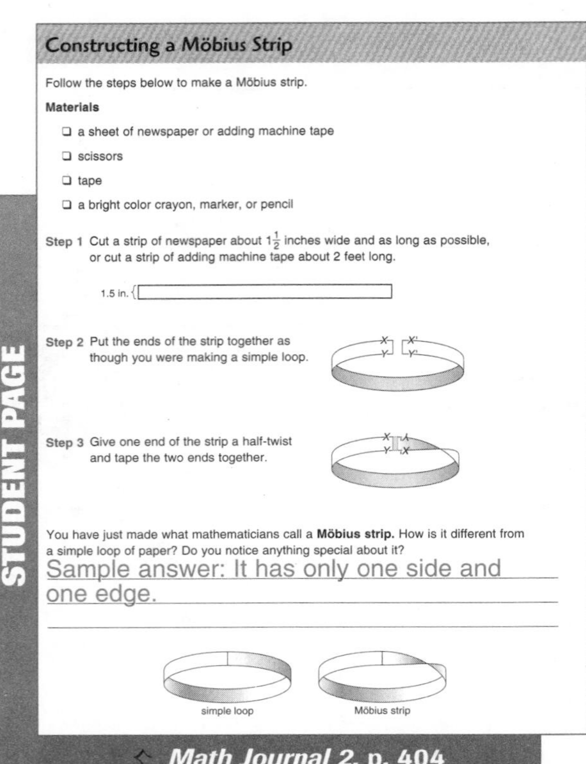

Constructing a Möbius Strip

Follow the steps below to make a Möbius strip.

Materials

- ❑ a sheet of newspaper or adding machine tape
- ❑ scissors
- ❑ tape
- ❑ a bright color crayon, marker, or pencil

Step 1 Cut a strip of newspaper about $1\frac{1}{2}$ inches wide and as long as possible, or cut a strip of adding machine tape about 2 feet long.

Step 2 Put the ends of the strip together as though you were making a simple loop.

Step 3 Give one end of the strip a half-twist and tape the two ends together.

You have just made what mathematicians call a **Möbius strip.** How is it different from a simple loop of paper? Do you notice anything special about it?

Sample answer: It has only one side and one edge.

STUDENT PAGE

Math Journal 2, p. 404

✦ Making a Möbius Strip (*Math Journal 2,* p. 404)

WHOLE-CLASS ACTIVITY

As a class, follow the directions on journal page 404 to make a Möbius strip. If possible, model the step-by-step procedure at the front of the class while students follow along at their desks. In order to complete the partner activities on journal pages 406 and 407, students must know how to construct a Möbius strip.

Adjusting the Activity Step 3 may be difficult for some students. Suggest that they first lay the strip flat on the desk or table and then flip one end over and tape the two ends together. Be certain that students are successful in making half-twists.

✦ Experimenting with Möbius Strips (*Math Journal 2,* pp. 406 and 407)

PARTNER ACTIVITY

Students do the Möbius strip experiments described on journal pages 406 and 407. Suggest that students work together to check the twist-and-cut combinations and to compare results. Encourage students to make the cuts on their own. (It's more fun!) Circulate and assist. When the class has completed the experiments, discuss the results.

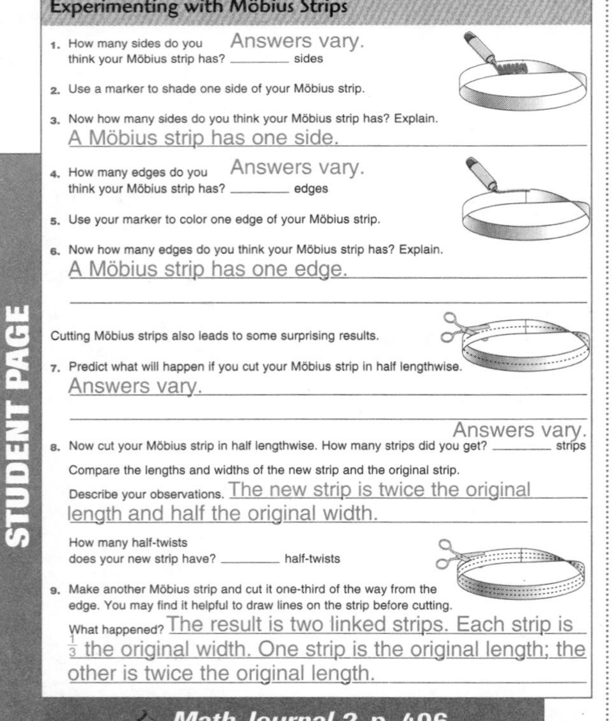

Experimenting with Möbius Strips

1. How many sides do you think your Möbius strip has? Answers vary. sides
2. Use a marker to shade one side of your Möbius strip.
3. Now how many sides do you think your Möbius strip has? Explain. A Möbius strip has one side.
4. How many edges do you think your Möbius strip has? Answers vary. edges
5. Use your marker to color one edge of your Möbius strip.
6. Now how many edges do you think your Möbius strip has? Explain. A Möbius strip has one edge.

Cutting Möbius strips also leads to some surprising results.

7. Predict what will happen if you cut your Möbius strip in half lengthwise. Answers vary.
8. Now cut your Möbius strip in half lengthwise. How many strips did you get? Answers vary. strips

   Compare the lengths and widths of the new strip and the original strip.

   Describe your observations. The new strip is twice the original length and half the original width.

   How many half-twists does your new strip have? ______ half-twists
9. Make another Möbius strip and cut it one-third of the way from the edge. You may find it helpful to draw lines on the strip before cutting.

   What happened? The result is two linked strips. Each strip is $\frac{1}{3}$ the original width. One strip is the original length; the other is twice the original length.

STUDENT PAGE

Math Journal 2, p. 406

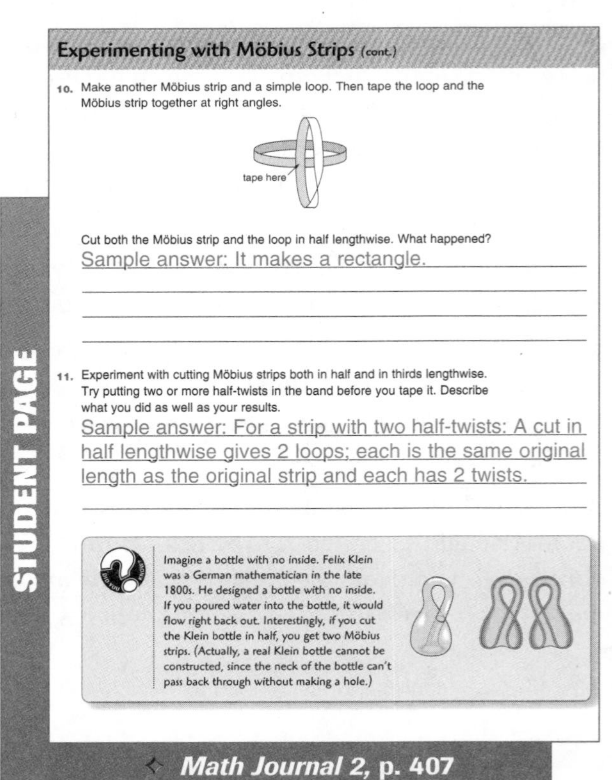

Experimenting with Möbius Strips (cont.)

10. Make another Möbius strip and a simple loop. Then tape the loop and the Möbius strip together at right angles.

Cut both the Möbius strip and the loop in half lengthwise. What happened?

Sample answer: It makes a rectangle.

11. Experiment with cutting Möbius strips both in half and in thirds lengthwise. Try putting two or more half-twists in the band before you tape it. Describe what you did as well as your results.

    Sample answer: For a strip with two half-twists: A cut in half lengthwise gives 2 loops; each is the same original length as the original strip and each has 2 twists.

Imagine a bottle with no inside. Felix Klein was a German mathematician in the late 1800s. He designed a bottle with no inside. If you poured water into the bottle, it would flow right back out. Interestingly, if you cut the Klein bottle in half, you get two Möbius strips. (Actually, a real Klein bottle cannot be constructed, since the neck of the bottle can't pass back through without making a hole.)

STUDENT PAGE

Math Journal 2, p. 407

Ongoing Learning & Practice

✦Reviewing Unit 10 Geometry Topics (*Math Journal 2,* p. 408)

INDEPENDENT ACTIVITY 

Students solve problems that review tessellations, rotations, and cross sections.

✦Math Boxes 10.6 (*Math Journal 2,* p. 405)

INDEPENDENT ACTIVITY 

Mixed Review Math Boxes in this lesson are paired with Math Boxes in Lesson 10.3.

✦Study Link 10.6 (*Math Masters,* p. 381)

Home Connection Students learn another topology trick that involves transference of curves. Point out to students that they will need paper clips, a rubber band, and a strip of paper to do the trick.

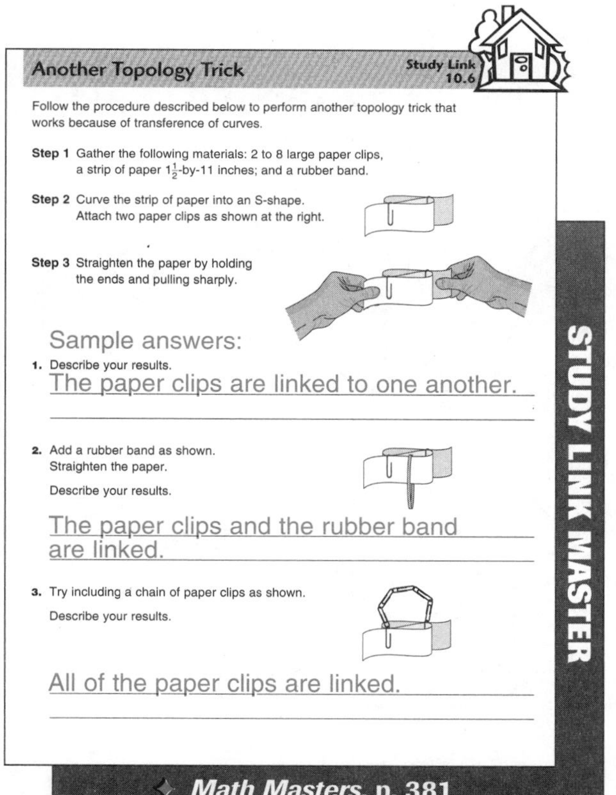

Another Topology Trick — Study Link 10.6

Follow the procedure described below to perform another topology trick that works because of transference of curves.

Step 1 Gather the following materials: 2 to 8 large paper clips, a strip of paper $1\frac{1}{2}$-by-11 inches; and a rubber band.

Step 2 Curve the strip of paper into an S-shape. Attach two paper clips as shown at the right.

Step 3 Straighten the paper by holding the ends and pulling sharply.

Sample answers:

1. Describe your results.
   The paper clips are linked to one another.
2. Add a rubber band as shown. Straighten the paper. Describe your results.
   The paper clips and the rubber band are linked.
3. Try including a chain of paper clips as shown. Describe your results.
   All of the paper clips are linked.

STUDY LINK MASTER

✧ Math Masters, p. 381

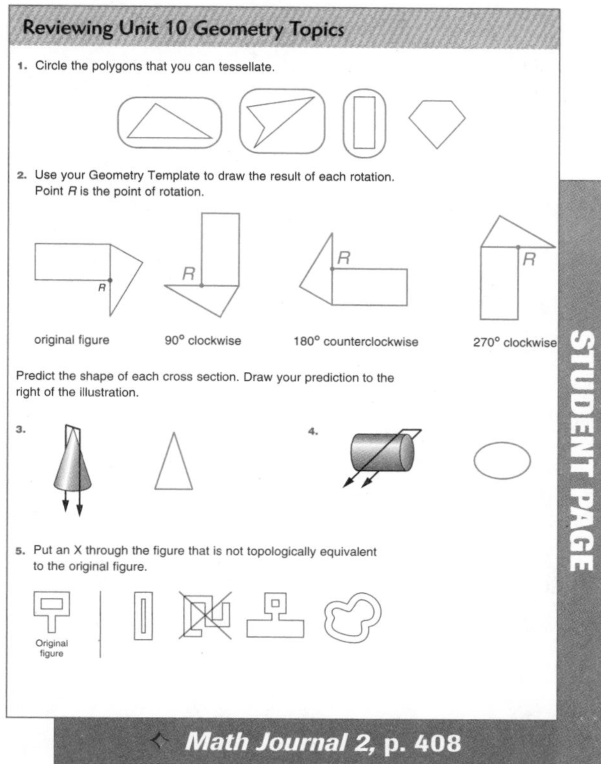

Reviewing Unit 10 Geometry Topics

1. Circle the polygons that you can tessellate.
2. Use your Geometry Template to draw the result of each rotation. Point *R* is the point of rotation.

Predict the shape of each cross section. Draw your prediction to the right of the illustration.

3.
4.

5. Put an X through the figure that is not topologically equivalent to the original figure.

STUDENT PAGE

✧ Math Journal 2, p. 408

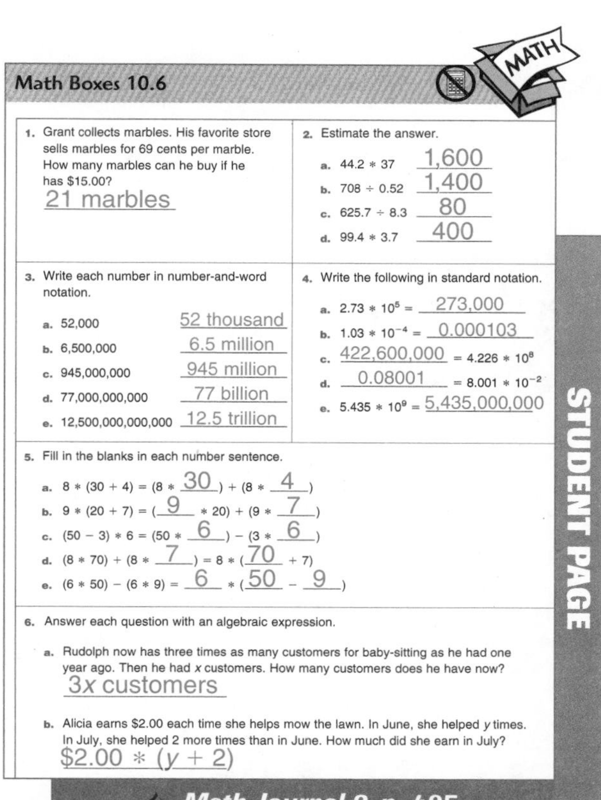

Math Boxes 10.6

1. Grant collects marbles. His favorite store sells marbles for 69 cents per marble. How many marbles can he buy if he has $15.00?
   21 marbles
2. Estimate the answer.
   a. 44.2 * 37 1,600
   b. 708 ÷ 0.52 1,400
   c. 625.7 ÷ 8.3 80
   d. 99.4 * 3.7 400
3. Write each number in number-and-word notation.
   a. 52,000 52 thousand
   b. 6,500,000 6.5 million
   c. 945,000,000 945 million
   d. 77,000,000,000 77 billion
   e. 12,500,000,000,000 12.5 trillion
4. Write the following in standard notation.
   a. $2.73 * 10^5$ = 273,000
   b. $1.03 * 10^{-4}$ = 0.000103
   c. 422,600,000 = $4.226 * 10^8$
   d. 0.08001 = $8.001 * 10^{-2}$
   e. $5.435 * 10^9$ = 5,435,000,000
5. Fill in the blanks in each number sentence.
   a. 8 * (30 + 4) = (8 * 30) + (8 * 4)
   b. 9 * (20 + 7) = (9 * 20) + (9 * 7)
   c. (50 − 3) * 6 = (50 * 6) − (3 * 6)
   d. (8 * 70) + (8 * 7) = 8 * (70 + 7)
   e. (6 * 50) − (6 * 9) = 6 * (50 − 9)
6. Answer each question with an algebraic expression.
   a. Rudolph now has three times as many customers for baby-sitting as he had one year ago. Then he had *x* customers. How many customers does he have now?
      3*x* customers
   b. Alicia earns $2.00 each time she helps mow the lawn. In June, she helped *y* times. In July, she helped 2 more times than in June. How much did she earn in July?
      $2.00 * (y + 2)

STUDENT PAGE

✧ Math Journal 2, p. 405

3 Options for Individualizing

✦ ENRICHMENT Reading an Essay about Möbius (*Student Reference Book,* p. 327)

INDEPENDENT ACTIVITY  **5–15 min** 

Students read about August Ferdinand Möbius and practical applications of Möbius strips on page 327 of the *Student Reference Book.*

✦ ENRICHMENT Reading a Mathematical Poem

PARTNER ACTIVITY  **5–15 min** 

Literature Link "The Möbius Strip" in *Math Talk: Mathematical Ideas in Poems for Two Voices* would be an ideal selection to share at this time. Some students may be interested in memorizing the poem in their spare time and then presenting it to the class.

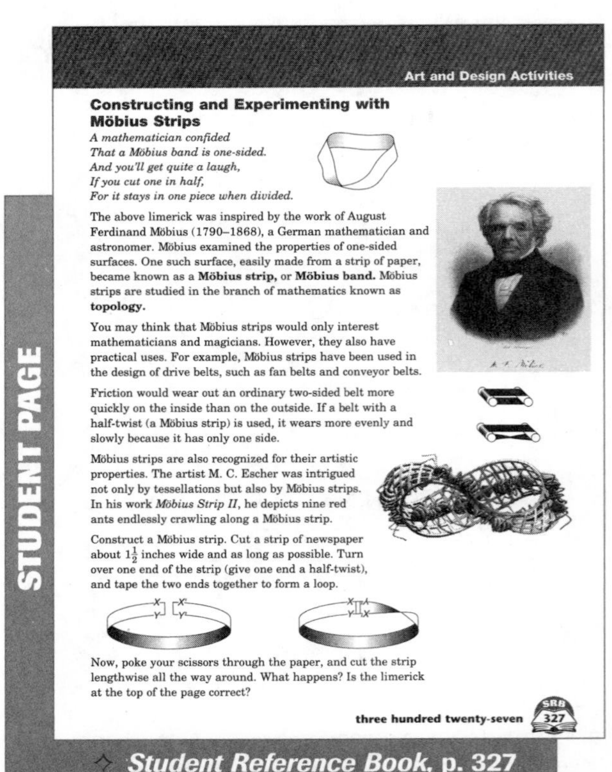

STUDENT PAGE

Art and Design Activities

Constructing and Experimenting with Möbius Strips

A mathematician confided
That a Möbius band is one-sided.
And you'll get quite a laugh,
If you cut one in half,
For it stays in one piece when divided.

The above limerick was inspired by the work of August Ferdinand Möbius (1790–1868), a German mathematician and astronomer. Möbius examined the properties of one-sided surfaces. One such surface, easily made from a strip of paper, became known as a **Möbius strip,** or **Möbius band.** Möbius strips are studied in the branch of mathematics known as **topology.**

You may think that Möbius strips would only interest mathematicians and magicians. However, they also have practical uses. For example, Möbius strips have been used in the design of drive belts, such as fan belts and conveyor belts.

Friction would wear out an ordinary two-sided belt more quickly on the inside than on the outside. If a belt with a half-twist (a Möbius strip) is used, it wears more evenly and slowly because it has only one side.

Möbius strips are also recognized for their artistic properties. The artist M. C. Escher was intrigued not only by tessellations but also by Möbius strips. In his work *Möbius Strip II*, he depicts nine red ants endlessly crawling along a Möbius strip.

Construct a Möbius strip. Cut a strip of newspaper about $1\frac{1}{2}$ inches wide and as long as possible. Turn over one end of the strip (give one end a half-twist), and tape the two ends together to form a loop.

Now, poke your scissors through the paper, and cut the strip lengthwise all the way around. What happens? Is the limerick at the top of the page correct?

three hundred twenty-seven SRB 327

✧ *Student Reference Book,* p. 327

10.7 Unit 10 Review and Assessment

OBJECTIVE **To review and assess students' progress on the material covered in Unit 10.**

1 Assess Progress

learning goals	activities
10a **Beginning Goal** Identify and use notation for semiregular tessellations. **(Lesson 10.1)**	❑ Written Assessment, Problems 4 and 5
10b **Developing Goal** Identify figures that can tessellate. **(Lesson 10.1)**	❑ Written Assessment, Problems 2 and 3
10c **Beginning Goal** Create nonpolygonal, translation tessellations. **(Lesson 10.2)**	❑ Written Assessment, Problem 9
10d **Beginning Goal** Explore rotation and point symmetry. **(Lesson 10.3)**	❑ Written Assessment, Problem 10
10e **Beginning Goal** Explore cross sections of solids. **(Lesson 10.4)**	❑ Oral Assessment, Problem 2 ❑ Slate Assessment, Problem 1 ❑ Written Assessment, Problems 6–8
10f **Beginning Goal** Perform topological transformations. **(Lessons 10.5 and 10.6)**	❑ Written Assessment, Problem 1

materials

- ☐ *Math Journal 2,* p. 409
- ☐ Study Link 10.6
- ☐ Teaching Masters (*Math Masters,* pp. 7–9)
- ☐ Assessment Masters (*Math Masters,* pp. 418 and 419; pp. 425–432, optional)
- ☐ compass ☐ straightedge

2 Build Background for Grade 7

summaries	materials
A family letter provides suggestions for summer math games and math reading.	☐ Study Link Masters (*Math Masters,* pp. 382–385)

Each **learning goal** listed above indicates a level of performance that might be expected at this point in the *Everyday Mathematics* K–6 curriculum. For a variety of reasons, the levels indicated may not accurately portray your class's performance.

Additional Information

Advance Preparation For additional information on assessment for Unit 10, see the *Assessment Handbook,* pages 68–70. For assessment checklists, see *Math Masters,* pages 452, 453, and 468–470.

Getting Started

Math Message

Answer the Time to Reflect *questions on journal page 409.*

Study Link 10.6 Follow-Up

Briefly review students' results. You might consider asking one or two students to demonstrate the tricks.

Time to Reflect

1. Which activity in this unit did you like best? Answers vary.

2. Did any of the activities make you curious about further mathematical study? Which one? What questions would you like to have answered about it?

3. Think about any art (figurines, posters, drawings, calendar photos) that you have in your room (or anywhere in your home). Do any of them use any kind of symmetry that you have studied this year? Describe the art and the kind of symmetry it has. If you don't have anything in your home, look around the classroom to find something to describe.

STUDENT PAGE

Math Journal 2, p. 409

NOTE: Some of these assessment suggestions relate to learning goals that have been addressed in previous units. Now is a good time to evaluate students' progress toward those goals.

1 Assess Progress

✦ Math Message Follow-Up
(*Math Journal 2,* p. 409)

WHOLE-CLASS DISCUSSION

Discuss students' interests in further mathematical study. Point out that many careers in graphic design, engineering, architecture, or other fields, use many of the topics explored in this unit. Mention mathematics courses (or courses in related fields of study) students might take in middle school and high school: algebra, trigonometry, calculus, geometry, art, CAD (drafting).

Allow time for students to describe the symmetric art pieces. Encourage students to look for symmetry in nature during the summer.

✦ Oral and Slate Assessments

WHOLE-CLASS ACTIVITY

If the suggested problems below are not appropriate for your class's level of performance, adjust the numbers or the problems themselves to better assess your students' abilities.

Oral Assessment Suggestions

1. Pose "fraction of" problems. *Suggestions:*
   - $\frac{3}{4}$ of 100 75
   - $\frac{4}{8}$ of 100 50
   - $\frac{1}{4}$ of 100 25
   - $\frac{5}{10}$ of 50 25
   - $\frac{1}{3}$ of 90 30
   - $\frac{3}{6}$ of 80 40
   - $\frac{2}{4}$ of 70 35
2. Ask students to describe the difference between the terms *2-dimensional* and *3-dimensional* and to provide an example of each kind of figure. *2-dimensional* describes figures with two measures, length and width: square, triangle, kite, circle, parallelogram. *3-dimensional* describes figures with three measures, length, width, and depth: cube, pyramid, sphere, rectangular prism. **Objective of Lesson 10.4**

Slate Assessment Suggestion

1. Review students' understanding of plane figures. Ask them to draw quick sketches of figures such as the following: kite, square, rhombus, parallelogram, acute triangle, obtuse triangle, equilateral triangle, trapezoid. Keep in mind that the sketches do not have to be exact, but should indicate that the students recognize these (and other) figures. **Objective of Lesson 10.4**

✦ Written Assessment
(*Math Masters,* pp. 418 and 419)

INDEPENDENT ACTIVITY 

Depending on the needs of students, you may want to work through an example together, reading a problem aloud, discussing it, and providing additional examples as necessary before students work the problem independently.

Each of the problems is listed below and paired with one or more of this unit's learning goals.

- Identify tessellations. (Problems 2 and 3) **Goal 10b, Lesson 10.1**
- Use tessellation notation. (Problems 4 and 5) **Goal 10a, Lesson 10.1**
- Understand how to create a nonpolygonal tessellation. (Problem 9) **Goal 10c, Lesson 10.2**
- Recognize topological equivalence. (Problem 1) **Goal 10f, Lesson 10.5**
- Predict the shape of cross sections of solids. (Problems 6–8) **Goal 10e, Lesson 10.4**
- Demonstrate an understanding of rotation symmetry. (Problem 10) **Goal 10d, Lesson 10.3**

✦ ALTERNATIVE ASSESSMENT OPTION
Make Tessellation Designs
(*Math Masters,* pp. 7–9)

INDEPENDENT ACTIVITY 

Art Link Provide students with any of the grids supplied in the *Math Masters* (1-inch, $\frac{1}{4}$-inch, or 1-centimeter). Students make and color tessellation designs or designs that use any form of symmetry. They label parts of the finished design with the type of symmetry displayed: flips, slides, rotations, point symmetry. Watch for students who show proficient understanding by combining more than one type of symmetry and labeling the types correctly.

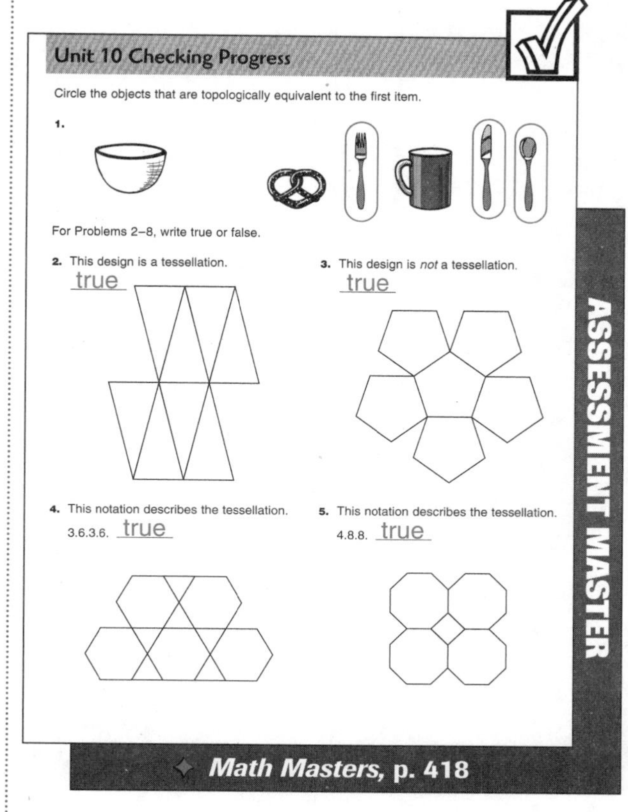

Unit 10 Checking Progress

Circle the objects that are topologically equivalent to the first item.

1.

For Problems 2–8, write true or false.

2. This design is a tessellation. true

3. This design is *not* a tessellation. true

4. This notation describes the tessellation. 3.6.3.6. true

5. This notation describes the tessellation. 4.8.8. true

ASSESSMENT MASTER

✦ *Math Masters,* p. 418

NOTE: The statements in Problems 2–8 on the written assessment were intentionally phrased to be true.

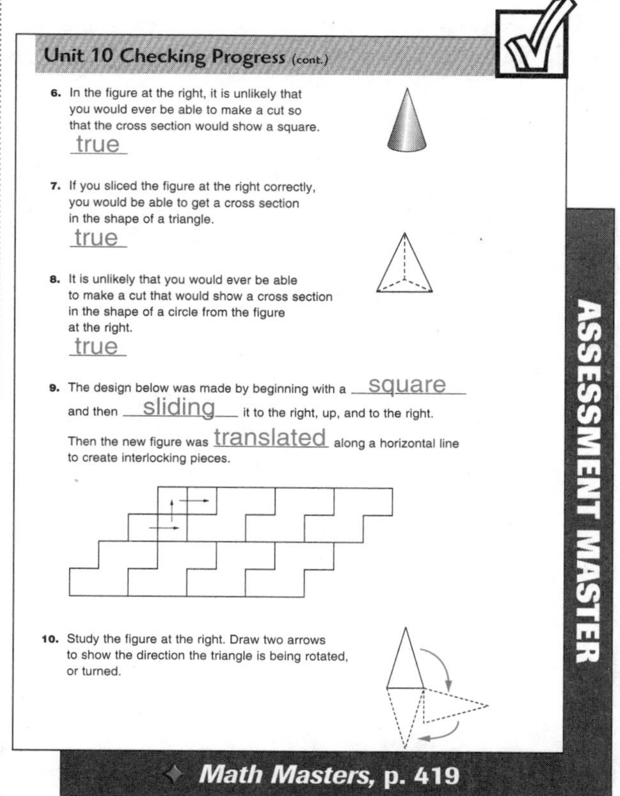

Unit 10 Checking Progress (cont.)

6. In the figure at the right, it is unlikely that you would ever be able to make a cut so that the cross section would show a square. true

7. If you sliced the figure at the right correctly, you would be able to get a cross section in the shape of a triangle. true

8. It is unlikely that you would ever be able to make a cut that would show a cross section in the shape of a circle from the figure at the right. true

9. The design below was made by beginning with a square and then sliding it to the right, up, and to the right. Then the new figure was translated along a horizontal line to create interlocking pieces.

10. Study the figure at the right. Draw two arrows to show the direction the triangle is being rotated, or turned.

ASSESSMENT MASTER

✦ *Math Masters,* p. 419

✦ ALTERNATIVE ASSESSMENT OPTION
Write Reports

INDEPENDENT ACTIVITY 

Language Arts Students write about any of the following topics: M. C. Escher, August F. Möbius, careers in graphic design, one computer art program (describing its functions and possible usefulness), or topology.

✦ End-of-Year Assessment
(*Math Masters*, pp. 425–432)

The End-of-Year Assessment provides an additional assessment opportunity that you may want to use as part of your balanced assessment plan. This test covers many of the important concepts and skills presented in *Sixth Grade Everyday Mathematics*. It should be used along with ongoing, product, and periodic assessments. Please see the *Assessment Handbook* for further information.

Build Background for Grade 7

✦ Study Link 10.7: Family Letter
(*Math Masters*, pp. 382–385)

Home Connection This Study Link thanks family members for their participation in *Sixth Grade Everyday Mathematics*, suggests activities that can be done at home during summer vacation, and provides a "sneak preview" of Grade 7 mathematics.

STUDY LINK MASTERS

Family Letter Study Link 10.7

Congratulations!

By completing *Sixth Grade Everyday Mathematics*, your child has accomplished a great deal. Thank you for all of your support.

This Family Letter is intended as a resource for you to use throughout your child's vacation. It includes an extended list of Do-Anytime Activities, directions for games that can be played at home, a list of mathematics-related books to get from your library, and a sneak preview of what your child might be learning in seventh grade. Enjoy your vacation!

Do-Anytime Activities

Mathematics means more when it is rooted in real-life situations. To help your child review many of the concepts that he or she has learned in sixth grade, we suggest the following activities for you and your child to do together over vacation. These activities will help your child build on the skills that your child has learned this year and help prepare him or her for a seventh grade mathematics course.

1. Practice quick recall of multiplication facts. Include "extended facts," such as $70 * 8 = 560$ and $70 * 80 = 5,600$.
2. Practice calculating with percents. Use a variety of contexts, such as sales tax, discounts, and sports performances.
3. Use measuring devices—rulers, metersticks, yardsticks, tape measures, thermometers, scales, and so on. Measure in both U.S. customary and metric units.
4. Estimate the answers to calculations, such as the bill at a restaurant or store, the distance to a particular place, the number of people at an event, and so on.
5. Play games like those in the *Student Reference Book*.

✦ *Math Masters*, pp. 382–385

Appendices

contents

Title	Page
Projects	828
Sixth Grade Key Vocabulary	871
Scope and Sequence	887
Index	908

PROJECT

1

Exploring the Solar System

OBJECTIVES **To learn about the solar system; and to read and compare large numbers.**

background information

Recommended Use: During or after Unit 2

See the discussion of Projects in the Management Guide section of the *Teacher's Reference Manual*.

materials

- ☐ *Math Masters*, pp. 178–185
- ☐ calculator (optional)

Project Information

This is the first of five linked projects (Projects 1–5). *Math Masters*, page 182 is also referenced in Project 5, Will It Be Possible to Travel to Other Planets in Your Lifetime?

Students read about the solar system and examine a table showing the diameter, average distance from the Sun, and surface temperature of each planet. They use diameter and distance information to develop a second table comparing other planets to Earth. This may take two days.

Vocabulary • **sphere** • **geocentric** • **heliocentric** • **significant figures** • **diameter of a sphere** • **endpoints** • **ellipses** • **astronomical unit**

Doing the Project

✦ Reading about the Solar System (*Math Masters,* pp. 178 and 179)

WHOLE-CLASS DISCUSSION 

Have students read the essays about the solar system and planetary movement on *Math Masters*, pages 178 and 179.

Discuss the essays. Elicit additional information students may have on specific planets (such as the collision of a comet with Jupiter in 1995), space probes, and so on.

✦ Considering Data about the Solar System (*Math Masters,* pp. 180 and 181)

WHOLE-CLASS DISCUSSION 

Follow your usual group reading procedure to read *Math Masters,* pages 180 and 181. If necessary, clarify *average diameter* and *average distance* terms appearing on the tables.

▷ The **diameter of a sphere** is the length of a line segment that passes through the center of the **sphere** and has **endpoints** on the sphere. Planets are not quite spheres, so "average diameter" is used in the data tables.

▷ Planets move around the Sun in orbits that are **ellipses** (ovals), somewhat perturbed by the gravitational pulls of other planets. Except for Mercury and Pluto, the orbits are very nearly circles, with the Sun at the center. Estimates of average distances from the Sun are accurate enough for anything done in these solar system projects.

Some big numbers are given in standard notation, and some are given in scientific notation. Have students read a few of each kind aloud.

The data are given in both U.S. customary and metric units. This is done for comparison, because in later explorations the class will choose which units to use.

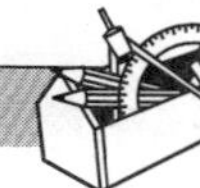

The Solar System

Our solar system consists of the Sun, nine planets and their moons, and a large number of asteroids, comets, and meteors. The Sun is at the center of the solar system.

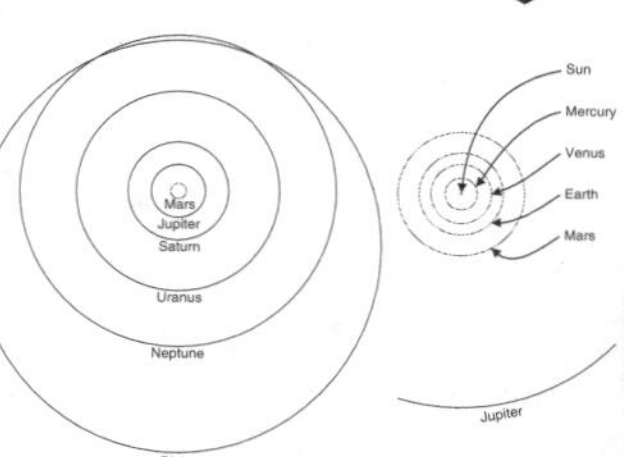

Astronomers estimate that the solar system was formed between 4 and 5 billion years ago. A huge, slowly rotating cloud of particles was pulled together to form the Sun. The planets, moons, and other objects were formed from particles in the outer portion of the cloud.

From time to time, you can see Mercury, Venus, Mars, Jupiter, and Saturn in the night sky. For most of history, people thought these were the only planets other than Earth. Then, using increasingly powerful telescopes, astronomers spotted Uranus in 1718, Neptune in 1846, and Pluto in 1930. Neptune and Pluto might never have been found if astronomers were not guided by mathematical predictions that told them where to aim their telescopes.

The four planets closest to the Sun—Mercury, Venus, Earth, and Mars—are called the "rocky dwarfs," because they are small and made mostly of rock. Jupiter, Saturn, Uranus, and Neptune are huge balls of frozen gas and liquid with small solid cores. They are called the "gas giants" or "Jovian planets." They have multiple moons and rings.

Knowledge of the solar system is growing rapidly. During the past thirty years, all of the planets except Pluto have been visited by one or more space probes. From these expeditions, we have learned that each planet is unique. The planets have different atmospheres, surfaces, and cores.

PROJECT MASTER

✦ Math Masters, p. 178

Movement of the Planets

Today, most people know that Earth revolves around the Sun.

Long ago, almost everyone believed that the entire universe revolved around Earth. That idea certainly corresponds to what we can see with our own eyes: Every day the Sun rises in the east and sets in the west. At night, the Moon, planets, and stars move steadily through the sky.

In the second century A.D., an Egyptian mathematician and astronomer named Claudius Ptolemaeus (Ptolemy) published a book called the *Almagest.* In it he gave a mathematical description of the universe as **geocentric** or Earth-centered. Ptolemy's theory of how the Sun, planets, and stars move through space was widely accepted for the next 1,400 years.

In 1543, the Polish astronomer Nicolaus Copernicus (1473–1543) described a different view of the universe in his book *On the Revolutions of the Celestial Spheres.* After 30 years of research, he concluded that the planets—including Earth—have a **heliocentric** movement: They actually revolve around the Sun. The apparent motion of heavenly bodies through the sky is due primarily to Earth's rotation. This idea had been proposed by Greek scholars as early as the third century B.C. but had been ignored.

Copernicus's theory did not perfectly explain the movement of all of the planets that were known at the time, but it led scientists in a new direction. Astronomer Tycho Brahe (1546–1601) gathered large quantities of data in a search for the true laws of planetary motion. Although Brahe died before he could complete his theory, his assistant, Johannes Kepler (1571–1630) developed mathematical models that correctly explained the observed motions of the planets. Kepler showed that planetary orbits are elliptical (oval) rather than circular. He also demonstrated that the Moon is a satellite of Earth.

In *Everyday Mathematics,* you have developed mathematical models to describe situations, represent relationships, and solve problems. These models have included number sentences and graphs. You are solving problems that are simpler than Kepler's, but you are following the same approach to problem solving that he used. You can read more about problem solving on pages 240 and 241 in the *Student Reference Book.*

PROJECT MASTER

✦ Math Masters, p. 179

PROJECT MASTER

Planet Data

The tables on this page and the next provide estimates of diameters, distances from the Sun, and surface temperatures of the planets, rounded to 2 **significant figures.** The data are presented in both U.S. customary and metric units. In your explorations, you can choose which units to work with.

The **diameter** of a **sphere** is the length of a line segment that passes through the center of the sphere and has **endpoints** on the sphere. Planets are not quite spheres, so "average diameter" is used in the data tables.

Planets move around the Sun in orbits that are **ellipses** (ovals), somewhat perturbed by the gravitational pulls of other planets. Except for Mercury and Pluto, the orbits are very nearly circles. Estimates of "average distances" from the Sun are accurate enough for anything done in the *Sixth Grade Everyday Mathematics* solar system projects.

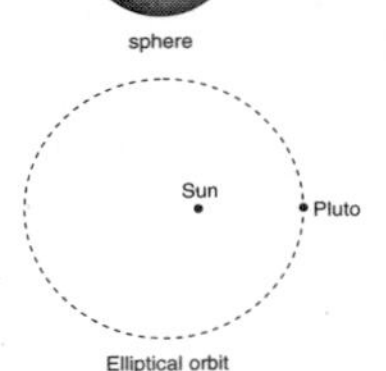

Solar System Data Table 1

Planet	Average Diameter (Miles)	Average Distance from the Sun (Miles)	Surface Temperature (Degrees Fahrenheit)
Mercury	3,000	36,000,000 or $3.6 * 10^7$	−290 to 800
Venus	7,500	67,000,000 or $6.7 * 10^7$	850 to 910
Earth	7,900	93,000,000 or $9.3 * 10^7$	−130 to 140
Mars	4,200	140,000,000 or $1.4 * 10^8$	−190 to 80
Jupiter	89,000	480,000,000 or $4.8 * 10^8$	−240 to −150
Saturn	75,000	890,000,000 or $8.9 * 10^8$	−290 to −150
Uranus	31,000	1,800,000,000 or $1.8 * 10^9$	−330
Neptune	30,000	2,800,000,000 or $2.8 * 10^9$	−310
Pluto	1,600	3,700,000,000 or $3.7 * 10^9$	−350
Sun	870,000		5,400 to 36,000,000

✦ *Math Masters,* p. 180

PROJECT MASTER

Planet Data (cont.)

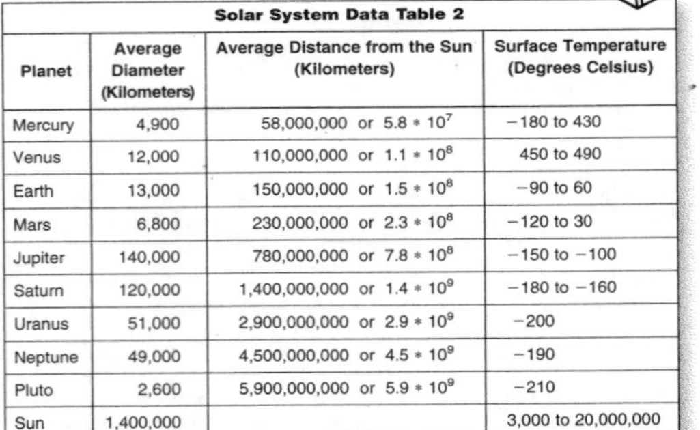

Solar System Data Table 2

Planet	Average Diameter (Kilometers)	Average Distance from the Sun (Kilometers)	Surface Temperature (Degrees Celsius)
Mercury	4,900	58,000,000 or $5.8 * 10^7$	−180 to 430
Venus	12,000	110,000,000 or $1.1 * 10^8$	450 to 490
Earth	13,000	150,000,000 or $1.5 * 10^8$	−90 to 60
Mars	6,800	230,000,000 or $2.3 * 10^8$	−120 to 30
Jupiter	140,000	780,000,000 or $7.8 * 10^8$	−150 to −100
Saturn	120,000	1,400,000,000 or $1.4 * 10^9$	−180 to −160
Uranus	51,000	2,900,000,000 or $2.9 * 10^9$	−200
Neptune	49,000	4,500,000,000 or $4.5 * 10^9$	−190
Pluto	2,600	5,900,000,000 or $5.9 * 10^9$	−210
Sun	1,400,000		3,000 to 20,000,000

Using Estimates and Comparing Big Numbers

Here is one strategy for comparing big numbers.

Problem Compare the distance of Earth from the Sun with the distances of Mars and Neptune from the Sun.

Think
Earth to Sun 150,000,000 km, or 150 million km
Mars to Sun 230,000,000 km, or 230 million km
Neptune to Sun 4,500,000,000 km, or 4,500 million km

Ask *About how many 150 millions are in 230 million? In 4,500 million?*

Another strategy is to compare distances in scientific notation. It is important to compare like powers of 10. Write equivalent names to make the division easier.

Think
Earth to Sun $1.5 * 10^8$ km, or $15 * 10^7$ km
Mars to Sun $2.3 * 10^8$ km, or $23 * 10^7$ km
Neptune to Sun $4.5 * 10^9$ km, or $45 * 10^8$ km, or $450 * 10^7$ km

Ask *About how many 15's are in 23? In 450?*

✦ *Math Masters,* p. 181

✦ Working with Solar System Data Tables (*Math Masters,* pp. 180–183)

INDEPENDENT ACTIVITY 

Students answer three questions on *Math Masters,* page 183 about the solar system data. When the majority of students have finished, bring the class together to share answers and ideas for each question.

The third question asks students to consider whether living things might exist on other planets, based on temperature data. *Math Masters,* page 182 discusses this issue, including recent evidence of bacterial life on Mars long ago. Some of your students might like to find out and report on the current scientific consensus, if any, on the question of past life on Mars.

✦ Comparing Other Planets to Earth (*Math Masters,* pp. 180, 181, and 184)

WHOLE-CLASS ACTIVITY

Students make a data table that compares the diameters of the other planets to the diameter of Earth, and compares the distances of the other planets from the Sun to the distance of Earth from the Sun.

Stimulate discussion with questions such as the following:

- How does the diameter of Mars compare to the diameter of Earth? Is it more or less? less What fraction of it? About $\frac{1}{2}$ of Earth's diameter
- How does the distance from Mars to the Sun compare to the distance from Earth to the Sun? Is it more or less? more About how many times more? About $1\frac{1}{2}$ times

Calculators may be useful, but the main focus of the activity should be on mental estimates with large numbers. A calculator can handle numbers in the billions and beyond only if it can represent them in scientific notation. Even then, entering large numbers is tedious, which is one reason why being able to perform mental estimates with large numbers is useful.

Math Masters, page 181 describes two strategies for estimating to compare large numbers. Applied to U.S. customary measurements, one strategy is to think of 93,000,000 as 93 million. Ask: *About how many 93 millions are in 140 million? In 480 million?* The distance to Neptune, 2,800,000,000 miles, can be thought of as 2,800 million miles, so that the question becomes, "How many 93 millions are in 2,800 million?"

Another strategy is to compare distances in scientific notation. It is important to compare like powers of 10. Students should feel free to write equivalent names to make the division easier.

Earth to Sun: $9.3 * 10^7$ miles

Mars to Sun: $1.4 * 10^8$ or $14 * 10^7$ miles

Ratio comparisons of numbers in standard notation can be simplified by striking out the same number of zeros in each number (in other words, by dividing both numbers by 10 or 100 or whatever power of 10 is appropriate).

Remind students that good estimates, not exact answers, are called for, and that answers can't be more accurate (have more significant figures) than the original data. Allow time to share strategies and solutions.

NOTE: Encourage students to use estimates freely. The data in the tables are averages of many measurements, which are themselves estimates. Students should not be surprised if data from various sources do not agree, although they should question large discrepancies of ±10% or more.

Life on Other Planets

Until recently, scientific studies of the other planets in the solar system found no signs of life. Jupiter's large moons have temperatures that could sustain life, but Voyager space probes examined these moons from 1979 to 1981 and found no life. Some scientists speculate that small organisms might live underground on Mars, where temperatures are moderate. Also, there are geological signs that Mars had water hundreds of thousands of years ago, which raises the possibility that life existed there in the past.

An article in the August 16, 1996 issue of *Science* magazine reported that there may have been life on Mars over 3 billion years ago. The evidence—possibly the remains of bacteria (a tiny, simple form of life)—was in a small rock found in Antarctica in 1984. The rock is thought to have come from Mars after that planet was struck by an asteroid 16 million years ago. There is certain to be considerable argument about this evidence. You may want to find out what has happened since this book was printed.

Photographs of the surface of Mars taken by *Viking I* in 1976 show a face-like object. Some people claim that it was built by intelligent beings. Astronomers, however, say that the face is just a combination of sunlight and shadow on eroded landforms.

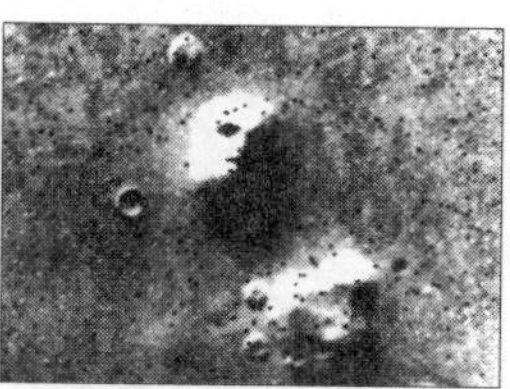

The photograph shows the north pole of Mars, which is covered by water in the form of ice. There might be liquid water under the ice cap. This is one of the regions where missions to Mars will look for signs of life.

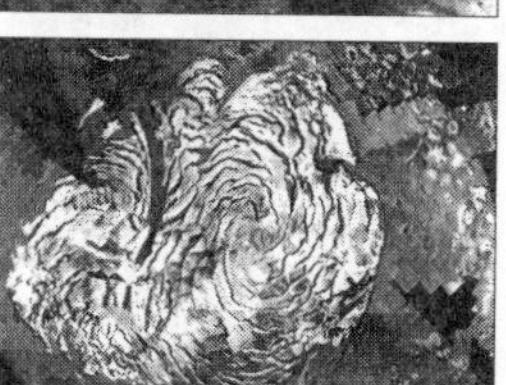

PROJECT MASTER

Math Masters, p. 182

What Can You Learn from the Data Tables?

1. Look at the data on planet diameters on *Math Masters,* pages 180 and 181.
   Do you see any patterns? Answers vary.
   If so, describe the patterns.
   List some ideas or questions that the data suggest to you.
   Answers vary.
2. Look at the data on average distance from the Sun. Are the planets evenly spaced?
   No. They are not.
   Describe any patterns you see. Sample answer: The distance between planets increases as distance from the Sun increases.
3. Look at the data on surface temperature. Is it likely that there is life on other planets today?
   Sample answer: Not life as we know it.
   Why or why not? Temperatures are either too hot or too cold to support life.

For more information about life on other planets, read *Math Masters,* page 182.

PROJECT MASTER

Math Masters, p. 183

Data Analysis

One way to explore and understand a data table is to make another table that compares the same information to a common measure. Use Solar System Data Table 1 or 2 to fill in the table, as described below.

1. Compare the diameters of the other planets with the diameter of Earth. Use estimates. For example, the diameter of Mars (4,200 miles, or 6,800 kilometers) is about $\frac{1}{2}$ of the diameter of Earth (7,900 miles or 13,000 kilometers).

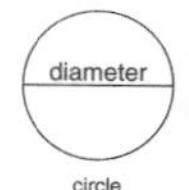

circle

sphere

2. The average distance from Earth to the Sun is called one **astronomical unit.** It is an important unit for measuring distance in the solar system.

   Compare each planet's distance from the Sun to Earth's distance from the Sun. Use estimates. For example, the distance of Jupiter from the Sun (480 million miles, or 780 million kilometers) is about 5 times the distance of Earth from the Sun (93 million miles, or 150 million kilometers).

How Do the Other Planets Compare to Earth?

Planet	Diameter Compared to Earth's Diameter	Distance from Sun Compared to Earth's Distance from Sun
Mercury	About $\frac{3}{8}$ or $\frac{1}{2}$	About $\frac{1}{3}$
Venus	About the same	About $\frac{3}{4}$
Mars	About $\frac{1}{2}$	About $1\frac{1}{2}$ times
Jupiter	About 11 times	About 5 times
Saturn	About 10 times	About 10 times
Uranus	About 4 times	About 20 times
Neptune	About 4 times	About 30 times
Pluto	About $\frac{1}{5}$	About 40 times

PROJECT MASTER

Math Masters, p. 184

Conclusions

How does Earth compare with the other planets? Discuss diameters, distances from the Sun, and any other measures you wish.

Sample answer: The diameter of Earth is larger than that of Mercury, Venus, Mars, and Pluto. It is smaller than that of Jupiter, Saturn, Uranus, and Neptune. Earth is third closest to the Sun. Its range of temperature (270°F) is equal to that of Mars and greater than the range of Venus or Jupiter.

Pursuing Planets

For centuries, people have wondered if there are planets beyond our solar system. Such planets would be tiny objects compared to the huge, bright stars they orbit, so it would be impossible to see them. Their existence would have to be deduced mathematically from information, such as wobbles (small changes) in the expected positions of the stars.

In 1995, astronomers located what seemed to be three planets beyond our solar system. One orbits a star in the constellation Ursa Major, also known as the Big Dipper; another orbits a star in the constellation Virgo. Both stars can be seen without a telescope. These two planets are like Jupiter—mostly gas—but larger, and both are about 35 light-years from Earth. (It would take a radio signal 35 years to reach them.) The third planet circles a star in the constellation Pegasus, about 45 light-years from Earth. It has a mass about one-half the mass of Jupiter and is closer to its star than Mercury is to our Sun.

Is there life on these planets? Probably not on the one in Pegasus, where the surface temperature is about 1,300°C. However, it is possible that liquid water exists on the other two, and water is necessary for life—at least for life as we know or can imagine it. Since 1995, astronomers have found evidence of more than 50 planets beyond our own solar system.

PROJECT MASTER

✦ *Math Masters,* p. 185

✦ Drawing Conclusions about Earth Compared to Other Planets (*Math Masters,* pp. 182 and 185)

PARTNER ACTIVITY 

Students discuss the Conclusions question with partners and then write their own thoughts. When most students have finished, take time to share and discuss conclusions.

2 Extending the Project

✦ Discussing Travel to Other Planets

WHOLE-CLASS DISCUSSION 

Although *Math Masters,* page 182 is used in Project 5, you might want to allow time at the end of this project to discuss it briefly.

PROJECT

2 Modeling the Solar System

OBJECTIVE **To apply a variety of skills to make a scale model of the planets and our solar system.**

background information

Recommended Use: During or after Unit 2

See the discussion of Projects in the Management Guide section of the *Teacher's Reference Manual.*

materials

- ☐ *Math Masters,* pp. 180, 181, and 186–193
- ☐ masking tape or transparent tape
- ☐ tape measure, yardstick, or meterstick
- ☐ construction paper (various colors)
- ☐ stick-on notes (optional)
- ☐ scissors
- ☐ compass
- ☐ ruler
- ☐ calculator

***See* Advance Preparation**

Project Information

In a two- to three-day exploration, the class makes a 2-dimensional scale model of our solar system. Because of the vast distances in the solar system, two scales are necessary, one for the sizes of planets and one for their distances from the Sun.

On the first day, in a whole-class discussion, students consider the sizes of the planets and the Sun and decide on a scale for their planet models. The class is divided into eight Planet Teams (there is no team for Earth; see the discussion in Part 1), and each team makes a model of its planet.

On the second day, students consider the distances of the planets from the Sun. They decide on a scale for distance and then assemble the model of the solar system. Each team records information on *Math Masters,* page 192, Planet Information Label, and posts it near the team's planet.

As much as possible, your role should be one of moderator and coach rather than director of the activities.

Results of this project will be used in Projects 3, 4, and 5.

Advance Preparation The first time you do this project, it will require significant advance preparation.

Decide how to divide the class into eight Planet Teams. Make nine copies of *Math Masters,* page 192—one per Planet Team and one for Earth.

You need to find suitable wall space to represent distances from the Sun. For the model of Pluto to be large enough, the model of the Sun must be at least nine feet in diameter.

A nice representation, including a full model of the Sun, fits in about 55 feet of wall space. In this model, the scale for distance from the Sun is one inch to ten million miles. The 55 feet can be found either in a hallway or, in some cases, within the classroom by placing the Sun in a corner or on an adjoining wall.

On the next two pages are several ways to set up the scale model of the solar system. If the walls are less than nine feet high, the top and bottom of the Sun can be cut off.

Vocabulary • **customary units** • **metric units** • **scale** • **scale model** • **midpoint**

Background Information

Using U.S. Customary Units

Full model of the Sun, with planets on both sides

- Needs about 35.5 feet on one wall and 19.5 feet on an adjoining wall.

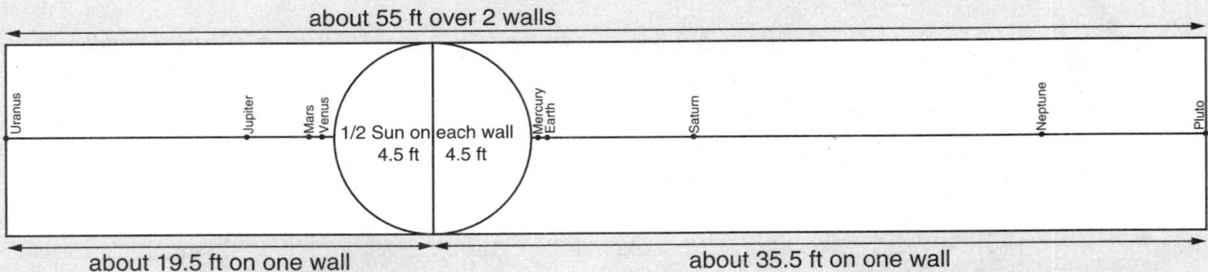

Half of the Sun, with planets all on one side

- Needs about 35.5 feet along one wall. The full model of the Sun can be used if there is about 40 feet of wall space.

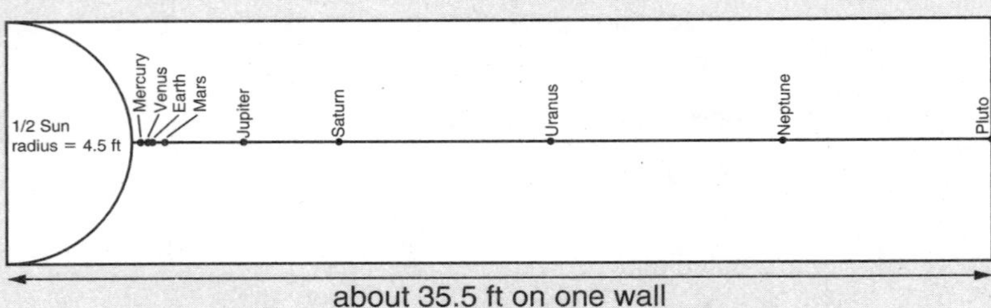

Using Metric Units

Full model of the Sun, with planets on both sides

- Needs about 24 feet (7.5 meters) along one wall and 14 feet (4.5 meters) along an adjoining wall.

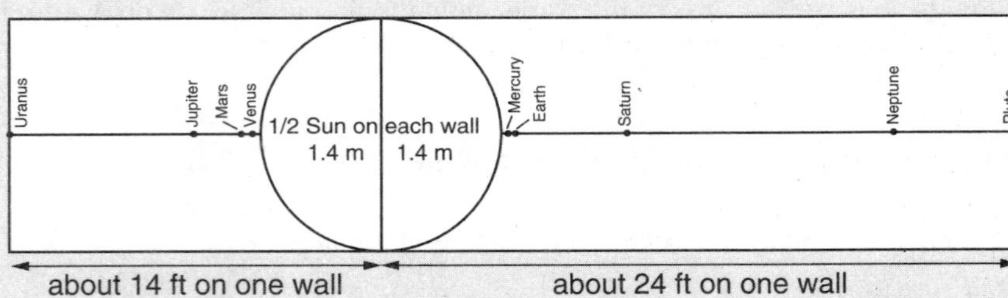

Half of the Sun, with planets all on one side

- Needs about 24 feet (7.5 meters) along one wall. The full model of the Sun can be used if there is about 29 feet (9 meters) of wall space.

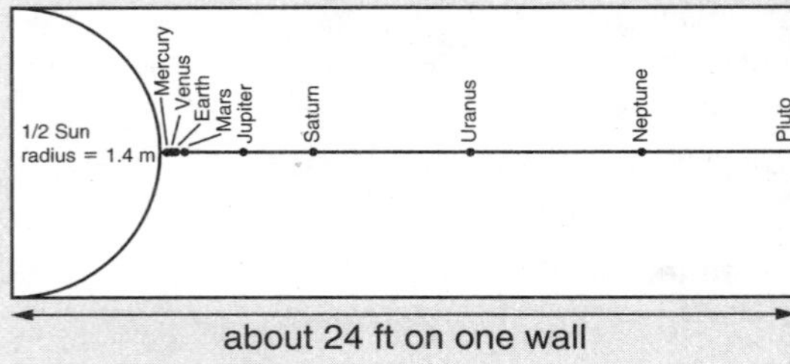

Estimate where the planets will fall to make sure that your placement of them avoids obstacles such as doors and bulletin boards. The planets' distances from the Sun for the two suggested scales are given in the following table.

Planet's Distances from the Sun in a Model Solar System

Planet	1 inch represents 10 million miles	1 centimeter represents 10 million kilometers
Mercury	$3\frac{1}{2}$ in.	5.8 cm, or 6 cm
Venus	$6\frac{3}{4}$ in.	11 cm
Earth	9 in., or $9\frac{1}{4}$ in.	15 cm
Mars	14 in.	23 cm
Jupiter	48 in., or 4 ft	78 cm
Saturn	90 in., or 7 ft 6 in.	140 cm
Uranus	180 in., or 15 ft	290 cm
Neptune	280 in., or 23 ft	450 cm
Pluto	370 in., or 31 ft	590 cm

In addition to wall space, you need supplies for making the Sun and planets. The art teacher may be able to help with such items as rolls of colored paper about three feet wide. Three pieces, each about nine feet long, can be taped together to make a square and then trimmed to form a circle representing the Sun. (*See Figure 1.*)

Another method is to outline the Sun with tape, pieces of construction paper, or stick-on notes. (*See Figure 2.*) Whatever method you choose, you should assemble the Sun and place it before Day Two of the project.

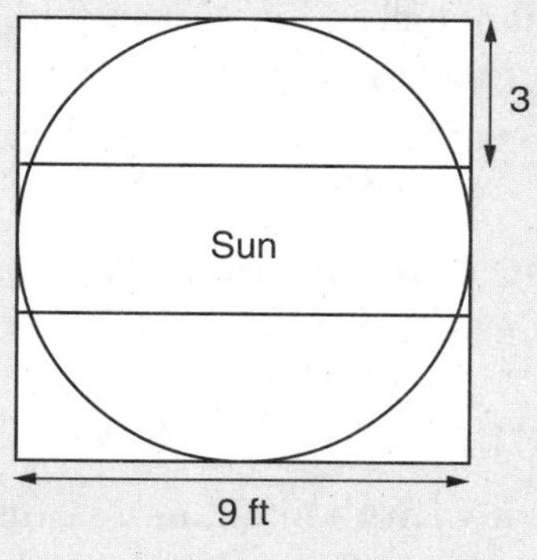

Figure 1

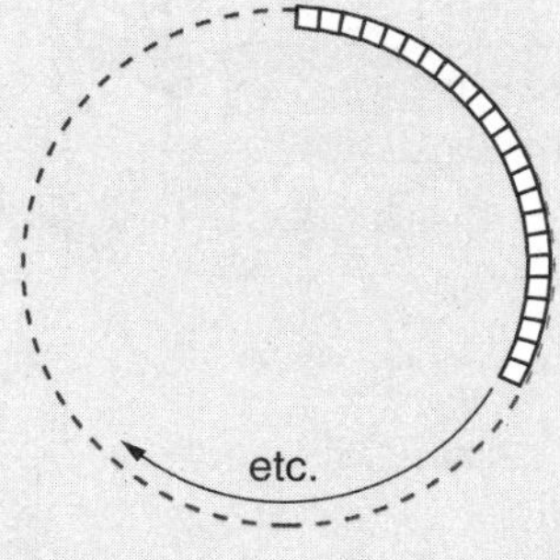

Figure 2

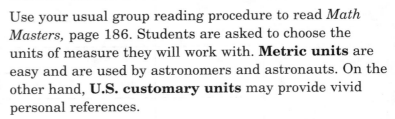

1 Doing the Project

DAY 1

✦ Beginning to Make Scale Models of the Sun and Planets (*Math Masters*, p. 186)

WHOLE-CLASS DISCUSSION 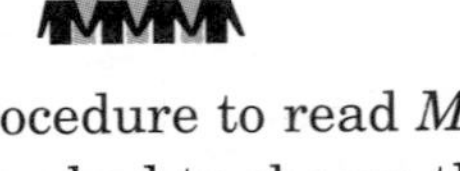

Use your usual group reading procedure to read *Math Masters,* page 186. Students are asked to choose the units of measure they will work with. **Metric units** are easy and are used by astronomers and astronauts. On the other hand, **U.S. customary units** may provide vivid personal references.

Point out that an important consideration is the space available to display the **scale model.** You may want to recommend one measurement system over the other based on where you intend to display the model.

Students select the scale they will use to model the Sun and planets. If the scale suggested will not work in your space, you will need to work with students to choose an alternative.

Divide the class into eight Planet Teams. There should not be a team for Earth, because it will be used for whole-class demonstrations. Assign planets, or let the teams select. Students will work in these same teams for Projects 2–5.

✦ Making the Planet Models (*Math Masters,* pp. 180, 181, and 186–188)

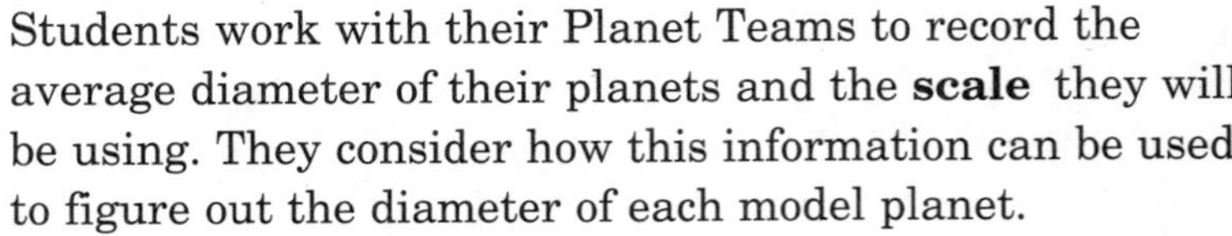

SMALL-GROUP ACTIVITY

Students work with their Planet Teams to record the average diameter of their planets and the **scale** they will be using. They consider how this information can be used to figure out the diameter of each model planet.

PROJECT MASTER

Starting the Model

1. **Choose a Measurement System**

   In order to build a scale model of the solar system, the class needs to make some decisions.

   - Will we measure in **U.S. customary units** (in. and mi) or **metric units** (cm and km)?

   Metric units are used by astronomers and astronauts. On the other hand, U.S. customary units may make the model easier to relate to personal references. For example, if the diameter of Earth is 1 inch (about the length of a toe), then the Sun's diameter is about 9 feet, almost twice the height of most students. Discuss the advantages and disadvantages of each measurement system. Then make a class decision.

   We will use Answers vary. units.

2. **Choose a Scale**

   Now the class needs to make another decision.

   - What scale will we use to model the relative sizes of the Sun and the planets?

   The **scale** tells how many units in the real solar system are represented by one unit in the scale model of the solar system. *Suggestions:*

   - **Using U.S. Customary Units** You might let 1 inch represent 8,000 miles (1 inch to 8,000 miles, or 1 in.:8,000 mi). 8,000 miles is approximately the diameter of Earth. If the diameter of Earth is represented by 1 inch, about how many inches would represent the diameter of Jupiter? 11 in.
   - **Using Metric Units** You might let 1 centimeter represent 5,000 kilometers (1 centimeter to 5,000 kilometers, or 1 cm:5,000 km). These are easy numbers to work with and to remember.

   We will use this scale for size: Answers vary.

3. **Divide into Planet Teams**

   The class should divide into eight Planet Teams, one for each planet except Earth. The model will be easier to build if you work in teams.

   My Planet Team will model this planet: Answers vary.

✦ *Math Masters,* p. 186

PROJECT MASTER

Modeling the Sizes of Planets and the Sun

1. My Planet Team's planet is Answers vary.
2. Its average diameter is ______

   (Remember to give the diameter in the same system of units—metric or U.S. customary—that you will use to build the model.)
3. In our scale model of planet size, ______ represents ______
4. How can you use the scale to figure out how large your planet should be in the model? Discuss with your teammates.
5. What will be the diameter of your planet in the model? ______
6. a. What will be the diameter of the Sun in the model? ______

   b. How many feet or meters is this? ______

✦ *Math Masters,* p. 187

For example, if one inch represents 8,000 miles, students need to figure out about how many 8,000s there are in their planet's diameter. In the case of Mercury, Venus, Mars, and Pluto, they need to figure out what fraction of 8,000 their planet's diameter is. Point out that only estimates are needed.

Some of the answers will be quite clear, but others will require more thought. One way to reason out some answers is by looking at a ruler. Mercury, for example, has a diameter of 3,000 miles. This is more than $\frac{1}{4}$ of 8,000 but less than $\frac{1}{2}$ of 8,000. Ask: *What marking on the ruler falls between $\frac{1}{4}$ and $\frac{1}{2}$?* Sample answer: $\frac{3}{8}$ Reasonable diameters for the two suggested scales are in the table below.

Diameters of Model Sun and Planets

Planet	1 inch represents 8,000 miles	1 centimeter represents 5,000 kilometers
Mercury	$\frac{3}{8}$ in.	1 cm
Venus	$\frac{15}{16}$, or $\frac{7}{8}$ in.	2.4, or 2.5 cm
Earth	1 in.	2.5 cm
Mars	$\frac{1}{2}$ in.	1.4, or 1.5 cm
Jupiter	11 in.	28 cm
Saturn	9 in.	24 cm
Uranus	4 in.	10 cm
Neptune	4 in.	10 cm
Pluto	$\frac{3}{16}$, or $\frac{1}{8}$ in.	0.6 cm, or 6 mm
Sun	108 in., or 9 ft	280 cm, or 2.8 m

Use Earth to demonstrate how the planets can be constructed. The color chart on *Math Masters*, page 188 suggests the color of paper to use, if possible, to reflect each planet's actual appearance. Earth is blue, brown, and green. Construction procedures are suggested on *Math Masters*, page 188. Some students may need help drawing larger circles.

Making a Scale Model of Your Planet

To make a 2-dimensional scale model of your planet, your Planet Team needs a pencil, ruler, scissors, tape, compass, and colored construction paper.

If possible, use the chart at the right to select the color(s) of paper for your planet. These are the main colors of the planets as seen from Earth and space probes.

Planet	Color
Mercury	Orange
Venus	Yellow
Earth	Blue, brown, green
Mars	Red
Jupiter	Yellow, red, brown, white
Saturn	Yellow
Uranus	Green
Neptune	Blue
Pluto	Yellow

1. With a ruler, draw a line segment equal in length to the diameter your planet should have in the model. If you are modeling Jupiter or Saturn, you may need to tape two pieces of paper together.
2. Find the **midpoint** (middle) of this line segment and mark a dot there.
3. Use a compass to draw a circle. The center of the circle should be at the midpoint you just marked. Put the point of the compass on the dot. Put the pencil on one endpoint of the line segment, and draw the circle.

If your compass is too small, tie a string around a pencil near the point. Hold the point of the pencil on one endpoint of the line segment. Pull the string tightly and hold it down at the dot (midpoint) on the line segment. Keeping the string tight, swing the pencil around to draw a circle.

4. Cut out and label the circle.
5. Share your work with the other Planet Teams.

PROJECT MASTER

Math Masters, p. 188

PROJECT MASTER

Modeling Distances in the Solar System

1. My Planet Team's planet is Answers vary.

2. Its average distance from the Sun is ______.

3. Now that you have modeled the size of your planet, you need to figure out how far it should be placed from the Sun. How could you do this?

To model the distances between the planets and the Sun, your class needs to make several decisions.

Finding a Scale

4. Can you use the same **scale** for distance that you used for size? This would provide an excellent picture of planetary sizes and distances but may not be possible. Why not? Discuss with your classmates.
Sample answer: There may not be room to accommodate the range of distances.

5. If 1 inch represents 8,000 miles, how many inches from the Sun should Earth be placed? 11,625 inches

6. How many feet is this? About 1,000 feet

7. Would a model of the entire solar system using this scale be possible anywhere in your school building? Answers vary.

You probably need a different scale for distances of the planets from the Sun than for diameters of the planets. Discuss with your class what scale to use. Two important points to consider:

- How much space do you have to display the model? Answers vary.
- How much space will be taken up by the Sun? ______

Math Masters, **p. 189**

PROJECT MASTER

Modeling Distances in the Solar System (cont.)

Deciding on a Scale Answers vary.

8. In the scale we are using for distance, ______ represents ______.

9. In the model, my Planet Team's planet should be placed ______ (how far?) from the Sun.

Building the Model

- First, the class should decide which part of the Sun to measure from.
- Then, working with your teammates, use a tape measure to place your planet the correct distance from the Sun.
- Finally, fill in as much information as you can on your team's Planet Information Label (*Math Masters,* page 192). You will fill in the remaining information later.

You can add details to the model by including some of the features of the solar system described on *Math Masters,* page 191.

Scaling Mount Everest

You saw that there is a problem in using the same scale to represent both planet size and distance in our solar system. There is a similar problem in representing mountains and other elevated regions on a globe or a 3-dimensional topographic map.

Since the diameter of Earth is about 8,000 miles, even an 8-mile-high mountain would be barely noticed on a world globe, because the mountain's height would be only one thousandth of the diameter of the globe. (The highest mountain in the world, Mount Everest, is about 6 miles high.)

Cartographers (map makers) solve this problem by greatly exaggerating the vertical scale of topographic maps. For example, on a map of California with 1 inch representing 50 miles, the mountains and valleys of the Sierra Mountain Range might be represented by 1 inch for 5 miles of elevation so that Mount Whitney (at 14,500 feet, the highest mountain in the Sierras) would be shown as a bump of about $\frac{1}{2}$ inch.

When you read a map that shows elevations in three dimensions, you should be sure to read the scale in the map key to find out whether different scales are used for distance and elevation.

Math Masters, **p. 190**

DAY 2

✦Modeling Distances in the Solar System (*Math Masters,* pp. 180, 181, 189, and 190)

SMALL-GROUP ACTIVITY

Students continue to work with their Planet Teams. They should find their planet's average distance from the Sun and record it on *Math Masters,* page 189 (Problem 2).

Next, they write their ideas for placing their planets.

When most of the teams are at this point, a class discussion may be useful to consider several features of modeling distance. Read as a class the questions under Finding a Scale on *Math Masters,* page 189. Students answer the questions in their teams, and then the class shares solutions and strategies. Questions such as the following may facilitate discussion.

- Where should the planets be placed in the model? The positions can be found by dividing the actual average distance of each planet from the Sun by the distance represented by one unit of the scale. For Earth, 93,000,000 miles divided by 8,000 miles per inch equals almost 12,000 inches or 1,000 feet.
- What are the pros and cons of using the same scale for size and distance? The same scale would provide the most accurate picture of the solar system. However, such a model wouldn't fit in a classroom.

- If the scale that is used for planet size is also used for distance from the Sun, how far would Earth be from the Sun in the model solar system? How far would Pluto be? Answers depend on the scale used for planet size.

Discuss what scale could be used for distance, given the space available for the model. Suggest the scale that you have predetermined as practical in the space available. Students record the scale at the top of *Math Masters*, page 190.

✦ Placing Planet Models
(*Math Masters,* pp. 190–192)

SMALL-GROUP ACTIVITY

Each Planet Team calculates how far its planet will be from the Sun, using the agreed upon scale. Then teams take turns putting their planets the proper distance from the Sun. They will need a tape measure, yardstick, or meterstick. They can add details to the model by including some of the solar system features described on *Math Masters,* page 191.

Reasonable distances for inch and centimeter scales are provided in the table on page 835.

Teams fill in as much as they can on their Planet Information Label (*Math Masters,* page 192). The remaining information can be added as it is found in Projects 3, 4, and 5. One student in each team should hang the Planet Information Label under the team's model planet.

Some Solar System Features

More detail can be added to the model by including some or all of the following celestial bodies.

Asteroids These are large pieces of rock too small to be considered planets. They range in size from big boulders to small mountains. Ceres, one of the largest asteroids, has a diameter of 580 miles, or 940 kilometers. Most asteroids are in what is known as the Asteroid Belt. The Asteroid Belt lies between Mars and Jupiter, roughly 180 to 270 million miles (290 to 430 million kilometers) from the Sun. To date more than 18,000 asteroids have been identified in this region of the solar system. They can be represented in the model by small pen dots on pieces of paper or stick-on notes.

Moons Mars, Jupiter, Saturn, Uranus, and Neptune each have two or more moons. Mercury and Venus have no moons. The largest moons of Jupiter and Saturn are larger than Mercury and Pluto. Jupiter has at least 17 moons. The four largest moons and their diameters are shown in the table.

Moon	Diameter	
Ganymede	3,200 mi	5,300 km
Callisto	2,900 mi	4,800 km
Io	2,200 mi	3,600 km
Europa	1,900 mi	3,100 km

Saturn has at least 18 moons. The largest is Titan. Its diameter is 3,100 miles (5,200 kilometers). Earth's moon has a diameter of 2,200 miles (3,750 kilometers). It is slightly less than $\frac{1}{3}$ the size of Earth.

Rings It has been known for a long time that Saturn is surrounded by large, beautiful rings. When the Voyager spacecraft visited Jupiter, Neptune, and Uranus in the 1980s, it discovered that these planets also have rings, although they are considerably smaller and less grand than Saturn's. Saturn has six rings of different colors. The rings are made up of frozen water particles ranging in size from tiny grains to blocks of ice 30 yards in diameter. The rings are only a few miles thick, but they extend out from the planet for 50,000 miles (80,000 kilometers).

PROJECT MASTER

✦ Math Masters, p. 191

Planet Information Label

Planet name: Answers vary. ______

Average diameter: ______

The planet's average diameter is about __?__ the diameter of Earth. ______

Average distance from the Sun: ______

How long would it take to fly from the planet to the Sun? ______

Time sunlight takes to reach the planet: ______

How long does it take the planet to orbit the Sun? ______

Since 1776, this planet has orbited the Sun about __?__ times. ______

At today's rate of manned space travel (10,000 miles per hour), the length of time it would take to reach the planet from Earth: ______

In our lifetime, humans in space might be able to travel 50,000 miles per hour. At this rate, how long would it take to reach the planet? ______

PROJECT MASTER

✦ Math Masters, p. 192

PROJECT MASTER

Conclusions

1. Suppose you had used the scale for planet diameters to also represent *distances* of planets from the Sun. Keep the same position for the Sun that you used in your model. Answers vary.
   a. How far away from your model Sun would Earth be? ______
   b. Where in your school or town might Earth be located? ______
   c. How far away from your model Sun would Neptune be? ______
   d. Where in your school or town might Neptune be located? ______

2. Suppose you had used the scale for distances of planets from the Sun to also represent the *diameter* of Earth. Answers vary.
   a. What would be the diameter of the model Earth? ______
   b. If the model Earth were made with exactly that diameter, could it be seen without a magnifying glass? (Pencil leads in some mechanical pencils are 0.5 mm or about $\frac{2}{1{,}000}$ of an inch thick.) ______

3. Suppose you were explaining to someone how huge the largest planet in the solar system is compared to Earth.
   a. What would be an easy multiple to use? Sample answer: 11
   b. What other comparison might you use to make the difference easier to understand (for example, the costs or sizes of two things in your world)? Answers vary.

4. Similarly, suppose you were explaining how huge the Sun is compared to even the largest planet in the solar system.
   a. What would be an easy multiple to use? Sample answer: 10
   b. What other comparison might you use to make the difference easier to understand? Answers vary.

5. Choose a fact you have learned about the solar system. Make up a question for a trivia game based on that fact. Answers vary.

✦ *Math Masters*, p. 193

✦ Answering the Conclusions Questions
(*Math Masters,* p. 193)

SMALL-GROUP ACTIVITY

Students should work in their Planet Teams to answer the questions under Conclusions. When most students have finished, provide time for discussion.

2 Extending the Project

✦ Finding Out about the Solar System

INDEPENDENT ACTIVITY 

Invite students to learn more about the solar system by reading newspapers, magazines, and books such as the following:

Janice VanCleave's The Solar System: Mind-Boggling Experiments You Can Turn into Science Fair Projects, by Janice Pratt VanCleave (Wiley, 2000).

The New Solar System, J. Kelly Beatty, Carolyn Collins Petersen, and Andrew L. Chaikin, editors (Cambridge University, 1998).

There are many Internet sites devoted to the solar system, astronomy, and space exploration. *For example:*

▷ NASA's site, with many links:
http://www.nasa.gov/

▷ The solar system:
http://www.seds.org/nineplanets/nineplanets

▷ Evidence of life on Mars found in rocks on Earth:
http://spaceflight.nasa.gov/mars/science/ancient/

▷ Exploration of Mars by orbiters and robots:
http://spaceflight.nasa.gov/mars/

▷ The search for planets:
http://science.nasa.gov/newhome/headlines/ast14nov99_1.htm
http://spaceflightnow.com/news/n0008/07newplanet/
http://www.spaceviews.com/2000/08/07a.html
http://exoplanets.org/

PROJECT

3

Distances in the Solar System

OBJECTIVES **To compare large numbers; and to calculate travel times.**

background information

Recommended Use: During or after Unit 2

See the discussion of Projects in the Management Guide section of the *Teacher's Reference Manual.*

materials

- □ Planet Information Label (*Math Masters,* p. 192)
- □ *Math Masters,* pp. 194–198
- □ Transparency (*Math Masters,* p. 195; optional)
- □ calculator

***See* Advance Preparation**

Project Information

This project uses information obtained in Project 2.

Students compare distances in the solar system to more familiar distances. They work in their Planet Teams to calculate how long it would take to fly at the speed of a jet airplane from each planet to the Sun and how long sunlight takes to reach each planet. Then they share their findings with the class to compile the information. Finally, students write a description of the distance of Pluto from the Sun to make the distance comprehensible to a friend. In an Extending the Project activity, students determine how long it would take to travel from Earth to the nearest star, Proxima Centauri.

Advance Preparation To help display data obtained by Planet Teams, make an overhead transparency of *Math Masters,* page 195, or draw on the board a copy of the table on that page.

Vocabulary • **light-year** • **speed of light**

Travel Times between Earth and the Sun

Distances in the solar system are huge. For example, the average distance from Earth to the Sun is about 93,000,000 miles, or 150,000,000 kilometers.

To understand distances in the solar system, it helps to compare them to distances you know or can understand more easily.

Distance from New York to San Francisco	about 3,000 miles (mi), or about 4,800 kilometers (km)
Time to fly by jet from New York to San Francisco	about 6 hours at 500 mi per hr, or about 6 hours at 800 km per hr
Speed of sunlight	about 186,000 mi per sec, or about 298,000 km per sec

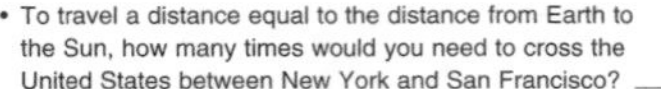

- To travel a distance equal to the distance from Earth to the Sun, how many times would you need to cross the United States between New York and San Francisco? 31,000 times
- If a plane flew at 500 miles per hour (800 kilometers per hour) without stopping, about how long would it take to travel the distance from Earth to the Sun? About 186,000 hours, or 7,750 days, or 21 years
- It takes sunlight about 8 minutes (how long?) to travel from the Sun to Earth.

Get Out Your Shades!

The temperature at the Sun's core is estimated to be 15 million degrees Celsius.

At this time, most astronomers agree that the Sun has been active for about 4.6 billion years and has enough fuel (hydrogen) to keep burning for another 5 billion years. Even after the Sun runs out of fuel, it may take a trillion years to cool off completely.

Source: NASA Spacelink (http://spacelink.msfc.nasa.gov)

PROJECT MASTER

✦ *Math Masters,* p. 194

Estimate Travel Times

Use what you have learned about travel times between Earth and the Sun to make similar comparisons for your model planet. Answers vary.

- The planet I helped model is ________________.
- Its average distance from the Sun is ________________.
- This distance is equal to crossing the United States ________ times.
- It would take about ________ to fly this distance at 500 miles per hour.
- It takes sunlight about ________ to reach this planet.

Add this information to your team's Planet Information Label.

Share your work with your classmates. Use their numbers to help you complete the following table. Answers are approximate.

Planet	Average Distance from Sun (Miles)	Number of Trips across U.S. to Equal Distance from Planet to Sun	Time to Fly the Distance from Planet to Sun (Years)	Time Sunlight Takes to Reach Planet (Minutes)
Mercury	36,000,000	12,000	8	3
Venus	67,000,000	22,000	15	6
Earth	93,000,000	31,000	21	8
Mars	140,000,000	47,000	32	13
Jupiter	480,000,000	160,000	110	43
Saturn	890,000,000	300,000	200	80
Uranus	1,800,000,000	600,000	410	160
Neptune	2,800,000,000	930,000	640	250
Pluto	3,700,000,000	1,200,000	840	330

PROJECT MASTER

✦ *Math Masters,* p. 195

1 Doing the Project

✦ Estimating Travel Times between Earth and the Sun (*Math Masters,* p. 194)

PARTNER ACTIVITY 

Partners work the problems on *Math Masters,* page 194 to estimate how long it would take to fly from Earth to the Sun and how long it takes sunlight to reach Earth.

Circulate and assist. When most partnerships have finished, take a few minutes to share strategies and estimates.

NOTE: If the calculators in your classroom don't accept entries in scientific notation, some numbers will be too large to work with. One trick to overcome this is to drop the same number of zeros from each number in ratio comparisons (equivalent to dividing both numbers by the same multiple of 10). For example, 3,000 miles across the U.S. compared to 140,000,000 miles from Mars to the Sun is the same as 3 compared to 140,000.

✦ Estimating Distances and Travel Times in the Solar System (*Math Masters,* pp. 192, 195, and 196)

SMALL-GROUP ACTIVITY

Discuss the best way to report flying time (hours, days, or years) and time for sunlight to reach a planet (seconds, minutes, or hours). Remind students that for the very large distances here, giving answers to two significant figures is fine. That means they will use rounding and write many zeros.

Students work in the same Planet Teams as they did in Project 2. Each team will make trip and time estimates for its own planet.

Planet Teams complete *Math Masters,* page 195 for their own planets. Circulate and assist as needed.

As teams finish, have them enter the additional information on their Planet Information Labels (*Math Masters,* page 192). Those who finish well ahead of the others can work on Extending the Project—described in Part 2, and with student activities on *Math Masters,* pages 197 and 198.

When the Planet Teams have finished, have them share their findings so that everyone can complete the table on *Math Masters,* page 195. It will help to use an overhead transparency of *Math Masters,* page 195, or copy the table onto the board.

The table below shows how the table might be completed. Remember that all values are estimates.

Planet	Average Distance from Sun (Miles)	Number of Trips across U.S. to Equal Distance from Planet to Sun	Time to Fly Distance from Planet to Sun (Years)	Time Sunlight Takes to Reach Planet (Minutes)
Mercury	36,000,000	12,000	8	3
Venus	67,000,000	22,000	15	6
Earth	93,000,000	31,000	21	8
Mars	140,000,000	47,000	32	13
Jupiter	480,000,000	160,000	110	43
Saturn	890,000,000	300,000	200	80
Uranus	1,800,000,000	600,000	410	160
Neptune	2,800,000,000	930,000	640	250
Pluto	3,700,000,000	1,200,000	840	330

✦ Describing a Distance
(*Math Masters,* p. 196)

WHOLE-CLASS DISCUSSION 

Students independently write a description of the enormous distance of Pluto from the Sun. Then volunteers share their answers with the class.

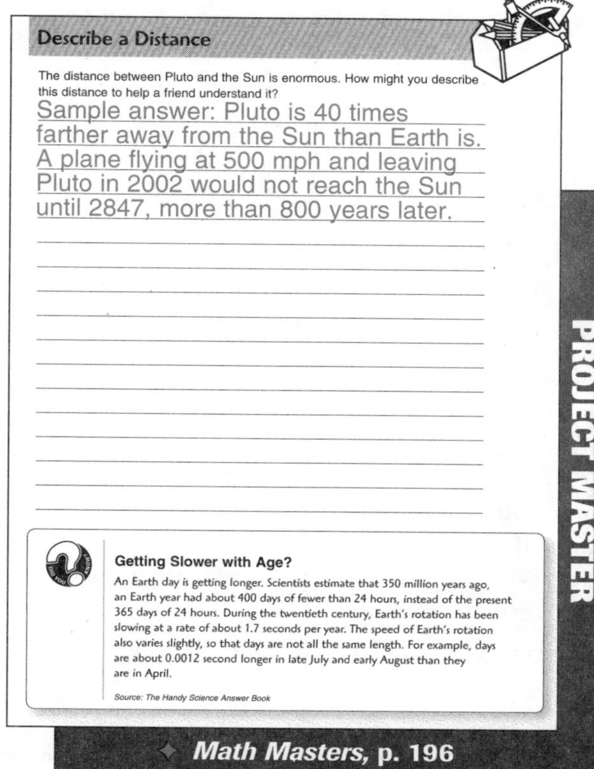

Describe a Distance

The distance between Pluto and the Sun is enormous. How might you describe this distance to help a friend understand it?

Sample answer: Pluto is 40 times farther away from the Sun than Earth is. A plane flying at 500 mph and leaving Pluto in 2002 would not reach the Sun until 2847, more than 800 years later.

Getting Slower with Age?
An Earth day is getting longer. Scientists estimate that 350 million years ago, an Earth year had about 400 days of fewer than 24 hours, instead of the present 365 days of 24 hours. During the twentieth century, Earth's rotation has been slowing at a rate of about 1.7 seconds per year. The speed of Earth's rotation also varies slightly, so that days are not all the same length. For example, days are about 0.0012 second longer in late July and early August than they are in April.

Source: The Handy Science Answer Book

PROJECT MASTER

✦ *Math Masters,* p. 196

2 Extending the Project

✦ Exploring Distances beyond Our Solar System (*Math Masters,* pp. 197 and 198)

WHOLE-CLASS ACTIVITY 

Students read the essay on *Math Masters,* page 197 as a class or individually, and then answer the question on *Math Masters,* page 198. Here is a possible solution:

Pioneer 10 took about 20 years to travel 5 billion miles.

At this rate, the time it would take to reach Proxima Centauri can be found by first dividing the total distance to the star (25,000 billion miles) by the distance already traveled (5 billion miles). The answer 5,000 means that the trip will be 5,000 times as long. Since it took about 20 years to travel 5 billion miles, it would take 5,000 ∗ 20 years, or 100,000 years, to reach the nearest star after the Sun (at the speed of *Pioneer 10*).

NOTE: The current status of *Pioneer 10* is reported on the Internet at the following web site: http://spaceprojects.arc.nasa.gov/Space_Projects/pioneer/PNStat.html

PROJECT MASTER

Beyond the Solar System

Our Sun is just an ordinary star, one of an estimated 100 billion in the Milky Way galaxy. The nearest star beyond our solar system, Proxima Centauri, is 25,000,000,000,000 miles from the Sun. That is about 7,000 times the average distance from the Sun to Pluto.

The huge distance to Proxima Centauri indicates how extremely large the universe is. To simplify calculations, astronomers usually measure distances beyond our solar system in **light-years.** A light-year is the distance light travels in 1 year: about 6 trillion miles ($6 * 10^{12}$ miles), or 9.5 trillion kilometers ($9.5 * 10^{12}$ kilometers).

Proxima Centauri is 4.3 light-years away. Some of the visible stars are 20 to 80 light-years away, or 5 to 20 times farther than Proxima Centauri. Many of the stars in the Milky Way galaxy are less than 35,000 light-years away. Astronomers, however, consider such stars to be relatively near. Andromeda, the galaxy nearest to the Milky Way, is about 2 million light-years away.

Four space probes launched in the 1970s, *Pioneer 10* and *11* and *Voyager 1* and *2,* are now heading beyond our solar system. *Pioneer 10* is the most distant man-made object in the universe. Launched in 1972, it was more than 7 billion miles from Earth in 2000. It is traveling toward outer space at 40,000 miles per hour.

These probes will send back important information about the outer edges of our solar system. Then scientists will lose contact with them. The probes, however, may travel through space for hundreds of centuries.

Source: Gerrit Vershuur, "Race to the Sun's Edge," *Air and Space,* April/May 1993

The **speed of light:**
about 186,000 miles per second
about 300,000 kilometers per second

1 **light-year:**
about 5.9 trillion miles ($5.9 * 10^{12}$ mi)
about 9.5 trillion kilometers ($9.5 * 10^{12}$ km)
about 63,000 astronomical units

✦ *Math Masters,* p. 197

PROJECT MASTER

Beyond the Solar System (cont.)

To appreciate distances beyond the solar system, read the information on *Math Masters,* page 197. Then try the following calculation.

It took *Pioneer 10* about 20 years to travel 5 billion miles. At this rate, how long would it take to travel to the nearest star, Proxima Centauri, which is 25 trillion or 25,000 billion miles away?

About 100,000 years

Explain how you got your answer. Sample answer: I divided 25,000 billion miles by 5 billion miles and got 5,000. So the distance to the star is 5,000 times the distance traveled in 20 years.
5,000 ∗ 20 years = 100,000 years

How Many Stars?

Some astronomers have estimated that there might be as many as 80 billion galaxies in the universe.

A galaxy contains 50 to 100 billion stars.

80 billion galaxies ∗ 100 billion stars per galaxy =
$8 * 10^{10} * 1 * 10^{11}$ stars $= 8 * 10^{21}$ stars

So there could be 8,000,000,000,000,000,000,000 stars in the universe. Does it seem likely or unlikely that there are fewer than 60 planets in all (9 in our solar system and 50 more possible planets found recently)?

✦ *Math Masters,* p. 198

PROJECT

4

Movement of the Planets

OBJECTIVES **To learn about Earth's rotation and revolution; and to calculate times of rotation and revolution.**

background information

Recommended Use: During or after Unit 2

See the discussion of Projects in the Management Guide section of the *Teacher's Reference Manual.*

materials

- ☐ Planet Information Label (*Math Masters,* p. 192)
- ☐ *Math Masters,* pp. 180, 181, and 199–203
- ☐ calculator
- ☐ globe (optional)

***See* Advance Preparation**

Project Information

Students learn about the daily rotation of Earth on its axis and the yearly revolution of Earth around the Sun. They calculate how far they have revolved and rotated in the past hour and past minute. Students work in their Planet Teams to compare the movement of the other planets with Earth and to estimate how many times each planet has traveled around the Sun since 1776. Students also estimate the minimum distance between each planet and Earth. In an Extending the Project activity, the Planet Teams calculate the maximum distance between each planet and Earth.

Advance Preparation A globe will be useful.

Vocabulary • **rotate** • **revolve** • **rotation** • **revolution**

Spaceship Earth

To be a successful space traveler, you must be able to find your way back to Earth. This may not be easy. You do not feel it, but at this moment you are traveling through space at incredible speeds.

Earth spins around like a top. In 24 hours, it makes one complete **rotation.** At the equator, the distance around Earth is about 25,000 miles. In the middle of the United States, the distance falls to about 21,000 miles. This means that if you live in the middle of the United States, you travel about 21,000 miles every day.

21,000 miles
25,000 miles

At the same time Earth is rotating, it is moving in its orbit around the Sun. In one year, Earth makes one complete **revolution,** or trip, around the Sun. This trip is approximately 600,000,000 (or $6 * 10^8$) miles long.

600,000,000 miles
Earth
Sun

Movement of the Planets around the Sun

All of the planets are in motion, rotating like tops and revolving around the Sun. Compared to Earth, some planets are fast, while others are quite slow. Understanding planetary motion is key for space travel. You must know where to aim the spaceship.

Solar System Data Table 3

Planet	Average Speed in Orbit: Miles per Earth Day	Time to Revolve Once around the Sun: Earth Days or Years	Time to Rotate Once: Earth Days or Hours
Mercury	2,600,000	88 days	59 days
Venus	1,900,000	223 days	243 days
Earth	1,600,000	365 days	24 hours
Mars	1,300,000	686 days	25 hours
Jupiter	700,000	12 years	10 hours
Saturn	520,000	29 years	11 hours
Uranus	360,000	84 years	16 hours
Neptune	290,000	165 years	18 hours
Pluto	250,000	249 years	6 days

Source: Richard Lewis. *The Illustrated Encyclopedia of the Universe.* Harmony Books, 1983

PROJECT MASTER

✦ *Math Masters,* p. 199

1 Doing the Project

✦ Estimating Distances of Rotation and Revolution (*Math Masters,* pp. 199 and 200)

WHOLE-CLASS ACTIVITY 

Use your usual group reading procedure to read the essay "Spaceship Earth" at the top of *Math Masters,* page 199. Ask students to suggest ways to find out how far they travel each day as Earth **rotates** on its axis and **revolves** around the Sun. If possible, demonstrate Earth's **rotation** and **revolution** with a globe.

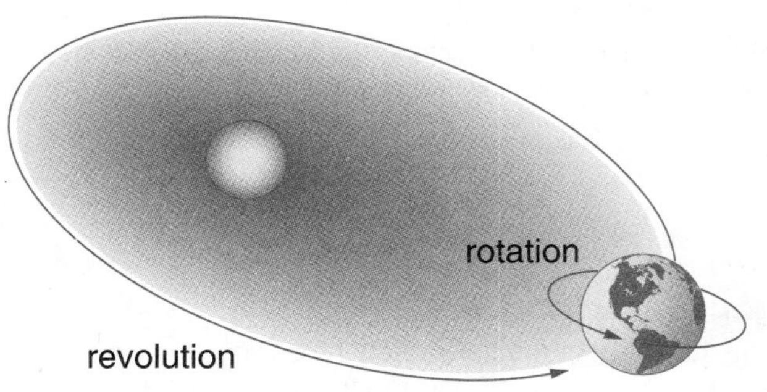

Discuss the text and the diagrams of Earth's movement. Ask whether your school is nearest the latitude lines at 25,000 miles (equator), at 21,000 miles, or at the North Pole. Ask for suggestions on how to estimate the distance a person travels in a 24-hour rotation of Earth.

On *Math Masters,* page 200, students are asked to use the information from *Math Masters,* page 199, to estimate how far they have rotated and revolved in the past hour and minute. They should use a calculator and round their results. Circulate, observe, and assist as necessary.

Rotating and Revolving with Earth

During one rotation of Earth, a person at the equator travels about 25,000 miles. The farther north of the equator a person is, the smaller the distance of rotation becomes.

City	Distance of One Rotation
Honolulu, HI	24,000 mi
Los Angeles, CA	21,000 mi
Philadelphia, PA	19,000 mi
Seattle, WA	17,000 mi
Anchorage, AK	13,000 mi

Sample answers:

1. Estimate how many miles a person travels during 1 hour of rotation.
   a. At the equator About 1,040 miles
   b. In Los Angeles About 880 miles
   c. In Seattle About 710 miles
   d. In Anchorage About 540 miles

2. a. Estimate the distance of one rotation for your location. For example, if you live in Chicago—which is farther from the equator than Philadelphia but closer than Seattle—you might say 18,000 miles. Answers vary. About ______ miles
   b. How far have you rotated in the past hour? About ______ miles
   c. How far have you rotated in the past minute? About ______ miles

3. Earth travels about 600,000,000 miles (in scientific notation: $6 * 10^8$) around the Sun in one year. Estimate how far Earth (with you on it) travels in its orbit around the Sun during various time periods. Complete the following statements.
   a. In one month, Earth travels about 50,000,000 ($5 * 10^7$) miles.
   b. In one day, it travels about 1,600,000 miles.
   c. In the past hour, it traveled about 68,000 miles.
   d. In the past minute, it traveled about 1,100 miles.

PROJECT MASTER

✦ *Math Masters,* p. 200

ONGOING ASSESSMENT

This is a good time for informal assessment. Check that students know the difference between *rotation* and *revolution.*

When most students have finished, bring the class together to share strategies and solutions.

✦ Examining the Movements of Planets around the Sun (*Math Masters,* pp. 199 and 201)

SMALL-GROUP ACTIVITY

Planet Teams examine Solar System Data Table 3 on *Math Masters,* page 199. Students look for patterns in the data and describe them on *Math Masters,* page 201, sharing their thoughts with others on the team and perhaps with other Planet Teams.

Students use the information in the table to estimate how many times their team's planet has traveled around the Sun since 1776. Teams share results so students can complete the table on *Math Masters,* page 201.

Movement of Planets around the Sun

Read the paragraph under Movement of the Planets around the Sun on *Math Masters,* page 199, and look at the information in Solar System Data Table 3. Then work with your Planet Team to complete the following.

1. Record some observations about the information in the table. For example, which planets rotate faster than Earth? About the same as Earth? Slower than Earth?
Sample answer: Faster—Jupiter, Saturn, Uranus, and Neptune; slower—Mercury, Venus, and Pluto; about the same—Mars

2. Since the Declaration of Independence was signed in 1776, about how many times has Earth revolved around the Sun? Sample answer: 225 times (as of 2001)

3. a. About how many times has your Planet Team's planet traveled around the Sun since 1776? Answers vary.

b. Share results with your classmates to complete the list below.
Sample answers: (as of 2001)

Revolutions around the Sun Since 1776					
Mercury	930	Mars	120	Uranus	2.7
Venus	370	Jupiter	19	Neptune	1.4
Earth	225	Saturn	7.8	Pluto	0.9

4. Use what you have learned to add information to your team's Planet Information Label.

PROJECT MASTER

✦ *Math Masters,* p. 201

✦ Calculating Minimum Distances from Earth to Other Planets (*Math Masters,* pp. 180, 181, 202, and 203)

SMALL-GROUP ACTIVITY

Still in Planet Teams, students read *Math Masters,* page 202. The diagrams show that from time to time the distance between Earth and Mars reaches a minimum: This can be inferred to be true for the other planets, as well. Except for Pluto, the orbits are almost circular and in the same plane. Hence, the approximate minimum distance can be calculated from Solar System Data Tables 1 or 2 on *Math Masters,* pages 180 and 181, when Earth and the other planet align on the same radius.

Because Pluto's eccentric orbit makes calculation difficult, you might have the Pluto Team disperse to other teams; or an especially capable group might attempt to write an explanation of why estimating the minimum Earth-to-Pluto distance from the data in the table would be difficult.

When teams have finished, discuss their work and share results so students can complete the Estimated Minimum Distance from Earth column in the table on *Math Masters,* page 203.

Minimum Distances

The constant movement of the planets complicates space travel. Since the planets move at different speeds, exact calculations are needed to figure out the directions spaceships should travel. Another problem is that the distances between Earth and the other planets are always changing.

Complex mathematical computer models are used to calculate the relationship of Earth to the other planets, and to plot the data needed to send space probes to other planets. But several fortunate facts make it possible to make rough estimates of some things that we might want to know for space travel.

All the planets except Pluto travel in nearly circular orbits, with the Sun at the center.

For all the planets except Pluto, those nearly circular orbits are almost in the same plane. This means that when the planets pass each other on the same radius from the Sun, that minimum distance can be calculated from the information in the Solar System Data Tables on *Math Masters,* pages 180 and 181. This can be seen in the diagram below.

Earth revolves quickly around the Sun compared with all of the planets except Mercury and Venus. This means that at least once a year, Earth and each of the outer planets line up on the same radius from the Sun, at the minimum distance. The times are predictable, too. It is harder to predict when Earth will line up with Mercury and Venus. However, they do line up from time to time. (For Pluto the situation is even more difficult. You might want to take on the problem as a challenge, but it can't be done using only the information on these pages.)

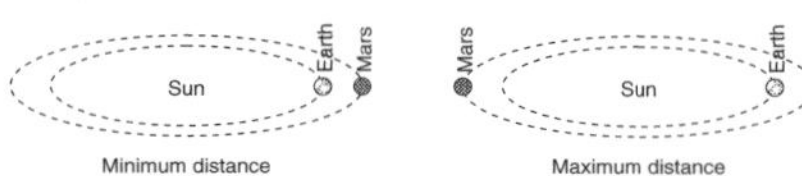

PROJECT MASTER

✦ *Math Masters,* p. 202

PROJECT MASTER

Minimum/Maximum Distances of Planets

Read the essay "Minimum Distances" on *Math Masters,* page 202.

Then work with your Planet Team, unless you are on the Pluto Team. Your teacher will tell the Pluto team what to do.

Use the information on *Math Masters,* page 180 or 181 to estimate the distance between Earth and your planet when they are closest. Round your estimate to 2 significant digits and write it in scientific notation. Share estimates with the other teams to fill in the estimated minimum distances in the table below.

Planet	Estimated Minimum Distance from Earth (mi or km)	Estimated Maximum Distance from Earth (mi or km)
Mercury	$5.7 * 10^7$ mi, $9.2 * 10^7$ km	$1.3 * 10^8$ mi, $2.1 * 10^8$ km
Venus	$2.6 * 10^7$ mi, $4.0 * 10^7$ km	$1.6 * 10^8$ mi, $2.6 * 10^8$ km
Mars	$4.7 * 10^7$ mi, $8.0 * 10^7$ km	$2.3 * 10^8$ mi, $3.8 * 10^8$ km
Jupiter	$3.9 * 10^8$ mi, $6.3 * 10^8$ km	$5.7 * 10^8$ mi, $9.3 * 10^8$ km
Saturn	$8.0 * 10^8$ mi, $1.3 * 10^9$ km	$9.8 * 10^8$ mi, $1.6 * 10^9$ km
Uranus	$1.7 * 10^9$ mi, $2.8 * 10^9$ km	$1.9 * 10^9$ mi, $3.1 * 10^9$ km
Neptune	$2.7 * 10^9$ mi, $4.4 * 10^9$ km	$2.9 * 10^9$ mi, $4.7 * 10^9$ km

Summary

1. How would you describe to a friend the motion of Earth on its axis and around the Sun? Answers vary.

2. When you return from a space trip, will Earth be in the same place as when you left? ______ Explain. Answers vary.

3. About how many times have you rotated and revolved since you were born?
Rotated: 4,380 Revolved: 12 Answers based on the age of 12. If leap years are used, the "rotated" answer might be 4,383.

✦ *Math Masters,* **p. 203**

✦ Summarizing (*Math Masters,* p. 203)

PARTNER ACTIVITY 

Students complete Questions 1, 2, and 3 on *Math Masters,* page 203 and then share their answers with the class. Filling in the third column on the table is considered an extension. See Part 2 for a discussion of that activity.

2 Extending the Project

✦ Calculating Maximum Distances from Earth to Other Planets (*Math Masters,* pp. 180, 181, 202, and 203)

SMALL-GROUP ACTIVITY 

As teams finish finding minimum distances, you might have them calculate the estimated maximum distance from Earth to their planets. They use the information to fill in the third column of the table on *Math Masters,* page 203.

PROJECT

Will It Be Possible to Travel to Other Planets in Your Lifetime?

OBJECTIVE To use data gathered previously to decide whether it will be possible to travel to other planets in students' lifetime.

background information

Recommended Use: During or after Unit 2

See the discussion of Projects in the Management Guide section of the *Teacher's Reference Manual.*

materials

- ☐ Planet Information Label (*Math Masters,* p. 192)
- ☐ *Math Masters,* pp. 180–182, 199, and 203–208

Project Information

Students use what they learned in the preceding projects as they explore the possibility of humans traveling to other planets in their lifetime. This project is designed to be a culminating activity.

In Projects 1–4, students worked with partners, Planet Teams, or the whole class. In this project, the authors suggest that students work independently to consider the feasibility of space travel to a planet of their choice, mainly by estimating how long a trip to that planet would take. They need not explore the planet they studied with their Planet Teams, but it is likely that many students will choose the same planet. Some planets may not be chosen by anyone. In an Extending the Project activity, students estimate how old they would be on three other planets—Venus, Mars, and Jupiter.

1 Doing the Project

✦ Deciding the Possibility of Travel to Other Planets in Students' Lifetime
(*Math Masters,* pp. 180–182, 199, and 203–207)

INDEPENDENT ACTIVITY 

Ask students to pick a planet to travel to and record it at the top of *Math Masters,* page 204. Encourage them to choose a diversity of planets. Ask a few students to tell which planets they chose and why.

NOTE: Students recorded their estimates of the minimum distance from Earth to each planet (except Pluto) on *Math Masters,* page 203. Use these figures to estimate travel times.

Students should work independently, perhaps using you or classmates as consultants. As much as possible, they should solve problems by themselves before checking with others. It may, however, be necessary to partner some students because of varying language, reading, or mathematical abilities.

Circulate, observe, and offer assistance as necessary.

After students have made calculations for the planet of their choice, they pool their information to fill in the table on *Math Masters,* page 205. Then have students read silently *Math Masters,* pages 182 and 207. If some students finish early, ask them to make estimates for any planets not chosen by other students, so that all blanks in the table can be filled in.

As they finish their estimates, students add information to the Planet Information Labels posted by each planet in the solar system model.

Finally, if time allows, or on another day, students share responses to Conclusions on *Math Masters,* page 206.

PROJECT MASTER

Travel to Other Planets in Your Lifetime?

You have explored the solar system. You have learned about the size, distance, and motion of each planet. You are ready to offer an informed opinion on travel to other planets.

Fill in the basic facts about the planet you plan to visit. Then estimate the answers to the questions on the rest of this page and the next page. Work on your own, but consult with your teacher or classmates if you are unsure about what to do.

My planet Answers vary.

Here are some facts I know about this planet.
(This information is on *Math Masters,* pages 180, 181, and 199.)

- Surface temperature ______
- Average diameter ______
- Average distance from the Sun ______
- Earth days or years to orbit the Sun ______

How Far Will You Need to Travel?

Estimated minimum distance from Earth
(See *Math Masters,* page 203.) ______

How Long Will It Take to Travel to Your Planet?

- Currently, a spaceship with people on it can travel at about 10,000 miles per hour. At this speed, how long will it take to reach your planet? See *Math Masters,* p. 205.
- If you could travel at 10,000 miles per hour, would it be possible to visit your planet and return to Earth in your lifetime? Answers vary.
- If not, how much faster would you need to travel? ______ times faster
- At the faster speed, how long would it take to go to your planet and return? See *Math Masters,* p. 205.

✦ **Math Masters, p. 204**

PROJECT MASTER

Travel to Other Planets in Your Lifetime? (cont.)

How long would your trip take if you could travel at Answers vary.

50,000 miles per hour? ______ 100,000 miles per hour? ______

Write the results for your planet in the table below. Share your results with your classmates, and get information from them to complete as much of the table as possible.

Estimated Travel Time in Hours to the Planets

Planet	Fastest Speed Now 10,000 miles/hour	In about 20 Years 50,000 miles/hour	In about 50 Years 100,000 miles/hour
Mercury	5,700 hours	1,100 hours	570 hours
Venus	2,600 hours	520 hours	260 hours
Mars	4,700 hours	940 hours	470 hours
Jupiter	39,000 hours	7,800 hours	3,900 hours
Saturn	80,000 hours	16,000 hours	8,000 hours
Uranus	170,000 hours	34,000 hours	17,000 hours
Neptune	270,000 hours	54,000 hours	27,000 hours
Pluto	360,000 hours	72,000 hours	36,000 hours

Try to complete the Planet Information Labels posted in the solar system model. Read *Math Masters,* pages 182 and 207.

Faster and Faster

It is difficult to predict how fast we will be able to travel in the future. Seventy-five years ago, the fastest that people could travel was about 100 miles per hour. Now astronauts can travel into space at 10,000 miles per hour. Using this fact and their knowledge of technology, some scientists estimate that within twenty years, astronauts could travel to other planets at speeds of up to 50,000 miles per hour. A few scientists estimate that speeds up to 100,000 miles per hour will be possible within the next 40 to 50 years.

Source: "Where to Next, Columbus?" Exhibit at National Air and Space Museum, Washington, D.C.

✦ **Math Masters, p. 205**

Extending the Project

✦ Figuring Out How Old You Would Be on Another Planet (*Math Masters,* pp. 199 and 208)

INDEPENDENT ACTIVITY 

Students estimate the number of Earth days they have been alive. Then they estimate how old they would be in Venus-years, Mars-years, and Jupiter-years, using data from Solar System Data Table 3 on *Math Masters,* page 199. (They can find the answers by dividing the number of days they have been alive by 223 for Venus, 686 for Mars, and 4,380 for Jupiter.) Because the numbers are large and involve estimates, students should not be surprised to find discrepancies between various sources other than these project worksheets.

✦ Finding Out More about Space Flight

INDEPENDENT ACTIVITY 

Invite students to learn more about current space flight activity by reading newspapers, magazines, and books, and by visiting Internet sites such as the NASA site http://spaceflight.nasa.gov.

Travel to Other Planets in Your Lifetime? (cont.)

Conclusions Answers vary.

1. Do you think it might be possible to travel to your planet and return in your lifetime? Why or why not?

2. Which planets are the most likely to be explored by humans? Why do you think so?

3. Some scientists believe that it makes sense to send people to explore other planets. Other scientists believe that the planets should be explored only with computers, cameras, and scientific instruments aboard space probes. Choose one of these positions, or one in between, and defend your choice.

4. If you were to be one of the first people to go on a trip to another planet, what items would you take to represent your beliefs and interests?

PROJECT MASTER

✦ *Math Masters,* p. 206

Missions to Mars

Because of its blood-red color, the Romans named Mars for their god of war. The Babylonians called the planet Nergal, for their god of death. The ancient Greeks called it Ares, for their god of battle.

In 1877, Italian astronomer Giovanni Schiaparelli reported seeing markings on Mars that he called "canals." American astronomer Percival Lowell claimed that the canals had been dug by intelligent beings to bring water from polar ice caps to irrigate their crops.

In 1950, Ray Bradbury published *The Martian Chronicles,* a collection of science-fiction short stories that became very popular. In these stories, Earth people colonize and corrupt a peaceful Martian civilization. Today we know that Mars is a cold, barren planet without intelligent life, although recent discoveries suggest that microscopic life may have existed there long ago. The question of "canals" was settled by pictures from a series of spacecraft that visited Mars. The first was *Mariner 4,* which flew past in 1965. In 1976, *Viking I* and *Viking 2* both landed on the surface of Mars and sent back thousands of images.

Exploration of Mars was delayed when the *Mars Observer,* a spacecraft sent to make maps, was lost in space in 1993. The United States launched two new missions to Mars in 1996. One of these, the *Mars Global Surveyor,* observed Mars from an orbit around the planet. The other, the *Mars Pathfinder,* landed on the surface July 4, 1997 and sent out a robot, the 25-pound Rover Sojourner, to investigate the terrain and send back images.

The *Mars Polar Lander* and two *Deep Space* probes, launched on January 3, 1999, arrived safely at Mars. Communications were scheduled to resume after the lander and probes reached the surface. However, efforts to contact them failed. That mission was a failure; but one result of all this exploration is that scientists now believe that the canals are simply an optical illusion. NASA plans to launch a Mars orbiter in 2001 and two large scientific rovers in 2003.

Our increasing knowledge of Mars and of space travel has stimulated people to think seriously about sending people to Mars. They argue that human exploration of Mars would advance our knowledge of the solar system, improve technology, establish a place beyond Earth where humans could survive, and inspire the people of the world.

Opponents claim that such a mission would be too expensive and too dangerous. Also, opponents say it would require the development of technologies that would not necessarily be useful on Earth.

Sources: BritannicaOnLine; NASA Exploring Mars (http://www.spaceflight.nasa.gov/mars/)

PROJECT MASTER

✦ *Math Masters,* p. 207

Your Age on Another Planet

We use the time it takes Earth to make one trip around the Sun to keep track of our ages. When you tell someone how old you are, you are telling how many times Earth has traveled around the Sun since you were born.

1. a. Today my age is 12 years, 0 months, and 0 days.
   b. So I have been on Earth a total of about 4,383 days.

Planet	Time to Orbit the Sun (Earth Days)
Mercury	88
Venus	223
Earth	365
Mars	686
Jupiter	4,380
Saturn	10,585
Uranus	30,660
Neptune	60,225
Pluto	90,885

Source: Universal Almanac

Answers above based on the age of 12, with 3 leap years.

If you lived on a different planet, you would have a different age counted in the "year" of that planet. For example, on Venus, one year (the time it takes for Venus to travel around the Sun) would equal 223 Earth days.

2. a. How many Earth days are there in a year on Mars? 686
   b. How many Earth days are there in a year on Jupiter? 4,380

3. Estimate how old you would be on the following planets by finding the number of times they have revolved around the Sun since you were born.

Venus 19.7 Mars 6.4 Jupiter 1

Answers for #3 based on the age of 12.

PROJECT MASTER

✦ *Math Masters,* p. 208

PROJECT

6

Anthropometry Project: Formulas for Body Height and Neck Circumference

OBJECTIVES To measure body parts and plot measurements as data pairs; and to investigate formulas that relate body measurements.

background information

Recommended Use: During or after Unit 3

See the discussion of Projects in the Management Guide section of the *Teacher's Reference Manual.*

materials

- ☐ *Math Masters,* pp. 209–215

For students:

- ☐ tape measure (inches)
- ☐ inch ruler and string (optional)
- ☐ yardstick
- ☐ calculator
- ☐ coloring pencils (red, blue, black)

For the teacher:

- ☐ scissors
- ☐ transparent tape or thumbtacks

***See* Advance Preparation**

Project Information

Students investigate two rules for estimating body measurements. One rule relates height to tibia length; the other relates neck circumference to wrist circumference.

Each student measures two adults and herself or himself. The class plots all of the students' results on two coordinate grids, one for each rule, using different symbols to distinguish adult males, adult females, and students. Students evaluate the tibia/height rule for various inputs and verify the graph for that rule.

Finally, students use the classroom graphs to answer questions such as, "How good is the rule for predicting?" and "Does the rule predict equally well for adults and for students?"

Advance Preparation You will need to make 8 copies of *Math Masters,* page 215 to make two large coordinate grids. (See directions on page 853.) Use either tape or thumbtacks to fasten papers to the board or bulletin board. This project will proceed smoothly if students complete several measurement and graphing activities before the class begins the project. Following is a suggested timetable.

7 school days before teaching the project: Have students read the background information about anthropometry on *Math Masters,* page 209. Also distribute copies of *Math Masters,* pages 210 and 211, which illustrate how, and with what precision, students are to measure the following: their own tibias and heights; the tibias and heights of two adults; their own necks and wrists; and the necks and wrists of two adults. Take time to illustrate the measuring process so students will know exactly *where* to measure. Remind students that all body measures should be in U.S. customary units—with the tibia and neck to the nearest $\frac{1}{4}$ inch, the height to the nearest $\frac{1}{2}$ inch, and the wrist to the nearest $\frac{1}{8}$ inch. Allow students 5 to 6 days to complete this assignment.

Avoid the knob.

Measure around skinny part of wrist.

6 days before teaching the project: Assemble two large classroom coordinate grids, as follows:

▷ Cut 4 copies of *Math Masters,* page 215 and tape them to form a coordinate grid as shown on page 855. Label the left axis Height and the bottom axis Tibia Length. Label the unit marks along the axes as follows:

Left and right axes in inches from 51" to 75"
Top and bottom axes in inches from 11" to 19"

▷ Cut 4 more copies of *Math Masters,* page 215, and assemble a second grid in the same way as shown on page 857. Label the left axis Neck Circumference and the bottom axis Wrist Circumference. Label the unit marks along the axes as follows:

Left and right axes in half-inches from 7" to 19"
Top and bottom axes in half-inches from $4\frac{1}{2}$" to $8\frac{1}{2}$"

▷ A prediction line is a line through the points that follow a rule exactly. Draw the prediction line for the rule

Circumference of neck = 2 * Circumference of wrist

on the coordinate grid. (The prediction line for the other grid will be done as a class demonstration. See Part 1.) As students plot their neck-and-wrist data pairs during the next several days, they will be able to conclude immediately, by looking at the prediction line, whether any data pair they add to the grid satisfies the rule.

▷ Tape or tack the prepared coordinate grids to the board or bulletin board.

5 days before teaching the project: Some students will have completed their body-size measurements. Demonstrate how they should plot their measures as data pairs on the two classroom coordinate grids. Cover the following points:

▷ Each student will have measures for an adult male, for an adult female, and for himself or herself. Therefore, each student will plot 3 points on each coordinate grid.

▷ Explain the color and symbol conventions for plotting:

Use solid red circles for adult female data.
Use open blue circles for adult male data.
Use solid black squares for student data.

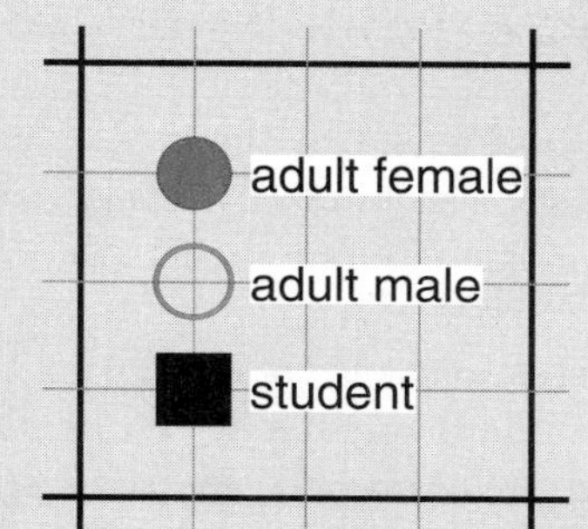

Each plotted point should be large—about 5 mm across—so students will be able to see the points from a distance. As students are bound to make mistakes when plotting, consider using coloring pencils that erase easily, rather than markers or pens.

Verify that students are reading the scales correctly when they locate number pairs. For example, the tibia axis has grid lines at each $\frac{1}{4}$ inch but is labeled only at whole inches. The height axis has grid lines at each $\frac{1}{2}$ inch but is labeled only at whole inches.

Have students discuss why a graph that visually differentiates adult male, adult female, and student data might be useful. There may be interesting patterns among plotted points. These patterns are more apparent when the points for men, women, and children are color-coded. These patterns may be overlooked if the points are not color-coded.

Remaining days before teaching the project: As students complete *Math Masters,* pages 210 and 211, have them plot their measures as data pairs onto the classroom grids. Encourage students who have not yet completed the measurements to do so.

It's likely that some number pairs will be identical. If the point for a student's number pair is already occupied, he or she should plot the pair as near the desired point as possible, without overlapping any points already marked.

Background Information **Anthropometry** is the study of human body sizes and proportions. An **anthropometrist** is a person who gathers data on the size of the body and its components. Body-size data are useful to engineers, architects, industrial designers, interior designers, clothing manufacturers, and artists. *For example:*

▷ Automotive engineers use body-size data in designing vehicles and child-safety seats.

- ▷ Architects take body-size data into account when designing stairs, planning safe kitchens and bathrooms, and providing access space for people who use wheelchairs.
- ▷ Clothing manufacturers use body-size data to create sewing patterns.
- ▷ No two people, including identical twins, are exactly alike. There are big differences in body sizes and proportions due to age, sex, and ethnic or racial group.
- ▷ This means there are no "perfect formulas" that can be used to predict one body measure exactly from another body measure. For example, there is no exact formula that can predict a person's weight from his height and no exact formula that can predict a person's height from his arm length.

There are "imperfect formulas" and "rules of thumb" that can be very useful in describing how one body measure is related to another body measure. The project will focus on activities that investigate two such "less-than-perfect" formulas.

Vocabulary • **anthropometry** • **anthropometrist** • **tibia (shinbone)** • **patella (kneecap)** • **prediction line**

NOTE: Measuring the tibia as directed on *Math Masters,* page 210, will very likely yield results that overestimate the length of the tibia by $\frac{1}{2}$ inch. However, the average $\frac{1}{2}$-inch overestimate is not a problem, because the formula takes that overestimate into account.

Anthropometry Project: Tibia and Height

1. Your **tibia** is your shinbone. The following rule is sometimes used to predict the height of an adult when the length of the person's tibia is known. Measurements are in inches.

   Height = (2.6 ∗ Length of Tibia) + 25.5

   Do you think that this rule can exactly predict a person's height when the length of his or her tibia is known? Sample answer: no

   Explain. People's proportions differ. The rule is intended to give only an approximate number.

2. Use the rule in Problem 1 to complete the table. Find the predicted height for each tibia length. You may use your calculator.

Tibia Length	Height Predicted
11 in.	54 in.
14 in.	62 in.
19 in.	75 in.
$17\frac{1}{2}$ in.	71 in.

3. Your teacher will draw a **prediction line** on the grid where you plotted your research data. It passes through points that exactly follow the rule for predicting height given the tibia length. Use the prediction line to answer the following questions.

   a. The predicted height for a person with a $15\frac{1}{4}$-inch tibia is about 65 inches.

   b. The predicted height for a person with a $13\frac{1}{4}$-inch tibia is about 5 ft 0 in.

   Sample answers:

4. a. How closely does the prediction line approximate the actual data points for adult males? Fairly closely

   Explain. Most of the data points fall near or slightly above the prediction line.

PROJECT MASTER

✦ *Math Masters,* p. 212

Doing the Project

✦ Applying a Rule (*Math Masters,* p. 212)

INDEPENDENT ACTIVITY 

Ask students to read and answer Problem 1 on *Math Masters,* page 212. Then have them share their responses to Problem 1. Students should have no difficulty understanding that anthropometric data cannot be described by perfect formulas that predict exactly. You may wish to share an example from the completed classroom plot of tibia/height measures to illustrate this point.

NOTE: Point out that the formula

Height = (2.6 ∗ Length of Tibia) + 25.5

applies to adults. Anthropometrists typically use separate formulas for males and females to describe relationships between two different body measures. The rule used for the activities in this lesson, Height = (2.6 ∗ Length of Tibia) + 25.5, is a compromise that acceptably fits both adult males and females.

- ▷ Find a **tibia** length that is common to several people. Notice that, most likely, not all these people have the same height.
- ▷ Find a height that is common to several people. Notice that, most likely, not all these people have the same tibia length.

Have students complete Problem 2 on *Math Masters,* page 212.

✦ Graphing the Prediction Line for Tibia and Height (*Math Masters,* pp. 212 and 213)

WHOLE-CLASS ACTIVITY

Gather the class, with their project master copies and calculators, around the classroom grid on which they plotted their tibia and height data.

Have students read their answers to Problem 2 on *Math Masters,* page 212 as you mark these four points on the grid. Indicate that these points fall on a straight line, which is called the **prediction line** for the formula: Then draw the prediction line. (*See margin.*) The prediction line is a "picture version" of the formula. It shows the values for which the formula is true.

Pose additional tibia lengths and have students use the formula and their calculators to find the predicted heights for those lengths. In each case, verify that each of these new tibia-predicted height pairs also falls on the line drawn.

As a class, use the prediction line to complete Problems 3 and 4. The discussion need not be a sophisticated analysis of the completed grid. Rather, simply guide students to see and verbalize some simple features of the data that are quite clear from looking at the completed grid.

Although the actual data pairs will vary from class to class, the following features are likely to be consistent:

- ▷ *Adult male data (open blue circles):* Some data points will fall on, or nearly on, the prediction line. For these people, the formula is predicting their height almost exactly. Of the remaining data points, more points will likely fall above the prediction line than below it. This means that, for men, the rule tends to predict heights that are a bit short. Very few of the data points will represent heights that differ from the predicted heights by more than 3 inches.
- ▷ *Adult female data (solid red circles):* These data points should be similar to those of the adult males. However, expect that more female points will fall below the prediction line than above it. This means that, for women, the rule tends to predict heights that are a bit tall.
- ▷ *Student data (black squares):* Most data points will fall below the prediction line. The rule predicts heights for students that are greater than their actual heights.

NOTE: The grid below shows actual data that were collected from adults and students. It should give you a good idea of how your class's completed grid will look.

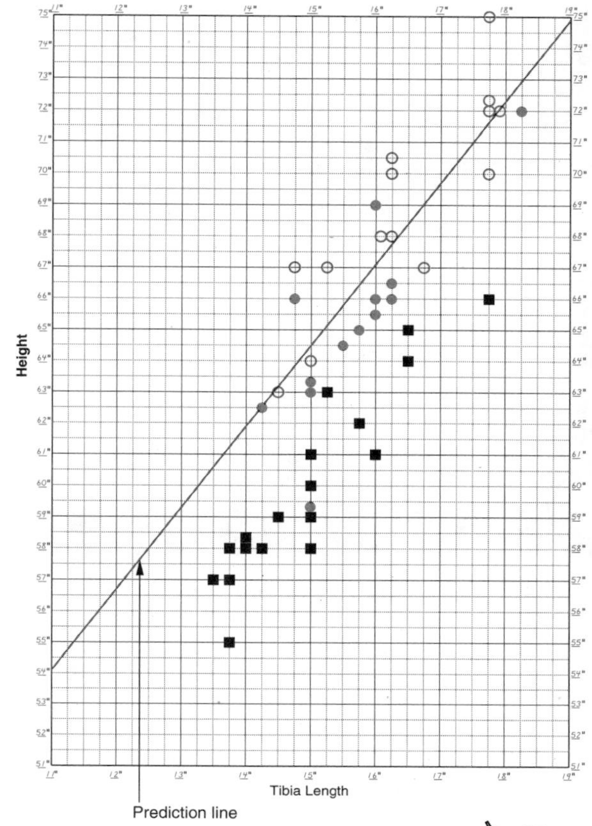

Anthropometry Project: Tibia and Height (cont.)

Sample answers:

b. How closely does the prediction line approximate the actual data points for adult females? Fairly closely

Explain. Most of the data points are close to or slightly below the prediction line.

c. How closely does the prediction line approximate the actual data points for students in your class? Not as closely as for adults.

Explain. Many of the student data points are quite a bit below the prediction line.

5. Scientists can use a single bone from a human skeleton to estimate the height of an adult who lived many centuries ago. If they have a tibia, they can use the rule:

Height = (2.6 * Length of Tibia) + 25.5

a. The skeleton of a Neanderthal man who lived about 40,000 years ago contained a tibia about $14\frac{3}{4}$ inches long. Estimate the man's height. 64 in.

b. The tibia of a partial skeleton of a 20,000-year-old adult was reconstructed and found to be about $12\frac{1}{2}$ inches long. Estimate the person's height. 58 in.

6. Paul measured his baby sister's tibia (4 inches long) and then used the rule to estimate her height. "That's crazy!" said Paul when he saw the result.

a. What was Paul's estimate of his baby sister's height? 36 in.

b. Why did he say that the estimate was "crazy"? Sample answer: Babies are not 3 feet long.

PROJECT MASTER

✦ *Math Masters,* p. 213

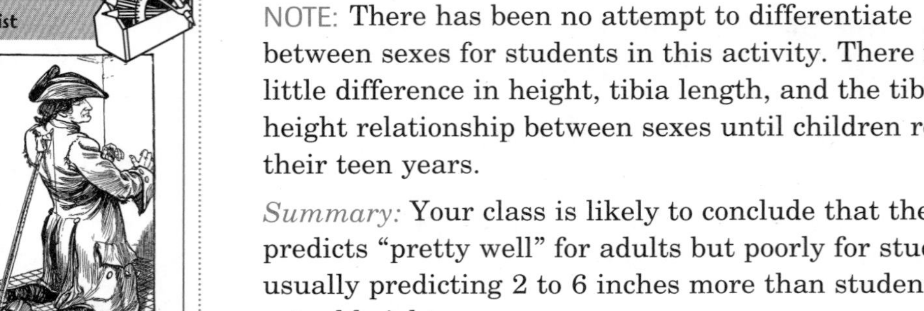

Anthropometry Project: Neck and Wrist

Use the neck and wrist data that you and your classmates collected on the graph posted in the classroom to answer the following questions about the wrist-to-neck rule.

Circumference of Neck = 2 * Circumference of Wrist

1. How closely does the prediction line approximate the actual data points

   for adult males? Not too closely

   for adult females? Not too closely

   for sixth graders? Fairly closely

The following passage is from *Gulliver's Travels* by Jonathan Swift. The setting is Lilliput, a country where the people are only 6 inches high.

"Two hundred seamstresses were employed to make me shirts … . The seamstresses took my measure as I lay on the ground, one standing at my neck, and another at my mid leg, with a strong cord extended, that each held by the end, while the third measured the length of the cord with a rule of an inch long. Then they measured my right thumb and desired no more; *for by a mathematical computation, that twice round the thumb is once round the wrist, and so on to the neck and the waist,* and by the help of my old shirt, which I displayed on the ground before them for a pattern, they fitted me exactly."

This passage provides three rules:

- Circumference of Wrist = 2 * Circumference of Thumb
- Circumference of Neck = 2 * Circumference of Wrist
- Circumference of Waist = 2 * Circumference of Neck

Sample answer:

2. Based on the data collected by you and your classmates, how well do you think Gulliver's new clothes fit? They may be snug.

   Explain. Most of the data points for adult males fall above the prediction line.

PROJECT MASTER

Math Masters, p. 214

NOTE: There has been no attempt to differentiate between sexes for students in this activity. There is very little difference in height, tibia length, and the tibia-to-height relationship between sexes until children reach their teen years.

Summary: Your class is likely to conclude that the rule predicts "pretty well" for adults but poorly for students, usually predicting 2 to 6 inches more than students' actual heights.

Testing the "Rule of Twice"

(*Math Masters,* pp. 213 and 214)

PARTNER ACTIVITY

Ask students to complete Problems 5 and 6 on *Math Masters,* page 213 (reproduced on page 855).

Then have them work in partnerships to complete *Math Masters,* page 214. When the majority of students have completed the pages, discuss the conclusions that they were able to draw.

Although actual data pairs will vary from class to class, the following features are likely to be consistent:

- *Adult male data (open blue circles):* More of the data points will likely fall above the prediction line than below it. This means that the rule tends to predict men's neck sizes that are a bit small. Few actual neck sizes will differ from the predicted sizes by more than 3 inches.
- *Adult female data (solid red circles):* These results should be similar to those of the adult males. However, expect that a few more female points than male points will fall below the prediction line. This means that the rule tends to predict women's neck sizes that are a bit small, but not so much so as for men.
- *Student data (black squares):* Some data points will fall on or near the prediction line. For these people, the rule predicts neck size almost exactly. Of the remaining data points, more will fall above the prediction line than below it.

NOTE: Once again, there has been no attempt to differentiate between sexes for students in this activity.

Summary: Your class is likely to conclude that the rule predicts "pretty well" for students but poorly for adults, usually predicting neck sizes less than actual.

NOTE: The completed grid in the margin shows actual data collected from adults and students. It should give you a fairly good idea of how your class's completed grid will look.

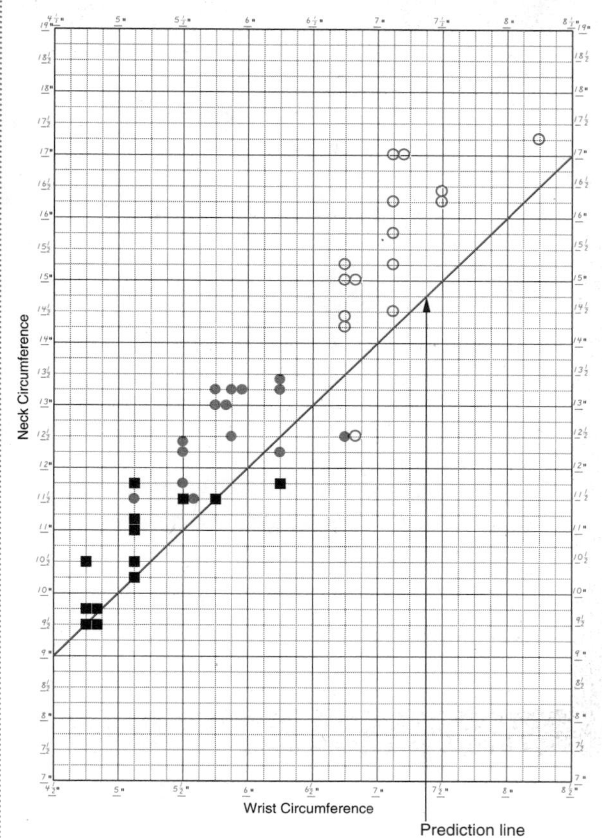

2 Extending the Project

✦ Collecting Data for Thumbs and Waists
(*Math Masters,* p. 215)

INDEPENDENT ACTIVITY 

Some students may be interested in collecting data for thumbs and waists to test the other formulas from *Gulliver's Travels.* Invite those students to share their findings with the class.

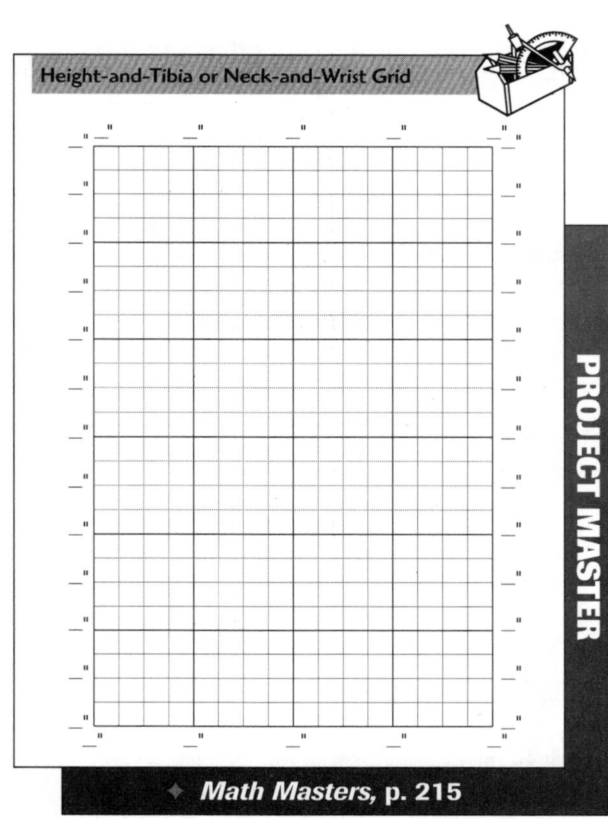

PROJECT MASTER

✦ *Math Masters,* p. 215

PROJECT

7

Paper-Throwing Experiments

OBJECTIVES **To decide on a testing protocol and follow detailed instructions; to organize test data in tables and bar graphs; and to evaluate tested airplanes.**

background information

Recommended Use: During or after Unit 5

See the discussion of Projects in the Management Guide section of the *Teacher's Reference Manual.*

materials

- ☐ *Math Masters,* pp. 216–227

For students:

- ☐ sheets of $8\frac{1}{2}$"-by-11" paper, 20 lb or 24 lb
- ☐ transparent tape
- ☐ inch ruler
- ☐ one tape measure or yardstick per group

For the teacher:

- ☐ 50-foot tape measure
- ☐ masking tape

See **Advance Preparation**

Project Information

Day 1: Students throw folded sheets of paper and examine the effects of the shape and surface area of the paper on the distance thrown. Each student designs a paper airplane and assembles it.
Day 2: Students test their airplanes and determine which three fly the farthest.
Day 3: Students make a second paper airplane using a prize-winning design.
Day 4: Students test their second airplanes and choose the three that fly the farthest. Then they test the three best student-designed airplanes and the three best prize-winning-designed airplanes and analyze the results.
To limit the project to *one day,* use the following version, which emphasizes geometry and minimizes data analysis.

1. Copy the design plan of the prize-winning airplane model.
2. Assemble the airplane.
3. Test each student's airplane for distance; compare the results.

Advance Preparation Students will need a supply of $8\frac{1}{2}$"-by-11" paper of a standard weight (20 or 24 lb, not construction paper or cardstock) and transparent tape. You will need a 50-foot tape measure and masking tape.

Day 1: Divide the class into groups of 3 or 4 students. (An odd number of groups is helpful in determining median distances.) Draw a table like the following on the board.

Class Distances

Group	Unfolded	1 Fold	2 Folds	3 Folds	4 Folds	5 Folds
1						
2						
(etc.)						

Distance testing of the folded paper can also be done as a whole-class activity. In this case, you will not need the table of Class Distances, since there will be no group results to record.

Students will need a long space (at least 50 feet) in which to throw the folded paper, such as a corridor, gymnasium, cafeteria, or outside area not subject to wind. Place a strip of masking tape on the floor as a baseline from which to throw the papers.

Day 2: Students will again require a long space in which to throw their paper airplanes. Stretch a 50-foot tape measure along the length of the area, or put masking tape on the floor at 10-foot intervals, starting at the baseline. You will use this area again on Day 4.

Day 3: To help guide students, you might build the paper airplane yourself, as directed on *Math Masters,* pages 222–224, before Day 3. You may want to make a master of your airplane for students who have difficulty copying the design.

Day 4: Use the same area as you did on Day 2.

You may want to enlist parent volunteers to help ensure that safety procedures are followed during the students' paper-throwing experiments.

Vocabulary • **resistance**

Doing the Project

DAY 1

◆ Throwing Paper

WHOLE-CLASS DISCUSSION

Ask: *How far do you think you can throw a sheet of notebook paper?*

Expect that students will want to know whether the sheet of paper can be folded or crumpled or must remain flat. Some will want to know if there is a specific way in which the paper must be folded or thrown. These are valid questions. Tell students that they will investigate how these factors affect the distance the paper will travel.

◆ Testing How Far a Sheet of Paper Can Be Thrown (*Math Masters,* pp. 216 and 217)

SMALL-GROUP ACTIVITY

Students work in groups of 3 or 4 to complete the paper-folding and distance-testing activities described on *Math Masters,* page 216. (Alternatively, the whole class can do these activities.) Review these procedures with the class before groups begin working.

Stress that a maximum of 3 inches of tape may be used on any sheet of paper. Students should consider this a rule of the testing procedure—more tape might give an unfair advantage over a sheet with less tape.

Each folded paper should be thrown three times. Each group records the *greatest* distance for each kind of fold

How Far Can You Throw a Sheet of Paper?

1. Paper Folding

Work in a group of three or four students. You will need six sheets of paper, transparent tape, and a tape measure or yardstick.

- Leave one paper unfolded.
- Fold one paper in half.
- Fold one paper in half two times.
- Fold one paper in half three times.
- Fold one paper in half four times.
- Fold one paper in half five times.

unfolded | 1 fold | 2 folds | 3 folds | 4 | 5

For each of the folded papers, use tape to secure the edges and keep the paper from unfolding. *Use no more than 3 inches of tape* for each folded paper. Write the number of folds on each folded paper.

2. Distance Testing

Agree on a baseline from which to throw each paper. Throw each paper (including the unfolded one) 3 times. Don't worry if the paper hits the floor, ceiling, or walls before it lands. You may throw the paper in any way you want. Try to throw each paper as far as possible.

a. Measure all distances to the nearest foot. Record the *best distance* for each kind of paper in the table below. Answers vary.

Group Distances

	Unfolded	1 Fold	2 Folds	3 Folds	4 Folds	5 Folds
Distance (to the nearest foot)						

b. If your teacher has put a table of Class Distances on the board, record the distances collected by your group in the table.

PROJECT MASTER

◆ *Math Masters,* p. 216

How Far Can You Throw a Sheet of Paper? (cont.)

PROJECT MASTER

3. Use the data in the completed table of Group Distances to complete the table below. Answers vary.

Landmarks for Class Distances

Landmark	Unfolded	1 Fold	2 Folds	3 Folds	4 Folds	5 Folds
Maximum						
Median						
Minimum						

4. Which paper(s) were consistently thrown the greatest distance? ______

The shortest distance? ______

How do you think the surface area of the paper, its shape, the method of throwing, and other factors affected how far the paper traveled?

Answers vary. See the discussion on *Teacher's Lesson Guide*, page 381.

5. Generations of students, much to the dismay of generations of teachers, have perfected a way of using the air to throw a sheet of paper a great distance. Can you describe how they do it?

Answers vary.

✦ *Math Masters,* p. 217

in the table of Group Distances in Problem 2 on *Math Masters,* page 216. When each group has completed this table, students enter their groups' results in the table of Class Distances on the board. (See Advance Preparation.)

If you prefer not to have individual groups conduct the distance-testing activities, consider this procedure. Allow about 10 minutes for groups to complete the folding and taping. Be sure to remind students to write the number of folds on each piece of paper. Place all of the folded papers in separate piles—one pile of unfolded papers, one pile of 1-fold papers, and so on. Students should take turns as "measurers" and "throwers," testing one pile at a time. Each paper should be thrown only once. After the last paper in a pile has been thrown, identify the minimum, maximum, and median throws. The measurers then measure these distances from the baseline and report them to the class. Students should record the measurements in the table of Landmarks for Class Distances in Problem 3 on *Math Masters,* page 217. Skip Problem 2 on *Math Masters,* page 216.

✦ Determining Landmarks for Class Distances (*Math Masters,* p. 217)

WHOLE-CLASS ACTIVITY

Discuss the data recorded in the table of Class Distances on the board. Students then use this table to complete the table of Landmarks for Class Distances in Problem 3 on *Math Masters,* page 217.

✦ Discussing the Effects of Various Factors on the Distance Paper Will Travel
(*Math Masters,* p. 217)

WHOLE-CLASS DISCUSSION

Problem 4 on *Math Masters,* page 217 asks students to consider why some of the folded papers might have traveled farther than others. Have students share ideas within their groups before opening the discussion to the entire class. Expect responses like the following:

▷ *Unfolded:* The unfolded paper probably traveled the shortest distance. Many students may note that the paper "flew back" at them when they tried to throw it forward. (Students may report a negative distance for a paper that lands behind the baseline.) Because the surface area of the paper is so large, air **resistance** greatly affects the forward motion of the paper.

▷ *1 Fold:* This paper probably traveled only slightly farther than the unfolded paper. Again, the paper may have "flown back" due to the amount of surface area.

▷ *2 and 3 Folds:* Several groups may have found that when these papers are thrown "like flying discs," they travel a fair distance. The thickness of the folded paper made a "flying disc throw" possible—unlike the unfolded and 1-fold papers. When the paper is thrown like a flying disc, the air is used to the thrower's advantage.

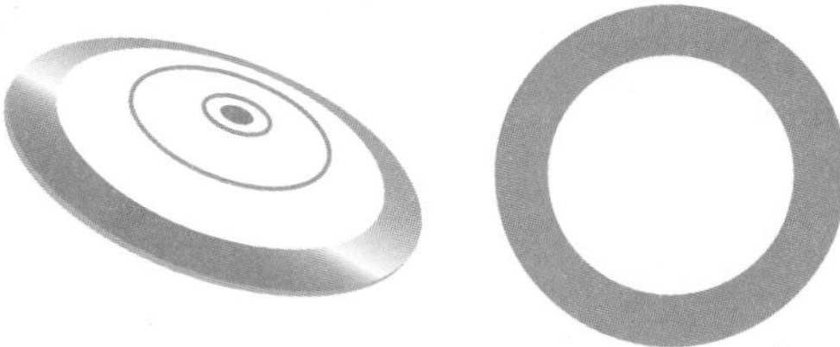
Flying Discs

▷ *4 and 5 Folds:* Most likely, these papers traveled the greatest distances. Some groups may have found that by throwing the paper with an edge slicing through the air, they were able to minimize the effect of air resistance. Also, these folded papers have the smallest surface area, thus limiting the effect of air resistance.

By the end of the discussion, students should conclude that the air either *resisted* or *assisted* the forward motion of the paper, depending on the way the paper was folded and the manner in which it was thrown.

Problem 5 on *Math Masters,* page 217 refers to paper airplanes. Tell students that during the next few days, they will experiment with paper airplane designs.

NOTE: *Math Masters,* pages 226 and 227 describe simple experiments with the "kite effect" and "vacuum effect" on flight. You may want to conduct these experiments as whole-class demonstrations or suggest that students consult these pages as they design their own paper airplanes in the assignment on *Math Masters,* page 219. (*See page 862.*)

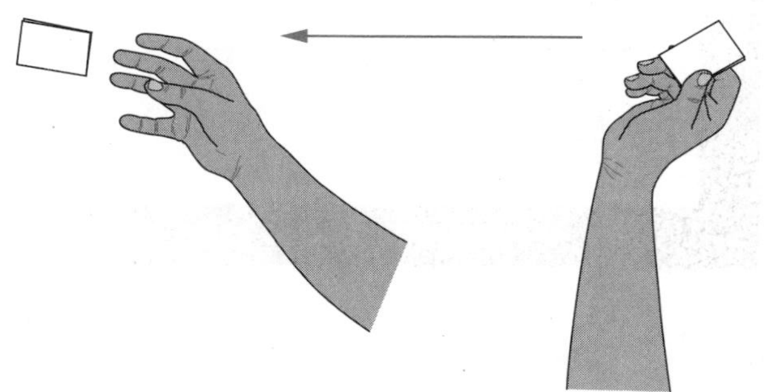
Overhand throw, viewed from the side

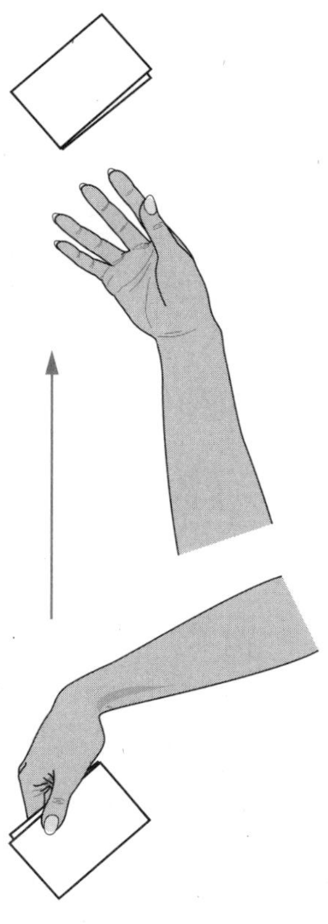
Flying disc throw, viewed from above

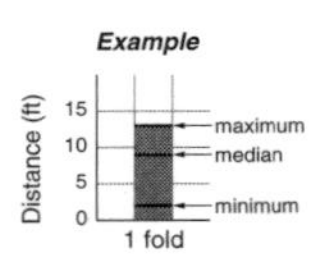

How Far Can You Throw a Sheet of Paper? (cont.)

6. Graphing the Test Data Answers vary.

Use the results in the Landmarks for Class Distances table on *Math Masters,* page 217 to make a bar graph.

The graph should have six bars. Draw one bar for "unfolded" paper, one bar for "1 fold," one bar for "2 folds," and so on.

The height of each bar should be the maximum distance thrown. The median and minimum distances should be marked on each bar, as shown at the right.

Example

Distance (ft): 0, 5, 10, 15 — maximum, median, minimum — 1 fold

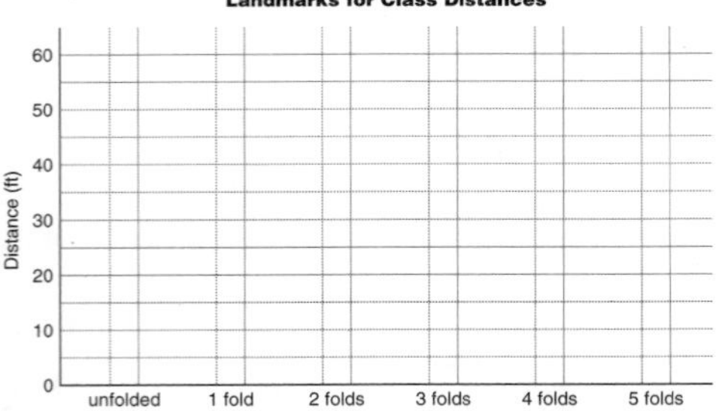

PROJECT MASTER

✦ **Math Masters, p. 218**

Build a Paper Airplane

Design Objective To produce a paper airplane that will fly the greatest possible distance.

Rules

1. Your paper airplane design must be original.
2. You must use $8\frac{1}{2}$"-by-11" paper, or smaller. The paper must be of normal thickness. Do not use construction paper or cardstock. You may construct your paper airplane out of this sheet, if you wish.
3. The plane may be assembled only by folding, cutting, and taping. Do not use more than 3 inches of tape. The 3 inches of tape may be cut into any number of smaller pieces. No glue or other adhesives, string, paper clips, or other objects may be used.

You may need to try several different designs before you are confident that you have found a design that you believe will fly the greatest possible distance.

Good luck!

PROJECT MASTER

✦ **Math Masters, p. 219**

✦ Graphing the Class Distances
(*Math Masters,* pp. 217 and 218)

INDEPENDENT ACTIVITY 

Students use the table of Landmarks for Class Distances on *Math Masters,* page 217 to complete the graph on *Math Masters,* page 218.

You may want to complete the first bar together as a class to make sure that students understand how to show the minimum and median with marks below the top of the bar. (See the example on *Math Masters,* page 218.) Students should catch on quickly and complete the remaining bars easily on their own. Circulate and assist as necessary.

NOTE: The bar on *Math Masters,* page 218 is similar to a statistical display called a "box-and-whiskers plot."

✦ Designing a Paper Airplane
(*Math Masters,* p. 219)

INDEPENDENT ACTIVITY 

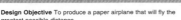

Students are to design a paper airplane that they think will fly the greatest possible distance. Review the design rules with the class. Assign this activity after the Day 1 activities, to be completed in time for the Day 2 activities. You may want to assign it over a weekend, or you might give students two nights to complete the assignment, and insert a Games Day or a regular lesson before beginning the Day 2 activities.

DAY 2

✦ Testing Student-Designed Paper Airplanes (*Math Masters,* p. 220)

WHOLE-CLASS ACTIVITY

Have students take their airplanes to the test area. Each airplane should be thrown once by its creator. Leave the planes where they land.

After all of the airplanes have been thrown, they will be lying on the floor at various distances from the baseline. Student helpers should then move each plane over to one of the walls, being careful not to change the plane's distance from the baseline. It is now possible to observe a line plot of flight-tested airplanes, and to identify and measure the landmark flight distances, as well as the three longest flights.

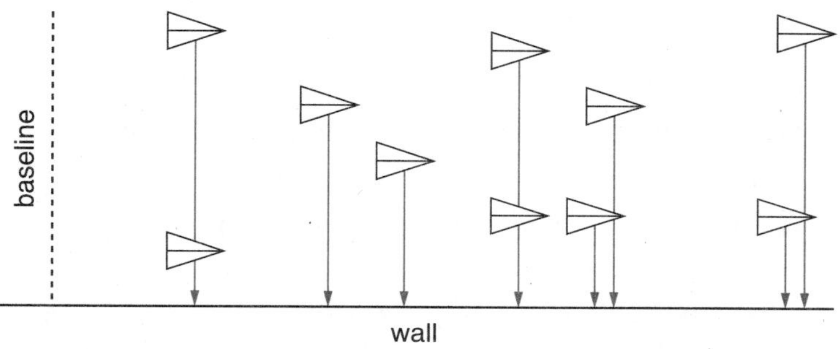

Have the class identify the airplanes that flew the minimum distance (closest to the baseline), maximum distance (farthest from the baseline), and median distance. Measure these distances to the nearest foot. Students record these landmark distances in Problem 1 on *Math Masters,* page 220 (to be used later in conjunction with *Math Masters,* page 225).

Important: Save the three airplanes that flew the farthest for further testing on Day 4.

DAY 3

✦ Reading about the First International Paper Airplane Competition (*Math Masters,* p. 221)

WHOLE-CLASS ACTIVITY 

Use your usual group reading procedure to read the essay on *Math Masters,* page 221. Tell students that they will construct paper airplanes from the design made by Louis Schultz, the nonprofessional winner of *The Leonardo*

Testing Paper Airplane Designs, Part 1

Student-Designed Airplanes

1. Complete the following after you conduct test flights of student-designed paper airplanes. Answers vary.
   a. Number of models tested ________
   b. Minimum distance ________ feet
   c. Median distance ________ feet
   d. Maximum distance ________ feet

Schultz-Designed Airplanes

2. Complete the following after you conduct test flights of Schultz-designed airplanes. Answers vary.
   a. Number of models tested ________
   b. Minimum distance ________ feet
   c. Median distance ________ feet
   d. Maximum distance ________ feet

3. Select the three student-designed and the three Schultz-designed airplanes that flew the farthest. Test these six planes again. Record the results in the table below.

Name of Model's Designer	Distance	Rank (1st to 6th)
Student	feet	
Student	feet	
Student	feet	
Louis Schultz	feet	
Louis Schultz	feet	
Louis Schultz	feet	

PROJECT MASTER

✦ *Math Masters,* p. 220

First International Paper Airplane Competition

The First International Paper Airplane Competition was held during the winter of 1966–67 and was sponsored by *Scientific American* magazine. The 11,851 entries (about 5,000 from children), from 28 different countries, were original designs for paper airplanes. They were entered into one of the following categories:

- Duration aloft (The winning designs flew for 9.9 and 10.2 seconds.)
- Distance flown (The winning designs flew 58 feet, 2 inches and 91 feet, 6 inches.)
- Aerobatics (stunts performed in flight)
- Origami (the traditional Japanese art or technique of folding paper into a variety of decorative or representational forms)

The Leonardo

Contestants were permitted to use paper of any weight and size. The smallest entry received, entered in the distance category, measured 0.08 inch by 0.00003 inch. However, this entry was found to be made of foil, not paper. The largest entry received, also entered in the distance category, was 11 feet long. It flew two times its length when tested.

Scientific American awarded a winner's trophy to two designers, a nonprofessional and a professional, in each category. Nonprofessionals were people not professionally involved in air travel. Professionals were "people employed in the air travel business, people who build non-paper airplanes, and people who subscribe to *Scientific American* because they fly so much." The winners received a trophy called *The Leonardo,* named after Leonardo da Vinci (1452–1519), whom *Scientific American* refers to as the "Patron Saint of Paper Airplanes."

Da Vinci, known for many accomplishments in the fields of painting and sculpture, was also an architect, engineer, and inventive builder. Studying the flight of birds, da Vinci believed that it would be possible to build a flying apparatus which would enable humans to soar through the air. He designed several wing-flapping machines, suggested the use of rotating wings similar to those of the modern helicopter, and invented the "air screw," similar to the modern propeller.

Self portrait of Leonardo da Vinci done in red chalk

More information about the First International Paper Airplane Competition, as well as templates and directions for making each of the winning designs, can be found in the book *The Great International Paper Airplane Book* by Jerry Mander, George Dippel, and Howard Gossage (Simon and Schuster, 1971).

PROJECT MASTER

✦ *Math Masters,* p. 221

PROJECT MASTER

A Winning Paper Airplane Design

The design plan shown below was submitted by Louis Schultz, an engineer. Schultz's paper airplane flew 58 feet, 2 inches and was a winner in the distance category for nonprofessionals. The professional winner in the distance category was Robert Meuser. His paper airplane flew 91 feet, 6 inches before it hit the rear wall of the testing site.

1. Follow the directions below to make an accurate copy of the design plan on an $8\frac{1}{2}$"-by-11" sheet of paper.

   a. Use a ruler to find the midpoints at the top and bottom of the paper. Mark these points. Draw a center line connecting the midpoints to match the subsequent labels.

   b. Mark two points that are $\frac{1}{4}$ inch away from the midpoint at the top of the paper.

   c. Use a protractor to make two 45° angles as shown.

   d. Use a protractor to make two 82° angles as shown.

Louis Schultz's Paper Airplane Design Plan

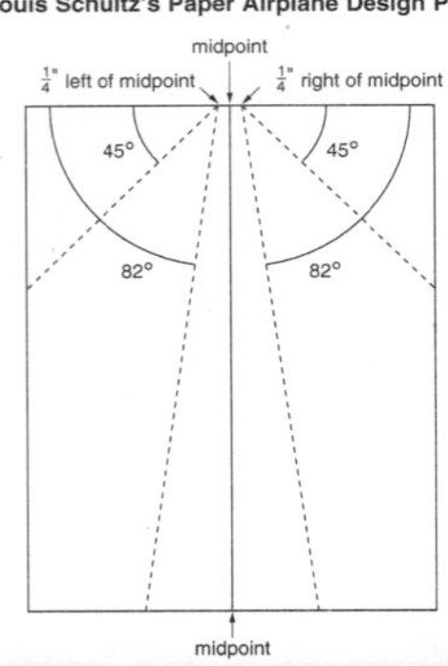

***Math Masters,* p. 222**

PROJECT MASTER

A Winning Paper Airplane Design (cont.)

2. Assemble the paper airplane as shown below. Be very careful to make precise folds. Make the folds on a table. When making a fold, first press down onto the paper with a finger. Then go over this fold with a pen or a ruler on its side. It is important that you **do not** use your fingernails to make folds. (Using your fingernail causes more than one fold to be made in a small area. This fold will move as you attempt to make the rest of the plane.)

   a. Fold the paper back and forth along the center line to get a nice crease. Then unfold.

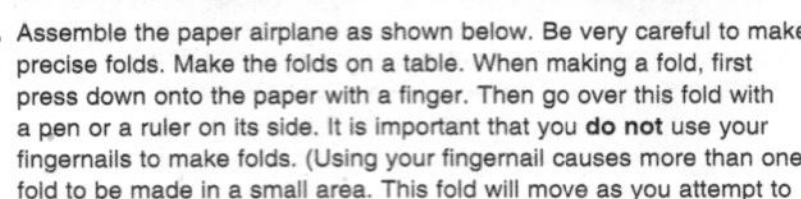

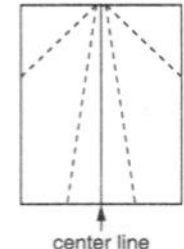

   b. Fold corners along the dashed lines as shown. Use a small piece of tape to secure each corner as shown in the sketch.

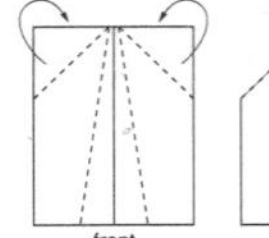

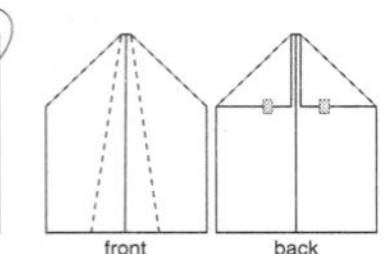

   c. With the back side of the paper facing you, fold the right side of the paper toward the center so that the edges highlighted in the sketch meet. Use a small piece of tape to secure the flap in the position shown in the sketch. Do the same to the other side.

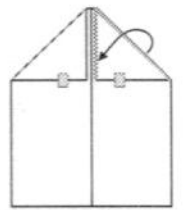

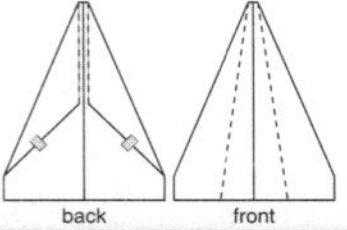

***Math Masters,* p. 223**

trophy in the distance category. They will then test their best planes (Day 2 test flight winners) against the best planes made according to Schultz's specifications (Day 4 test flight winners).

✦ Copying a Design and Assembling an Airplane (*Math Masters,* pp. 222–224)

PARTNER ACTIVITY 

The design plan on *Math Masters,* page 222 is an accurate scale drawing of Schultz's design, but it is less than 50% of the required size. Students are asked to copy this design, enlarging it to fit exactly on an $8\frac{1}{2}$"-by-11" sheet of paper, while preserving all the ratios of lengths and angle measures. Enlarging the design plan of the winning airplane model provides practice with following an annotated plan, as well as measuring and drawing angles.

Expect that some students will have difficulty drawing the 45° and 82° angles, since the edge of the paper is one side of each angle. You might want to demonstrate how to draw these angles before students begin copying the design.

When students have copied the design plan, they should follow the directions for assembling the plane, given on *Math Masters,* pages 223 and 224. Stress the need for precise folding. Circulate and assist as necessary.

DAY 4

✦ Testing the Schultz-Designed Airplanes (*Math Masters,* p. 220)

WHOLE-CLASS ACTIVITY

The Schultz-designed paper airplanes are tested in the same way as the student-designed airplanes were tested on Day 2. Students record the minimum, maximum, and median distances in Problem 2 on *Math Masters,* page 220.

Important: Save the three best Schultz-designed planes for additional testing.

✦ Testing Student Planes against Schultz Planes (*Math Masters,* p. 220)

WHOLE-CLASS ACTIVITY

The final test pits the three best student-designed airplanes against the three best airplanes built to Louis Schultz's specifications. Throw each plane only once. After the last plane is thrown, measure the distance each plane flew to the nearest foot. Students record these distances in Problem 3 on *Math Masters*, page 220.

✦ Reporting Test Results (*Math Masters,* p. 225)

INDEPENDENT ACTIVITY 

Students complete the bar graph on *Math Masters,* page 225. The report describing the test results (Problem 5) should make full use of *all* collected data.

- ▷ Problems 1 and 2 on *Math Masters,* page 220 show landmarks for the tests of all the paper airplanes that were made.
- ▷ Problem 3 on *Math Masters,* page 220 shows information for the *best three* paper airplanes of each type.

A Winning Paper Airplane Design (cont.)

PROJECT MASTER

d. Flip the paper to the front side. Fold in half along the center line so that the front side is now in the inside. Your paper airplane should now look like this.

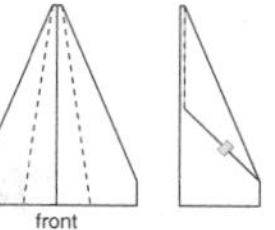

e. Take the top flap of the paper and fold it outward along the dashed lines. (Look for these dashed lines on the inside of the plane.) Do the same to the other flap. Your paper airplane should now look like this.

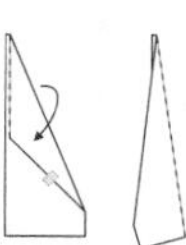

f. First, tape the wings together on top of the airplane. Then tape the bottom as shown, making sure that all loose flaps are secured.

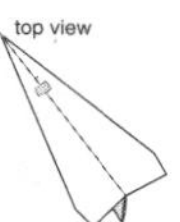

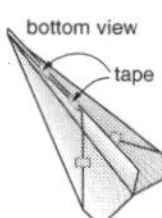

✦ **Math Masters, p. 224**

Testing Paper Airplane Designs, Part 2

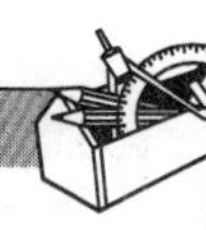

PROJECT MASTER

Answers vary.

4. Draw a bar graph below to show the distance traveled by each of the six planes as recorded in the table on *Math Masters,* page 220.

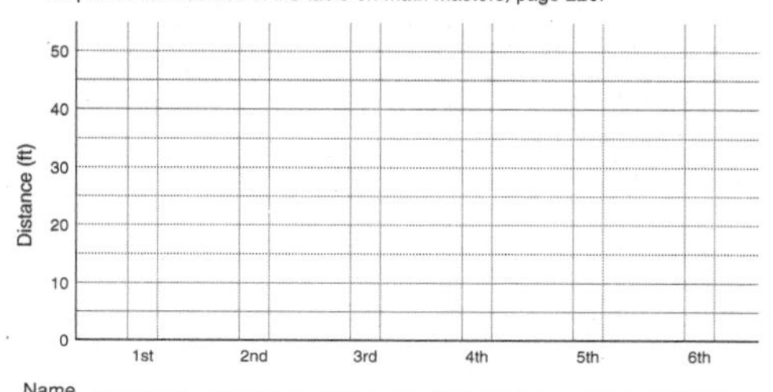

5. Describe the test flight results. Did student-designed airplanes perform better or worse than airplanes built using Schultz's design?

____

____

____

____

6. Which do you think works best for distance?

a. a paper airplane that uses the air to assist the motion of the paper; or

b. a piece of paper, folded very tightly (like the 5-fold paper), which cuts through the air? Explain.

____

____

____

____

✦ **Math Masters, p. 225**

PROJECT MASTER

Experiments with Air

Air is a real substance, just as water, earth, and maple syrup are real substances. Because air is a substance, it offers **resistance** or opposition to the movement of objects through it.

Imagine dropping a penny into a bottle of maple syrup. The penny will eventually fall to the bottom of the bottle, but the maple syrup will slow its progress—the maple syrup will offer resistance to the movement of the penny. Air works in much the same way—objects can move through it, but the air offers resistance to the movement of those objects.

Did you know that this resistance can serve a helpful purpose? Try the following experiments to see how resistance can be used to help an object, such as an airplane, move through the air more efficiently.

The "Kite Effect"

1. Hold one end of an $8\frac{1}{2}$"-by-11" sheet of paper as illustrated—forefinger on top, supported by the thumb and second finger on the bottom. Notice that the paper in the illustration is tilted slightly so that the opposite end of the paper is a bit higher than the end that you are holding.

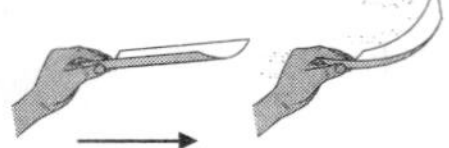

2. *Push* the paper directly forward as illustrated.

You will notice that the end of the paper, opposite the end that you are holding, tilts up. When the tilted surface of the paper pushes against the air, the air pushes back. This partially slows the paper down and partially lifts it up.

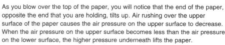

The sheet of paper has some of the characteristics of an airplane wing. The wings of an airplane are set at an angle so that their front edge is higher than their back edge. In this way, the lower surface of the airplane wing uses the air resistance to achieve a small amount of lift.

◇ *Math Masters,* p. 226

PROJECT MASTER

Experiments with Air (cont.)

The "Vacuum Effect"

1. Hold the small end of a 2"-by-6" strip of paper between your thumb and forefinger as illustrated—thumb on top. The paper should fall in a curve.
2. Blow over the top of the paper as shown.

As you blow over the top of the paper, you will notice that the end of the paper, opposite the end that you are holding, tilts up. Air rushing over the upper surface of the paper causes the air pressure on the upper surface to decrease. When the air pressure on the upper surface becomes less than the air pressure on the lower surface, the higher pressure underneath lifts the paper.

This sheet of paper also has some of the characteristics of an airplane wing. Only the lower surface of an airplane wing is flat; the upper surface is curved or arched. In this way, the upper surface of the airplane wing also uses the air resistance to achieve lift. Both the "kite effect" and the "vacuum effect" contribute to the total lift of an airplane. However, the "vacuum effect" is responsible for about 80% of it.

Additional Sources of Information about Paper Airplanes

Here are three books about paper airplanes:

- *The Best Paper Airplanes You'll Ever Fly* by the editors of Klutz (Klutz, 1998).
- *The Great International Paper Airplane Book* by Jerry Mander, George Dippel, and Howard Gossage (Simon and Schuster, 1971, and Galahad Books, 1998).
- *The World Record Paper Airplane Book* by Ken Blackburn and Jeff Lamers (Workman, 1994).

Internet sites come and go. The following two may no longer exist, but there will be new ones. Search for "paper airplanes."

- http://www.geocities.com/CapeCanaveral/1817/ A site maintained by Ken Blackburn, creator of the paper airplane that holds the Guinness world record for time in the air, 27.6 seconds, set in 1998.
- http://www.webpointers.com/papair.html (includes links to additional sites)

◇ *Math Masters,* p. 227

2 Extending the Project

✦ Finding Out More about Paper Airplanes (*Math Masters,* pp. 226 and 227)

INDEPENDENT ACTIVITY 

Invite students to learn more about paper airplanes. Some suggested books, Internet sites, and software are listed on *Math Masters,* page 227.

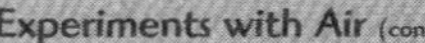

PROJECT

8

Mathematics and Poetry

OBJECTIVE **To learn about the mathematical structures of four kinds of poems.**

background information

Recommended Use: During or after Unit 6

See the discussion of Projects in the Management Guide section of the *Teacher's Reference Manual.*

materials

- ☐ *Math Masters,* pp. 228–232
- ☐ children's literature selections

***See* Advance Preparation**

Project Information

Students read about four types of poems and their mathematical structures. They read poems of these types and try to write their own.

Advance Preparation *Math Masters,* pages 228–232 describe four types of poems: haiku, sonnet, free verse, and limerick. Decide how you want students to work—with some or all types, independently or with a partner. Also decide whether to bring the class together to talk about the poems and share their work.

Gather books of poems—preferably books that illustrate the haiku, sonnet, free verse, and limerick. *For example:*

Haiku Handbook: How to Write, Share, and Teach Haiku, by William J. Higginson and Penny Harter (Kodansha, 1992).

The Essential Haiku: Versions of Basho, Buson, and Issa, Robert Hass editor (HarperCollins, 1995).

Great Sonnets, Paul Negri, editor (Dover, 1994).

Americans' Favorite Poems, Robert Pinsky and Maggie Dietz, editors (Norton, 1999).

The 20th Century Children's Poetry Treasury, Jack Prelutsky, editor (Knopf, 1999).

A Book of Nonsense, by Edward Lear (Everyman Library, 1992).

Complete Sonnets of William Shakespeare (Dover, 1991).

Basho and the Fox, by Tim Myers (Cavendish, 2000).

Vocabulary • **haiku** • **sonnet** • **free verse** • **limerick**

Haiku

A **haiku** is a poem with 3 lines and 17 syllables. The first line has 5 syllables, the second line has 7 syllables, and the third line has 5 syllables. Haikus originated in Japan, where they are still popular. Some newspapers print haikus about the day's events on their front page.

In every haiku
the lines are five, seven, five,
in every haiku.

This design has a kind of symmetry, with the two shorter lines around the longer middle line. The variation keeps the lines from becoming too rhythmic or sing-song. The form forces the poet to treat words as precious. Traditionally, haikus are about nature.

Here are translations of four traditional haikus by Japanese poets.

Wet with morning dew
and splotched with mud, the melon
looks especially cool.
Basho (1644–1694)

Clinging to the bell
he dozes so peacefully,
this new butterfly.
Buson (1715–1783)

Those falling blossoms
all return to the branch when
I watch butterflies.
Moritake (1452–1540)

The barnyard rooster
tries to act like a lion
by preening feathers.
Kikaku (1661–1707)

Notice that each haiku has a surface meaning and a deeper meaning as well. Haikus are often about contrasts, such as the beauty of a melon spotted by mud, or the calm of a butterfly just before a bell rings. The power of haikus comes from compressing content into a small form. Also, the symmetry of the form, and the asymmetry (lack of symmetry) of the individual lines, contribute to the poem's effectiveness.

Try These

1. Find several haikus in a book or magazine. Write a paragraph describing their surface meanings and any deeper meanings you see.
2. Try to write a haiku. Notice how it forces you to choose your words with care.

PROJECT MASTER

Math Masters, p. 228

Sonnet

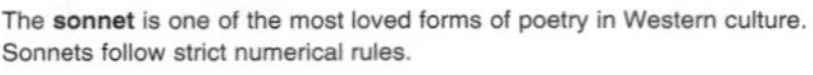

The **sonnet** is one of the most loved forms of poetry in Western culture. Sonnets follow strict numerical rules.

- A sonnet must be 14 lines long.
- In a traditional English sonnet, each line must have 10 syllables.

Sonnets are usually divided into parts. In one type of sonnet, the first eight lines might state a problem or ask a question. The last six lines might solve the problem or answer the question.

In another type of sonnet, there are three parts of four lines each, followed by one part of two lines. The lines in a traditional sonnet must rhyme. There are several rhyming patterns, one of which is shown in Sonnet XVIII on *Math Masters,* page 230.

The 14 lines of a sonnet give the poet time to make an argument, but they also force the poet to be careful with words. A line is long enough for a sentence, but sentences can also continue from one line to the next.

The 14 lines also keep the sonnet from becoming too symmetrical. A poem of 16 lines, for example, would be more regular, but possibly less interesting.

Sonnets are not easy to write. Sometimes they are hard to read. Try reading Sonnet XVIII on *Math Masters,* page 230. It was written by William Shakespeare (1564–1616), probably the greatest sonnet writer in the English language.

PROJECT MASTER

Math Masters, p. 229

1 Doing the Project

✦ Introducing Mathematics and Poetry

WHOLE-CLASS DISCUSSION 

Say that students will explore mathematics and poetry. Make the following points:

- ▷ Poetry might not seem to have much to do with mathematics, but you might be surprised. Both poets and mathematicians work within a *system of rules*, follow *patterns*, and make beauty with *abstract forms*.
- ▷ A poet chooses a form for a poem in order to express meaning through language, just as a mathematician might use a graph or an equation to express relationships.
- ▷ The form that the poet or mathematician chooses can affect meaning. The forms of poetry in this project involve numbers, and each form contributes to the feeling of the poem.

Discuss students' favorite poems, poems studied in class, and any forms of poetry with which students are familiar.

✦ Learning about Poems (*Math Masters,* pp. 228–232)

INDEPENDENT ACTIVITY 

Have students read about forms of poetry and do the suggested activities. Point out any poetry books available in the classroom.

- ▷ *Math Masters,* page 228 is about the haiku.
- ▷ *Math Masters,* pages 229 and 230 are about the sonnet.
- ▷ *Math Masters,* page 231 is about free verse.
- ▷ *Math Masters,* page 232 is about the limerick, sums up the project, and suggests further work with poets and poetry.

Extending the Project

✦ Sharing Students' Poems

WHOLE-CLASS ACTIVITY 

Have students talk about the poems they have written. For example, was it hard or easy to work in the form? How did they come up with an idea? Ask students to read their poems to the class or post them on the bulletin board. If students found poems they like by other people, they could share those as well, and point out any mathematical patterns in the poems.

✦ Finding Out about Poetry and Poets

(*Math Masters,* p. 232)

INDEPENDENT ACTIVITY

Invite students to learn more about poems and poets, as suggested at the bottom of *Math Masters,* page 232.

Sonnet (cont.)

Sonnet XVIII

Shall I compare thee to a summer's day?
Thou art more lovely and more temperate:
Rough winds do shake the darling buds of May,
And summer's lease hath all too short a date:
Sometimes too hot the eye of heaven shines,
And often is his gold complexion dimm'd,
And every fair from fair sometimes declines,
By chance or nature's changing course, untrimm'd;
But thy eternal summer shall not fade,
Nor lose possession of that fair thou ow'st;
Nor shall Death brag thou wander'st in his shade,
When in eternal lines to time thou grow'st;
So long as men can breathe, or eyes can see,
So long lives this, and this gives life to thee.

Shakespeare is comparing his beloved to summer, and saying that she is more beautiful, pleasing, and lasting. He uses the sonnet to convince us of this. Each group of four lines is called a *quatrain.* In the first quatrain, Shakespeare asks which is more beautiful—summer or his beloved—and begins to answer by showing that summer is not perfect.

The second quatrain continues this answer, so that the first eight lines are linked. Shakespeare does not always use the fewest possible words, as a haiku must. For example, he could have referred to "the eye of heaven" in fewer words. (He means the Sun.)

When the third quatrain begins (line 9), Shakespeare shifts from summer to his beloved, saying that she will never grow old. As in a haiku, he is using contrast. At first this quatrain might seem like a riddle, since everyone grows old. But the riddle is answered in the last two lines, called the rhymed couplet. The sonnet itself will keep its subject alive.

Like a haiku, this sonnet is about more than one idea. It is a love poem, but it is also about the power of art to keep its subject alive.

Try These

1. Notice that the last words in the first and third lines rhyme: "day" and "May." What is the rhyme pattern for the entire sonnet—that is, which lines rhyme?
2. Find a sonnet in a book or magazine. Write a paragraph describing its content and structure.

PROJECT MASTER

✦ *Math Masters,* p. 230

Free Verse

Many poets have written in what is called **free verse.** The name is misleading. While a free-verse poem might not follow an established pattern like a haiku or a sonnet, its form has been carefully chosen by the poet.

Artistic forms might be compared to geometric shapes. There are basic shapes—triangles, rectangles, trapezoids, and so on—but there are also unusual or complex shapes, such as a convex nine-sided polygon, which can still be studied and explained with geometry. Poets, painters, and other artists who use unusual or complex forms do not do so because they can't use the basic ones; they use them because the form matches the content.

Read this free-verse poem written by William Carlos Williams (1883–1963).

Poem

As the cat
climbed over
the top of
the jamcloset
first the right
forefoot
carefully
then the hind
stepped down
into the pit of
the empty
flowerpot

Did you notice the very short lines, the irregular rhythm, and the number of syllables? We think of patterns and forms as being "regular," but Williams is actually making a pattern out of irregularity. Why? Have you ever seen a cat climbing over something uneven? The cat takes its time and tests each step carefully. By using a short line length, the poet makes us feel the cat's movements.

Try These

1. Try to write a free-verse poem. Remember, a free-verse poem does not have to follow an established pattern. However, its form should be carefully chosen to express the ideas and emotions you want to convey.
2. Find a free-verse poem you like in a book or magazine. Write a paragraph describing its content and structure. Are any parts difficult to understand?

PROJECT MASTER

✦ *Math Masters,* p. 231

Limericks

Limericks are short poems (five lines) with a definite rhyming pattern and strong rhythm. Both of these features support the limerick's usually humorous or silly topic.

A mathematician confided
That a Möbius band is one-sided.
And you'll get quite a laugh
If you cut one in half,
For it stays in one piece when divided.

A tutor who taught on the flute
Tried to teach two tooters to toot.
Said the two to the tutor,
"Is it harder to toot, or
To tutor two tooters to toot?"

Try These

1. Figure out the rhythms and rhyming pattern of limericks.
2. Find other limericks (for example, by Edward Lear), and write some of your own.

Summing Up

For poets and other artists, form and structure and pattern are not separate from meaning. Since mathematics is so much about form and structure and pattern, there are many similarities between art and mathematics.

- Are you starting to recognize how a poem's meaning is affected by its design—how many syllables there are in a line, how many lines are grouped together, how repetition and rhyme and strong and weak syllables create patterns?
- Are you starting to notice properties that poems share with geometric shapes, such as symmetry and asymmetry (lack of symmetry)?
- Can you feel that when a poet stretches a sentence across two lines, or changes the rhythm, that the poet is playing with form, just as in mathematics you might transform a geometric shape or vary a pattern?

If you answered "yes," or even "maybe," to these questions, you are on your way to thinking like a poet as well as a mathematician.

Try These

1. Find out about another form of poetry, such as the ballad, lyric, epic, or ode. What are some examples of this form? Compare the form with one of the forms in this project. How are the two forms similar? Different?
2. Read about the life and work of a poet—for example, Shakespeare, William Carlos Williams, William Wordsworth, Emily Dickinson, Robert Frost, or Jack Prelutsky.

PROJECT MASTER

✦ *Math Masters,* p. 232

Grade 6 Key Vocabulary

accurate As near as possible to a true result. For example, an accurate measure or count is one with little or no error. Compare to *precise*.

acute angle An angle with a measure greater than 0° and less than 90°.

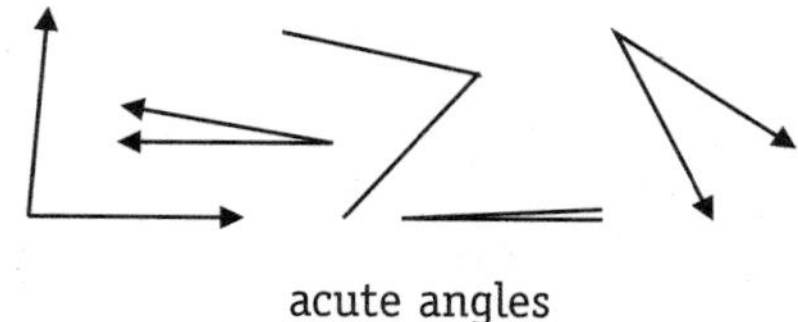

acute angles

adjacent angles Two angles with a common side and vertex that do not otherwise overlap.

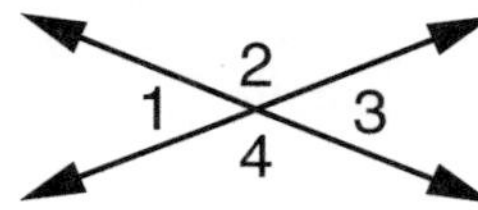

Angles 1 and 2, 2 and 3, 3 and 4, and 4 and 1 are pairs of adjacent angles.

algebraic expression An expression that contains a variable. For example, if Maria is 2 inches taller than Joe and if the variable M represents Maria's height, then the algebraic expression $M - 2$ represents Joe's height.

arc Part of a circle, from one point on the circle to another. For example, a semicircle is an arc with endpoints that are the endpoints of a diameter of the circle. An arc is named by its endpoints.

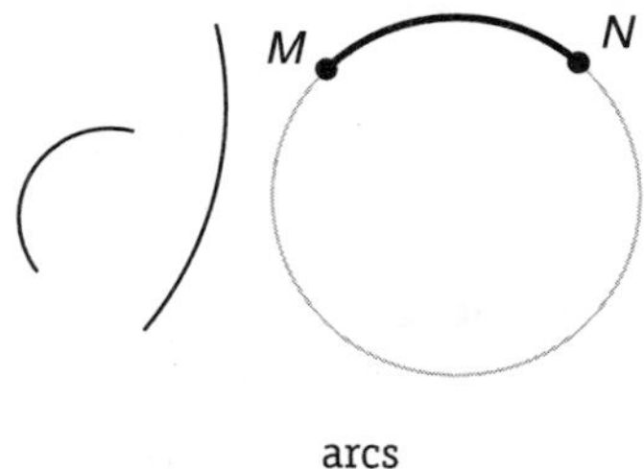

arcs

area A measure of a bounded surface. The boundary might be a triangle or rectangle in a plane or the boundaries of a state or country on the earth's surface. Area is expressed in square units such as square miles, square inches, or square centimeters, and can be thought of as the approximate number of non-overlapping squares that will "tile" or "cover" the surface within the boundary.

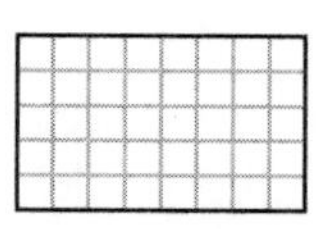

40 square units 21 square units

The area of the United States is about 3,800,000 square miles.

axis (1) Either of the two number lines used to form a coordinate grid. Plural *axes*.

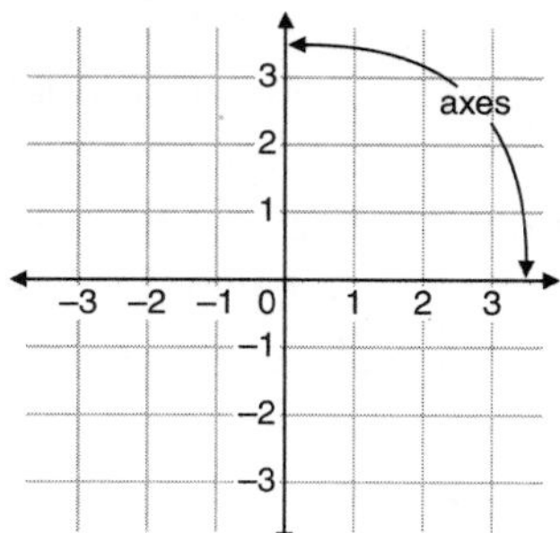

(2) A line about which a solid figure rotates.

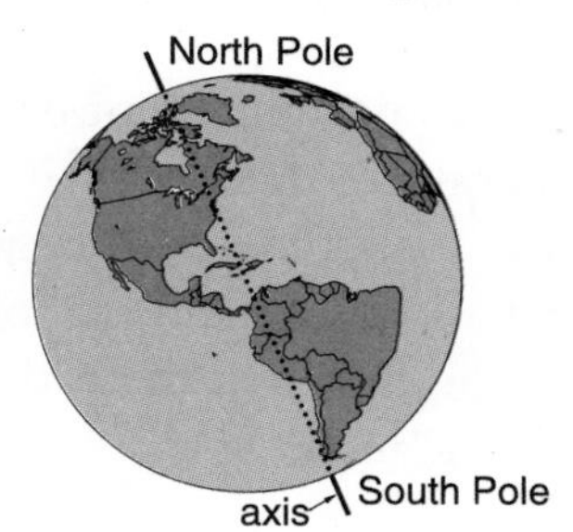

bar graph A graph that shows the relationships in data by the use of bars to represent quantities.

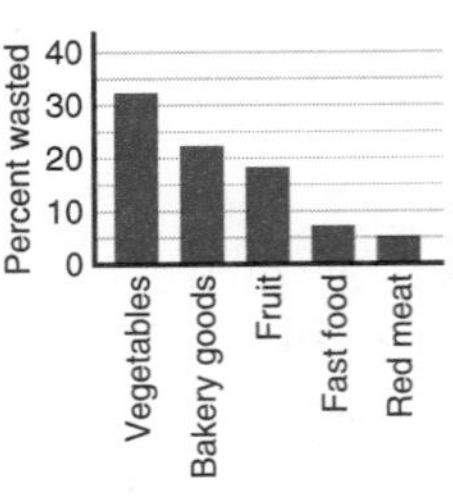

Source: *The Garbage Product*

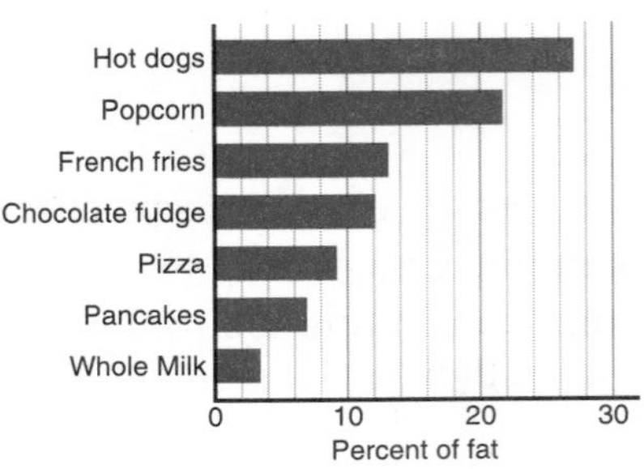

Source: *The New York Public Library Desk Reference*

base (1) Geometry: A side of a polygon, usually used for area computations along with the "altitude," or height, perpendicular to it.

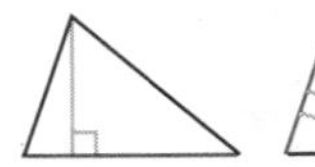
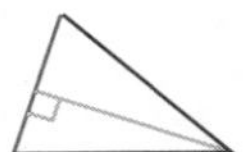

Bases are shown in blue, altitudes in grey.

(2) Geometry: Either of two parallel and congruent faces that define the shape of a prism or cylinder, or the face that defines the shape of a cone or pyramid.

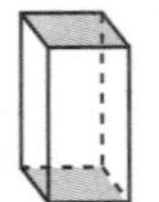

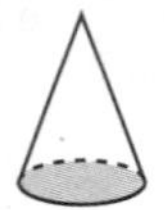
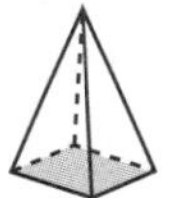

Bases are shown in blue.

(3) Arithmetic: See *exponential notation*.
(4) Arithmetic: The foundation number for a numeration system. For example, our ordinary system for writing numbers is a base-10 place-value system, with 1, 10, 100, 1000 and other powers of 10 as the values of the places in whole numbers. In electronics and computers, bases of two, eight, or sixteen are usual, instead of base ten.

$$356 = 300 + 50 + 6$$

expanded notation for a base-ten number

benchmark An important count or measure that can be used to evaluate the reasonableness of other counts, measures, or estimates. A benchmark for land area is that a football field is about one acre. A benchmark for length is that the width of a man's thumb is about one inch.

broken-line graph Same as *line graph*.

calorie A unit for measuring the amount of energy a food will produce when it is digested by the body. One calorie is the amount of energy required to raise the temperature of 1 liter of water 1° Celsius. (Technically, this is a "large calorie" or kilocalorie. A "small calorie" is one thousandth of a large calorie.)

circle The set of all points in a plane that are equally distant from a given point in the plane called the *center* of the circle. The distance from the center to the circle is the *radius*. The circle is the boundary only. A circle together with its interior is called a *disk* or a *circular region*.

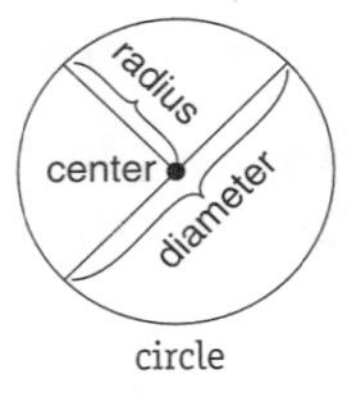

circle

circular region

circle graph A graph in which a circle and its interior are divided into parts to represent the parts of a set of data. The whole circle represents the whole set of data. Also called a *pie graph*.

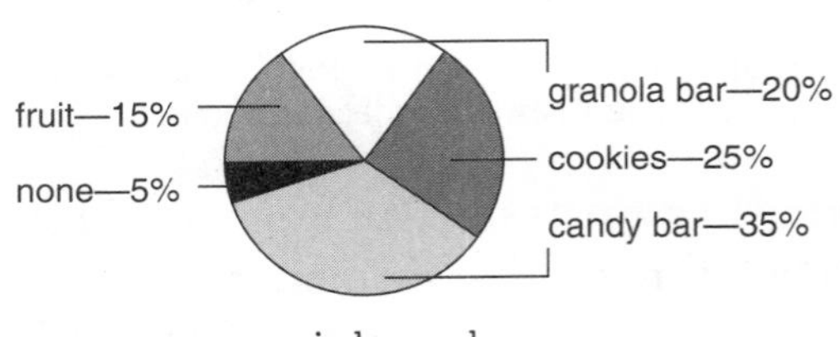

circle graph

column (1) A vertical arrangement of objects or numbers in an array or a table.

(2) A section of cells lined up vertically in a spreadsheet.

common denominator Any nonzero number that is a multiple of the denominators of two or more fractions. For example, the fractions $\frac{1}{2}$ and $\frac{2}{3}$ have common denominators 6, 12, 18, and so on.

common factor Any number that is a factor of two or more numbers. The common factors of 18 and 24 are 1, 2, 3, and 6. See *factor*.

commutative property A property of addition and multiplication (but not division or subtraction) that says that changing the order of the elements being added or multiplied will not change the sum or product.

For addition: $a + b = b + a$, so $5 + 10 = 10 + 5$
For multiplication: $a \times b = b \times a$, so $5 \times 10 = 10 \times 5$.

compass (1) A tool used to draw circles and arcs and copy line segments. Certain geometric figures can be drawn using only a compass and a straightedge. See *compass-and-straightedge construction.*

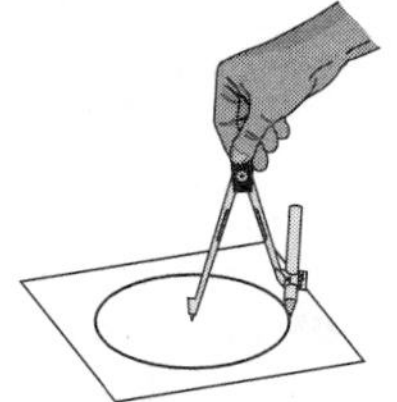
Using a compass to draw a circle

(2) A tool used to determine geographic direction.

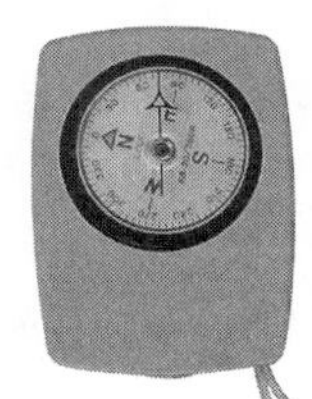
directional compass

compass-and-straightedge construction A drawing of a geometric figure made using only a compass and a straightedge.

concentric circles Circles that have the same center but radii of different lengths.

congruent Having the same size and shape. Two figures are congruent if a combination of slides, flips, and turns can be used to move one of the figures so that it exactly fits "on top of" the other figure. In diagrams of congruent figures, the congruent sides may be marked with the same number of tick marks. The symbol ≅ means "is congruent to."

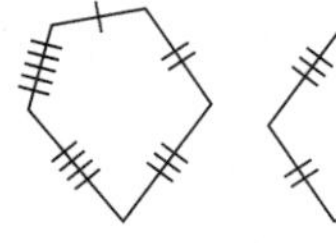

congruent pentagons

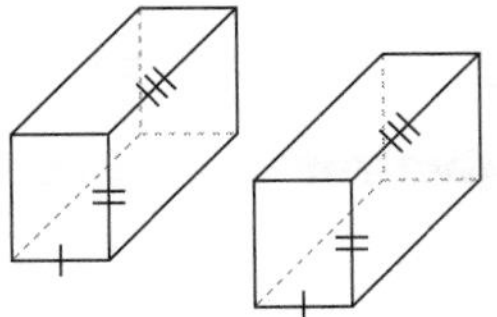
congruent prisms

consecutive Following one another in an uninterrupted order. For example, A, B, C, and D are four consecutive letters of the alphabet; 6, 7, 8, 9, and 10 are five consecutive whole numbers.

consecutive angles Two angles in a polygon that share a common side.

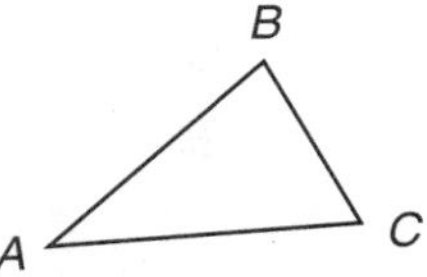

Angles A and B, B and C, and C and A are pairs of consecutive angles.

coordinate A number used to locate a point on a number line, or one of two numbers used to locate a point on a coordinate grid.

corresponding angles (1) Of angles in figures: two angles in the same relative position.

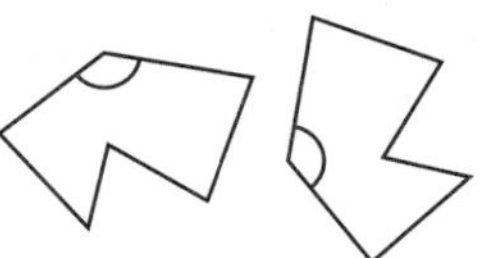

(2) Of angles formed by lines cut by a transversal: Two angles in similar locations in relation to a transversal intersecting two lines. In the diagram, $\angle a$ and $\angle e$, $\angle b$ and $\angle f$, $\angle d$ and $\angle h$, and $\angle c$ and $\angle g$ are corresponding angles. If any two corresponding angles are congruent, then the lines are parallel.

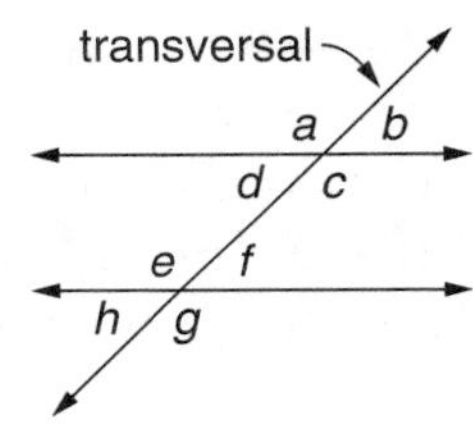

corresponding sides Two sides in the same relative position in two figures. In the diagram, corresponding sides are marked with the same number of tick marks.

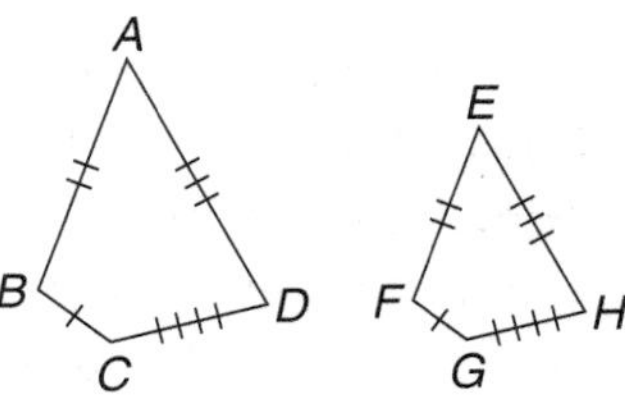

counting numbers The numbers used to count things. The set of counting numbers is {1, 2, 3, 4, ...}. Sometimes 0 is included. Counting numbers are also in the set of whole numbers, the set of integers, the set of rational numbers, and the set of real numbers, but those sets also include numbers that are not counting numbers.

cover-up method A method for finding the solution of an equation by covering up a part of the equation containing a variable.

cross section A shape formed by the intersection of a plane and a geometric solid.

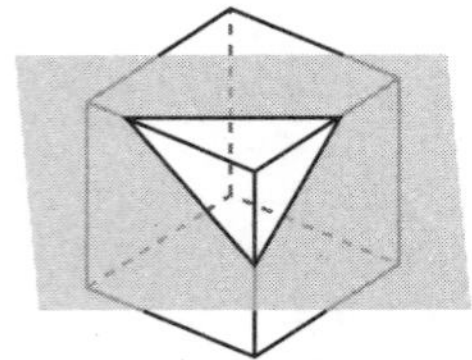

cross section of a cube

cup In the U.S. customary system, a unit of capacity equal to 8 fluid ounces; $\frac{1}{2}$ pint.

discount The amount by which the regular price of an item is reduced, expressed as a fraction or percent of the original price. For example, a $4.00 item that is on sale for $2.00 is discounted by 50 percent or by $\frac{1}{2}$. Or, when a $10.00 item has a discount percent of 10% (or the equivalent discount fraction of $\frac{1}{10}$) its sale price is $9.00.

display bar In a spreadsheet, a place where data or formulas entered from the keyboard are shown.

distributive property A property that relates two operations on numbers, usually multiplication and addition or multiplication and subtraction. This property gets its name because it "distributes" the factor outside the parentheses over the terms within the parentheses.

For multiplication over addition:
$a \times (x + y) = (a \times x) + (a \times y)$,
so $2 \times (5 + 3) = (2 \times 5) + (2 \times 3) = 10 + 6 = 16$

For multiplication over subtraction:
$a \times (x - y) = (a \times x) - (a \times y)$,
so $2 \times (5 - 3) = (2 \times 5) - (2 \times 3) = 10 - 6 = 4$

dividend In division, the number that is being divided. For example, in $35 \div 5 = 7$, the dividend is 35.

divisor
dividend quotient
35 / 5 = 7

divisor
dividend quotient
40 ÷ 8 = 5

quotient → 3
divisor → 12)36 ← dividend

division of fractions property A rule for dividing: Division by any number is equivalent to multiplication by the number's reciprocal. If the divisor is a fraction, the reciprocal is obtained by exchanging the numerator and the denominator, so $n \div \frac{c}{d} = n \times \frac{d}{c}$. If both the dividend and the divisor are fractions, the rule becomes $\frac{a}{b} \div \frac{c}{d} = \frac{a}{b} \times \frac{d}{c}$. Examples:

$$5 \div 8 = 5 \times \frac{1}{8} = \frac{5}{8}$$

$$15 \div \frac{3}{5} = 15 \times \frac{5}{3} = \frac{75}{3} = 25$$

$$\frac{1}{2} \div \frac{3}{5} = \frac{1}{2} \times \frac{5}{3} = \frac{5}{6}$$

divisor In division, the number that divides another number (the dividend). For example, in $35 \div 7 = 5$, the divisor is 7.

divisor
dividend quotient
35 / 5 = 7

divisor
dividend quotient
40 ÷ 8 = 5

quotient → 3
divisor → 12)36 ← dividend

enlarge To increase the size of an object or figure.

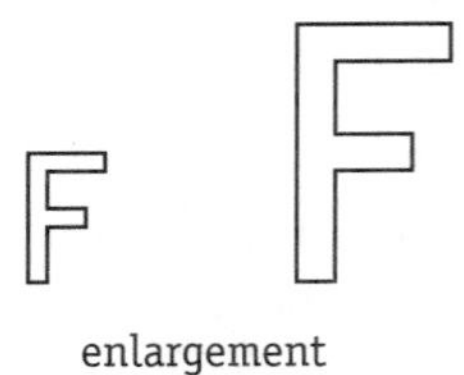

enlargement

equation A mathematical sentence that asserts the equality of two quantities.

equivalent equations Equations that have the same solutions. For example, $2 + x = 4$ and $6 + x = 8$ are equivalent equations; their solution is 2.

equivalent fractions Fractions that have different numerators and denominators but represent the same number.

equivalent ratios Ratios that make the same comparison. Equivalent ratios can be expressed by equivalent fractions. For example, $\frac{1}{2}$ and $\frac{4}{8}$ are equivalent ratios. See *equivalent fractions.*

evaluate (1) An algebraic expression: To replace each variable in an algebraic expression with a

particular number and then to calculate the value of the expression.
(2) A numerical expression: To carry out the operations in a numerical expression to find the value of the expression.
(3) A formula: To find the value of one variable in the formula when the values of the other variables are given.

expected outcome The average outcome over a large number of repetitions of a random experiment. For example, the expected outcome of rolling one die is the average number of spots showing over a large number of rolls. Since each face of a fair die has equal probability, the expected outcome will be $(1 + 2 + 3 + 4 + 5 + 6) / 6 = 21 / 6 = 3\frac{1}{2}$. This means that the average of many rolls of a fair die will be about $3\frac{1}{2}$. (More formally, the expected outcome is defined as an average over infinitely many repetitions.)

exponent See *exponential notation*.

exponential notation A way of representing repeated multiplication by the same factor. For example, 2^3 is exponential notation for $2 * 2 * 2$. The small, raised 3, called the *exponent*, indicates how many times the number 2, called the *base*, is used as a *factor*.

$$2^3 = 2 * 2 * 2 = 8$$
$$4^5 = 4 * 4 * 4 * 4 * 4 = 1{,}024$$

factor (1) A number being multiplied in a multiplication number model. In the number model $6 * 0.5 = 3$, 6 and 0.5 are factors and 3 is the product. (2) A whole number that can divide another whole number without a remainder. For example, 4 and 7 are both factors of 28 because 28 is divisible by both 4 and by 7. (3) To represent a number as a product of factors. To factor 21, for example, is to write it as $7 * 3$.

fair game A game in which every player has the same chance of winning. If any player has an advantage or disadvantage at the beginning (for example, by playing first), then the game is not fair.

false number sentence A number sentence that is not true; a number sentence in which the relation symbol does not accurately relate the two sides. For example, $8 = 5 + 5$ is a false number sentence. Compare to *true number sentence*.

fluid ounce In the U.S. Customary System, a unit of capacity equal to $\frac{1}{16}$ of a pint. One fluid ounce is 29.574 milliliters.

formula A general rule for finding the value of something. A formula is often written symbolically using letters, called variables, to stand for the quantities involved. For example, a formula for distance traveled can be written as $d = s \times t$, where d stands for distance, s for speed, and t for time.

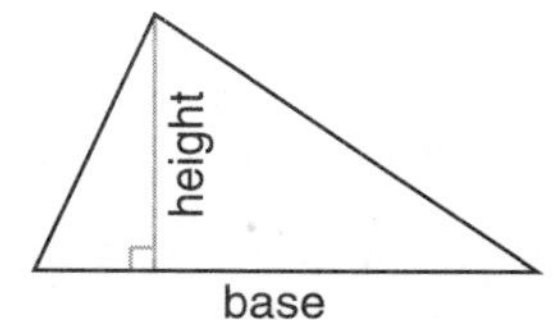

Area of triangle = 1/2 base × height
$A = 1/2\ b \times h$

fulcrum (1) The center support of a pan balance.

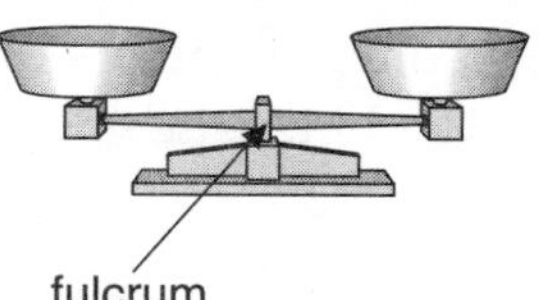

(2) The support on which a lever turns.

(3) The point on a mobile at which a rod is suspended.

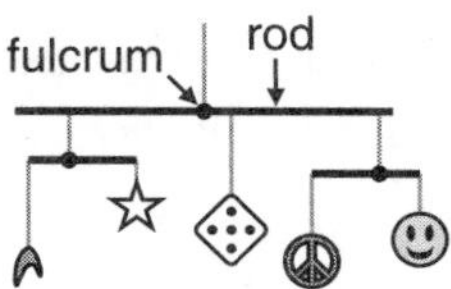

gallon (gal) In the U.S. customary system, a unit of capacity equal to 4 quarts.

genus In topology: The number of holes in a geometric shape. Shapes with the same genus are topologically equivalent. See *topology*.

Genus 0

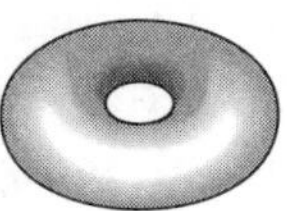
Genus 1

Golden Ratio A particular ratio, approximately equal to 1.618 to 1. The Golden Ratio is sometimes denoted by the Greek letter phi: ϕ.

The Golden Ratio is an irrational number equal to $\frac{1+\sqrt{5}}{2}$.

Golden Rectangle A rectangle in which the ratio of the longer side to the shorter side is the *Golden Ratio*, or about 1.618 to 1. A standard index card, 5 inches by 3 inches, is nearly a Golden Rectangle.

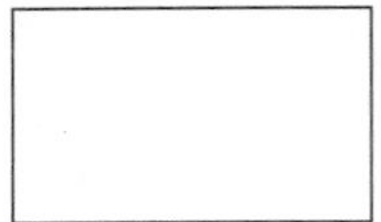

a Golden Rectangle

graph key An annotated list of the icons and other symbols used in a graph. A graph key explains how to read the graph.

greatest common factor (GCF) The largest factor that two or more numbers have in common. For example, the common factors of 24 and 36 are 1, 2, 3, 4, 6, and 12. Thus, the greatest common factor of 24 and 36 is 12.

horizon Where the earth and sky appear to meet; if nothing is in the way, as when looking out to sea, the horizon looks like a line.

hypotenuse In a right triangle, the side opposite the right angle.

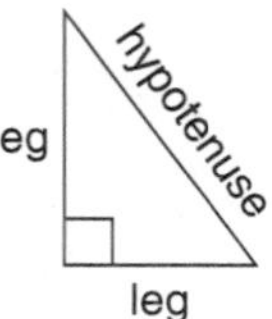

image A figure that is produced by a transformation of another figure. See *transformation*. Compare to *preimage*.

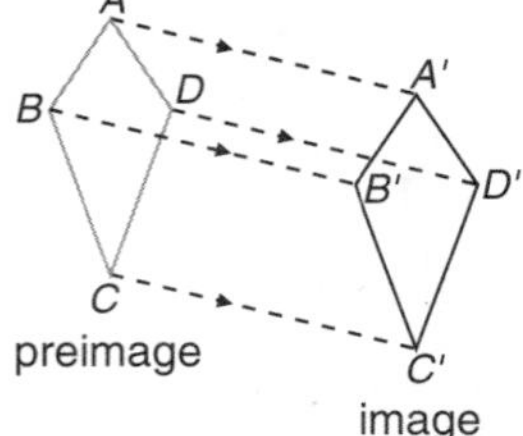

improper fraction A term for a fraction whose numerator is greater than or equal to its denominator. An improper fraction names a number greater than or equal to 1. For example, $\frac{4}{3}$, $\frac{5}{2}$, $\frac{4}{4}$, and $\frac{24}{12}$ are all improper fractions. In *Everyday Mathematics*, improper fractions are sometimes called top-heavy fractions.

indirect measurement The determination of heights, distances, and other quantities that cannot be measured directly.

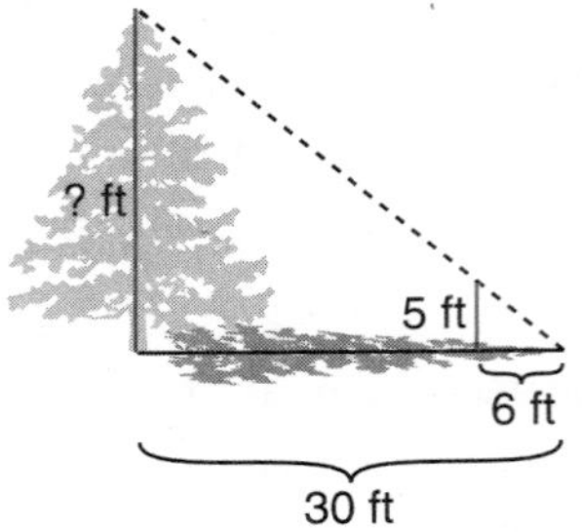

Using indirect measurement, the height of the tree is found to be 25 ft.

inequality A number sentence stating that two quantities are not equal, or might not be equal. Relation symbols for inequalities include $\neq$, $<$, $>$, $\geq$, and $\leq$.

inscribed polygon A polygon all of whose vertices are points on a circle.

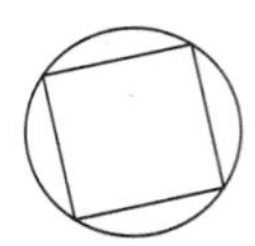

inscribed square

integer A number in the set {... –4, –3, –2, –1, 0, 1, 2, 3, 4, ...}. All integers are rational numbers, but not all rational numbers are integers. (For example, $-\frac{1}{2}$ is a rational number but is not an integer.) All whole numbers are integers, but not all integers are whole numbers. (For example, –3 is an integer, but not a whole number.) Compare to *whole number*, *rational number*, *irrational number*, and *real number*.

interest Money paid for the use of someone else's money. Interest is usually a percentage of the amount borrowed.

interior The set of all points in a plane "inside" a closed two-dimensional figure, such as a polygon or circle. Also, the set of all points in space "inside" a closed three-dimensional figure, such as a polyhedron or sphere. The interior is usually not considered to be part of the figure.

interior

irrational number A number that cannot be written as a fraction where both the numerator and denominator are integers and the denominator is not zero. For example, $\sqrt{2}$ and π are irrational numbers. An irrational number can be represented by a nonterminating, nonrepeating decimal. For example, the decimal for π, 3.141592653..., continues without a repeating pattern. The number 1.10100100010000... is also irrational; although there is a pattern in the decimal, it does not repeat.

isometry transformation A transformation such as a translation (*slide*), a reflection (*flip*), a rotation (*turn*), or a combination of these that preserves distances between points and angle measures. As a result, isometries preserve both the shape and the size of figures, but not necessarily the position or the orientation. (From the Greek word *isometros*, of equal measure.) See *transformation*, *translation*, and *rotation*.

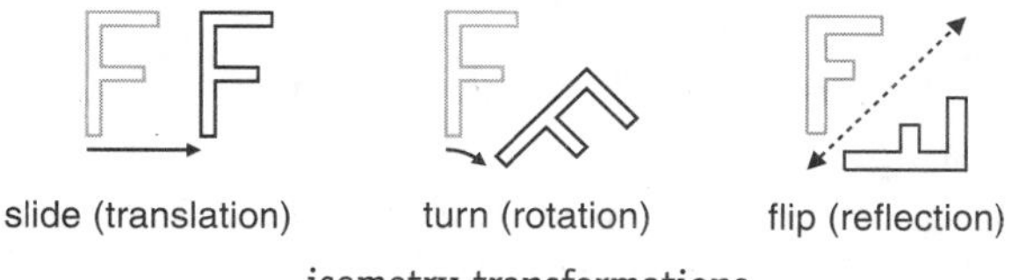

isometry transformations

label (1) A descriptive word or phrase used to put a number or numbers in context. Using a label reinforces the idea that numbers refer to something. Flags, snowballs, and scary monsters are examples of labels.
(2) In a spreadsheet or graph, words or numbers used to provide information such as the title of the spreadsheet, the heading for a row or column, or the variable on an axis.

landmark A notable feature of a data set. Landmarks include *median*, *mode*, *maximum*, *minimum*, and *range*.

least common denominator The *least common multiple* of the denominators of every fraction in a given collection. For example, the least common denominator of $\frac{1}{2}$, $\frac{4}{5}$, and $\frac{3}{8}$ is 40.

least common multiple (LCM) The smallest number that is a multiple of two or more given numbers. For example, while some common multiples of 6 and 8 are 24, 48, and 72, the least common multiple of 6 and 8 is 24.

leg of a right triangle A side of a right triangle that is not the hypotenuse. Compare to *hypotenuse*.

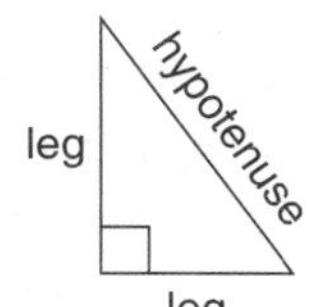

like terms In an algebraic expression, either the constant terms or any terms that contain the same variable(s) raised to the same power(s). For example, $4y$ and $7y$ are like terms in the expression $4y + 7y - z$. To "combine like terms" means to rewrite the sum or difference of like terms as a single term. For example, $5a + 6a$ can be rewritten as $11a$, because $5a + 6a = (5 + 6)a = 11a$. Similarly, $16t - 3t$ can be rewritten as $13t$.

line graph A graph in which data points are connected by a line or line segments. Same as *broken line graph*.

line of reflection A line halfway between a plane figure (preimage) and its reflected image. The line of reflection is the perpendicular bisector of the line segments connecting points on the preimage with the corresponding points on the image. Also know as *mirror line*.

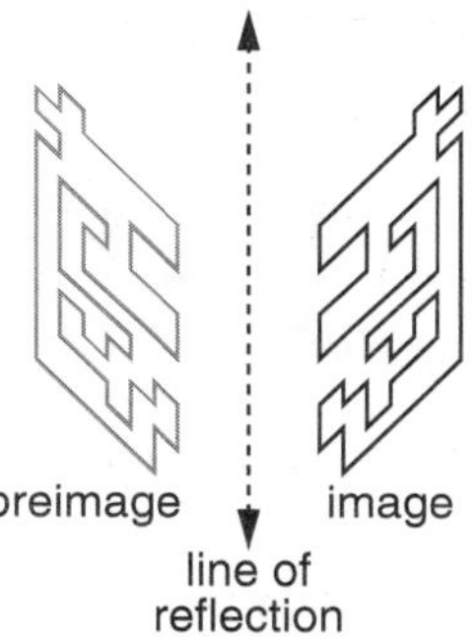

line plot A sketch of data in which check marks, Xs, or other symbols above a labeled line show the frequency of each value.

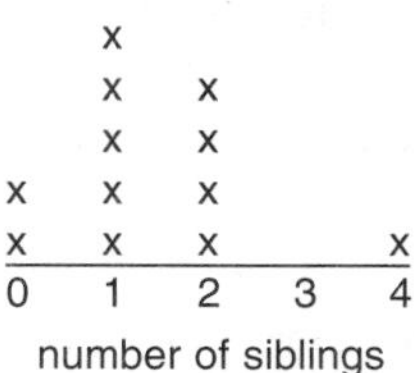

lowest terms Same as *simplest form*.

magnitude estimate A rough estimate of the size of a numerical result—whether it is in the 1s, 10s, 100s, 1000s, and so on. In *Everyday Mathematics*, students are often asked to give magnitude estimates for problems like "How many dimes in \$200?" or "How many halves are in 30?"

maximum The largest amount; the greatest number in a set of data. Compare to *minimum*.

mean A measure of central tendency. It is found by adding the numbers in the set and dividing the sum by the number of numbers. It is often referred to as the average. Compare to *median* and *mode.*

median The middle value in a set of data when the data are listed in order from least to greatest (or greatest to least). If there is an even number of data points, the median is the mean of the two middle values. The median is also known as the *middle value*. Compare to *mean* and *mode*.

minimum The smallest amount; the smallest number in a set of data. Compare to *maximum*.

mixed number A number that is written using both a whole number and a fraction. For example, $2\frac{1}{4}$ is a mixed number equal to $2 + \frac{1}{4}$.

Möbius strip or Möbius band A shape with only one side and one edge; named for mathematician Augustus Ferdinand Möbius.

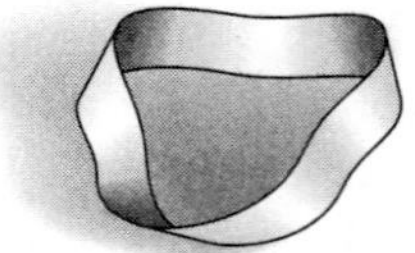

Möbius strip

mode The value or values that occur most often in a set of data. Compare to *median* and *mean*. In the data set 3, 4, 4, 4, 5, 5, 6, the mode is 4.

multiples (1) Repeated groups of the same amount. Multiples of a number are the products of that number and the numbers 1, 2, 3, . . . For example, the multiples of 7 are 7, 14, 21, 28, . . . (2) Products of a number and an integer. The multiples of 7 are . . ., –21, –14, –7, 0, 7, 14, 21, . . .

multiplicative inverses Two numbers whose product is 1. For example, the multiplicative inverse of 5 is $\frac{1}{5}$; the multiplicative inverse of $\frac{3}{5}$ is $\frac{5}{3}$. Multiplicative inverses are also called *reciprocals* of each other.

***n*-to-1 ratio** A ratio of a number to 1. Every ratio can be converted to an *n*-to-1 ratio. For example, to convert the ratio of 3 girls to 2 boys to an *n*-to-1 ratio, divide 3 by 2. The *n*-to-1 ratio is 1.5 to 1.

name-collection box In *Everyday Mathematics*, a box-like diagram tagged with a given number and used for collecting equivalent names for that number.

16
4^2
$\sqrt{256}$
$(4 + 6) * 6 - 4 * 11$
XVI

A typical name-collection box for 16—there are infinitely many possibilities

negative power of 10 A number that can be written as a product using only 0.1, or 10^{-1}, as a factor. For example, 0.01 is a negative power of 10 because it is equal to 0.1×0.1, or 10^{-2}. See *power of 10*. Compare to *positive power of 10*.

number-and-word notation A notation consisting of the significant digits of a number and words for the place value. For example, 27 billion is number-and-word notation for 27,000,000,000.

obtuse angle An angle measuring more than 90° and less than 180°.

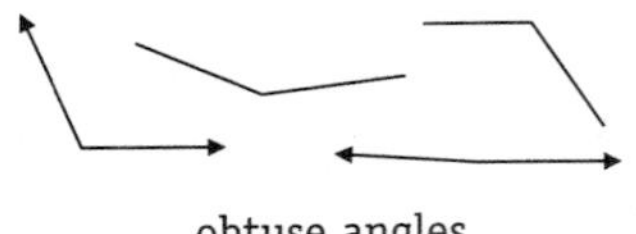

obtuse angles

open sentence A number sentence which is neither true nor false because one or more variables hold the place of missing numbers. For example, the number sentences 9 + __ = 15 and __ – 24 < 10 are open. As an introduction to algebra, *Everyday Mathematics* regards a ?, blank, or frame as a variable or "place holder," in, for example, "missing addend" problems.

$9 + ? = 15$	$5 - ? \geq 3$
$9 + \_\_ = 15$	$5 - \_\_ \geq 3$
$9 + \square = 15$	$5 - \square \geq 3$
$9 + x = 15$	$5 - x \geq 3$

open sentences

operation symbol A symbol used in number sentences to stand for a particular mathematical operation. The operation symbols most often used in school mathematics are:

+ for addition
– for subtraction
×, ∗, and • for multiplication
÷ and / for division

OPP key The change-of-sign key on certain calculators. Pressing the OPP key changes the sign of the number in the display, making a negative number positive and a positive number negative. OPP stands for opposite.

opposite of a number A number that is the same distance from zero on the number line as the given number, but on the opposite side of zero. The opposite of any number n is written as (op)n or $-n$. If n is a negative number, (op)n or $-n$ will be a positive number. For example, if $n = -5$, then $-n$, or (op)n, is (op)$-5 = 5$. The sum of a number and its opposite is zero.

ordered pair 1) A pair of numbers used to locate a point on a coordinate grid. The first number corresponds to position along the horizontal axis, and the second number corresponds to position along the vertical axis. 2) Any pair of objects or numbers in a particular order.

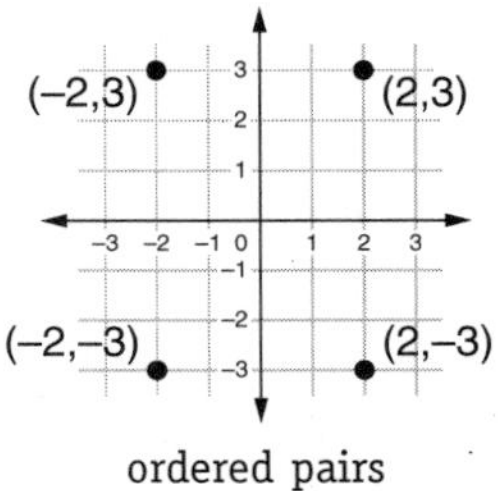

ordered pairs

origin The zero point in a coordinate system. In two-dimensional Cartesian coordinates, the origin is the point at which the x-axis and y-axis intersect.

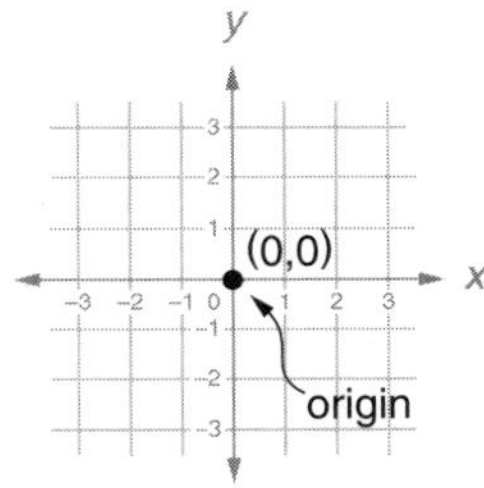

outcome A possible result of a random process. HEADS and TAILS are the two possible outcomes of tossing a coin.

pan balance A device used to weigh objects or compare their weights.

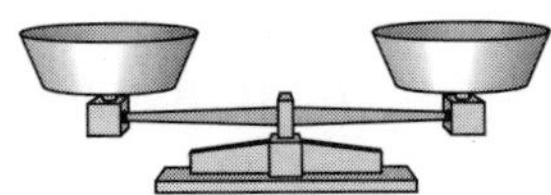

part-to-part ratio A ratio that compares a part of a whole to another part of the same whole. For example, the statement "There are 8 boys for every 12 girls" expresses a part-to-part ratio. See *ratio*. Compare to *part-to-whole ratio*.

part-to-whole ratio A ratio that compares a part of a whole to the whole. For example, the statement "8 out of 20 students are boys" expresses a part-to-whole ratio. The statement "12 out of 20 students are girls" also expresses a part-to-whole ratio. See *ratio*. Compare to *part-to-part ratio*.

partial-products method A multiplication procedure in which products of the digits of two factors are computed separately and then added to yield the final product.

		67
		× 53
50 × 60	→	3000
50 × 7	→	350
3 × 60	→	180
3 × 7	→	+ 21
		3551

partial-quotients method A division procedure in which the quotient is found in several steps. In each step, a partial quotient is found. The partial quotients are then added to find the final quotient.

22)400		
− 220	10	(10 [22s] in 400)
180		
− 110	5	(5 [22s] in 180)
70		
− 44	2	(2 [22s] in 70)
26		
− 22	1	(1 [22] in 26)
4	18	

400/22 → 18 R4

percent (%) Per hundred, or out of a hundred. 1% means $\frac{1}{100}$ or 0.01. For example, "48% of the students in the school are boys" means that out of every 100 students in the school, 48 are boys.

Percent Circle A device on the Geometry Template used to measure or draw figures (such as circle graphs) involving percents.

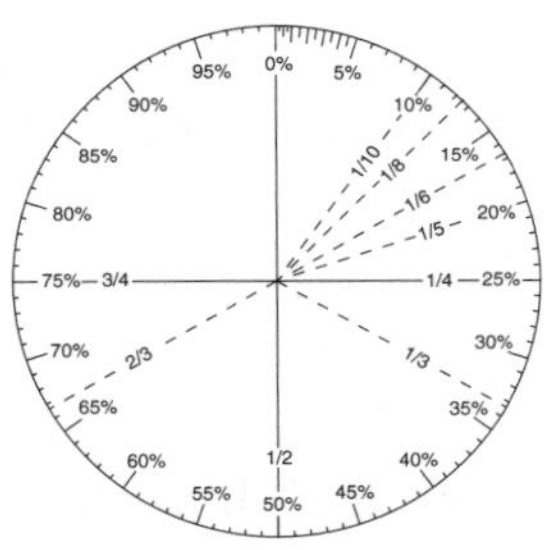

perimeter The distance around a closed plane figure or region. *Peri-* comes from the Greek word for "around," and *meter* comes from the Greek word for "measure"; perimeter means "around measure."

perpendicular Rays, lines, line segments, or planes that form right angles are perpendicular to each other.

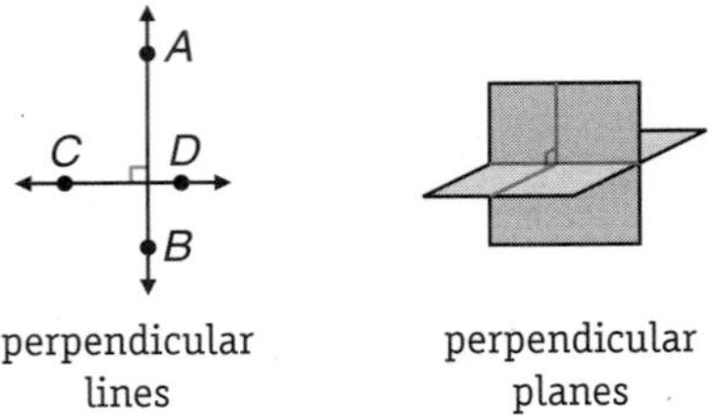

perpendicular lines

perpendicular planes

pint In the U.S. customary system, a unit of capacity equal to 2 cups or 16 fluid ounces. A handy saying to remember is "A pint's a pound the world around," which refers to the fact that a pint of water *weighs* about 1 pound (or 16 ounces).

point symmetry The property of balance in a figure that can be rotated 180° about a point in such a way that the resulting figure (the image) exactly matches the original figure (the preimage). Point symmetry is rotational symmetry in which the turn is 180°.

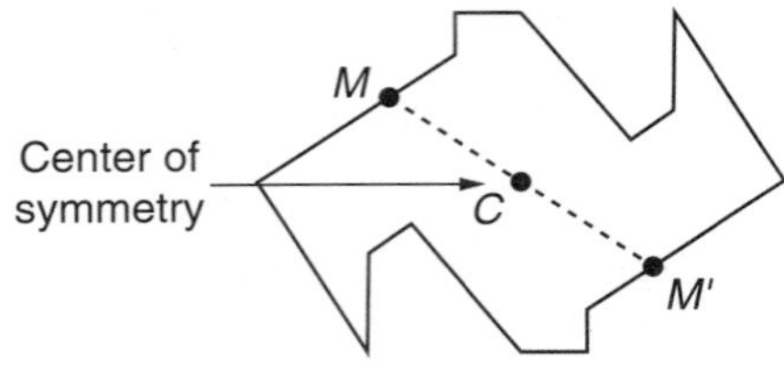

2-D shape with point symmetry

positive power of 10 A power of 10 greater than 1. The positive powers of 10 are 10, 100, 1000, and so on. See *power of 10*. Compare to *negative power of 10*.

power (1) The exponent to which a "base" number is raised in exponential notation; the number a in n^a, where n is the base. If n is any number and a is a positive whole number, a tells how many times to use n as a factor in a product. For example, $5^3 = 5 * 5 * 5 = 125$, and is read "5 to the third power." See *power of 10* for more examples, including examples in which a is a negative integer. (2) The result of a "powering" or "exponential" operation x^y. In mathematics beyond grades K–6, exponentiation goes beyond repeated multiplication, so that y can be a fraction or a decimal.

power of 10 (1) A whole number that can be written as a product using only 10 as a factor; also called a positive power of 10. For example, 100 is equal to $10 * 10$, or 10^2. 100 can also be called ten squared, the second power of 10, or 10 to the second power. (2) More generally, any number that can be written as a product using only 10s or $\frac{1}{10}$s as factors. For example, 0.01 is equal to $0.1 * 0.1$, or 10^{-2}. Other powers of 10 include $10^1 = 10$ and $10^0 = 1$. See *power, positive power of 10*, and *negative power of 10*.

powers key The [^] or [y^x] key on a calculator, used to calculate powers. Keying in 4 [^] 5 gives 4 raised to the fifth power, or 4^5, which equals $4 * 4 * 4 * 4 * 4$, or 1,024. See *power*.

precise In everyday language, a fine measurement or scale. The smaller the unit, or fraction of a unit used, the more precise the measurement or scale. For example, a measurement to the nearest inch is more precise than a measurement to the nearest foot. A ruler with $\frac{1}{16}$-inch markings is more precise than a ruler with $\frac{1}{4}$-inch markings. Compare to *accurate*.

preimage A geometric figure that is operated on by a transformation—such as a reflection, rotation, or translation—to produce another figure. See *transformation*. Compare to *image*.

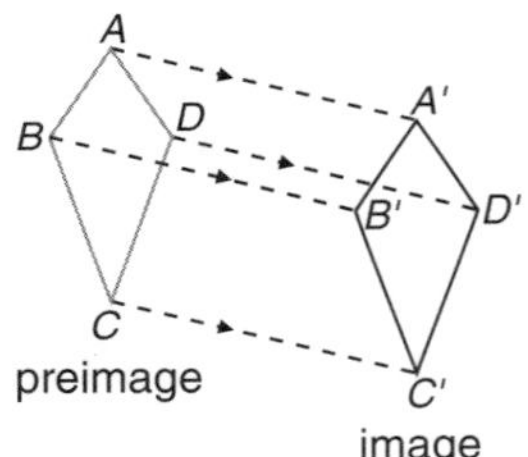

probability A number from 0 to 1 that indicates the likelihood that an event will happen. The closer a probability is to 1, the more likely that the event will happen. The closer a probability is to 0, the less likely that the event will happen. For example, the probability that a fair coin will show heads is 1/2.

proper fraction The traditional term for a fraction in which the numerator is less than the denominator; a proper fraction names a number less than 1. For example, 3/4, 2/5, and 12/24 are proper fractions. Compare to *improper fraction*.

proportion A number sentence, possibly including variables, that equates two fractions. Often the fractions in a proportion represent rates or ratios. Many problem situations can be modeled by proportions. For example, the problem, "Alan's speed is 12 miles per hour. At the same speed, how far can he travel in 3 hours?" can be modeled by the proportion:

$$\frac{12 \text{ miles}}{1 \text{ hour}} = \frac{n \text{ miles}}{3 \text{ hours}}$$

Pythagorean Theorem The proposition that for any right triangle, the area of the square on the hypotenuse is equal to the sum of the areas of the squares on the other two sides. Symbolically, the theorem can be stated as follows: If the legs of a right triangle have lengths a and b, and the hypotenuse has length c, then $a^2 + b^2 = c^2$.

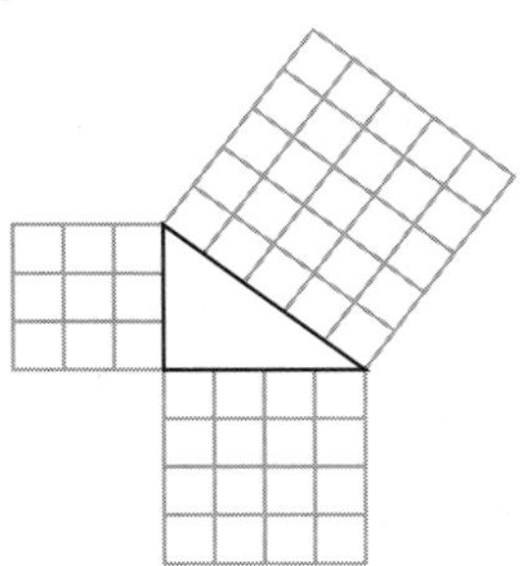

quart In the U.S. customary system, a unit of capacity equal to 32 fluid ounces, 2 pints, or 4 cups.

quick common denominator The product of the denominators of two or more fractions. The quick common denominator of $\frac{a}{b}$ and $\frac{c}{d}$ is $b \times d$. For example, the quick common denominator of $\frac{3}{4}$ and $\frac{5}{6}$ is 4×6 or 24.

quotient The result of dividing one number by another number. In the division model $10 \div 5 = 2$, the quotient is 2.

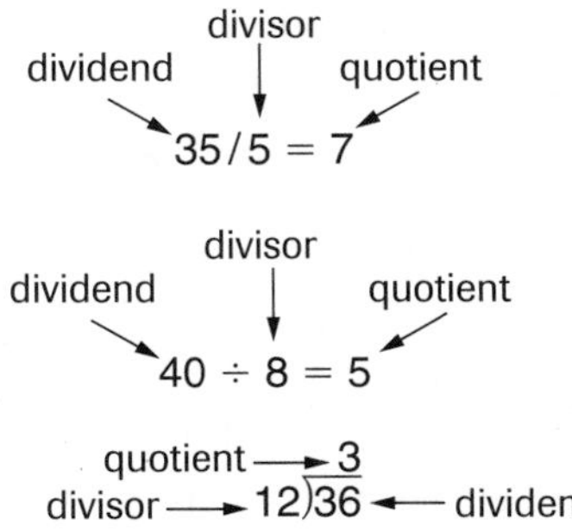

radius A line segment from the center of a circle (or sphere) to any point on the circle (or sphere); also, the length of such a line segment.

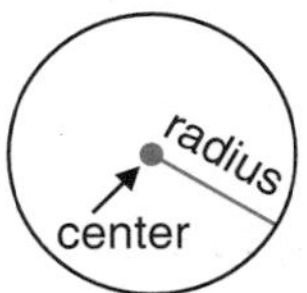

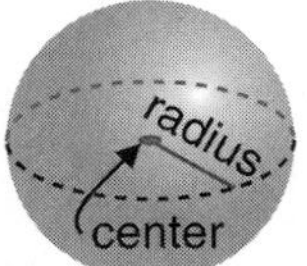

random number A number produced by a random process, such as rolling a die or spinning a spinner. A random number has the same chance of appearing as any other possible number.

range The difference between the greatest and least values in a set of data.

rate A comparison by division of two quantities with different units. For example, traveling 100 miles in 2 hours can be expressed as 100 mi/2 hr or 50 miles per hour. In this case, the rate compares distance (miles) to time (hours). Compare to *ratio*.

rate table A means of displaying rate information. See *rate*.

miles	35	70	105	140	175	210
gallons	1	2	3	4	5	6

rate table

ratio A comparison by division of two quantities with the same units. Ratios can be expressed as fractions, decimals, or percents, as well as in words. Ratios can also be written with a colon between the two numbers being compared. For example, if a team wins 3 games out of 5 games played, the ratio of wins to total games is $\frac{3}{5}$, 3/5, 0.6, 60%, 3 to 5, or 3:5 (read "three to five"). Compare to *rate*.

rational number Any number that can be represented in the form a/b, where a and b are integers and $b \neq 0$. A rational number can always be represented by either a terminating decimal or a repeating decimal. For example, 2/3, –2/3, 0.5, 20.5, and 0.333… are all rational numbers.

real number Any rational or irrational number. For every real number there is a corresponding point on the number line, and for every point on the number line there is a real number.

recall survey A survey in which data are gathered by asking people what they remember about a particular topic. For example, a recall survey might ask people to list what soft drinks they have consumed in the previous week.

rectangular coordinate grid A system for locating points by means of perpendicular lines called axes.

reduce (1) To make an object or shape smaller. (2) To reduce fractions: To put into simpler form. See *simplest form.*

reflex angle An angle measuring between 180° and 360°.

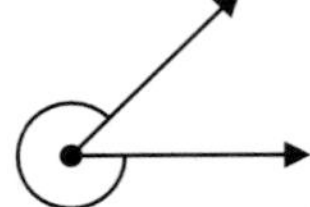

regular polygon A polygon whose sides are the same length and whose angles are all equal.

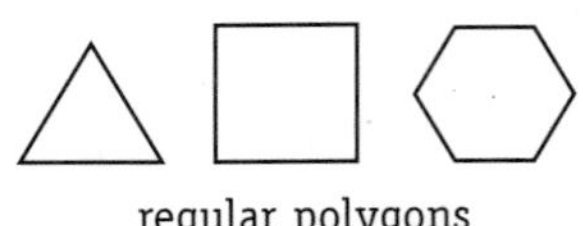

regular polygons

regular polyhedron A polyhedron whose faces are all congruent regular polygons and with the same number of faces meeting at every vertex, all at the same angle. There are five regular polyhedra, known as the Platonic solids:

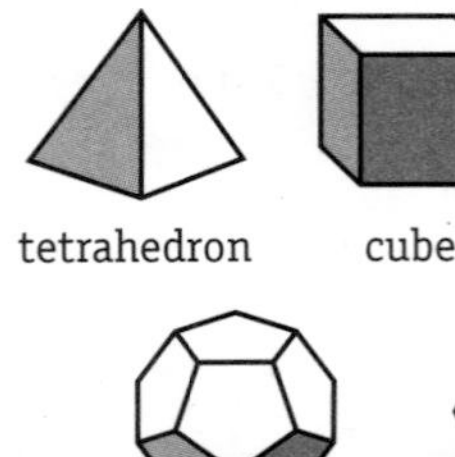

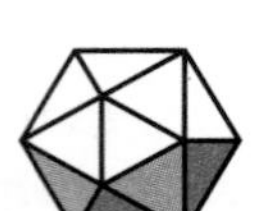

tetrahedron cube octahedron

dodecahedron icosahedron

tetrahedron:	4 faces, each an equilateral triangle
cube:	6 faces, each a square
octahedron:	8 faces, each an equilateral triangle
dodecahedron:	12 faces, each a regular pentagon
icosahedron:	20 faces, each an equilateral triangle

regular tessellation A tessellation made up of only one kind of regular polygon. There are only three regular tessellations.

 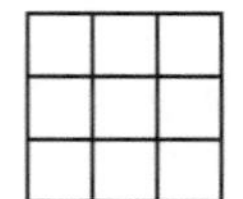 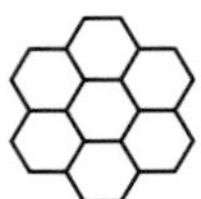

the three regular tessellations

relation symbol A symbol used to express a relationship between two quantities. Some relation symbols used in number sentences include: = for "is equal to," ≠ for "is not equal to," < for "is less than," > for "is greater than," ≤ for "is less than or equal to," and ≥ for "is greater than or equal to."

remainder An amount left over when one number is divided by another. In the division number model 16 ÷ 3 → 5R1, the remainder is 1.

repeating decimal A decimal in which one digit, or a group of digits, is repeated without end. For example, 0.3333. . . and $0.\overline{147}$ are repeating decimals. Compare to *terminating decimal.*

right (1) Of an angle: An angle whose measure is 90°.

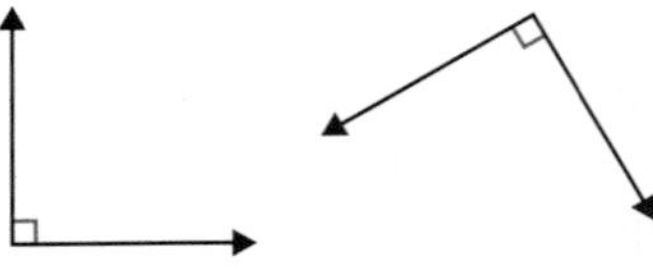

right angles

(2) Of a prism or cylinder: Having lateral faces or surfaces that are all perpendicular to their bases.

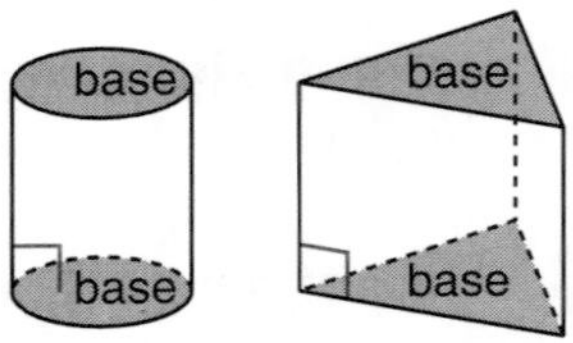

a right circular cylinder and a right triangular prism

(3) Of a pyramid or cone: Having an apex directly above the center of its base.

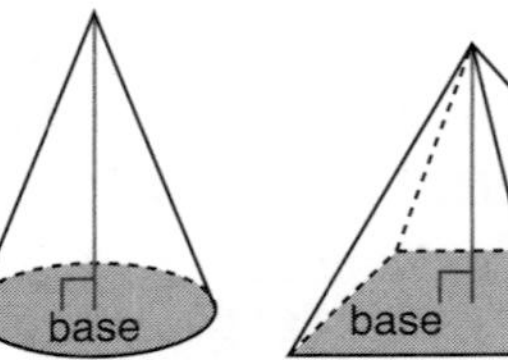

a right circular cone and a right square pyramid

(4) Of a triangle: Having a right angle.

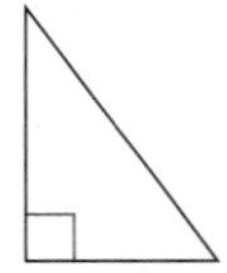

right triangle

rotation A transformation that "turns" an object around a fixed point or axis. The point or axis, called the *center* or *axis of rotation,* can be inside or outside of the original image. Same as *turn.* See *transformation.*

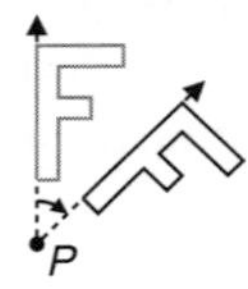

rotation

rotational symmetry (1) In a plane, a figure has rotational symmetry if it can be rotated less than one full turn around a point so that the resulting figure (the image) exactly matches the original figure (the preimage).

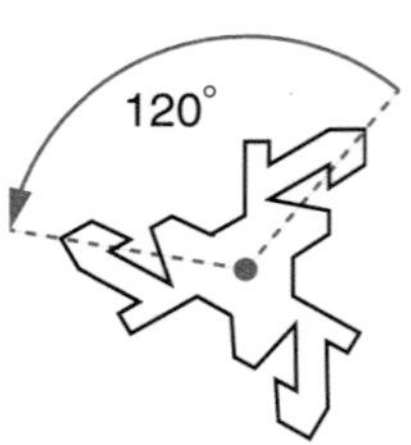

figure with rotational symmetry

(2) A 3-D figure has rotational symmetry if it can be rotated less than a full turn around an axis so that the resulting figure exactly matches the original figure.

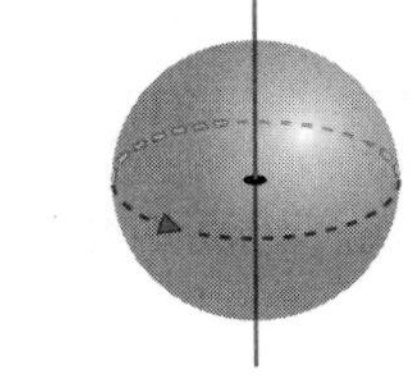

3-D shapes with rotational symmetry

row (1) A horizontal arrangement of objects or numbers in an array or table. (2) A section of cells lined up horizontally in a spreadsheet.

scale model A model that represents an object or display in fixed ratio to its actual size. The ratio is called the scale factor. For example, many model trains or airplanes are scale models of actual vehicles.

scientific notation A system for representing numbers in which a number is written as the product of a power of 10 and a number that is at least 1 and less than 10. Scientific notation allows writing big and small numbers with only a few symbols. For example, 4,300,000 in scientific notation is 4.3×10^6, and 0.00001 in scientific notation is 1×10^{-5}. Compare to *standard notation*.

sector A region bounded by an arc and two radii of a circle. A sector resembles a slice of pizza. The word *wedge* is sometimes used instead of sector.

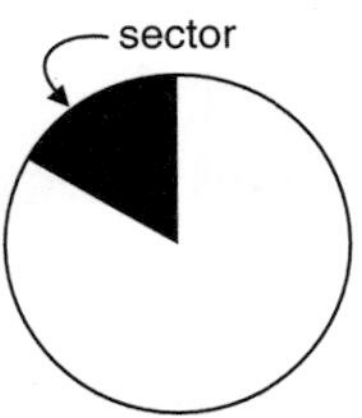

semiregular tessellation A tiling in which every tile is a regular polygon and the angles around every vertex point are congruent to the angles around every other vertex point. A semiregular tessellation must have more than one kind of regular polygon; otherwise it would be a regular tessellation. Every vertex in a semiregular tessellation looks the same. There are eight semiregular tessellations. Compare to *regular tessellation*.

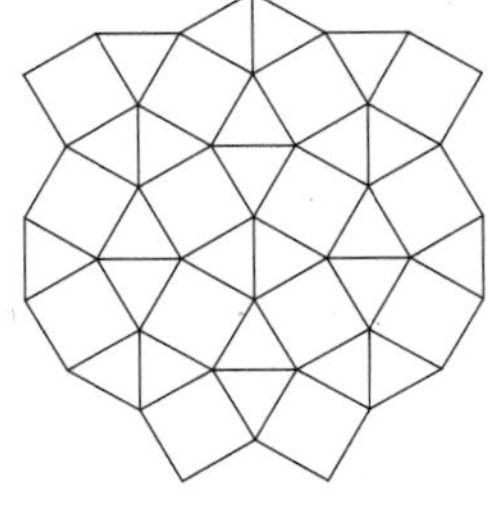

a semiregular tessellation

side-by-side bar graph A bar graph that uses adjacent bars to show two related sets of data. The side-by-side bar graph below shows both road miles and air miles from Los Angeles to different cities.

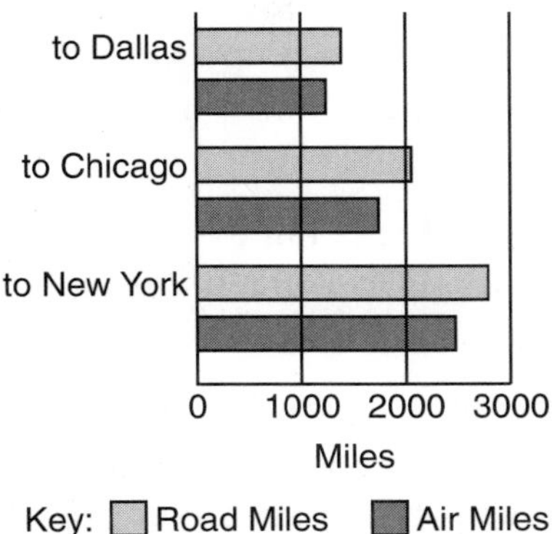

side-by-side bar graph

similar Having the same shape but not necessarily the same size. All squares are similar to one another. Compare to *congruent*.

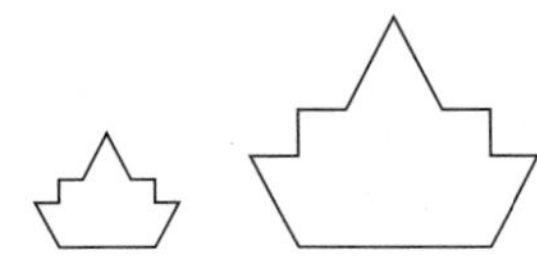

similar figures

simplest form (1) Of proper fractions: Having numerator and denominator with no common factors (other than 1). For example, $\frac{10}{15}$ and $\frac{2}{3}$ are equivalent fractions. However, $\frac{10}{15}$ is not in simplest form because the numerator and denominator can each be divided by 5; $\frac{2}{3}$ is in simplest form because 2 and 3 have no common factors (other than 1).
(2) Of mixed numbers: Having a fraction part that is proper and in simplest form. For example, $1\frac{7}{3}$ is not in simplest form because the fraction part is not proper. Same as *lowest terms*.
Note: Simplest form is not emphasized in *Everyday Mathematics* because other equivalent forms are often equally or more useful. For example, when comparing or adding fractions, fractions written with a common denominator are easier to work with than those in simplest form.

simplify (1) Of a fraction: To express in simplest form, or lowest terms. See *simplest form*.
(2) Of an equation: To rewrite an equation by clearing parentheses and combining like terms and constants on each side of the equal sign. Equations that have been simplified are often easier to solve.

(3) Of an expression: To rewrite by removing parentheses and by combining like terms. For example, $7y + 4 + 5 + 3y$ can be simplified as $10y + 9$ and $3(2y + 5) - y$ can be simplified as $5y + 15$.

size change An enlargement or reduction of an original.

size-change factor A number that indicates the amount of an enlargement or reduction. See *size change*.

skew lines Lines in space that do not lie in the same plane. Skew lines do not intersect and are not parallel. An east-west line on the floor and a north-south line on the ceiling are skew.

Skew lines can be modeled with 2 pencils.

solution (1) Of an open sentence: A value or values for the variable(s) which make the sentence true. For example, the open sentence 4 + __ = 10 has the solution 6. See *open sentence*.
(2) Of a problem: The answer or the method by which the answer was obtained.

speed A rate that compares distance traveled with the time taken to travel that distance. See *rate*.

spreadsheet A computer application in which numerical information is arranged in cells in a grid. Values in the cells are either constants that have been entered by the user or are based on formulas defined by the user. Values in a cell may depend on values in other cells. When the value of a cell changes, the values of all cells dependent on that cell also change.

Class Picnic ($$)

	A	B	C	D
1		budget for class picnic		
2				
3	quantity	food items	unit price	cost
4	6	packages of hamburgers	2.79	16.74
5	5	packages of hamburger buns	1.29	6.45
6	3	bags of potato chips	3.12	9.36
7	3	quarts of macaroni salad	4.50	13.50
8	4	bottles of soft drinks	1.69	6.76
9			subtotal	52.81
10			8% tax	4.23
11			total	57.04

The name *spreadsheet* comes from ledger worksheets for financial records. Such sheets were often taped together and then spread out for examination.

square number A number that is the product of a whole number and itself; a whole number to the second power. For example, 25 is a square number, because $25 = 5 * 5$. A square number can be represented by a square array.

square of a number The product of a number and itself. The square of a number is symbolized by a raised 2. For example, $3.5^2 = 3.5 * 3.5 = 12.25$.

square root of a number The square root of a number n is a number which, when multiplied by itself, results in the number n. For example, 4 is a square root of 16, because $4 * 4 = 16$. Normally, square root refers to the positive square root, but the opposite of a positive square root is also a square root. For example, -4 is also a square root of 16 because $(-4) * (-4) = 16$.

square root key The [√] key on certain calculators. The [√] key undoes the result of squaring a non-negative number.

squaring key The [x^2] key on certain calculators. The [x^2] key squares the number in the display. To find the square of 24 on such a calculator, you would key in 2 4 [x^2] [=], and the display would show 576.

stacked bar graph A bar graph in which the bars are sub-divided to show additional information. A stacked bar graph can be used to show how a total is made up of several parts. See *bar graph*. Compare to *side-by-side bar graph*.

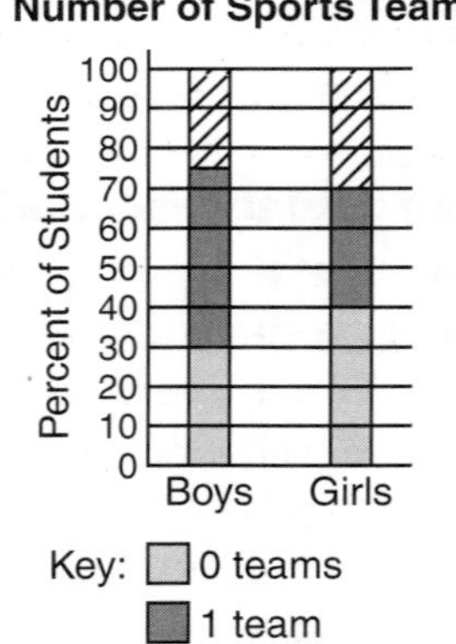

stacked bar graph

standard notation The most familiar way of representing whole numbers, integers, and decimals. Standard notation is base-10 place-value numeration. For example, standard notation for three hundred fifty-six is 356.

step graph A graph that looks like steps because the values are the same for an interval and then change (or "step") for another interval. The horizontal axis of a step graph often represents time.

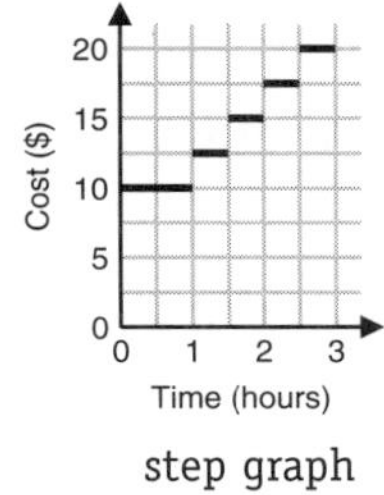

step graph

straight angle An angle measuring 180°.

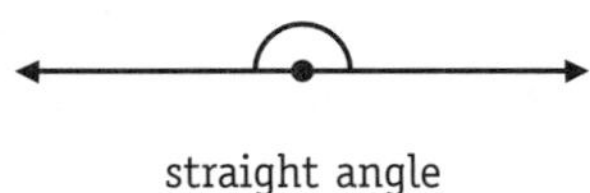

straight angle

substitute To replace one thing with another; in a formula, to replace variables with numerical values. For example, if $b = 4.5$ and $h = 8.5$, then these values can be substituted in the formula $A = b * h$ to yield $A = 4.5 * 8.5 = 38.25$.

supplementary angles Two angles whose measures total 180°.

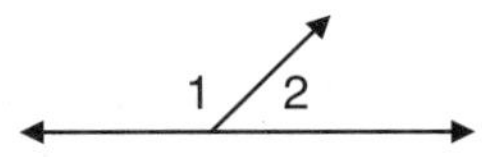

$\angle 1$ and $\angle 2$ are supplementary angles.

terminating decimal A decimal that ends. For example, 0.5 and 0.125 are terminating decimals. A terminating decimal can be thought of as a repeating decimal in which only 0 repeats. Since 0.5 and 0.125 can be written with repeating 0s as 0.500... and 0.12500..., respectively, they terminate. Compare to *repeating decimal.*

test number A number used to replace a variable during the process of solving an equation by trial and error. Test numbers are useful for "closing in" on the exact solution of an equation. See *trial-and-error method.*

theorem A mathematical statement that can be proved to be true. For example, the Pythagorean Theorem states that if the legs of a right triangle have lengths a and b and the hypotenuse has length c, then $a^2 + b^2 = c^2$. The Pythagorean Theorem has been proved in hundreds of ways over the past 2,500 years.

time graph A graph that is constructed from a story that takes place over time. A time graph shows what happened through a progression of times.

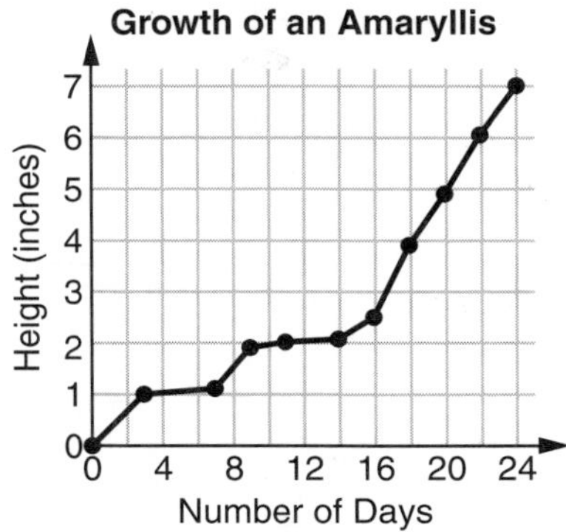

topology The study of the properties of shapes that are unchanged by shrinking, stretching, twisting, bending, and similar transformations. (Tearing, breaking, and sticking together, however, are not allowed.)

transformation An operation on a geometric figure that produces a new figure, called the image, from the original figure, called the preimage. Transformations are sometimes thought of as moving a figure from one place to another and sometimes changing its size or shape. The study of transformations is called *transformation geometry.*

See *isometry transformation, rotation,* and *translation.*

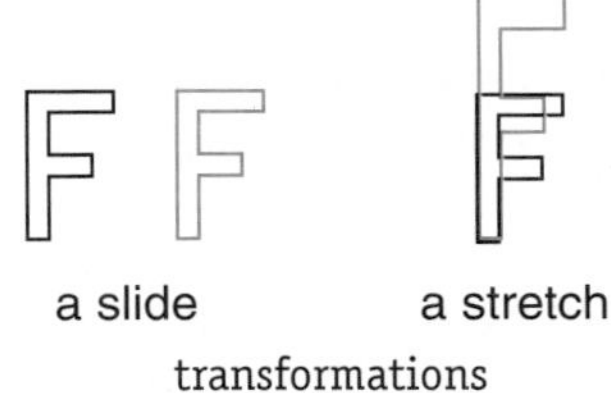

transformations

transformation geometry The study of the geometry of transformations.

translation The motion of "sliding" an object or picture along a line segment. Same as *slide*. See *transformation.*

translation tessellation A tessellation created by translating (sliding) curves from one side of a figure (such as a square) to the opposite side. The resulting figure is then translated to create the interlocking pieces in the tessellation. M. C. Escher created many beautiful and elaborate translation tessellations. See *translation.*

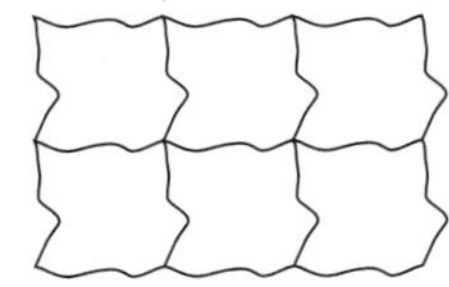

transversal A line that intersects two or more other lines.

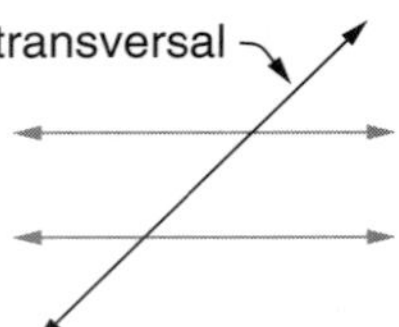

trapezoid A quadrilateral that has exactly one pair of parallel sides. No two sides need be the same length.

tree diagram A network of points connected by line segments and containing no closed loops. One special point is the root of the tree. Tree diagrams can be used to factor numbers and to represent probability situations in which there is a series of events. The first tree diagram below shows the prime factorization of 30. The second tree diagram represents flipping one coin two times.

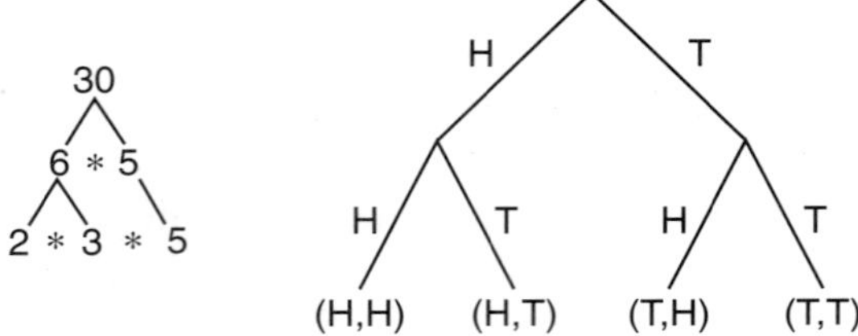

trial-and-error method A method for finding the solution of an equation by trying a series of test numbers. See *test number*.

true number sentence A number sentence in which the relation symbol accurately reflects the relation between the two sides of the sentence. $75 = 25 + 50$ is a true number sentence. Compare to *false number sentence*.

truncate (1) To replace all digits to the right of a particular place with 0s. For example, 3,654 can be truncated to 3,650 or 3,600 or 3,000. Truncation is similar to rounding but always makes the number smaller (unless all the truncated digits are 0s). (2) To cut off a vertex of a solid figure.

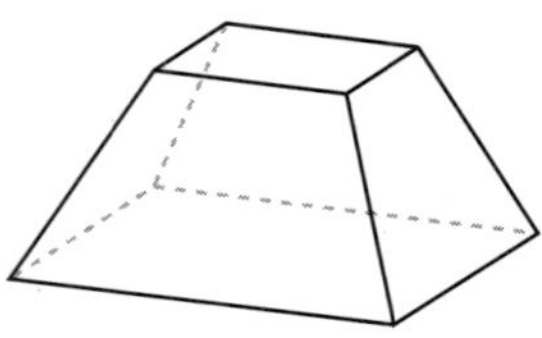

truncated pyramid

turn An informal name for a rotation transformation. See *rotation* and *transformation*.

unfair game A game in which every player does not have the same chance of winning. Compare to *fair game*.

variable A letter or other symbol that represents a number. A variable need not represent one specific number; it can stand for many different values. For example, in the expression $2x + 3y$, x and y are variables, and in the equation $a + 12 = 2b + 6$, a and b are variables.

Venn diagram A picture that uses circles to show relationships among sets.

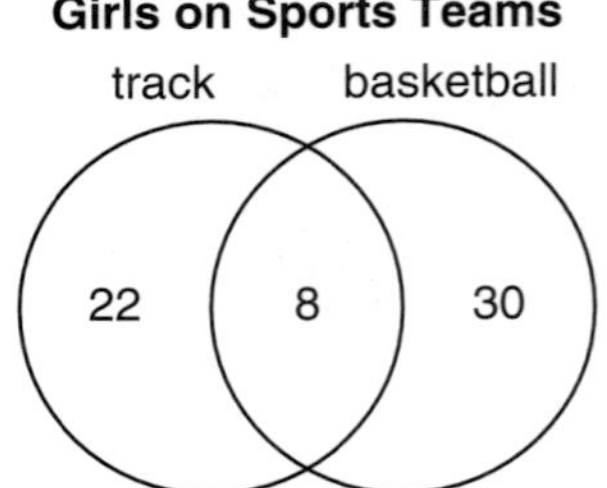

vertex The point at which the rays or line segments of an angle, the sides of a polygon, or the edges of a polyhedron meet.

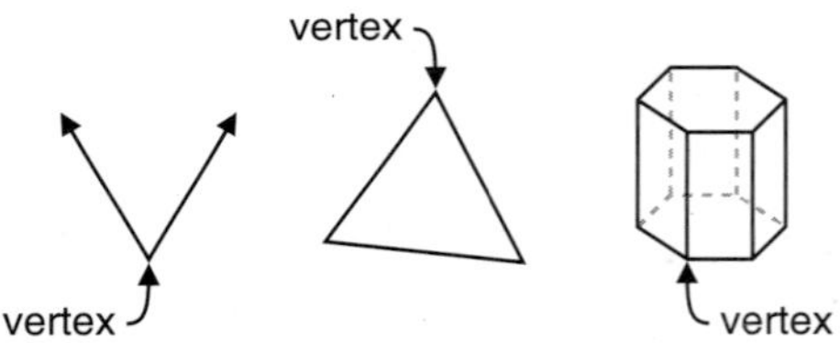

vertical angles When two lines intersect, the angles that do not share a common side; the angles opposite each other. Vertical angles have equal measures.

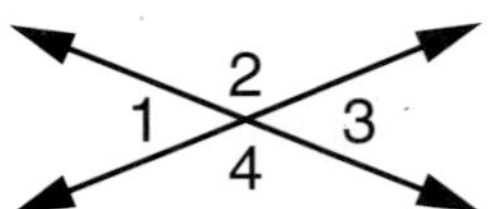

Angles 1 and 3 and Angles 2 and 4 are pairs of vertical angles.

whole number Any of the numbers 0, 1, 2, 3, 4, and so on.

Scope and Sequence Chart

Throughout *Everyday Mathematics,* students repeatedly experience concepts and skills in each of the mathematical strands. Each exposure builds on and extends students' understanding. They study important concepts over consecutive years through a variety of formats. The Scope and Sequence Chart shows the units in which exposures occur and the developmental level of the skill or concept. The three levels of skill and concept development used in the chart are Beginning, Developing, and Secure. These levels refer here to unit content within the *K–6 Everyday Mathematics* curriculum rather than performance expectations for students.

The skills and concepts are divided according to the mathematical strands below.

Mathematical Strands	**Pages**
Numeration	888 and 889
Operations and Computation	890–893
Patterns, Functions, and Algebra	894–896
Geometry	897–900
Measurement and Reference Frames: Measurement	901–904
Measurement and Reference Frames: Reference Frames	905
Data and Chance	906 and 907

How to Read the Scope and Sequence Chart

Each section of the chart includes a mathematical strand title, three grade level columns divided by units, and a list of specific skills and concepts grouped by major concepts.

Numeration

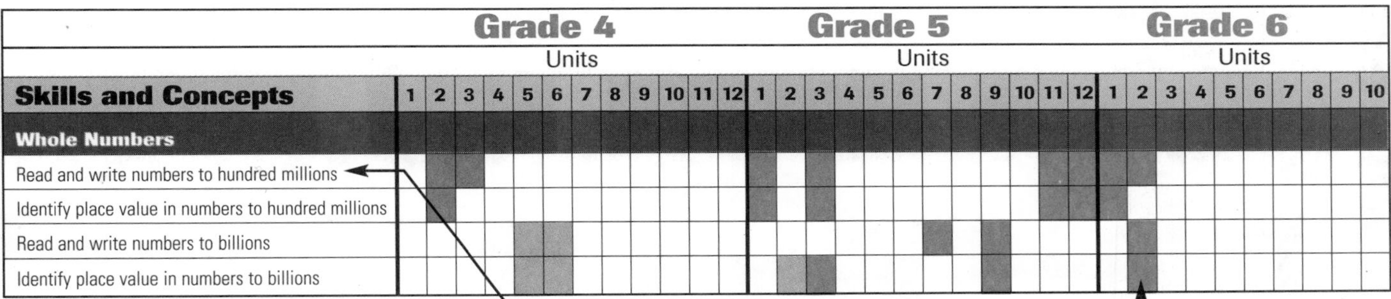

Major mathematical concepts within each strand. A list of related skills and concepts appear below this head.

Find specific skills and concepts in this list and then follow across the row for units in which they appear at each grade level.

The shading in the cells indicates the skill and concept development level for a particular exposure. The lightest shading shows beginning exposures, the medium shading designates developing exposures, and the darkest shading indicates secure exposures.

Numeration

	Grade 4												Grade 5												Grade 6									
	Units												Units												Units									
Skills and Concepts	1	2	3	4	5	6	7	8	9	10	11	12	1	2	3	4	5	6	7	8	9	10	11	12	1	2	3	4	5	6	7	8	9	10
Whole Numbers																																		
Read and write numbers to hundred millions																																		
Read and write numbers to billions																																		
Explore numbers to trillions																																		
Read and write numbers to trillions																																		
Identify place value in numbers to hundred millions																																		
Identify place value in numbers to billions																																		
Name the values of digits in numbers to billions																																		
Compare larger numbers																																		
Find equivalent names for numbers																																		
Identify even and odd numbers																																		
Find and identify factors of numbers																																		
Identify prime and composite numbers																																		
Find the prime factorization of numbers																																		
Find the least common multiple of two numbers																																		
Find the greatest common factor of two numbers																																		
Understand and apply powers of 10																																		
Rename numbers written in exponential notation																																		
Understand and apply exponential notation																																		
Understand and apply scientific notation																																		
Understand square numbers and their square roots																																		
Understand properties of rational numbers																																		

Skill
Money and Decimals
Read and write decimals to thousandths
Identify place value in decimals to thousandths
Round decimals to a given place
Fractions
Find equivalent fractions
Compare and order fractions
Convert between mixed numbers and fractions
Find common denominators
Rename fractions and mixed numbers
Identify the whole for fractions
Find a fraction of a number
Relate fractions and decimals
Give equivalencies between fractions, decimals, and percents
Use a calculator to rename a fraction as a decimal or percent
Find opposites and reciprocals of numbers
Positive/Negative Numbers (Integers)
Explore uses for positive and negative numbers
Compare and order positive and negative numbers
Ratio, Proportion, and Percent
Find a percent of a number
Estimate and calculate percent
Find the whole, given a percent of the whole
Convert between fractions, decimals, mixed numbers, and percents
Estimate equivalent percents for fractions

Beginning **Developing** **Secure**

Operations and Computation

	Grade 4												Grade 5												Grade 6									
	Units												Units												Units									
Skills and Concepts	1	2	3	4	5	6	7	8	9	10	11	12	1	2	3	4	5	6	7	8	9	10	11	12	1	2	3	4	5	6	7	8	9	10
Addition and Subtraction																																		
Solve addition/subtraction number stories																																		
Practice basic facts and extended facts																																		
Use mental arithmetic to add/subtract																																		
Add/subtract multidigit numbers																																		
Use column addition																																		
Use estimation to add/subtract																																		
Use addition/subtraction algorithms																																		
Add/subtract positive and negative numbers																																		
Addition and Subtraction with Decimals																																		
Add/subtract money amounts/decimals																																		
Add/subtract 1- and 2-digit decimals																																		
Solve decimal addition/subtraction number stories																																		
Add/subtract multidigit whole numbers and decimals																																		
Addition and Subtraction with Fractions																																		
Add/subtract fractions with like denominators																																		
Find a common denominator																																		
Add/subtract fractions with unlike denominators																																		
Solve fraction addition/subtraction number stories																																		
Add/subtract mixed numbers with like denominators																																		

Addition and Subtraction with Fractions (cont.)
Estimate sums/differences of fractions
Add/subtract mixed numbers with unlike denominators
Multiplication and Division
Solve multiplication/division number stories
Interpret a remainder in division problems
Investigate properties of multiplication/division
Practice multiplication/division facts
Practice extended multiplication/division facts
Use arrays to model multiplication
Use estimation to multiply/divide
Make magnitude estimates for products
Find the product of multidigit whole numbers
Solve multiplication/division problems involving multiples of 10, 100, and 1,000
Solve multidigit multiplication/division problems
Use the lattice method for multiplication
Use a calculator to multiply/divide
Use mental arithmetic to multiply/divide
Multiply/divide multiples of 10, 100, and 1,000 by 1-digit numbers
Multiply/divide money amounts
Use multiplication/division algorithms
Use divisibility tests
Express remainders as fractions or decimals
Express quotients as mixed numbers or decimals

Beginning **Developing** **Secure**

Operations and Computation (cont.)

	Grade 4												Grade 5												Grade 6									
	Units												Units												Units									
Skills and Concepts	1	2	3	4	5	6	7	8	9	10	11	12	1	2	3	4	5	6	7	8	9	10	11	12	1	2	3	4	5	6	7	8	9	10
Multiplication and Division (cont.)																																		
Divide by 1-digit numbers																																		
Divide by 2-digit numbers																																		
Solve open number sentences																																		
Use parentheses in number sentences																																		
Understand and apply the order of operations																																		
Multiply/divide positive and negative numbers																																		
Multiply by positive and negative powers of 10																																		
Multiplication and Division with Decimals																																		
Use estimation to multiply/divide decimals by whole numbers																																		
Multiply decimals by whole numbers																																		
Multiply decimals by decimals																																		
Divide decimals by whole numbers																																		
Estimate products and multiply decimals																																		
Estimate the quotient and divide decimals and whole numbers																																		
Round a decimal quotient to a specified place																																		
Locate the decimal point in a product																																		
Multiply/divide decimals by powers of 10																																		
Solve multiplication/division decimal number stories																																		

Multiplication and Division with Fractions
Relate fractions and division
Use an algorithm to multiply fractions
Use an algorithm to multiply mixed numbers
Use a common denominator to divide fractions
Use an algorithm to divide fractions and mixed numbers
Solve multiplication/division fraction number stories
Ratio, Proportion, and Percent
Find unit rates
Calculate unit prices
Collect and compare rate data
Use rate tables
Represent rates with formulas, tables, and graphs
Solve rate and ratio number stories
Explore uses of ratios and ways of expressing ratios
Write open proportions to solve model problems
Solve problems involving a size-change factor
Use cross-multiplication to solve proportion problems

Beginning **Developing** **Secure**

Notes on Scope and Sequence

Patterns, Functions, and Algebra

	Grade 4												Grade 5												Grade 6									
	Units												Units												Units									
Skills and Concepts	1	2	3	4	5	6	7	8	9	10	11	12	1	2	3	4	5	6	7	8	9	10	11	12	1	2	3	4	5	6	7	8	9	10
Visual Patterns																																		
Create patterns with 2-dimensional shapes																																		
Explore and extend visual patterns																																		
Define and create tessellations/frieze patterns																																		
Number Patterns																																		
Find patterns in addition, subtraction, multiplication, and division facts																																		
Investigate square numbers																																		
Plot points on a coordinate grid																																		
Find locations on a map or globe																																		
Find number patterns in data																																		
Find and extend numerical patterns																																		
Functions																																		
Complete a table of values																																		
Collect and compare rate data																																		
Solve rate number stories																																		
Represent rates with formulas, tables, and graphs																																		
Number Sentences and Equations																																		
Write/solve addition and subtraction number sentences																																		
Write/solve multiplication number sentences																																		
Write/solve division number sentences																																		
Apply the use of parentheses in number sentences																																		
Solve open sentences																																		
Determine if number sentences are true or false																																		

Number Sentences and Equations (cont.)
Apply the order of operations to evaluate expressions and solve number sentences
Translate number stories into expressions
Determine the value of a variable
Solve equations with a variable
Use variables to describe general patterns
Use a spreadsheet
Use variables and formulas in spreadsheets
Interpret mystery graphs
Evaluate formulas
Use formulas to solve problems
Apply the distributive property
Inequalities and Expressions
Compare numbers using < and > symbols
Evaluate expressions using <, >, and = symbols
Write algebraic expressions to describe situations
Evaluate algebraic expressions
Describe a pattern with a number sentence that has one or two variables
Solve and graph solutions for inequalities
Simplify expressions and equations that have parentheses
Combine like terms to simplify expressions and equations
Write and identify equivalent expressions and equivalent equations
Write and solve equations that represent problem situations

Beginning **Developing** **Secure**

Patterns, Functions, and Algebra (cont.)

	Grade 4												Grade 5												Grade 6									
	Units												Units												Units									
Skills and Concepts	1	2	3	4	5	6	7	8	9	10	11	12	1	2	3	4	5	6	7	8	9	10	11	12	1	2	3	4	5	6	7	8	9	10
Positive/Negative Numbers (Integers)																																		
Compare and order positive and negative numbers																																		
Use properties of positive and negative numbers																																		
Compute with positive and negative numbers																																		

Notes on Scope and Sequence

Geometry

	Grade 4												Grade 5												Grade 6									
	Units												Units												Units									
Skills and Concepts	1	2	3	4	5	6	7	8	9	10	11	12	1	2	3	4	5	6	7	8	9	10	11	12	1	2	3	4	5	6	7	8	9	10
2-Dimensional Shapes (Polygons)																																		
Identify 2-dimensional shapes																																		
Explore shape relationships																																		
Identify characteristics of 2-dimensional shapes																																		
Construct/draw 2-dimensional shapes																																		
Solve problems involving 2-dimensional shapes																																		
Classify and name polygons																																		
Identify properties of polygons																																		
Use a compass and a straightedge to construct geometric figures																																		
Classify quadrilaterals according to side and angle properties																																		
Name, draw, and label angles, triangles, and quadrilaterals																																		
Identify types of triangles																																		
Verify and apply the Pythagorean Theorem																																		
Define and create tessellations/frieze patterns																																		
3-Dimensional Shapes																																		
Identify 3-dimensional shapes																																		
Identify characteristics of 3-dimensional shapes																																		
Construct 3-dimensional shapes																																		
Identify faces, edges, vertices, and bases of prisms and pyramids																																		

Beginning **Developing** **Secure**

Geometry (cont.)

	Grade 4												Grade 5												Grade 6									
	Units												Units												Units									
Skills and Concepts	1	2	3	4	5	6	7	8	9	10	11	12	1	2	3	4	5	6	7	8	9	10	11	12	1	2	3	4	5	6	7	8	9	10
3-Dimensional Shapes (cont.)																																		
Describe properties of geometric solids																																		
Perform topological transformations																																		
Symmetry																																		
Identify symmetrical figures																																		
Identify lines of symmetry																																		
Rotate figures																																		
Translate figures																																		
Identify lines of reflection, reflected figures, and figures with line symmetry																																		
Explore transformations of geometric figures in a plane																																		
Congruence and Similarity																																		
Identify congruent figures																																		
Identify similar figures																																		
Draw or form a figure congruent to a given figure																																		
Points, Lines, and Angles																																		
Draw line segments to a specified length																																		
Identify parallel and nonparallel line segments																																		
Identify and name points																																		
Identify and name line segments																																		
Identify and name lines																																		
Identify and name intersecting lines																																		

Points, Lines, and Angles (cont.)
Identify and name rays
Draw lines and rays
Name, draw, and label line segments, lines, and rays
Identify and describe right angles, parallel lines, and line segments
Explore the relationship between endpoints and midpoints
Solve construction problems
Identify and name angles
Model clockwise/counterclockwise turns/rotations
Measure angles with degree units
Solve degree problems
Identify acute, obtuse, straight, and reflex angles
Make turns and fractions of turns; relate turns to angles
Use full-circle and half-circle protractors to measure and draw angles
Determine angle measures based on relationships among angles
Estimate the measure of an angle
Find angle sums for geometric shapes
Use a compass to draw a circle and angles formed by intersecting lines
Measure angles formed by intersecting lines
Apply properties of supplementary angles and vertical angles
Apply properties of angles formed by two parallel lines and a transversal
Apply properties of angles and parallelograms

Beginning Developing Secure

Geometry (cont.)

	Grade 4												Grade 5												Grade 6									
	Units												Units												Units									
Skills and Concepts	1	2	3	4	5	6	7	8	9	10	11	12	1	2	3	4	5	6	7	8	9	10	11	12	1	2	3	4	5	6	7	8	9	10
Points, Lines, and Angles (cont.)																																		
Calculate the degree measure of each sector in a circle graph; use a protractor to construct the graph																																		
Apply properties of sums of angle measures of triangles and quadrilaterals																																		

Notes on Scope and Sequence

Measurement and Reference Frames: Measurement

	Grade 4												Grade 5												Grade 6									
	Units												Units												Units									
Skills and Concepts	1	2	3	4	5	6	7	8	9	10	11	12	1	2	3	4	5	6	7	8	9	10	11	12	1	2	3	4	5	6	7	8	9	10
Length																																		
Estimate and compare distances																																		
Estimate and compare lengths/heights of objects																																		
Measure to the nearest foot																																		
Measure to the nearest inch																																		
Measure to the nearest centimeter																																		
Investigate the meter																																		
Measure to the nearest $\frac{1}{2}$ inch																																		
Measure to the nearest $\frac{1}{2}$ centimeter																																		
Identify equivalent customary units of length																																		
Identify equivalent metric units of length																																		
Investigate the mile																																		
Solve length/height/distance number stories																																		
Use a map scale																																		
Use a mileage map																																		
Use a scale drawing																																		
Identify locations for given latitudes and longitudes																																		
Find latitude and longitude for given locations																																		
Measure to the nearest $\frac{1}{4}$ inch																																		
Measure to the nearest $\frac{1}{8}$ inch																																		
Measure to the nearest millimeter																																		
Measure diameter and circumference																																		

Beginning **Developing** **Secure**

Measurement and Reference Frames: Measurement (cont.)

	Grade 4												Grade 5												Grade 6									
	Units												Units												Units									
Skills and Concepts	1	2	3	4	5	6	7	8	9	10	11	12	1	2	3	4	5	6	7	8	9	10	11	12	1	2	3	4	5	6	7	8	9	10
Length (cont.)																																		
Express metric measures with decimals																																		
Convert between metric measures																																		
Establish personal references for metric units of length																																		
Establish personal references for customary units of length																																		
Capacity and Volume																																		
Understand the concept of capacity																																		
Identify customary units of capacity																																		
Identify equivalent customary units of capacity																																		
Identify metric units of capacity																																		
Identify equivalent metric units of capacity																																		
Calculate capacity																																		
Solve capacity number stories																																		
Understand the concept of volume of a figure																																		
Understand the relationships between the volumes of pyramids and prisms, and the volumes of cones and cylinders																																		
Find volume																																		
Estimate volume																																		
Use formulas to calculate volumes of 3-dimensional shapes																																		
Examine the relationships among the liter, milliliter, and cubic centimeter																																		

Weight
Use a pan balance/spring scale
Solve pan-balance problems
Solve weight number stories
Identify customary units of weight
Identify metric units of weight
Estimate and compare weights
Identify equivalent customary units of weight
Identify equivalent metric units of weight
Estimate/weigh objects in ounces or grams
Perimeter and Area
Investigate area
Estimate area
Find the perimeters of irregular shapes
Find the perimeters of regular shapes
Find the areas of regular shapes
Compare perimeter and area
Find the areas of irregular shapes
Find the area of a figure by counting unit squares
Use formulas to find areas of rectangles, parallelograms, and triangles
Estimate surface area
Identify the bases and heights of triangles and parallelograms
Use a formula to find the circumference of a circle
Use a formula to find the area of a circle

Beginning Developing Secure

Measurement and Reference Frames: Measurement (cont.)

	Grade 4												Grade 5												Grade 6									
	Units												Units												Units									
Skills and Concepts	1	2	3	4	5	6	7	8	9	10	11	12	1	2	3	4	5	6	7	8	9	10	11	12	1	2	3	4	5	6	7	8	9	10
Perimeter and Area (cont.)																																		
Distinguish between circumference and area in circle problems																																		
Find the surface areas of prisms, cylinders, and pyramids																																		
Find an approximate value for π (pi)																																		
Use personal references for common units of area																																		
Money																																		
Solve money number stories																																		
Add/subtract money amounts																																		
Estimate costs																																		
Divide money amounts																																		
Calculate unit price																																		
Determine the better buy																																		
Multiply money amounts																																		
Identify/find fractional parts of units of money																																		

Measurement and Reference Frames: Reference Frames

	Grade 4												Grade 5												Grade 6									
	Units												Units												Units									
Skills and Concepts	1	2	3	4	5	6	7	8	9	10	11	12	1	2	3	4	5	6	7	8	9	10	11	12	1	2	3	4	5	6	7	8	9	10
Time																																		
Calculate elapsed time																																		
Tell time to the nearest minute																																		
Convert units of time																																		
Temperature																																		
Convert units of temperature																																		

Beginning Developing Secure

Notes on Scope and Sequence

Data and Chance

	Grade 4												Grade 5												Grade 6									
	Units												Units												Units									
Skills and Concepts	1	2	3	4	5	6	7	8	9	10	11	12	1	2	3	4	5	6	7	8	9	10	11	12	1	2	3	4	5	6	7	8	9	10
Collecting Data																																		
Collect data by counting/interviewing																																		
Collect data from print sources																																		
Collect data from a map																																		
Make predictions about data																																		
Explore random sampling																																		
Conduct a survey																																		
Record/compare numerical data																																		
Organize and tabulate survey data																																		
Collect and compare rate data																																		
Recording/Displaying Data																																		
Make a tally chart																																		
Make a bar graph																																		
Record data in a table/chart																																		
Record data on a map																																		
Make a line plot																																		
Draw a circle graph																																		
Construct a stem-and-leaf plot																																		
Construct a step graph																																		
Construct a Venn diagram																																		

Evaluating Data
Find/use the range
Find/use the mode
Find/use the median
Find/use the mean
Compare two sets of data
Find/use the minimum/maximum
Interpret tables, graphs, and maps
Use data in problem solving
Summarize and interpret data
Understand how sample size affects results
Interpret stem-and-leaf plots
Explore misleading ways of presenting data
Probability and Chance
Explore equal-chance events
Predict outcomes
Record outcomes
Conduct experiments
Explore *fair* and *unfair* games
Solve problems involving chance outcomes
Use tree diagrams
Compute the probability of equally-likely outcomes
Calculate the probability of simple events
Apply the concept of random numbers to probability situations
Understand how increasing the number of trials affects experimental results

Beginning **Developing** **Secure**

Index

A

Absolute value, 468
Actual results, 558
Acute angle, 293
Acute triangle, 293
Addition
  decimal, 80, 86–90
  fraction, 229–234, 325, 715
  mixed number with like denominators, 235–239
  mixed number with unlike denominators, 240–244, 290, 325
  negative number, 462–469
  positive number, 462–469
  whole number, 90
Adjacent angles, 296, 332
Algebra, 714, 776–777
Algebraic expressions, 151, 162–165, 576, 756, 807
  evaluating, 164
  simplifying, 695, 716–717
  writing to represent situations described in words, 164
Algorithms
  division, 83–85, 457–461
  fraction multiplication, 245–248
  lattice method, 81, 98
  partial-products, 694
  partial-quotients, 126–129, 694
Anchor (of a compass), 321
Angles
  acute, 293
  adjacent, 296, 332
  bisecting, 327
  classification of, 290–294
  consecutive, 338
  corresponding, 316, 661
  games, 292, 565
  measuring and drawing, 290–294, 312, 713
  modeling, 293
  opposite, 296
  problems, solving, 758
  reflex, 291
  relationships, 296–297
  right, 291
  straight, 291
  sums, 298
  supplementary, 296, 332
  vertical, 296, 332
Arc, 48
Area, 52–56, 490
  circle, 739
  floor space, calculating, 741–742
  formulas, 738–742, 744
  number stories, 759
  parallelograms, 740, 742, 777
  problems, 747, 758
  rectangles, 703
  trapezoids, 744
  triangles, 742, 744, 777
Area model, 700–703
  for distributive property, 700–703
Art link, 146, 157, 282, 334, 594, 678, 690, 730, 782, 794, 797, 825
Assessment, 5, 75, 145, 209, 281, 441, 531, 593, 689, 781
  end-of-year, 826
  oral, 69, 138–139, 202–203, 273–274, 342, 524, 586, 681, 774–775, 824
  slate, 69, 139, 203, 274, 343, 525, 587, 682, 775, 825
  written, 69–70, 139–140, 204, 275, 343–344, 525–526, 587–588, 683, 776, 825
Average. *See* Mean
Axis, 305

B

Ballpark estimate, 103
Bar graphs, 12, 38–41
  side-by-side, 39
  stacked, 39–40
Base, 110, 113
Base-10 blocks, 86, 253
  modeling addition and subtraction of decimals, 90
  modeling fractions, decimals, and percents, 256
Billions, 104
Bisect, 327
Bisecting angles, 327
Bisecting line segments, 327
Brick-wall formula, 169–170
Broken-line graphs, 12, 33–37, 41
  making "yarn", 36–37
  persuasive, 60

C

Calculator
  converting standard notation to scientific notation, 124
  displaying and reading large numbers, 107
  exponents on a, 113–114
  powers key, 83, 112–115
  reciprocals, finding, 455
  scientific, 486, 526
  scientific notation on a, 121–124
  TI-15, 25, 150, 173, 750
Calories, 621–626
  calculating, 629
  planning a healthful lunch, 630–631
Capacities, comparing, 747–748
Capacity, units of
  kitchen, 62–66
Cells, in spreadsheets, 184
Centimeter, 745
Circle, 48
  area of, 739
  circumference, 740
  concentric, 321
  estimating percents and fractions of a, 264
  formulas, 740
  interior of a, 48
  pi, 740
  radius, 48
Circle graphs, 13, 47–51, 65, 263–267, 287, 299–303, 307, 323, 632–633, 650
  displaying survey data, 267
  human, 51
Circumference formula, 740
Clock, 235
Coefficient, 513
Coin flipping, 566, 577
Columns, in spreadsheets, 184
Combine like terms, 711
Common denominators, 226–227
  least, 226
  in operations with fractions, 214–215
  quick, 226, 231
Commutative Property, 159
Compass, 263, 304, 314, 320, 325, 330, 336, 659, 674, 800
Computer spreadsheets, 186, 695, 732–737
Concentric circle, 321
Cones, 810
Congruence, 287–288
  exploring with pentominoes, 319

Congruent figures, 314–319, 660
Consecutive numbers, 498
Consecutive angles, 338
Constant terms, 513
Constructions with compass and straightedge, 320–329
angles, 332, 338
Golden Rectangle, 601, 671, 676
hexagon, 294
inscribed square, 327
line segments, 322
parallel lines, 332
parallelogram, 336–340
triangles, 322, 324
Consumer Education link, 6, 43, 64–65, 76, 98, 146, 186, 197, 269, 532, 560, 594, 644
Conversions
between decimals and percents, 258–262
Coordinate, 305
Coordinate geometry, 287, 304–308
Coordinate grid
solving polygon problems on the, 306
Corresponding angles, 316, 661
Corresponding sides, 316, 660
Counters, 468
Counting numbers, 476–477
Cross-curricular links, 6, 76, 146, 210, 282, 442, 532, 594, 690, 782
Cross multiplication, solving proportions by, 617–619
Cross products, 616
using to solve proportions, 617–619
Cross sections of solids, 786, 806–811
using clay, 809–810
using fruits and vegetables, 807–808
Cubic centimeter, 745–746
Cup (C), 63
Cylinders
volume, 745–748

D

Data, 2–71
collecting and analyzing, 66
displaying in graphs, 12–13, 303
landmarks, 10, 22
line plots of, 10, 20–23
persuasive, 57–61
Decimal computation problems, 140
Decimal point, locating the, 97
Decimal quotients
practicing division, 164
Decimals, 72–141, 253–257
adding, 80, 86–90, 95, 118
dividing, 132–136
by a decimal, 672
by whole numbers, 619
division algorithm, 83–85
history of notation, 214
modeling addition and subtraction with base-10 blocks, 90
modeling with base-10 blocks, 256
multiplying, 91–98, 118
by powers of 10, 81, 101
notation, 214, 216
number stories, 89
products of, 92–93
products with, 80–81
renaming as percents, 259–260
repeating, 477
rounding, 87–88
subtracting, 80, 86–90, 95, 118
terminating, 477–478
unrealistic data, 80
Denominator
common, 226
common multiples of the, 231
finding missing in pairs of equivalent fractions, 221
least common, 226
quick common, 226, 231
Designs, reducing, 666
Diagrams
tree, 537, 556–566, 568, 575–576
Venn, 538, 567–572
Discount, 269
Discounted price. *See* Sale price
Distances
ball-throwing experiment, 181
for freely-falling objects, 178–179
formula, 178–179, 188–189
Distributive Property, 694, 704–709, 723
Dividend, 135
Division
algorithm, 83–85, 457–461
decimals, 132–136
fractions, 446, 457–461, 485
games, 131
mental, 21
mixed numbers, 446, 457–461
negative numbers, 470–474
positive numbers, 470–474
practicing with decimal quotients, 164, 729
problems, 112, 725
renaming fractions as percents, 260–261
rules for positive and negative numbers, 471–472
whole numbers, 125–131
zero by, 474
Division of Fractions Property, 459–461
Divisor, 128
Drawing tools, 286

E

"Easy"
fractions, renaming as percents, 646
multiples, 84, 130
Ecology, 267
Enlargement, 654, 666, 684
using a grid, 665
Equally likely, 542
Equations, 488
formula, 755–760
inventing, 510
pan-balance, 507–511
simple, 493–498
simplifying, 717, 720–724
solving, 449–450, 496, 510, 512–516, 695, 697, 720–724, 749–754
using to solve mobile problems, 725–731
writing, 496
Equivalent equations, 512–516, 721
Equivalent fractions, 218–223, 452, 455, 457, 508–509
Fraction Cards, 223
pattern blocks, 223
Equivalent rate, 605
Equivalent ratios, 636, 673, 733
Equivalents
finding close, 262
Estimation
percent equivalents for fractions, 648–649, 651, 653
percents and fractions of a circle, 264
products of decimals, 92–93
Exit slip, 22, 36, 114, 179, 559, 569, 713
Expanded notation, 83
Expected outcomes, 557
Exponential notation, 82, 110, 112–115, 547
renaming to standard form, 295
Exponents, 110, 113
on a calculator, 113–114
Expressions, 150
evaluating, 484, 486, 491
simplifying, 710–714

F

Fact families, 472, 474
Fact Triangles, 472, 474
Factors, 113, 183, 187
game, 694, 703
greatest common, 183, 187
size-change, 654, 656
Fair games, 538, 573–578, 580, 588
False sentence, 488
Fat, 628
content in foods, 646–651
Fibonacci sequence, 679
relationship with the Golden Ratio, 679
Flips. *See* Reflections
Fluid ounces (fl. oz.), 64
Food labels, 629
Formulas, 150, 151–152, 166–175, 196–200, 696, 753
area, 738–742

bowler's handicap, 757
brick-wall, 169–170
circumference, 740
distance, 178–179, 188–189
equations, 755–760
evaluate, 167–169, 204
perimeter, 740
speed, 179
in spreadsheets, 152, 182–190, 734, 737
tibia-to-height, 757
using to solve problems, 756–757
volume, 743–748
words-to-age, 756
Fraction
multiplication algorithm, 245–248
conversions to decimal and percent notations, 216
"Fraction of" problems, 789
Fraction-of-a-fraction problems, 551
Fraction Cards, 223
Fraction computation
prerequisite skills for, 185, 199
strategy, 277, 639
Fractions, 253–257
addition, 229–234, 255, 325, 715
common denominators in, 214–215
comparing, 224–228
division, 446, 457–461, 485
"easy", renaming as percents, 646
Egyptian method of writing, 233
equivalent, 218–223, 452, 455
estimating percent equivalents for, 648–649, 651, 653
to express amounts of time, 239
history of notation, 214
improper, 236, 700
improper, renaming as mixed numbers, 236
modeling with base-10 blocks, 256
multiplying, 261, 309, 325, 446, 452–456
number stories, 277
ordering, 228
proper, 236
renaming as decimals and percents, 540
renaming as decimals using division, 664
renaming as mixed or whole numbers, 162
renaming as percents using division, 260, 270
renaming in simplest form, 220, 245, 540
renaming mixed and whole numbers as, 154, 158
subtracting, 229–234, 255, 325
sums of like, 230
Fulcrum, 726
Full-circle protractor, measuring angles with, 290–294, 312, 713
Function tables. *See* "What's My Rule?" problems

G

Galileo, 181
Gallon (G), 63
Games
Algebra Election, 491–492, 522, 714
Angle Tangle, 292, 565
Broken Calculator, 495, 504, 515
Buzz, 228
Carnival Games, 544–545
Credits/Debits Game (Advanced Version), 469
Division Dash, 131
Doggone Decimal, 102, 124
Exponent Ball, 114, 124
Frac-Tac-Toe, 257, 559
Fraction Action, Fraction Friction, 234, 544
Fraction Top-It, 228
Getting to One, 754
Greedy, 555
Hidden Treasure, 200, 308, 736
High-Number Toss, 111
Landmark Shark, 29–32, 35, 55
Multiplication Wrestling, 694, 703
Name That Number, 28, 497, 526, 583, 702
Polygon Capture, 335, 708
Scientific Notation Toss, 120
Solution Search, 520, 521, 816
Spoon Scramble, 276, 665
Spreadsheet Scramble, 184, 188, 190
3-D Shape Sort, 765
Top-It, 473
General patterns, 155
number sentences, 156
special cases, 159–161
two variables, 158–161
Genus, 815
Geography link, 146, 189, 210, 243
Geometric patterns, 165
Geometric solids, 786, 806–811
games, 765
volume, 744, 754
Geometric transformations, 786
Geometry, 278–345
congruent figures, 314–319, 660
coordinate, 287, 304–308
games, 292, 335, 565, 708, 765
Golden Rectangle, 601, 671, 676
hexagon, 294
line segments, 307, 322
parallel lines, 288, 331–334, 337, 339, 344
parallelograms, 288, 336–340, 740, 742, 777
polygons, 659–666, 789
rays, 291
tessellations, 788–799
topology, 786–787, 812–817
transformation, 310–311
triangles, 322, 324
Geometry Template, 47, 62, 235, 263, 290, 295, 314, 627, 652, 659, 788, 812
Golden Ratio, 601, 674–679
relationship with the Fibonacci sequence, 679
Golden Rectangle, 601, 671, 676
Googol, 107
Googolplex, 107
Graph key, 39
Graphs, 151–152, 171–175, 196–200, 753
bar, 12, 38–41
broken-line, 12, 33–37, 41, 60
circle, 13, 47–51, 65, 263–267, 287, 299–303, 307, 323, 632–633, 650
constructing from a "time story", 193
drawing, 191–195
interpreting, 198
line, 34, 172–173
mystery, 194–195, 204
persuasive, 14, 57–61
pictograph, 14, 59–60
reading, 191–195
side-by-side bar, 39
to solve problems, 13
stacked bar, 39–40
step, 12, 42–46, 98
summer job profit data, 198
time, 193–194
using to investigate perimeter and area, 52–56
Greatest common factor, 183, 187, 218, 220
Grids
coloring, 157
using to draw an enlargement, 665

H

Health link, 6, 59–60, 594, 623, 628, 632–633, 649–650
Hexagon, 294
History link, 146, 181, 210, 233
Horizontal bar graph, 39
Human circle graph, 51
Hypotenuse, 764

I

Illustrating terms, 658
Image, 310
Improper fractions, 236, 700
Indirect measurement, 698, 768–772
Inequalities, 451, 517–522
graphing, 521
Inequality, 488
Input-output rules, 150
Inscribed square, 327
Integers, 477
Interest, 269
Interior of a circle, 48
Interpolate, 41
Irrational numbers, 478

Isometry transformations, 287–288, 309–313, 786
exploring with pentominoes, 319

K

Kitchen units of capacity, 62–66
converting between, 63–64

L

Labels, in spreadsheets, 734
Landmarks, 11, 22, 27
Language Arts link, 6, 17, 76, 115, 146, 155, 282, 310, 442, 480, 532, 584, 594, 624, 690, 719, 782, 826
Language diversity, 46, 66, 102, 157, 271, 294
Large numbers, 103–107
displaying and reading on a calculator, 107
number-and-word notation for, 104–106
scientific notation for, 116–120
using prefixes to express, 115
writing and reading, 121
Lattice method of multiplication, 81, 98, 694
Learning goals, 4, 74, 144, 208, 280, 440, 530, 592, 688, 780
Least common denominator (LCD), 226
Least common multiples, 171, 176, 224
Legs of a right triangle, 764
Life expectancy, 192–193
Like terms, 711
combining, 710–714
Linear measurements, converting, 628
Line graphs, 34
representing speed with, 172–173
Line of reflection, 313
Line plots, 10, 20–23, 27
mystery, 10, 22, 23
Line segments, 307, 322
bisecting, 327
construction of, 322
Lines
parallel, 288, 331–334, 337, 339, 344
List price. *See* Regular price
Literature link, 6, 19, 76, 107, 146, 161, 210, 239, 282, 298, 324, 532, 545, 594, 620, 679, 690, 760, 782, 799, 822
Logic problems, 298

M

Magnitude benchmarks, 117
Map scale, 657
Mathematical Scavenger Hunt, 478–479
Maximum, 22, 38
Maze problems, 559
Mean, 11, 24–28, 38, 65
Measurement
angle, 290–294, 312, 713
area
parallelogram, 740, 742, 777
rectangle, 703
triangle, 742, 744, 777
indirect, 698, 768–772
U.S. customary system, 356
volume
cylinders and cones, 745–748
geometric solids, 745, 754
rectangular prisms, 754
spheres, 744
Measurement tools, 286
Median, 10–11, 22, 24–28, 38, 65
Meter, 115
Metric system, 745–746
Midpoint, 307
Millimeter, 745
Millions, 104–105
Minimum, 22, 38
Mixed numbers
adding and subtracting, with like denominators, 235–239, 255
adding and subtracting, with unlike denominators, 240–244, 255, 290, 325
computation strategy, 277, 639
division of, 446, 457–461
to express amounts of time, 239
multiplying, 249–252, 261, 309, 325, 446, 452–456
operations with, 215–216
renaming as fractions, 154, 158
renaming fractions as, 162, 166
renaming improper fractions as, 236
in simplest form, 237, 245
writing in simplest form, 236–237
Mobile, 726
problems, 725–731
Möbius strips, 818–822
Mode, 22, 38
Multiple-choice tests, strategies for, 538–539, 579–584
Multiples
least common, 171, 176, 224
of 4, 171, 176
of 6, 176
of 3, 171
Multiplication
decimal, 91–98
facts, 16, 21
fraction, 245–248, 261, 309, 325, 446, 452–456
lattice method of, 81, 98
mental, 91
mixed number, 249–252, 261, 309, 325, 446, 452–456
negative number, 470–474
positive number, 470–474
whole number, 94, 98
Multiplication property of −1, 471
Multiplying
decimals by 100, 258
by powers of 10, 99–102, 108
Mystery graphs, 194–195, 204
Mystery plot routine, 10, 22

N

n-to-1 ratio, 654
Name-collection boxes, 25, 28
Negative numbers, 33, 196, 446–447, 520
addition of, 462–469
division of, 470–474
modeling, 468
multiplication of, 470–474
subtraction of, 462–469, 470
Negative powers of 10, 117
Number line
adding positive and negative numbers, 464
subtracting positive and negative numbers, 464–465
Number pairs, plotting ordered, 305
Number patterns
using variables to describe, 154–157
Number sentences, 487–492
to describe general patterns, 156
representing area problems, 702
Number stories
area, 759
decimal, 89
distributive property, 776
division with fractions, 485
fraction, 277
fraction multiplication, 248
involving rates, 175, 608
ratio, 640, 684
solving, 94, 479
volume, 759
writing, 709
Number systems
development of, 447–448
properties of, 475–480
Numbers
associating with their applications, 798
counting, 476–477
irrational, 478
large, 103–107
mixed, 154, 639
negative, 33, 196, 520
positive, 33, 196, 520
rational, 477–478
real, 478
rounding, 87–88, 317
small, 108–111
square, 762
triangular, 793
whole, 72–141, 154, 477
Numerator, 221

Nutrition
  information, 599, 627–633
  labels, 610

O

Open sentence, 150, 494
Operation symbols, 488
Operations
  with common denominators in fractions, 214–215
  with mixed numbers, 215–216
  order of, 448–449, 481–486
  with positive and negative numbers, 446–447
Opposite angles, 296
Opposite of a number, 463
Order of operations, 448–449, 481–486
Ordered number pairs, 305
Origin, 305
Outcome, 542, 547

P

Pan balance, 450–451, 499, 749
  equations, 507–511, 549
  problems, 450–451, 499–506, 526, 549, 724
Parallel line segments, 332, 339
Parallel lines, 288, 332, 337, 339, 344
  and angle relationships, 330–335
Parallelograms, 288, 336–340
  area, 740, 742, 777
Parentheses, removing, 715–719
Partial-products multiplication method, 694
Partial-quotients division method, 126–129
Part-to-part ratio, 636, 638
Part-to-whole ratio, 636, 638
Pattern blocks, 223, 235, 239, 309, 788
  using to explore similar polygons, 661–663
Patterns
  general, 155, 156, 158–161
  geometric, 165
  making by coloring grids, 157
  number, 154–157
  tessellating, 794
Pentominoes, 319
Percent Circle, 47–51
Percent notation
  conversions to decimal and fraction notations, 216
Percent of a number, 268–271
"Percent of" problems, 292, 609
Percent problems, using proportions to solve, 641–645
Percents, 253–257
  applications of, 217
  calculators, 261, 264, 647
  fraction equivalents for, 667
  modeling with base-10 blocks, 256
  renaming as decimals, 260
  renaming as fractions, 268
Perimeter, 52–56
  formula, 740
  problems, 747, 758, 760
  relationship to size-change factor, 658
Perpendicular, 327
  bisectors, 327, 329
Persuasive data, 57–61
Persuasive graphs, 14, 57–61
Per-unit rate method, 604
Per-unit rates, 603
Physical Education link, 594, 626
Pi (π), 740, 746
Pictograph, persuasive, 14, 59–60
Pie graph. *See* Circle graph
Pint (P), 63
Place value, 104, 105, 109–111, 256
Point symmetry, 802
  magic trick, 804
Polygon problems, 306
Polygons
  regular, 789
  similar, 659–666
Portfolio ideas, 23, 28, 41, 51, 56, 61, 66, 70, 89, 115, 120, 140, 161, 169, 175, 181, 195, 204, 233, 252, 267, 271, 277, 294, 303, 313, 319, 324, 329, 344, 345, 474, 486, 497, 505–506, 511, 521, 544, 560, 584, 588, 632–633, 665, 673, 683, 684, 703, 714, 737, 741–742, 759, 766, 771, 776, 777, 794, 805
Positive numbers, 33, 196, 446–447, 520
  addition, 462–469
  division, 470–474
  modeling, 468
  multiplication, 470–474
  subtraction, 462–469, 470
Positive powers of 10, 117
Power, 110
Powers key, 83, 112–115
Powers of 10, 110
  division, 796
  multiplication, 81, 99–102, 108, 796
  positive and negative, 117
  and scientific notation, 82
Precision, 88
Preimage, 310, 786
Prisms
  volume, 754
Probability
  chance outcomes, 536
  dice rolling, 813
  equally likely outcomes, 540–545
  tree diagrams, 562–565
Probability meter, 541
Problem-solving diagram, 479–480
Proof, studying a, 461
Proper fraction, 236
Properties of number systems, 150
Proportions, 605
  open, 610–612
  solving by cross multiplication, 615–620
  solving rate problems with, 609–614
  using to model rate-problem solutions, 605
  using to solve percent problems, 641–645
Protractor, 287, 290, 299–303, 304, 307, 309, 314, 320, 325, 336, 646, 659, 710, 800
Puzzles, solving, 480
  topological, 817
Pythagorean Theorem, 697–698, 761–767
  studying a proof, 764
  using to find missing lengths, 765
  verifying, 764

Q

Quadrangles
  noncongruent, 329
  sums of angles, 298
  tessellations, 799
Quart (Q), 63
Quick common denominator (QCD), 226, 231
Quotient, 128
  rounding to nearest tenth or hundredth, 656

R

Radius, 48
Random digit table, 550
Random numbers, 537, 546–550
  using, 554
Random-number simulation, 551–555
Range, 22, 38
Rate problems, solving, 175, 598–599, 606, 621, 633
  with proportions, 609–614
Rate tables, 602–608
  simplified, 610–612
Rate units, 172, 603–604, 608, 610–612, 622, 625
Rates, 172–174, 598, 602–608
  comparing ways to represent, 174
  number stories, 175, 608
Rate-table method, 604–605
Rational numbers, 206–277, 477–478
  addition of, 229–244
  collecting examples of, 256
  division of, 260–261
  multiplication of, 245–252, 261
  negative, 33, 196, 446–447, 520
  positive, 33, 196, 520
  properties of, 480
  subtraction, 229–244
Ratios, 598, 600, 634–640
  comparing, 601, 667–673

equivalent, 636, 673, 733
Golden, 601, 674–679
interpreting, 736
number stories, 640, 684
part-to-part, 636, 638
part-to-whole, 636, 638
problems, solving, 637–640
reading, 673
using to describe size changes, 600, 652–658
Rays, 291
Real Number Line Poster, 462, 475
Real numbers, 478
Recall survey, 14, 64
Recipes, calculating amounts of ingredients, 683
Reciprocals, 446, 453–457, 556
Rectangles
area of, 703
Golden, 601, 671, 676
perimeter, 52–56
Rectangular coordinate grid, 305
Rectangular prism, maximizing the volume of a, 754
Reduction, 654, 666
Reflection
line of, 313
symmetry, 804
Reflections, 310
Reflex angle, 291
Regular
hexagon, 294
polygon, 789
tessellation, 790, 794
price, 269
Relation symbol, 488
reminder cards, 492
Remainder, 128, 136
division, expressing to a given decimal place, 613
renaming as a decimal, 728
Repeating decimals, 478
Review and assessment, 67–71, 137–141, 201–205, 272–277, 341–345, 523–527, 585–589, 680–685, 773–777, 823–826
Right angle, 291
Right triangle, 764
legs of a, 764
Rotation symmetry, 800–805
order of, 802–803, 805
Rotations, 310
Rounding
decimals, 87–88
quotients to nearest tenth or hundredth, 656
Rows, in spreadsheets, 184
Ruler, 166, 290, 314, 320, 325, 336, 457, 573, 652, 659, 674, 738

S

Sale price, 269
Scale, 573
Scale models, finding dimensions of objects based on, 658
Science Experiment, 152, 176–181
Science link, 6, 34–35, 39–41, 76, 115, 146, 177, 181, 210, 234, 266, 267, 532, 570, 582, 690, 745–746
Scientific notation, 82, 83, 547
on a calculator, 121–124
for large and small numbers, 116–120
translating to standard notation, 117–118, 124
Sector, 48, 300
Semiregular tessellation, 788–794
Shapes, sorting, 345
Side-by-side bar graphs, 39
Sides, corresponding, 316, 660
Similar figures, 660, 663
Similar polygons, 659–666
using pattern blocks to explore, 661–663
Simple equations, 493–498
Simplest form fractions, 220, 245
Simplifying expressions,
combining like terms, 710–714
removing parentheses, 715–719
Simulation, 552
random-number, 551–555
tournament, 552–553
Size changes, using ratios to describe, 652–658
Size-change factor, 654, 656
finding lengths and volumes in similar figures, 769–770
relationship to perimeter, 658
Slides. *See* Translations
Small numbers, 108–111
reading and writing in standard notation, 109–110
scientific notation for, 116–120
using prefixes to express, 115
Social Studies link, 76, 120, 146, 169–170, 192–193, 442, 491, 532, 580–581, 594, 657, 668–669
Solid geometry, 786, 806–811
Solids, cross sections of, 786, 806–811
Solution set, 519
Solution to an open sentence, 494
Special case, 155
Speed, 172
ball-throwing experiment, 181
formula, 179
of free-falling objects, 179
representing with a table and a line graph, 172
Sphere, volume of a, 744
Spreadsheet program, 733
comparing mean and median, 27–28
Spreadsheets, 182–190
address box, 734
address of a cell, 734
cell, 734
computer, 186, 695, 732–737
display bar, 734
formulas, 734, 737
labels, 734
numbers, 734
updating or revising, 183
Square of a number, 762
Square-root function, 698
Square root of a number, 698, 762
Square-root problems, solving, 763
Standard notation, 82, 104, 110, 738
translating to scientific notation, 117–118, 124
Stem-and-leaf plot, 644–645
Step graphs, 12, 42–46, 98
for plumber's rates, 45
for taxi cab fares, 44–45
Straight angle, 291
Student Reference Book, 10
Subtraction
decimal, 80, 86–90
fraction, 229–234
mixed numbers with like denominators, 235–239
mixed numbers with unlike denominators, 240–244, 290
negative number, 462–470
positive number, 462–470
rule for positive and negative numbers, 466
whole number, 90
Supplementary angles, 296, 332
Survey
data, displaying, 303
recall, 14, 64
taking and interpreting a, 271
Symmetry
point, 802, 804
reflection, 804
rotation, 800–805

T

Tables, 151–152, 171–175, 196–200, 753
calorie, 623
comparing the profits for summer jobs, 197
rate, 602–608
relating Venn diagrams and, 570–571
representing speed with, 172–173
Tape measure, 166
Technical language, recognizing, 633
Technology link, 690, 737, 763, 782, 794
Temperature, 448
Terminating decimal, 477
Terms of the equation, 513
Tessellating patterns, 794
Tessellation, 790
demiregular, 791
designs, 794, 799, 825
Escher-type translation, 795–799
quadrangle, 799

regular, 790, 794
semiregular, 788–794
using a computer program to explore, 794
Test numbers, 751
Theorem, 764
Thermometer, 463
Thousands, 104–105
Time
graphs, 193–194
using fractions and mixed numbers to express, 239
Tools, measuring and drawing, 286
Topological equivalent, 815
Topological transformation, 815–816
Topology, 786–787, 812–817
properties, 816
puzzles, 817
Transformation, 310
Transformational geometry, 310–311
Translations, 310
Transversal, 332, 339
Tree diagrams, 537, 556–560, 568, 575–576
calculate probabilities, 561–566
Trial and error, 495
solving equations by, 697, 749–754
Trial-and-error method, 750–752
Triangles
area, 742, 777
constructing, 322, 324
enlarging with rubber bands, 666
sum of angles, 298
Triangular numbers, 793
Trillions, 105
True sentence, 488
Truncated quotient, 135
Turns. *See* Rotations

U

Unfair games, 538, 573–578
Unit fractions, using to find the whole, 625–626
Unit percents, using to find the whole, 631
Unit rates, 602–608
U.S. customary system, 356

V

Variable terms, 513
Variables, 150, 494
in general patterns, 158–161
in spreadsheets, 152, 182–190
substitute numerical values for, 167
using to describe number patterns, 154–157
Venn diagrams, 538, 567–572
from Internet searches, 571–572, 589
relating tables and, 570–571
Vertex, *plural:* vertices, 790–791
Vertex point, 790–791
Vertical angles, 296, 332
Vertical bar graph, 39
Volume
of cylinders, 745–748
formulas, 743–748
of geometric solids, 786, 806–811
of a human body, 745–746
metric system for, 745–746
number stories, 759
of prisms, 754
problems, solving, 757
of spheres, 744

W

Weight, 266
"What's My Rule?" problems, 150–151, 165, 168–169, 173–175, 197, 469, 494
rate problems, 614
Whole, 223
using unit fractions to find the, 625–626
using unit percents to find the, 631
Whole numbers, 72–141, 477
addition, 90
divided by whole numbers, 607
dividing decimals by, 619
division, 125–131
division algorithm, 83–85
division with decimal answers, 134–135
multiplication, 94, 98
multiplying by powers of 10, 81
renaming as fractions, 154, 158
renaming fractions as, 162, 166
subtraction, 90

Z

Zeno's paradox, 233
Zero
in decimals, 93, 101, 104–105, 109, 259
in division, 261, 474, 476–477
on number lines, 458, 463–466, 477
as a placeholder, 88, 101–102, 104–105
powers of 10, operations with, 100–101, 110, 114, 117, 510